D1093655

UNITED STATES DEPARTMENT OF THE INTERIOR

BUREAU OF RECLAMATION

DESIGN OF SMALL DAMS

A Water Resources Technical Publication

First Edition, 1960
Second Edition, 1973
Revised Reprint, 1977
Third Edition, 1987

As the Nation's principal conservation agency, the Department of the Interior has responsibility for most of our nationally owned public lands and natural resources. This includes fostering the wisest use of our land and water resources, protecting our fish and wildlife, preserving the environmental and cultural values of our national parks and historical places, and providing for the enjoyment of life through outdoor recreation. The Department assesses our energy and mineral resources and works to assure that their development is in the best interests of all our people. The Department also has a major responsibility for American Indian reservation communities and for people who live in Island Territories under U.S. Administration.

For sale by the U.S. Government Printing Office
Superintendent of Documents, Mail Stop: SSOP, Washington, DC 20402-9328

Mission of the Bureau of Reclamation

The Bureau of Reclamation of the U.S. Department of the Interior is responsible for the development and conservation of the Nation's water resources in the Western United States.

The Bureau's original purpose "to provide for the reclamation of arid and semiarid lands in the West" today covers a wide range of interrelated functions. These include providing municipal and industrial water supplies; hydroelectric power generation; irrigation water for agriculture; water quality improvement; flood control; river navigation; river regulation and control; fish and wildlife enhancement; outdoor recreation; and research on water-related design, construction, materials, atmospheric management, and wind and solar power.

Bureau programs most frequently are the result of close cooperation with the U.S. Congress, other Federal agencies, States, local governments, academic institutions, water-user organizations, and other concerned groups.

Preface to the Third Edition

The second edition of *Design of Small Dams* has been very popular throughout the world; it has been published in a number of different languages and used extensively in the United States. Since the second edition was published in 1974, there have been significant revisions in the approaches and procedures related to the design of dams. Because of these revisions and the continued demand for this manual, it was decided that this new third edition be prepared and published.

The purpose of this third edition has been changed in scope and intent from that of the second edition. The title *Design of Small Dams* has been retained even though some of the information in the third edition relates to large dams. Many of the theoretical concepts presented can be applied to large or small structures; however, it is recommended that the procedures and methods presented be used only as guidelines. When preparing the design of large or complicated structures, especially those located where they create a high hazard, the owner should rely on experienced dam engineers, experienced consultants, or refer to more detailed references.

Some of the chapters and appendixes have been revised extensively, while others reflect only minor revisions. Chapter 1, "Plan Formulation," has been condensed to briefly cover only the basic concepts of plan formulation. The authors of this chapter concluded that a detailed discussion of plan formulation was not appropriate because the primary focus of this manual is on design, not project planning. Also, a discussion of plan formulation, particularly with an emphasis on Federal plan formulation requirements, would not be of interest to a majority of dam designers. The chapter thus provides a brief discussion of the steps of plan formulation and some of the fundamental tests for the viability of proposed plans.

Chapter 2, "Ecological and Environmental Considerations," has been revised to include a discussion on the management of fish and wildlife resources at completed projects, in addition to new design considerations. An expanded section on water quality implications to dam design and operation is also included.

Chapter 3, "Flood Hydrology Studies," has been completely revised, including incorporating the previous appendix A, "Estimating Rainfall Runoff from Soil and Cover Data," into the chapter. Reference to the Soil Conservation Services' curve number approach for assigning infiltration losses, the triangular unit-hydrograph approach, and all discussions and plates providing guidance for estimating probable maximum precipitation have been eliminated. These topics have been replaced by a treatment of infiltration losses as actually applied by the Bureau of Reclamation, expanded consideration and guidance relative to the development of unit hydrographs using the dimensionless unigraph and S-graph approaches, and specific reference to the National Weather Service's Hydrometeorological Report series as the basis for developing probable maximum precipitation estimates for the contiguous United States.

Chapter 5, "Foundation and Construction Materials," has been updated to incorporate current standards in foundation and construction materials investigations. A reservoir studies section has been added to the section on scope of investigations. The sections on soil and rock classification have been updated to reflect current standards, and a new section on engineering geophysics has been added to summarize the capabilities of these methods. The sections on subsurface explorations and sampling have been revised extensively to represent new technology. The logging of explorations has also been revised to reflect current standards, and the field and laboratory test section has been updated. Changes in soil mechanics terminology and soil testing procedures generated by revision of the Bureau's *Earth Manual* are reflected in this chapter. The previous table 8, "Average Properties of Soils," which is now table 5-1, was recompiled to include laboratory test results obtained since the last edition. Figure 5-14, "Permeability of Soils," was added to this edition to illustrate ranges of permeability measured on compacted soil specimens tested at the Bureau's laboratory in Denver. The bibliography has been updated to include selected sources of information for foundation and construction materials investigation.

Chapter 6, "Earthfill Dams," has been revised to update terminology and reflect design philosophy, procedures, and standards that have evolved since 1974. The major change is greater emphasis on internal filtering and drainage to control seepage and internal erosion within embankment dams. New figures have been added that show current dam embankments that have been designed and constructed by the Bureau of Reclamation. Other illustrations have been replaced or revised to reflect current thinking and technology. Liberal reference is made to design standards that have been developed as guides for Bureau engineers.

Chapter 7, "Rockfill Dams," required only minor revisions; however, the Bureau does not have extensive experience with the design and construction of rockfill dams. Design and construction procedures for rockfill dams have changed over the last two or three decades and continue to do so. The chapter gives a good general background for the design of rockfill dams; however, the designer should also refer to the literature on the subject.

Chapter 8, "Concrete Gravity Dams," now includes additional topics, clarification, and more detail. This chapter has also been revised to address concerns for concrete dams of any height. Sections on material properties and foundation considerations have also been added. More complete discussions are now included for forces acting on the dam, requirements for stability, and stress and stability analyses. Discussions addressing the analysis of cracked dams have been clarified and expanded to include analysis during an earthquake. Also, a general iterative approach for cracked dam analysis, applicable for static and dynamic conditions, is now included.

The "Spillways" and "Outlet Works" chapters, 9 and 10, respectively, now include two new hydraulic designs for energy dissipators. These designs are a modified low Froude number basin as an alternative to basin 4 design, and modifications in the design criteria for baffled apron spillways to permit their use for higher unit discharges. Other contemporary spillway concepts are introduced, although design criteria are not included because they are still under development. Included in this category are labyrinth weirs where large flows must be discharged in a limited space such as a narrow canyon, and the use of air slots (aerators) in spillways where there is high potential for cavitation damage. Plunge-pool design criteria have been somewhat improved by the addition of several references to recent research. The suggested method for calculating the discharge under radial gates has been revised to reflect up-to-date criteria developed by the U.S. Army Corps of Engineers, Waterways Experiment Station. The section on siphon spillways has been omitted from this edition because they are seldom used as flow control structures for dams. The bibliography has been revised by the removal of references that were hard to obtain and by the addition of many new references that reflect the current state-of-the-art.

Chapter 12, "Operation and Maintenance," now includes additional topics, clarification, and more detail. The new topics added are "Changes in Operating Plan," which addresses modification to a structure to add additional storage or to change the purpose of allocation of storage; "Emergency Preparedness Plan," which addresses instructions to an operator during emergency situations; and "Dam Operators Training," which outlines the requirements for the training of operators to assure that operation and maintenance of a facility are performed in an accurate and responsible manner.

Chapter 13 is a new chapter dealing with dam safety. Although dam safety is always an underlying consideration in the design, construction, operation, and monitoring of a dam, the passage of legislation on Safety of Dams has placed additional emphasis on dam safety; and the inclusion of a chapter on this subject was believed to be important. This chapter presents procedures and references to other procedures for the evaluation and analyses of dam safety issues for both new and existing dam structures.

The appendix designations have been revised. The previous appendix A is now part of chapter 3, and the original appendix H, "Sedimentation," is now appendix A. A new appendix H, "Operation and Maintenance," presents a checklist for Operation and Maintenance inspections.

Appendix D, "Soil Mechanics Nomenclature," was updated to reflect current terminology in use from ASTM Designation D-653, "Standard Definitions of Terms and Symbols Relating to Soil and Rock Mechanics," and from USBR 3900, "Standard Definitions of Terms and Symbols Relating to Soil Mechanics." The latter reference is from the Bureau's recently revised *Earth Manual*, volume 2, "Test Designations."

Appendix E, "Construction of Embankments," has been revised to emphasize and more fully describe construction control philosophy and procedures. Several photographs of more modern equipment and construction techniques have been added. The "Rapid Method of Compaction Control" has been eliminated; the reader is now referred to the Bureau's *Earth Manual* for that procedure. Terminology has been updated to that currently used within the Bureau of Reclamation.

A discussion on concrete erosion has been added, and the discussion on abnormal set of concrete has been expanded in appendix F, "Concrete in Construction." The design of concrete mixes has been revised and includes revisions to tables, forms, and the steps involved in concrete mix design.

Appendix G, "Sample Specifications," has been updated to include guide specifications currently used by the Bureau of Reclamation.

Throughout the third edition, figures and illustrations have been revised and many new figures have been added.

The intent of this third edition is to expand discussion of concepts for design of small to large dams and to update the different approaches and procedures being employed in the current state-of-the-art of planning, design, construction, operation, and evaluation processes. The text is not intended in any way to encourage assumption of undue responsibility on the part of unqualified personnel, but rather to point out the importance of specialized training. Engineers who do not have specialized training in dam engineering should seek advice from experienced consultants.

This manual was prepared by personnel of the Bureau of Reclamation, U.S. Department of the Interior, Denver, Colorado, under the direction of Darrell Webber, Assistant Commissioner, Engineering and Research, with contributions from the staff of other Assistant Commissioners. Neil Parrett, Chief, Division of Dam and Waterway Design, established a three-man team to coordinate the assembly of this new edition: Harold K. Blair, Chairman, Head, Design Section No. 2 of the Concrete Dams Branch; Thomas N. McDaniel, Design Manager, Embankment Dams Branch; and Ronald D. Mohr, General Engineer, Document Systems Management Branch. Numerous engineers, technicians, and support personnel participated with this team in the preparation of this third edition and their efforts are greatly appreciated. Special recognition to the many authors, both current and past, is appropriate:

	Current Author(s)	*Past Author(s)*
Chapter 1	W.C. Dunkin, C.W. Huntley	A.F. Johnson
Chapter 2	J.C. Hokenstrom	E.A. Seamen, L.W. Davidson
Chapter 3	A.G. Cudworth, Jr.	D.L. Miller, R.A. Clark, S. Schamach
Chapter 4	T.N. McDaniel, H.K. Blair	H.G. Arthur
Chapter 5	S.R. Bartlett, R.C. Hatcher	J.W. Hilf
Chapter 6	T.N. McDaniel	H.G. Arthur
Chapter 7	T.N. McDaniel	R.W. Bock, L.W. Davidson
Chapter 8	H.L. Boggs, C.C. Hennig	A.T. Lewis, J.S. Conrad, E.L. Watson, L.M. Christiansen
Chapter 9	H.K. Blair, T.J. Rhone	C.J. Hoffman
Chapter 10	H.K. Blair, T.J. Rhone	C.J. Hoffman
Chapter 11	T.N. McDaniel, H.K. Blair	E.R. Lewandowski
Chapter 12	W.P. Gersch, L.J. Yocom	H.G. Arthur
Chapter 13	H.J. Warren, D.G. Achterberg, D.J. Trieste	
Appendix A	R.I. Strand, E.L. Pemberton	R.I. Strand

	Current Author(s)	Past Author(s)
Appendix B	R.I. Strand, T.J. Rhone	C.J. Hoffman, J.M. Lara, R.I. Strand
Appendix C	R.A. Simonds, H.K. Blair	P.K. Bock, C.J. Hoffman
Appendix D	R.A. Young	J.W. Hilf
Appendix E	T.N. McDaniel	J.W. Hilf
Appendix F	J.L. Hart	J.E. Backstrom, L.C. Porter, E.L. Ore, G.B. Wallace
Appendix G	J.L. Hart, R. Wright, R.H. Restad, T.N. McDaniel	R.E. Fink, N.F. Larkins, E.R. Lewandowski
Appendix H	W.P. Gersch, L.J. Yocom	

Preparation of the manuscript for publication was performed by the personnel of the Planning and Editing Section, Document Systems Management Branch, A. J. Huber, Branch Chief.

The Bureau of Reclamation expresses appreciation to the organizations who have permitted the use of their material in this text. There are occasional references to proprietary materials or products in this publication. These references are not to be construed in any way as an endorsement because the Bureau does not endorse proprietary products or processes of manufacturers or the services of commercial firms.

Preface to the Second Edition

The first edition of "Design of Small Dams" was published to serve primarily as a guide to safe practices for those concerned with the design of small dams in public works programs in the United States. Its publication was warmly received and, in the intervening years since then, it has been widely used in the United States, reprinted numerous times, and translated into many foreign languages, including Korean, Spanish, Japanese, and Chinese.

Since publication of the first edition of "Design of Small Dams," a large body of new literature has become available to dam designers, and many new design procedures used at the Bureau of Reclamation have been changed to reflect more modern techniques. As the number of changes in design techniques increased, it became apparent that their incorporation in a second edition would be beneficial to those individuals and agencies concerned with small dams.

The purpose of the second edition remains essentially the same as for the first edition. Many of the design procedures proposed in the first edition remain virtually unchanged. However, a number of new procedures have been developed by the Bureau and are currently in use. To make this new information available generally, it is included in the second edition. The increased concern of the Bureau of Reclamation with environmental problems is reflected by the inclusion of chapter II, "Ecological and Environmental Considerations." This chapter outlines some of the practical measures which may be taken to reduce the environmental and ecological impact of a project. Chapter III has been extensively revised to include current methods of design flood computation and to incorporate new graphical data.

Chapter V has been revised to reflect the availability of current information concerning foundation design and to include supplemental foundation investigation procedures. Chapter VI contains additional material on the design of earth dams, a discussion of the slurry trench method of cutoff construction, earthquake considerations, soil-cement design criteria, additional design details, and a more extensive reference list. The discussion of rockfill dam design has been considerably expanded in chapter VII to reflect the recent interest in rockfill dams and the growth of available information on this subject. Baffled spillway design procedures have been incorporated in chapter IX, and additional information on tunneling has been presented in chapter X. Appendix A includes new information on the estimation of rainfall runoff from soil cover data, and an expanded discussion of flow in natural channels is contained in appendix B. Appendix C includes new tables for the design of both reinforced concrete pressure pipe and cast-in-place conduits, and appendix E has a more complete discussion of the rapid method of compaction control. Appendix G has been expanded to include specifications concerning air and water pollution, and each specification has been updated to reflect current Bureau requirements. A new appendix on reservoir sedimentation is presented in appendix H, which outlines current procedures used to estimate the rate of sedimentation and the period of time before sediment will interfere with the useful functions of the reservoir. A convenient list of conversion factors is presented in appendix I to facilitate the increased utilization of metric units. Many minor changes have been made throughout the text to reflect current design and construction techniques.

It is intended that this book will provide the designer with an important source of information. However, this text is not intended in any way to encourage the assumption of undue responsibility on the part of unqualified personnel, and the use or application of the methods and data contained herein is strictly the responsibility of the person utilizing the material. Designs should reflect the actual site conditions and should not merely be patterned after a successful design used at another location.

Periodically, the names of Bureau of Reclamation projects and features are changed by acts of Congress, Federal agencies, etc., and therefore there may be a few inconsistencies in the project and feature names referred to in the text.

Some recent changes include the following:

Cachuma Dam to Bradbury Dam
Wasco Reservoir to Clear Lake
Soap Park Reservoir to Milly K. Goodwin Lake
Missouri River Basin Project to Pick-Sloan Missouri Basin Program.

There are occasional references to proprietary materials or products in this publication. These must not be construed in any way as an endorsement since the Bureau cannot endorse proprietary products or processes of manufacturers or the services of commercial firms for advertising, publicity, sales, or other purposes.

The second edition was prepared by the engineers of the Bureau of Reclamation, U.S. Department of the Interior, at its Engineering and Research Center in Denver, Colo. A number of engineers and technicians participated in the preparation of the second edition and in its critical review, and the efforts of these persons are greatly appreciated. Special recognition is given to H. G. Arthur, Director of Design and Construction, for his overall guidance in preparation of the text and to Dr. J. W. Hilf, Chief of the Division of Design, for his technical advice.

The second edition of the text was coordinated, edited, and much supplemental technical information provided by L. W. Davidson, Civil Engineer, Earth Dams Section. Detailed editorial guidance, final review, and preparation of the manuscript for publication was performed by W. E. Foote of the Technical Services Branch.

The Bureau of Reclamation again expresses grateful appreciation to those organizations which have permitted the use of material from their publications, especially the National Oceanic and Atmospheric Administration, U.S. Department of Commerce, for material used in chapter III; the Soil Conservation Service, U.S. Department of Agriculture, whose material was used in appendix A; the U.S. Geological Survey of the Department of the Interior, who supplied material used in chapter V; and the Corps of Engineers, U.S. Department of the Army, whose report on slurry trench construction was used in the preparation of chapter VI. Acknowledgments to other organizations which furnished lesser amounts of material are given throughout the text.

Preface to the First Edition

This book presents instructions, standards, and procedures for use in the design of small dams. It is intended to serve primarily as a guide to safe practices for those concerned with the design of small dams in public works programs in the United States. The book will serve this purpose in three ways: (1) It will provide engineers with information and data necessary for the proper design of small dams, (2) it will provide specialized and highly technical knowledge concerning the design of small dams in a form that can be used readily by engineers who do not specialize in this field, and (3) it will simplify design procedures for small earthfill dams.

An earlier publication, "Low Dams" which was prepared in 1938 by the National Resources Committee, presented much useful information on the design of small dams. In the 20 years that have elapsed since the printing of that book, however, there have been many technical advances in the design of dams, and the need for a new work incorporating the latest design techniques has become increasingly evident. It is believed that this book, "Design of Small Dams," will fill that need. The new book retains much of the format of "Low Dams" and some of the material from the earlier publication has been incorporated in the new one, but most of the text is wholly new.

Although this text is related almost exclusively to the design of small dams and appurtenant structures, it is important that the designer be familiar with the purposes of the project, the considerations influencing its justification, and the manner of arriving at the size and type of structure to be built. For these reasons, an outline discussion of a desirable project investigation has been included in chapter I.

Only the more common types of small dams now being constructed are discussed. These include concrete gravity, earthfill (rolled-type), and rockfill dams. Emphasis is placed on the design of rolled earthfill dams because they are the most common type. For the purpose of this book, small dams include those structures with heights above streambed not exceeding 50 feet except for concrete dams on pervious foundations. For the latter structures, the maximum height is further limited to dams whose maximum net heads (headwater to tailwater) do not exceed 20 feet. The text is not intended to cover dams of such large volumes that significant economies can be obtained by utilizing the more precise methods of design usually reserved for large dams. In recognition of the limited engineering costs justified for small dams, emphasis is placed on efficiency and relatively inexpensive procedures to determine the necessary design data. Simplified design methods are given to avoid the complex procedures and special investigations required for large dams or for unusual conditions. Adequate but not unduly conservative factors of safety are used in the simplified design methods.

Small dams are properly considered to be associated with small streams and drainage areas of limited extent. For these situations or for those in which spillway capacity is obtainable at relatively low cost, a sufficient approximation of the inflow design flood discharge may be determined by procedures given in this text. For important projects, particularly where the spillway cost is a major item of project cost and thus may have an important bearing on project feasibility, more exact and complex studies which are beyond the scope of this text may be justified.

This text is addressed to the designer of the structure and does not include in its scope the field of construction practices or methods. However, as the integrity of the design requires adherence to limiting specifications for materials and to the practice of good workmanship in construction, appendixes are included on "Construction of Embankments," "Concrete in Construction," and "Sample Specifications." More detailed specifications will be required to ensure proper construction of any specific dam.

This text is not intended in any way to encourage assumption of undue responsibility on the part of unqualified personnel, but rather to point out the importance of specialized training and to stimulate wider use of technically trained and experienced consultants.

This text should be of service to all concerned with the planning of small water storage projects, but in no way does it relieve any agency or person using it of the responsibility for safe and adequate design. The stated limitations of the design procedures should be heeded.

This book was prepared by the engineers of the Bureau of Reclamation, U.S. Department of the Interior, at Denver, Colo., under the direction of Grant Bloodgood, Assistant Commissioner and Chief Engineer, and L. G. Puls, Chief Designing Engineer. More than 30 engineers and many technicians participated in the preparation of the book or in its critical review, and the efforts of all of these are gratefully acknowledged. Special recognition is given to O. L. Rice, Chief of the Dams Branch, for his guidance and counsel, especially in determining the scope and treatment of the text.

The text was coordinated and edited by H. G. Arthur, Supervisor, Design Unit, Earth Dams Section, and final review and preparation of the manuscript for the printer was by E. H. Larson, Head, Manuals and Technical Records Section.

The Bureau of Reclamation expresses grateful appreciation to those organizations which have permitted the use of material from their publications, especially the Soil Conservation Service, U.S. Department of Agriculture, whose material was used in appendix A; and the Corps of Engineers, U.S. Department of the Army, whose Technical Manual TM 5-545 was freely used in the preparation of part D of chapter V. Acknowledgments to other organizations furnishing a lesser amount of material are given throughout the text.

CONTENTS

Section *Page*

F. CONCRETE SPECIFICATIONS

1. Concrete Specifications for Small Jobs

2. Concrete Specifications for Large Jobs

G. MISCELLANEOUS

TABLES

FIGURES

Figure *Page*

Figure *Page*

Figure *Page*

Figure *Page*

Figure *Page*

Figure *Page*

Chapter 1

Plan Formulation

The plan formulation process consists of identifying water-related needs and opportunities, developing alternative plans that provide for those needs and opportunities, and selecting the plan from among those alternatives that most effectively and efficiently provides for those needs and opportunities. Identification of the needs and opportunities is done primarily through public involvement, which includes the client and interested agencies. Plan formulation includes economic, social, environmental, engineering, hydrologic, land classification, legal, and institutional considerations.

Some of the more common water-related needs and opportunities are agricultural irrigation, municipal and industrial uses, power generation, flood control, instream flow augmentation, groundwater recharge, recreation, fish and wildlife habitat, and pollution abatement.

Plan formulation is an iterative process of comparing and selecting from alternative plans until the most acceptable plan is identified.

The following sequence of steps can serve as a helpful guide in plan formulation for a water resources study:

a. Preliminary identification of needs and opportunities.
b. Preliminary decisions on possible alternative plans for providing for the needs and opportunities.
c. Preliminary estimate of prospective differences among the alternatives, expressed in physical or nonmonetary terms.
d. Translation of descriptions of the differences among the alternatives into rough estimates of the benefits and costs in monetary terms, their times of occurrence, and their conversions to approximately equivalent values for a common time period.
e. Evaluation of nonmonetary effects of the plan, such as expected environmental and social effects.
f. Analysis and comparison of the rough monetary and nonmonetary estimates, and selection of those alternatives justifying further study.
g. Progressive refinements in physical, economic, environmental, and social evaluations; and selection of the more promising alternatives for more detailed study.
h. Progressive reexamination of problems and opportunities, alternative plans previously considered, and new alternatives that may be conceived in light of the results and refinements of progressive investigations and analyses.
i. Selection among the few remaining alternatives, giving consideration to more detailed studies, to comparative benefits and costs in monetary terms, and to differences among alternatives that are not readily reducible to monetary terms.
j. Selection of a single plan from the surviving alternatives, with further analysis using progressive levels of development to determine the optimum project size, and with consideration given to such concerns as pertinent laws, interstate compacts, and fiscal and administrative policies of relevant governing and financing organizations.

In practice, the relationships of engineering, economic, hydrologic, environmental, and social principles and criteria of plan formulation should be well understood. These relationships should be applied at all stages of the planning investigations and analyses from the beginning resource inventories and field inspections, through the increasing stages of refinement, to the time that one plan is selected for detailed investigation and evaluation.

The viability of proposed plans can be tested to a substantial degree by applying four tests: (1) completeness, (2) effectiveness, (3) efficiency, and (4) acceptability. These four tests are set out in the "Economic and Environmental Principles and Guidelines for Water and Related Land Resources Implementation Studies," dated March 10, 1983, as published by the U.S. Water Resources Council. While the tests, as extracted from that document and stated below, are intended for guidance for Federal agencies, they are appropriate for the evaluation of any plan for use of water resources.

The four tests are:

(1) *Completeness.*—The extent to which a given alternative plan provides and accounts for all necessary investments or other actions to ensure the realization of the planned effects. This may require relating the plan to other types of public and private plans if the other plans are crucial to realization of the contributions to the objective.

(2) *Effectiveness.*—The extent to which an alternative plan alleviates the specified problems and achieves the specified opportunities.

(3) *Efficiency.*—The extent to which an alternative plan is most cost effective in alleviating the specified problems and realizing the specified opportunities, consistent with protecting the nation's environment.

(4) *Acceptability.*—The workability and viability of the alternative plan with respect to acceptance by State and local entities and the public; and compatibility with existing laws, regulations, and public policy.

Ecological and Environmental Considerations

A. INTRODUCTION

2.1. ***Planning.***—Proper planning of dams requires a heightened awareness of our natural and human environment. Concern for environmental quality includes concern for the air and water, our natural ecological systems, and our cultural resources. Many laws and regulations now reflect this concern and require the consideration of environmental factors in planning.

Recent legislation and public concern require agencies to provide detailed statements of the significant environmental impacts of the proposed actions that can affect the quality of the environment. Reports meeting this requirement have become widely known as EIS's (Environmental Impact Statements). The demand for these reports has resulted in the establishment of numerous companies whose primary purpose is to develop technically adequate EIS's and extensive literature on environmental assessment methods [1, 2, 3, 4, 5, 6][1]. In many instances, the objective appears to be the development of an EIS; however, the goal is not better documents but decisions that better balance the use of water resources with the protection and enhancement of environmental quality.

Legislation and public concern have fostered a multiobjective approach to water development and more serious consideration of the potential environmental consequences of development. Environmental aspects must be considered from the initial planning and design of a project through its construction and operation [7, 8]. This requires the actions of an interdisciplinary (and in some cases interagency) team representing a wide range of expertise, including economics, engineering, design, biology, recreation, hydrology, and sociology. The disciplines involved in each study should be based on the natural and physical resources involved in that study. It is through the effective interactions of the team members that arrangements are made to accommodate environmental concerns early in the planning rather than through mitigating actions after the project is completed.

The enhancement of existing resources and the complete avoidance of adverse environmental effects are not always possible. In addition, benefits to one resource may result in the loss of another resource; e.g., impounding a stream may create a dependable water supply but eliminate terrestrial resources within the permanent pool area. It is the job of a planning team to develop plans that result in impacts that are more positive than negative. In many cases, adverse environmental impacts can be reduced significantly through the careful design, construction, and operation of project features.

The purpose of this chapter is to describe ways to plan for environmental resources and to identify some practical solutions to the common environmental problems that frequently confront project planners and designers. Because each project presents unique problems, the reader is encouraged to consult the publications referenced in the bibliography at the end of this chapter (sec. 2.10) and other publications on this subject. Designers and planners are encouraged to consult experts in the environmental sciences to identify the opportunities for enhancing natural resources and to develop creative solutions for lessening adverse impacts.

[1]Numbers in brackets refer to entries in the bibliography (sec. 2.10).

B. GENERAL ENVIRONMENTAL ISSUES

2.2. *Requirements.*—Subsequent sections of this chapter deal with the environmental issues generally encountered in all water resource development projects. A list of environmental factors that might be important in a specific project would be extensive. Therefore, each study should identify, or "scope," the environmental issues that could significantly affect planning. In many instances, these issues are specific legal requirements (local, State, or Federal regulations) that must be addressed. The appropriate agencies should be consulted for compliance procedures. In the United States, the appropriate Federal agencies include the Fish and Wildlife Service, Forest Service, National Park Service, National Marine Fisheries Service, and the Environmental Protection Agency. State agencies include game and fish, recreation, public health, historic preservation, and water resource organizations. Each study should involve a unique combination of agencies, depending on the resources involved.

2.3. *Categories of Resources.*—The general categories of resources that should be considered include air quality, water quality, prime and unique farmlands, wild and scenic rivers, endangered species, wetlands, unique natural areas, wilderness areas, sound quality, visual quality, and geologic formations [9].

C. FISH AND WILDLIFE CONSIDERATIONS

2.4. *General.*—Experience in Federal water resources development indicates that fish and wildlife resources may represent a major portion of the environmental concerns that should be addressed before project construction and operation. These resources include animal species with economic importance because of their uses as food and for commerce, species with recreational importance because of their uses in hunting and fishing, and endangered species with ecological importance because of the concern for their protection. Species that are indicators of environmental health and species with esthetic appeal should also be considered.

Because of the complexity of fish and wildlife resource problems that, on the surface, appear simple, it is imperative that professional fish and wildlife biologists be actively involved in project planning and design. Those professionals familiar with the resources in the planning area should be consulted early in the planning phase. The appropriate agencies can supply valuable information on local wildlife habitats and populations. Their involvement can result in the avoidance of critical resource areas, and their suggestions can help enhance particular resources. Where adverse impacts are unavoidable, they can recommend actions (designs and management methods) that can partially or completely mitigate project impacts.

Reservoirs can be of significant benefit to certain fish and wildlife species when the biological requirements of these species are considered during the planning, design, and operation of the reservoir project. The following sections discuss how fish and wildlife may be affected by dams and reservoirs, and describe certain features that can be incorporated into a project design to reduce adverse impacts or to directly benefit certain groups of species.

2.5. *Ecological and Environmental Considerations for Fish.*—Impacts to fish and other aquatic life resulting from the construction of a dam and subsequent impoundment of water can be caused by the change from flowing to standing water conditions, by the modification of downstream flows, by changes in temperature and water quality conditions, or by the addition of physical barriers to both upstream and downstream movements.

The most dramatic impact is caused by the conversion of a portion of a free-flowing stream or river system to a standing-water system. Depending on the numerous physical and chemical variables of the site, the temperature and water quality conditions could change so as to significantly affect project uses, including fish and wildlife and recreation. Water quality issues in reservoir design are discussed in greater detail in part E of this chapter.

In most instances, either the species of fish that occupy the new reservoir are different from those in the stream, or the ratio of the various species contributing to the total population is significantly changed. If a significant fishery exists in the stream or if the project is to provide fishing opportunities, the planning study needs data accurate enough to assist in the design of alternatives that will maximize fishery benefits in the new reservoir, but will avoid adverse impacts downstream. The agencies responsible for fish management should be consulted for such a project.

Assessment of existing and potential fishery resources may, depending on the significance of the resource and the amount of available data, require sophisticated population or habitat studies. Where migratory species (salmon, trout, shad, striped bass, etc.) are important, tagging or radio-tracking techniques may be necessary. In recent years, there has been an increased emphasis on more accurate determination of the flow conditions that optimize fish habitat for the various life stages (spawning, fry, juvenile, and adult) [10, 11, 12]. Depending on the resource involved, the study methods can vary in the amount of time, money, and technical expertise needed to obtain adequate information. Predictions of reservoir populations are often made by comparing the physical and chemical properties with those of other reservoirs in the same area [13].

In cases where stored water will be used to generate hydroelectric power in a peaking pattern, the installation of a reregulation dam downstream from the discharge point should be considered if a significant fishery resource exists, or high recreational use is expected. This reregulation structure should balance high and low flow conditions which, if unregulated, could strand fish and recreationists, expose spawning areas, and scour the stream bottom, possibly reducing the production of aquatic food.

In relatively small rivers and streams, it is often possible to create habitat conditions that increase fish populations. Where pools are limiting, the construction of bank deflectors or small dams can direct the current so that scour holes are developed [14, 15] (see fig. 2-1). These structures can be very effective, yet they require little maintenance if properly located and constructed. Wing deflectors can be placed to direct the stream current to avoid excessive erosion, permitting the area to stabilize and reducing the amount of sediment entering the stream. Riprap and rock-filled gabions can also effectively control erosion. Underbank (escape) cover can be developed through the construction of overhanging structures: using logs securely anchored into the bank and covered by planking and sod (fig. 2-2). Where spawning habitat is limited or inaccessible because of the dam, construction of spawning channels and riffle areas have sometimes been beneficial (fig. 2.3).

When the construction of a dam will create a barrier to upstream and downstream fish movements where fish populations are an important resource (e.g., salmon), the design should include facilities for fish passage. Several design features are possible alternatives. Although none of these are completely effective in passing fish, they can reduce adverse impacts significantly. The types of structures include fishways (or ladders), conduits, and turbine bypasses [14]. At some facilities, trapping and hauling have been selected as the most cost-effective solution.

The fish ladder is perhaps the most common method used to facilitate fish passage. These structures generally consist of a series of stepped pools separated by weirs. Another type of passage structure, the Denil-type fishway, consists of a chute with energy dissipating vanes in the sides and bottom that reduce the water velocity enough to permit fish to ascend. Figure 2-4 shows yet another design, the Alaska steep pass fishway, at Ice Harbor Dam in Alaska. [14].

To direct fish to passage areas and to reduce the possibility of their entry into intake structures, several types of excluding devices have been used. These devices include stationary and moving screens (fig. 2-5), louvered deflectors, and electric weirs [14]. Where specific requirements for fish passage or exclusion are required, designs may be developed with the help of the U.S. Fish and Wildlife Service or the State fishery agency.

Within the reservoir, there are several factors that should be considered and evaluated to enhance the value of the anticipated fishery. Results from water quality and temperature studies should indicate whether the reservoir will thermally stratify. If stratification is expected, the reservoir may be suitable for management as a "two-story" fishery, with warm-water species occupying the upper layer (epilimnion), and cool or cold-water species established in the lower layer (hypolimnion). Management of the hypolimnion assumes that oxygen will be available in an acceptable concentration, which is determined in the water-quality studies. In stratified reservoirs, the installation of a multilevel intake structure may be desirable for both reservoir and downstream management.

When preparing the reservoir area, it is often advantageous to leave some trees and shrubs in the

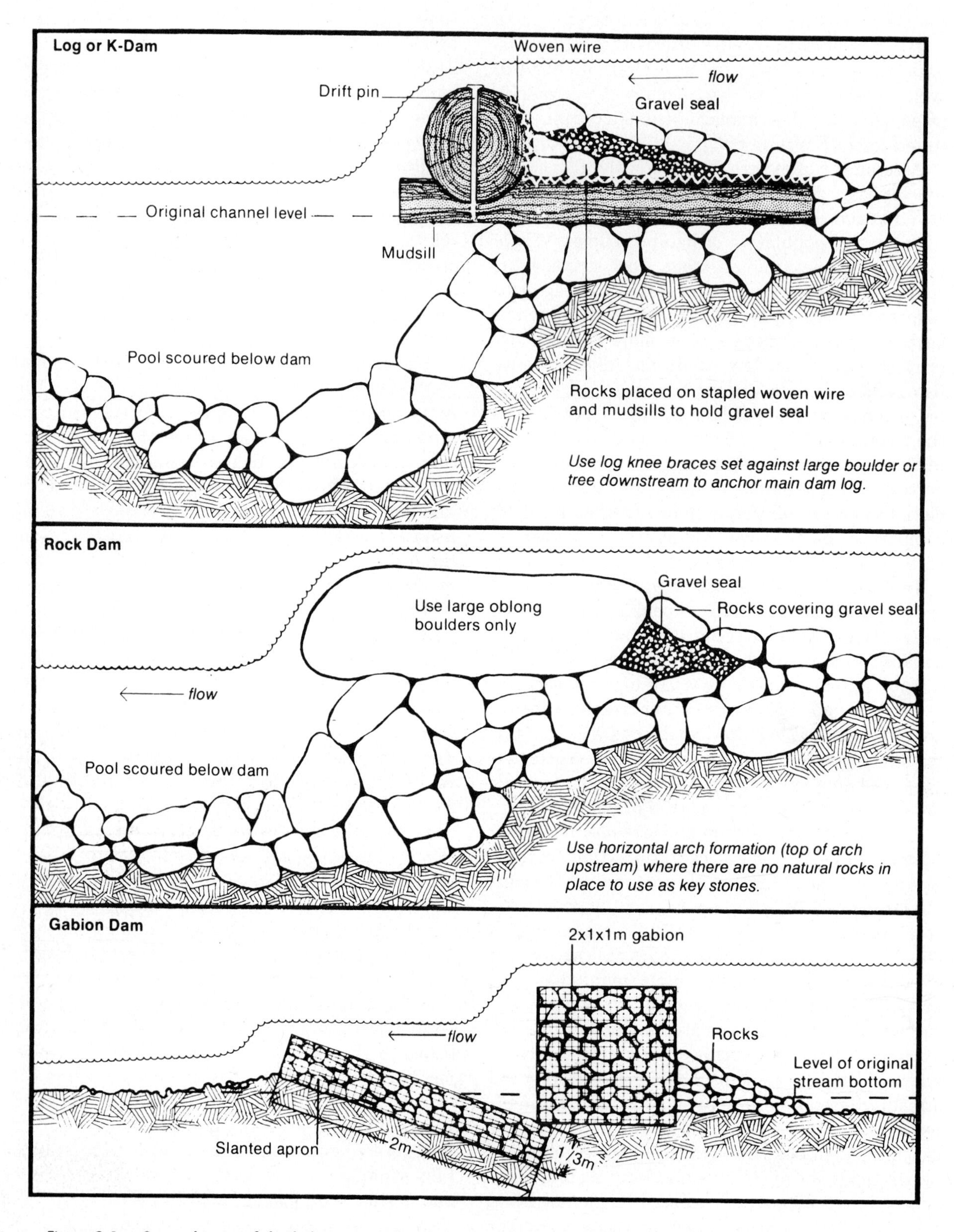

Figure 2-1.—Several types of check dams. Scour holes developed by these dams create habitat conditions that increase fish populations. 103–D–1793.

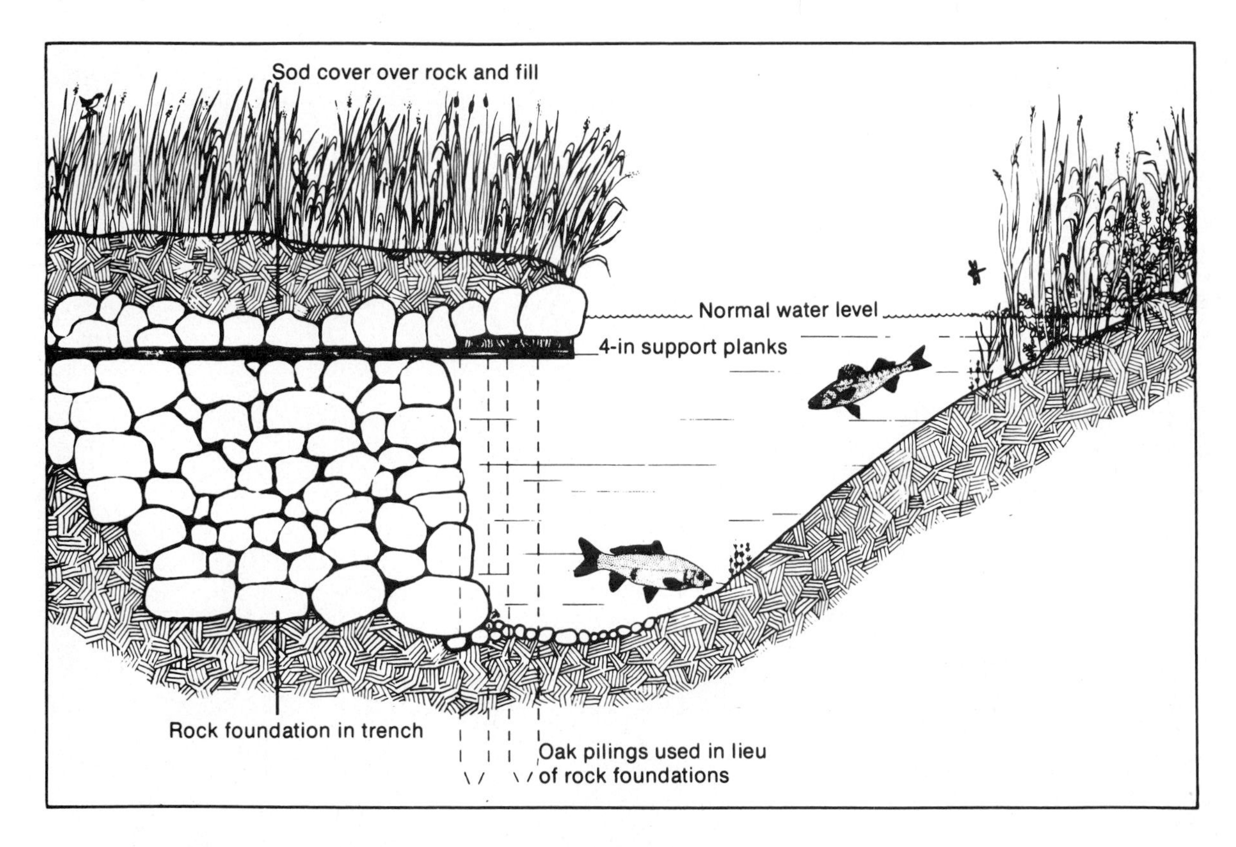

Figure 2-2.—Construction schematics for artificial overhead cover structures. From [16]. 103–D–1794.

Figure 2-3.—Artificial spawning channels along the Tehama-Colusa Canal. Part of the Central Valley Project, California. P801–D–81027

Figure 2-4.—Alaska steep pass fishway, fish ladder. Ice Harbor Dam, Alaska. P801-D-81028

permanent pool area as cover and feeding areas for fish [16]. This should be balanced with the recreational objectives of boating and water skiing. Artificial spawning areas can also be developed with successful results in certain situations (e.g., using stone substitutes).

It may be desirable to eradicate fish from drainages contributing to the reservoir to reduce the influence of undesirable species on a new reservoir and to provide stocked sport fish with at least a temporary advantage. The use of fish toxicants, such as rotenone, is usually the preferred method. The decision to use fish toxicants should be made after consultation with Federal and State fish agencies as part of an overall fish-management plan.

Where possible, the reservoir should contain a permanent conservation pool to ensure the continued survival of fish species. When pool levels are lowered in response to other project purposes, the changes should generally be gradual to avoid stranding desirable species. However, it may be advantageous at times to effect a rapid drawdown to strand eggs of undesirable species, such as carp. At other times, the fish manager may recommend increasing the water level, then holding it constant to enhance the spawning of desirable species.

2.6. *Ecological and Environmental Considerations for Wildlife.*—Impacts to wildlife resulting from the construction and operation of a reservoir can be caused by the loss and modification of their habitat and the disruption of movement patterns. These impacts may be caused by direct and by indirect actions. Certain impacts, such as inundation of habitat within the reservoir area, are unavoidable if project purposes are to be met. Nevertheless, other impacts can be reduced through design considerations, and still others can be offset only by including separable wildlife features.

Ecological complexities and legal requirements make it imperative that wildlife agencies be involved from the initial project planning. An important contribution of these agencies can be the identification of important or critical wildlife areas. Foreknowledge of this kind can often be used to

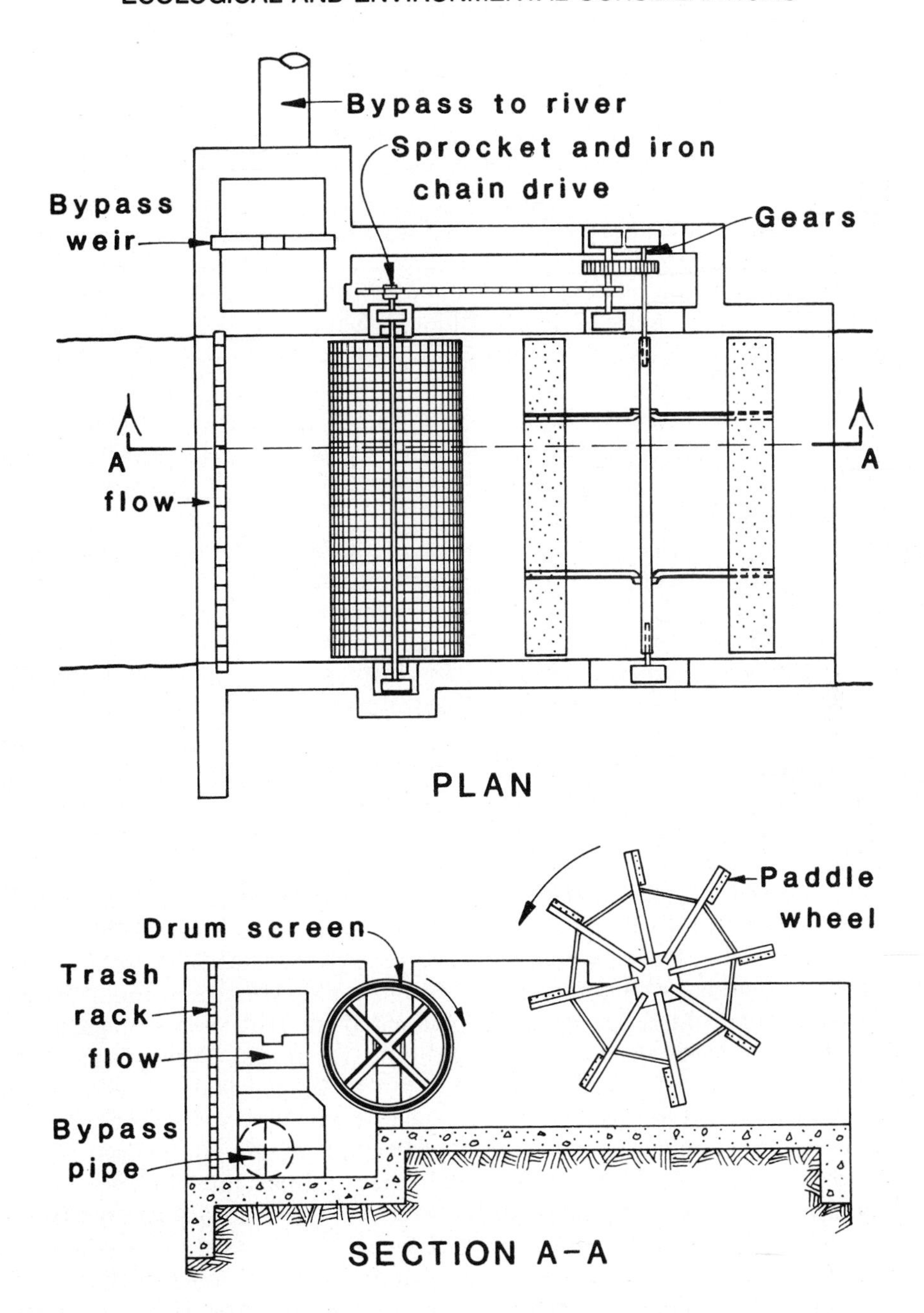

Figure 2-5.—Horizontal drum-screen, fish-passage structure. From [14]. 103-D-1795.

avoid adverse impacts to these resource areas.

In the past, the importance of a wildlife resource was measured, to a large extent, by its significance as a recreation base (hunting, nature study, etc.). However, in the past 10 to 12 years, the emphasis has shifted to methods that measure various ecological factors. These methods vary in both the type of information developed and their time and cost of application. The methods now used include population census, remote sensing, radio telemetry, habitat analysis, and mathematical models [17, 18, 19, 20].

To offset the loss of inundated wildlife habitat, the wildlife value of noninundated areas may be increased (increase carrying capacity). Perhaps the most widely used practice to increase the value of an area for wildlife is to exclude livestock (and humans in some instances) by fencing, while allowing wildlife to pass. Fencing is also used to exclude wildlife from hazardous areas and from areas where wildlife could interfere with project operations (e.g., canals) or could be a hazard to humans (e.g., in an automobile collision). The kinds of animals to be excluded must be considered in the design of the fence. By varying the fence design, livestock can be excluded while permitting antelope to pass over or under the fence (fig. 2-6).

Wildlife habitat can also be improved through the selective planting of the trees, shrubs, and grasses that provide needed food and cover (fig. 2-7). Depending on the frequency and length of inundation, areas within the boundaries of the fluctuating pool can be managed effectively for wildlife. The types of plants selected are of critical importance and should be selected by experienced wildlife managers [21, 22]. Where project lands are already under agricultural development or where lands are suitable for cropping, wildlife benefits can be obtained through a share-cropping arrangement, in which the user is required to leave a portion of each year's crop to provide winter food and cover. Proceeds from the lease of the land can be used to help offset annual wildlife operation and management costs.

Enhancement of the habitat for some species may occur as a result of dam construction. Additional nesting sites for certain wildlife species (e.g., ducks, geese, and raptors) can be developed through the use of constructed nesting devices (fig. 2-8). Constructed islands can also serve as excellent nest sites provided water-level fluctuations are not great during the nesting season (fig. 2-9). The construction of subimpoundments within the main pool area can provide pair and brood habitat for waterfowl and habitat for other marsh species. These subimpoundments can also serve as sediment and nutrient traps in areas on the contributing watershed where erosion is a problem.

At projects where power is produced, high-voltage towers, poles, and transmission wires can pose serious obstacles for birds. In addition to strikes (flying into a structure), large birds, such as eagles and hawks, risk electrocution. The careful design of these features can greatly reduce their potential for adverse impacts [23]. In addition, transmission-line rights-of-way can be planted with vegetation that will not interfere with operation or maintenance, but will benefit many species of wildlife.

Operation (storage and release of water) of the reservoir can usually be modified to benefit wildlife and fish without affecting other project purposes. Figure 2-10 presents a graphic representation of typical seasonal water-level fluctuations at a warm-water reservoir. In such reservoirs, operational plans can be devised that increase game and forage fish production and waterfowl use, while decreasing turbidity and rough fish populations.

Canals associated with many reservoir projects pose special problems to wildlife and wildlife managers [24, 25]. Although canals may not cause a significant loss of habitat, they can trap thirsty or migrating animals unless certain design features are incorporated. The problem occurs when wildlife are attracted to open canals for water or try to cross a canal that has interrupted a seasonal or daily migration route. An animal can become trapped and eventually drown in a canal because of its steep or smooth sides or its high water velocity. This problem can be especially critical in areas with large populations of deer and antelope.

To reduce the severity of this problem, canals can be fenced or even covered in certain critical, high-use areas. Where canals are fenced, drinking access areas should be provided. This usually involves a simple flattening of the side slopes. To permit crossing, bridges should be constructed at specified intervals and at regular crossing points (fig. 2-11). In areas where fencing or covering are impractical, the canal side slopes should be roughened or provided with cleats to allow escape. In addition, turnouts and deflectors can be installed to direct animals into the areas of reduced current where escape ramps are located (fig. 2-12). Once a project is operational, it may be necessary to add certain escape or access restriction features after problem areas have been empirically identified. Nevertheless, animal drowning cannot be completely avoided.

Wildlife and water resource development can exist in harmony if there is a commitment on the part of developers and environmental groups to compromise. The important point is that a wildlife management plan should be developed by professional wildlife managers. A well-formulated plan can benefit wildlife resources, generate revenues to help offset management costs, and help create a positive public image.

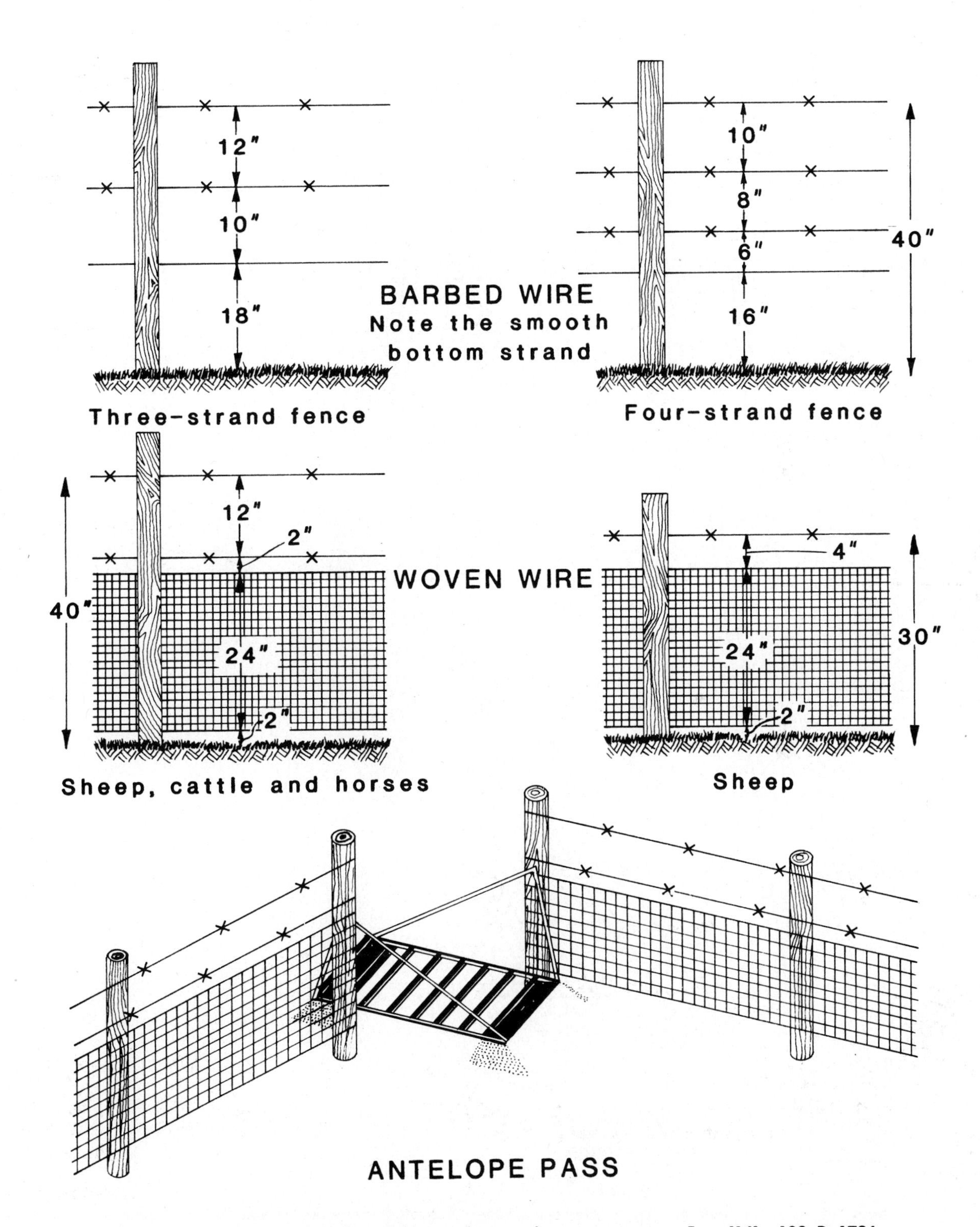

Figure 2-6.—Fences passable for antelope and an antelope pass structure. From [14]. 103–D–1796.

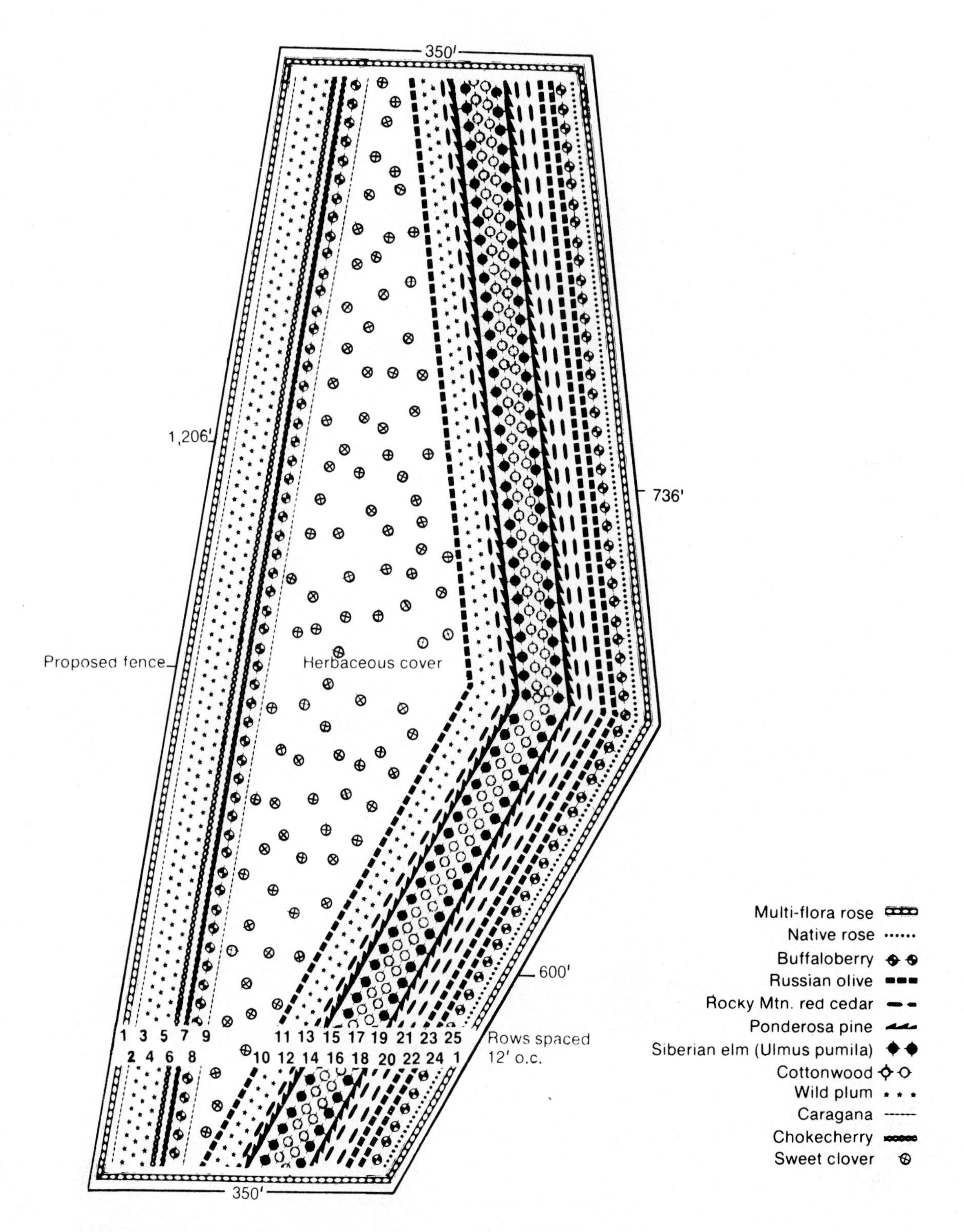

Figure 2-7.—Typical food and cover planting scheme. Angostura Reservoir, South Dakota. From [14]. 103–D–1797.

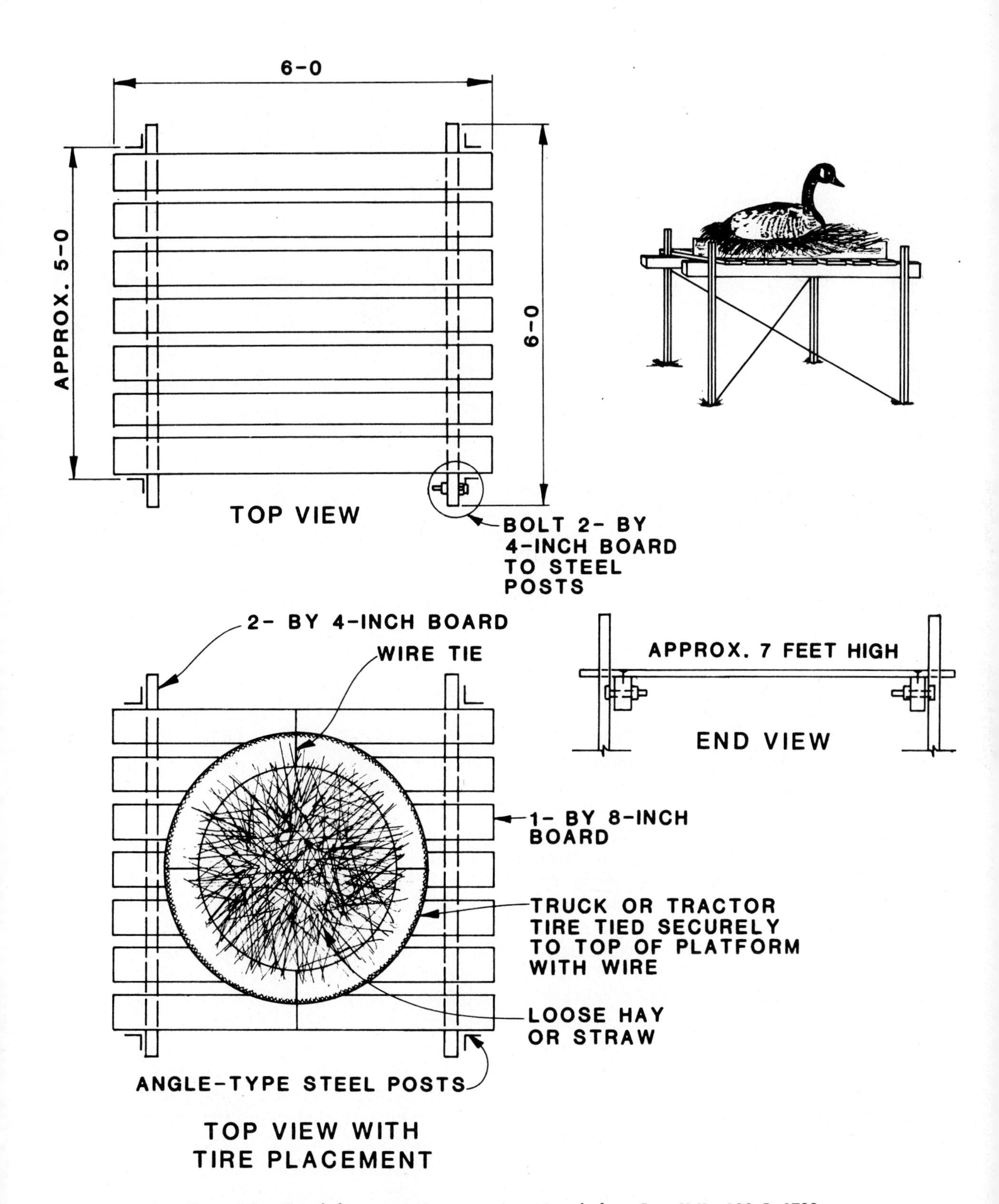

Figure 2-8.—Details for constructing a goose-nesting platform. From [14]. 103–D–1798.

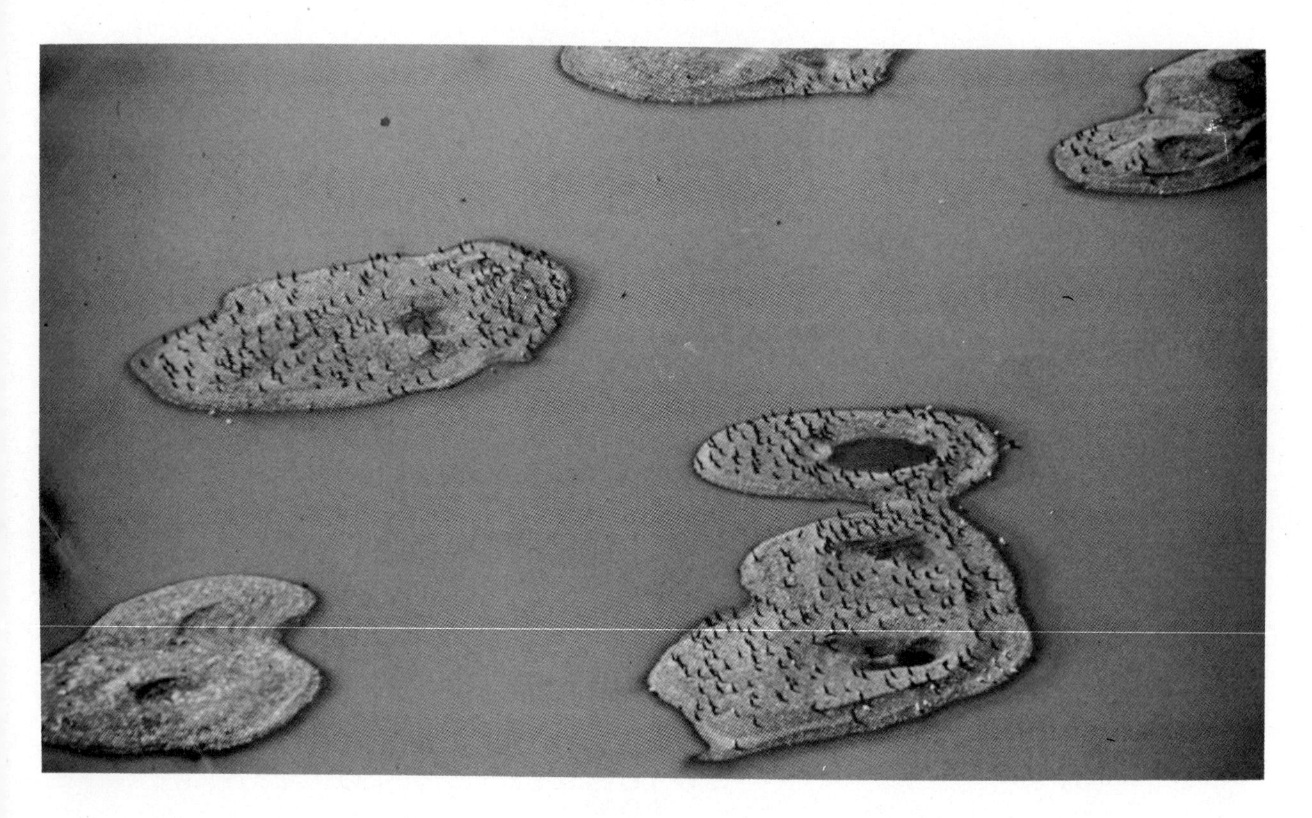

Figure 2-9.—Constructed nesting islands. Canyon Ferry Reservoir, Montana. From [14]. P801–D–81029

D. WATER QUALITY

2.7 *General.*—The quality of the water impounded by a dam must be considered in the planning and design of a project. If the water is of inferior quality for intended users (irrigators, municipalities, industry), if it unnecessarily impairs the habitat for the fish and wildlife in the reservoir or downstream, or if the reservoir is subject to excessive algal growth that reduces the attractiveness of the area for recreation, then the reservoir should be considered a partial failure because anticipated project benefits will not be fully realized.

In the past, water quality issues were seldom considered except as an afterthought. More recently, attempts have been made to evaluate these effects as part of the environmental impact analysis. Like other environmental issues, water quality considerations should be an integral part of the planning and design process to avoid water quality-related failures. In general, the analyses described in the following paragraphs should be completed for each reservoir. If any of these analyses indicate potential problems, the project should be reexamined to determine whether changes can reduce these problems to an acceptable level.

(a) *Water Quality Analysis.*—The suitability of the water quality for the intended uses should be determined. A sufficient number of water samples should be collected and analyzed to accurately characterize the water to be stored. The number of samples and the extent of laboratory analysis required depends somewhat on the intended uses.

Water intended solely for irrigation may be described adequately by the analysis of 12 to 20 representative samples collected over a typical annual cycle and analyzed for common ions and boron. However, water for human consumption should be analyzed for all contaminants listed in the appropriate drinking water standard (e.g., "Environmental Protection Agency National Primary and Secondary Drinking Water Regulations"). Several years of data may be required to properly evaluate the suitability of potable water. For aquatic life,

Calendar Period	Level Manipulation	Habitat and Population Improvement Purposes
Jan 1 – Feb 28	Hold low	Provide spring runoff and flood capacity; allow weather to clean rocky shorelines of algae, silt.
Mar 1 – May 15	Increase gradually	Inundate vegetation and rocks for improved spawning; reduce walleye losses through dam outlets.
May 16 – Jun 30	Hold high	Maintain fish nursery habitat; decompose vegetation for nutrients and turbidity control.
Jul 1 – Jul 15	Decrease abruptly	Expose shorelines for revegetation; dessicate rough fish spawn.
Jul 16 – Sep 30	Hold low	Expose forage fish to predation; allow vegetation to mature.
Oct 1 – Nov 15	Increase gradually	Partially inundate vegetation for increased waterfowl food and cover.
Nov 16 – Dec 15	Hold intermediate	Maintain for maximum waterfowl use.
Dec 16 – Dec 31	Decrease gradually	Reduce ice and wave damage to vegetation; prepare for next season.

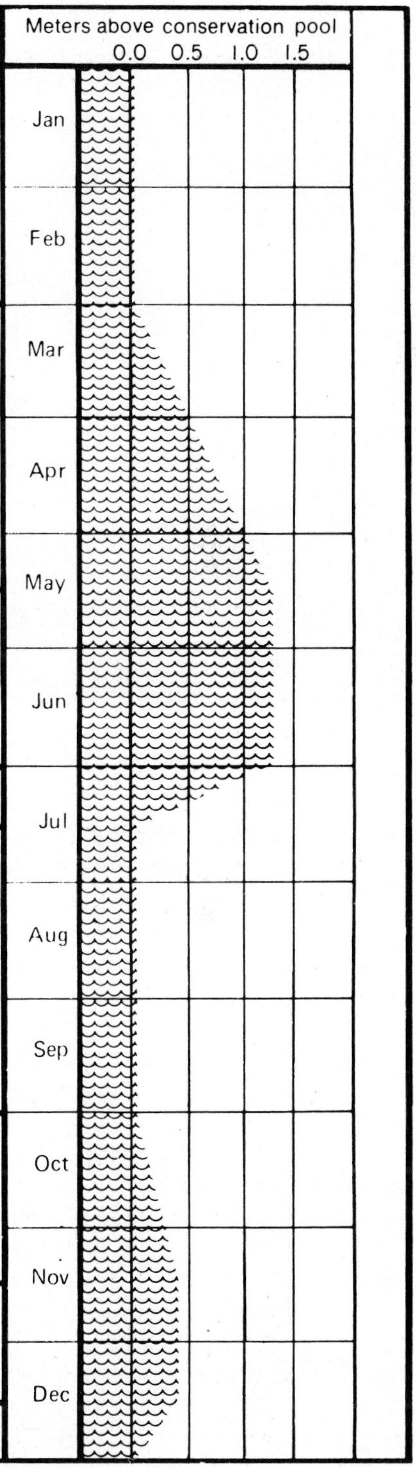

Figure 2-10.—Typical water-level manipulation plan for a warm-water reservoir. From [26]. 103–D–1799.

Figure 2-11.—Fenced wildlife crossing over Tiger Creek Canal, California. From [14]. P801-D-81030

other water-quality parameters are important: an appropriate sampling program generally focuses on common ions, physical properties, dissolved gasses, trace metals, pesticides, and nutrients. The extent of sampling for each of the above groups depends on the intended uses of the water and the results of initial analyses.

(b) *Effects of Design and Operating Criteria.*— The effects of proposed design and operating criteria on the water quality should be evaluated both in the reservoir and downstream. Various tools are available to perform some of the required analyses. One of the basic factors that affects most water-quality parameters is the temperature regime. Fortunately, fairly reliable temperature simulation models are available to predict temperature profiles in reservoirs [27, 28, 29]. From the temperature simulation, it is possible to determine the time of initial stratification, the strength of the thermocline, and the temperature profile. Some of the significant factors affecting the thermal regime are solar radiation, air temperature, sky cover, wind speed, location (latitude, longitude, and elevation), amount and location of inflows and discharges, and the depth, surface area, and volume of the reservoir. The temperature regime influences many of the other measures of water quality both in the reservoir and below the dam.

Some of these other parameters, such as the TDS (total dissolved solids), dissolved oxygen, and nutrients, can be also modeled [28]. However, except for the TDS and to a lesser extent dissolved oxygen, mathematical simulations of these parameters for planned reservoirs are generally less reliable than temperature simulation models. Other tools useful in water quality analyses include physical modeling, algal assay tests, and anaerobic lake-bottom simulations. The procedures for assessing the eutrophication potential of planned reservoirs have been described in other texts [30].

Water quality can be affected by the design and operational features of the reservoir. The obvious impacts are those associated with the location of outlets. Bottom withdrawals result in cooler water

Figure 2-12.—Revised Richmond deer-escape ramp. Water flow is from left to right. From [14]. P801-D-81031

downstream and warmer water in the reservoir. Withdrawals from the epilimnion (from near the surface) result in warmer water downstream and cooler water in the reservoir. Bottom withdrawals also tend to flush nutrients and sediment out of the reservoir. The timing of releases can also influence the water quality. Other effects may be more subtle. It is clear, however, that water quality aspects should be evaluated for various reservoir and outlet configurations.

Once the reservoir models are operational, it is fairly easy to evaluate the effects on the water quality of changes in the reservoir—its size, outlet configuration, or operating procedures. The analysis of those constituents not subject to direct simulation is usually aided by temperature and dissolved oxygen models.

(c) *Design Considerations.*—Water quality is affected by various elements of the design. The primary factor in controlling water quality is the selection of the damsite. Ideally, the dam should be located on a reach of stream that has high quality water. Obvious sources of pollution, such as contaminated tributaries, old mine spoils rich in heavy metals, and saline springs, should be avoided. Once the site is selected, water quality can be controlled somewhat by designing the outlet works, as discussed previously in section 2.7(b). It is important to specify the water-quality goals of the project in advance because of the possible tradeoff between water quality in the reservoir and water quality downstream. Other design factors include the extent to which vegetation is removed from the reservoir and the possibility of eliminating potential sources of pollution, e.g., excavation of mine tailings in the watershed or pool area.

The design should provide some flexibility to deal with water quality problems. For example, multilevel outlets can be provided so that water from different elevations can be blended to control (within limits) the quality of the outflows (fig. 2.13).

Nevertheless, if a reservoir does not stratify, multilevel outlets are ineffective. In the early 1960's, a reservoir was constructed in Kansas with a four-

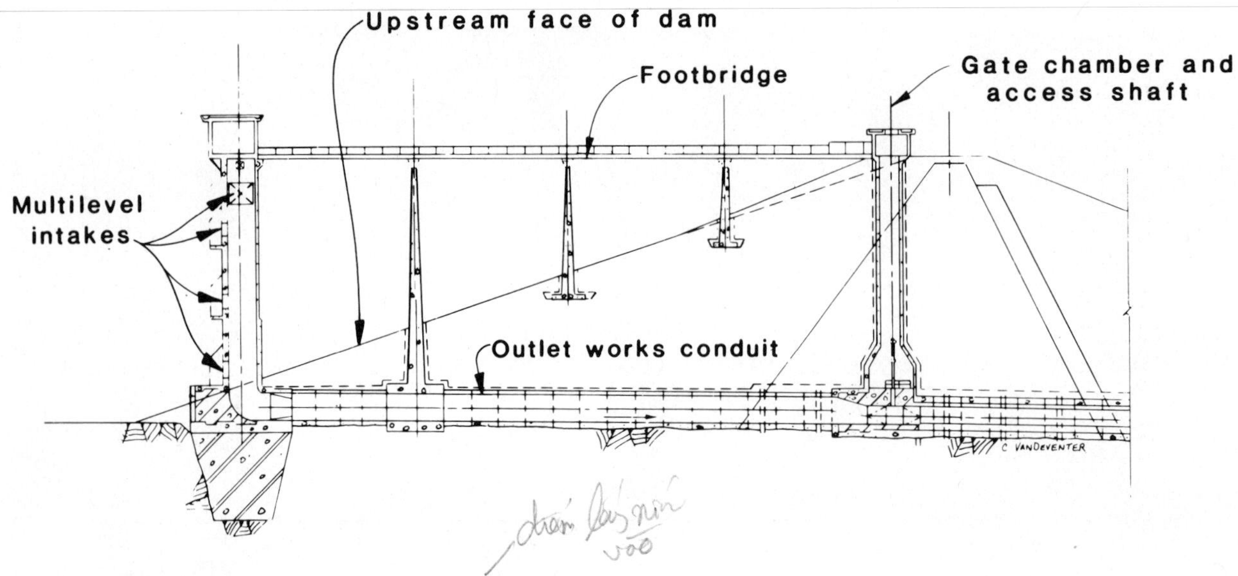

Figure 2-13.—Multipurpose intake structure with multilevel outlet potential. 103–D–1800.

level outlet structure. However, because its reservoir is wide, shallow, and subject to considerable wind action, the waters are consistently well-mixed; therefore, the multiple outlets have little effect on the water quality. Thus, a thorough understanding of stratification is vital for an effective design.

An aeration system can be designed to improve the quality of the reservoir water by destratifying the water column and increasing the dissolved oxygen content (fig. 2-14). An aeration system can also reduce the concentrations of many contaminants, which remain in solution only under the anaerobic (no oxygen) conditions that occur in the hypolimnion of a stratified reservoir.

At a reservoir in Colorado, which may have a tendency to develop excessive concentrations of heavy metals at certain times of the year, the underwater portion of a reaeration system (perforated pipes and the necessary supports) was designed and constructed before the reservoir was filled. The rest of the reaeration system (motors and compressors to provide air to the underwater pipes) will be installed, if needed, when the reservoir is operational. A reaeration system could also be designed and installed after the reservoir is completed. Some reservoirs in California have been successfully retrofitted with diffused-air systems, which provide partial destratification and control the temperature and dissolved oxygen in the reservoir. These systems have improved the water quality substantially.

Other designs that benefit water quality include the modification of turbines to increase the dissolved oxygen in discharges through powerplants and the installation of deflectors on outlet works to reduce nitrogen supersaturation below the dam. However, these problems do not normally affect small dams.

E. ARCHEOLOGICAL AND HISTORICAL CONSIDERATIONS

2.8. *Requirements.*—During the planning of a water development project, a professional archeologist should conduct a thorough search of the records relating to the location of known historic and archeological sites within the project area. The Government agencies responsible for the preservation of such resources should be consulted about the legal requirements. Furthermore, the entire project area should be surveyed to identify previously undiscovered sites. Emphasis should be placed on those areas that are to be physically modified (e.g., the reservoir area, damsite, and recreation sites). Before construction, the entire project area should be subjected to a complete ground survey [31]. If historical or archeological sites are discovered during construction, activity should be stopped and a professional archeologist should be contacted.

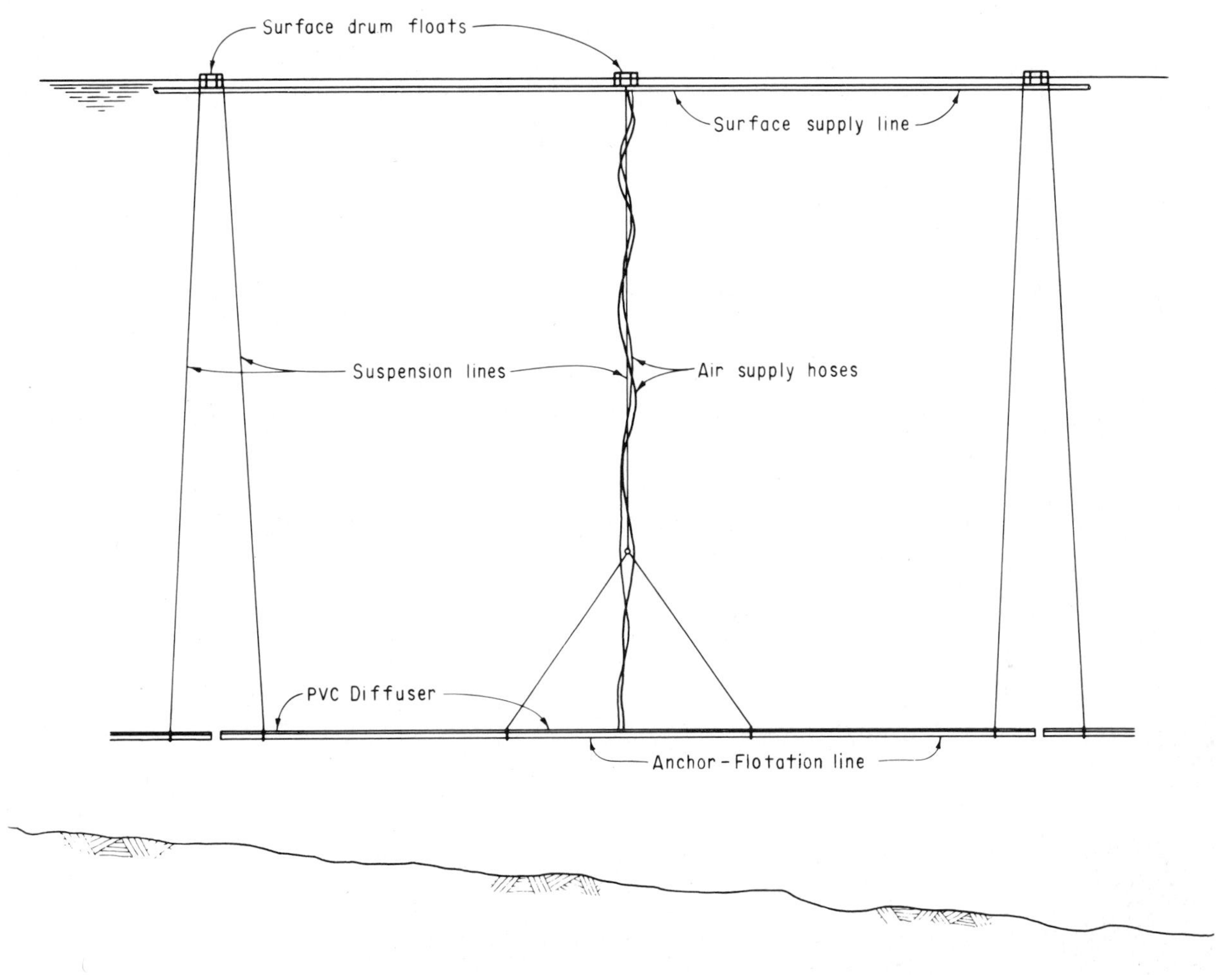

Figure 2-14.—Diffused-air reservoir aeration system. 103–D–1801.

F. RECREATION CONSIDERATIONS

2.9. ***Planning for Recreation Facilities.***—It is generally acknowledged that, if access is available, a reservoir will be used for recreation. Water attracts people as a recreation medium (e.g., for swimming, fishing, and boating) and as a general feature of the area that enhances other activities, such as picnicking, camping, and sightseeing. In the planning and design of a reservoir, every effort should be made to maximize recreation benefits in a manner consistent with other project purposes. In most instances, recreation is not a major purpose of small projects, but can make an important contribution to overall benefits.

Before serious planning can be undertaken, the type and amount of use for recreation must be estimated. Assistance should be sought from the Governmental outdoor recreation agencies, and the State Comprehensive Outdoor Recreation Plans should be consulted. In developing a recreation plan for a reservoir, it is necessary to estimate total use and determine how the use will be distributed between day use and overnight, or long-term, activities. The proximity to population centers, unique qualities of the area, and project purposes affect the type and amount of use expected.

Where minimal use is anticipated or where sponsors cannot be found to share the costs of recreation facilities and management, minimum facilities for health and safety may be provided. This may involve one or more parking areas with sanitation facilities, trash disposal sites, and a boat ramp.

When more than the minimum facilities are

needed, design and planning become much more complex. In these situations, the recreation planner, landscape architect, fish and wildlife biologists, and representatives of the other necessary disciplines must work together to avoid conflicts with other project purposes.

Reservoir operation has perhaps the most significant effect on the location and design of recreation facilities. For irrigation and flood-control reservoirs, and to a much lesser extent hydroelectric power reservoirs, the extent and duration of water-level fluctuations determine the location of recreation features. If boat docks and launch facilities are to be installed in these types of reservoirs, they must be designed to be functional over the range of water levels expected (fig. 2-15 shows a Corps of Engineers' design for a floating dock that is functional over a range of water levels). In addition, facilities to be located within the flood pool must be designed to withstand specified periods of inundation without significant damage.

Usually, water-dependent features should not be located at the upstream end of a reservoir. Deposition of sediment over time can result in the recession of the shoreline and the creation of marsh-type conditions, leaving the facilities "high and dry."

In many cases, zoning both the water and land surfaces can reduce the conflicts among the interests of people, fish and wildlife, and project operations. Power boating may be excluded from all or parts of a reservoir to avoid conflicts in areas expected to experience much fishing, in areas of critical importance to breeding waterfowl or nesting raptors, in fish-spawning areas, and around swimming areas. Land areas can be zoned to separate day-use from overnight facilities and trailers from tent camps, and to limit activities in areas intended for low-intensity use.

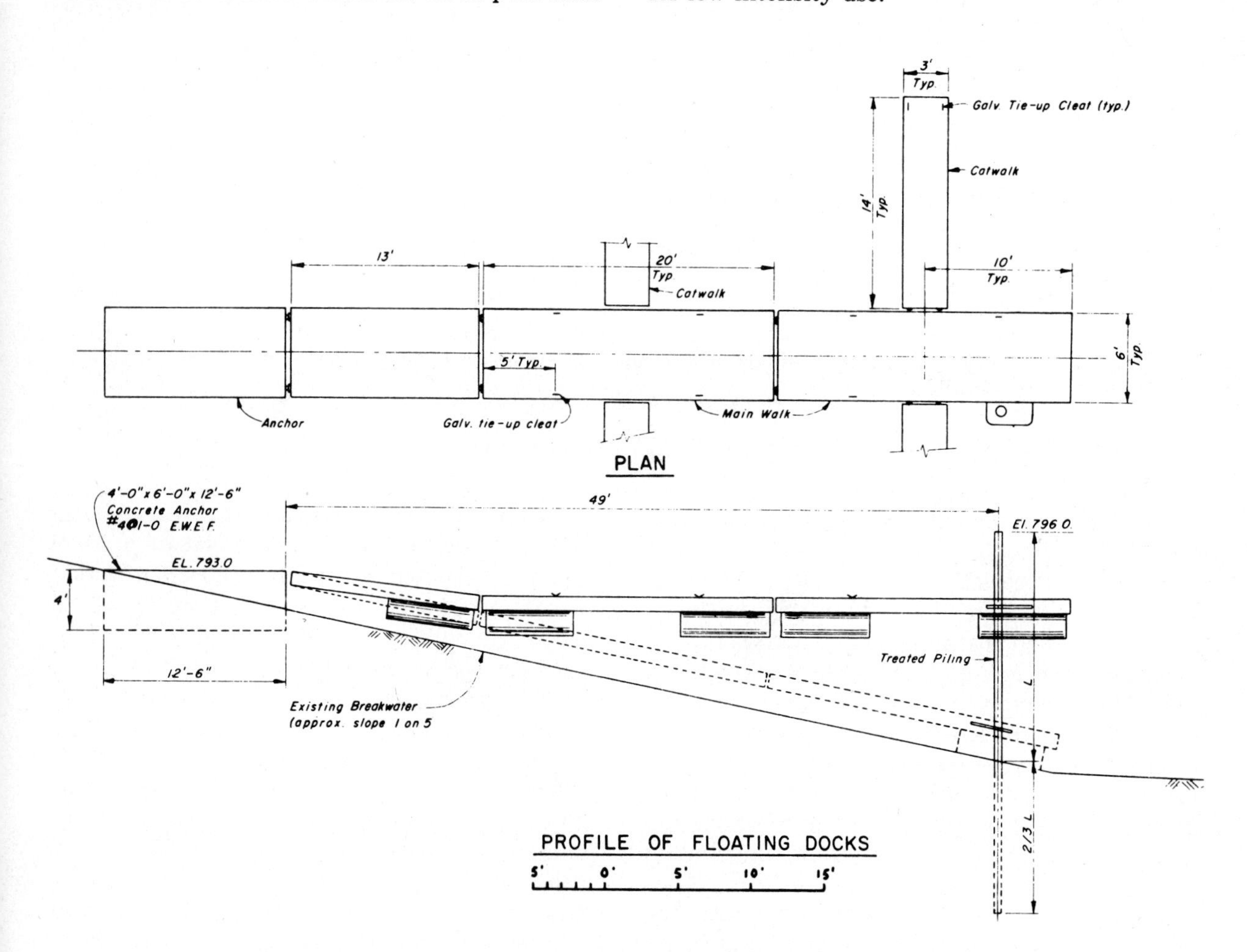

Figure 2-15.—Floating dock, functional at various water levels. 103-D-1802.

Ideally, recreation facilities should be located and designed so that they will be in harmony with the natural setting. Whenever possible, these facilities should be constructed with natural materials so that they will be unobtrusive.

Where high use is anticipated, a visitors' center can be built at the damsite or at an appropriate viewing location. Exhibits explaining the purpose of the project, its history, local cultural and historical features, local wildlife, and other aspects of the area can enhance a visitor's enjoyment and appreciation.

Downstream areas can also be developed for fishing, boating, and hiking. Where reservoir operation results in significant flow fluctuations (velocity and rapid elevation change caused by hydropeaking), safety features should be included. These features can include fencing to prevent access to high-risk areas and sound alarms and signs to warn of changing conditions.

Effective maintenance of the facilities is important if the anticipated recreation benefits are to be realized. Trash-disposal facilities should be provided at convenient locations, and toilet facilities should be available at all camping areas and near all areas of heavy use. Camping should be restricted to designated areas and limited to the identified carrying capacity to avoid a decrease in the quality of the recreation experience.

G. BIBLIOGRAPHY

2.10. *Bibliography*

[1] Canter, L. W., *Water Resources Assessment—Methodology and Technical Sourcebook*, 2,529 pp., Ann Arbor Science Publishers, Inc., Ann Arbor, MI, 1979.

[2] Golden, J., R. P. Ouellette, S. Saari, and P. N. Cheremisinoff, *Environmental Impact Data Book*, 864 pp., Ann Arbor Science Publishers, Inc., Ann Arbor, MI, 1979.

[3] States, J. B., P. T. Haug, T. G. Shoemaker, L. W. Reed, and E. B. Reed, *A System Approach to Ecological Baseline Studies*, FWS/OBS-78/21, 392 pp., U.S. Fish and Wildlife Service, Office of Biological Services, March 1978.

[4] Warner, M. L., J. L. Moore, S. Chatterjee, D. C. Cooper, C. Ifeadi, W. T. Lawhon, and R. S. Reimers, *An Assessment Methodology for the Environmental Impact of Water Resource Projects*, EPA Report No. 600/5-74-016, 221 pp., U.S. Government Printing Office, Washington, D.C., 1974.

[5] Ward, Diana V., *Biological Environmental Impact Studies: Theory and Methods*, Academic Press, 157 pp., New York, NY, 1978.

[6] Henderson, Jim E., "Handbook of Environmental Quality Measurement and Assessment: Methods and Techniques," Instruction Report E-82-2, U.S. Army Corps of Engineers Waterways Experiment Station, CE, Vicksburg, MS, 1982.

[7] American Society of Civil Engineers, *Environmental Effects of Large Dams*, 225 pp., 1978.

[8] Soil Conservation Society of America, *Wildlife and Water Management: Striking a Balance*, 48 pp., 1973.

[9] Canter, L. W., and L. G. Hill, *Handbook of Variables for Environmental Impact Assessments*, 203 pp., Ann Arbor Science Publishers, Inc., Ann Arbor, MI, 1979.

[10] Wesche, T. A., and P. S. Richard, *A Summary of Instream Flow Methods for Fisheries and Related Needs*, Eisenhower Consortium Bulletin No. 9, Eisenhower Consortium for Western Environmental Forestry Research, 122 pp., U.S. Government Printing Office, Washington, D.C., 1980.

[11] Binns, N. A., and F. M. Eiserman, "Quantification of Fluvial Trout Habitat in Wyoming," *Transactions*, Am. Fish. Soc. 108(3): pp. 215-228, 1979.

[12] Bovee, Ken D., *A Guide to Stream Habitat Analysis Using the Instream Flow Incremental Methodology*, FWS/OBS-81/47, U.S. Fish and Wildlife Service, Office of Biological Services, September 1981.

[13] Jenkins, R. M., "Prediction of Fish Production in Oklahoma Reservoirs on the Basis of Environmental Variables," Ann. Okla. Acad. Sci. No. 5: pp. 11-20, 1976.

[14] Nelson, Wayne R., Gerald C. Horak, and James E. Olson, *Western Reservoir and Stream Habitat Improvements Handbook*, FWS/OBS-78/56, U.S. Fish and Wildlife Service, Office of Biological Services, 1978.

[15] Cooper, C. O., and T. A. Wesche, "Stream Channel Modification to Enhance Trout Habitat Under Low Flow Conditions," Water Resources Series No. 58, 107 pp., University of Wyoming, 1976.

[16] White, R. J., and O. M. Brynildson, "Guidelines for Management of Trout Stream Habitat in Wisconsin," Wisconsin Department of Natural Resources, Division of Conservation, Technical Bulletin No. 39, 1967.

[17] Schemnitz, Sanford D., editor, *Wildlife Management Techniques Manual*, 4th ed., 686 pp., The Wildlife Society, Inc., Washington, D.C., 1980.

[18] U.S. Fish and Wildlife Service, "Habitat Evaluation Procedures," *USDI Ecological Services Manual*, No. 102, 1980.

[19] U.S. Army Corps of Engineers, Fort Worth District, "Walnut and Williamson Creeks, Expanded Flood Plain Information Study—Environmental Considerations," vol. III, May 1980.

[20] Hays, R. L., C. Summers, and W. Seitz, *Estimating Wildlife Habitat Variables*, FWS/OBS-81/47, U.S. Fish and Wildlife Service, 111 pp., 1981.

[21] U.S. Fish and Wildlife Service, Office of Biological Services, *Rehabilitation of Western Wildlife Habitat: A Review,* FWS/OBS-78/86, 238 pp., December 1978.

[22] U.S. Forest Service, *Wildlife Habitat Improvement Handbook,* Catalog No. FSH 2609.11, August 1969.

[23] U.S. Fish and Wildlife Service, Office of Biological Services, *Management of Transmission Line Rights-of-Way for Fish and Wildlife,* vol. I-III, FWS/OBS-79/22, 1979.

[24] Seaman, E. A., *Wild and Domestic Mammal Control in Concrete-Lined Canals,* Bureau of Reclamation, August 1977.

[25] Latham, H. S., and J. M. Verzuh, *Reducing Hazards to People and Animals on Reclamation Canals,* Bureau of Reclamation Report No. REC-ERC-71-36, Denver, CO., September 1971.

[26] Groen, C. L., and T. A. Schroeder, "Effects of Water Level Management on Walleye and Other Coolwater Fishes in Kansas Reservoirs," presented at the North American Coolwater Fisheries Symposium, St. Paul, MN, 1978.

[27] Smith, D. J., "Water Quality for River Reservoir Systems (Draft)," U.S. Army Corps of Engineers, Hydrologic Engineering Center, 25 pp., Davis, CA, 1978.

[28] U.S. Army Corps of Engineers, CE-QUAR-RI, *A Numerical One-Dimensional Model of Reservoir Water Quality User's Manual,* Environmental Laboratory, Waterways Experiment Station, Vicksburg, MS, 1982.

[29] Sartoris, J. J., *User's Manual: Corps/WRE Reservoir Temperature Simulation Model,* Bureau of Reclamation, Engineering and Research Center, 88 pp., Denver, CO, 1978.

[30] Mueller, D. K., D. C. Craft, R. L. George, P. L. Johnson, and R. A. Roline, "Guidelines for Studies of Potential Eutrophication," Bureau of Reclamation, Water Quality Planning Technical Memorandum, 32 pp., December 1981.

[31] Bureau of Reclamation, *Environmental Guidebook for Construction,* 1973.

Chapter 3

Flood Hydrology Studies

3.1. ***Purpose and Scope.***—The information in this chapter is intended for use by hydrologic engineers in the preparation of flood hydrology studies necessary for the design of dams and their appurtenant features. This chapter provides general guidance for estimating both the magnitude and frequency of floods. Directions are also provided for the preparation of flood hydrology reports, which document the bases for and the results of flood hydrology studies.

3.2. ***Background.***—Design-flood hydrographs or parts thereof (peak or volume) are required for sizing the hydraulic features of a variety of water-control and conveyance structures. In the case of dams and their appurtenant features, flood hydrographs are required for the sizing of spillways and attendant surcharge storage spaces. A flood hydrograph is a graphical or tabular representation of the variation of discharge over time, at a particular point on a watercourse. Various types of flood hydrographs represent different conditions:

(a) *PMF Hydrograph.*—The PMF (probable maximum flood) hydrograph represents the maximum runoff condition resulting from the most severe combination of hydrologic and meteorologic conditions considered reasonably possible for the drainage basin under study. The PMF is used by design and construction organizations as a basis for design in those cases where the failure of the dam from overtopping would cause loss of life or widespread property damage downstream.

(b) *Specific-Frequency Flood Hydrograph.*—The second type of flood hydrograph includes those that represent an assigned, or specific, frequency of occurrence. In the field of flood hydrology, "frequency of occurrence" is defined as the probability of a flood of a given magnitude being equaled or exceeded within a specified period, usually one year. Specific-frequency flood hydrographs are primarily used in the design of facilities to provide for the care and diversion of flows during the construction of water-control structures, such as dams. Where the hazard potential below the proposed damsite is negligible, a flood of a specific frequency or one that is a percentage of the PMF may be used for determining the spillway size and surcharge storage requirement. Specific-frequency flood hydrographs or their peak discharges are also used in the design of cross-drainage facilities.

3.3. ***Basic Hydrologic and Meteorologic Data.***—The compilation and analysis of hydrologic and meteorologic data accumulated during and after severe flood events is necessary for every flood-hydrology study. Hydrologic data include records of runoff accumulated at continuous recording streamflow gauges and at crest-stage streamflow gauges, indirect peak-discharge measurements, and reservoir operation records from which inflow hydrographs may be determined. Meteorologic data include precipitation, temperature, and wind records collected at official National Weather Service first- and second-order climatological stations, data from supplemental precipitation surveys (commonly called bucket surveys) conducted immediately after severe storm events to supplement data collected at official National Weather Service stations, and snow surveys conducted by Federal, State and local agencies in areas susceptable to significant snowmelt runoff.

3.4. ***Hydrologic Data.***—(a) *Recorded Streamflow Data.*—These data are collected primarily by the USGS (U.S. Geological Survey) at continuous-recording streamflow gauging stations. They are compiled and published by the USGS in a series of "Water Supply Papers." Generally, these publications present the streamflow in terms of the average daily flow for each day for the period the stream gauge has been in operation. However, their value is limited for flood hydrograph analyses, for all but the largest drainage basins and, therefore, they are rarely used in such analyses. Average daily-flow values are developed from recorder charts that provide a continuous record of river stage versus time, at each gauging site. River stage is shown on the recorder chart as the elevation, in feet, above some arbitrary datum. Copies of these charts can be obtained from the USGS together with the rating curve for each gauging station. The rating curve presents the relationships between the discharge, in cubic feet per second, and the river stage above the arbitrary datum, in feet. A hydrograph representing the discharge in cubic feet per second can then be developed for a particular location by reading the river stage values at selected time intervals from the recorder chart and converting these values to discharge, using the rating curve for that station. The time interval selected is important to successful flood-hydrograph analysis. The rationale and method for selecting an appropriate time interval is discussed in section 3.9(b) "Unit Hydrograph Lag Time."

"Water Supply Papers" also present the instantaneous peak discharge for each gauging station for every year that station has been in operation. These data form the basis for developing annual peak discharge-frequency relationships, discussed in section 3.12, and peak discharge envelope curves, discussed in section 3.11.

(b) *Peak Discharge Data.*—Because the cost of installing, operating, maintaining, compiling, and publishing the data is high, there are relatively few continuous-recording stream gauges, considering the number of rivers and streams in the United States. To supplement the recording stream-gauge network, networks of crest-stage gauges have been established in many regions of the country. These are simple devices consisting of a length of 2-inch-diameter pipe mounted vertically on a post or bridge pier. The pipe is capped at each end, and the lower cap is perforated on the side facing the flow to permit the entry of water. A graduated rod is placed inside the pipe and granulated cork is placed inside the pipe at the bottom. The water that enters during floods causes the cork to rise and adhere to the rod up to the maximum stage reached. This maximum stage is then related to the discharge by using a rating curve, if one exists, or by the slope-area method of indirect peak-discharge measurement.

3.5. *Meteorologic Data.*—Systematic acquisition of precipitation data is accomplished primarily through the efforts of the NWS (National Weather Service). The NWS maintains a network of "first order" weather stations. Each station in this network collects continuous precipitation, temperature, wind, and relative humidity data.

Supplemental data on historical and recent storms are acquired for the determination of PMF's and the development of operating procedures for flood routing through reservoirs. Because more recording rain gauges operate now than ever before, more complete data are available for recent storms. However, the network of precipitation stations is still far from sufficient to provide the data necessary for detailed analyses of storm precipitation. It is therefore necessary, after outstanding storms, to supplement the data obtained at rain gauges with "unofficial" observations made by individuals, radio and T.V. stations, and city and county departments.

3.6. *Field Reconnaissance of Drainage Basins for Flood Hydrology Studies.*—Before the initiation of the flood hydrology study, except those conducted at the appraisal level, a field reconnaissance should be made of the subject drainage basin. The purpose of this reconnaissance is to identify and to document in a trip report the pertinent physical features of the basin, including existing water-control facilities, that will affect the magnitude and timing of flood runoff. The reconnaissance party should observe and document the following four primary characteristics of the drainage basin.

(a) *Drainage Network.*—Particular emphasis should be placed on observing and documenting the hydraulic roughness characteristics of the drainage network, or hydraulic systems, of the basin. This is most readily accomplished by visually inspecting representative reaches of the network and assigning average Manning's n (roughness coefficient) values to these reaches. It should be kept in mind that the n values assigned are to reflect extreme flood conditions, specifically considering overbank flow, meander cutoff, scour, and the time of year the flood is likely to occur. The values and the reaches should be delineated on the maps used in the field reconnaissance. These values will be averaged and will form the basis for selecting an appropriate coefficient for the unit hydrograph lag equation. An excellent guide for use in the selection of Manning's n values is the USGS "Water Supply Paper 1849: Roughness Characteristics of Natural Channels." This publication provides measured Manning's n values for a variety of natural channel and overbank conditions, accompanied by color photographs of the measured sections and associated channel reaches.

The channels should be described in the reconnaissance report. The description should include a discussion of the type of channel (swale, well-incised, etc.), the character of the overbank areas (heavily wooded, grass covered, etc.), and the materials (boulders, cobbles, native soil, etc.) that form the channel bed and overbank areas. This information is also useful for future reference.

Photographs, preferably in color, should be included as supplementary information in each reconnaissance report and should be appropriately referenced in the narrative portion of the report.

The density of the well-defined channels that make up the drainage network should be observed and described in the reconnaissance report. These descriptions will necessarily be somewhat subjective, but will enhance information shown on topographic maps. The discussion should also include information on the extent of overland flow. This type of flow occurs in those portions of a basin where runoff must flow in sheets before reaching a point where it is concentrated in a channel or swale.

(b) *Soil and Geologic Conditions.*—Soil conditions, the types of soils in the drainage basin and the locations of each type of soil, should be observed and documented on a suitable map. In general, the soils should be classified using the four general Soil Conservation Service types discussed in section 3.9(e) "Infiltration and Other Losses." Systematic observations and adequate documentation of these observations should provide the basis for selecting the appropriate minimum infiltration rates used in the development of PMF hydrographs.

The general geologic setting should be described in the reconnaissance report. In a number of areas in the United States underlain with limestone beds, depressions in the land surface have developed. These depressions, called "sinkholes" or "playas," usually impound water that does not contribute to the runoff. These areas can have a significant effect on the flood runoff that can be expected from a drainage basin. Therefore, it is of prime importance that such areas be identified, delineated on a map, and assessed regarding their impounding capability. Such features should also be fully discussed in the field reconnaissance report. This discussion should be supplemented with color photographs as appropriate.

(c) *Vegetative Cover.*—To adequately estimate infiltration-loss characteristics and unit hydrograph parameters, it is necessary to be familiar with the vegetative cover of the drainage basin. Therefore, during the field reconnaissance, it is necessary to observe and document the types, area, and location of vegetation in the basin. Ground observation supplemented, if possible, with aerial photographs is probably the best way to accomplish this task. The results should be delineated on the map used in the field reconnaissance and should be discussed in the reconnaissance report, which should also include color photographs.

(d) *Land Use.*—Most drainage basins above proposed dams are natural or undeveloped basins. If this is the case, it should be so stated in the reconnaissance report. However, portions of drainage basins are sometimes used for agriculture (including both crops and livestock grazing), forestry (tree harvesting, particularly in the Pacific Northwest), or urban development. The extent and intensity of agricultural and forestry land uses should be determined during the field inspection and properly documented in the reconnaissance report.

To assess urban development, future developments as well as those existing should be considered. Therefore, when inspecting an area near an expanding urban center, the local government should be contacted and a projected land-use map secured. Knowledge of projected urban land use is of considerable importance because the rainfall-runoff response of an urbanized drainage basin is usually significantly different from the response the same basin would experience in a nonurbanized condition. For example, in a relatively flat area of central Texas, the peak discharge for a particular basin increased by a factor of almost eight after the basin was completely urbanized, although the rainfall stayed essentially the same. If urbanization becomes a factor in a flood study, the projected urban development map should be obtained from a reliable governmental source and included in the flood study report.

(e) *Significant Nearby Basins.*—If the route of travel to or from the basin to be inspected passes near a basin where a significant flood event has been recorded, that basin should also be inspected. Observations of the types listed in this section should be made and documented in the reconnaissance report for the nearby basin. These observations may help confirm or determine hydrologic parameters used in the flood study for the subject basin or for other ungauged basins within the hydrologically homogeneous region.

3.7. *Field Reconnaissance Report.*—This document should be prepared as soon after the field inspection is completed as practicable. The report should, as a minimum, contain the following items:

(a) The date or dates of the field reconnaissance and the names and offices of those on the field reconnaissance team

(b) The places and offices visited and the individuals contacted

(c) The purpose of the trip, including appropriate references to the formal and informal correspondence that prompted the field reconnaissance

(d) A synopsis of the trip, including a description of the route traveled and the observations made to define the drainage network, soil and geologic conditions, vegetative cover, land use, and pertinent water control facilities in the drainage basin

(e) Conclusions reached on hydrologic parameters, including the unit hydrograph lag time, time versus rate-of-change of discharge, infiltration rates, and relative forest cover (for snowmelt analyses)

3.8. *Development of Probable Maximum Storms.*—Probable maximum storms for drainage basins in the United States located east of the 105° meridian are developed using regionalized criteria contained in National Weather Service *HMR (Hydrometeorological Report) 51* and *52*. Probable maximum storms for drainage basins located west of the Continental Divide are developed using criteria presented in *HMR 36, 43,* and *49*. For the region between the 105° meridian and the Continental Divide, probable maximum storms are developed using *HMR 55*.

The paragraphs that follow discuss, in general terms, the methodologies used in the hydrometeorological reports mentioned above.

(a) *Hydrometeorological Reports 51 and 52.*—PMP (probable maximum precipitation) estimates for the United States east of the 105° meridian for storms with areas of 10 to 20,000 mi² and durations from 6 to 72 hours are provided in *HMR 51*. Using the procedures contained in *HMR 52*, these precipitation estimates can be applied to a specific drainage to derive the site-specific basin average PMP. In addition, *HMR 52* expands upon the storm-related estimates found in *HMR 51* by providing a temporal distribution for durations less than 6 hours.

The PMP values derived from procedures contained in *HMR 51* are regionalized estimates; that is, isolines of PMP are given on a map that allows determination of storm-related PMP over a region, within the limits set on area and duration in the report. Derivation of these estimates began with obtaining maximum observed area precipitation data for various durations of recorded major storms. The observed areal precipitation values from each storm were adjusted for maximum moisture potential. This adjustment involved increasing the storm precipitation to a value consistent with the maximum moisture in the atmosphere that could reasonably be expected at the location and time (month) of occurrence. These adjusted precipitation values were then transposed to the limits of a homogeneous region relative to the terrain and meteorological features associated with the storm that produced the particular rainfall. A set of regional charts for selected storm areas and durations were developed on which the adjusted-transposed area precipitation from each critical storm was plotted. Smooth regional isohyets were analyzed on each chart. The general shape and gradients of the isohyets were patterned after several rainfall indexes, such as minimum envelopment of greatest daily and weekly rainfall amounts, 100-year rainfall analysis, and regional distributions of maximum persisting 12-hour dewpoints. A grid was established for these charts, from which area-duration precipitation values were read. These values were then enveloped by area and duration and plotted on a new set of area-duration charts, from which a revised, smooth regional analysis was developed and checked. The envelopment process was considered necessary to compensate for the random occurrence of large rainfall events. In other words, a particular region may not have experienced equally efficient storm mechanisms for all pertinent storm areas and durations.

Final charts of PMP are presented in *HMR 51*. These charts present the PMP's for storms of 6, 12, 24, 48, and 72 hours and with areas of 10, 200, 1,000, 5,000, and 10,000 mi². From these charts, the storm PMP can be obtained for any storm with an area and duration within the limits set by the report, in the region in the United States east of the 105° meridian.

Procedures are provided in *HMR 52* that translate the storm average PMP area values obtained from *HMR 51* to a spatially and temporally distributed estimate of storm PMP. The results of the application of those procedures found in *HMR 52* to a particular basin are estimates of site-specific, basin average PMP.

The temporal distribution of rainfall, included in *HMR 52* for use in PMF studies, was derived by examination of the actual occurrence of incremental precipitation from critical storms of record. Analysis of these storms also led to the adoption of an elliptically shaped isohyetal storm pattern having a major to minor axis ratio of 2.5 to 1. The storm PMP is reduced to account for the restrictions or preferences of the orientation of the probable maximum storm pattern relative to the orientation of the subject drainage basin. Using the depth-area-duration information from critical storms of record, the spatial distributions of rainfall (the degree of precipitation concentration within the isohyetal pattern) was developed. Determination of the proper spatial distribution led to the concept of residual precipitation, which is the rainfall outside the PMP portion of the rainfall pattern and not considered to be equal to the PMP in magnitude. Use of this important concept permits the determination of concurrent precipitation; i.e., the precipitation occurring on an adjacent drainage basin.

The combined use of *HMR 51* and *HMR 52* permits the development of site-specific drainage average PMP for the subject drainage basin. Accordingly, this value provides the PMF that will be derived from the hydrologic analysis.

(b) *Regionalized Procedures West of the Continental Divide.*—Probable maximum storm estimates for basins west of the Continental Divide may be developed using procedures presented in *HMR 43, Probable Maximum Precipitation, Northwest States; HMR 49, Probable Maximum Precipitation, Colorado River and Great Basin Drainage;* and *HMR 36, Interim Report-Probable Maximum Precipitation in California.* In these regionalized studies, the local storm (thunderstorm) is considered unique and is not enveloped with general storm depth duration data, as was the case for regionalized general storm criteria for the region east of the 105° meridian.

To compute general storm PMP for a drainage basin, characteristics such as the size, width, elevation, and location of the basin must be known. Convergence precipitation is determined by referring to the regionalized convergence precipitation index map for basin locations and refining the values taken from the map for basin area and temporal distribution. The orographic PMP component is determined by reading the average basin index from regional maps and refining that index the account for the basin area, basin width with respect to inflow winds, and temporal distribution. The indexes for each time increment for both the convergence and orographic PMP's are added to determine the total PMP. The PMP temporal distribution can then be rearranged using several generalized distributions presented in the reports, or it may be patterned after a historic severe storm that has occurred in or near the basin.

The general storm isohyetal pattern is assumed to fit perfectly over the drainage basin being studied, and the average basin precipitation for 72 hours should equal the total PMP calculated by the general method. If an isohyetal pattern or area distribution is necessary, a severe historic storm pattern and distribution is used.

Temperature, dew point, and wind values may be computed from criteria presented in the reports for snowmelt calculations. Seasonal variations of PMP for use in frozen-ground, rain-on-snow, or snowmelt-flood computations may be determined using the generalized criteria, nomograms, tables, and graphs in *HMR 36, HMR 43,* and *HMR 49.*

Estimates of the local, or thunderstorm, PMP may be determined for the Colorado River and Great Basin drainages and for the California region using the criteria in *HMR 49.* Local-storm procedures for the Northwestern States are in *HMR 43.*

To derive a local storm for areas less than 500 mi^2 and for durations less than 6 hours, the average 1-hour, 1-mi^2 PMP is chosen from regionalized charts in the appropriate HMR. These values are then reduced for basin elevation and area and distributed over time. Elliptically shaped isohyetal patterns are used to calculate PMP so that the basin shape and storm center locations are considered for appropriate hydrologic analysis.

The methodology for determining PMP is set fourth in the HMR's in simple, easy-to-follow, sequential procedures. Supporting data, upon which the criteria were developed, are also shown in these publications: *HMR 37, Meteorology of Hydrologically Critical Storms in California*; and *HMR 50, Meteorology of Important Rainstorms in the Colorado River and Great Basin Drainages.*

Revision and refinement of regionalized PMP procedures, techniques, and methodology in the data-deficient West is an ongoing process. As new, severe storms are recorded, regionalized procedures are evaluated for their adequacy. When deficiences are noted, revisions and refinements are made and documented in subsequent reports.

3.9. *Flood Runoff from Rainfall.*—In 1932, Leroy K. Sherman was the first to propose the unit hydrograph approach to convert rainfall on a drainage basin to runoff from that basin. Sherman's approach, which was formally presented in the April 7, 1932 issue of *Engineering News-Record*, has, with continued use, undergone considerable refinement since that time. The advent of high-speed electronic computers led hydrologists to devise approaches using complex watershed models as alternatives to the unit hydrograph model to predict the runoff response to the rainfall in a drainage basin. Because these complex watershed models generally require considerable calibration to adequately represent the physical properties of a basin, much effort is needed in the field and office to acquire data on these properties.

In the final analysis, the relative worth of an approach is measured by how well that approach reproduces actual, recorded flood events. Comparative studies have indicated that both approaches can satisfactorily reproduce these events, and neither is superior to the other. Accordingly, the Bureau of Reclamation has retained the unit hydrograph approach because if its simplicity, its reliability, and the relatively low costs of applying it in flood hydrology studies.

(a) *Basic Unit Hydrograph Theory.*—The basic concept of the unit hydrograph theory can be understood by considering a situation in which a storm of, say, 1-hour duration produces rainfall at a constant rate, uniformly over the drainage basin above a recording stream gauging station. Assume that the rainfall rate is such that 1 inch of the total rainfall does not infiltrate into the soil, but runs off over the ground surface to tributary watercourses, eventually arriving at the stream gauging station. The runoff at the gauging station will be recorded to form a hydrograph representing the temporal distribution of discharge from 1 inch of "rainfall excess" occurring in 1 hour. This hydrograph is the "1-hour unit hydrograph" for the drainage basin tributrary to the gauging station. The unit hydrograph in this case is said to have a "unit duration" of 1 hour.

Now consider the situation for the same basin in which the rainfall excess is 2 inches in a 1-hour period. The unit hydrograph theory assumes that the 1-hour hydrograph ordinates are proportional to the rainfall excess. It then follows that the runoff hydrograph at the gauging station resulting from these 2 inches of rainfall excess can be predicted by multiplying each of the 1-hour unit hydrograph ordinates by 2. This, of course, is true for any multiple or fraction of an inch of rainfall excess, as shown on figure 3-1.

Until now the discussion has considered an isolated rainfall event sustained for a time equal to the unit duration of the unit hydrograph. Nature, unfortunately, does not usually behave in such a simplistic manner. The severe storms that occasionally occur at every drainage basin, regardless of location, are both longer in duration and more varied in intensity from one "unit" period to another.

Figure 3-2 depicts, in graphical form, the manner in which the unit hydrograph approach takes complex storms into consideration. Note that each of the five increments of precipitation excess results in an incremental runoff hydrograph. These are shown by the plots labled 1.5, 1.2, 0.8, 0.6, and 0.4 inches. Each incremental runoff hydrograph is determined by multiplying the increments of rainfall excess by the unit hydrograph ordinates. The total runoff from the complex rainfall event (of which only the excess is depicted on fig. 3-2) can be determined by adding the ordinates of each incremental runoff hydrograph at discrete time intervals, usually equal to the unit duration of the unit hydrograph. The resulting runoff hydrograph can be drawn by graphically connecting these points on a curve.

In actual practice, the hydrologic engineer is usually faced with the problem of providing a flood hydrograph for design purposes at a location where no streamflow data have been accumulated. These flood hydrographs are developed using hypothetical rainfall amounts for the drainage basin, appropriate infiltration loss rates, and a synthetic unit hydrograph.

Synthetic unit hydrographs are developed from parameters representing the salient characteristics of the rainfall-runoff phenomena found by reconstructing observed flood events on similar drainage basins. Reconstruction of observed events generally provides two significant items of information. The first item is an indication of infiltration rates expected with certain types of soils. The second item

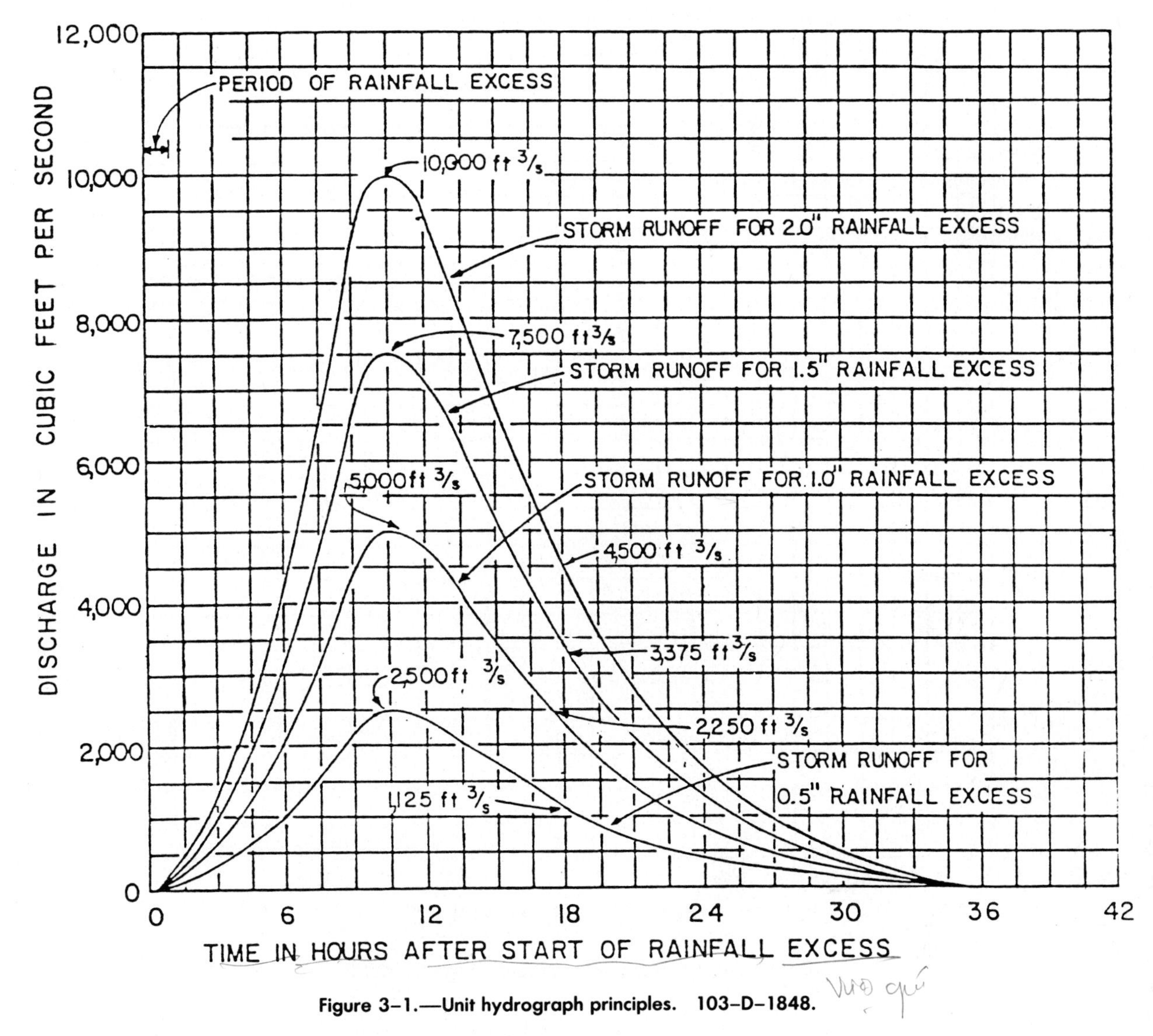

Figure 3-1.—Unit hydrograph principles. 103-D-1848.

is a unit hydrograph for each of the basins analyzed. Associated with each unit hydrograph are two characteristics used to determine synthetic unit hydrographs for ungauged drainage basins. These characteristics, discussed below, are the lag in time between the rainfall and the rise in runoff (unit hydrograph lag time) and the time versus discharge rate of change realtionship (temporal distribution of unit runoff).

(b) *Unit Hydrograph Lag Time.*—Over the years many observed floods have been reconstructed using the unit hydrograph approach. Analyses of these reconstructions has led to the conclusion that the lag time of a unit hydrograph varies as a function of certain measurable basin parameters. Lag time was originally defined by Horner and Flynt [1][1] as the ". . .time difference between. . .center of mass of rainfall and center of mass of runoff. . ." The following general relationship between lag time, L_g, and measurable basin parameters was developed:

$$L_g = C \left(\frac{LL_{ca}}{S^{0.5}} \right)^N \tag{1}$$

where:

L_g = unit hydrograph lag time, in hours,
C = constant,

[1]Numbers in brackets refer to entries in the bibliography (sec. 3.14).

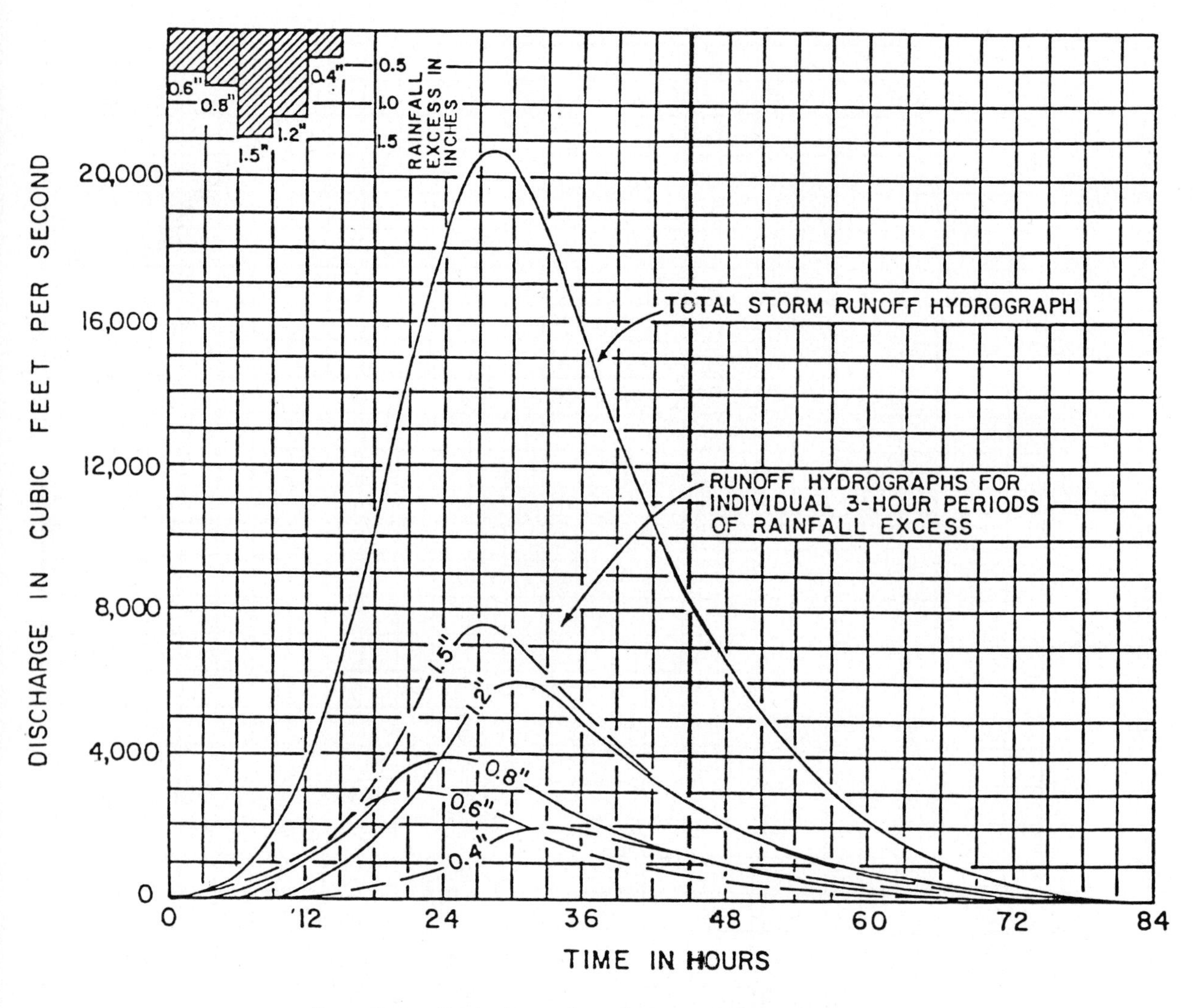

Figure 3-2.—Unit hydrograph application. 103-D-1849.

N = constant,

L = the length of the longest watercourse from the point of concentration to the boundary of the drainage basin, in miles. The point of concentration is the location on the watercourse where a hydrograph is desired,

L_{ca} = the length along the longest watercourse from the point of concentration to a point opposite the centroid of the drainage basin, in miles, and

S = the overall slope of the longest watercourse (along L), in feet per mile.

Subsequent analyses of unit hydrograph data, as they have become available, have led to the conclusion that the exponent N should be 0.33, regardless of the location of the drainage basin. Additional analyses of these data have led investigators to conclude that C should be 26 times the average Manning's n value representing the hydraulic characteristics of the drainage network. This average Manning's n value is identified as K_n in subsequent consideration of lag time in this manual. Thus, $C = 26K_n$. It should be emphasized that K_n is primarily a function of the magnitude of discharge and normally decreases with increasing discharge.

Current Bureau of Reclamation practice uses two definitions of unit hydrograph lag time that are somewhat different from those originally proposed by Horner and Flynt [1]. The lag time definition used depends on which of the two techniques for synthetic unit hydrograph development, listed below, is selected.

(1) *Dimensionless Unit Hydrograph Technique.* This lag time is the time from the midpoint of the unit rainfall excess to the time that 50 percent of the volume of unit runoff from the drainage basin has passed the concentration point.

(2) *S-Graph Technique.* This lag time is the time from the start of a continuous series of unit rainfall excess increments to the time when the resulting runoff hydrograph reaches 50 percent of the ultimate discharge. The ultimate discharge is an equilibrium rate achieved when the entire drainage basin is contributing runoff at the concentration point from the continuous series of unit rainfall excess increments.

To help determine an appropriate lag time, many flood hydrograph reconstructions have been examined. These reconstructions represent flood runoff from natural basins throughout the contiguous United States west of the Mississippi River and from urbanized basins for several locations throughout the United States. Data for urbanized basins are included in this edition because of the increased interest in the hydrology of such areas, particularly with respect to the impact on runoff from various intensities of development.

As a result of the examination of these reconstructions, 162 flood hydrographs considered representative of surface runoff from rainfall events were selected. Those not included were considered to represent either interflow runoff or runoff that included significant contribution from snowmelt. The 162 examples were then segregated on a regional and topographic basis, as displayed on figures 3-3 through 3-8. The supporting data for these figures are listed in tables 3-1 through 3-6, which include the station index number, station name and location, drainage area (in some cases only the area contributing to the flood runoff), the basin factor ($LL_{ca}/\sqrt{S}$), the unit hydrograph lag time determined from the flood hydrograph reconstruction, and the computed K_n value. These data may be used as a guide during the field reconnaissance in establishing an appropriate K_n value for the drainage basin being studied. It is also valuable to visit the basins included in the data to understand the physical conditions that are indicative of the K_n value.

Figure 3-3 and the data in table 3-1 represent conditions on the Great Plains west of the Mississippi River and east of the foothills of the Rocky Mountains. They reflect K_n values from about 0.070 to as low as 0.030. The upper limit value generally reflects basins with considerable overland flow before reaching moderately well-defined water courses. Many upper reach watercourses are swales. Well-defined drainage networks are limited to the lower parts of the basins. Overbank flow conditions reflect relatively high Manning's n values. The lower limit value generally reflects a well-defined drainage network reaching points near the basin boundary. Overland flow occurs for fairly short distances before entering a well-defined watercourse. Overbank conditions reflect fairly low Manning's n values.

Figure 3-4 and the data in table 3-2 represent conditions in the Rocky Mountains. Included are the Front, Sangre de Christo, San Juan, Wasatch, Big Horn, Absoroka, Wind River, and Bitteroot ranges of New Mexico, Colorado, Wyoming, Utah, Idaho, Oregon, and Montana. Data representing basins at the higher elevations of these mountain ranges are generally lacking. In addition, the infrequency of severe rainstorms in these areas and in the Northern States precludes acquisition of a good data base representing severe event phenomena. Examination of the available data leads to the conclusion that they represent two types of storm phenomena: the low-intensity general storm and the high-intensity thunderstorm event.

Accordingly, two sets of relationships are presented on figure 3-4, one for each type meteorologic event. Data representing the general storm phenomena indicate K_n values ranging from 0.260 to 0.130. Because most of the data reflect low-intensity storms, a K_n of 0.160 or less should be used in the development of PMF hydrographs. This value is consistent with data for the Sierra Nevada of California, which have hydrologic characteristics very similar to those of the Rocky Mountains.

Higher values are considered appropriate for developing flood hydrographs of more common frequency than, say, the 100-year event. Data representing the thunderstorm phenomena indicate K_n values ranging from 0.073 to 0.050. Selection of a value within these limits depends primarily on the character of flow retarding vegetation in the portions of the basin where overland flow will occur in the overbank flow areas, and on the bed material in the channels. It also depends on the extent to

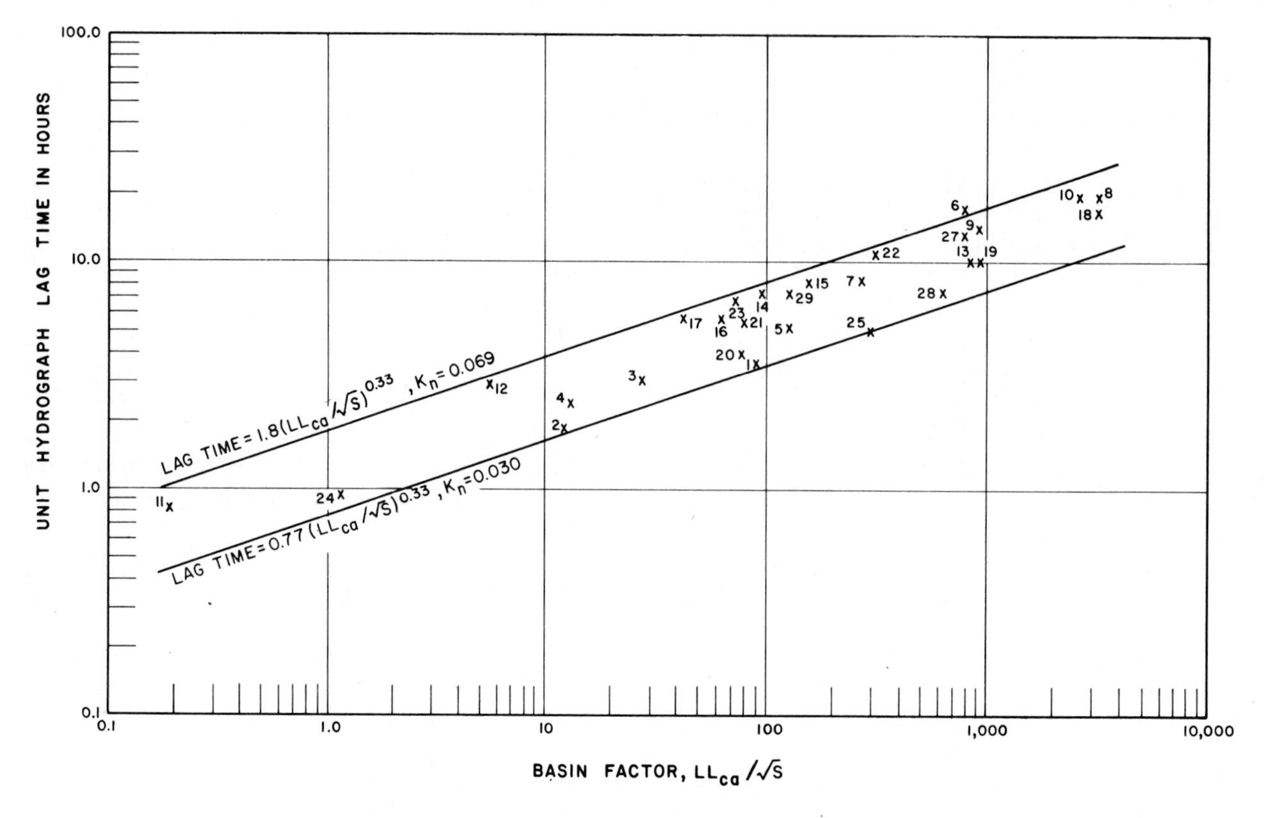

Figure 3-3.—Unit hydrograph lag relationships, Great Plains. 103-D-1850.

which the drainage network has been developed by erosion.

Figure 3-5 and the data in table 3-3 represent conditions in the Southwest Desert, Great Basin, and Colorado Plateau regions of Southern California, Nevada, Utah, Arizona, and western Colorado and New Mexico. Basins in this arid region are generally typified by sparse vegetation, fairly well-defined drainage networks, and terrain varying from rolling to very rugged in the more mountainous areas.

Reflecting relatively high hydraulic efficiencies, regional K_n values range from a high of 0.070 to a low of 0.042. The higher value is indicative of decreased basin hydraulic efficiency consistent with the coniferous forests at the higher elevations, and the lower value is typical of the usual desert terrain. In addition, the third lag curve, the dashed line on figure 3-5, represents a partially urbanized basin in the desert region. Its position, below the two limiting curves, reflects the increased hydraulic efficiency associated with urbanization of a drainage basin.

Figure 3-6 and the data in table 3-4 represent conditions in the Sierra Nevada of California. Basins in this region normally have well-developed drainage networks and substantial coniferous growth throughout those parts of the basins above about elevation 2000. River and stream channels are well incised into the bedrock. In general, the hydrologic and hydraulic characteristics of the Sierra Nevada basins are quite similar to those of the Rocky Mountains. However, the data available for the Sierra Nevada reflect flood hydrograph reconstructions for floods resulting from major, intense storms. Such is not the case for the Rockies, which is the reason for establishing the upper limit K_n at 0.150 (used for generating PMF's for basins in the Rocky Mountain region). Reflecting the varying degrees of hydraulic efficiency, K_n ranges from a high of 0.150 to a low 0.064. However, considering the few points shown on figure 3-6 at or near the lower value, care should be exercised before selecting a low K_n to ensure that the basin being studied has essentially the same hydraulic efficiency characteristics in terms of geology, drainage network development, and stream roughness.

Figure 3-7 and the accompanying data tabulated in table 3-5 represent conditions in the Coast and Cascade ranges of California, Oregon, and Washington. At the high end of the K_n range, a value of 0.150 is indicative of very heavy coniferous growth extending into the overbank flood plain, which lowers the hydraulic efficiencies of these basins. At the low end of the K_n range, a value of 0.080 is typical of the low lying basins where considerably sparser vegetation results in a higher hydraulic efficiency.

Figure 3-8 and data in table 3-6 represent urban conditions at several locations throughout the United States. The range in K_n values, from 0.033 to 0.013, primarily reflects the density and type of development and the extent to which engineered floodwater collection systems have been constructed. A high-density development combined with a good collection system is typical of drainage basins with the lower K_n values. Low-density or partial development with only minor floodwater collection facilities are typical of basins with the higher K_n values. As a result, it is imperative that anticipated future developments be considered. Most urban development eventually tends to become high-density and, with continued flooding problems, also tends to have more formal collection systems. The hydrologic engineer must anticipate such eventualities and assign lower K_n values that could reasonably be expected over the functional life of the project.

(c) *Temporal Distribution of Unit Runoff.*—The lag time of a drainage basin is only half the information required for developing a synthetic unit hydrograph. The other half is the means by which the runoff from the unit rainfall is temporally distributed, or expressed another way, the time versus the discharge rate of change relationship. This distribution is accomplished by using a dimensionless form of an observed unit hydrograph for a similar

Table 3-1.—Unit hydrograph lag data, Great Plains.

Index No.	Station and location	Drainage area, mi²	Basin factor, $LL_{ca}/\sqrt{S}$	Lag time, h	K_n
1	Black Squirrel Cr. nr. Ellicot, CO	353.0	92.9	3.5	0.030
2	Jimmy Camp Cr. nr. Widefield, CO	54.3	12.2	1.8	.030
3	Dry Creek nr. Lamar, CO	73.0	27.9	3.1	.040
4	Willow Cr. nr. Lamar, CO	40.5	13.3	2.5	.041
5	Clay Cr. above Clay Cr. Dam nr. Lamar, CO	213.0	129.0	5.2	.040
6	Smokey Hill R. nr. Ellsworth, KS	[1]1050.0	787.0	17.9	.076
7	Cimmaron R. nr. Boise City, OK	2150.0	275.0	8.4	.051
8	North Fk. Red R. nr. Granite, OK	[1]2005.0	3230.0	20.0	.053
9	Elm Fk. of North Fk. Red R. nr. Magnum, OK	838.0	920.0	14.5	.076
10	Salt Fk. Red R. nr. Magnum, OK	1566.0	2045.0	21.0	.060
11	Beaver Cr. No. 3 NE (Central Plains Experiment Station)	2.0	0.19	0.88	.059
12	Beaver Cr. No. 8, NE (Central Plains Experiment Station)	25.0	5.7	3.1	.067
13	Washita R. at Clinton, OK	794.0	860.0	10.5	.043
14	Barnitze Cr. nr. Arapaho, OK	243.0	99.9	7.5	.063
15	Pond Cr. nr. Ft. Cobb, OK	300.0	156.0	8.4	.061
16	Rock Cr. nr. Dougherty, OK	134.0	65.9	5.8	.056
17	Red Willow Cr. nr. McCook, NE	[1]68.0	44.4	5.8	.064
18	Pecos R. at Puerto D. Lune, NM	3970.0	3300.0	17.0	.045
19	Pecos R. at Anton Chico, NM	1050.0	890.0	10.5	.043
20	Vermejo R. at Dawson, NM	299.0	83.0	4.2	.038
21	Vermejo R. at Dawson, NM (2d reconstruction)	299.0	83.0	5.7	.051
22	Rio Hondo nr. Diamond A Ranch, NM	960.0	312.0	11.0	.064
23	Rio Ruidoso nr. Hondo, NM	307.0	73.5	7.0	.065
24	Buckhorn Cr. nr. Masonville, CO	[1]6.9	1.2	1.0	.036
25	Washita R. nr. Cheyenne, OK	353.0	306.0	5.1	.030
26	Medicine Cr. nr. Cambridge, NE	722.0	797.0	13.5	.057
27	Little Beaver Cr. above Marmath, ND	550.0	648.0	7.7	.035
28	Middle Fk. Powder R. above Kaycee, WY	980.0	131.0	7.7	.059

[1]Contributing area

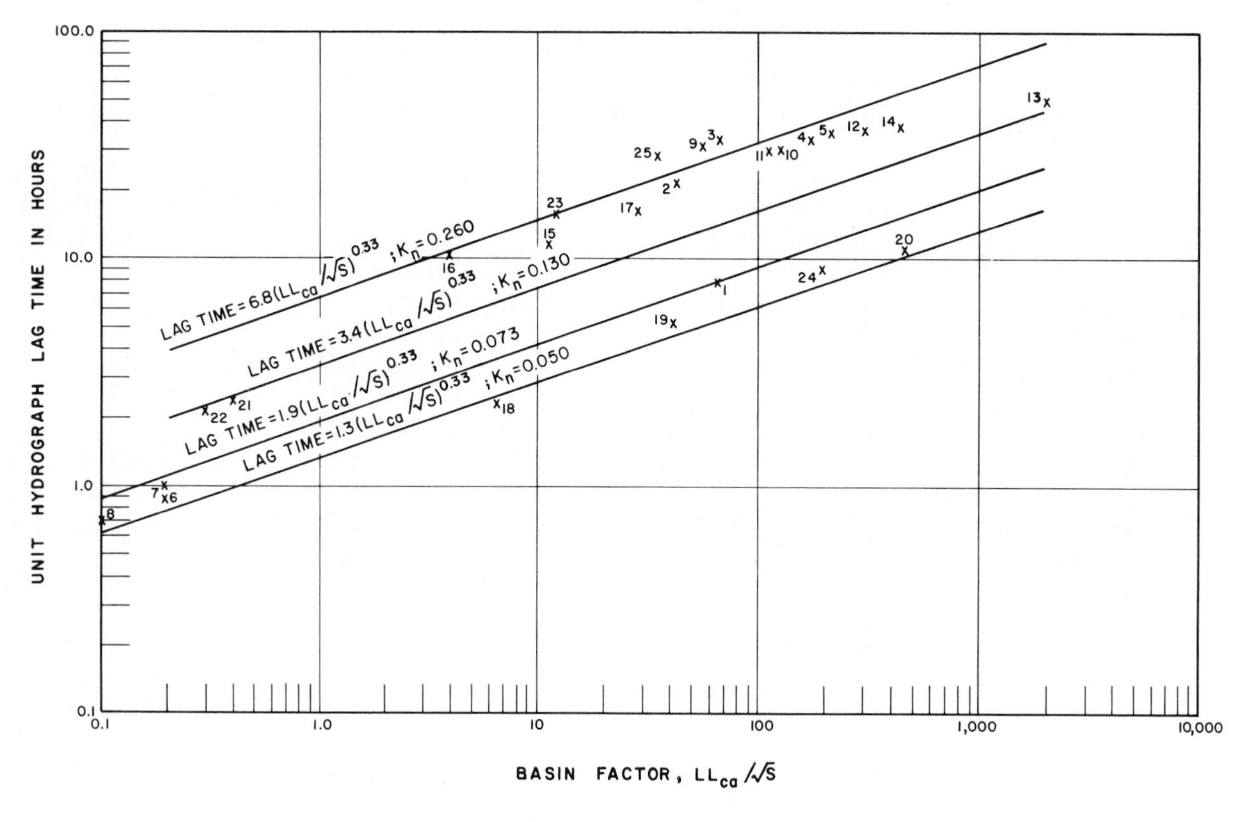

Figure 3-4.—Unit hydrograph lag relationships, Rocky Mountains. 103-D-1851.

drainage basin. Through this dimensionless form, differences in basin size and variations in the unit hydrograph lag time and in the unit duration are automatically taken into account.

In the dimensionless unit hydrograph technique, unit hydrographs developed from recorded flood events are converted to dimensionless form as follows:

(1) The time base is expressed on the abscissa scale (x axis) in terms of time as a percent of the lag time of half the unit rainfall duration (i.e., the semiduration).

(2) Dimensionless discharge is expressed on the ordinate scale (y axis) in terms of unit hydrograph discharge (in cubic feet per second) times the lag time plus the semiduration (in hours) divided by the unit runoff in cubic feet per second-days. Mathematically, this is expressed as $q(L_g + D/2)/Vol;$ where q is the dimensionless discharge ordinate, L_g is the lag (in hours), D is the duration of unit rainfall (in hours), and *Vol.* is the volume of the unit runoff (in cubic feet per second-days.)

In the S-graph technique, unit hydrographs developed from recorded events are converted to dimensionless form as follows:

(1) A summation hydrograph is first developed by algebraically adding the ordinates of a continuous series of identical unit hydrographs, each successively out of phase by one unit period. The lag time for this particular technique is determined by reading (from the plotted summation hydrograph) the elapsed time from the beginning of rainfall to the time when 50 percent of the ultimate discharge is reached.

(2) The dimensionless unit hydrograph is then developed from the summation hydrograph by converting the time base (abscissa) to time in percent of lag time, and the ordinate values to discharge as a percent of the ultimate discharge.

(d) *Development of Synthetic Unit Hydrographs.*—(1) *Determining Synthetic Unit Hydrograph Lag Time.*—Considerable attention has been given to specific observations that should be made in a field reconnaissance of a drainage basin. Observations of the drainage network of a basin or its

Table 3-2.—Unit hydrograph lag data, Rocky Mountains. New Mexico, Colorado, Utah, Wyoming, Montana, Idaho, and Oregon.

Index No.	Station and location	Drainage area, mi^2	Basin factor, $LL_{ca}/\sqrt{S}$	Lag time, h	K_n
1	Purgatoire R. at Trinidad, CO	742.0	69.8	8.0	0.076
2	Wood R. nr. Meeteetse, WY	194.0	41.9	21.5	.241
3	Grey Bull R. nr. Meeteetse, WY	681.0	68.3	34.0	.324
4	San Miguel R. at Naturita, CO	1080.0	174.0	34.0	.238
5	Uncompaghre R. at Delta, CO	1110.0	216.0	36.0	.235
6	Dry Gulch nr. Estes Park, CO	2.1	0.2	0.9	.059
7	Rabbit Gulch nr. Estes Park, CO	3.4	0.2	1.0	.065
8	North Fk. Big Thompson R. nr. Glen Haven, CO	1.3	0.1	0.7	.058
9	Uintah R. nr. Neola, UT	181.0	59.0	32.0	.324
10	South Fk. Payette R. nr. Garden Valley, OR	779.0	123.0	30.0	.236
11	Malheur R. nr. Drewsey, OR	910.0	114.0	30.0	.242
12	Weiser R. above Craney Cr. nr. Weiser, OR	1160.0	310.0	37.0	.214
13	Madison R. nr. Three Forks, MT	2511.0	2060.0	50.0	.155
14	Gallitin R. at Logan, MT	1795.0	443.0	38.0	.196
15	Surface Cr. at Cedaredge, CO	43.0	11.3	11.3	.195
16	South Piney Cr. at Willow Park, WY	28.9	3.8	10.5	.260
17	Piney Cr. at Kearney, WY	106.0	29.0	16.5	.209
18	Coal Cr. nr. Cedar City, UT	92.0	6.6	2.4	.050
19	Sevier R. nr. Hatch, UT	260.0	41.0	5.1	.058
20	Sevier R. nr. Kingston, UT	1110.0	469.0	11.0	.056
21	Centerville Cr. nr. Centerville, UT	3.9	0.4	2.4	.124
22	Parrish Cr. nr. Centerville, UT	2.0	0.3	2.2	.126
23	Florida R. nr. Hermosa, CO	69.4	12.5	15.5	.259
24	Dolores R. nr. McPhee, CO	793.0	193.0	9.0	.061
25	Los Pinos R. nr. Bayfield, CO	284.0	35.0	28.5	.339

hydraulic system form the primary basis for establishing the appropriate K_n to be used in estimating the synthetic unit hydrograph lag time. In assigning the K_n value for a particular basin, consideration should also be given to K_n values developed from analyses of observed flood hydrographs for basins that have similar channel and floodplain characteristics and drainage-network densities.

Once the value of K_n has been determined, L and L_{ca}, are measured using a suitable topographic map. S, the slope of the longest watercourse, is also determined using data from the topographic map. These physical parameters, K_n, L, L_{ca}, and S, are then entered into the general equation for lag time, equation (1), which yields the synthetic unit hydrograph lag time, in hours.

$$L_g = 26K_n \left(\frac{LL_{ca}}{S^{0.5}} \right)^{0.33}$$

(2) *Selecting an Appropriate Dimensionless Unit Hydrograph or S-Graph.*—It is recognized that most readers do not have access to an extensive file of data representing either dimesionless unit hydrographs or dimensionless S-graphs that could be used in developing unit hydrographs for specific drainages. Examination of data available in the Bureau of Reclamation has led Bureau flood hydrologists to the conclusion that six dimensionless relationships are suitable for the regions identified in the previous discussion of unit hydrograph lag relationships. It should be kept in mind that a unit hydrograph developed from a flood hydrograph reconstruction of a major flood event in the basin under study can be considered superior to those recommended for the region in which the basin is located.

In accordance with the regional breakdown for the unit hydrograph lag relationships, tables 3-7 through 3-18 represent dimensionless unit hydrographs and comparable dimensionless S-graphs for these regions. These data may be used by the reader to plot the dimensionless unit hydrographs on semilogarithmic paper or the S-graph on rectangular coordinate paper. This will facilitate extracting ordinate values at discrete percentage values of either lag plus semiduration values or time in percent of lag. These discrete values are required for the development of a particular unit hydrograph.

Tables 3-7 and 3-8 provide data for a dimensionless unit hydrograph and a comparable dimensionless S-graph that are considered suitable for the Great Plains Region. Tables 3-9 and 3-10 provide similar data for use in developing unit hydrographs for PMF's resulting from general-type probable maximum storms in the Rocky Mountain Region. Tables 3-11 and 3-12 provide data suitable for use in developing unit hydrographs for basins in the Rocky Mountain Region when estimating thunderstorm generated PMF's. Tables 3-13 and 3-14 provide data for use in the Southwest Desert, Great Basin, and Colorado Plateau regions. Tables 3-15 and 3-16 provide data considered suitable for use in both the Sierra Nevada Region of California and the Coast and Cascade regions of California, Oregon, and Washington. Finally, tables 3-17 and 3-18 are a dimensionless unit hydrograph and a comparable dimensionless S-graph, respectively, that may be used in the development of unit hydrographs for urban basins.

(3) *Computing the Synthetic Unit Hydrograph Ordinates.*—When the unit hydrograph lag time has been determined and the dimensionless unit hydrograph or S-graph selected, it is basically a mechanical process to determine the synthetic unit hydrograph ordinates. This process is discussed in the following paragraphs for each of the two techniques currently used by the Bureau.

a. Dimensionless Unit Hydrograph Technique.—The first item that must be determined is the unit duration of the synthetic unit hydrograph. To provide adequate definition near and at the peak of the unit hydrograph, many investigators have shown that the unit duration should approximate the lag time divided by 5.5. The result of this division, the adopted unit duration, should always be rounded down to the closest of the following: 5, 10, 15, or 30 minutes, or 1, 2, or 6 hours. If the result is greater than 6 hours, the basin, should probably be subdivided into subbasins, and a unit hydrograph developed for each subbasin. The runoff hydrographs resulting from the application of rainfall to each subbasin should be routed and combined at the concentration point to determine the final hydrograph.

The dimensionless unit hydrograph is expressed in terms of time in percent of lag time plus the semiduration of unit rainfall on the abscissa scale. The ordinate values are determined by multiplying the discharge by the number found by adding the lag time and the semiduration of unit rainfall, then dividing by the volume of 1 inch of runoff from the subject basin. Because the lag time is known and the volume of 1 inch of runoff can be determined from the area of the drainage basin, the selected dimensionless unit hydrograph can be used to compute the unit hydrograph. This methodology is best explained by an example.

Consider a 300-mi^2 drainage basin whose unit hydrograph lag time has been determined to be 9 hours. Assume that a unit time of 2 hours has been selected for use in developing the unit hydrograph. Assume also that the dimensionless unit hydrograph shown on figure 3-9 has been selected as the basis for developing the unit hydrograph for the subject basin.

The lag time plus the semiduration of unit rainfall equals $9 + 2/2 = 10$ hours. The volume of 1 inch of runoff equals 300 times the conversion factor 26.89, or 8,067 ft^3/s-d. After these values are determined, a table is set up as shown on figure 3-9. The conversion factor 26.89 is used to convert 1 inch of rainfall excess over a 1-mi^2 area in 24 hours to runoff, in cubic feet per second-days. The first column lists the time in hours; each increment is equal to the unit rainfall duration. Values in the second column, labeled "% of $L_g + D/2$" (percent of lag time plus the semiduration of unit rainfall), are determined by dividing the corresponding value in the first column by the sum of the lag time and the semiduration value, $D/2$, then multiplying by 100 to convert to percentages. Values in the third column are obtained by reading the ordinate value from the dimensionless unit hydrograph for the corresponding percent of lag time plus the semiduration value in the second column. The unit hydrograph discharge ordinates listed in the fourth column are calculated by multiplying values in the third column by the quotient of the 1-inch runoff volume (8,067 ft^3/s-d) divided by the lag time plus semiduration value. The ordinates so developed represent the unit hydrograph discharge at the end of the respective time period.

When the unit hydrograph ordinates are determined, the points should be plotted on graph paper and connected by a smooth curve. Although this curve will not pass through all the points, the final

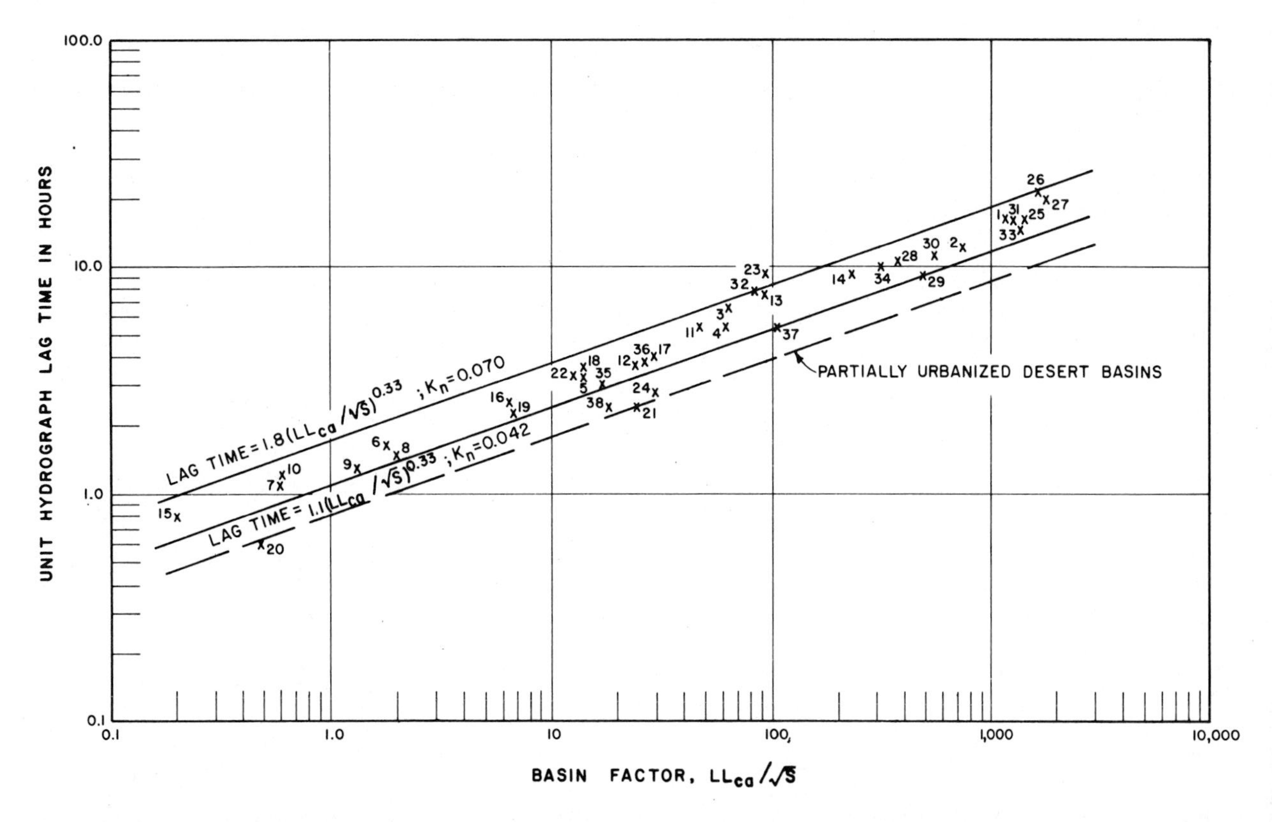

Figure 3-5.—Unit hydrograph lag relationships, Southwest Desert, Great Basin, and Colorado Plateau. 103-D-1852.

unit hydrograph ordinates used in developing a flood hydrograph should be the values read from the curve rather than the computed values. A plot of the final unit hydrograph and a table of the final ordinates should be included in every flood study report.

b. Dimensionless S-Graph Technique.—As with the dimensionless unit hydrograph technique, the unit duration should be the first item determined. The same constraints apply to this technique relative to determining the unit duration that apply to the dimensionless unit hydrograph technique relative to determining the unit duration and the subdivision of the drainage basin.

The dimensionless S-graph is expressed in terms of time (in percent of unit hydrograph lag time) on the abscissa scale, and discharge is expressed as a percentage of the ultimate discharge on the ordinate scale. The ultimate discharge is an equilibrium rate of discharge achieved when the entire basin is contributing runoff at the concentration point from a continuous series of unit-rainfall excess increments. The ultimate discharge for a drainage basin is found by multiplying the drainage area, in square miles, by the conversion factor 645.3 and dividing the result by the unit duration of rainfall. The conversion factor 645.3 converts 1 inch of rainfall excess over a 1-mi^2 area in 1 hour to runoff, expressed as 1h-ft^3/s. When both the lag time and the ultimate rate of discharge are known, application of these values to the appropriate dimensionless S-graph yields a synthetic unit hydrograph, as described in the following example.

Consider a drainage basin with an area of 250 mi^2 and a lag time of 12 hours. The theoretical unit duration is 12/5.5, or 2.18 hours. This is rounded downward to 2 hours for computational purposes. The ultimate discharge for this basin from a continuous series of rainfall excess increments of 1 inch in each 2-hour period would be 250(645.3)/2 or 80,662.5 2-h-ft^3/s. The dimensionless S-graph shown on figure 3-10 is assumed to be appropriate for the hypothetical basin under consideration and is selected for use in this example. The synthetic unit hydrograph, truncated at hour 18 for brevity, is then developed as shown in table 3-19.

The time is shown in the first column at increments equal to the unit duration. Time is expressed as a percentage of lag time in the second column and is found by dividing the time increment in the first column by the unit hydrograph lag time. Values entered in the third column represent ordinates read from the dimensionless S-graph at corresponding values (time in percent of lag) in the second column. Each value in the third column is multiplied by the ultimate to arrive at the summation hydrograph ordinates shown in the fourth column. Each unit hydrograph ordinate in the fifth column is the difference between the corresponding value in the fourth column and the preceding value in the fourth column.

The unit hydrograph ordinates should be plotted on graph paper for the proper time intervals, and a smooth curve should be drawn through the points. The final unit hydrograph ordinates should reflect the position of the smooth curve rather than the computed ordinates.

Table 3-3.—Unit hydrograph lag data, Southwest Desert, Great Basin, and Colorado Plateau.

Index No.	Station and location	Drainage area, mi^2	Basin factor, $LL_{ca}/\sqrt{S}$	Lag time, h	K_n
1	Salt River at Roosevelt, AZ	4341.0	1261.0	16.0	0.058
2	Verde R. above E. Verde and below Jerome, AZ	3190.0	760.0	12.0	.052
3	Tonto Cr. above Gun Cr., AZ	678.0	66.3	6.5	.063
4	Agua Fria R. nr. Mayor, AZ	590.0	63.2	5.4	.053
5	San Gabriel R. at San Gabriel Dam, CA	162.0	14.4	3.3	.053
6	West Fk. San Gabriel R. at Cogswell Dam, CA	40.4	1.8	1.6	.051
7	Santa Anita Cr. at Santa Anita Dam, CA	10.8	0.6	1.1	.050
8	Sand Dimas Cr. at San Dimas Dam, CO	16.2	2.0	1.5	.046
9	Eaton Wash at Eaton Wash Dam, CA	9.5	1.3	1.3	.046
10	San Antonio Cr. nr. Claremont, CA	16.9	0.6	1.2	.055
11	Santa Clara R. nr. Saugus, CA	355.0	48.2	5.6	.060
12	Temecula Cr. at Pauba Canyon, CA	168.0	24.1	3.7	.050
13	Santa Margarita R. nr. Fallbrook, CA	645.0	99.2	7.3	.062
14	Santa Margarita R. at Ysidora, CA	740.0	228.0	9.5	.061
15	Live Oak Cr. at Live Oak Dam, CA	2.3	0.2	0.8	.052
16	Tujunga Cr. at Big Tujunga Dam, CA	81.4	6.5	2.5	.052
17	Murrieta Cr. at Temecula, CA	220.0	28.9	4.0	.051
18	Los Angeles R. at Sepulveda Dam, CA	152.0	14.3	3.5	.056
19	Pacoima Wash at Pacoima Dam, CA	27.8	6.8	2.4	.049
20	East Fullerton Cr. at Fullerton Dam, CA	3.1	0.5	0.6	.029
21	San Jose Cr. at Workman Mill Rd. CA	81.3	24.8	2.4	.032
22	San Vincente Cr. at Foster, CA	75.0	12.8	3.2	.053
23	San Diego R. nr. Santee, CA	380.0	95.4	9.2	.078
24	Deep Cr. nr. Hesperia, CA	137.0	28.1	2.8	.036
25	Bill Williams R. at Planet, AZ	4730.0	1476.0	16.2	.056
26	Gila R. at Conner No. 4 Damsite, AZ	2840.0	1722.0	21.5	.071
27	San Francisco R. at Jct. with Blue R., AZ	2000.0	1688.0	20.6	.068
28	Blue R. nr. Clifton, AZ	790.0	352.0	10.3	.057
29	Moencopi Wash nr. Tuba City, AZ	2490.0	473.0	9.2	.046
30	Clear Cr. nr. Winslow, AZ	607.0	570.0	11.2	.053
31	Puerco R. nr. Admana, AZ	2760.0	1225.0	15.9	.058
32	Plateau Cr. nr. Cameo, CO	604.0	89.9	7.9	.069
33	White R. nr. Watson, UT	4020.0	1473.0	15.7	.054
34	Paria R. at Lees Ferry, AZ	1570.0	296.0	10.2	.060
35	New River at Rock Springs, AZ	67.3	16.5	3.1	.047
36	New River at New River, AZ	85.7	26.3	3.7	.048
37	New R. at Bell Road nr. Phoenix, AZ	187.0	108.0	5.3	.043
38	Skunk Cr. nr. Phoenix, AZ	64.6	18.7	2.4	.035

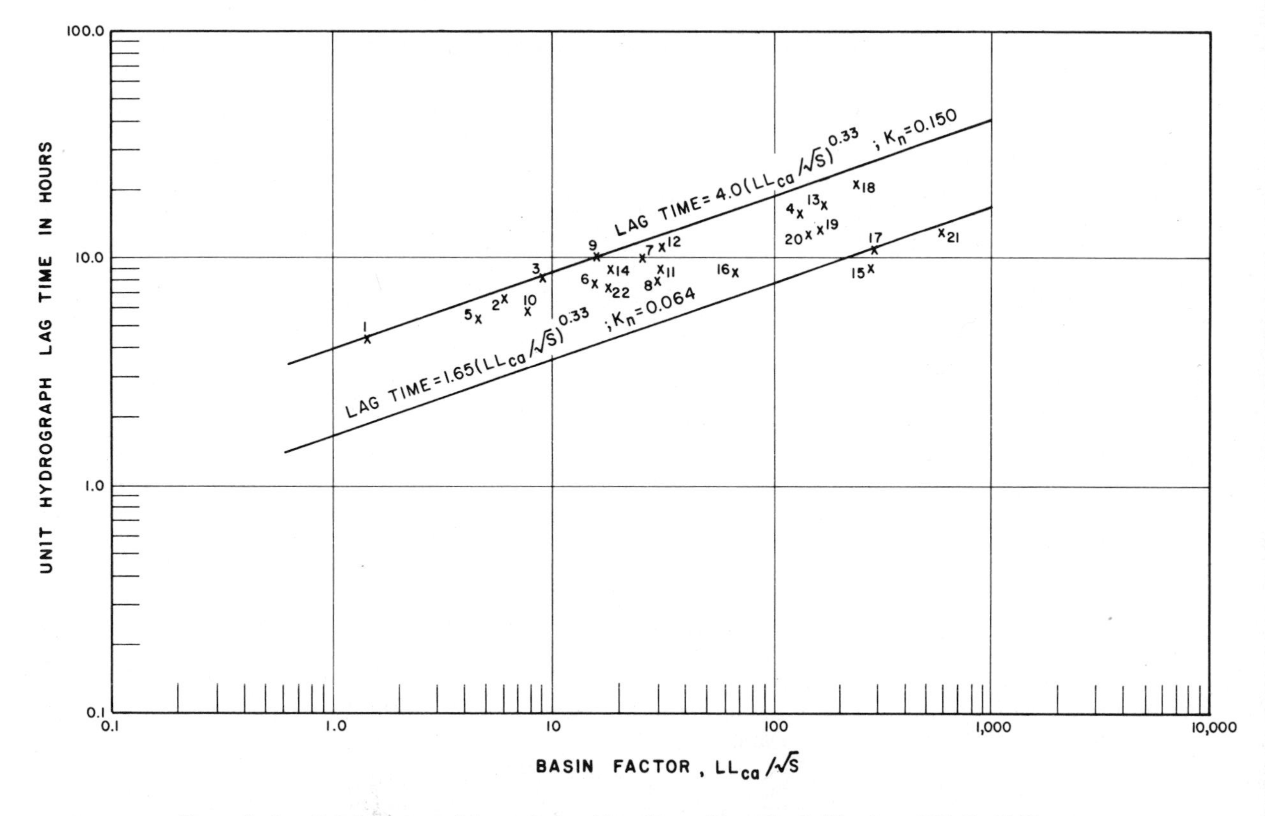

Figure 3-6.—Unit hydrograph lag relationships, Sierra Nevada, California. 103-D-1853.

(e) *Infiltration and Other Losses.*—Rainfall or snowfall separates into several components when it reaches the ground. The flood hydrologist recognizes four types of losses:

(1) *Interception* by vegetation and subsequent evaporation or retardation from reaching the ground surface.

(2) *Evaporation* from the ground surface during prolonged rainfall events or when accumulated in frozen form from snowfall.

(3) *Depression storage* in surface depressions, which act as miniature reservoirs and do not release their waters until their storage capacity is exceeded (and then only to a stage-versus-discharge relationship comparable with that of an engineered uncontrolled spillway for a water-impounding structure).

(4) *Infiltration* into the receiving soil, rock, or combination thereof. Any of the constituents (both natural and artificial) of the earth's mantle can absorb water—whether it be a concrete parking area or the sandiest soils.

Overland runoff occurs when the rate of rainfall or the rate of snowmelt has satisfied the first three losses and exceeds the capacity of the soil to absorb the water.

The first three of the losses listed above are usually minor compared with infiltration losses when rainfall intensities are sufficient to produce severe flood events. Under such conditions they are often grouped with part of the infiltration loss and termed "initial losses."

To illustrate the phenomena that occur in the soil when water is applied in the form of rain, consider a condition at the onset of a rainstorm where the soil is comparatively dry because no precipitation has occurred in recent days. Initially, part of the precipitation is intercepted by vegetation. However, once the vegetation has reached its capacity to retain water, additional precipitation simply runs off and falls to the ground. The rest of the rainfall falls directly on the ground surface and enters the soil or is retained in depression storage. In actuality, some of this precipitation evaporates into the atmosphere. However, in the hydrologic analysis of extreme flood events, interception and evaporation losses are so small compared with the magnitude of the precipitation that they are neglected. Precipitation at first filters rather rapidly into most soils to satisfy the soil-moisture deficiency. Thereafter,

Table 3-4.—Unit hydrograph lag data, Sierra Nevada, California.

Index No.	Station and location	Drainage area, mi²	Basin factor, $LL_{ca}/\sqrt{S}$	Lag time, h	K_n
1	Pitman Cr. below Tamarack Cr., CA	22.7	1.4	4.4	0.151
2	North Fk. Kings R. nr. Cliff Camp, CA	[1]70.0	6.2	6.7	.141
3	North Fk. Kings R. below Rancheria, CA	[1]116.0	9.2	8.4	.155
4	Cosumnes R. at Michigan Bar, CA	537.0	133.0	16.0	.123
5	Cosgrove Cr. nr. Valley Springs, CA	20.6	4.6	5.5	.128
6	Woods Cr. nr. Jacksonville, CA	98.4	15.1	7.8	.122
7	North Fk. Calaveras R. nr. San Andreas, CA	85.7	25.4	10.0	.132
8	Calaveras R. at Calaveras Reservoir, CA	395.0	30.6	8.5	.106
9	Calaveritas Cr. nr. San Andreas, CA	53.0	15.6	10.0	.155
10	North Fk. Cosumnes R. at Cosumnes Mine, CA	36.9	7.7	6.0	.118
11	Tule R. at Success Dam, CA	388.0	31.4	8.8	.109
12	Kaweah R. at Terminus Dam, CA	560.0	30.4	11.5	.143
13	Kings R. at Pine Flat Dam, CA	1542.0	168.0	17.2	.122
14	Big Dry Cr. Reservoir, CA	86.0	18.5	9.2	.135
15	Stanislaus R. at Melones Dam, CA	897.0	269.0	9.2	.056
16	Calaveras R. at Hogan Reservoir, CA	363.0	66.0	8.6	.083
17	American R. at Folsom Dam, CA	1875.0	290.0	10.9	.065
18	Kern R. at Isabella Dam, CA	2075.0	235.0	21.5	.136
19	North Yuba R. at Bullard's Bar Dam, CA	481.0	164.0	13.2	.094
20	Yuba R. at Englebright Dam, CA	990.0	143.0	12.5	.093
21	San Joaquin R. at Friant Dam, CA	1261.0	497.0	13.7	.068
22	South Fk. Cosumnes R. nr. River Pines, CA	64.3	17.7	7.6	.113

[1]Contributing area.

water in excess of that required to satisfy the soil-moisture deficiency moves downward under the effect of gravity until it enters the ground-water reservoir.

The minimum rate at which a soil in a saturated condition can absorb water is generally termed the "infiltration capacity" of the soil.

The rate at which a given soil absorbs rainfall is a function of infiltration and transmissibility. The infiltration rate is primarily controlled by surface conditions where the water enters the ground. The transmissibility, or transmission rate, is the rate at which the water moves through the soil in either the vertical or horizontal direction. However, in flood hydrology studies both the infiltration and the transmission rates are combined under the designation "infiltration rates."

In practice, all these phenomena, as they relate to severe flood occurrences, can be represented by a decay-curve function. In 1940, Horton [2] proposed the following equation to represent this function:

$$f = f_c + (f_o - f_c)e^{-kt} \qquad (2)$$

where:

f = resulting infiltration rate at time t,
f_c = minimum infiltration rate,
f_o = initial rate of infiltration capacity,
e = base of the Naperian logarithms,
k = constant dependent primarily on soil type and vegetation, and
t = time from the start of rainfall.

In the development of PMF's, the hydrologic engineer is primarily concerned with the magnitude of f_c.

The Soil Conservation Service has proposed subdividing soils into four groups, relative to their respective infiltration capacities. These groups, as defined by that agency, are essentially as follows:

(1) *Group A Soils* (low runoff potential) have high infiltration rates even when saturated. This group mainly consists of well to mod-

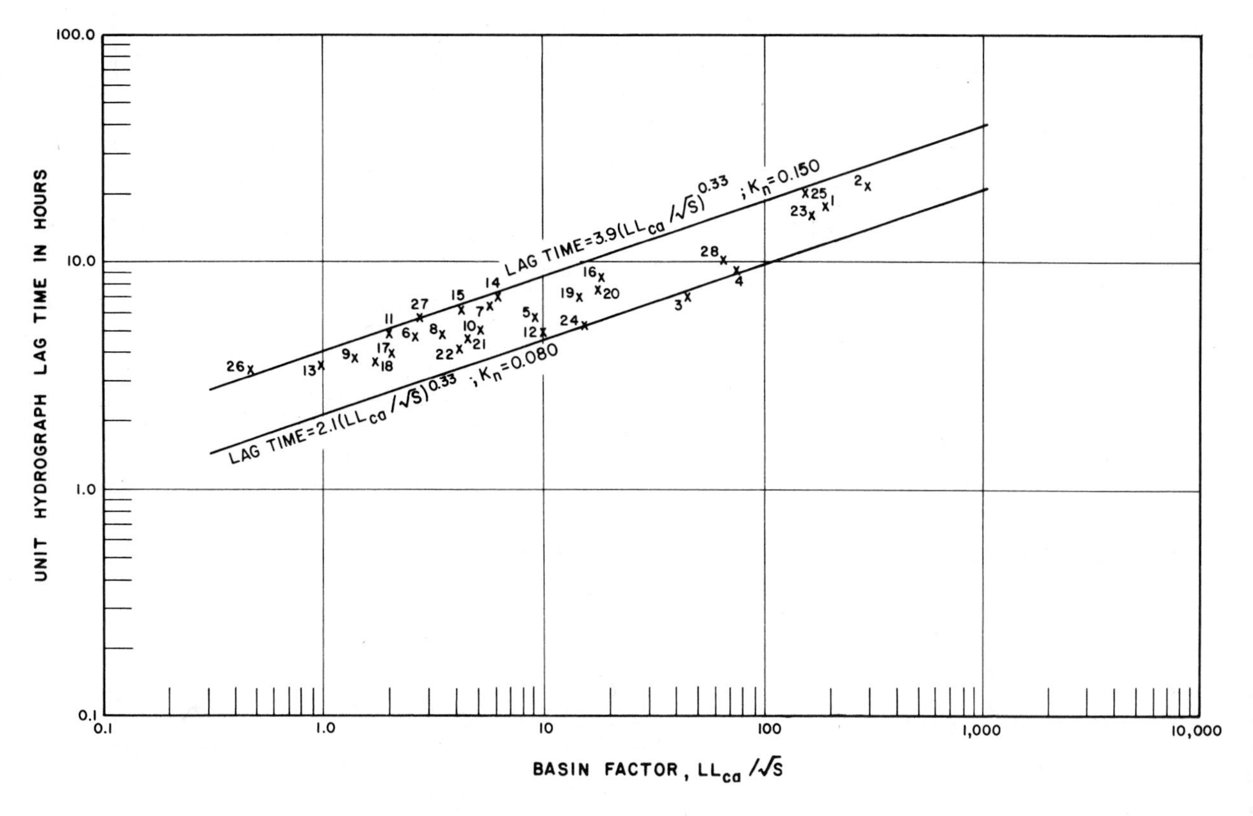

Figure 3-7.—Unit hydrograph lag relationships, Coast and Cascade ranges of California, Oregon, and Washington. 103-D-1854.

erately well-drained sands or gravels. These soils have a high transmission rate. Minimum infiltration rates for these soils range from 0.3 to 0.5 inch per hour.

(2) *Group B Soils* have moderate infiltration rates when throughly wetted. This group mainly consists of moderately deep to deep and moderately well to well-drained soils. They have fine to moderately coarse textures and include sandy loams and shallow loess. Minimum infiltration rates for those soils range from 0.15 to 0.30 inch per hour.

(3) *Group C Soils* have low infiltration rates when throughly wetted. This group mainly consists of soils with a layer that impedes downward movement of water and soils with moderately fine to fine texture. These soils have a low transmission rate. Many clay loams, shallow sandy loams, soils low in organic matter, and soils high in clay content are in this group. Minimum infiltration rates for these soils range from 0.05 to 0.15 inch per hour.

(4) *Group D Soils* (high runoff potential) have very low infiltration rates when throughly wetted. This group mainly consists of clay soils with high swelling potential, soils with a permanently high water table, soils with a claypan or clay layer at or near the surface, and shallow soils over nearly impervious material. This group includes heavy plastic clays and certain saline soils. These soils have a very low transmission rate. Minimum infiltration rates for these soils range from values approaching 0 to 0.05 inch per hour.

Hydrologic analyses leading to PMF estimates should be based on the assumption that minimum infiltration rates prevail for the duration of the probable maximum storm. This assumption is based on consideration of conditions that have been shown to exist before extreme storm events. Historical conditions have shown that it is quite reasonable to expect one or more storms preceding or antecedent to the extreme event. Accordingly, it is assumed that antecedent storms satisfy all soil-moisture deficiencies and interception, evaporation,

Table 3-5.—Unit hydrograph lag data, Coast and Cascade ranges. California, Oregon, and Washington.

Index No.	Station and location	Drainage area, mi^2	Basin factor, $LL_{ca}/\sqrt{S}$	Lag time, h	K_n
1	Putah Cr. nr. Winters, CA	577.0	190.0	17.5	0.119
2	Stony Cr. nr. Hamilton City, CA	764.0	288.0	21.8	.129
3	Huasna R. nr. Santa Maria, CA	119.0	45.4	7.0	.076
4	Sisquoc R. nr. Garey, CA	465.0	76.8	8.9	.082
5	Salinas R. nr. Pozo, CA	114.0	9.0	5.7	.106
6	Corte Madera Cr. at Ross, CA	18.1	2.6	4.6	.129
7	East Fk. Russian R. nr. Calpella, CA	93.0	5.9	6.5	.139
8	Novato Cr. nr. Novato, CA	17.5	3.5	4.7	.120
9	Pinole Cr. nr. Pinole, CA	10.0	1.4	3.8	.131
10	San Francisquito Cr. nr. Stanford University, CA	38.3	4.8	4.8	.110
11	San Lorenzo Cr. at Hayward, CA	37.5	2.0	4.9	.150
12	Sonoma Cr. at Boyes Hot Springs, CA	62.2	10.0	4.8	.086
13	Corralitos Cr. nr. Corralitos, CA	10.6	0.97	3.4	.132
14	Austin Cr. nr. Cadzadero, CA	63.0	6.2	6.8	.143
15	Dry Cr. nr. Napa, CA	17.4	4.3	6.0	.143
16	South Fk. Eel R. nr. Branscomb, CA	43.9	17.8	8.1	.120
17	Branciforte Cr. at Santa Cruz, CA	17.3	2.1	3.9	.117
18	Matadero Cr. at Palo Alto, CA	7.2	1.7	3.7	.119
19	Napa R. at St. Helena, CA	81.1	14.8	6.8	.107
20	San Lorenzo R. at Big Trees, CA	111.0	17.8	8.0	.119
21	Uvas Cr. at Morgan Hill, CA	30.4	4.4	4.4	.104
22	Feliz Cr. nr. Hopland, CA	31.2	4.0	3.9	.095
23	Redwood Cr. at Orick, CA	278.0	170.0	16.0	.113
24	Russian R. at Ukiah, CA	99.6	14.5	5.1	.081
25	Trinity R. at Lewiston, CA	726.0	157.0	20.0	.145
26	Powell Cr. nr. Williams, OR	8.6	0.47	3.4	.168
27	Slate Cr. nr. Wonder, OR	30.9	2.8	5.6	.153
28	Arroyo Del Valle nr. Livermore, CA	147.0	66.5	10.0	.096

and depression storage losses; and that infiltration rates are lowest at the onset of the probable maximum storm.

(f) *Base Flow and Interflow.*—These two components of a flood hydrograph are graphically depicted on figure 3-11. The base-flow component generally consists of the water that reaches the watercourses after flowing a considerable distance underground as ground water. The hydrograph is generally depicted as a recession curve, indicating a gradually decreasing rate of surface flow. This flow continues to decrease until the water surface in the stream is in equilibrium with the surface of the adjacent water table, and the flow is maintained by inflow from the ground-water reservoir. When the water table is at a level below the channel bed, there is no surface flow in the stream, but there may be subsurface flow in the river gravels. For this case the recession curve approaches and finally goes to zero.

The interflow component, sometimes called the subsurface storm flow, is generated by precipitation that enters the ground by infiltration, but emerges as a direct contribution to the surface runoff within a relatively short time. Current thinking is that this phenomenon occurs during every severe flood event in varying degrees, depending on the characteristics of the drainage basin.

Quantification of the base-flow and interflow components in a flood study are usually based on the results of flood hydrograph reconstructions. A typically shaped recession curve and an interflow representation are shown on figure 3-11 as the dashed line and the alternating long and short dashed line, respectively. The separation of the observed flood hydrograph into three components requires a considerable amount of judgement because the interflow and base flow (or recession flow) are

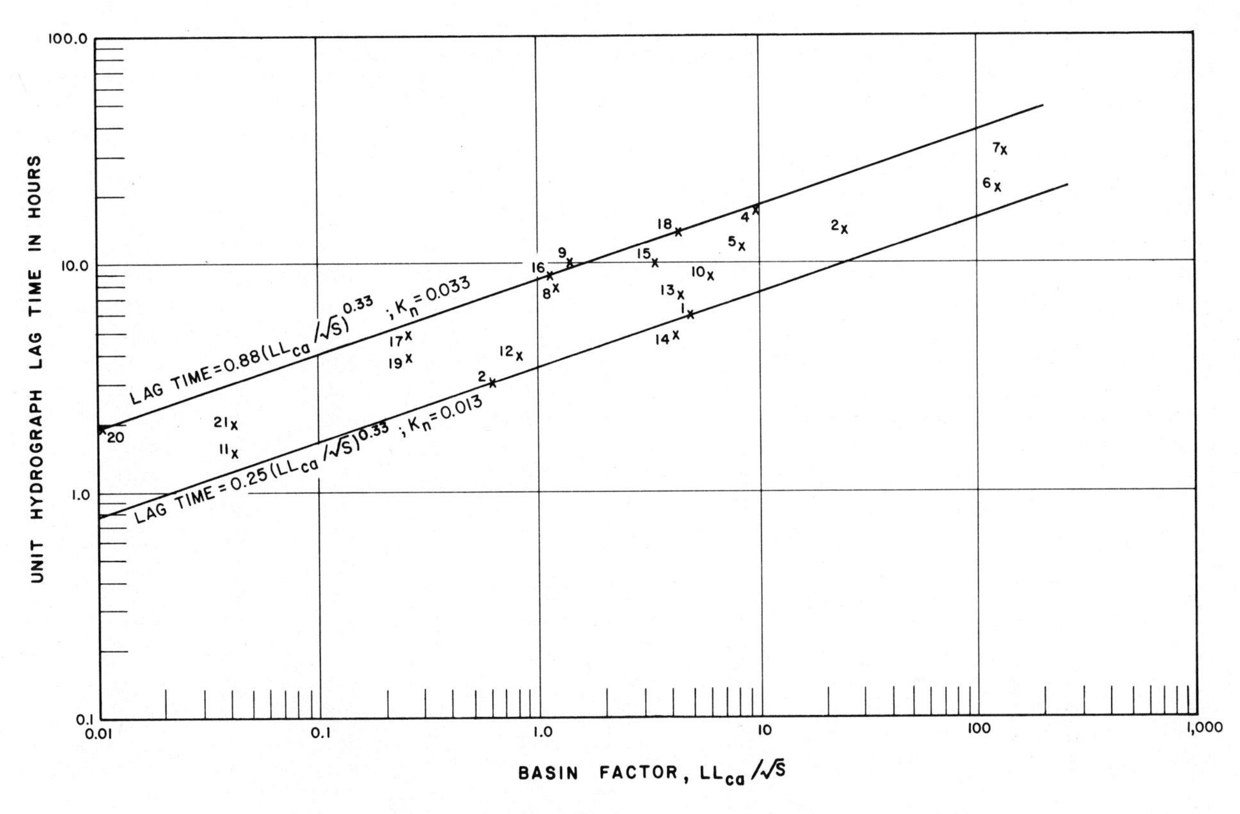

Figure 3-8.—Unit hydrograph lag relationships, urban basins. 103-D-1855.

Table 3-6.—Unit hydrograph lag data, urban basins.

Index No.	Station and location	Drainage area, mi^2	Basin factor, $LL_{ca}/\sqrt{S}$	Lag time, h	K_n
1	Alhambra Wash above Short St., Monterey Park, CA	14.0	4.8	0.6	0.011
2	San Jose Cr. at Workman Mill Rd, Whittier, CA	81.3	24.8	2.4	.032
3	Broadway Drain at Raymond Dike, CA	2.5	0.6	0.3	.014
4	Compton Cr. below Hooper Ave. Storm Drain, L.A., CA	19.5	9.7	1.8	.033
5	Ballona Cr. at Sawtelle Blvd., L.A., CA	88.6	8.3	1.2	.023
6	Brays Bayou, Houston, TX	88.4	121.0	2.1	.017
7	White Oak Bayou, Houston, TX	92.0	134.0	3.1	.024
8	Boneyard Cr., Austin, TX	4.5	1.2	0.8	.029
9	Waller Cr., Austin, TX	4.1	1.4	1.0	.034
10	Beargrass Cr., Louisville, KY	9.7	5.6	0.9	.020
11	17th Street Sewer, Louisville, KY	0.2	0.04	0.15	.017
12	Northwest Trunk, Louisville, KY	1.9	0.8	0.4	.014
13	Southern Outfall, Louisville, KY	6.4	4.4	0.7	.017
14	Southwest Outfall, Louisville, KY	7.5	4.1	0.50	.012
15	Beargrass Cr., Louisville, KY	6.3	3.4	1.0	.026
16	Tripps Run nr. Falls Church, VA	4.6	1.1	0.9	.033
17	Tripps Run at Falls Church, VA	1.8	0.26	0.5	.030
18	Four Mile Run at Alexandria, VA	14.4	4.2	1.4	.034
19	Little Pimmit Run at Arlington, VA	2.3	0.25	0.4	.024
20	Piney Branch at Vienna, VA	0.3	0.01	0.2	.035
21	Walker Avenue Drain at Baltimore, MD	0.2	0.04	0.2	.022

Table 3-7.—Dimensionless unit hydrograph data, Great Plains. $q = Q\,(L_g + ½D)/Vol.$

% of $(L_g + ½D)$	q	% of $(L_g + ½D)$	q	% of $(L_g + ½D)$	q	% of $(L_g + ½D)$	q	% of $(L_g + ½D)$	q	% of $(L_g + ½D)$	q
5	0.10	105	15.04	205	3.18	305	1.37	405	0.65	505	0.30
10	.20	110	13.52	210	2.98	310	1.32	410	.62	510	.29
15	.81	115	12.51	215	2.79	315	1.27	415	.60	515	.29
20	1.66	120	11.40	220	2.67	320	1.23	420	.58	520	.27
25	3.23	125	10.50	225	2.52	325	1.18	425	.56	525	.26
30	4.83	130	9.59	230	2.41	330	1.14	430	.54	530	.26
35	7.06	135	8.88	235	2.32	335	1.10	435	.52	535	.25
40	9.18	140	8.26	240	2.24	340	1.05	440	.50	540	.24
45	11.10	145	7.57	245	2.15	345	1.02	445	.48	545	.24
50	14.03	150	6.96	250	2.08	350	0.98	450	.46	550	.23
55	16.25	155	6.36	255	2.00	355	.94	455	.44	555	.22
60	18.07	160	5.95	260	1.92	360	.91	460	.43	560	.21
65	20.19	165	5.45	265	1.85	365	.87	465	.41	565	.20
70	21.40	170	5.05	270	1.79	370	.84	470	.40	570	.20
75	22.91	175	4.64	275	1.72	375	.81	475	.38	575	.19
80	24.02	180	4.39	280	1.66	380	.78	480	.37	580	.18
85	22.81	185	4.04	285	1.59	385	.75	485	.35	585	.18
90	20.59	190	3.78	290	1.54	390	.72	490	.34	590	.17
95	18.37	195	3.53	295	1.48	395	.70	495	.33	595	.16
100	16.65	200	3.38	300	1.42	400	.67	500	.32	600	.16

Table 3-8.—Dimensionless S-graph data, Great Plains.

Time, % of L_g	Discharge, % of ultimate	Time, % of L_g	Discharge, % of ultimate	Time, % of L_g	Discharge, % of ultimate	Time, % of L_g	Discharge, % of ultimate	Time, % of L_g	Discharge, % of ultimate	Time, % of L_g	Discharge, % of ultimate
5	0.02	105	53.28	205	83.76	305	92.60	405	96.81	505	98.85
10	.06	110	56.25	210	84.42	310	92.89	410	96.95	510	98.93
15	.21	115	58.94	215	85.05	315	93.17	415	97.08	515	99.00
20	.52	120	61.43	220	85.63	320	93.44	420	97.21	520	99.08
25	1.11	125	63.71	225	86.19	325	93.70	425	97.34	525	99.15
30	2.01	130	65.81	230	86.72	330	93.95	430	97.46	530	99.22
35	3.31	135	67.74	235	87.22	335	94.19	435	97.58	535	99.29
40	5.02	140	69.53	240	87.70	340	94.43	440	97.69	540	99.35
45	7.11	145	71.20	245	88.16	345	94.65	445	97.80	545	99.41
50	9.70	150	72.73	250	88.61	350	94.87	450	97.91	550	99.48
55	12.76	155	74.15	255	89.04	355	95.08	455	98.01	555	99.53
60	16.20	160	75.46	260	89.46	360	95.28	460	98.11	560	99.59
65	20.02	165	76.67	265	89.86	365	95.48	465	98.20	565	99.65
70	24.17	170	77.80	270	90.25	370	95.66	470	98.29	570	99.70
75	28.57	175	78.84	275	90.62	375	95.85	475	98.38	575	99.76
80	33.23	180	79.80	280	90.98	380	96.02	480	98.47	580	99.81
85	37.95	185	80.70	285	91.33	385	96.19	485	98.55	585	99.86
90	42.39	190	81.54	290	91.66	390	96.35	490	98.63	590	99.91
95	46.40	195	82.33	295	91.99	395	96.51	495	98.70	595	99.95
100	50.00	200	83.07	300	92.30	400	96.66	500	98.78	600	100.00

Table 3-9.—General storm dimensionless unit hydrograph data, Rocky Mountains. $q = Q\ (L_g + ½D)/Vol.$

% of $(L_g + ½D)$	q	% of $(L_g + ½D)$	q	% of $(L_g + ½D)$	q	% of $(L_g + ½D)$	q	% of $(L_g + ½D)$	q	% of $(L_g + ½D)$	q
5	0.26	105	11.91	205	3.72	305	1.63	405	0.74	505	0.34
10	.90	110	11.21	210	3.55	310	1.57	410	.71	510	.33
15	2.00	115	10.61	215	3.40	315	1.50	415	.68	515	.32
20	3.00	120	10.01	220	3.25	320	1.45	420	.65	520	.31
25	5.00	125	9.40	225	3.10	325	1.39	425	.63	525	.29
30	6.00	130	8.80	230	3.00	330	1.34	430	.60	530	.28
35	7.70	135	8.25	235	2.87	335	1.28	435	.56	535	.27
40	9.00	140	7.70	240	2.75	340	1.23	440	.58	540	.26
45	14.51	145	7.25	245	2.65	345	1.19	445	.54	545	.25
50	18.11	150	6.80	250	2.52	350	1.13	450	.52	550	.24
55	21.51	155	6.40	255	2.42	355	1.09	455	.50	555	.23
60	24.01	160	6.00	260	2.33	360	1.05	460	.48	560	.23
65	22.81	165	5.65	265	2.24	365	1.01	465	.46	565	.22
70	21.21	170	5.35	270	2.15	370	0.97	470	.44	570	.21
75	19.31	175	5.00	275	2.07	375	.93	475	.42	575	.20
80	16.91	180	4.80	280	1.99	380	.90	480	.41	580	.19
85	15.21	185	4.55	285	1.91	385	.86	485	.40	585	.19
90	14.21	190	4.30	290	1.83	390	.83	490	.38	590	.18
95	13.41	195	4.10	295	1.76	395	.80	495	.37	595	.17
100	12.71	200	3.90	300	1.70	400	.77	500	.35	600	.17

Table 3-10.—General storm dimensionless S-graph data, Rocky Mountains.

Time, % of L_g	Discharge, % of ultimate	Time, % of L_g	Discharge, % of ultimate	Time, % of L_g	Discharge, % of ultimate	Time, % of L_g	Discharge, % of ultimate	Time, % of L_g	Discharge, % of ultimate	Time, % of L_g	Discharge, % of ultimate
5	0.05	105	52.51	205	81.06	305	91.68	405	96.55	505	98.82
10	.23	110	54.87	210	81.83	310	92.02	410	96.71	510	98.89
15	.62	115	57.10	215	82.56	315	92.35	415	96.86	515	98.96
20	1.20	120	59.21	220	83.26	320	92.67	420	97.01	520	99.04
25	2.15	125	61.20	225	83.93	325	92.97	425	97.15	525	99.11
30	3.46	130	63.08	230	84.57	330	93.26	430	97.29	530	99.19
35	4.97	135	64.84	235	85.18	335	93.55	435	97.42	535	99.26
40	6.72	140	66.50	240	85.78	340	93.82	440	97.54	540	99.33
45	9.33	145	68.05	245	86.35	345	94.08	445	97.66	545	99.39
50	12.74	150	69.51	250	86.89	350	94.33	450	97.78	550	99.46
55	16.84	155	70.88	255	87.42	355	94.58	455	97.89	555	99.52
60	21.47	160	72.17	260	87.92	360	94.81	460	98.00	560	99.58
65	26.17	165	73.39	265	88.41	365	95.03	465	98.11	565	99.64
70	30.58	170	74.53	270	88.87	370	95.25	470	98.21	570	99.69
75	34.66	175	75.62	275	89.32	375	95.45	475	98.31	575	99.75
80	38.32	180	76.64	280	89.75	380	95.65	480	98.40	580	99.80
85	41.57	185	77.61	285	90.17	385	95.85	485	98.49	585	99.85
90	44.55	190	78.54	290	90.57	390	96.03	490	98.58	590	99.90
95	47.35	195	79.43	295	90.95	395	96.21	495	98.66	595	99.95
100	50.00	200	80.26	300	91.32	400	96.38	500	98.74	600	100.00

Table 3-11.—Thunderstorm dimensionless unit hydrograph data, Rocky Mountains. $q = Q\ (L_g + ½D)/Vol.$

% of $(L_g + ½D)$	q	% of $(L_g + ½D)$	q	% of $(L_g + ½D)$	q	% of $(L_g + ½D)$	q	% of $(L_g + ½D)$	q	% of $(L_g + ½D)$	q
5	0.14	105	20.76	205	2.75	305	1.05	405	0.43	505	0.18
10	.21	110	18.84	210	2.61	310	1.00	410	.42	510	.17
15	.33	115	16.81	215	2.44	315	0.96	415	.40	515	.17
20	.51	120	14.99	220	2.31	320	.92	420	.38	520	.16
25	.84	125	12.86	225	2.17	325	.88	425	.36	525	.16
30	1.62	130	11.04	230	2.04	330	.84	430	.35	530	.15
35	3.74	135	9.52	235	1.95	335	.81	435	.33	535	.15
40	6.38	140	8.41	240	1.84	340	.77	440	.32	540	.14
45	8.61	145	7.50	245	1.76	345	.74	445	.31	545	.14
50	10.94	150	6.69	250	1.69	350	.71	450	.29	550	.13
55	13.26	155	5.98	255	1.62	355	.68	455	.28	555	.13
60	15.70	160	5.47	260	1.55	360	.65	460	.27	560	.12
65	18.23	165	4.97	265	1.49	365	.62	465	.26	565	.12
70	20.76	170	4.55	270	1.42	370	.59	470	.25	570	.11
75	23.30	175	4.25	275	1.36	375	.57	475	.24	575	.11
80	25.83	180	3.89	280	1.30	380	.55	480	.23	580	.10
85	28.36	185	3.59	285	1.24	385	.52	485	.22	585	.10
90	26.53	190	3.34	290	1.19	390	.50	490	.21	590	.09
95	24.71	195	3.13	295	1.14	395	.48	495	.20	595	.09
100	22.68	200	2.93	300	1.09	400	.46	500	.19	600	.08

Table 3-12.—Thunderstorm dimensionless S-graph data, Rocky Mountains.

Time, % of L_g	Discharge, % of ultimate	Time, % of L_g	Discharge, % of ultimate	Time, % of L_g	Discharge, % of ultimate	Time, % of L_g	Discharge, % of ultimate	Time, % of L_g	Discharge, % of ultimate	Time, % of L_g	Discharge, % of ultimate
5	0.03	105	54.43	205	87.87	305	95.09	405	98.11	505	99.40
10	.07	110	58.48	210	88.44	310	95.31	410	98.21	510	99.44
15	.14	115	62.14	215	88.97	315	95.52	415	98.30	515	99.48
20	.24	120	65.42	220	89.47	320	95.72	420	98.38	520	99.52
25	.40	125	68.32	225	89.95	325	95.92	425	98.46	525	99.55
30	.70	130	70.83	230	90.39	330	96.10	430	98.54	530	99.58
35	1.39	135	72.98	235	90.81	335	96.28	435	98.62	535	99.62
40	2.57	140	74.86	240	91.22	340	96.45	440	98.69	540	99.65
45	4.21	145	76.53	245	91.60	345	96.61	445	98.76	545	99.68
50	6.31	150	78.02	250	91.96	350	96.77	450	98.82	550	99.71
55	8.86	155	79.35	255	92.31	355	96.92	455	98.89	555	99.73
60	11.88	160	80.55	260	92.64	360	97.06	460	98.95	560	99.76
65	15.39	165	81.65	265	92.96	365	97.20	465	99.01	565	99.78
70	19.41	170	82.65	270	93.27	370	97.33	470	99.06	570	99.82
75	23.92	175	83.57	275	93.57	375	97.46	475	99.12	575	99.85
80	28.93	180	84.44	280	93.85	380	97.58	480	99.17	580	99.88
85	34.43	185	85.22	285	94.12	385	97.69	485	99.22	585	99.91
90	39.99	190	85.95	290	94.38	390	97.81	490	99.27	590	99.94
95	45.18	195	86.64	295	94.63	395	97.91	495	99.31	595	99.97
100	50.00	200	87.27	300	94.86	400	98.01	500	99.36	600	100.00

Table 3-13.—Dimensionless unit hydrograph data, Southwest Desert, Great Basin, and Colorado Plateau. $q = Q\,(L_g + ½D)/Vol.$

% of $(L_g + ½D)$	q	% of $(L_g + ½D)$	q	% of $(L_g + ½D)$	q	% of $(L_g + ½D)$	q	% of $(L_g + ½D)$	q	% of $(L_g + ½D)$	q
5	0.19	105	18.92	205	3.47	305	1.15	405	0.38	505	0.12
10	.32	110	16.08	210	3.28	310	1.08	410	.36	510	.12
15	.48	115	14.19	215	3.10	315	1.02	415	.34	515	.11
20	.74	120	12.61	220	2.93	320	0.97	420	.33	520	.10
25	1.21	125	11.04	225	2.75	325	.91	425	.30		
30	1.81	130	9.99	230	2.63	330	.86	430	.28		
35	2.63	135	9.04	235	2.47	335	.82	435	.27		
40	3.68	140	8.20	240	2.33	340	.78	440	.26		
45	5.47	145	7.36	245	2.22	345	.74	445	.24		
50	8.41	150	6.78	250	2.10	350	.69	450	.23		
55	12.61	155	6.20	255	1.99	355	.66	455	.22		
60	16.50	160	5.83	260	1.88	360	.63	460	.21		
65	20.50	165	5.47	265	1.78	365	.59	465	.20		
70	23.97	170	5.15	270	1.68	370	.56	470	.19		
75	27.75	175	4.84	275	1.59	375	.53	475	.18		
80	28.91	180	4.57	280	1.50	380	.50	480	.17		
85	28.07	185	4.31	285	1.43	385	.47	485	.16		
90	26.38	190	4.10	290	1.36	390	.45	490	.15		
95	24.18	195	3.87	295	1.28	395	.42	495	.15		
100	21.55	200	3.68	300	1.21	400	.40	500	.13		

Table 3-14.—Dimensionless S-graph data, Southwest Desert, Great Basin, and Colorado Plateau.

Time, % of L_g	Discharge, % of ultimate	Time, % of L_g	Discharge, % of ultimate	Time, % of L_g	Discharge, % of ultimate	Time, % of L_g	Discharge, % of ultimate	Time, % of L_g	Discharge, % of ultimate	Time, % of L_g	Discharge, % of ultimate
5	0.04	105	54.19	205	86.64	305	95.65	405	98.75	505	99.85
10	.10	110	57.86	210	87.36	310	95.89	410	98.84	510	99.89
15	.20	115	61.02	215	88.04	315	96.13	415	98.92	515	99.93
20	.34	120	63.83	220	88.68	320	96.35	420	98.99	520	99.97
25	.57	125	66.33	225	89.29	325	96.56	425	99.06	525	100.00
30	.91	130	68.53	230	89.86	330	96.75	430	99.13		
35	1.40	135	70.53	235	90.41	335	96.94	435	99.20		
40	2.08	140	72.34	240	90.93	340	97.12	440	99.26		
45	3.08	145	73.99	245	91.42	345	97.29	445	99.32		
50	4.57	150	75.47	250	91.88	350	97.45	450	99.37		
55	6.79	155	76.84	255	92.32	355	97.60	455	99.42		
60	9.79	160	78.10	260	92.74	360	97.74	460	99.47		
65	13.55	165	79.28	265	93.14	365	97.88	465	99.52		
70	18.03	170	80.40	270	93.51	370	98.01	470	99.57		
75	23.22	175	81.44	275	93.87	375	98.14	475	99.61		
80	28.90	180	82.43	280	94.21	380	98.25	480	99.65		
85	34.64	185	83.37	285	94.52	385	98.36	485	99.69		
90	40.15	190	84.25	290	94.83	390	98.47	490	99.73		
95	45.30	195	85.09	295	95.12	395	98.57	495	99.77		
100	50.00	200	85.88	300	95.39	500	98.66	500	99.81		

Table 3-15.—Dimensionless unit hydrograph data, Sierra Nevada, Coast, and Cascade ranges. $q = Q\,(L_g + \tfrac{1}{2}D)/Vol.$

% of $(L_g + \frac{1}{2}D)$	q	% of $(L_g + \frac{1}{2}D)$	q	% of $(L_g + \frac{1}{2}D)$	q	% of $(L_g + \frac{1}{2}D)$	q	% of $(L_g + \frac{1}{2}D)$	q	% of $(L_g + \frac{1}{2}D)$	q
5	0.65	105	13.83	205	3.89	305	1.92	405	1.00	505	0.43
10	1.30	110	12.53	210	3.73	310	1.85	410	0.96	510	.40
15	1.95	115	11.36	215	3.58	315	1.78	415	.93	515	.38
20	2.60	120	10.29	220	3.44	320	1.73	420	.90	520	.34
25	3.25	125	9.33	225	3.30	325	1.67	425	.87	525	.31
30	4.23	130	8.73	230	3.18	330	1.62	430	.84	530	.28
35	5.51	135	8.17	235	3.08	335	1.57	435	.82	535	.25
40	7.17	140	7.65	240	2.98	340	1.52	440	.80	540	.22
45	9.34	145	7.15	245	2.88	345	1.47	445	.77	545	.19
50	12.17	150	6.69	250	2.79	350	1.42	450	.75	550	.16
55	13.88	155	6.33	255	2.69	355	1.38	455	.72	555	.14
60	15.83	160	5.99	260	2.60	360	1.34	460	.69	560	.13
65	18.05	165	5.67	265	2.50	365	1.30	465	.66		
70	20.59	170	5.36	270	2.41	370	1.26	470	.63		
75	23.48	175	5.07	275	2.33	375	1.22	475	.61		
80	21.54	180	4.85	280	2.26	380	1.18	480	.58		
85	19.77	185	4.63	285	2.18	385	1.14	485	.55		
90	18.13	190	4.43	290	2.11	390	1.11	490	.52		
95	16.63	195	4.24	295	2.05	395	1.06	495	.49		
100	15.26	200	4.06	300	1.98	400	1.03	500	.46		

Table 3-16.—Dimensionless S-graph data, Sierra Nevada, Coast, and Cascade ranges.

Time, % of L_g	Discharge, % of ultimate	Time, % of L_g	Discharge, % of ultimate	Time, % of L_g	Discharge, % of ultimate	Time, % of L_g	Discharge, % of ultimate	Time, % of L_g	Discharge, % of ultimate	Time, % of L_g	Discharge, % of ultimate
5	0.14	105	52.79	205	80.49	305	91.47	405	97.00	505	99.66
10	.43	110	55.32	210	81.25	310	91.84	410	97.19	510	99.73
15	.86	115	57.60	215	81.98	315	92.20	415	97.38	515	99.79
20	1.44	120	59.66	220	82.68	320	92.55	420	97.56	520	99.84
25	2.17	125	61.57	225	83.35	325	92.89	425	97.73	525	99.89
30	3.13	130	63.35	230	84.00	330	93.22	430	97.90	530	99.92
35	4.38	135	65.01	235	84.63	335	93.53	435	98.06	535	99.96
40	6.04	140	66.56	240	85.24	340	93.83	440	98.22	540	99.99
45	8.21	145	68.01	245	85.83	345	94.13	445	98.36	545	100.00
50	10.94	150	69.38	250	86.40	350	94.41	450	98.51		
55	14.06	155	70.67	255	86.94	355	94.69	455	98.64		
60	17.64	160	71.89	260	87.47	360	94.96	460	98.78		
65	21.73	165	73.04	265	87.98	365	95.22	465	98.90		
70	26.42	170	74.13	270	88.47	370	95.47	470	99.02		
75	31.28	175	75.16	275	88.94	375	95.71	475	99.13		
80	35.72	180	76.15	280	89.40	380	95.94	480	99.23		
85	39.78	185	77.10	285	89.84	385	96.17	485	99.33		
90	43.50	190	78.00	290	90.27	390	96.39	490	99.42		
95	46.91	195	78.87	295	90.69	395	96.60	495	99.51		
100	50.00	200	79.70	300	91.08	400	96.81	500	99.59		

Table 3-17.—Dimensionless unit hydrograph data, urban basins. $q = Q\,(L_g + \frac{1}{2}D)/Vol.$

% of $(L_g + \frac{1}{2}D)$	q	% of $(L_g + \frac{1}{2}D)$	q	% of $(L_g + \frac{1}{2}D)$	q	% of $(L_g + \frac{1}{2}D)$	q	% of $(L_g + \frac{1}{2}D)$	q	% of $(L_g + \frac{1}{2}D)$	q
5	0.64	105	14.50	205	3.73	305	1.64	405	0.81	505	0.40
10	1.56	110	13.08	210	3.55	310	1.60	410	.78	510	.39
15	2.52	115	12.19	215	3.37	315	1.53	415	.75	515	.37
20	3.57	120	11.31	220	3.24	320	1.49	420	.73	520	.36
25	4.36	125	10.27	225	3.04	325	1.42	425	.69	525	.34
30	5.80	130	9.63	230	2.93	330	1.39	430	.67	530	.33
35	6.95	135	8.96	235	2.75	335	1.32	435	.64	535	.32
40	8.38	140	8.27	240	2.67	340	1.28	440	.62	540	.31
45	9.87	145	7.75	245	2.53	345	1.23	445	.60	545	.30
50	11.52	150	7.22	250	2.47	350	1.21	450	.58	550	.29
55	13.19	155	6.75	255	2.37	355	1.15	455	.56	555	.28
60	15.18	160	6.27	260	2.30	360	1.11	460	.54	560	.27
65	17.32	165	5.94	265	2.21	365	1.07	465	.52	565	.26
70	19.27	170	5.55	270	2.12	370	1.03	470	.50	570	.25
75	19.74	175	5.24	275	2.04	375	1.00	475	.49	575	.24
80	20.00	180	4.92	280	1.98	380	0.97	480	.48	580	.24
85	19.74	185	4.63	285	1.90	385	.93	485	.46	585	.23
90	19.27	190	4.39	290	1.83	390	.90	490	.45	590	.22
95	17.72	195	4.18	295	1.78	395	.87	495	.43	595	.21
100	16.12	200	3.93	300	1.71	400	.84	500	.41	600	.21

Table 3-18.—Dimensionless S-graph data, urban basins.

Time, % of L_g	Discharge, % of ultimate	Time, % of L_g	Discharge, % of ultimate	Time, % of L_g	Discharge, % of ultimate	Time, % of L_g	Discharge, % of ultimate	Time, % of L_g	Discharge, % of ultimate	Time, % of L_g	Discharge, % of ultimate
5	0.14	105	52.94	205	82.34	305	92.18	405	96.82	505	99.05
10	.48	110	55.64	210	83.06	310	92.51	410	96.98	510	99.12
15	1.04	115	58.13	215	83.75	315	92.82	415	97.13	515	99.19
20	1.82	120	60.42	220	84.40	320	93.12	420	97.27	520	99.26
25	2.84	125	62.53	225	85.02	325	93.40	425	97.41	525	99.33
30	4.11	130	64.50	230	85.60	330	93.68	430	97.54	530	99.39
35	5.64	135	66.32	235	86.17	335	93.95	435	97.67	535	99.45
40	7.49	140	68.01	240	86.71	340	94.21	440	97.79	540	99.51
45	9.67	145	69.59	245	87.23	345	94.46	445	97.91	545	99.57
50	12.21	150	71.06	250	87.73	350	94.69	450	98.03	550	99.62
55	15.14	155	72.42	255	88.22	355	94.92	455	98.14	555	99.67
60	18.51	160	73.71	260	88.68	360	95.15	460	98.25	560	99.72
65	22.33	165	74.91	265	89.13	365	95.36	465	98.35	565	99.77
70	26.47	170	76.04	270	89.56	370	95.57	470	98.45	570	99.82
75	30.71	175	77.10	275	89.98	375	95.77	475	98.54	575	99.87
80	34.95	180	78.10	280	90.38	380	95.96	480	98.64	580	99.91
85	39.12	185	79.04	285	90.77	385	96.15	485	98.73	585	99.95
90	43.09	190	79.94	290	91.14	390	96.33	490	98.81	590	99.99
95	46.72	195	80.78	295	91.50	395	96.50	495	98.89	595	100.00
100	50.00	200	81.58	300	91.85	400	96.66	500	98.97		

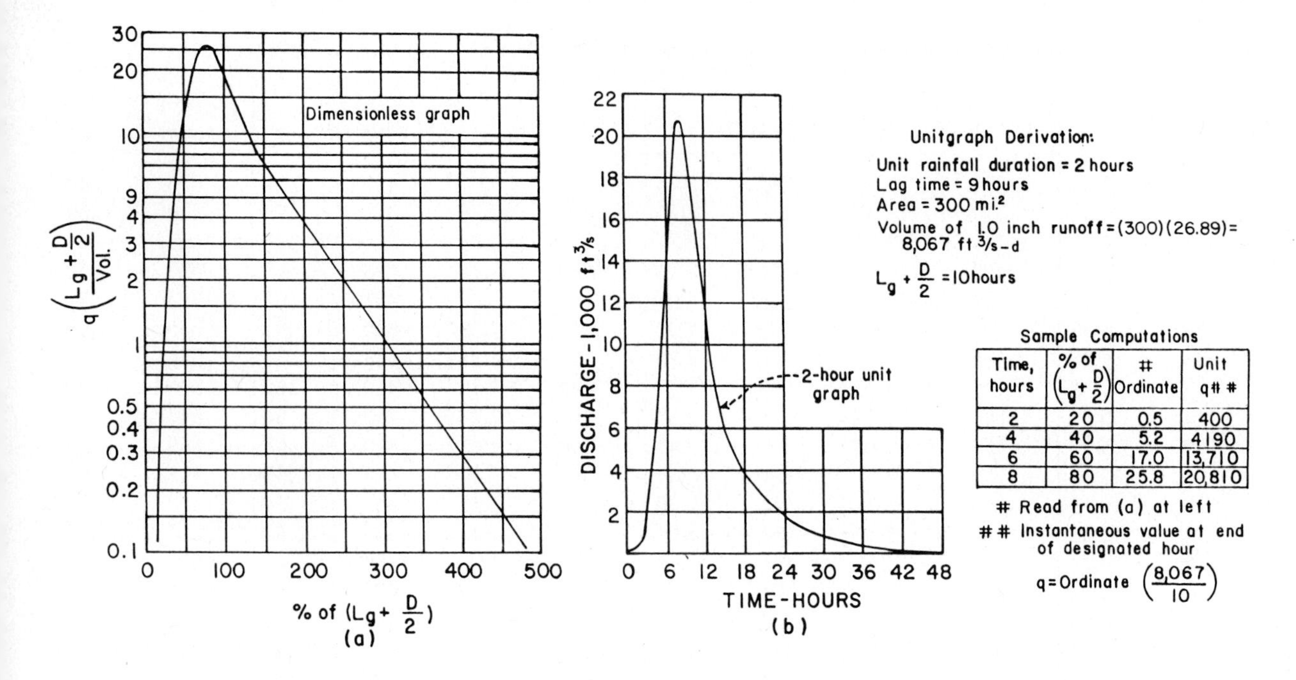

Time, hours	% of $(L_g+\frac{D}{2})$	# Ordinate	Unit q##
2	20	0.5	400
4	40	5.2	4190
6	60	17.0	13,710
8	80	25.8	20,810

Figure 3-9.—Dimensionless unit hydrograph and sample computations. 103-D-1856.

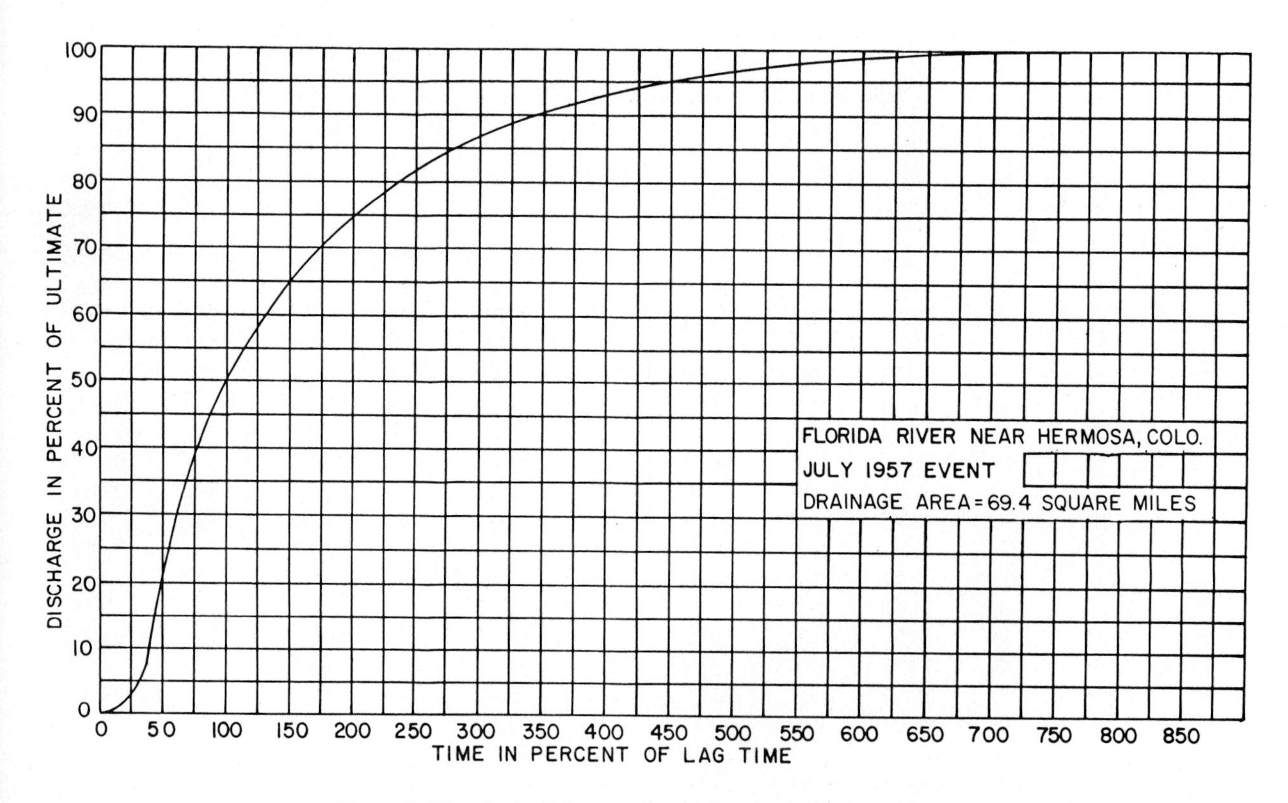

Figure 3-10.—Typical dimensionless S-graph. 103-D-1857.

Table 3-19.—Synthetic unit hydrograph data.

(1) Time, h	(2) Time, % of lag	(3) Discharge, % of ultimate	(4) Summation hydrograph, ft³/s	(5) Unit hydrograph, ft³/s
0	0	0	0	0
2	17	1	807	807
4	34	6	4840	4033
6	51	21	16939	12099
8	68	35	28232	11293
10	85	44	35491	7259
12	102	51	41138	5647
14	119	57	45978	4840
16	136	62	50011	4033
18	153	66	53237	3226

considerably more indeterminate than the surface flow component.

The magnitude of the base flow of a storm is largely dependent on antecedent storm conditions: the magnitude of that storm and the time between its occurrence and the onset of the subject storm. If sufficient data are available (which is rarely the case), a complete recession curve representing the base-flow component for a given drainage basin can be determined. The recession, or base flow, used in the development of PMF's should represent conditions that are consistent with antecedent storm conditions provided for in the storm study report. For example, a higher recession flow should be used in the case where there is a 1-day separation between the antecedent and probable maximum storm than would be used in the case where a 5-day separation between storms is assumed. When preparing a flood study for an ungauged watershed, results of observed flood reconstructions on hydrologically similar drainage basins, relative to the base-flow component, are used to estimate this component for the ungauged basin. This may be accomplished by converting the observed component to cubic feet per second per square mile of basin area. The result is then applied to the area of the subject ungauged basin to determine its appropriate rate of base flow. Assuming that the base, or recession, flow rate is uniform for the entire duration of the PMF hydrograph is entirely proper.

The interflow component is essentially determined by a trial and error approach in the course of observed flood hydrograph reconstructions. After subtracting the base, or recession, flow component, the remaining observed flood hydrograph is composed of the surface flow and interflow components. In separating the surface flow and interflow components, care must be taken to ensure that neither too much nor too little flow is assigned to the interflow component. A balance is achieved by adequate selection of infiltration loss rates.

When an ungauged watershed is studied, interflow information from observed flood hydrograph reconstructions for nearby, hydrologically similar watersheds may be used to estimate the magnitude and rate of change of discharge over time. As for the base-flow component, the conversion from the observed hydrograph to that for the ungauged basin is based on a direct ratio of the respective drainage-basin areas. The resulting interflow hydrograph should incorporate a slowly rising limb, a rather broad peak, and a long recession limb.

(g) *Design-Flood Hydrographs.*—The PMF hydrographs represent the maximum runoff condition resulting from the most severe combination of hydrologic and meteorologic conditions considered reasonably possible for a drainage basin. Accordingly, because the unit hydrograph approach is used to develop the design-flood hydrograph, the following considerations should be used in computing the flood hydrograph.

(1) The PMF is, by definition, based on a probable maximum storm. The temporal distribution of the storm rainfall, unless provided in the appropriate hydrometeorological report, should be arranged so that the maximum peak discharge and the maximum concentration of discharge around the peak is achieved.

(2) Infiltration rates subtracted from the storm rainfall to obtain the excess amounts available for surface runoff should be the lowest rates consistent with the soil types and the underlying geologic conditions of the subject basin. These minimum rates should be assumed to prevail for the duration of the probable maximum storm.

(3) The unit hydrograph used to compute the PMF should represent extreme discharge conditions. When studies are prepared for gauged basins for which the results of the observed flood hydrograph analyses are available, care should be taken to ensure that

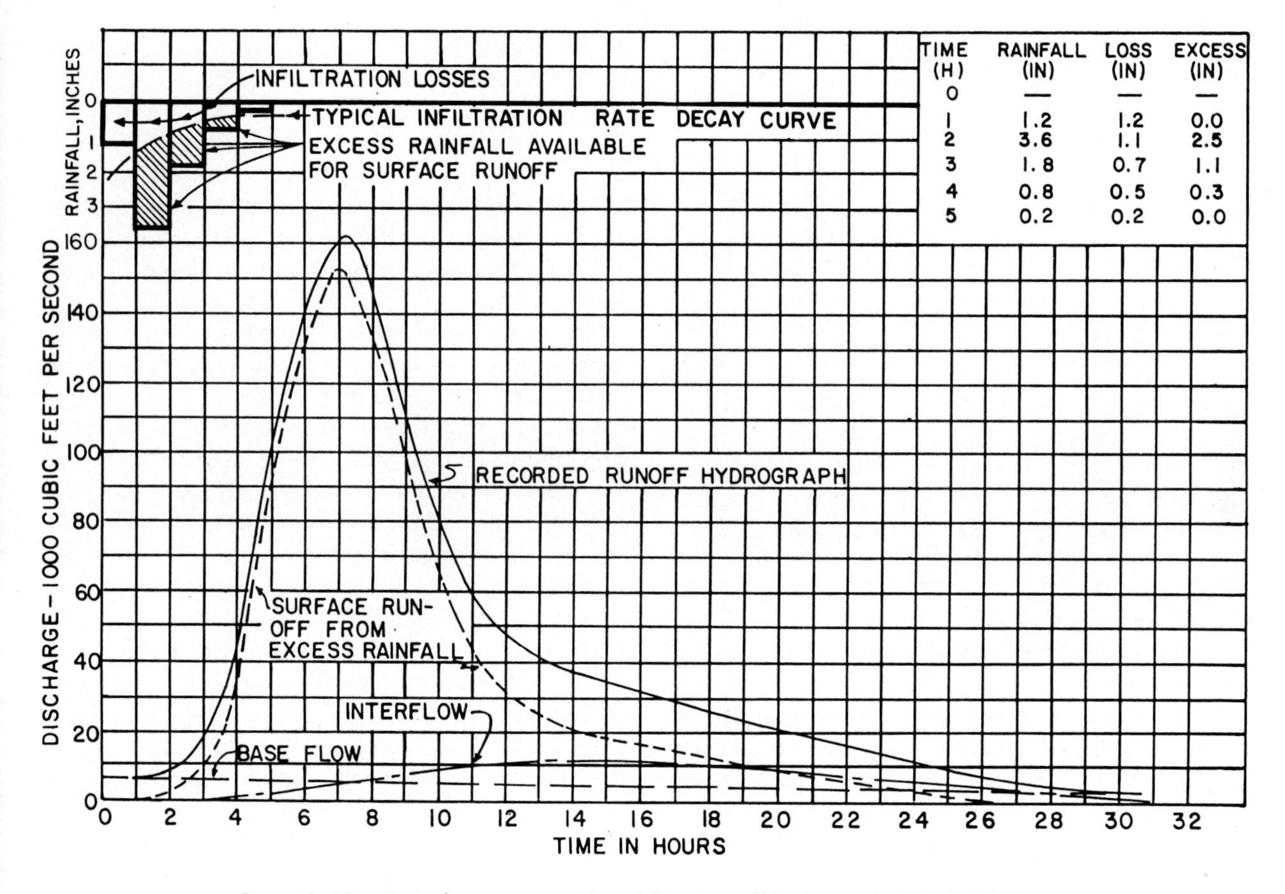

Figure 3-11.—Typical components of total flood runoff hydrograph. 103-D-1858.

the unit hydrograph parameters adequately reflect the streamflow conditions likely in a probable maximum event. It is entirely appropriate to decrease K_n in the general unit hydrograph lag equation to reflect the increased hydraulic efficiency of the drainage network associated with an extreme runoff event. When the flood study involves an ungauged basin, considerable judgement must be exercised to ensure that K_n approximates the expected hydraulic efficiency of the basin during a probable maximum event.

(4) The base-flow hydrograph component should reflect the maximum rates of discharge consistent with the magnitude and timing of the antecedent flood event.

(5) The interflow component should reflect conditions expected from a probable maximum storm event. However, this component will probably not differ significantly from that experienced in a relatively minor event because the hydraulic efficiency of the subsurface media through which this component passes is essentially fixed.

The hydrograph representing surface runoff is computed by applying the unit hydrograph to the rainfall excess by the method of superposition, discussed previously. Hydrographs representing the base-flow and interflow components are then added to the surface-runoff hydrograph to obtain the total PMF hydrograph.

In many cases a rain-on-snow PMF hydrograph is desired. The basis and rationale for adding a snowmelt runoff component to the rainflood hydrograph is discussed in section 3.10.

3.10. *Flood Runoff From Snowmelt.*—The Bureau of Reclamation has used a method called, "Snow Compaction Method for the Analyses of Runoff From Rain on Snow." This method requires air temperatures, wind speeds, forest cover percentages, snow depths, and now densities at various elevation bands. When the snowmelt runoff is expected to contribute to the PMF, the wind speeds and air temperatures are usually furnished by Bureau meteorologists as a part of the probable maximum storm study. From a search of records, the hydrologist determines the snow depths and densities considered reasonable for initial watershed conditions. In most cases the drainage basin is divided into elevation bands. These elevation bands are usually selected at 500- or 1000-foot intervals, depending on the size of the basin and the elevation differences. Basins that are relatively flat may be considered one elevation band. The probable maximum precipitation contribution is added to the snowmelt contribution from each elevation band. The combined contribution is then averaged over the total basin.

This method of determining the total flood runoff from snowmelt requires several decisions by the hydrologic engineer. Several trial arrangements of the rainfall, wind speeds, and air temperatures are usually required to ensure that the largest flood has been computed. The initial snow depths and densities may also need adjustment to ensure that a reasonable amount of snow has been melted and not too much rain has been trapped in the snow remaining in the upper-elevation bands. Without experience and care, this method can become erratic. Thus, for consistency and ease of application, the use of a 100-year snowmelt flood combined with the probable maximum rainflood is considered a suitable alternative to the snow compaction method.

The normally accepted practice of the Bureau of Reclamation is to combine the probable maximum rainflood with a snowmelt flood reasonably expected at the time of year that the probable maximum storm occurs. Of course, this practice is only used for those areas where significant snowpacks occur.

The most common and simplest method of accounting for snowmelt is to use a 100-year snowmelt flood. A frequency analysis of the maximum annual snowflood volume is made, and the 100-year flood is determined. The usual period of runoff selected is 15 days. The 100-year snowmelt flood is then distributed over time using the largest recorded snowmelt flood as the basis for distribution. The resulting snowmelt-flood hydrograph is generally expressed in terms of mean daily flows for the 15-day period, with diurnal fluctuations neglected.

The rainflood hydrograph is then superimposed on the snowmelt flood hydrograph with the rain assumed to occur during the day or days of the greatest snowmelt flooding. This assumption is made so that the maximum rain occurs during the warmest period. The resulting combined rain-on-snow flood is the PMF.

3.11. *Envelope Curves of Prior Flood Discharges.*—Each flood hydrology study should consider information on the flood peak and the volumes that have been experienced in the hydrologic region. This information is presented in the form of a curve enveloping the data points representing the peak discharge or the flow volume for a specified time duration versus the drainage area contributing to the flood runoff. Figure 3-12 depicts an example of this relationship.

These curves are particularly valuable in the development of PMF estimates because they provide definitive information on the magnitude of floods that have occurred over various size drainage basins in a hydrologically homogeneous region. They should not be construed as indicating the limit of the magnitude of future flood events. As time passes and more data are collected, each envelope curve will inevitably be altered upward. PMF values should always be higher than the properly drawn envelope curve. If this is not the case, both the envelope curve and the PMF estimate must be carefully reviewed to determine whether some hydrologic or meteorologic parameter has been neglected or improperly used.

When preparing these envelope curves, the hydrologic engineer must exercise care to ensure that the flood values used represent flood events with similar causative factors. Four primary causative factors should be recognized, and the data should be segregated accordingly: (1) thunderstorm-type events, in which the resulting flood is caused by high-intensity, short-duration rainfall; (2) general rain-type events, in which the resulting flood is caused by moderate-intensity, long-duration rainfall; (3) snowmelt floods, resulting from the melting of an accumulated snowpack; and (4) floods resulting from rain falling on a melting snowpack. Each envelope curve should provide information on the causative factor represented.

The hydrologic engineer must ensure that the basins represented are hydrologically homogeneous. For example, it is improper to include data representing steep mountainous basins with those representing low-relief plains basins. In many instances, severe storms cover only a part of a large basin, but produce an extremely high flood. In these cases the drainage area used in developing the envelope curve should be that of the storm not the entire basin area above the stream gauge.

The basic source of data used to develop envelope curves is the USGS "Water Supply Paper" series. Particularly important in the development of peak discharge envelope curves are the papers in this series titled, "Magnitude and Frequency of Floods in the United States." The 10 volumes in this series, which covers the entire United States, summarize all recorded peak discharges at the USGS stream-gauging network up to 1 or 2 years before their publication. The records for subsequent years in the annual "Water Supply Papers" for gauges in the region should be closely examined to determine whether the values in the "Magnitude and Frequency . . . ." series have been exceeded. If so, they should be recorded for further use. The annual "Water Supply Papers" are also used to develop volume envelope curves generally representing 5-, 10- and 15-day volumes. Several State governments, generally through either their water resource agency or highway department, have installed networks of crest-stage gauges. Records of peak discharges at these gauges are published at various intervals. The hydrologic engineer should contact these agencies and obtain these data, if available. In many cases, these data provide a valuable supplement to the systematic data acquired and published by the USGS. There are other sources of data, such as reports prepared by the Corps of Engineers, USGS, National Weather Service, Bureau of Reclamation, and some local and county governments, that provide considerable information on specific flood events.

The procedure for developing envelope curves is relatively simple:

(1) On a small-scale map, outline the limits of the geographical area where the character of hydrologic and meterologic phenomena are similar.
(2) Locate all streamflow gauging stations (both recording and crest-stage) within the geographic area and plot them on the small-scale map. They should be properly identified with the conventional USGS station number or name (e.g., Arkansas River at Pueblo, Colorado).
(3) Arrange the data in tabular form as follows: column 1, the identifying number for cross referencing the data point on the map and on the envelope curve with this tabulation; column 2, the name of the stream or river as shown in the "Water Supply Papers"; column 3, the location of the gauge on the river or stream, as listed in the "Water Supply Papers"; column 4, the drainage area in square miles (if only the contributing area of the storm is used, list that area and provide a footnote to that effect); column 5, the date of the flood event; column 6, the peak discharge in cubic feet per second; column 7, the flood volume recorded over the desired period (this period should be specified in the column heading).
(4) Plot the data on log-log paper having enough cycles to cover the range in discharges and area sizes represented by the data. In all cases the area is to be on the abscissa scale and the discharge on the ordinate scale.
(5) Draw a smooth preliminary curve that envelopes the plotted data points.
(6) It will now be apparent that only a few of the data points control the position of the envelope curve. Analyze the data for each control point to ensure that the data represent runoff from basins that have topography, soils, vegetation, and meteorological characteristics comparable with those of the subject basin. Eliminate points associated with inconsistencies.
(7) After verifying that the control points are suitable, draw the final envelope curve, as shown on figure 3-12.

3.12. *Estimates of Frequency of Occurrence of Floods.*—Estimates of the magnitude of floods having probabilities of being equaled or exceeded of 1 in 5, 1 in 10, or 1 in 25 years are helpful in estimating the requirements for stream diversion during the construction of a dam and its appurtenent features. These floods are normally termed the "5-, 10-, and 25-year floods," respectively. The magnitude of a more rare event, such as a 50- or 100-year flood, may be required to establish the sill location of emergency spillways, to design diversion dams, and for other purposes. The common expression, "x-year flood," should not lead to the conclusion that the event so described can occur only once in x years or, having occurred, will not occur again for another x years. It *does* mean that the x-year flood has a probability of $1/x$ of being equaled or exceeded in any year. Floods occur randomly; they may be bunched or spread out unevenly with respect

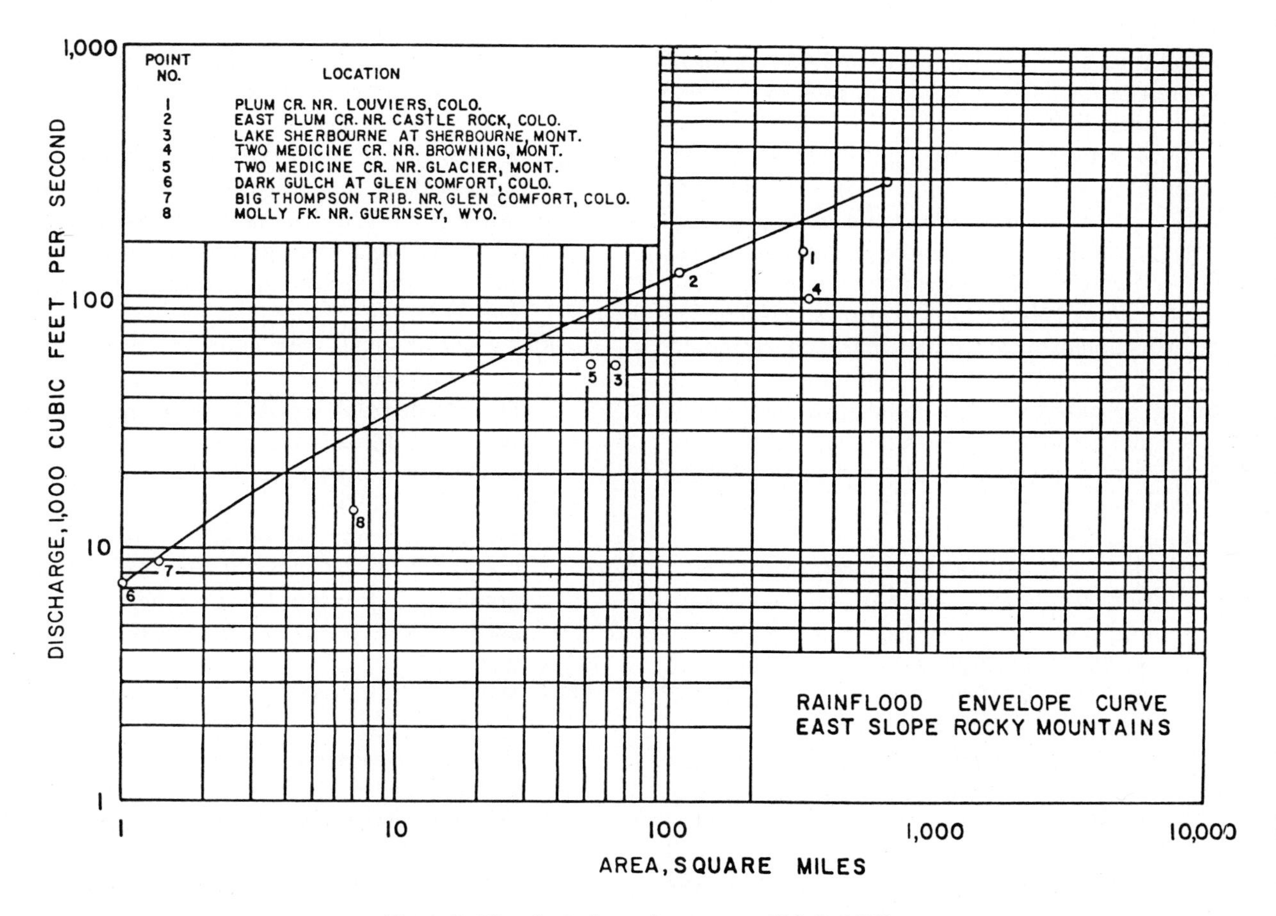

Figure 3-12.—Typical envelope curve. 103-D-1859.

to time. No predictions are possible for determining their distribution: the PMF may even occur the first year after a dam is completed, although the odds are heavily against it.

The hydrograph of a flood of a particular frequency is usually sketched to conventional shape using the peak-discharge value and corresponding volume values obtained from computed volume frequency curves. In some instance, the peak discharge and associated volume of a recorded flood correspond closely with a particular frequency value; in which case the recorded flood hydrograph is used.

If streamflow data for a period of 20 years or more are available for the subject watershed or for comparable watersheds, frequency-curve computations yield acceptable results for estimates up to the 25-year flood. The frequency curve data may even be extrapolated to indicate the 100-year flood with a fair chance of obtaining acceptable values. However, in no case should the frequency curve be extrapolated beyond twice the length of record or 100 years, whichever is greater.

Many methods of flood-frequency determinations based on streamflow data have been published. Although these methods are all based on acceptable statistical procedures, the differences in methodology can cause appreciably different results when extensions are made beyond the range of adequate data. To standardize Federal water resources planning, the Water Resources Council has recommended that all Government agencies use the Log-Pearson Type III distribution as a base method. This method is described in their Bulletin 17B, "Guidelines for Determining Flood Flow Frequencies," dated September 1981.

For watersheds where runoff originates from rainfall and for which streamflow data are not available (usually small watersheds), an indication of flood frequencies can be obtained by estimating probable runoff from precipitation data of the desired frequency. Probable rainfall intensities for short durations can be obtained from National Weather Service publications or, in some instances, by direct frequency analyses of records at nearby precipitation stations. These data provide means of obtaining probable "x-year" precipitation values for various periods. These precipitation values are converted to runoff using the unit hydrograph approach discussed in section 3.9. The uncertainties inherent in estimating the amount of runoff from a given amount of rainfall make this procedure less reliable than the use of streamflow data.

3.13. *Flood Hydrology Reports.*—A report clearly documenting all the assumptions, rationale, methodology, and results of hydrologic analyses must be prepared for each flood hydrology study. These reports should include sufficient detail to enable the reader to independently reproduce all flood values in the report. Each report should include the following 13 items.

(1) *Authority.*—Cite the appropriate legislation, regulations, etc., and include the general purpose or purposes of the project.

(2) *Summary of study results.*—Include peak and volume information for the PMF and for floods of specific frequencies. Include a summary statement of the reservoir routing recommendations and cite the level of study; e.g., appraisal, feasibility.

(3) *General.*—Include a discussion of all formal and informal agreements reached by the various organizational levels on the technical aspects of the flood study. Present a brief discussion of each previous flood study with a summary of its results.

(4) *Basin description.*—Cite the geographic location of the basin and its area, and describe the terrain features, including the elevation range, basin development, drainage network, geological setting, soils, and vegetative cover. Include a discussion and the pertinent data for existing water-control facilities in the basin. The discussion of basin development should include a statement on anticipated future development based on projections made by the most authoritative source available.

(5) *Storm study.*—Reference pertinent summary data from the storm study (for a self-contained report, it is desirable to include the complete storm study as an appendix). This reference should include a discussion of the basin and regional climatology.

(6) *Unit hydrograph.*—Cite the basis and rationale for selecting the dimensionless unit hydrograph and the lag curve. If a selection is based on a reconstruction of an observed event, the reconstruction study should be thoroughly described.

(7) *Loss rates.*—Provide the basis and rationale for selecting the infiltration rates used to develop the PMF. If these are based on an observed flood hydrograph reconstruction, refer to the section on unit hydrographs (sec. 3.9).

(8) *Snowmelt.*—Cite the assumptions on the extent of snow cover, snowpack depth and density, distribution over the basin, and the percent of forest cover.

(9) *Probable maximum flood.*—Provide a brief discussion of abstraction of losses from rainfall and unit hydrograph application of excess rainfall to arrive at the PMF hydrograph. Include information on the base-flow assumptions, and summarize peak and volume data.

(10) *Frequency analysis.*—Provide a peak discharge-frequency curve to determine construction diversion requirements and for possible use in risk-based analyses. The narrative should provide information on the source of the streamflow data, length of records available, and use of a regionalized approach (if applicable). If specific-frequency floods developed by the rainfall-runoff model approach are used to define the discharge-frequency curve, information cited in paragraphs (5) through (8) above should be presented.

(11) *Antecedent flood.*—Provide the basis and rationale for the antecedent flood selected, particularly in regard to its magnitude and timing (with respect to the PMF). Together the antecedent flood and the PMF make up the PMF series and should be presented as such in the report.

(12) *Reservoir routing criteria.*—Provide recommendations on the pool level assumed at the onset of the PMF series. Include flood-control regulations, if appropriate. Discuss the assumptions relative to the use of hydraulic release features during the PMF and antecedent floods.

(13) *Envelope curves.*—Show all points used to position the curve. Label each point with either the station name or a number referring to an accompanying table that lists the name and location of each station.

3.14. *Bibliography.*

[1] Horner, W.W., and F.L. Flynt, ASCE *Proceedings*, "Relation Between Rainfall and Runoff from Small Urban Basins," vol. 60, pp. 1,135-1,178, 1934.

[2] Horton, Robert E., *Surface Runoff Phenomena*, Publication 101, Edward Brops., Ann Arbor, MI, 1940.

Unitgraph Procedures, Bureau of Reclamation, November 1952.

Effects of Snow Compaction on Runoff from Rain or Snow, Bureau of Reclamation, Engineering Monograph No. 35, June 1966.

Flood Hydrograph Analyses and Computations, U.S. Army Corps of Engineers, EM-1110-2-1405.

Flood Prediction Techniques, Department of the Army, TB-5-550-3, February 1957.

Routing of Floods Through River Channels, U.S. Army Corps of Engineers, EM-1110-2-1408, March 1960.

Drainage for Areas Other than Airfields, U.S. Army Corps of Engineers, EM-1110-345-284, August 14, 1964.

Flood Flow Frequency Analyses, Water Resources Council, Bulletin 17B, September 1981.

Chapter 4

Selection of Type of Dam

A. CLASSIFICATION OF TYPES

4.1. *General.*—Dams may be classified into a number of different categories, depending upon the purpose of the classification. For the purposes of this manual, it is convenient to consider three broad classifications: Dams are classified according to their use, their hydraulic design, or the materials of which they are constructed.

4.2. *Classification According to Use.*—Dams may be classified according to the broad function they serve, such as storage, diversion, or detention. Refinements of these classifications can also be made by considering the specific functions involved.

Storage dams are constructed to impound water during periods of surplus supply for use during periods of deficient supply. These periods may be seasonal, annual, or longer. Many small dams impound the spring runoff for use in the dry summer season. Storage dams may be further classified according to the purpose of the storage, such as water supply, recreation, fish and wildlife, hydroelectric power generation, irrigation, etc. The specific purpose or purposes to be served by a storage dam often influence the design of the structure and may establish criteria such as the amount of reservoir fluctuation expected or the amount of reservoir seepage permitted. Figure 4-1 shows a small earthfill storage dam, and figure 4-2 shows a concrete gravity structure serving both diversion and storage purposes.

Diversion dams are ordinarily constructed to provide head for carrying water into ditches, canals, or other conveyance systems. They are used for irrigation developments, for diversion from a live stream to an off-channel-location storage reservoir, for municipal and industrial uses, or for any combination of the above. Figure 4-3 shows a typical small diversion dam.

Detention dams are constructed to retard flood runoff and minimize the effect of sudden floods. Detention dams consist of two main types. In one type, the water is temporarily stored and released through an outlet structure at a rate that does not exceed the carrying capacity of the channel downstream. In the other type, the water is held as long as possible and allowed to seep into pervious banks or into the foundation. The latter type is sometimes called a water-spreading dam or dike because its main purpose is to recharge the underground water supply. Some detention dams are constructed to trap sediments; these are often called debris dams.

Although it is less common on small projects than on large developments, dams are often constructed to serve more than one purpose. Where multiple purposes are involved, a reservoir allocation is usually made to each distinct use. A common multipurpose project combines storage, flood control, and recreational uses.

4.3. *Classification by Hydraulic Design.*—Dams may also be classified as overflow or nonoverflow dams.

Overflow dams are designed to carry discharge over their crests or through spillways along the crest. Concrete is the most common material used for this type of dam.

Nonoverflow dams are those designed not to be overtopped. This type of design extends the choice of materials to include earthfill and rockfill dams.

Often the two types are combined to form a composite structure consisting of, for example, an overflow concrete gravity dam with earthfill dikes. Figure 4-4 shows such a composite structure built by the Bureau of Reclamation.

4.4 *Classification by Materials.*—The most common classification used for the discussion of design procedures is based upon the materials used to build the structure. This classification also usually recognizes the basic type of design, for example, the "concrete gravity" dam or the "concrete arch" dam.

This text is limited in scope to consideration of

Figure 4-1.—Crescent Lake Dam, a small earthfill storage dam on Crescent Creek in Oregon. 806–126–92.

the more common types of dams constructed today; namely, earthfill, rockfill, and concrete gravity dams. Other types of dams, including concrete arch, concrete buttress, and timber dams, are discussed briefly with an explanation of why their designs are not covered in this text.

4.5. *Earthfill Dams.*—Earthfill dams are the most common type of dam, principally because their construction involves the use of materials from required excavations and the use of locally available natural materials requiring a minimum of processing. Using large quantities of required excavation and locally available borrow are positive economic factors related to an earthfill dam. Moreover, the foundation and topographical requirements for earthfill dams are less stringent than those for other types. It is likely that earthfill dams will continue to be more prevalent than other types for storage purposes, partly because the number of sites favorable for concrete structures is decreasing as a result of extensive water storage development. This is particularly true in arid and semiarid regions where the conservation of water for irrigation is a fundamental necessity.

Although the earthfill classification includes several types, the development of modern excavating, hauling, and compacting equipment for earth materials has made the rolled-fill type so economical as to virtually replace the semihydraulic- and hydraulic-fill types of earthfill dams. This is especially true for the construction of small structures, where the relatively small amount of material

Figure 4-2.—Black Canyon Dam, a concrete-gravity storage and diversion structure on the Payette River in Idaho.

to be handled precludes the establishment of the large plant required for efficient hydraulic operations. For these reasons, only the rolled-fill type of earthfill dam is treated in this text. Rolled-fill earthfill dams are further classified as "homogeneous," "zoned," or "diaphragm," as described in chapter 6.

Earthfill dams require appurtenant structures to serve as spillways and outlet works. The principal disadvantage of an earthfill dam is that it will be damaged or may even be destroyed under the erosive action of overflowing water if sufficient spillway capacity is not provided. Unless the site is offstream, provision must be made for diverting the stream past the damsite through a conduit or around the damsite through a tunnel during construction. A diversion tunnel or conduit is usually provided for a concrete dam; however, additional provisions can be made for overtopping of concrete blocks during construction. A gap in an embankment dam is sometimes used for routing the river through the damsite during construction of portions of the dam on either or both sides of the gap. See chapter 11 for a more detailed description of diversion during construction.

4.6. *Rockfill Dams.*—Rockfill dams use rock of all sizes to provide stability and an impervious membrane to provide watertightness. The membrane may be an upstream facing of impervious soil, a concrete slab, asphaltic-concrete paving, steel plates, other impervious elements, or an interior thin core of impervious soil.

Figure 4-3.—Knight Diversion Dam, a small diversion structure on the Duchesne River near Duchesne, Utah. P66-400-3167.

Like the earth embankments, rockfill dams are subject to damage or destruction by the overflow of water and so must have a spillway of adequate capacity to prevent overtopping. An exception is the extremely low diversion dam where the rockfill facing is designed specifically to withstand overflows. Rockfill dams require foundations that will not be subject to settlements large enough to rupture the watertight membrane. The only suitable foundations, therefore, are rock or compact sand and gravel.

The rockfill type dam is suitable for remote locations where the supply of good rock is ample, where the scarcity of suitable soil or long periods of high rainfall make construction of an earthfill dam impractical, or where the construction of a concrete dam would be too costly. Rockfill dams are popular in tropical climates because their construction is suitable for long periods of high rainfall.

4.7. *Concrete Gravity Dams.*—Concrete gravity dams are suitable for sites where there is a reasonably sound rock foundation, although low structures may be founded on alluvial foundations if adequate cutoffs are provided. They are well suited for use as overflow spillway crests and, because of this advantage, are often used as spillways for earthfill or rockfill dams or as overflow sections of diversion dams.

Gravity dams may be either straight or curved in plan. The curved dam may offer some advantage in both cost and safety. Occasionally the dam curvature allows part of the dam to be located on a

Figure 4-4.—Olympus Dam, a combination earthfill and concrete-gravity structure on the Big Thompson River in Colorado. The concrete section contains the spillway and an outlet works to a canal. 245–704–3117.

stronger foundation, which requires less excavation. The concept of constructing concrete dams using RCC (roller-compacted concrete) has been developed and implemented. Several RCC dams have been constructed in the United States and in other countries. The technology and design procedures, however, are not presented in this manual because procedures and approaches are relatively new and are still being developed.

4.8. ***Concrete Arch Dams.***—Concrete arch dams are suitable for sites where the ratio of the width between abutments to the height is not great and where the foundation at the abutments is solid rock capable of resisting arch thrust.

Two types of arch dams are defined here: the single and the multiple arch dam. A single arch dam spans a canyon as one structure and is usually limited to a maximum crest length to height ratio of 10:1. Its design may include small thrust blocks on either abutment, as necessary, or a spillway somewhere along the crest. A multiple arch dam may be one of two distinct designs. It may have either a uniformly thick cylindrical barrel shape spanning 50 feet or less between buttresses, such as Bartlett Dam in Arizona, or it may consist of several single arch dams supported on massive buttresses spaced several hundred feet on centers. The dam's purpose, whether it be a permanent major structure with a life expectancy of 50 years or a temporary cofferdam with a useful life of 5 years, will directly influence the time for design and construction, the quality of materials in the dam and foundation, the foundation treatment, and the hydraulic considerations. Structural and economic aspects prohibit the design of an arch dam founded on stiff soil, gravel, or cobblestones. Uplift usually does not affect arch dam stability because of the relative thinness through the section, both in the dam and at the concrete-rock contact.

Historically, both permanent and temporary concrete dams have survived partial and complete inundation, both during and after construction.

Because the design of an arch dam is specialized, a detailed discussion is not included in this book. Refer to *Design of Arch Dams*, a Bureau of Reclamation publication, for discussions on design, loads, methods of analysis, safety factors, etc.

4.9. *Concrete Buttress Dams.*—Buttress dams are comprised of flat deck and multiple arch structures. They require about 60 percent less concrete than solid gravity dams, but the increased formwork and reinforcement steel required usually offset the savings in concrete. A number of buttress dams were built in the 1930's, when the ratio of labor costs to material costs was comparatively low. The cost of this type of construction is usually not competitive with that of other types of dams when labor costs are high.

The design of buttress dams is based on the knowledge and judgment that comes only from specialized experience in that field. Because of this fact and because of the limited application for buttress dams under present-day conditions, their design is not covered in this text.

4.10. *Other Types.*—Dams of types other than those mentioned above have been built, but in most cases they meet some unusual local requirement or are of an experimental nature. In a few instances, structural steel has been used both for the deck and for the supporting framework of a dam. And before 1920, a number of timber dams were constructed, particularly in the Northwest. The amount of labor involved in the timer dam, coupled with the short life of the structure, makes this type of structure uneconomical for modern construction. Timber and other uncommon types of dams are not treated in this text.

B. PHYSICAL FACTORS GOVERNING SELECTION OF TYPE

4.11. *General.*—During the early stages of planning and design, selection of the site and the type of dam should be carefully considered. It is only in exceptional circumstances that only one type of dam or appurtenant structure is suitable for a given damsite. Generally, preliminary designs and estimates for several types of dams and appurtenant structures are required before one can be proved the most suitable and economical. It is, therefore, important to understand that the project is likely to be unduly expensive unless decisions regarding the site selection and the type of dam are based upon adequate study.

The selection of the type of dam requires cooperation among experts representing several disciplines—including planners; hydrologists; geotechnical, hydraulic, and structural engineers; and engineering geologists—to ensure economical and appropriate designs for the physical factors, such as topography, geology and foundation conditions, available materials, hydrology, and seismicity.

Protection from spillway discharges, limitations of outlet works, the problem of diverting the stream during construction, availability of labor and equipment, accessibility of the site, physical features of the site, the purpose of the dam, and dam safety all affect the final choice of the type of dam. Usually, the final choice of the type of dam is based on a comparison of the costs to construct the various dam types studied. The following paragraphs discuss important physical factors in the choice of the type of dam.

4.12. *Topography.*—Topographic considerations include the surface configuration of the damsite and of the reservoir area and accessibility to the site and to construction materials. Topography, in large measure, dictates the fist choice of the type of dam. A narrow stream flowing between high, rocky walls would naturally suggest a rockfill or concrete overflow dam. On the other hand, low, rolling plains would suggest an earthfill dam. Intermediate conditions might suggest other choices, such as a composite structure. The point is that topography is of major significance in choosing the dam type.

Topography may also have an important influence on the selection of appurtenant structures. For example, if there are natural saddles, it may be possible to locate a spillway through a saddle. If the reservoir rim is high compared with the dam height, and it is unbroken, a chute or tunnel spillway might be necessary. The spillway considerations can influence the type of dam. In a deep, steep-walled canyon, it might be more economical to construct a concrete dam with an overflow spillway than to provide a spillway for a rockfill dam.

4.13. *Geology and Foundation Conditions.*— The suitability of the various types of rock and soil as foundation and construction materials are geologic questions that must be considered. The foundation geology at a damsite often dictates the type of dam suitable for that site. The strength, thickness, and inclination of strata; permeability; fracturing; and faulting are all important considerations in selecting the dam type. Some of the different foundations commonly encountered are discussed below.

(a) *Rock Foundations.*—Competent rock foundations, which are free of significant geologic defects, have relatively high shear strengths, and are resistant to erosion and percolation, offer few restrictions as to the type of dam that can be built upon them. The economy of materials or the overall cost should be the ruling factor. The removal of disintegrated rock together with the sealing of seams and fractures by grouting is frequently necessary. Weaker rocks such as clay shales, some sandstones, weathered basalt, etc., may present significant problems to the design and construction of a dam and may heavily influence the type of dam selected.

(b) *Gravel Foundations.*—Gravel foundations, if well compacted, are suitable for earthfill or rockfill dams. Because gravel foundations are frequently subjected to water percolation at high rates, special precautions must be taken to provide adequate seepage control or effective water cutoffs or seals.

(c) *Silt or Fine Sand Foundations.*—Silt or fine sand foundations can be used for low concrete gravity dams and earthfill dams if properly designed, but they are generally not suitable for rockfill dams. Design concerns include nonuniform settlement, potential soil collapse upon saturation, uplift forces, the prevention of piping, excessive percolation losses, and protection of the foundation at the downstream embankment toe from erosion.

(d) *Clay Foundations.*—Clay foundations can be used for the support of earthfill dams, but require relatively flat embankment slopes because of relatively lower foundation shear strengths. Clay foundations under dams can also consolidate significantly. Because of the requirement for flatter slopes and the tendency for clay foundations to settle a lot, it is usually not economical to construct a rockfill dam on a clay foundation. Clay foundations are also ordinarily not suitable for concrete gravity dams. Tests of the foundation material in its natural state are usually required to determine the consolidation characteristics of the foundation strata and their ability to support the superimposed load.

(e) *Nonuniform Foundations.*—Occasionally, situations occur where reasonably uniform foundations of any of the types described above cannot be found and where a nonuniform foundation of rock and soft material must be used if the dam is to be built. Nevertheless, such conditions can often be counterbalanced by special design features. Even damsites that are not highly unusual present special problems requiring the selection of appropriate treatment by experienced engineers.

The details of the foundation treatments mentioned above are given in the appropriate chapters on the design of earthfill, rockfill, and concrete gravity dams (chs. 6, 7, and 8, respectively).

4.14. *Materials Available.*—Materials for dams of various types that may sometimes be available at or near the site are:

- Soils for embankments
- Rock for embankments and riprap
- Concrete aggregate (sand, gravel, crushed stone)

Elimination or reduction of transportation expenses for construction materials, particularly those used in great quantities, reduce the total cost of the project considerably. The most economical type of dam is often the one for which a large quantity of materials can be found within a reasonable distance from the site.

The availability of suitable sand and gravel for concrete at a reasonable cost locally and, perhaps, even on property to be acquired for the project is a factor favorable to the selection of a concrete structure. The availability of suitable rock for rockfill is a factor favorable to the selection of a rockfill dam. Every local resource that reduces the cost of the project without sacrificing the efficiency and quality of the final structure should be used.

4.15. *Hydrology.*—Hydrologic studies examine the project purposes stated in section 4.2 in the paragraph on storage dams. There is a close relationship between the hydrologic and economic factors governing the choice of the type of dam and appurtenant structures. Streamflow characteristics and precipitation may appreciably affect the cost of construction by influencing the treatment and diversion of water and extending the construction time. Where large tunnels are required for diversion, conversion of the tunnels to tunnel spillways may provide the most economical spillway alternative.

4.16. *Spillway.*—A spillway is a vital appurtenance of a dam. Frequently, its size and type and the natural restrictions in its location are the controlling factors in the choice of the type of dam. Spillway requirements are dictated primarily by the runoff and streamflow characteristics, independent of site conditions or type or size of the dam. The selection of specific spillway types should be influenced by the magnitudes of the floods to be passed. Thus, it can be seen that on streams with large flood potential, the spillway is the dominant structure, and the selection of the type of dam could become a secondary consideration.

The cost of constructing a large spillway is frequently a considerable portion of the total cost of the project. In such cases, combining the spillway and dam into one structure may be desirable, indicating the selection of a concrete overflow dam. In certain instances, where excavated material from separate spillway channels can be used in the dam embankment, an earthfill dam may prove to be advantageous. Small spillway requirements often favor the selection of earthfill or rockfill dams, even in narrow damsites.

The practice of building overflow concrete spillways on earth or rock embankments has generally been discouraged because of the more conservative design assumptions and added care needed to forestall failures. Inherent problems associated with such designs are unequal settlements of the structure caused by differential consolidations of the embankment and foundation after the reservoir loads are applied; the need for special provisions to prevent the cracking of the concrete or opening of joints that could permit leakage from the channel into the fill, with consequent piping or washing away of the surrounding material; and the requirement for having a fully completed embankment before spillway construction can be started. Consideration of the above factors coupled with increased costs brought about by more conservative construction details, such as arbitrarily increased lining thickness, increased reinforcement steel, cutoffs, joint treatment, drainage, and preloading, have generally led to selection of alternative solutions for the spillway design. Such solutions include placing the structure over or through the natural material of the abutment or under the dam as a conduit.

One of the most common and desirable spillway arrangements is the use of a channel excavated through one or both of the abutments outside the limits of the dam or at some point removed from the dam. Where such a location is adopted, the dam can be of the nonoverflow type, which extends the choice to include earthfill and rockfill structures. Conversely, failure to locate a spillway site away from the dam requires the selection of a type of dam that can include an overflow spillway. The overflow spillway can then be placed so as to occupy only a portion of the main river channel, in which case the remainder of the dam could be either of earth, rock, or concrete. Olympus Dam (fig. 4-4) is an example of this type of dam.

4.17. *Earthquake.*—If the dam lies in an area that is subject to earthquake shocks, the design must provide for the added loading and increased stresses. Earthquake design considerations for earthfill, rockfill, and concrete gravity dams are discussed in chapters 6, 7, and 8, respectively. For earthquake areas, neither the selection of type nor the design of the dam should be undertaken by anyone not experienced in this type of work.

C. LEGAL, ECONOMIC, AND ESTHETIC CONSIDERATIONS

4.18. *Statutory Restrictions.*—Statutory restrictions exist with respect to control of the waters of navigable streams. Plans for diversion or control of waters in such streams are subject to approval by the Corps of Engineers, U.S. Department of the Army. There are numerous other Federal and State regulations relating to dam construction and operation that may affect the choice of the type of structure. Almost every State has laws and regulations governing the design, construction, and operation of all dams and reservoirs of appreciable size. Engineers or owners considering dam construction in any of the 50 States should contact the proper State authorities before proceeding with detailed designs.

4.19. *Purpose and Benefit-Cost Relation.*— Consideration of the purpose a dam is to serve often suggests the type most suitable. For example, selection of the type of dam can be based on whether its principal function is to furnish continuous and dependable storage of the water supply for irrigation, power, or domestic use; to control floods by detention; to regulate the flow of the streams; or to be a diversion dam or a weir without storage features.

Few sites exist where a safe and serviceable dam could not be built. But in many instances, conditions inherent in the site result in a project cost in excess of the justifiable expenditure. The results of a search for desirable damsites often determine whether a project can be built at a cost consistent with the benefits to be derived from it. Accepted procedures are available for evaluating the benefits from waterpower, irrigation, and water-supply uses. However, the procedures are less well-defined for flood control, and there is no satisfactory measure of the value of recreational projects.

Justification for recreational development must be based on an evaluation of the population that will benefit, the locations of other similar projects, and the trend of development in the district (appreciative and depreciative)—all as related to the cost of the project and the money available. In a case where a development is desired, but the number of people that would be served is limited, the development of an expensive site may not be justified. In another case, the present need may be great, but declining population and property values must be considered. In both instances, the development selected should be as inexpensive as possible—probably a low dam of small storage capacity.

4.20. *Appearance.*—In general, every type of structure should have a finished, workmanlike appearance, compatible with its functional purpose. The alignment and texture of finished surfaces should be true to the design requirements and free from unsightly irregularities. Esthetic considerations may have an important bearing on the selection of the type of structure, especially one designed primarily for recreational use.

Chapter 5

Foundations and Construction Materials

A. SCOPE OF INVESTIGATIONS

5.1. ***General.***—Information on foundation and reservoir conditions and on the natural materials available for construction is essential for the design of all dams. Investigations to gather such information are conducted in the field and in the laboratory, and analyses and reference work are performed in the office. For efficiency, these investigations must be properly planned. Subsurface explorations should not be started until all available geologic and soils data have been evaluated. The investigator needs a working knowledge of engineering geology, including the classification requirements of soil, rock, and landforms. The investigator should also be familiar with mapping, with logging and sampling methods, and with field and laboratory testing. Such a background and a knowledge of the capabilities and limitations of the various methods of subsurface exploration will lead to the selection of the most appropriate field methods and will save the time and effort that would otherwise be lost through ineffective procedures and duplication of effort.

The scope of investigations for foundations, for various types of construction materials, and for reservoir studies are given in this part of the chapter. Parts B through K provide information on the techniques and procedures for making these investigations.

5.2. ***Foundations.***—Thorough foundation investigations and the interpretation of the data obtained are required to ascertain whether a safe and economical structure can be built at a selected site. The type of structure should be determined based on the factors outlined in chapter 4. The construction of a dam whose failure would result in a destructive flood, possibly involving the loss of life, involves a serious public responsibility; many damaging floods have been caused by failures of small dams. Investigations have shown that many of these failures were the result of poor foundations or a lack of knowledge of the site conditions. A considerable number of failures attributed to other causes probably originated in defective foundations. It is undoubtedly true that many failures could have been averted by more thorough investigations leading to the selection of safer sites or to the adoption of the design and construction provisions necessary to overcome foundation defects.

Investigations for a potential dam primarily consist of three stages, or levels, of study. These stages, ranked in progressive order of complexity, consist of appraisal, feasibility, and design investigations. Each level of study uses the results obtained from previous investigations as a starting point for further investigations.

The first and one of the most important steps in the appraisal investigation of a proposed reservoir is a site reconnaissance to select the most favorable of the potential damsites based on existing data, topography, and geology of the area. Such a reconnaissance should be performed by both an engineer and an engineering geologist and should be entrusted only to those with thorough knowledge and experience in these fields. The actual reconnaissance field work should be preceded by a study of all available data relating to the water course and to the area under consideration, including examination of maps, aerial photographs, other remote sensing data, and reports. Reports and maps available from the USGS (U.S. Geological Survey), SCS (U.S. Soil Conservation Service), and various State agencies are excellent sources of data. Part C of this chapter discusses the various sources of information. A thorough site reconnaissance leading to the selection of the best damsite or to the elimination of as many potential damsites as possible can save considerable dollars in exploratory work.

Foundation conditions often can be determined from a visual inspection of erosional features, of outcrops, and of excavations such as highway or railroad cuts, building excavations, abandoned pits, and quarries in the general area of the damsite. Information on ground-water conditions often can be obtained from local wells. The results of appraisal field studies should be prepared, preferably on topographic base maps (although aerial photographs may be used), and on preliminary geologic sections. At the appraisal stage of investigation, these drawings should show the contacts between surficial deposits and bedrock units, the rock outcrops, the locations of faults, shear zones, and other geologic structures, and the strike and dip of geologic features such as joints, bedding, contacts, and shear zones.

The geologic maps and sections should be accompanied by a report describing the various geologic conditions, including bedrock and soil classifications and the types of cementing materials that may occur in the rock and soil. The appraisal stage report should discuss the relationship of the geologic conditions to the present and future permeability of the reservoir and dam foundation, and to the future stability and performance of the dam, spillway, and other structures. Readily apparent geologic problems requiring further investigations also should be discussed, and a tentative program outlining the extent and character of more detailed explorations for the feasibility stage of investigation should be recommended. The reservoir and damsite area should be examined for potential landslides that could be activated by construction.

In the feasibility stage of the investigation, subsurface exploration of the foundation is needed to determine (1) the depth to bedrock at the damsite and (2) the character of both the bedrock and the soils under the dam and under appurtenant structures. A number of drill holes are usually required at a damsite to determine the bedrock profile along the proposed axis. Because any axis selected in the field is necessarily tentative and subject to adjustment for design reasons, additional drill holes upstream and downstream from the axis are desirable. The number of drill holes required for foundation exploration of small dams should be determined by the complexity of geologic conditions, but the depth of the drill holes should be greater than the height of the dam.

In the feasibility stage of the investigation, it is also necessary to determine the subsurface conditions at possible locations for the appurtenant structures, such spillways, outlets, cutoff trenches, and tunnel portals. Exploration holes for appurtenant structures, including the diversion dam, usually should have a maximum spacing of 100 feet, should extend below the foundation at least 1½ times the base width of the structure, and should be arranged in a pattern dictated by the complexity of the foundation.

Exploration methods that offer an opportunity for sampling and testing the foundation without excessive disturbance are recommended for exploring foundations. Consequently, wash borings (for example) are not discussed in this text. Test pits, dozer and backhoe trenches, adits or shafts, and large-diameter auger borings that permit visual examination of the foundation are excellent methods of determining the character of the foundation materials and are recommended wherever practical. The recommended boring methods for exploring soil foundations for small dams are rotary drilling, using standard core barrels or Denison and Pitcher samplers, and drive sampling (including the standard penetration test). Inplace unit weight testing and determining the moisture content of soils above the water table also are required. Borings in bedrock require rotary drilling with core barrels to obtain samples. Approximate values for the permeability of rock strata and of surficial deposits can be determined by water tests in bore holes. In each subsurface exploratory hole, it is important to measure and record the depths to the water tables and the dates of these measurements.

The report prepared after completion of the feasibility stage foundation investigation should include a map showing the surface geology, the locations of all explorations, and the locations of geological sections. The map units should be basically geologic, and modified or subdivided to show the distribution of materials with significantly different engineering or physical properties. Cross sections should be prepared showing the known and interpreted subsurface geologic features. Logs of all holes should be included. Figure 5-1 includes an example of a geologic map of a damsite and a cross section along the centerline of the proposed dam.

Design investigations will require additional surface and subsurface explorations in the foundation. These investigations will resolve critical geologic considerations or issues so that detailed design analyses and construction drawings can be prepared. Additional samples and laboratory tests also may be necessary to establish foundation design parameters.

During construction, geologic drawings should be revised or new drawings completed to show the conditions actually revealed in construction excavations. Such a map may prove to be an invaluable "as-built" record of operation and maintenance if geologic problems, such as anomalies in foundation behavior or excessive seepage, are encountered later.

5.3. *Embankment Soils.*—Some damsites require considerable excavation to reach a competent foundation. In many cases, the excavated material is satisfactory for use in portions of the embankment. Excavations for a spillway or outlet works also may produce usable materials for filters, for an impervious core, or for other zones in the embankment. However, designated borrow areas will be required in most cases for embankment materials.

Investigation for embankment materials is a progressive procedure, ranging from a cursory inspection during the appraisal stage to extensive studies of possible sources of material during final design. A reconnaissance for borrow materials should be made at each prospective damsite. Careful examination of existing maps, soil surveys, aerial photographs, and geologic reconnaissance reports usually indicates the areas to be examined in the field. Highway and railroad cuts, arroyos, and banks along stream channels should be examined because they can provide valuable clues to the nature of the materials underlying a borrow area.

It is rarely necessary to excavate test pits or auger holes during the appraisal investigation stage. Quantities can be determined by consideration of topographic features and by a few rough measurements, either on the ground or on maps. The appraisal report should include a map showing the locations of potential borrow areas with respect to the damsite and the character and probable quantity of the materials in each area. Local factors that could affect the use of a borrow source should be discussed in the report. In addition to the engineering properties of the soils, many other facets should be considered, including proximity, accessibility, natural moisture content, and workability of the materials; costs of rights-of-way and stripping; thicknesses of deposits; and environmental considerations. It is good practice to limit the locations of borrow areas so that excavation does not take place within 500 feet of the toe of a small dam.

A systematic plan for selecting borrow areas should be followed during the feasibility investigation stage after final selection of the damsite. To avoid overlooking nearby areas, the investigations should start at the damsite and extend outward in all directions. Potential borrow areas near the dam should be investigated before more distant sources. Where possible, borrow from the proposed reservoir should be considered to mitigate environmental concerns. Holes should be excavated at approximately 500-foot centers on a rough grid system in all practicable locations. Augers should be used wherever possible, but test pits also should be excavated, especially where oversize materials or cemented materials are encountered. Auger holes should extend about 25 feet below the ground surface, except where bedrock or the water table is encountered first. Holes should be sampled and logged in accordance with the procedures given in parts I and J of this chapter. Exploration within the reservoir at probable locations of cutoff trenches, foundation stripping, and exploration for spillways and outlet works should be given high priority in the investigation plan. More detailed work in these areas is justified because of their possible early use as sources of embankment materials and for obtaining additional foundation information. When it becomes evident that a sufficient quantity of suitable materials cannot be found within a short haul distance of the damsite, more distant areas or the use of processed materials should be investigated.

The ultimate purpose of a detailed borrow investigation is to determine available borrow quantities and the distribution of these materials in the embankment. This can be accomplished only if enough explorations are completed to determine the soil profiles in the borrow area. The plotting of profiles on 500-foot centers, or closer, will indicate whether additional explorations are needed. It is evident that the more homogeneous the soil in a borrow area, the fewer the explorations required to establish the profile. Figure 5-2 shows an example of an exploration program for dam embankment materials. Soil classifications should be verified by laboratory tests on representative samples of the various materials encountered. Inplace unit weight tests should be made in each borrow

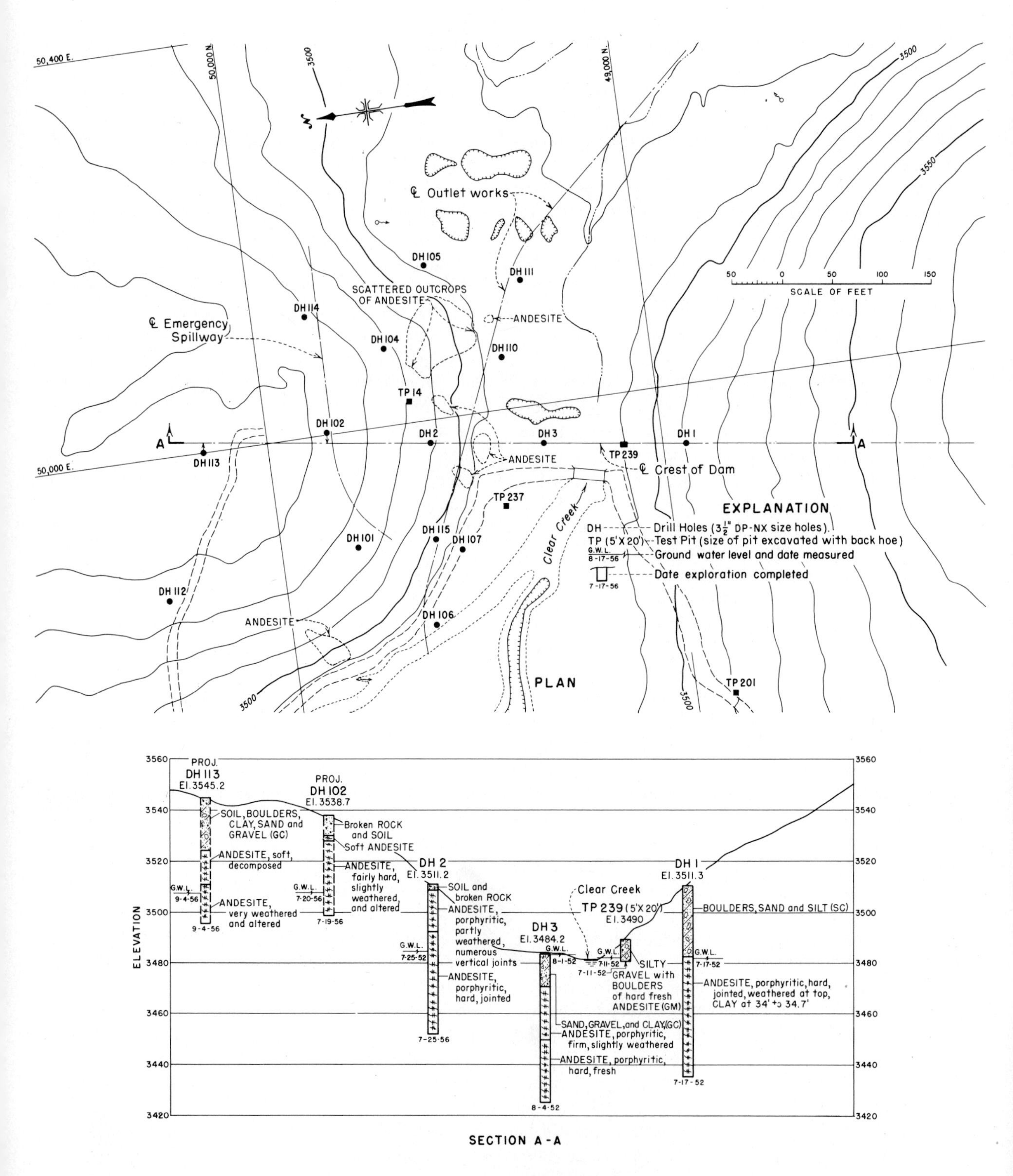

Figure 5-1.—Geologic map and cross section of a damsite. 288–D–2470.

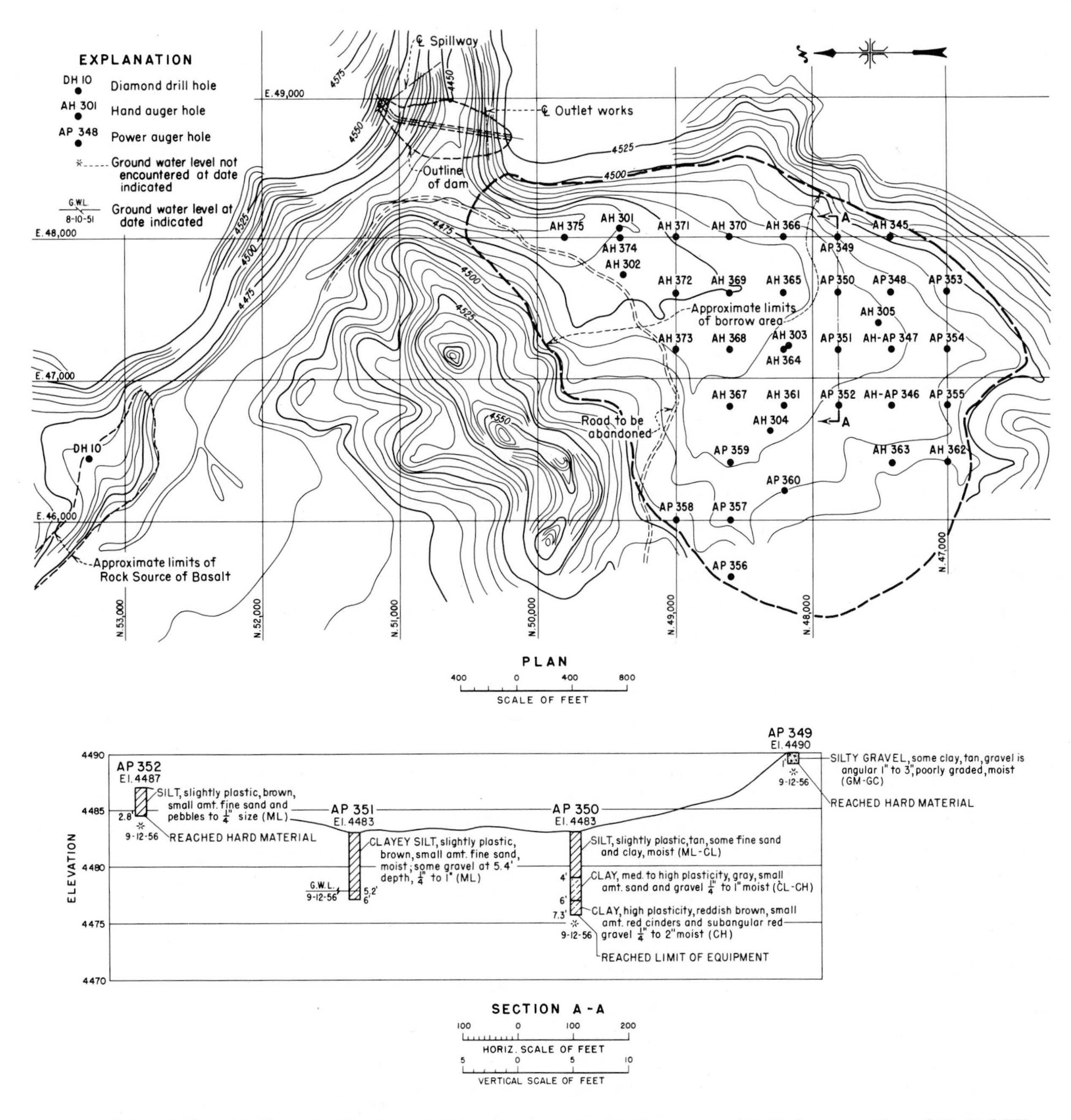

Figure 5-2.—Exploration for embankment materials—borrow area location map and typical cross section. 288–D–2471.

area to determine the shrinkage factor to be applied between the borrow area and compacted embankment. The procedures for this test are given in section 5.47.

Because of changed plans, estimating errors and other contingencies, large safety factors should be used in estimating available quantities from borrow areas. The following criteria will ensure adequate quantities for an appraisal report: when estimates of less than 10,000 yd^{3}of a material are needed, 10 times the estimated amount should be located; for requirements larger than 100,000 yd^3, 5 times the estimated quantity should be located. Even for well-explored borrow areas, at least 1.5 times the required quantity customarily is specified to ensure adequate quantities regardless of the contractor's choice of equipment or methods of excavation. Larger safety factors are often used when the existing information indicates that deposits are expected to be erratic. Filter materials and other special embankment zones may require extensive processing or may be purchased from commercial sources.

5.4. ***Riprap and Rockfill.***—Riprap is a layer of large, durable rock fragments placed on a slope to prevent erosion from wave action or from stream currents. Rockfill is that portion of an embankment constructed of rock fragments in earth and rockfill dams.

The search for suitable sources of riprap and rockfill is conducted in the same general sequence as the search for earth embankment materials. Because riprap is almost always essential for an embankment dam, it is impractical to limit the area to be searched. Explorations should extend radially outward from the damsite until a suitable rock quarry is located that will meet the anticipated cost and quantity requirements. The best possible use should be made of existing data, such as geologic maps, aerial photographs, topographic maps, publications of State, Federal, or private agencies, and known commercial sources. From a study of these data, existing quarries, outcrops, and other promising areas can be located on a map or photograph for later field investigation. At some point in the investigation, it may be more economical to consider alternative methods of slope protection, such as soil cement, asphaltic concrete, or rubble.

The primary criteria for riprap are quality and size. During the investigations, inspection and testing should be performed to evaluate the ability of the rock to resist wave action, freezing and thawing, and other detrimental forces, and to determine whether the quarry will yield sufficient material of the required sizes. The most obvious place to begin exploration of the rock source is where durable rock crops out. Vertical faces cut back to unweathered material should be thoroughly examined for fracture patterns, bedding and cleavage planes, and for zones of unsuitable material. The joint, cleavage, and bedding plane joint systems are especially important because they indicate the maximum sizes that can be produced.

The explorations required for determining the characteristics of potential riprap sources are usually accomplished with boreholes, trenches, or both. Core drilling is normally the most practicable and reliable method of determining the areal extent, volume, depth of overburden, waste material, weathering, and fracture pattern of the rock source. In the example shown on figure 5-2, only one borehole (DH 10) was used in the rock source to establish the depth of the extensively exposed basalt. Usually more than one borehole is required.

Where the bedrock is not suitable for riprap, other sources must be investigated. In several cases surface boulders have been gathered and used for riprap on earthfill dams because suitable quarry rock of quality could not be found within 100 miles of the damsite. The use of this type of riprap is normally feasible only when the boulders occur in fairly well-concentrated accumulations, and there are sufficient numbers to provide significant riprap quantities. Nevertheless, using several widely separated sources to obtain the quantity required for one dam is not uncommon.

Occasionally, talus slopes are found that contain durable rock of the required sizes and that are of sufficient extent to make quarrying from other sources unnecessary. Such slopes are especially desirable when they are easily accessible. Explorations for talus materials usually consist of making a thorough survey to determine the characteristics of the rock, the quantity available, and testing to determine the range of sizes and durability. Good photographs, which should be part of the exploratory data for all riprap and rock sources, are especially valuable when talus slopes are being considered. Figure 5-3 shows a talus deposit of igneous rock suitable for riprap.

The availability of riprap or rockfill materials has a significant effect on the design of a structure; consequently, very careful studies of their quantities must be made. It is occasionally possible to use readily accessible and less durable material rather than to procure a superior rock at considerably greater cost. On the other hand, using lesser quantities of superior materials sometimes offsets their higher unit cost. Information on the sampling of riprap sources is given in section 5.34(e).

5.5. ***Concrete Aggregate.***—Field investigations for concrete materials before construction are confined chiefly to existing aggregate sources and to locating, exploring, and sampling potential sources. Those locating potential sources or testing existing sources should be familiar with the effects

Figure 5-3.—Typical talus deposit suitable for riprap. At base of basalt cliffs in Grant County, Washington. 3PPG–1.

of gradation, physical characteristics, and aggregate composition on the properties of concrete. Good judgment and thoroughness in conducting preliminary field investigations are usually reflected in the durability and economy of the finished structures.

Most factors pertaining to the suitability of aggregate deposits are related to the geologic history of the area. These factors include size, and location of the deposit; thickness and character of the overburden; types and condition of the rock; gradation, roundness, and degree of uniformity of the aggregate particles; and ground-water level. Aggregate may be obtained from deposits of natural sand and gravel, from talus, or from quarries. Fine sand can sometimes be obtained from windblown deposits.

Stream deposits are the most common and, generally, the most desirable aggregate source because (1) they are easy and inexpensive to excavate or process; (2) streams naturally sort deposits (which can sometimes improve the gradation); and (3) abrasion caused by stream transportation and deposition eliminates some of the weaker materials. Alluvial fans may be used as sources of aggregate, but they often require more than normal processing. Glacial deposits provide sand and gravel, but they are generally restricted to the northern latitudes or high elevations. Those glacial deposits not influenced by fluvial agents are usually too heterogeneous to be suitable as aggregate and, at best, are usable only after elaborate processing.

When natural sand and gravel are not available, it is necessary to produce concrete aggregate by quarrying and processing rock. Quarrying in the

Western States normally is done only when other materials of adequate quality and size cannot be obtained economically. Quarry deposits may contain stratified materials that make it difficult to obtain representative samples of the undeveloped source. Furthermore, the presence of layers or zones of undesirable materials, such as clay or shale, sometimes necessitates selective quarrying and special processing.

The extent and justifiable expense of explorations for concrete aggregate are determined largely by the size and the purpose of the structure. When searching for suitable aggregate, it is important to remember that ideal materials are seldom found. Deficiencies or excesses of one or more sizes are common, and objectionable rock types, coated and cemented particles, or flat or slabby-shape particles may occur in excessive amounts.

The promising deposits should be explored and sampled by cased test holes, open test pits, or trenches, and the suitability of the aggregate should be determined by testing. The methods of geophysical exploration, subsurface exploration, sampling, logging, and testing are presented in parts G, H, I, J, and K, respectively, of this chapter. The quality and gradation requirements for aggregates are discussed in appendix F.

5.6. Reservoir Studies.—The geologic adequacy of a proposed reservoir is as important as the adequacy of a damsite foundation. Reservoir-wide investigations must be planned with comparable care; a concurrent study of both the reservoir and the damsite is best. If a major defect is uncovered in either, investigations should be reoriented or stopped before a disproportionately large exploration investment accrues on a site that may be abandoned.

(a) *General.*—Evaluating and exploring the proposed reservoir requires that attention be given to all factors that affect reservoir adequacy or use. The principal factors are rim stability, water-holding capability, bank storage, potential sources of pollution, and effects of borrow removal on stability and seepage. In addition, related foundation problems, including the relocation of highway, railroad, or other facilities must be considered. The degree of attention given to each problem should be appropriate to its importance and to the stage of planning or design. The detailed character of investigations should be determined by the purpose of each specific reservoir. Typically, the investigations should include distribution of bedrock and surficial deposits, outcrops, discontinuities and structural features, ground-water occurrence and behavior, mineral resources, observed and potential geologic hazards, landslides and rim stability, reservoir integrity and potential seepage, and sources of contamination of reservoir water.

(b) *Reservoir Maps.*—An effective reservoir geologic map is essential for planning and conducting the investigations. Inadequate geologic maps that present incomplete or poorly chosen data waste money and technical effort and can lead to erroneous conclusions. Inadequate geologic maps can even force binding decisions to be made on the basis of scanty or incomplete data. On geologic maps prepared for engineering and related geologic studies, the range of data to be shown and the scale to be used should be determined by (1) the purpose of the investigation, (2) the detail that can be shown, and (3) the extent to which quantitative data must be presented or derived from the map (e.g., distances, volumes of potential slide masses, differences in elevation, thicknesses of surficial deposits and bedrock units, and details of outcrop boundaries or geologic contacts). The choice of a suitable scale is important because it influences the detail and the legibility of the map.

In regional or project maps, the principal objective is to graphically present the general distribution of major site conditions. In contrast, site maps are detailed representations of geologic features. In the two types of maps, scales may range from 1:62,500 (regional) to 1:250 (site map). The usual scales of reservoir maps range from 1:24,000 (1 inch equals 2,000 feet) to 1:5,000 (1 inch equals approximately 400 feet).

The reservoir geologic map should not be restricted to the immediate area of the proposed reservoir. It must be supplemented by a regional-type map that relates the reservoir position, elevation, and distance to adjacent valleys. As a minimum, this map should show ridge and valley outlines with elevations.

The reservoir geologic map should be supplemented by several specialized maps or overlays and/or by smaller-scale inserts or separate maps showing detailed geologic conditions in critical areas of potential seepage or landslides. Similarly, small-scale inserts may be used to show gross relations of topographic saddles and adjacent drainages. Supplemental maps, charts, or graphs portraying regional ground-water contours or data (estimated if necessary) are desirable, particularly if potential leakage or anomalous ground-water conditions exist. Geologic sections and overlays showing generalized geologic structure, landslides, faults, buried channels, etc., should also be prepared.

The basic reservoir mapping should extend above the maximum reservoir level to characterize the geologic environment and facilitate evaluation of reservoir-rim stability and water-holding capability. There may be extensive areas below minimum reservoir level in which appraisal level mapping will be entirely adequate. For some areas of the reservoir, more detailed mapping may be necessary to define landslide or leakage problems.

Only occasionally or in certain types of terrain does the entire reservoir require detailed mapping and study. Commonly, the study and detailed mapping are done only so far as needed to establish geologic adequacy and to identify principal defects.

(c) *Investigation Methods.*—Field examination and aerial photograph interpretation are the basic methods by which geologic data are secured and collated on drawings for study and interpretation. The reservoir geologic map is the initial and principal medium through which geologic studies are planned or conducted and by which the nature and scope of reservoir defects are recognized and evaluated. Whatever the stage of the investigations, the map is a combination of fact and interpretation which, from an engineering-geology viewpoint, defines the geologic environment and aids in recognizing geologic defects or issues. Direct subsurface investigations, such as drilling, may or may not be a part of the overall study.

A variety of techniques or investigation approaches can be used in conducting reservoir studies. It is assumed that reservoir studies will be planned and conducted by engineering geologists and ground-water geologists trained in basic geologic principles and in standard methods of geologic investigation. The outline that follows is a checklist of the principal techniques that can assist in selecting the specific investigation methods most effective for the reservoir site study.

(1) *Geomorphologic Interpretation.*—Stream patterns, topographic and geologic maps, and aerial photographs can provide information such as:

a. Geologic structure, regional and local joint patterns, location of geologic contacts, sinkholes, and subterranean drainage
b. Aggrading stream history producing deep valley fill; degrading stream history producing landforms such as gravel-veneered (aggregate deposits) or rock-defended (low aggregate volume) terraces
c. Potential sources for embankment materials
d. Ground-water conditions and reservoir leakage potential
e. Existing and potential landslides

(2) *Hydrogeologic Studies.*—These studies yield information or require analysis such as:

a. Ground-water conditions, such as location, direction and velocities of flow, elevations, and contours of static and piezometer water levels. These can be determined using methods such as drill hole water-level measuring devices, down-hole flowmeters, dye and radioisotope tagging, and water sampling and analysis.
b. Ground-water ages (relative) as determined by tritium, carbon dioxide, or dissolved oxygen content.
c. Differentiation of ground-water bodies and evaluation of water quality by chemical analyses (analyze graphically by Stiff diagrams), conductivity, pH, and temperature studies.
d. Flow estimates or measurements of springs and small watercourses. Data such as spring flow and volume and ground-water levels in drill holes may be essential to define changes in the original ground-water conditions caused by reservoir leakage. Data collection must be started and completed before reservoir filling to establish the character of normal prereservoir conditions. Measurements of hydrostatic head may be necessary to judge whether spring flow may be reversed when subject to reservoir head.
e. Estimates of bank storage volume, inflow, and outflow rates.

(3) *Subsurface Investigations.*—Subsurface investigations may include geophysical tests; bailing tests as needed to determine water-table elevations and movement; packer or pump-out tests to estimate permeability, or exploratory drilling to obtain landslide thickness, depth and nature of surficial material in saddles, location of buried bedrock channels, or glaciofluvial permeable outwash channels in till deposits.

(4) *Remote Sensing.*—Natural-color or false-color infrared aerial photographs or sidescanning radar imagery can assist in mapping contacts, land-

forms, or geologic structures. Infrared imagery detects surface geothermal anomalies that may indicate near-surface ground water, faults, lineaments, or contacts.

B. COLLECTION AND PRESENTATION OF DATA

5.7. *General.*—The ability of a foundation to support the loads imposed by the various structures is primarily dependent on the deformation, stability, and ground-water conditions of the foundation materials. Judgment and intuition (empirical methods) alone are not adequate for the safe design of dams. It has become ever more imperative to properly develop foundation design data because recent advancements in soil and rock mechanics and new analytical procedures enable engineers and geologists to assess more conditions analytically than previously possible. To accommodate these techniques, foundation data must not only be accurate and concise, but must be quantified as much as possible. In addition, this quantifiable data must be sufficient to adequately ensure that the analytical models are representative of field conditions.

5.8. *Presentation of Data.*—This section provides general guidelines for the collection and presentation of geologic information required for the design and construction of small dams. In applying these guidelines, investigators should use good judgement and elaborate upon them as required by the particular geologic setting and engineering requirements. These guidelines are not intended to include all requirements or topics for every foundation or construction materials investigation. However, they do provide adequate guidance to formulate a data acquisition program for planning studies and for final design investigations.

The data required and methods of obtaining these data depend on the purpose of the investigations, the time and funds available for explorations, the amount and reliability of previous investigations, and the type of report required. The general guidelines for the data necessary for foundations and for construction materials are described in subsections (a) through (j) below.

(a) Compile, summarize, and document all investigations in the project area and describe the sequence and results of studies and explorations. Some of the sources of information for the initial investigations are described in part C. Types of exploration, sampling, logging, and testing are discussed in parts F through K.

(b) Prepare drawings showing the locations of explorations. Develop a stratigraphic column, surface geology maps, and geologic cross sections at appropriate scales to portray surface and subsurface conditions. Prepare special-purpose drawings (such as joint-contour diagrams and contour maps for top of rock, weathering, water levels, etc.) for sites with complex geology or design concepts.

(c) Prepare narrative descriptions of surficial deposits, specifying engineering properties, especially those that can affect design or construction. These descriptions may include, but are not restricted to, the presence of swelling minerals, low-density materials, gypsum and other sulfates, caliche, dispersive soils, loose deposits subject to liquefaction or consolidation, permeable materials, erodibility, and oversize materials. Instructions for logging and describing soils in geologic explorations are provided in parts D and J of this chapter. The descriptions should include the general classification of materials according to the Unified Soil Classification System and their physical characteristics (e.g., color, grain size, consistency or compactness, cohesion, cementation, moisture content, mineral deposits, and content of expansive or dispersive minerals, alteration, fissures, or fractures). The investigator should use descriptors established for the Unified Soil Classification System. The narrative should also describe the distribution, occurrence, and relative age; relationship with present topography; and correlation with features such as terraces, dunes, undrained depressions, and anomalies.

(d) Descriptions of bedrock should identify the engineering-geology properties such as strength, swelling minerals, presence of gypsum and other sulfates, depths of weathering, joints, faults and other planes of weakness. The following checklist can be useful as a general, though not necessarily complete, guide for bedrock descriptions.

(1) *Bedrock Units.*—Traceable lithologic units of similar physical properties should be identified and characterized.

- Identification as to rock type (e.g., granite, silty sandstone, mica schist), relative age and, where possible, correlation with named formations
- Physical characteristics (e.g., color; texture; grain size; nature of stratification, bedding, fol-

iation, or schistosity; hardness; chemical features such as cementation; mineral deposits; and alterations other than weathering-related)
- Distribution and dimensional characteristics (e.g., thickness, outcrop width, areal extent)

(2) *Distribution and Extent of Weathering and Alteration.*—Weathering should be divided into categories that reflect definable physical changes in the rock mass. Weathering profiles should be developed.

(3) *Structural Features.*—Bedding plane partings, cleavage, joints, contact shear and fault zones, folds, zones of contortion or crushing.
- Occurrence and distribution
- Orientation and changes in attitude
- Dimensional characteristics (e.g., width, spacing, continuity)
- Physical characteristics and their effect upon the rock mass (the conditions of planar surfaces, such as openness, roughness, waviness of surfaces, striations, mineralization, alteration, and infilling or healing)
- Statistical evaluations of distribution, orientation, and physical characteristics
- Relative ages (where pertinent)
- Specific features of shears or faults (e.g., description of composition of the fault, zones of gouge and breccia, displacment, attitude of slickensides, relative age of movements)

(4) *Response to Natural Surface and Near-Surface Processes.*—For example, raveling, gullying, and mass movement.

(e) Include laboratory determinations of engineering properties of surficial deposits and bedrock. See part K of this chapter.

(f) Provide black-and-white photographs of geologic conditions, drill hole cores, samples, outcrops, trenches, and test pits. Color photographs or transparencies also should be furnished if appropriate.

(g) Summarize data from remote-sensing and geophysical surveys (seismic, resistivity, etc.), if performed, and correlate with other geologic information.

(h) Describe investigation of ground-water conditions. Note water levels or piezometric surfaces and their seasonal fluctuation, the occurrence of unconfined and confined aquifers, seepage potential, water-producing capabilities, chemistry, and related ground subsidence. The following checklist can be used as a general, though not necessarily complete, guide for descriptions:
- Distribution, occurrence, and relationship to topography (e.g., streams, ponds, swamps, springs, seeps, subsurface basins)
- Recharge sources and permanence, variations in amounts of water and dates the measurements were recorded
- Evidence for earlier occurrence of water at localities now dry (e.g., vegetation, mineral leaching or deposition, relict karst, historic records)
- The effect of water on the properties of the inplace materials, including field and laboratory observations

(i) Prepare accurate and complete logs of explorations, using terminology consistent with the narrative. Give consideration to appropriate indexes; e.g., RQD (rock quality determination) and PR (penetration resistance).

(j) Evaluate landslides, avalanches, rockfalls, erosion, floods, etc. The following checklist may be useful as a general, though not necessarily complete, guide of descriptions:
- Features representing accelerated erosion (e.g., cliff reentrants, badlands, advancing gully heads)
- Features indicating subsidence, settlement, or creep (e.g., fissures, bulges, scarplets, displaced or tilted reference features, historic records, measurements)
- Slump and slide masses in bedrock and surficial deposits, their distribution, geometric characteristics, correlation with topographic and geologic features, age, and rates of movements

C. SOURCES OF INFORMATION

5.9. *Topographic Maps.*—Topographic maps are indispensable in the design and construction of a dam. They are necessary for the exploration of dam foundations and when exploring for construction materials. The locations of subsurface explorations and geologic contacts can be placed on a topographic map before detailed geologic maps are prepared. Information on the origin and characteristics of some of the simpler landforms is given in part F of this chapter because they may indicate foundation properties and the materials present. Before making the map, a thorough search should be made for maps of the reservoir, the damsite, and potential sources of construction materials. The USGS should be contacted for information on the availability of maps. The USGS produces standard topographic maps, which cover the United States, Puerto Rico, Virgin Islands, Guam, American Samoa, and the Trust Territory of the Pacific Islands.

The unit of survey for USGS maps is usually a quadrangle bounded by parallels of latitude and meridians of longitude. Quadrangles covering 7.5 minutes of latitude and longitude are generally published at the scale of 1:24,000 (1 inch equals 2,000 feet). Quadrangles covering 15 minutes of latitude and longitude are published at the scale of 1:62,500 (1 inch equals approximately 1 mile). A series of topographic maps at the scale of 1:250,000 (1 inch equals approximately 4 miles) has also been published, in units of 1° of latitude and 2° of longitude; it covers the entire country. Many special maps are published at other scales.

In addition to published topographic maps, information that can be of great assistance to engineers and geologists is available for mapped areas from the USGS. This information includes the locations and true geodetic positions of triangulation stations and the elevations of permanent benchmarks. In addition, map manuscripts at the 1:24,000 scale may be available 1½ to 2 years before publication of the final map. Large index maps that illustrate the types of maps by State or large geographic area are also available from the USGS.

River survey maps are often helpful to the investigator. These are strip maps that show the course and fall of the stream and nearby topographic and cultural features. River survey maps are prepared largely in connection with the classification of public lands for water resource development. Most of them are of rivers in the Western States. If a valley is less than 1 mile wide, topography is shown to 100 feet or more above the water surface; if the valley is flat and wide, topography is shown for a strip of 1 to 2 miles.

Potential reservoir sites are usually mapped on a scale of 1:24,000. The normal contour interval is 20 feet, except in the vicinity of the normal water surface where it is 5 feet. Many of these maps include damsites on a large scale and have a profile of the stream. The standard map size is 22 by 28 inches.

The availability of river survey maps and other special maps, including those of national parks and monuments, and a list of agents for topographic maps are indicated on the topographic map index. These indexes are also available from the USGS. Requests for indexes and inquiries concerning published maps and the availability of map manuscripts and related information should be directed to U.S. Geological Survey, Denver Federal Center, Denver, CO 80225 or to U.S. Geological Survey, Reston, VA, 22092.

5.10. *Geologic Maps.*—For appraisal studies, considerable useful engineering information may be obtained from published geologic maps. These maps identify the rock units and geologic structures underlying the reservoir and damsite and in the surrounding area. Geologic map requirements at the feasibility and final design stage are discussed in section 5.2. The characteristics of rocks are of major importance in the selection of a damsite and in the design of the dam. Subsurface conditions can be inferred or interpreted from the information on geologic maps.

On geologic maps, rock units are identified by their general lithologic character and geologic age. The smallest rock unit mapped is generally a formation or unit of relatively uniform lithology that extends over a fairly large area and can be clearly differentiated from overlying or underlying units. The areal extent of these formations is indicated on geologic maps by letter symbols, color, and symbolic patterns.

Letter symbols indicate the formation and geologic period. For example, "Jm" might stand for the Morrison Formation of the Jurassic Period. In general, standard color and pattern conventions are followed on USGS maps. Tints of yellow and orange are used for different Cenozoic units, tints of green for Mesozoic rocks, tints of blue and purple for Paleozoic rocks, and tints of russet and red for Precambrian rocks. Variations of dot and line patterns are used for sedimentary rocks; wavy lines for metamorphic rocks; and checks, crosses, or crystallike patterns for igneous rocks.

Geologic maps portray the attitude or orientation of the rock strata or other planar features by standardized symbols. In addition, geologic maps commonly carry one or more geologic structure sections showing the projected geologic units and structures in depth along an arbitrary line marked on the map. Sections prepared solely from surface data are not as accurate as those prepared from subsurface data obtained from drilling or mining records. Geologic sections are interpretive and must be used with caution.

A map showing a plan view of the bedrock in the area is a surface geology map. Such a map indicates the boundaries of the exposed structure and units and their inferred distribution where covered by soil or plant growth. Except for thick deposits of alluvium, most bedrock geologic maps do not delineate soil units. Some geologic maps differentiate the surface deposits of the area; they indicate the areal extent, characteristics, and geologic age of the surficial materials.

Most geologic maps are accompanied by explanations giving the relative ages and brief descriptions of the units distinguished on them. Where descriptions of units are lacking, an experienced geologist can determine their characteristics by making analogies with other areas. For more certain identification of the lithology and for details, geologic literature on the whole area must be consulted.

By studying the basic geologic map, together with all the collateral geologic data that pertain to an area, it is possible to prepare a special map that interprets the geology in terms of its engineering characteristics. Suitability of formations for construction materials, foundation and excavation conditions, and surface and ground-water data can also be interpreted from geologic maps. Such information is valuable in preliminary planning, but is not a substitute for detailed field investigations in the feasibility and design stages.

The USGS now publishes a series entitled "Geologic Quadrangle Maps of the United States," which replaces the *Geologic Atlas of the United States*, published from 1894 to 1945. Most maps in this series are large scale (1:62,500 or larger) and are printed in color. Most have structural sections and other graphic means of presenting geologic data and a brief explanatory text. Full descriptions of the areas shown on these maps and detailed interpretations of geologic history are commonly compiled in other publications, such as USGS bulletins and professional papers. The USGS also publishes geologic maps under a series known as "Miscellaneous Geologic Investigations Maps," "Mineral Resources Maps and Charts," "Geophysical Investigations," and "Hydrologic Investigation Atlases." Maps in these series have a wide range of scales and formats to meet specific purposes.

Several geologic maps are of special interest to designers of dams. A series of such maps resulted from geologic mapping and general resources investigations conducted by the USGS as part of the Department of the Interior plan for study and development of the Missouri River Basin. These include maps showing construction materials and nonmetallic mineral resources, including sand and gravel deposits, of several of the States in the Missouri River Basin.

Detailed information about published geologic maps for individual States is given in the series of geologic map indexes available from the USGS. Each published geologic map is outlined on a State base map, with an explanatory key giving the source and date of publication, the author, and the scale.

5.11. *Agricultural Soil Maps.*—A large portion of the United States has been surveyed by the USDA (Department of Agriculture). These investigations are surficial, extending to depths up to 6 feet, and consist of classifying soils according to color, structure, texture, physical constitution, chemical composition, biological characteristics, and morphology. The Department of Agriculture publishes reports of their surveys in which the different soils are described in detail. The suitability of these soils for various crops and, in the more recent reports, the limited engineering properties and uses of these soils are given. Included in each report is a map of the area (usually a county), which shows the various types of soils that occur by the pedologic classification .

These USDA surveys are available for purchase from the Superintendent of Documents, Washington, D.C. County extension offices may have local examples to examine or purchase. Out-of-print maps and other unpublished surveys may be available for examination from the USDA, county extension agents, colleges, universities, and libraries. The Bureau of Reclamation has made surveys for irrigation suitability in most river basins in the 17 Western States. These were made to identify and classify lands for irrigation. Maps and reports on these surveys are available in local project or regional offices of the Bureau of Reclamation. These data are quite useful for engineering purposes because they provide detailed soil data and considerable information relating to the geology and drainage conditions. In addition, the soils data usually include laboratory and field measurements of chemical and physical properties to at least a 10-foot depth and often some information on deeper materials.

To apply soil survey maps to explorations of foundations and construction materials, some knowledge of soil classification systems is necessary. The USDA uses a classification system entitled "Soil Classification, a Comprehensive System, Seventh Approximation," which is referred to as simply the "seventh approximation."

The category at the highest level of generalization is the "order," of which there are 10. The next category is the "suborder." This limits the ranges in soil moisture and temperature regimes, the kinds of horizons, and the composition, according to which is most important. Additional categories (in descending order) include "great groups," "subgroups," "families," and "series." The soil "series" is a commonly used term. It refers to a group of soils having horizons similar in differentiating characteristics and arrangements in the soil profile, except for texture of the surface portion.

The final subdivision of a soil series is the soil "phase." This is a subdivision of soil that concerns the characteristics affecting its use and management, but which does not vary sufficiently to differentiate it as a separate soil series. Phases of soil series are the major components of the soil mapping units currently being shown on detailed soil maps.

Although it is not a part of the soil classification system now being used, "soil type," a subdivision of soil series based on surface texture, is commonly used in most of the published soil survey data.

The textural classification system used in describing soil types or phases in USDA soil survey reports or in Bureau of Reclamation irrigation surveys is shown on figure 5-4. This is different from the Unified Soil Classification System commonly used by the Bureau of Reclamation for engineering purposes (see part D of this chapter). Figure 5-4 shows the terminology used for different percentages of clay (defined as particles smaller than 0.002 mm), silt (0.002 to 0.05 mm), and sand (0.05 to 2.0 mm). Note the use of the term "loam," which is defined in the chart as a mixture of sand, silt, and clay within certain percentage limits. Other terms used as adjectives to the names obtained in the triangle classification are "gravelly" for rounded and subrounded particles from approximately 1/16 inch to 3 inches, "cherty" for gravel sizes of chert, and "stony" for sizes greater than 10 inches.

The textural classification given as part of the soil name in soil types or phases refers to the material in the "A" horizon only and, therefore, is not indicative of the entire soil profile. However, the combination of a series name and textural classification provides a considerable amount of significant data. For each soil series, the texture, degree of compaction, presence or absence of hardpan or rock, lithology of the parent material, and chemical composition can be obtained. Similar and, frequently, more detailed data for specific sites can often be obtained from irrigation suitability surveys made by the Bureau of Reclamation. From the engineering point of view, both the USDA reports and the Bureau of Reclamation surveys have some limitations, but can often be used to advantage in reconnaissance-type studies.

Considerable useful information is contained in modern soil profile descriptions and in modern soil survey reports. This information is not only useful to farmers, but also to engineers and geologists attempting to interpret such properties as the suitability of the soil for road subgrades, road fills, building foundations, dikes, levees, and embankments. In addition, modern soil survey reports show not only the USDA textural classification [1][1], but also the Unified and AASHTO (American Association of State Highway and Transportation Officials) classifications for all soils included in the report. Such reports are quite useful for both agricultural and engineering purposes. Figure 5-4 shows a comparison of particle size scales for the Unified, ASSHTO, and USDA soil classification systems.

5.12. *Remote Sensing.*—Many new methods of remote sensing now available complement standard black-and-white photography. These include SLAR (side-looking airborne radar), LANDSAT (satellite), high-altitude (commonly U-2) and low sun-angle photography and sensing. Remote-sensing data may incorporate topographic, geophysical, and geochemical data, using thermal and fixed-color imagery, all of which can be computer enhanced.

An aerial photograph is a pictorial representation of a portion of the earth's surface taken from the air. It may be a vertical photograph, in which the axis of the camera is vertical, or nearly so, or an oblique photograph, in which the axis of the camera is inclined. High oblique photographs include the horizon; low obliques do not. The vertical photograph is commonly used as the basis for topographic mapping, agricultural soil mapping, and geological mapping and interpretations.

Except where dense forest cover or shadows from

[1]Numbers in brackets refer to entries in the bibliography (sec. 5.51).

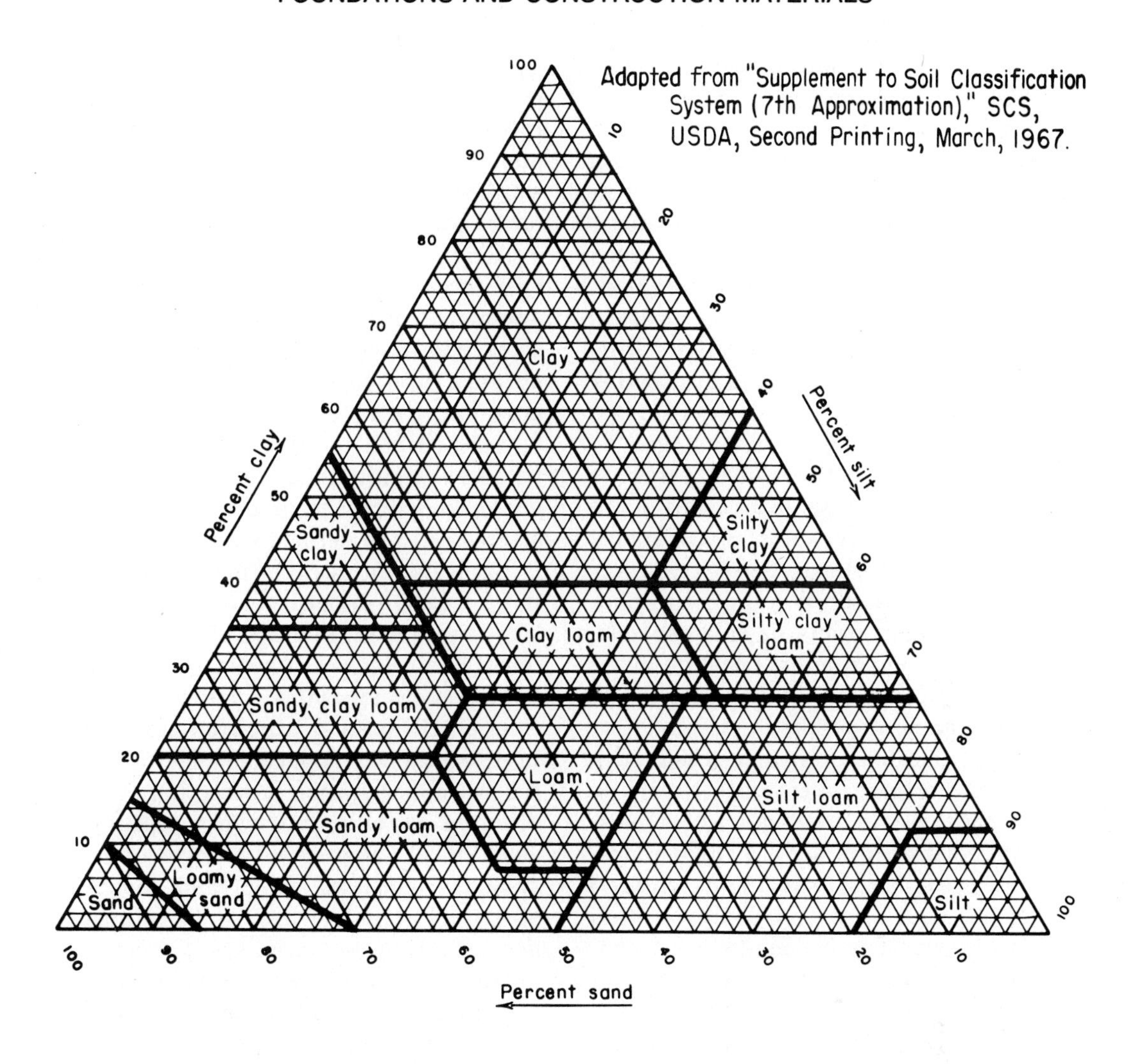

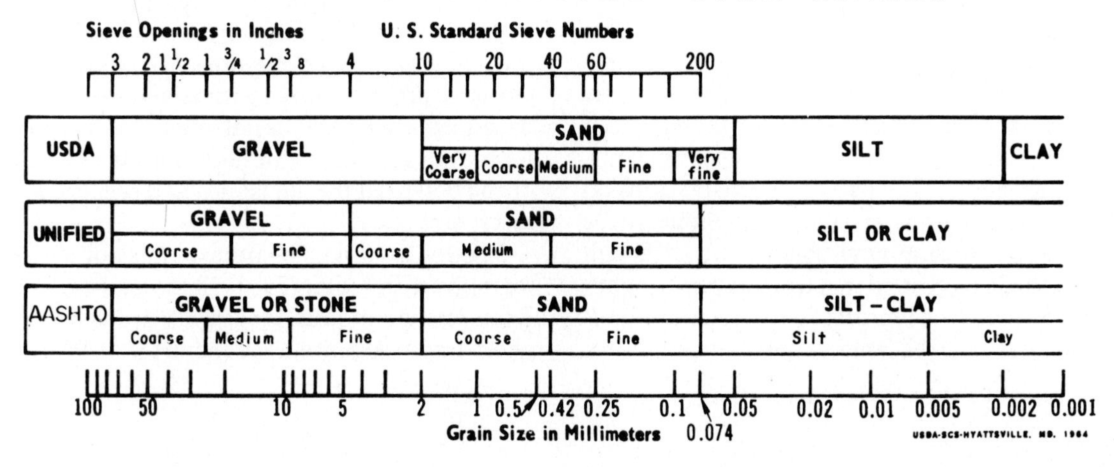

Figure 5-4.—Soil triangle of the basic soil textural classes. (U.S. Soil Conservation Service). 288–D–2782.

landforms obscure large areas from view, an aerial photograph will reveal natural and constructed features in detail. Some relationships are exposed that could not be found from the ground. Identification of features shown on the photograph can be facilitated by stereoscopic examination. The features are then interpreted for a particular purpose, such as geologic mapping, land use, or engineering uses. Knowledge of geology and soil science will assist in interpreting aerial photographs for engineering uses. Aerial photographs are often used for locating areas to be examined and sampled in the field and as substitutes for maps in the appraisal stage.

Virtually the entire area of the United States has been covered by remote sensing. Index maps of the United States, available from the U.S. Geological Survey, show which Government agency can provide prints for particular areas. When ordering photographs, specify contact prints or enlargements, glossy or matte finish, and location. Location in the Western States should be given by range, township, section, latitude, longitude, State, and county, or the location should be shown on an enclosed index map of the area. Stereoscopic coverage should be requested for most uses. Aerial mosaics of most areas of the United States are also available. A mosaic is an assemblage of aerial photographs matched and mounted to form a continuous representation of the earth's surface. They include halftone photolithographic reproductions from mosaic negatives known as "photo maps." Index maps showing the status of aerial mosaics for the United States (including the coverage and the agencies holding mosaic negatives) are available from the USGS.

Remote-sensing interpretation of earth materials and geologic features requires experience. The diagnostic features include terrain position, topography, drainage and erosional features, color tones, and vegetative cover. Interpretation is limited mainly to surface and near-surface conditions. There are special cases, however, where features on the photograph permit reliable predictions to be made of deep, underground conditions. Although interpretation can be rendered from any sharp photograph, the scale is a limiting factor because small-scale photos limit the amount of detailed information that can be obtained. Scales of 1:20,000 are usually satisfactory for engineering and geologic interpretation of surface materials. Large-scale photos often have applications to highly detailed work, such as for reservoir clearing estimates, and for geologic mapping of damsites, and reservoirs.

Aerial photographs can be used to identify certain terrain types and land forms. These topographic features are described in part F of this chapter. Inspection of stereoscopic photographs of an area, with particular attention to regional topography, local terrain features, and drainage conditions, suffice to identify the common terrain types. This permits the possible range in the soil and rock materials to be anticipated and their characteristics to be defined within broad limits.

Geologic features that may be highly significant to the location or performance of engineering structures can sometimes be identified from aerial photographs. In many instances these features can be more readily identified on the aerial photograph than on the ground. However, aerial photography interpretation is applicable only to those features that have recognizable surface expressions, such as drainage patterns, hummocky topography, scarps or cliffs, and alignment of ridges or valleys. Joint systems, landslides, faults and zones, folds, and other structural features can sometimes be identified quickly in an aerial photograph, but may be difficult to find on the ground. However, all interpretations derived from remote sensing should be verified in the field.

Items that can be identified by remote sensing are important in locating a dam and its appurtenant works. The general distribution of surface deposits and rock units, bedding or cleavage, and jointing of attitudes, as well as the presence of dikes and intrusions, ground-water barriers and seeps, often can be interpreted from aerial photographs. Such information is valuable in determining the existence of the potential for landslides and seepage losses in reservoirs.

Figures 5-5 and 5-6 are examples of aerial photographs with readily identifiable geologic features. Examples of typical landforms studied on aerial photographs are discussed in part F of this chapter.

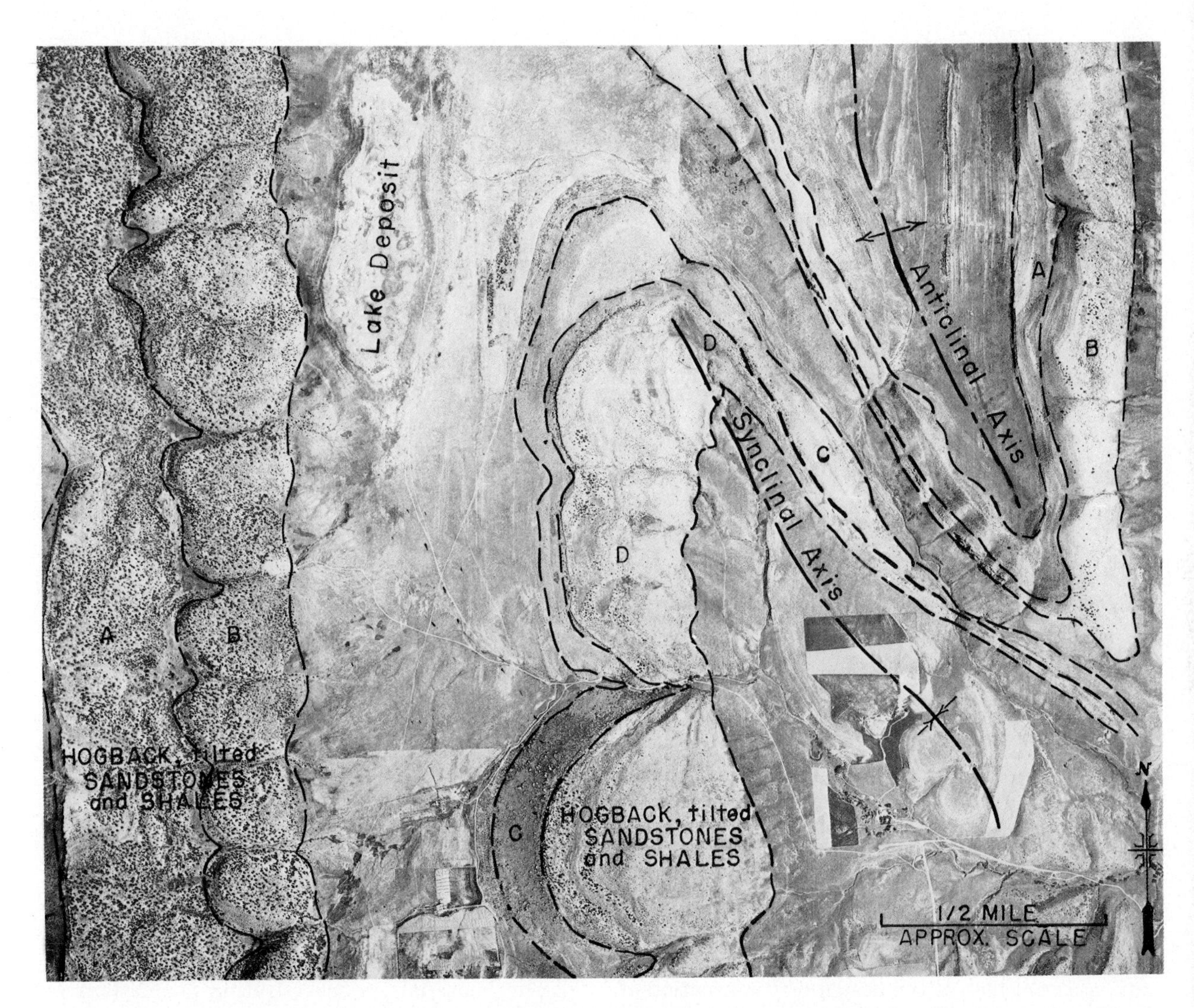

Figure 5-5.—Rock strata illustrating folding in sedimentary rocks. (A) Satanka formation, (B) Lyons formation, (C) Morrison formation, and (D) Lower and Middle Dakota formation. (U.S. Forest Service). PX–D–16265.

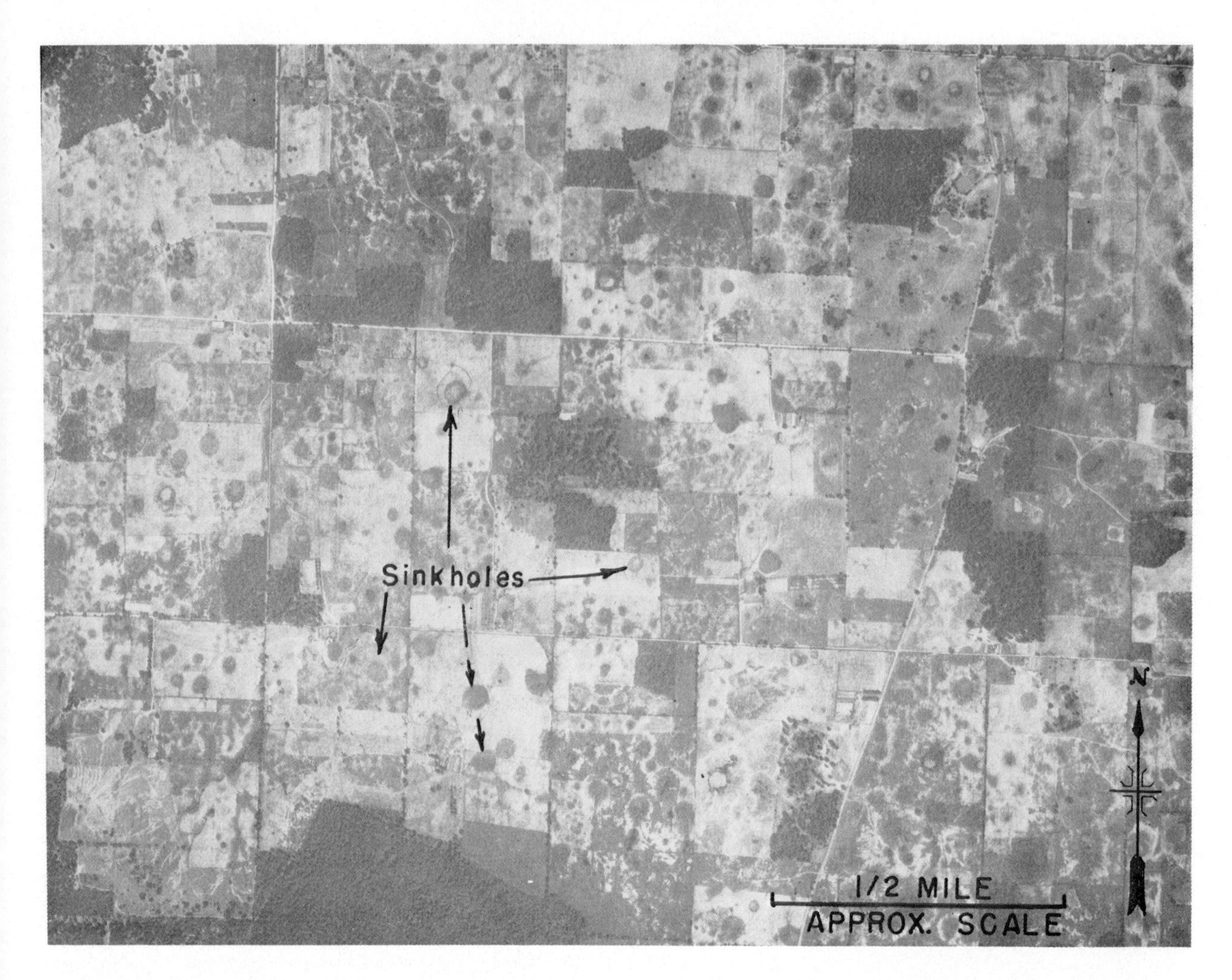

Figure 5-6.—Sinkhole plain indicating deep plastic soils over cavernous limestone, developed in humid climate. (U.S. Agricultural Stabilization and Conservation Service). PX–D–16264.

D. SOIL CLASSIFICATION

5.13. *General.*—In engineering applications, soil may be defined as generally nonindurated accumulations of solid particles produced by the physical and/or chemical disintegration of bedrock, and which may or may not contain organic matter. To engineers engaged in the design or construction of foundations and earthwork for dams, the physical properties of soils, such as unit weight, permeability, shear strength, and compressibility, and their interaction with water are of primary importance.

It is advantageous to have a standard method of identifying soils and classifying them into categories or groups that have distinct engineering properties. This enables engineers in the design office and those engaged in field work to speak the same language, thus facilitating the exchange of information. Knowledge of soil classification, including the typical engineering properties of the various soil groups, is especially valuable to engineers exploring materials or investigating foundations for structures. To a limited extent, soil classifications can be used for appraisal estimates of the engineering characteristics of soils intended for use in small dams.

In 1952, the Bureau of Reclamation and the Corps of Engineers, with Professor Arthur Casagrande of Harvard University as consultant, agreed on a modification of Professor Casagrande's airfield classification, which they named the "Unified Soil Classification System." This system which is particularly applicable to the design and construction of dams, takes into account the engineering properties of soils, is descriptive and easy to associate with actual soils, and has the flexibility of being adaptable to both field and laboratory applications. Probably its greatest advantage is that a soil can be classified readily by visual and manual examination without laboratory testing. The USCS (Unified Soil Classification System) is based on the size of the particles, the amounts of the various sizes, and the characteristics of the very fine grains. Laboratory classification is discussed in more detail in USBR 5000, and the visual classification of soils is discussed in USBR 5005, both in the Bureau's *Earth Manual* [7].

A soil mass consists of solid particles and pore fluids. The solid particles generally are mineral grains of various sizes and shapes, occurring in every conceivable arrangement. These solid particles can be divided into various components, each of which contributes its share to the physical properties of the whole. Soil classification can best be understood by first considering the properties of these soil components. Accordingly, sections 5.14, 5.15, and 5.16 describe the constituents of soil and introduce the concepts used in the system. Section 5.17 gives the essentials of the classification system for soils found in nature, as shown in the Unified Soil Classification Chart (fig. 5-12). Figure 5-4 gives a comparison of the particle size scales for the Unified, AASHTO, and USDA soil classification systems. In addition to proper classification, it is important to include an adequate description of the soil in reports or logs of explorations. The classification chart contains information required for describing soils and includes examples. Additional information on soil descriptions is given in part J. Section 5.18 contains a comparison of the engineering properties of typical soils of each classification group.

5.14. *Soil Components.*—(a) *Size.*—Particles larger than 3 inches are excluded from the USCS. The amount of each oversized material, however, may be important in the selection of sources for embankment material. Therefore, logs of explorations always contain information on the quantity and size of particles larger than 3 inches. For definitions of terms for materials larger than 3 inches (cobbles and boulders) see appendix D.

Within the size range of the system there are two major divisions: coarse grains and fine grains. Coarse grains are those larger than the No. 200 sieve size (0.075 mm), and they are further divided as follows:

- Gravel (G), 3 inches to No. 4 (3/16 inch):
  - Coarse gravel, 3 inches to 3/4 inch
  - Fine gravel, 3/4 inch to No. 4 sieve
- Sand (S), No. 4 to No. 200 sieve:
  - Coarse sand, No. 4 to No. 10 sieve
  - Medium sand, No. 10 to No. 40 sieve
  - Fine sand, No. 40 to No. 200 sieve

For visual classification, 1/4 inch is considered equivalent to the No. 4 sieve size, and the No. 200 size is about the smallest size of particles that can be distinguished individually by the unaided eye.

Fines smaller than the No. 200 size consist of two types: silt (M) and clay(C). Older classification systems defined clay variously as those particles smaller than 0.005 millimeters or 0.002 millimeters, and they defined silt as fines larger than clay particles (see fig. 5-4). It is a mistake, however, to think that the typical engineering characteristics of silt and clay correspond to their grain sizes. Natural deposits of rock flour that exhibit all the properties of silt and none of clay may consist entirely of grains smaller than 0.005 millimeters. On the other hand, typical clays may consist mainly of particles larger than 0.005 millimeters, but may contain small quantities of extremely fine, colloidal-sized particles. In the USCS, the distinction between silt and clay is not made by particle size, but rather by their behavior.

Organic material (O) is often a component of soil, but it has no specific grain size. It is distinguished by the composition of its particles rather than by their sizes, which range from colloidal-sized particles of molecular dimensions to fibrous pieces of partly decomposed vegetation several inches in length.

(b) *Gradation.*—The amounts of the various sizes of grains in a soil can be determined in the laboratory by sieve analysis for the coarse grains, and by hydrometer analysis for the fines, as described in section 5-49(a). The laboratory results are usually presented in the form of a cumulative grain-size curve. The grain-size distribution reveals something about the physical properties of soils consisting mainly of coarse grains. However, the grain size is much less significant for soils containing mostly fine grains.

Typical gradations of soils are:

- Well-graded (W), good representation of all particle sizes from largest to smallest
- Poorly graded (P), uniform gradation (most particles are about the same size); or skip (gap) gradation (one or more intermediate sizes are absent)

In the field, soil is estimated to be well-graded or poorly graded by visual examination. For laboratory purposes the type of gradation can be determined by the use of criteria based on the range of sizes and on the shape of the grain-size curve. The measure of size range is called the coefficient of uniformity, Cu, which is the ratio of the 60-percent-finer-than size (D_{60}) to the 10-percent-finer-than size (D_{10}). The shape of the grain-size curve is indicated by the coefficient of curvature, Cc, which equals $(D_{30})^2/(D_{60})(D_{10})$, where D_{30} is the 30-percent-finer-than size. A typical gradation curve is shown on figure 5-7.

(c) *Angularity.*—The angularity of the individual soil particles can affect the physical properties of a soil. Angularity of particles are described as rounded, subrounded, subangular, and angular. These ranges of angularity are shown on figure 5-8. A range of angularity may be used, for example, "subrounded to rounded."

(d) *Shape.*—Shape is distinct from angularity and can have a significant effect on the engineering and the physical properties of a soil. The shape of the gravel, cobbles, and boulder portion of a soil are described as flat, elongated, or flat and elongated. Otherwise, no mention of shape is required. The fraction of the particles having a particular shape should be indicated, for example, "one-third of the gravel particles are flat."

5.15. *Soil Moisture.*—A typical soil mass has three constituents: soil grains, air, and water. In soils consisting largely of fine grains, the amount of water present in the voids has a pronounced effect on the soil properties. Three main states of fine soil consistency, which are dependent upon the moisture content, are recognizable:

1. Liquid state, in which the soil is either in suspension or behaves like a viscous fluid
2. Plastic state, in which the soil can be rapidly deformed or molded without rebounding elastically, changing volume, cracking or crumbling
3. Solid state, in which the soil will crack when deformed or will exhibit elastic rebound.

In describing these soil states it is customary to consider only the fraction of soil smaller than the No. 40 sieve size (the upper limit of the fine sand component). For this soil fraction, the water content in percentage of dry weight at which the soil passes from the liquid state to a plastic state is called the liquid limit (LL). A device (fig. 5-9) that causes the soil to flow under certain conditions is used in the laboratory to determine the liquid limit as described in section 5.49(c). Similarly, the water content of the soil at the boundary between the plastic state and the solid state is called the plastic limit (PL). The laboratory test described in section 5.49(c) consists of repeatedly rolling threads of the soil to ⅛-inch diameter until they crumble, and then determining the water content (fig. 5-10).

The difference between the liquid limit and the plastic limit corresponds to the range of water contents within which the soil is plastic. This difference of water content is called the plasticity index (PI). Soils with high plasticity have high PI values. In a nonplastic soil the plastic limit and the liquid limit are the same and the PI equals 0.

These limits of consistency, which are called "Atterberg limits" after a Swedish scientist, are used in the USCS as the basis for laboratory differentiation between materials of appreciable plasticity (clays) and slightly plastic or nonplastic materials (silts), as shown on figure 5-12. With sufficient experience a soils engineer may acquire the ability to estimate the Atterberg limits of a soil. However, three simple hand tests have been found adequate for field identification and classification of fine soils and for determining whether fine-grained fraction of a soil is silty or clayey, without requiring estimation of Atterberg limits. These hand tests, which are part of the field procedure in the Unified Soil Classification System (see USBR 5005 [7]), are tests of:

- Dilatancy (reaction to shaking)
- Dry strength (crushing characteristics)
- Toughness (consistency near plastic limit)

They are discussed in the following section.

5.16. *Properties of Soil Components.*—

(a) *Gravel and Sand.*—Both coarse-grained soils (gravel and sand) have similar engineering properties, that differ mainly in degree. The division of gravel and sand sizes by the No. 4 sieve is arbitrary and does not correspond to a sharp change in properties. Well-graded, compacted gravels or sands are stable materials. Coarse-grained soils that are devoid of fines are pervious, easy to compact, affected little by moisture, and not subject to frost action.

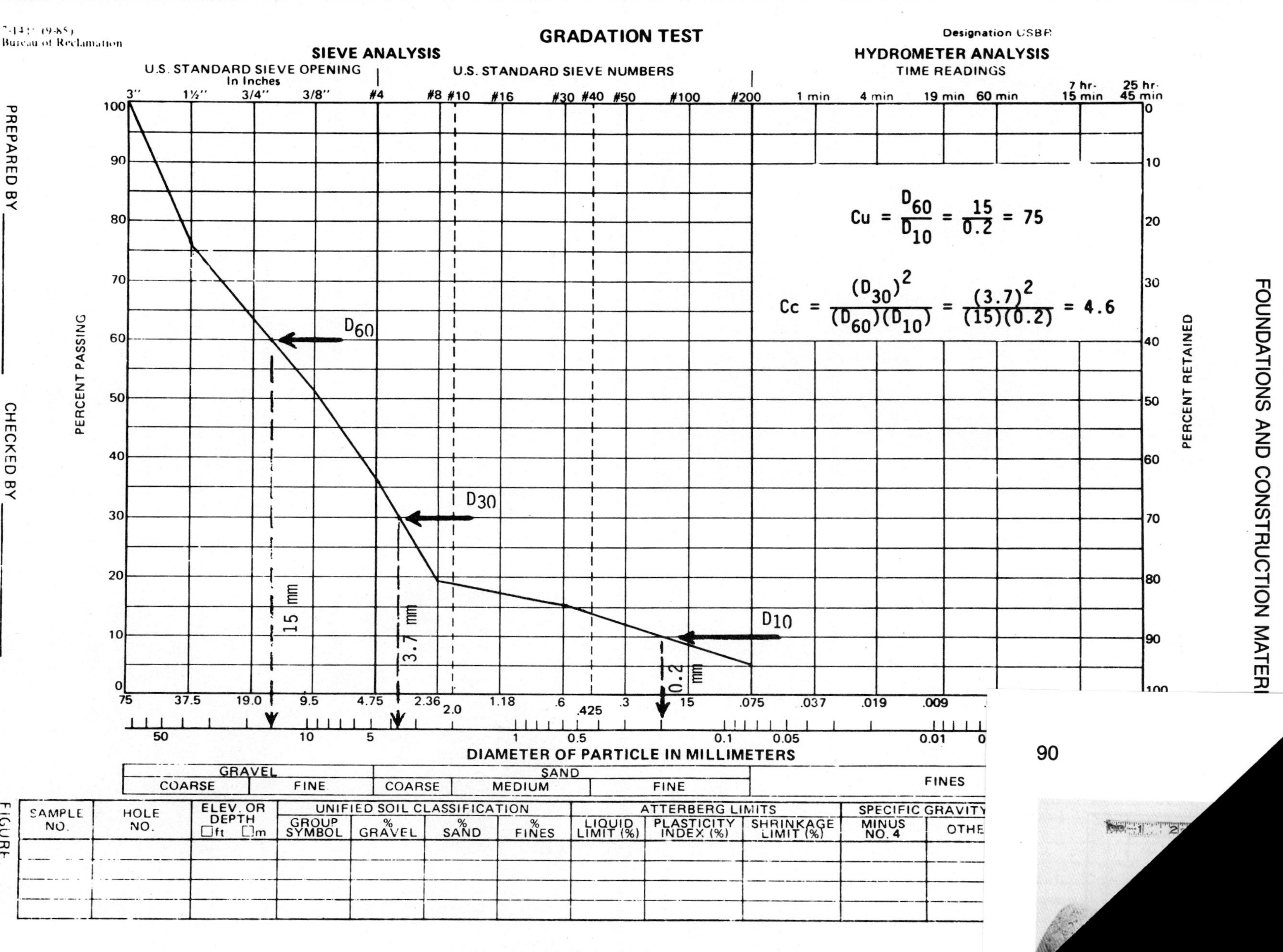

Figure 5-7.—Typical soil gradation curve.

Figure 5-8.—Typical angularity of bulky grains. PX-D-16266.

Figure 5-9.—Test for liquid limit. PX-D-17009.

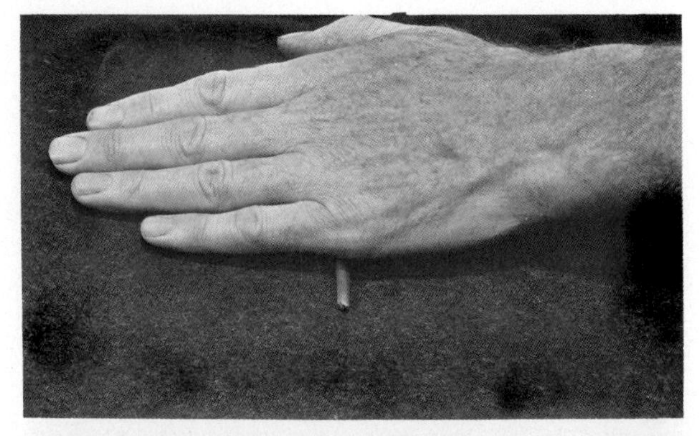

Figure 5-10.—Test for plastic limit. PX-D-16530.

Although grain shape and gradation, as well as size, affect these properties, gravels are generally more pervious, more stable, and less affected by water or frost than are sands, for the same amount of fines.

As a sand becomes finer and more uniform, its characteristics approach those of silt, with corresponding decreases in permeability and reduction in stability in the presence of water. Very fine, uniform sands are difficult to distinguish visually from silt. Dried sand, however, exhibits no cohesion and feels gritty, in contrast with the very slight cohesion and smooth feel of dried silt.

(b) *Silt and Clay.*—Even small amounts of fines can have significant effects on the engineering properties of soils. If as little as 10 percent of the particles in sand and gravel are smaller than the No. 200 sieve size, the soil can be virtually impervious, especially when the coarse grains are well-graded. Moreover, serious frost heaving in well-graded sands and gravels can be caused by fines making up less than 10 percent of the total soil weight. The utility of coarse-grained materials for surfacing roads can be improved by the addition of a small amount of clay to act as a binder for the sand and gravel particles.

Soils containing large quantities of silt and clay are the most troublesome to the engineer. These materials exhibit marked changes in physical properties with changes in water content. A hard, dry clay, for example, may be suitable as a foundation for heavy loads so long as it remains dry, but it may become unstable when wet. Many of the fine soils shrink on drying and expand on wetting, which may adversely affect structures founded upon them or constructed of them. Even when the water content does not change, the properties of fine soils may vary considerably between their natural condition in the ground and their state after being disturbed. Deposits of fine particles that have been subjected to loading in geologic time frequently have a structure that gives the material unique properties in the undisturbed state. When the soil is excavated for use as a construction material or when the natural deposit is disturbed, for example by driving piles, the soil structure is destroyed and the properties of the soil are changed radically.

Silts are different from clays in many important respects, but because of their similar appearance, they are often mistaken for each other, sometimes with unfortunate results. Dry, powdered silt and clay are indistinguishable, but they are easily identified by their behavior in the presence of water. Recognition of fines as either silt or clay is an essential part of the USCS.

Silts are the nonplastic fines. They are inherently unstable in the presence of water and have a tendency to become "quick" when saturated; that is, they assume the character of a viscous fluid and can flow. Silts are fairly impervious, difficult to compact, and highly susceptible to frost heaving. Silt masses undergo change of volume with change of shape (the property of dilatancy), in contrast with clays, which retain their volume with change of shape (the property of plasticity). The dilatancy of silt together with its quick reaction to vibration affords a means of identifying typical silt in the loose, wet state. The dilatancy test is illustrated by the photographs on figure 5-11, and is described in more detail in USBR 5005 [7]. When dry, silt can be pulverized easily under finger pressure (indicative of very slight dry strength), and has a smooth feel between the fingers unlike the grittiness of fine sand.

Silts differ among themselves in size and shape of grains. This is reflected mainly in the property of compressibility. Generally, the higher the liquid limit of a silt, the more compressible it is. The liquid limit of a typical bulky-grained, inorganic silt is about 30 percent; whereas, highly micaceous or diatomaceous silts (elastic silts), consisting mainly of flaky grains, may have liquid limits as high as 100 percent.

(A) REACTION TO SHAKING.

(B) REACTION TO SQUEEZING.

Figure 5-11.—Dilatancy test for silt. PX-D-16335.

Clays are the plastic fines. They have low resistance to deformation when wet, but they dry to hard, cohesive masses. Clays are virtually impervious, difficult to compact when wet, and impossible to drain by ordinary means. Large expansion and contraction with changes in water content are characteristics of clays. The small size, flat shape, and mineral composition of clay particles combine to produce a material that is both compressible and plastic. Generally, the higher the liquid limit of a clay, the more compressible it will be. Therefore, in the USCS, the liquid limit is used to differentiate

CRITERIA FOR ASSIGNING GROUP SYMBOLS AND GROUP NAMES USING LABORATORY TESTS [a]				SOIL CLASSIFICATION	
				GROUP SYMBOL	GROUP NAME [b]
COARSE-GRAINED SOILS more than 50% retained on No. 200 sieve	GRAVELS More than 50% of coarse fraction retained on No. 4 sieve	CLEAN GRAVELS Less than 5% fines [c]	Cu $\geq$ 4 and 1 $\leq$ Cc $\leq$ 3 [e]	GW	Well-graded gravel [f]
			Cu < 4 and/or 1 > Cc > 3 [e]	GP	Poorly graded gravel [f]
		GRAVELS WITH FINES More than 12% fines [c]	Fines classify as ML or MH	GM	Silty gravel [f,g,h]
			Fines classify as CL or CH	GC	Clayey gravel [f,g,h]
	SANDS 50% or more of coarse fraction passes No. 4 sieve	CLEAN SANDS Less than 5% fines [d]	Cu $\geq$ 6 and 1 $\leq$ Cc $\leq$ 3 [e]	SW	Well-graded sand [i]
			Cu < 6 and/or 1 > Cc > 3 [e]	SP	Poorly graded sand [i]
		SANDS WITH FINES More than 12% fines [d]	Fines classify as ML or MH	SM	Silty sand [g,h,i]
			Fines classify as CL or CH	SC	Clayey sand [g,h,i]
FINE-GRAINED SOILS 50% or more passes the No. 200 sieve	SILTS AND CLAYS Liquid limit less than 50	inorganic	PI > 7 and plots on or above "A" line [j]	CL	Lean clay [k,l,m]
			PI < 4 or plots below "A" line [j]	ML	Silt [k,l,m]
		organic	$\frac{\text{Liquid limit - oven dried}}{\text{Liquid limit - not dried}} < 0.75$	OL	Organic clay [k,l,m,n] Organic silt [k,l,m,o]
	SILTS AND CLAYS Liquid limit 50 or more	inorganic	PI plots on or above "A" line	CH	Fat clay [k,l,m]
			PI plots below "A" line	MH	Elastic silt [k,l,m]
		organic	$\frac{\text{Liquid limit - oven dried}}{\text{Liquid limit - not dried}} < 0.75$	OH	Organic clay [k,l,m,p] Organic silt [k,l,m,q]
Highly organic soils		Primarily organic matter, dark in color, and organic odor		PT	Peat

a. Based on the material passing the 3-in (75-mm) sieve.
b. If field sample contained cobbles and/or boulders, add "with cobbles and/or boulders" to group name.
c. Gravels with 5 to 12% fines require dual symbols
 GW-GM well-graded gravel with silt
 GW-GC well-graded gravel with clay
 GP-GM poorly graded gravel with silt
 GP-GC poorly graded gravel with clay
d. Sands with 5 to 12% fines require dual symbols
 SW-SM well-graded sand with silt
 SW-SC well-graded sand with clay
 SP-SM poorly graded sand with silt
 SP-SC poorly graded sand with clay

e. $Cu = D_{60}/D_{10}$ $\quad Cc = \frac{(D_{30})^2}{D_{10} \times D_{60}}$

f. If soil contains $\geq$ 15% sand, add "with sand" to group name.
g. If fines classify as CL-ML, use dual symbol GC-GM, SC-SM.
h. If fines are organic, add "with organic fines" to group name.
i. If soil contains $\geq$ 15% gravel, add "with gravel" to group name.
j. If the liquid limit and plasticity index plot in hatched area on plasticity chart, soil is a CL-ML, silty clay.
k. If soil contains 15 to 29% plus No. 200, add "with sand" or "with gravel" whichever is predominant.
l. If soil contains $\geq$ 30% plus No. 200, predominantly sand, add "sandy" to group name.
m. If soil contains $\geq$ 30% plus No. 200, predominantly gravel, add "gravelly" to group name.
n. PI $\geq$ 4 and plots on or above "A" line.
o. PI < 4 or plots below "A" line.
p. PI plots on or above "A" line.
q. PI plots below "A" line.

Figure 5-12.—Soil classification chart (laboratory method). (Sheet 1 of 2).

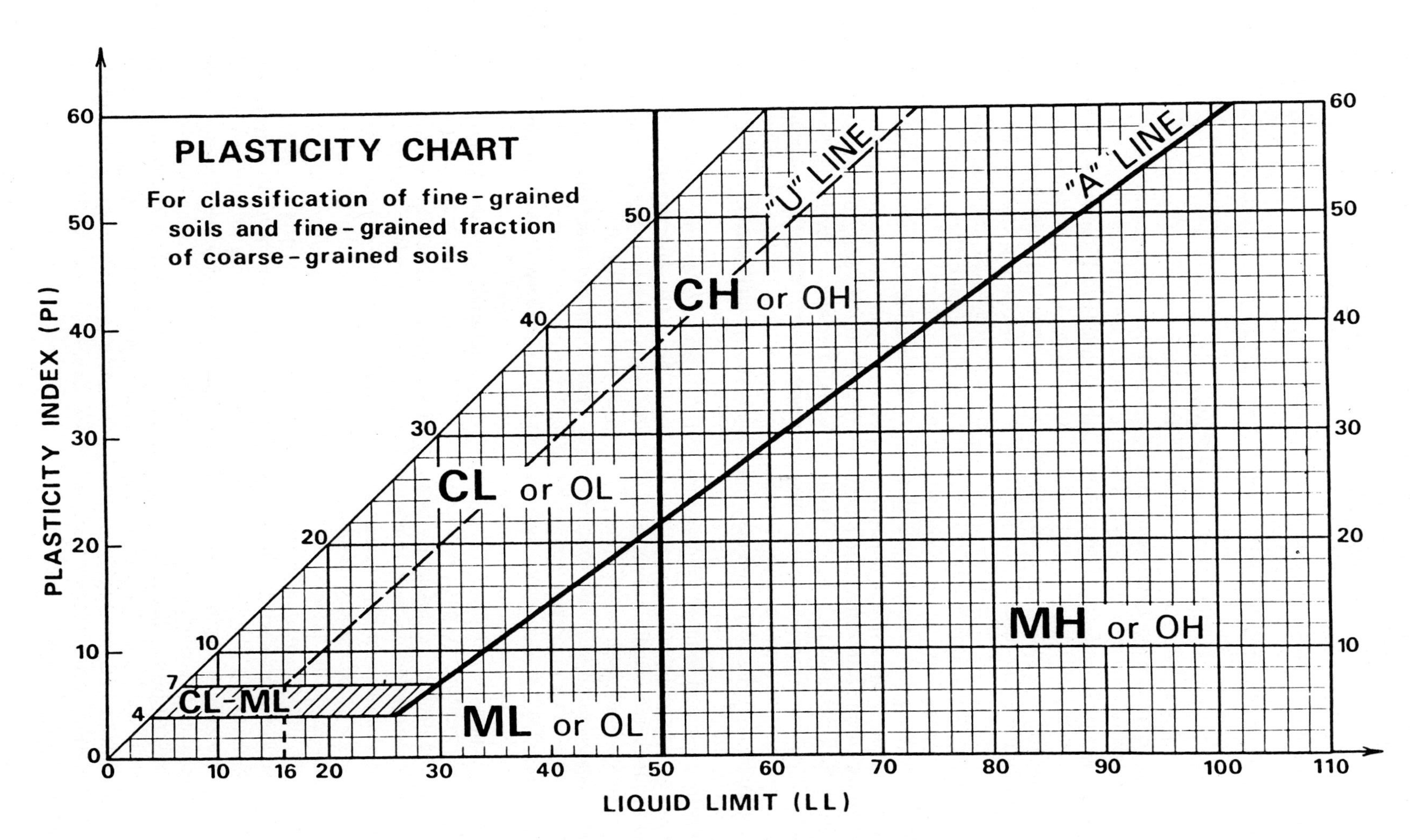

Figure 5-12.—Soil classification chart (laboratory method). (Sheet 2 of 2).

between clays of high compressibility (H) and those of low compressibility (L). Differences in the plasticity of clays are reflected by their plasticity indexes. At the same liquid limit, the higher the plasticity index, the more cohesive the clay.

Field differentiation among clays is accomplished by the toughness test, in which the moist soil is molded and rolled into threads until crumbling occurs, and by the dry strength test, which measures the resistance of the clay to breaking and pulverizing. The toughness and the dry strength are described in detail in USBR 5005 [7]. With a little experience in performing these tests, the clays of low compressibility and low plasticity, lean clays (L), can be readily differentiated from the highly plastic, highly compressible fat clays (H).

(c) *Organic Material.*—Organic material in the form of partly decomposed vegetation is the primary constituent of peaty soils. Varying amounts of finely divided vegetation are found in plastic and in nonplastic sediments and often affect their properties sufficiently to influence their classification. Thus, there are organic silts and clays of low plasticity and organic silts and clays of medium to high plasticity. Even small amounts of organic material in colloidal form in a clay will result in an appreciable increase in the liquid limit of the material without increasing its plasticity index. Organic soils are dark gray or black and usually have a characteristic odor of decay. Organic clays feel spongy in the plastic range as compared with inorganic clays. The tendency for soils high in organic content to create voids as a result of decay or to change the physical characteristics of a soil mass through chemical alteration makes them undesirable for engineering use. Soils containing even moderate amounts of organic matter are significantly more compressible and less stable than inorganic soils and, therefore, are undesirable for engineering use.

5.17. *Unified Soil Classification System.*—

(a) *General.*—Soils in nature seldom exist separately as gravel, sand, silt, clay, or organic material, but are usually found as mixtures with varying proportions of these components. The USCS is based on recognition of the type and predominance of these soil components, considering grain size, gradation, plasticity, and compressibility. The system divides soil into three major divisions: coarse-grained soils, fine-grained soils, and highly organic (peaty) soils. In the field, identification is accomplished by visual examination for the coarse grains and by a few simple hand tests for the fine-grained soils or portion of soils. In the laboratory the grain-size curve and the Atterberg limits can be used. The organic soils (Pt) are readily identified by color, odor, spongy feel, and fibrous texture, and are not further subdivided in the classification system.

(b) *Field Classification.*—A representative sample of soil (excluding particles larger than 3 inches) is first classified as coarse-grained or as fine-grained by estimating whether 50 percent, by dry mass, of the particles can be seen individually by the unaided eye. If the soil is predominantly coarse-grained (at least 50 percent of particles can be seen by eye), it is then identified as being a gravel or a sand by estimating whether 50 percent or more, by mass, of the coarse grain material is larger (gravel) or smaller (sand) than the No. 4 sieve size (about ¼ inch).

If the soil is a gravel, it is next identified as being either "clean" (containing little or no fines) or "dirty" (containing an appreciable amount of fines). For clean gravels the final classification is made by estimating the gradation: the well-graded gravels belong to the GW group, and the uniform and skip-graded gravels belong to the GP group. Dirty gravels are of two types: those with nonplastic (silty) fines (GM) and those with plastic (clayey) fines (GC). The determination of whether the fines are silty or clayey is made using the three manual tests for fine-grained soils.

For sands the same steps and criteria are used as for gravels to determine whether the soil is a well-graded sand (SW), poorly graded sand (SP), sand with silty fines (SM), or sand with clayey fines (SC).

If a material is predominantly (more than 50 percent by weight) fine-grained, it is classified into one of six groups (ML, CL, OL, MH, CH, OH) by estimating its dilatancy (reaction of shaking), dry strength (crushing characteristics), and toughness (consistency near the plastic limit), and by identifying it is as organic or inorganic.

Soils typical of the various groups are readily classified by the above procedures. Many natural soils, however, have property characteristics of two groups because they are close to the borderline between the groups either in percentages of the various sizes or in plasticity characteristics. For these soils, boderline classifications are used; that is, the two group symbols most nearly describing the soil are given, such as GC/SC.

5.18. *Engineering Characteristics of Soil Groups.*—(a) *General.*—Although there is no substitute for thorough testing to determine the important engineering properties of a particular soil, approximate values for typical soils of each USCS group can be given as a result of statistical analysis of available data (table 5-1). The attempt to put soils data into quantitative form involves the risk of (1) the data not being representative, and (2) using the values in design without adequate safety factors. In the early stages of planning, when different borrow areas and design sections are being studied, these averaged values of soil properties can be taken as useful qualitative guides. Because the values pertain to the soil groups, proper soil classification becomes of vital importance. Verification of field identification by laboratory gradation and Atterberg limits tests for design must be made on representative samples of each soil group encountered.

Table 5-1 is a summary of values obtained from more than 1,500 soil tests performed between 1960 and 1982 in the engineering laboratories of the Bureau of Reclamation in Denver, Colorado. The data, which were obtained from reports for which laboratory soil classifications were available, are arranged according to the USCS groups. The soils are from the 17 Western States in which the Bureau operates. Although the sampling area of the soils tested is limited, it is believed that the USCS is relatively insensitive to geographical distribution. The procedure for determining which of the many submitted samples should be tested was conducive to obtaining a representative range of values because samples were selected from the coarsest, the finest, and the average soil from each source.

For each soil property listed, the average, the standard deviation, the number of tests performed, the minimum test value, and the maximum test value are listed in table 5-1. Because all laboratory tests, except large-sized permeability tests, were made on compacted specimens of the minus No. 4 fraction of the soil, data on average values for the gravels were not available for most properties. The averages shown are subject to uncertainties that may arise from sampling fluctuations, and tend to vary widely from the true averages when the number of tests is small.

The values for laboratory maximum dry unit weight, optimum moisture content, specific gravity, and maximum and minimum index unit weight were obtained by tests described in section 5.49. The MH and CH soil groups have no upper boundary of liquid limits in the classification; therefore, it is necessary to give the range of those soils included in the table. The maximum liquid limits for the MH and the CH soils tested were 82 and 86 percent, respectively. Soils with higher liquid limits than these have inferior engineering properties.

(b) *Shear Strength.*—Two shear strength parameters are given for the soil groups under the headings c' and ϕ'. The values of c' and ϕ' are the vertical intercept and the angle of the envelope, respectively, of the Mohr strength envelope on an effective stress basis. (The Mohr plot is shown on fig. 5-13). The Mohr strength envelope is obtained by testing several specimens of compacted soil in a triaxial shear apparatus in which pore-fluid pressures developed during the test are measured.

The effective stresses are obtained by subtracting the measured pore-fluid pressures in the specimen from the stresses applied by the apparatus. The data used in compiling the values in table 5-1 are taken from UU (unconsolidated-undrained) and CU (consolidated-undrained) triaxial shear tests with pore-fluid pressure measurements and from CD (consolidated-drained) triaxial shear tests.

These values for shear strength are applicable for use in Coulomb's equation:

$$s = c' + (\sigma - \mu) \tan \phi' \qquad (1)$$

where:

s = shear strength,
u = pore-fluid pressure,
σ = applied normal stress,
ϕ' = effective angle of internal friction, and
c' = effective cohesion.

A discussion of the significance of pore-fluid pressure in the laboratory tests is beyond the scope of this text. The application of pore-pressure measurements to the shear strength of cohesive soils is discussed in [7]. The effective-stress principle, which takes the pore-fluid pressures into account, was used in arriving at recommended slopes given in chapter 6.

(c) *Permeability.*—The voids in the soil mass provide passages through which water can move. Such passages vary in size, and the paths of flow are tortuous and interconnected. If, however, a sufficiently large number of paths of flow are considered as acting together, an average rate of flow for

Table 5-1.—Average engineering properties of compacted soils. From the Western United States. Last updated October 6, 1982.

USCS soil type	Specific gravity		Compaction: Laboratory		Compaction: Index unit weight		Shear strength: Avg. placement		Shear strength: Effective stress		Values listed
	No. 4 minus	No. 4 plus	Maximum unit weight, lb/ft³	Optimum moisture content, %	Max., lb/ft³	Min., lb/ft³	Unit weight, lb/ft³	Moisture, content, %	c′ lb/in²	φ′, degrees	
GW	2.69	2.58	124.2	11.4	133.6	108.8	—	—	—	—	Average of all values
	0.02	0.08	3.2	1.2	10.4	10.2	—	—	—	—	Standard deviation
	2.65	2.39	119.1	9.9	113.0	88.5	—	—	—	—	Minimum value
	2.75	2.67	127.5	13.3	145.6	132.9	—	—	—	—	Maximum value
	16	9	5		16		0				Total number of tests
GP	2.68	2.57	121.7	11.2	137.2	112.5	127.5	6.5	5.9	41.4	Average of all values
	0.03	0.07	5.9	2.2	6.3	8.3	7.2	1.2	—	2.5	Standard deviation
	2.61	2.42	104.9	9.1	118.3	85.9	117.4	5.3	5.9	38.0	Minimum value
	2.76	2.65	127.7	17.7	148.8	123.7	133.9	8.0	5.9	43.7	Maximum value
	35	12	15		34		3				Total number of tests
GM	2.73	2.43	113.3	15.8	132.0	108.0	125.9	10.3	13.4	34.0	Average of all values
	0.07	0.18	11.5	5.8	3.1	0.2	0.9	1.2	3.7	2.6	Standard deviation
	2.65	2.19	87.0	5.8	128.9	107.8	125.0	9.1	9.7	31.4	Minimum value
	2.92	2.92	133.0	29.5	135.1	108.1	126.9	11.5	17.0	36.5	Maximum value
	34	17	36		2		2				Total number of tests
GC	2.73	2.57	116.6	13.9	—	—	111.1	15.9	10.2	27.5	Average of all values
	0.08	0.21	7.8	3.8	—	—	10.4	1.6	1.5	7.2	Standard deviation
	2.67	2.38	96.0	6.0	—	—	96.8	11.2	5.0	17.7	Minimum value
	3.11	2.94	129.0	23.6	—	—	120.9	22.2	16.0	35.0	Maximum value
	34	6	37		0		3				Total number of tests
SW	2.67	2.57	126.1	9.1	125.0	99.5	—	—	—	—	Average of all values
	0.03	0.03	6.0	1.7	6.0	7.1	—	—	—	—	Standard deviation
	2.61	2.51	118.1	7.4	116.7	87.4	—	—	—	—	Minimum value
	2.72	2.59	135.0	11.2	137.8	109.8	—	—	—	—	Maximum value
	13	2	1		12		0				Total number of tests
SP	2.65	2.62	115.6	10.8	115.1	93.4	103.4	5.4	5.5	37.4	Average of all values
	0.03	0.10	9.7	2.0	7.2	8.8	14.6	—	3.0	2.0	Standard deviation
	2.60	2.52	106.5	7.8	105.9	78.2	88.8	5.4	2.5	35.4	Minimum value
	2.77	2.75	134.8	13.4	137.3	122.4	118.1	5.4	8.4	39.4	Maximum value
	36	3	7		39		2				Total number of tests
SM	2.68	2.18	116.6	12.5	110.1	84.9	112.0	12.7	6.6	33.6	Average of all values
	0.06	0.11	8.9	3.4	8.7	7.9	11.1	5.4	5.6	5.7	Standard deviation
	2.51	2.24	92.9	6.8	88.5	61.6	91.1	1.6	0.2	23.3	Minimum value
	3.11	2.63	132.6	25.5	122.9	97.1	132.5	25.0	21.2	45.0	Maximum value
	149	9	123		21		17				Total number of tests
SC	2.69	2.17	118.9	12.4	—	—	115.6	14.2	5.0	33.9	Average of all values
	0.04	0.18	5.9	2.3	—	—	14.1	5.7	2.5	2.9	Standard deviation
	2.56	2.17	104.3	6.7	—	—	91.1	7.5	0.7	28.4	Minimum value
	2.81	2.59	131.7	18.2	—	—	131.8	22.7	8.5	38.3	Maximum value
	88	4	73		0		10				Total number of tests
ML	2.69	—	103.3	19.7	—	—	98.9	22.1	3.6	34.0	Average of all values
	0.09	—	10.4	5.7	—	—	11.5	8.9	4.3	3.1	Standard deviation
	2.52	—	81.6	10.6	—	—	80.7	11.1	0.1	25.2	Minimum value
	3.10	—	126.0	34.6	—	—	119.3	40.3	11.9	37.7	Maximum value
	65	0	39		0		14				Total number of tests
CL	2.71	2.59	109.3	16.7	—	—	106.5	17.7	10.3	25.1	Average of all values
	0.05	0.13	5.5	2.9	—	—	7.8	5.1	7.6	7.0	Standard deviation
	2.56	2.42	90.0	6.4	—	—	85.6	11.6	0.9	8.0	Minimum value
	2.87	2.75	121.4	29.2	—	—	118.7	35.0	23.8	33.8	Maximum value
	270	3	221		0		31				Total number of tests
MH	2.79	—	85.1	33.6	—	—	—	—	—	—	Average of all values
	0.25	—	2.3	1.6	—	—	—	—	—	—	Standard deviation
	2.47	—	82.9	31.5	—	—	—	—	—	—	Minimum value
	3.50	—	89.0	35.5	—	—	—	—	—	—	Maximum value
	10	0	5		0		0				Total number of tests

Table 5-1.—Average engineering properties of compacted soils. From the Western United States. Last updated October 6, 1982. —Continued.

USCS soil type	Specific gravity		Compaction				Shear strength				Values listed
			Laboratory		Index unit weight		Avg. placement		Effective stress		
	No. 4 minus	No. 4 plus	Maximum unit weight, lb/ft^3	Optimum moisture content, %	Max., lb/ft^3	Min., lb/ft^3	Unit weight, lb/ft^3	Moisture, content, %	c' lb/in^2	ϕ', degrees	
	2.73	—	95.3	25.0	—	—	93.6	25.7	11.5	16.8	Average of all values
	0.06	—	6.6	5.4	—	—	8.1	5.7	7.4	7.2	Standard deviation
CH	2.51	—	82.3	16.6	—	—	79.3	17.9	1.5	4.0	Minimum value
	2.89	—	107.3	41.8	—	—	104.9	35.3	21.5	27.5	Maximum value
	74	0	36		0		12				Total number of tests

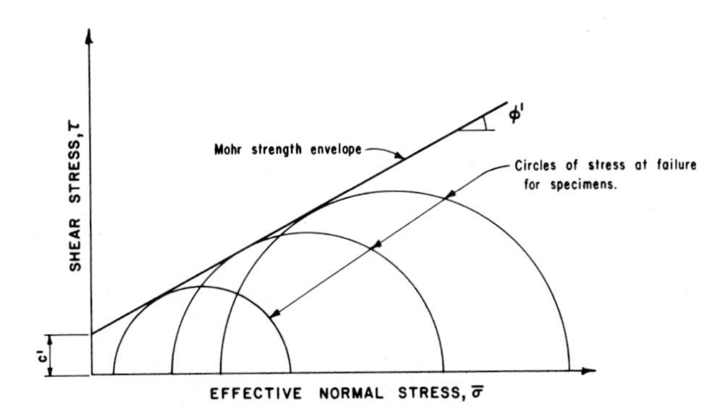

Figure 5-13.—Shear strength of compacted soils. 288-D-2474.

the soil mass can be determined under controlled conditions that will represent a property of the soil.

In 1856, H. Darcy showed experimentally that the rate of flow of water, q, through a soil specimen of cross-sectional area A was directly proportional to the imposed hydraulic gradient ($i = \Delta h/L$) or $q = kiA$. The coefficient of proportionality, k, has been called "Darcy's coefficient of permeability," "coefficient of permeability" (also referred to as hydraulic conductivity) or "permeability." Permeability is the soil property that indicates the ease with which water will flow through the soil. The use of k in estimating flow through soils is discussed in section 6.9(b). Many units of measurement are commonly used for expressing the coefficient of permeability. The units used on figure 5-14 are feet per year (or cubic feet per square foot per year at unit gradient). One foot per year is virtually equal to 10^{-6} cm/s.

Permeability in some soils is very sensitive to small changes in unit weight, water content, or gradation. Because of the possible wide variation in permeability, the numerical value of k should be considered only as an order of magnitude. It is customary in the Bureau of Reclamation to describe soils with permeabilities less than 1 ft/yr as impervious; those with permeabilities between 1 and 100 ft/yr as semipervious; and soils with permeabilities greater than 100 ft/yr as pervious. These values, however, are not absolute for the design of dams. Successful structures have been built whose various zones were constructed of soils with permeabilities not within these respective ranges.

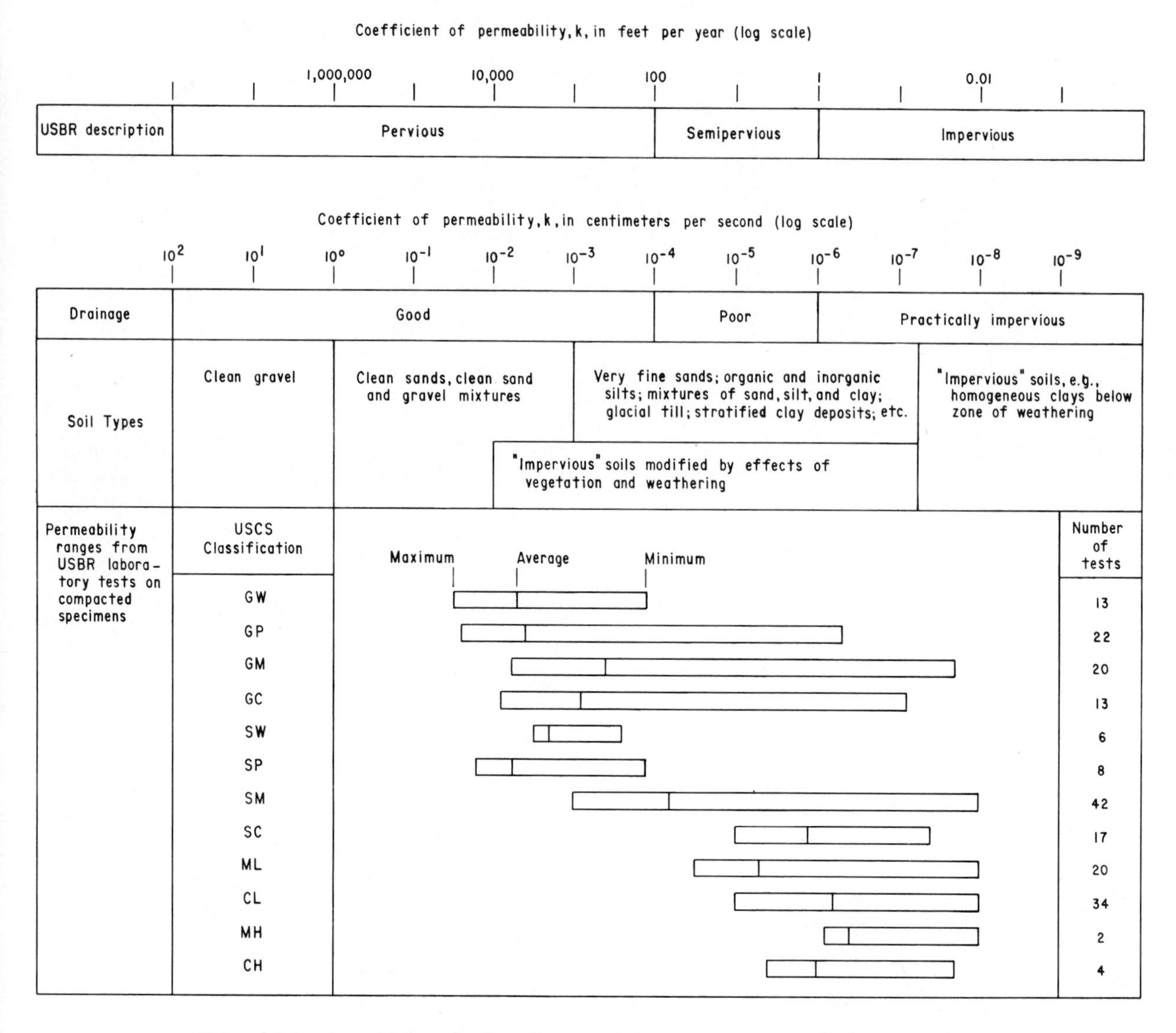

Figure 5-14.—Permeability of soils. (After Casagrande and Fadum, 1940). 103–D–1860.

E. ROCK CLASSIFICATION AND DESCRIPTION OF PHYSICAL PROPERTIES OF ROCK

5.19. *General.*—(a) *Definition and Types.*—Rock is defined as an aggregate of one or more minerals. However, to the engineer the term "rock" usually signifies hard or lithified substances that require mechanical or explosive methods to excavate. Based on their principal mode of origin, rocks are grouped into three large classes: igneous, sedimentary, and metamorphic. These are discussed in more detail in sections 5.20, 5.21, and 5.22, respectively.

(b) *Mineral Identification.*—The physical properties of a mineral, which are controlled by its chemical composition and molecular structure, are valuable aids in its identification and, consequently, in rock identifications. These properties include hardness, cleavage, fracture, luster, color, and streak. Those characteristics that can be determined by simple field tests are introduced to aid in the identification of minerals and indirectly in the identification of rocks.

(1) *Hardness.*—The hardness of a mineral is a measure of its ability to resist abrasion or scratch-

ing. A simple scale based on empirical tests for hardness has been universally accepted. The ten minerals selected to form the standard of comparison are listed in order of increasing hardness from 1 to 10:

Mineral	*Hardness*
Talc or mica	1
Gypsum (fingernail about 2)	2
Calcite	3
Flourite (copper coin between 3 and 4)	4
Apatite (knife blade about 5)	5
Orthoclase feldspar (glass about 5.5)	6
Quartz	7
Topaz or beryl	8
Corundum	9
Diamond	10

When testing the hardness of a mineral always use a fresh surface, and always rub the mark to make sure it is really a grove made by scratching.

(2) *Cleavage.*—A material is said to have cleavage if smooth, plane surfaces are produced when the mineral is broken. Some minerals have one cleavage; others have two, three, or more different cleavage directions, which may have varying degrees of perfection. The number of cleavage directions and the angle at which they intersect serve to help identify a mineral (fig. 5-15).

(3) *Fracture.*—The broken surface of a mineral, in directions other than those of cleavage planes, is called the fracture. In some cases this property may be very helpful in field identification. The common types of fracture are conchoidal if the fracture has concentric curved surfaces like the inside of a clamshell; irregular if the surface is rough; and splintery if it has the appearance of wood.

(4) *Luster.*—the luster of a mineral is the appearance of its surface based on the quality and intensity of the light reflected. Two major kinds are recognized, metallic and nonmetallic. Metallic minerals are opaque, or nearly so; whereas, nonmetallic minerals are transparent on their thin edges.

(5) *Color.*—Using color for identification must be done with proper precaution because some minerals show a wide range of color without a perceptible change in composition.

(6) *Streak.*—The color of the fine powder of a mineral, obtained by rubbing it on the unglazed portion of a porcelain tile is known as its streak. The streak of a mineral is quite consistent within a given range, even though its color may vary.

(c) *Common Rock-Forming Minerals.*—Only about 12 of the 2,000 known varieties of minerals are found in most common rocks. The primary rock-forming minerals or mineral groups are described below.

- *Quartz.*—Silicon dioxide. Quartz is the second most common rock-forming mineral. Hardness, 7, scratches glass easily; no cleavage; fracture, conchoidal; luster, vitreous; common varieties, usually white or colorless; streak, white or colorless.
- *Feldspar group.*—Potassium-aluminum silicates or sodium-calcium-aluminum silicates. Feldspars are the most common rock-forming minerals. Hardness, 6, scratches glass with difficulty; luster, vitreous; streak, white. Orthoclase is a common potassium-rich variety that is typically colorless, white, gray, pink, or red, and has two good directions of cleavage that intersect at 90° to each other (No. 1 on fig. 5-15). The sodium-calcium-rich feldspars, commonly referred to as plagioclase feldspar, are typically of various shades of gray, have two cleavage directions that intersect at angles of nearly 90° to each other, and can be differentiated from orthoclase feldspar by the presence of fine, parallel lines (striations) that appear on the basal cleavage surface.
- *Mica group.*—Complex potassium-aluminum silicates, often with magnesium, iron and sodium. Hardness, 2 to 3, can be scratched with the thumbnail; good cleavage in one direction; luster, vitreous to pearly; transparent, with varying shades of yellow, brown, green, red, and black in thicker specimens; streak, white. The true characteristic of this group is the capability of being split (cleavage) very easily into extremely thin and flexible sheets. Biotite

Figure 5-15.—Mineral cleavage. 288-D-2918.

(black) and muscovite (white) are two representative varieties.

- *Amphibole group.*—Complex calcium-magnesium-iron silicates. Hardness, 5 to 6; cleavage in two directions at angles 56° and 124°; color, light to dark green to black; streak, white to grayish-green. Hornblende is a common variety that can usually be differentiated from other amphiboles by its dark color.
- *Pyrozene group.*—Complex calcium-iron silicates, closely analogous chemically to the amphibole group. Hardness, 5 to 6; two directions of cleavage, making angles of about 87° and 93°, an important characteristic useful in differentiating between the minerals of the pyroxene and amphibole groups; color, light to dark green to black; streak, white to grayish-green. Augite is a common variety that can be differentiated from hornblende by the cleavage angles.
- *Olivine.*—Magnesium-iron silicate. Hardness 6.5 to 7; no cleavage, luster, vitreous; color, olive to grayish-green to brown; streak, white to colorless. An important characteristic of this mineral is its friability, or tendency to crumble into small grains, which is due to its granular texture.
- *Calcite and dolomite.*—Calcium carbonate and calcium-magnesium carbonate. Hardness, 3 and 3.5 to 4; perfect cleavage in three directions(No. 2 on fig. 5-15); luster, vitreous to pearl; usually white or colorless, but may appear in shades of gray, red, green, blue, or yellow; streak, white. Calcite may develop in large crystals; whereas, dolomite is commonly found in coarse, granular masses. Besides being common rock-forming minerals, these two carbonates are important cementing agents.
- *Clay minerals.*—Extremely complex hydrous aluminum silicates. Hardness, 2 to 2.5; luster, dull to earthy; color, white, gray, greenish, and yellowish-white. The three most important groups of clay minerals are kaolinite, smectite, and illite. Almost all clays contain one or more of these three groups. Clay minerals can be identified only under the microscope and with the aid of x-ray equipment. They occur typically in extremely fine-grained masses of thin, micalike scales.
- *Limonite and hematite.*—Hydrous ferric oxide and ferric oxide. Hardness, 5.5 and 6.5; no cleavage; color, dark brown to black and reddish-brown to black, depending on the variety. Limonite has a yellowish-brown streak and is characteristically found in dark brown, nodular earthy masses with no apparent crystal structure. Hematite has a light to dark Indian-red streak and usually occurs in earthy masses. Limonite and hematite are important coloring and cementing minerals in many different rocks, especially in the sedimentary group.

5.20. *Igneous Rocks.*—(a) *General.*—Igneous rocks are those that have solidified from a molten mass (magma) deep within the earth (intrusive rocks) (fig. 5-16) or from lava extruded on the earth's surface (extrusive rocks). Igneous rocks owe their variation in significant characteristics to differences in the chemical composition of the magma and to differences in physical conditions under which the molten mass solidified.

Dikes are tabular igneous bodies that are commonly intruded at an angle to the bedding or the foliation of the country rock (fig. 5-17). Sills are igneous rocks that are usually intruded parallel to the bedding or foliation of the rocks that enclose them. The thickness of a dike or a sill may vary from inches to several hundred feet, but this dimension is usually quite small in relation to the length and width of the intrusive body. Large, irregular, intrusive masses with exposures larger than 40 mi² are called batholiths. Although originally deeply buried beneath the earth's surface, they have become exposed through a process of uplift and erosion. A striking example of an exposed batholith is the one in central Idaho, which has an estimated area of over 80,000 mi². Intrusive masses covering less than 40 mi² are called stocks.

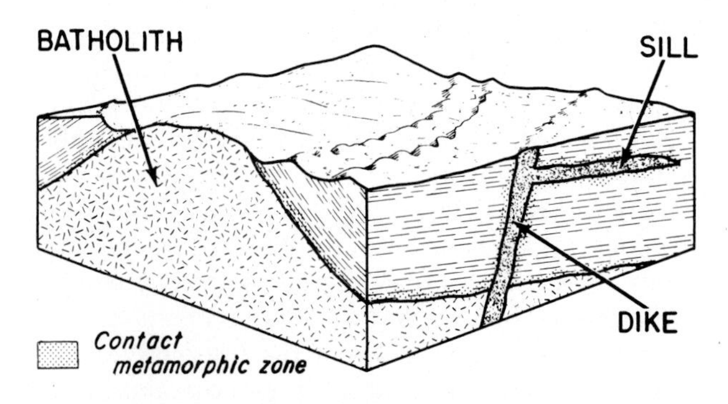

Figure 5-16.—Intrusive igneous masses. (U.S. Army Corps of Engineers). 288-D-2919.

Figure 5-17.—Three dikes cutting sedimentary beds. (U.S. Army Corps of Engineers.) 288–D–2920.

Extrusive igneous rocks include lava flows and volcanic ejecta. Lava flows issue from fissures in the earth's crust or pour out of volcanoes. These flows are the most common modes of occurrence of extrusive igneous rocks. Among the most notable of the enormous lava flows in the world is the Columbia River Plateau of Washington, Oregon, and Idaho. The lava sheets cover approximately 200,000 mi^2, and the succession of flows has a known cumulative thickness of more than 4,000 feet. Explosive volcanoes frequently eject great quantities of broken and pulverized rock material and molten lava, which solidify before striking the ground. These volcanic ejecta are termed pyroclastic material. They very in size from great blocks weighing many tons through small cinders of lapilli to fine dust-sized particles referred to as ash (fig. 5-18). The classification of pyroclastics is shown on figure 5-27.

(b) *Classification of Igneous Rocks.*—Chemical composition and texture are used to classify igneous rocks. Magma is a complex solution containing the oxide of silicon, which behaves as an acid, and oxides of iron, aluminum, calcium, magnesium, potassium, and sodium, which behave as bases. If more acid is available than is necessary to satisfy the bases in the magma, the surplus will show itself as free silicon dioxide (quartz), and the resulting rock is said to be acidic. If the bases are in excess, iron-magnesium minerals will be present and the rock is said to be basic. As a rule, acidic rocks are light colored, and basic rocks are dark to black.

Texture refers to the size and arrangement of the mineral grains in the rock (fig. 5-19). These factors are influenced primarily by the rate at which the molten mass, magma or lava, cools. A constant rate of cooling produces rocks in which the constituent mineral grains are approximately the same size. In general, the slower the molten material cools, the larger the size of the mineral grains. A change in the rate of cooling from an initial slow phase followed by a more rapid phase usually produces porphyritic texture (No. 4 on fig. 5-19). These rocks are characterized by mineral grains of two dominant sizes: phenocrysts, or large grains, in a ground mass or background of smaller grains. Textural terms used in the classification of igneous rocks are contained in table 5-2.

Figure 5-20 lists the various types of igneous rocks. Those of similar chemical composition or mineral content are listed in the vertical columns; those of similar texture are listed in the horizontal rows. Common igneous rocks and their constituent minerals are described in the following paragraphs.

Granite and rhyolite are composed primarily of quartz and feldspar (mainly of the orthoclase variety), and as a rule contain mica (generally the biotite variety).

Diorite and andesite are composed of feldspar (mainly plagioclase varieties) and one or more dark minerals (biotite, hornblende, or pyroxene).

Gabbro and basalt differ from diorite in that the dark minerals (hornblende, pyroxene, and olivine) predominate. All feldspar is plagioclase, and biotite, although present in some gabbros, is uncommon.

Obsidian and pitchstone correspond in composition to granite and rhyolite. Both are commonly referred to as volcanic glasses. Obsidian is dark-colored to black with a brilliant luster (No. 3 on fig. 5-19). Pitchstone is lighter colored and with a dull luster.

Pumice is a porous or cellular glass, usually white or gray, and commonly has the composition of rhyolite.

(c) *Primary Structural Features.*—With the exception of those varieties that exhibit an aphanitic texture, igneous rocks are composed of interlocking grains of different minerals. On this basis they can be distinguished from crystalline sedimentary and massive metamorphic rocks, which normally contain crystals of the same mineral. The distinctive

Figure 5-18.—Blocky type of solidified lava flows. Layer of volcanic ejecta (ash) covers area at left and in foreground. (U.S. Army Corps of Engineers). 288–D–2921.

structural features common to some, but not all, igneous rocks are described below.

Flow structure may be exhibited by the glassy-textured igneous rocks, such as obsidian, and by the fine-grained extrusives, such as rhyolite.

Vesicular or scoriaceous structure is commonly present in extrusive igneous rocks (fig. 5-21). Such rock contains tiny spherical to almond-shaped openings called vesicles, formed by gas bubbles in or rising through the lava.

Lamellar or platy structure may be found in some of the coarser grained igneous rocks. This structure is due to the parallel orientation of such minerals as mica or hornblende, and most commonly occurs near the contacts of intrusive bodies where the friction between the wall rock and the molten material causes the platy minerals to align themselves in the direction of flow.

5.21. *Sedimentary Rocks.*—(a) *General.*—Sedimentary rocks are of secondary origin. They are formed in layerlike masses of sediment that have hardened through cementation, compaction, or recrystallization. The inorganic material entering into the composition of most sedimentary rocks is derived from the disintegration and decomposition of preexistent igneous, sedimentary, and metamorphic rocks. This material is then moved from its original position by water, wind, or glaciers in the form of solid particles or dissolved salts. Rock particles dropped from suspension produce deposits of clastic or fragmental sediment. By chemical reaction the dissolved salts become insoluble and form precipitated sediments, or by evaporation of the water medium they form evaporites.

Based on the mode of origin, sediments can be classified as clastic, chemical, or organic. The clastic, or fragmental, sediments include gravel, sand, silt, and clay, which are differentiated by the dimensions of the particles. All types of rock contribute to clastic material. Each size of clastic particle may be transported by several agencies. The terms gravel, sand, silt, and clay soils are defined in section 5.14. However, the differentiation between "clay" and "silt" when classifying rock is based solely on the grain size of the particle, not the plasticity characteristics. Chemically deposited and organic sediments are classified on the basis of their chemical composition.

The conversion of sediment into rock, sometimes called lithification, is brought about by a combination of the following processes:

- Compaction, in which the rock or mineral particles are brought closer together by the pressure of overlying materials, as in the conversion of clay to shale and the conversion of peat to coal
- Cementation, in which porous materials are bound together by minerals precipitated from water solution such as silicon dioxide (quartz), calcium carbonate (calcite), and the iron oxides (limonite and hematite)
- Recrystallization, in which a rock with an interlocking crystalline fabric or grain, such as crystalline limestone, is developed by the continued growth of the mineral grains in a sediment or by the development of new minerals from water

(b) *Characteristics.*—Clastic rocks commonly show separate grains. The chemical precipitates and evaporites, on the other hand, either have interlocking crystals or are in earthy masses. The organically formed rocks commonly contain easily recognized animal and plant remains such as shells, bones, stems, or leaves. Figure 5-22 lists the sedimentary rock classifications used by the Bureau of Reclamation.

(1) *Coarse-Grained Sedimentary Rocks.*—The minerals commonly found in the coarse-grained sedimentary rocks, such as conglomerates (fig. 5-23) and sandstone, are quartz as grains or cementing material; feldspar; mica minerals; clay minerals; and limonite, hematite, or calcite, as cementing material.

(2) *Fine-Grained Sedimentary.*—The minerals commonly found in predominantly fine-grained sedimentary rocks, like shale and siltstone, are clay minerals; quartz as fine grains or cementing material; mica minerals; and limonite, hematite, and calcite as cementing materials.

(3) *Crystalline Sedimentary Rocks.*—The minerals commonly found in crystalline sedimentary rocks, such as limestone, chalk, dolomite, and coquina, are calcite, dolomite and quartz.

(c) *Primary Structural Features.*—The primary structural features inherent in the sediment before consolidation are valuable in the field recognition of sedimentary rocks. A universally prevalent structural feature of sedimentary rocks is their stratification, as indicated by differences in composition, texture, hardness, or color in approximately parallel bands. These strata may be flat lying, or nearly so, as originally deposited, or they may be tilted or folded as a result of movement within the earth's crust. Each stratum or bed is separated from the one immediately above and below by bedding planes.

Some sedimentary deposits, usually those composed of granular materials such as sand commonly exhibit laminae lying at an angle to the true bedding plane. This feature of sedimentary rock is known as crossbedding. Sediment deposited in low, flat places, such as flood plains of rivers or intermittent lakes, may develop mud cracks that separate the mass into irregular polygonal blocks. These may harden sufficiently to be preserved during the lithification of the sediment. Parallel ridges, known as ripple marks, developed in sediment moved by wind

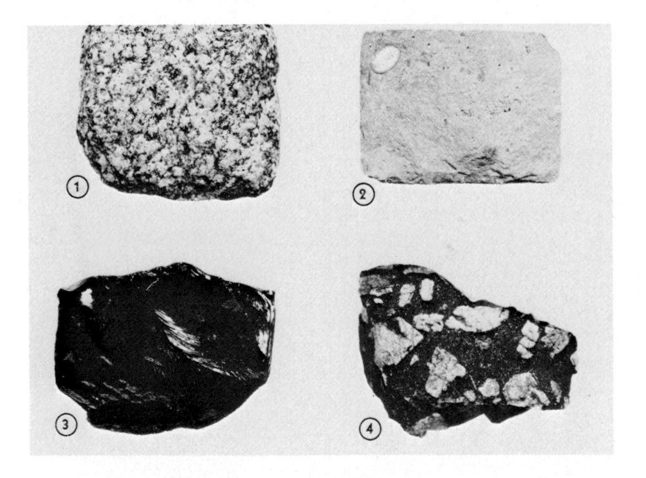

Figure 5-19.—Textures of igneous rocks. ① Coarse-grained, ② fine-grained, ③ glassy, and ④ porphyritic. (U.S. Army Corps of Engineers). 288-D-2922.

Table 5-2.—Igneous textural descriptors.

Descriptor	Average crystal diameter, in inches
Very coarse-grained or pegmatitic	>3/8
Coarse-grained	3/16 to 3/8
Medium-grained	1/32 to 3/16
Fine-grained	0.04 to 1/32
Aphanitic (cannot be seen with the unaided eye)	<0.04

	COLOR	LIGHT →							DARK		SPECIAL TYPES
	QUARTZ	> 10%	< 10%	> 10%	< 10%	> 10%		< 10%		CHIEFLY PYROXENE AND/OR OLIVINE	
	FELDSPAR	POTASSIUM FELDSPAR > 2/3 TOTAL FELDSPAR		POTASSIUM FELDSPAR 1/3-2/3 TOTAL FELDSPAR		PLAGIOCLASE > 2/3 TOTAL FELDSPAR					
						K-SPAR > 10% TOTAL	SODIC PLAGIOCLASE		CALCIC PLAGIOCLASE		
	CHIEF ACCESSORY MINERALS	HORNBLENDE BIOTITE MUSCOVITE		HORNBLENDE BIOTITE PYROXENE		HORNBLENDE, BIOTITE, PYROXENE			PYROXENE OLIVINE	SERPENTINE IRON ORE	
Fine to coarse > 0.1 mm	EQUIGRANULAR Batholiths, lopoliths, stocks, large laccoliths, thick dikes and sills.	GRANITE	SYENITE	QUARTZ MONZONITE	MONZONITE	GRANODIORITE	QUARTZ DIORITE	DIORITE	GABBRO	PERIDOTITE	PEGMATITE - Very coarse grained, normally silicic, rock (or small irregular mass). APLITE - Fine-grained rock having sugary texture. LAMPROPHYRE - Dark rock with high percentage FeMg minerals as phenocrysts and in ground mass.
PORPHYRITIC *	FINE TO COARSE GRAIN GROUND MASS Laccoliths, dikes, sills, plugs, small stocks, margins, of larger masses.	GRANITE PORPHYRY	SYENITE PORPHYRY	QUARTZ MONZONITE PORPHYRY	MONZONITE PORPHYRY	GRANODIORITE PORPHYRY	QUARTZ DIORITE PORPHYRY	DIORITE PORPHYRY	GABBRO PORPHYRY	PERIDOTITE PORPHYRY	
PORPHYRITIC *	APHANITIC GROUND MASS Dikes, sills, laccoliths, surface flows, margins of larger masses, welded tuffs.	RHYOLITE PORPHYRY	TRACHYTE PORPHYRY	QUARTZ LATITE PORPHYRY	LATITE PORPHYRY	DACITE PORPHYRY		ANDESITE PORPHYRY	BASALT PORPHYRY	RARE	* TRAP - dark-colored aphanitic rock. * FELSITE - light-colored aphanitic rock.
APHANITIC < 0.1 mm	MICROCRYSTALLINE Dikes, sills, surface flows, margins of larger masses, welded tuffs.	RHYOLITE	TRACHYTE	QUARTZ LATITE	LATITE	DACITE		ANDESITE	BASALT		
APHANITIC < 0.1 mm	GLASSY Surface flows, margins of dikes and sills, welded tuffs.	OBSIDIAN - dark colored PITCHSTONE - resinous VITROPHYRE - porphyritic PERLITE - concentric fractures PUMICE - light colored, finely vesicular SCORIA - dark colored, coarsely vesicular		Normally it is not possible to determine the composition of these rocks. They are customarily designated by the names at the left. Basic glass is rare so rocks named, except scoria, will normally be silicic. If the approximate composition (by close association) can be determined, the name may be prefixed by the name of the appropriate aphanitic rock, for example, "trachyte obsidian" or "latite vitrophyre". In general, scoria is basic; basic obsidian is called "tachylite"; and spherulite tachylite is "variolite".							* These are somewhat vague terms and generally should not be used.

* The names in these rows should be used if there are > 50% phenocrysts. If there are < 50% phenocrysts, the adjective "porphyritic" should be used, for example, "porphyritic granite".

Figure 5-20.—Field classification of igneous rocks. Modified from [3]. 103–D–1861.

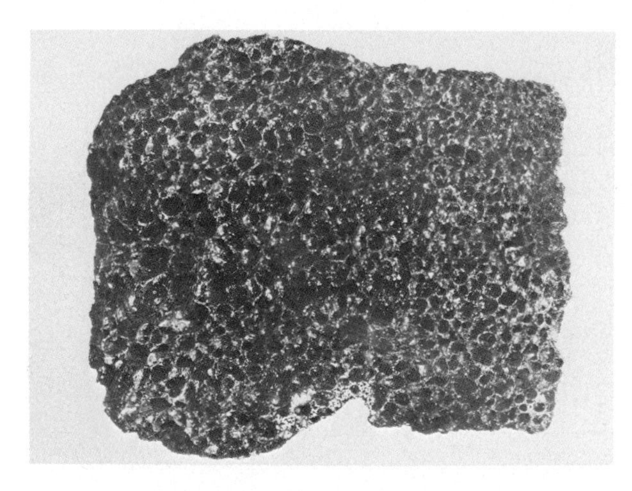

Figure 5-21.—Scoriaceous structure in extrusive lava rock. (U.S. Army Corps of Engineers). 288–D–2923.

or water are often preserved when the sediment is consolidated. Fossils, the remains or impressions of animals and plants, are not structural features, but they are important to the field identification of sedimentary rocks (see fig. 5-24).

5.22. *Metamorphic Rocks.*—(a) *General.*—Metamorphic rocks are those formed from preexisting igneous or sedimentary rocks as a result of adjustments of these rocks to environments different from those in which they were originally formed. These adjustments may include the formation within the rock of new structures, textures, and minerals.

Temperature, pressure, and chemically active fluids and gases are the major interrelated factors involved in metamorphism. Each factor is capable of accomplishing metamorphic work as follows:

(1) *Temperature.*—The effect of heat is twofold: it increases the solvent action of fluids, and it helps break up and change chemical compounds. Extremely high temperatures may result from the intrusion of molten masses or from deep burial.

The zone of altered rock formed adjacent to a molten mass is called the contact metamorphic zone (fig. 5-16). Heat may also be related to the depth of burial. In this case the earth's own heat produces metamorphism.

(2) *Pressure.*—The compressive forces that accompany movements in the earth's crust are mainly responsible for the pressures to which many rocks are subjected. By the action of these movements, rocks are reformed in which the crystals, grains, and rock fragments are flattened and elongated or pulverized as a result of the pressure.

(3) *Fluids and Gases.*—Water, in either fluid or gas form, is the most important of the liquids and gases involved in metamorphism. Under heat and pressure, water becomes a powerful chemical agent. It acts as a solvent, promotes recrystallization, and takes part in the composition of minerals for which it is essential. Water may be accompanied locally by carbon dioxide and other fluids or gases issuing from igneous magmas.

(b) *Classification.*—Metamorphic rocks, on the basis of their primary structure, are readily divided into two groups: foliated and nonfoliated. The foliated metamorphic rocks display a pronounced primary banded or layered structure as a result of the differential pressure to which they have been subjected (fig. 5-25). The nonfolidated or massive metamorphic rocks do not exhibit primary structural features. Metamorphism has apparently been limited to the process of recrystallization without the action of differential pressure. These structural differences are used as the basis for the simplified classification of the common metamorphic rocks listed on figure 5-26. The characteristics of several common types of metamorphic rocks are described in the following paragraphs.

Gneiss is characterized by rough, relatively coarse banding or foliation. The bands, often of unlike minerals, commonly appear as alternating light and dark lens-shaped masses in the body of the rock. The common minerals or mineral groups present in gneisses are quartz and the feldspar, mica, amphibole, and pyroxene mineral groups. The specific name assigned is determined by the predominant mineral in the rock. For example, gneiss with a predominance of the mineral hornblende would be called hornblende gneiss.

Schist is more homogeneous in appearance and composition than gneiss. Its foliations are much thinner, generally more uniform in thickness, finer textured, and often folded to a much greater degree than the bands of most gneisses. The minerals are, in general, the same as for gneiss, except that talc, chlorites, serpentine, and graphite may be dominant in some schists. As in gneiss, the specific name of a schist is determined by the predominant mineral present.

Slate is very fine-grained and homogeneous. Foliation is developed to a very great degree, enabling the slate to split into thin sheets with relatively

TEXTURE →	GRAIN SIZE < 0.0625 mm			GRAIN SIZE 0.0625 - 2 mm						GRAIN SIZE > 2 mm	
	CRYSTALLINE, CLASTIC, AMORPHOUS, BIOCLASTIC, ETC.			CLASTIC						CLASTIC	
COMPOSITION OF MAJOR FRACTION → / COMPOSITION OF MINOR FRACTION ↓	CLAY MINERALS or Clay-size Materials	Composition as indicated in left column	CHIEFLY CALCITE or DOLOMITE	CHIEFLY QUARTZ	QUARTZ with 10-25% FELDSPAR	QUARTZ with > 10% ROCK FRAGMENTS	QUARTZ with > 25% FELDSPAR	QUARTZ FELDSPAR, ROCK FRAGMENTS	PYROCLASTICS	CHIEFLY ONE CONSTITUENT Homogeneous breccias and conglomerates	SEVERAL CONSTITUENTS Mixed breccias and conglomerates
< 10% MINOR FRACTION			LIMESTONE DOLOMITE ETC.	QUARTZOSE SANDSTONE	FELDSPATHIC SANDSTONE	LITHIC SANDSTONE	ARKOSE	GRAYWACKE		Name consists of chief constituent and size, as QUARTZ COBBLE CONGLOMERATE LIMESTONE PEBBLE BRECCIA, ETC.	Name consists of "mixed" and size, as MIXED BOULDER BRECCIA. Name may include composition as ANDESITE-CHERT-ARKOSE CONGLOMERATE
CLAY MINERALS or Clay-size materials	CLAYSTONE, SILTSTONE - nonfissile SHALE - fissile ARGILLITE - highly indurated BENTONITE - sodium montmorillinite		ARGILLACEOUS LIMESTONE, MARL, ETC.	ARGILLACEOUS QUARTZOSE SANDSTONE	ARGILLACEOUS FELDSPATHIC SANDSTONE	ARGILLACEOUS LITHIC SANDSTONE	ARGILLACEOUS ARKOSE	ARGILLACEOUS GRAYWACKE	Refer to Figure 3-4 for classification of Pyroclastics	ARGILLACEOUS (size) CONGLOMERATE	ARGILLACEOUS MIXED CONGLOMERATE GLACIAL TILL FANGLOMERATE
SILICA Opal Chalcedony Quartz Chert	SILICEOUS SHALE, SILICEOUS CLAYSTONE ETC.	DIATOMITE RADIOLARITE SILICEOUS OOLITE OOLITE CHERT	SILICEOUS LIMESTONE, CHERTY CHERTY LIMESTONE, ETC.	SILICEOUS QUARTZOSE SANDSTONE	SILICEOUS FELDSPATHIC SANDSTONE	SILICEOUS LITHIC SANDSTONE	SILICEOUS ARKOSE	SILICEOUS GRAYWACKE		SILICEOUS (size) CONGLOMERATE	SILICEOUS MIXED (size) CONGLOMERATE
CALCITE or DOLOMITE	CALCAREOUS SHALE, ETC.	LIMESTONE DOLOMITE CALICHE - lime-rich deposit formed near surface OOLITIC LIMESTONE FOSSILIFEROUS LIMESTONE CHALK	CLASTIC LIMESTONE	CALCAREOUS QUARTZOSE SANDSTONE	CALCAREOUS FELDSPATHIC SANDSTONE	CALCAREOUS LITHIC SANDSTONE	CALCAREOUS ARKOSE	CALCAREOUS GRAYWACKE		CALCAREOUS (size) CONGLOMERATE	CALCAREOUS MIXED (size) CONGLOMERATE

Rocks including significant quantities of iron, carbon, or miscellaneous salts follow the above format. For example: ferruginous quartzose sandstone, coal, carbonaceous shale, gypsum, phosphatic limestone.

Figure 5-22.—Field classification of sedimentary rocks. Modified from [3].

Figure 5-23.—Conglomerate. (U.S. Army Corps of Engineers). 288–D–2925.

Figure 5-24.—Fossiliferous limestone. (U.S. Army Corps of Engineers). 288–D–2926.

smooth surfaces. The predominant minerals in slate are quartz, mica, chlorite, and sometimes graphite.

Quartzite is a metamorphic rock derived from sandstone by the recrystallization of or cementation by quartz. Quartzite formed by recrystallization may bear little resemblance to the parent rock. However, quartzite formed by cementation exhibits much the same physical appearance as the rock from which it is derived.

Marble is massive metamorphic rock that has essentially the same mineral content as the crystalline sedimentary rocks from which it is derived.

5.23. *Rock Classification.*—Numerous systems are used for field and petrographic classification of rocks. Many classifications require detailed petrographic laboratory tests and thin sections; others require limited petrographic examination and field tests. The Bureau of Reclamation has established a classification system that is modified from the one

Figure 5-25.—Foliation in metamorphosed sedimentary rocks. (U.S. Army Corps of Engineers). 288–D–2927.

developed by R. B. Travis [3]. Although the Bureau's system is not based entirely on field tests or field identification of minerals, many of the classification categories are sufficiently broad that field identification is possible. The differences in the mineral constituents that cannot be determined precisely in the field are usually not significant enough to affect the engineering properties of the rock. Detailed mineralogic identification and petrographic classification can be performed on hand samples or core samples submitted to the E&R (Engineering and Research) Center Petrographic Laboratory.

The engineering geologist must remember that engineering-geologic rock units should bear simplistic, general rock names based on either field identification, existing literature, or detailed petrographic examination. One must resist overclassification. For example, a rock unit should be called "hornblende schist" or "amphibolite" rather than "sericite-chlorite-calcite-hornblende schist." The term "granite" would convey more to a designer than the petrographically correct term "nepheline-syenite porphyry." Detailed mineralogic descriptions for various rock units may be used in reports and may be required to correlate between observations. But mineralogic classifications are not desirable as a rock unit name unless the mineral constituents or fabric are significant to engineering properties.

The classification for igneous, sedimentary, and metamorphic rocks are shown on figures 5-20, 5-22, and 5-26, respectively. These figures are condensed and modified slightly from Travis's more detailed classifications, which may also be used. The classification of pyroclastics is shown on figure 5-27.

(a) *Unit Names and Identification.*—Rock unit names are required for identification. They may also provide indications of formation and geologic history, geotechnical characteristics, and correlations with other areas. a simple descriptive name and map symbol should be assigned to indicate the possible engineering characteristics of the rock type. The rock unit names may be stratigraphic, lithologic, generic, or a combination of these, such as Navajo sandstone (Jn), Tertiary shale (Tsh), Jurassic chlorite schist (Jcs), Precambrian ganite (PCgr), or metasediments (ms). The *engineering*

COLOR	CHIEF MINERALS	ACCESSORY MINERALS	NONDIRECTIONAL STRUCTURE (MASSIVE OR GRANULOSE)		DIRECTIONAL STRUCTURE (LINEATED OR FOLIATED)					
			CONTACT METAMORPHISM		MECHANICAL METAMORPHISM	REGIONAL METAMORPHISM (HIGHLY FOLIATED ← → LESS FOLIATED)				PLUTONIC METAMORPHISM
			FINE	FINE TO COARSE	CATACLASTIC	SLATY	PHYLLITIC	SCHISTOSE	GNEISSOSE	MIGMATITIC
						APHANITIC	FINE	FINE TO COARSE		
LIGHTER ↔ DARKER	FELDSPAR	ACTINOLITE, ALBITE, ANDALUSITE, ANTHOPHYLLITE, BIOTITE, CHIASTOLITE, CHLORITE, CHLORITIOD, CHONDRODITE, CORDIERITE, DIOPSIDE, ENSTATITE, EPIDOTE, GARNET, GLAUCOPHANE, GRAPHITE, KYANITE, MUSCOVITE, OLIVINE, PHLOGOPITE, PYROPHYLLITE, SCAPOLITE, SERICITE, SERPENTINE, SILLIMANITE, STAUROLITE, TOURMALINE, TREMOLITE, WOLLASTONITE	HORNFELS	METAQUARTZITE	These rocks are formed by crushing with only minor recrystallization CATACLASITE - Nondirectional. MYLONITE - Foliated, aphanitic. PHYLLONITE - Foliated, fine grain, resembles a phyllite. FLASER GRANITE, FLASER DIORITE, FLASER CONGLOMERATE, ETC. - Flaser structure, lenses and layers of original or relatively unaltered granular minerals surrounded by matrix of highly sheared and crushed material. AUGEN GNEISS - Augen structure	SLATE	PHYLLITE	SCHIST (AMPHIBOLITE)	GNEISS	These rocks have a gneissose, streaked, or irregular structure produced by intimate mixing of metamorphic and magmatic materials. When they can be recognized as "mixed rock", they are called migmatite gneiss. They may originate by injection (injection migmatite, injection gneiss, or lit-par-lit gneiss), or by differential fusion. Many so-called migmatites probably originate by partial granitization or by metamorphic differentiation. But at great depth these processes apparently do not differ substantially from the igneous processes forming migmatite, so the products are usually indistinguishable. Migmatites are named by prefixing the rock name of the granitic material to the appropriate root as "granite mignatite", "monzonite injection mignatite", etc.
	QUARTZ									
	MICA			AMPHIBOLITE						
	HORNBLENDE								AUGEN GNEISS	
	CHLORITE									
	ACTINOLITE									
LIGHTER ↔ DARKER	TREMOLITE							GNEISSIC SCHIST	SCHISTOSE GNEISS	
	TALC			SOAPSTONE						
	CALCITE AND/OR DOLOMITE			MARBLE						
	CALC-SILICATES			SKARN						
	SERPENTINE			SERPENTINITE				SERPENTINITE		

Naming a metamorphic rock consists chiefly of prefixing the structural term with mineral names or an appropriate rock name. The rock name indicates either the original rock, if recognizable, or the new mineral composition. The prefix "meta", as "Metagabbro", "metasandstone", "metatuff", etc., is applied to rocks that have undergone considerable recrystallization but have largely retained their original fabric. Most of the minerals listed as accessories are genetically important and if present should be included in the rock name regardless of their quantity.

Figure 5-26.—Field classification of metamorphic rocks. Modified from [3]. 103-D-1863.

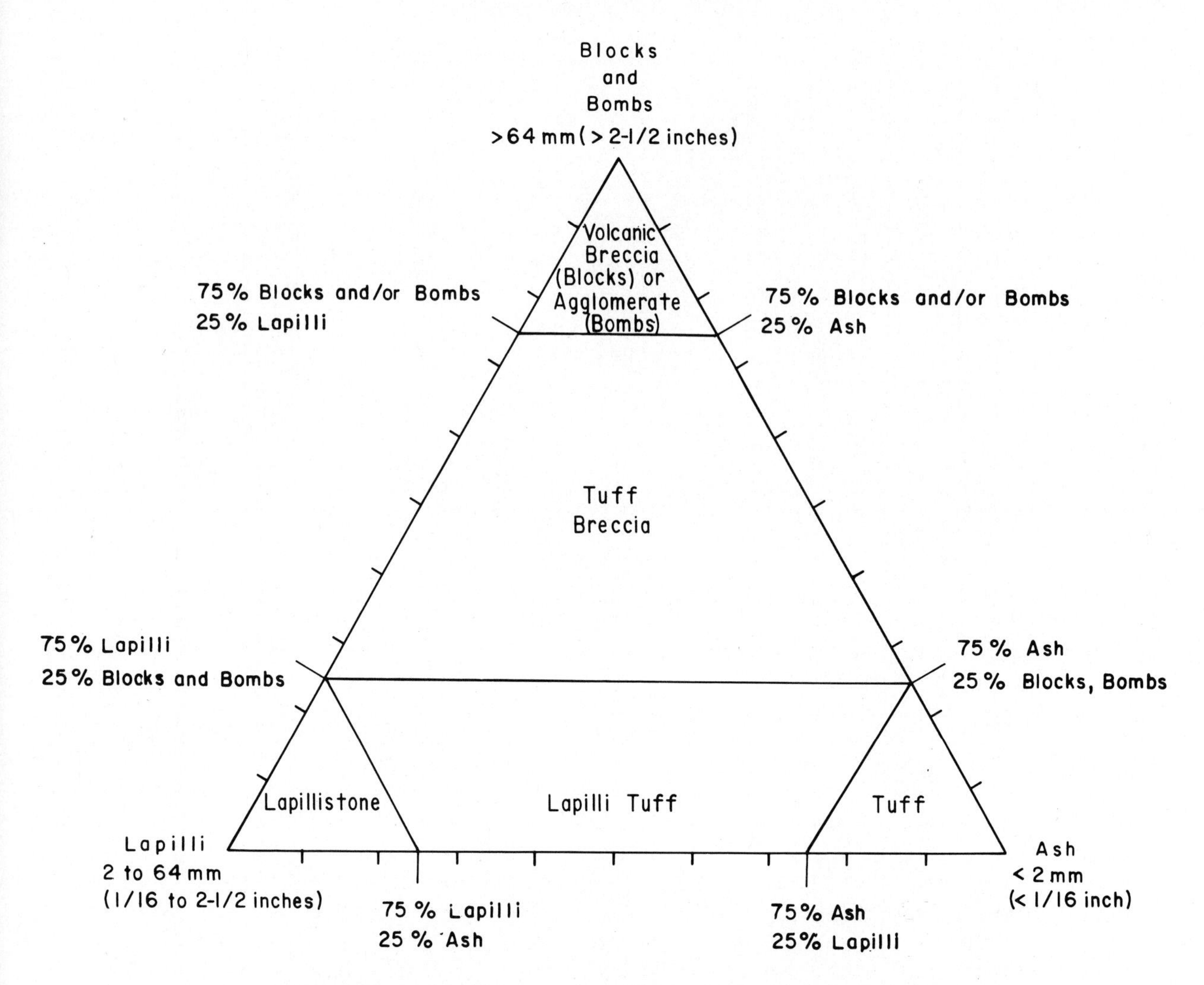

NOTE: Blocks are angular to subangular clasts >64 mm (>2-1/2 inches). Determine percent of each size present (ash, lapilli, blocks, and bombs), and list in decreasing order after rock name. Precede rock name with the term "welded" for pyroclastic rocks that have retained enough heat to fuse after deposition. Rock names for such deposits will usually be selected from the lower right portion of the classification diagram.

Figure 5-27.—Field classification of pyroclastic rocks. Modified from [4] and [5].

significance of bedrock units of similar physical properties should be delineated and identified. Every attempt should be made to identify and delineate units as early as posible during each geologic study. For appraisal planning studies, reservoir maps and other large-scale drawings may require the use of geologic fomrations of groups of engineering-geologic units with descriptions of their engineering significance in accompanying discussions. When more detailed mapping is performed, each unit should be individually identified and delineated.

Significant units should be differentiated, where it is possible to do so, by engineering properties but not necessarily by formal stratigraphic units. Although stratigraphic names are not required, bedrock units should be correlated to stratigraphic names in the data report or by an illustration, such as a stratigraphic column. This may require research and consultation to establish proper stratigraphic nomenclature. Stratigraphic names and ages (formation, member, etc.) descriptive enough to identify rock properties may be used as rock unit names. For engineering studies, each particular stratigraphic unit may require further subdivisions to identify different engineering parameters, such as susceptibility to weathering, presence of alteration, dominant discontinuity characteristics, hardness, strength, deformability, and the presence of deleterious minerals or beds (such as swell susceptibility in sulfates or clays). For example, a shale unit, Tsh, may be differentiated as Tsh_1 or Tsh_2 if unit 2 contains bentonite interbeds and unit 1 does not, and Tsh_C may be used as a unit name for the bentonite beds. A chlorite schist unit, Cs, may be differentiated as Cs_A or Cs_B where unit A contains higher percentages of chlorite or talc and is significantly softer (i.e., has different deformation properties) than unit B. A meta-sediment unit, Ms, may be further differentiated on more detailed maps and logs as Ms_{sh} (shale) or Ms_{ls} (limestone). All differentiated units should be assigned distinctive map symbols.

(b) *Descriptors and Descriptive Criteria for Physical Characteristics.*—Descriptive criteria for physical characteristics of rock are based on lithology, bedding (or foliation and flow) textures, weathering or alteration, hardness, discontinuities, contacts, and permeability. The descriptors are discussed in the following paragraphs. A more complete discussion of these descriptors can be found in chapter II-4 of the Bureau of Reclamation's *Engineering Geology Manual* [6].

(1) *Lithologic Descriptors (Composition, Grain Size, and Texture).*—Brief lithologic descriptions of the rock units should be provided. These include a general description of mineralogy, degree of induration, cementation, crystal sizes and shapes, textural adjectives, and color. Lithologic descriptors are especially important for the description of engineering-geology subunits when rock unit names are not specific, such as metasediments, Tertiary intrusives, Quaternary volcanics, etc.

(2) *Bedding, Foliation, and Flow Texture.*—These features give the rock anisotrophic properties or represent potential failure surfaces. Continuity and thickness of these features influence rock mass properties and cannot always be tested in the laboratory. Typical thickness descriptors for these features are listed in table 5-3.

(3) *Weathering, Alteration and Slaking.*—These three characteristics significantly affect the engineering properties and must be adequately described in identifying rock for engineering purposes.

a. Weathering.—Weathering, the chemical or mechanical degradation of rock, can significantly affect the engineering properties of the rock and rock mass. The term "weathering" for engineering-geology descriptions includes both chemical disintegration (decomposition) and mechanical disaggregation as agents of alteration. Weathering affects generally decrease with depth, although zones of differential weathering can occur and may modify a simple sequence of weathering. Examples of these are (1) differential weathering within a single rock unit, apparently caused by relatively higher premeability along fractures; (2) differential weathering between different or the same rock units, usually caused by compositional or textural differences; (3) differential weathering of contact zones associated with thermal effects, such as interflow zones within volcanics; and (4) directional weathering along permeable joints, faults, shears, or contacts that act as conduits along which weathering agents penetrate more deeply into the rock mass.

Weathering does not correlate directly with the specific geotechnical properties used for many rock mass classifications. However, weathering is important because it may be the primary criterion for determining depth of excavation, cut slope design, method and ease of excavation, and use of excavated materials. Porosity, absorption, compressibility,

Table 5-3.—Bedding, foliation, and flow texture descriptors.

Descriptor	Thickness
Massive	>10 feet
Very thickly (bedded, foliated, or banded)	3 to 10 feet
Thickly	1 to 3 feet
Moderately	0.3 to 1 feet
Thinly	0.1 to 0.3 feet
Very thinly	0.03 (3/8 inch) to 0.1 feet
Laminated (intensely foliated or banded)	<0.03 feet (<3/8 inch)

shear and compressive strengths, unit weight, and resistance to erosion are major engineering parameters influenced by weathering. Weathering is generally indicated visually by changes in the color and the texture of the rock mass, the condition of fracture fillings and surfaces, grain boundary conditions, and physical properties like hardness.

b. Alteration.—Chemical alteration effects distinct from chemical and mechanical degradation (weathering), such as hydrothermal alteration, may not fit into the weathering definitions discussed in the previous paragraph. When the alteration does not relate well to the weathering characteristics, the geologist must adjust the description to emphasize alterations. Many of the general characteristics may not change, but their degree could be very different. Appropriate descriptors, such as "moderately altered," "intensely altered," etc., may be assigned for each alteration category.

c. Slaking.—Slaking is another type of disintegration that affects the parameters used for design and construction. Terminology and descriptive criteria to identify this deleterious property are difficult to standardize because some materials air slake, many water slake, and some slake only after one or more wet-dry cycles. The durability index in table 5-4 provides a simplified method for describing slaking. The criteria for the index are based on the time exposed and the effects noted in the field. However, the Bureau of Reclamation has not established laboratory tests for quantifying slaking durability. These simplified criteria do not specify whether the specimen or exposure is wetted, dried, or subjected to cyclic wetting and drying, or freeze-thaw, all of which are critical in quantifying slaking durability.

(4) *Hardness-Strength.*—Hardness can be related to rock strength as a qualitative indication of unit weight or of resistance to breaking or crushing. Strength is a necessary engineering parameter for design that is frequently not assessed, but plays a dominant role in engineering design and construction. Tunnel support requirements, bit wear for drilling or TBM (tunnel boring machines) operations, allowable bearing pressures, and excavation methods and support all depend on the rock strength. The large differences in hardness are more important than the subtle differences. The hardness and strength of intact rock are usually functions of the individual rock type, but may be modified by weathering or alteration.

Table 5-4.—Durability index descriptors.

Descriptor	Criteria
D10	Rock specimen remains intact with no deleterious cracking after exposure longer than 1 year
D11	Rock specimen develops hairline cracking on surfaces within 1 month, but no disaggregation within 1 year of exposure
D12	Rock specimen develops hairline cracking on surfaces within 1 week and/or disaggregation within 1 month of exposure
D13	Specimen may develop hairline cracks in 1 day and displays pronounced separation of bedding and/or disaggregation within 1 week of exposure
D14	Specimen displays pronounced cracking and disaggregation within 1 day (24 hours) of exposure; generally ravels and degrades to small fragments

Hardness and, especially, strength are difficult characteristics to express with field tests. Nevertheless, there are two field tests that can be used; one is a measure of the ability to scratch the surface of a specimen with a knife, and the second is the resistance to fracturing by a hammer blow. Both of these tests should be used to determine the hardness and strength descriptors shown on table 5-5.

(5) *Discontinuities.*—All discontinuities, such as joints, fractures, shears, faults, and shear-fault zones, and significant contacts should be described. The descriptions should include all observable characteristics, such as orientation, spacing, continuity, openness, surface conditions, and fillings. Appropriate terminology, descriptive criteria, descriptors, and examples pertaining to discontinuities are presented in chapter II-5 of the Bureau of Reclamation's *Engineering Geology Manual* [6].

(6) *Contacts.*—Contacts between various rock units or rock-soil units must be described. In addition to their geologic classification, their engineering characteristics, such as their planarity or irregularity, should be described.

The descriptors that apply to the geologic classification of contacts are:

- Conformable

- Unconformable
- Welded (contact between two lithologic units, one of which is igneous, that has not been disrupted tectonically)
- Concordant (intrusive rocks)
- Discordant (intrusive rocks)

Descriptors pertinent to the engineering classification of contacts are:

- Jointed (contact not welded, cemented, or healed—a fracture)
- Intact
- Healed (by secondary process)
- Sharp
- Gradational
- Sheared
- Altered (baked or mineralized)
- Solutioned

(7) *Permeability Data.*—Hydraulic conductivity is an important physical characteristic that should be described. Suggested methods for testing, terminology, and descriptors are available in the Bureau's *Earth Manual* [7] and *Ground Water Manual* [8]. Numerical values for *K* (hydraulic conductivity) can be determined using any of several computer programs. These values may be shown on drill hole logs.

F. SURFACE EXPLORATIONS

5.24. *General.*—A relationship between topographic features or landforms and the characteristics of the subsurface soils has been shown repeatedly. Thus, the ability to recognize terrain features on maps, on aerial photographs, and during reconnaissance, combined with an elementary understanding of geologic processes, can be of great assistance in locating sources of construction materials and in making a general appraisal of foundation conditions.

The mechanisms that develop soil deposits are water, ice, and wind action for transported soils; and the mechanical-chemical action of weathering for residual soils. For the transported soils, each type of action tends to produce a group of typical landforms, modified to some extent by the nature of the parent rock and climatic conditions. Soils found in similar locations within similar landforms usually have similar physical properties. The engineering geologist and engineer responsible for foundation and construction materials investigations for small dams should become familiar with landforms and with the associated soils. Such knowledge is of great assistance during the appraisal stage of investigations and may be useful in determining the extent of investigations for feasibility and design investigations.

5.25. *Fluvial-Lacustrine Soils.*—(a) *Definition.* **Soils whose properties are predominantly affected by the action of water are designated fluvial soils when associated with running water, such as streams and rivers, and lacustrine soils when deposited in still water, such as lakes and reservoirs. Frequently, there is considerable sorting action, so** that a deposit is likely to be stratified or lenticular. Individual strata may be thin or thick, but the material in each stratum will generally have a small range of grain sizes. The three principal types of fluvial-lacustrine soils, reflecting the water velocity during deposition, are identified as outwash deposits, flood plain deposits, and lacustrine deposits. These soils are discussed in the following subsections.

(b) *Outwash Deposits.*—The typical landforms of this type are alluvial cones and alluvial fans. They vary in size and character from small, steeply sloping deposits of coarse rock fragments to gently sloping plains of fine-grained alluvium, very extensive in area. The deposition results from the abrupt flattening of the stream gradient that occurs at the juncture of mountainous terrain and adjacent valleys or plains. Figure 5-28 includes an aerial photograph and a topographic map of an alluvial fan. The coarser material is deposited first and, therefore, is found on the steeper slopes at the head of the fan; whereas, the finer material is carried to the outer edges. In arid climates where mechanical rather than chemical weathering predominates, the cones and fans are composed largely of rock fragments, gravel, sand, and silt. In humid climates where the landforms have less steep slopes and chemical weathering has a greater influence, the material contains much more sand, silt, and clay.

Sand and gravel from these deposits are generally subrounded to subangular in shape, reflecting movement over relatively short distances, and the deposits have only poorly developed stratification. The outwash deposits are likely sources of sand and

Table 5-5.—Rock hardness and strength descriptors.

Descriptor	Hardness	Criteria
H1	Extremely hard	Core, fragment, or outcrop cannot be scratched with knife or sharp pick; can only be chipped with repeated heavy hammer blows
H2	Very hard	Cannot be scratched with knife or sharp pick; core or fragment breaks with repeated heavy hammer blows
H3	Hard	Can be scratched with knife or sharp pick with difficulty (heavy pressure); heavy hammer blow required to break specimen
H4	Moderately hard	Can be scratched with knife or sharp pick with light or moderate pressure; core or fragment breaks with moderate hammer blow
H5	Moderately soft	Can be grooved 1/16 inch deep by knife or sharp pick with moderate or heavy pressure; core or fragment breaks with light hammer blow or heavy manual pressure
H6	Soft	Can be grooved or gouged easily by knife or sharp pick with light pressure; can be scratched with fingernail; breaks with light to moderate manual pressure
H7	Very soft	Can be readily indented, grooved, or gouged with fingernail, or carved with a knife; breaks with light manual pressure

Any bedrock softer than H7 (very soft) is to be described using Bureau of Reclamation Standard 5000 Series consistency descriptors.

Note: Although sharp pick is included in these criteria, descriptions of ability to be scratched, grooved, or gouged by a knife is preferred.

gravel for pervious and semipervious embankment materials and for concrete aggregate. The presence of boulders is likely to limit their usefulness for some types of fill materials. The soils are typically skip-graded, resulting in a GP or SP classification. Because this type of deposit is consolidated only by its own weight, settlement should be anticipated when it is used as a foundation for a structure. Normally, outwash deposits are too pervious and do not provide satisfactory abutments for dams. If it is necessary to locate a dam near such a deposit, the dam should be placed along the upstream edge of the fan.

(c) *Flood Plain Deposits.*—Flood plain deposits are generally finer, better stratified, and better sorted than outwash deposits. The degree of variation caused by the water depends largely on the volume of water and on the gradient of the stream. The surface of these stream deposits is nearly flat. The nature of the materials in the deposit can be deduced from the characteristics of the stream. Braided streams usually indicate the presence of silt, sand, and gravel; whereas, meandering streams in broad valleys are commonly associated with fine-grained soils (silts and clays).

Flood plain deposits of sand and gravel are common sources of concrete aggregate and pervious zone materials for dam embankments. The soils in the various strata of river deposits may range from pervious to impervious; therefore, the permeability of the resulting material sometimes can be influenced appreciably by the depth of cut. A high water table is a major obstacle in the use of these deposits, especially as a source of impervious material. Furthermore, the removal of materials from the reservoir floor just upstream from a damsite may be undesirable when a positive foundation cutoff is not feasible. When considering borrowing from a river deposit downstream from a dam, it should be remembered that such operations may change the tailwater characteristics of the stream channel, and that the spillway and outlet works will have to be designed for the modified channel conditions. If tailwater conditions will be affected, borrow operations must produce a predetermined channel and explorations for the design must accurately define conditions within this channel.

Stream deposits vary in competency as foundations for dams. Potential difficulties include high water table, variation in soil properties, seepage, consolidation and, possibly, low shear strengths.

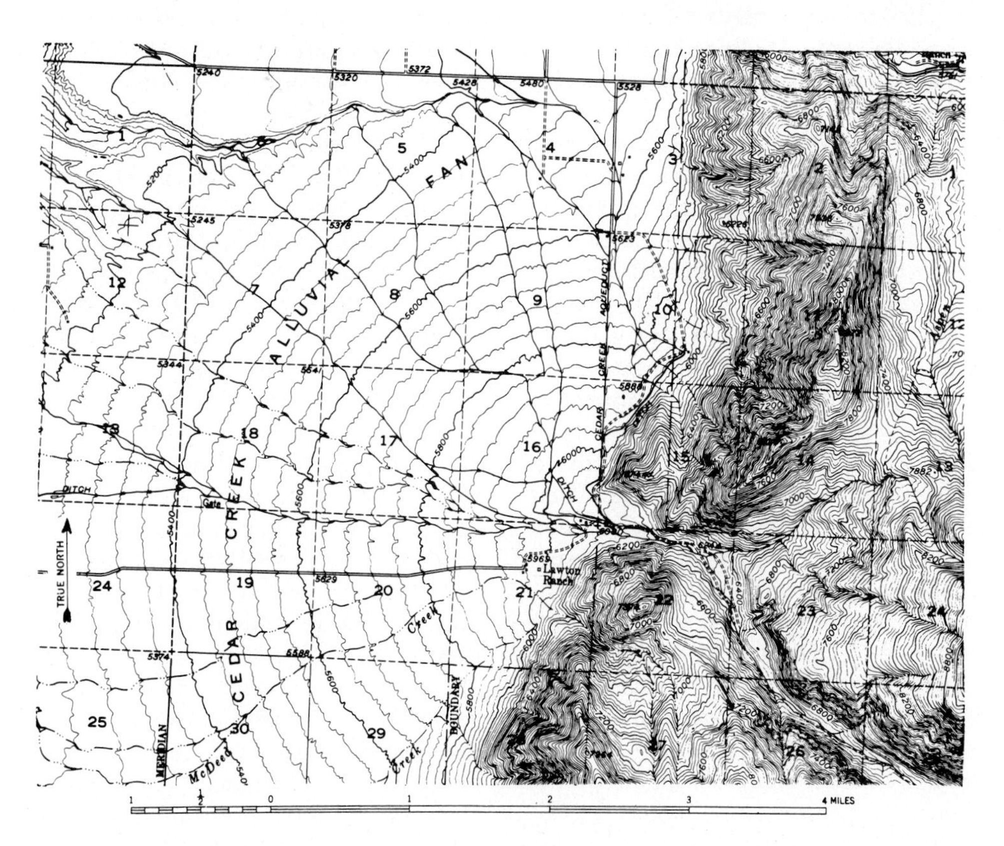

Figure 5-28.—Aerial view and topography of an alluvial fan. A potential source of sand and gravel. 288–D–2928 and 288–D–2929.

Although flood plain deposits are usually acceptable as foundations for small dams, their depths and characteristics must be investigated thoroughly during explorations.

An important type of stream deposit is the terrace. It represents an earlier level of valley development. Remnants of such deposits are recognized by their flat tops and steep faces, usually persistent over an extended reach of the valley. Examination of the eroded faces facilitates classification and description of the deposits, and the extent of the drainage network developed on the terrace helps determine the relative permeability. Free-draining material has almost no lateral erosion channels; whereas, impervious clays are finely gullied laterally. Terraces are found along streams throughout the United States and are prevalent in the glaciated regions of the Northern States. Sands and gravels from terrace deposits usually occur in layers and are generally well-graded. They provide excellent sources of construction materials. Figure 5-29 includes an aerial photograph and a topographic map showing river alluvium and terrace deposits.

(d) *Lacustrine Deposits.*—Lake sediments, or lacustrine deposits, are the result of sedimentation in still water. Except near the edges of the deposits where alluvial influences are important, the materials are very likely to be fine-grained silt and clay. The stratification is frequently so fine that the materials appear to be massive in structure. Lacustrine deposits are recognizable by their flat surfaces surrounded by high ground. The materials they contain are likely to be impervious, compressible, and low in shear strength. Their principal use is for impervious cores of earthfill dams. Moisture control in these soils is usually a problem because their water content is difficult to change. Lake sediments usually provide poor foundations for structures. Their use as foundations for dams is beyond the scope of this text, and should not be attempted without special field and laboratory testing and thorough study.

5.26. *Glacial Deposits.*—(a) *General.*—Advances and retreats of the great North American continental ice sheets during glacial times created recognizable landforms. These landforms are important sources of construction materials and may be encountered in dam foundations. Smaller scale glacial landforms are found in high mountain valleys of the Rocky Mountains and the Sierra Nevada (in some instances the glaciers still exist). Glacial deposits are generally heterogeneous and are therefore difficult to explore. They contain a wide range of particle sizes, from clay or silt up to boulders, and the particle shapes of the coarse grains are typically subrounded or subangular, sometimes with flat faces.

(b) *Glacial Till.*—Glacial till is deposited directly from the ice with little or no transportation by water. It consists of a heterogeneous mixture of boulders, cobbles, gravel, and sand in an impervious matrix of generally nonplastic fines. Gradation, type of rock minerals, and degree of weathering found in till vary considerably, depending on the type of rocks in the path of the ice and the degree of leaching and chemical weathering. Glacial tills usually produce impervious materials with satisfactory shear strength; however, the oversized materials must be removed for the soil to be compacted satisfactorily. Fairly high inplace unit weight makes morainal deposits satisfactory for foundations of small dams.

Typical landforms containing glacial till are ground moraines, which have flat to slightly undulating poorly drained surfaces; end (or terminal) moraines, ridges at right angles to the direction of ice movement, and often curve so that the center is farther downstream than the ends; and lateral and medial moraines, which occur as ridges parallel to the direction of ice movement. Low, cigar-shaped hills occurring on a ground moraine, with their long axis parallel to the direction of ice movement, are called drumlins. They commonly contain unstratified fine-grained soils. Figure 5-30 includes an aerial photograph and topographic map showing a typical terminal moraine.

(c) *Glacial Outwash.*—Deposits from the glacial outwash (melt water) consist of several types. Glacial outwash plains of continental glaciation and their alpine glaciation counterparts, the valley trains, commonly contain poorly stratified silt, sand, and gravel similar to the alluvial fans of outwash deposits, which they resemble in mode of formation. Eskers are prominent winding ridges of sand and gravel that are the remnants of the beds of glacial streams that flowed under the ice. Eskers generally run parallel to the direction of ice movement, have an irregular crestline, are characterized by steep flanks (about 30°), and are 20 to 100 feet high. Eskers usually contain clean sand and gravel, with some boulders and silty strata that are irregular and exhibit fair to poor stratification. Eskers are excellent sources of pervious materials and

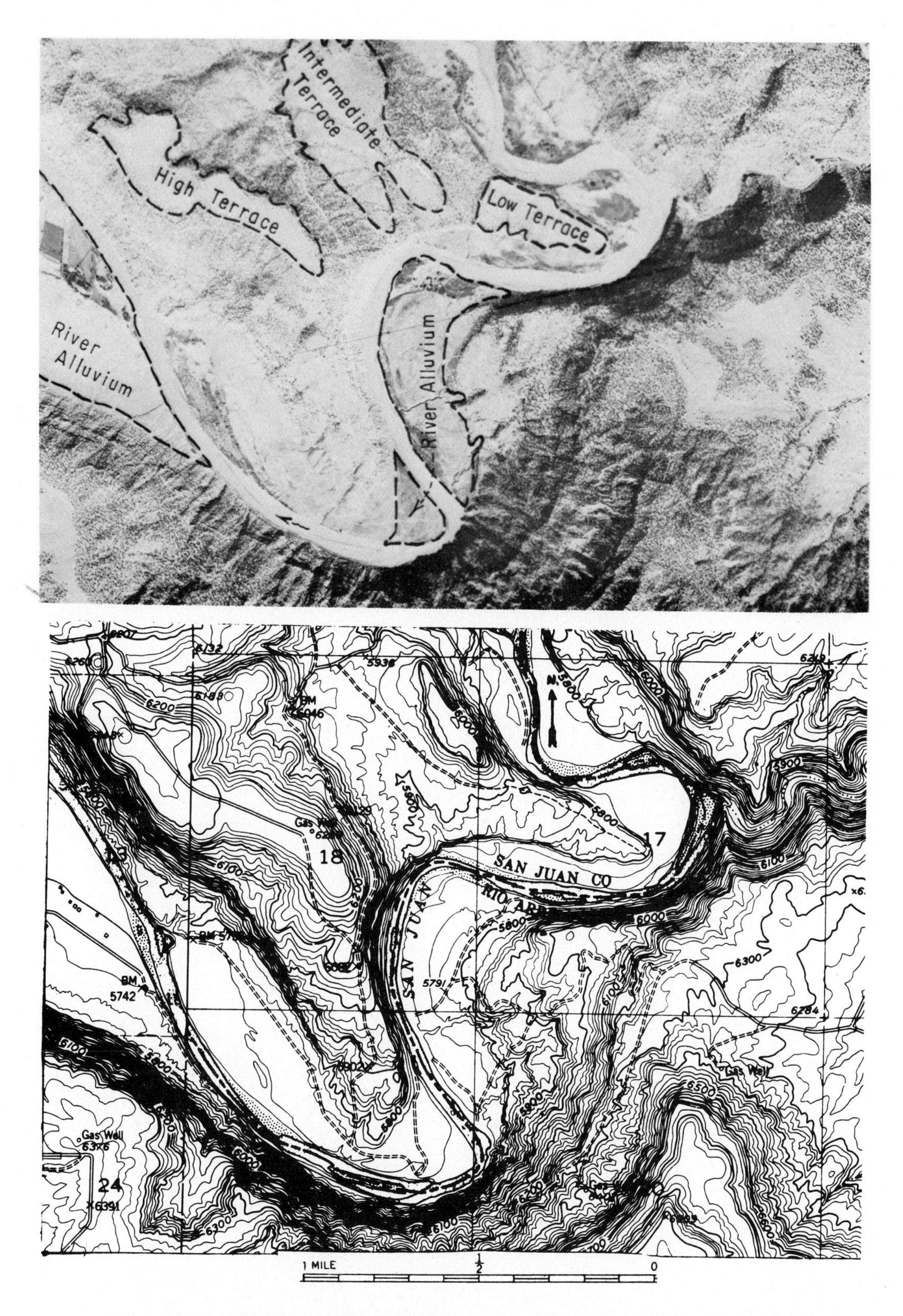

Figure 5-29.—Aerial view and topography of stream deposit showing river alluvium and three levels of gravel terraces. (Photograph by USGS). PX–D–16259.

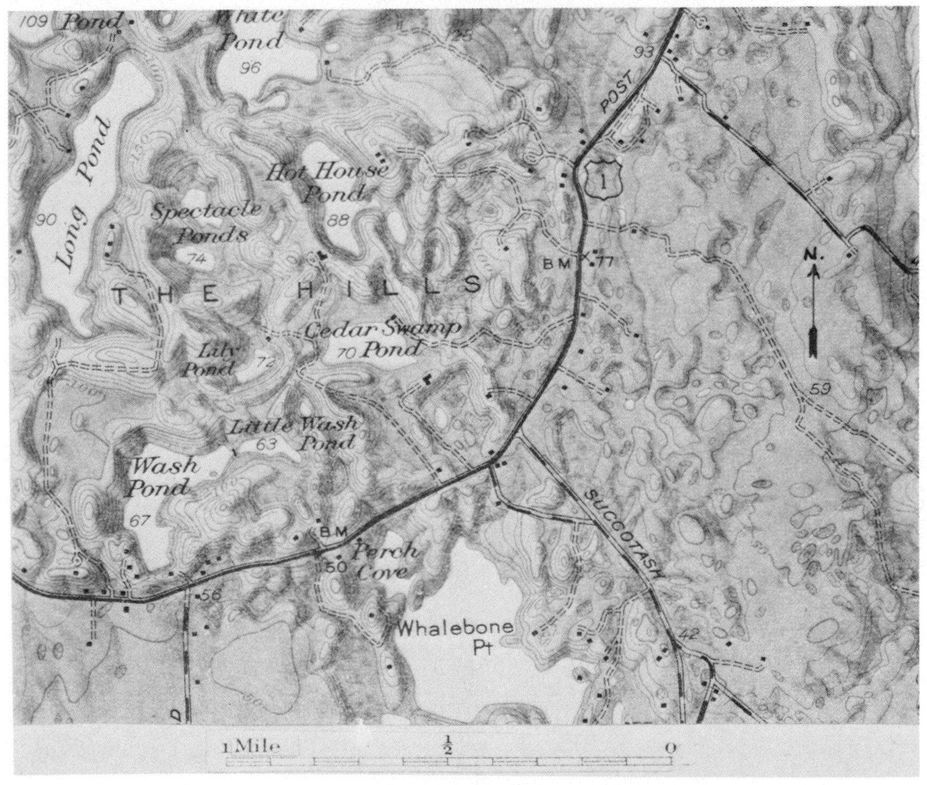

Figure 5-30.—Aerial view and topography of terminal moraine of continental glaciation. (Photograph by U.S. Commodity Stabilization Service). PX–D–16260.

concrete aggregate. Kames are low, dome-shaped partially stratified deposits of silt, sand, and gravel formed by hidden glacial streams. They are round to elliptical in plan, and the long axes are generally at right angles to the direction of ice movement. Their slopes, contents, and uses are similar to those of eskers. Glacial lake deposits, formed in temporary lakes, are generally similar in character and in engineering uses to fluvial-lacustrine deposits. However, they are normally more coarsely stratified (varyed) than the recent lake deposits, and they may contain fine sand.

5.27. *Aeolian Deposits.*—Soils deposited by the wind are known as Aeolian deposits. The two principal classes that are readily identifiable are dunes and loess. Dune deposits are recognizable as low elongated or crescent-shaped hills, with a flat slope windward and a steep slope leeward of the prevailing winds. Usually, these deposits have very little vegetative cover. The material is very rich in quartz, and its characteristics include limited range of grain size, usually in the fine or medium range sand; no cohesive strength; moderately high permeability; and moderate compressibility. They generally fall in the SP or SM group of the USCS.

Loess (windblown) deposits cover extensive areas in the plains regions of the temperate zone. They have a remarkable ability for standing in vertical walls. Figure 5-31 shows typical loessial topography by map and aerial photograph. Loess consists mainly of angular particles of silt or fine sand, with a small amount of clay that binds the soil grains together. In its natural state, true loess has a characteristic structure formed by remnants of small vertical root holes that makes it moderately pervious in the vertical direction. Although they have low unit weight, naturally dry loessial soils have a fairly high strength because of the clay binder. This strength, however, may be lost readily upon wetting, and the structure may collapse. When remolded, loess soils are impervious and moderately compressible and have low cohesive strength. They usually fall in the ML group or in the boundary ML-CL group of the USCS. Figure 5-32 shows a 90-foot, almost vertical, cut in loess.

Aeolian deposits are normally unacceptable as foundations for dams, and such deposits should be avoided if it is practicable to do so. However, they can be used when properly explored and evaluated. Information on the inplace unit weight of Aeolian soils is a critical criterion in evaluating their usefulness for foundations of structures.

5.28. *Residual Soils.*—As weathering action on rock progresses, the material decomposes to a point where it assumes all the characteristics of soil. It is difficult to clearly define the dividing line between rock and residual soil, but for engineering purposes a material is usually considered soil if it can be removed by common excavating methods.

A differentiating feature of many residual soils is that their individual grains are angular but soft. Handling residual soils during construction reduces their grain size appreciably, which makes predicting their performance by laboratory tests difficult. Appreciable settlement and change of material characteristics after handling are also detrimental factors. As a consequence, residual soils should be avoided if other types can be readily secured.

It is difficult to recognize and appraise residual soils on the basis of topographic forms. Their occurrence is quite general wherever none of the other types of deposits, with their characteristic shapes, are recognizable and where the material is not clearly bedrock. Talus (fig. 5-3) and landslides are easily recognizable forms of residual soils. Because the type of parent rock has a very pronounced influence on the character of the residual soil, the rock type should always be determined in assembling data for the appraisal of a residual deposit. Residual soils can usually provide satisfactory foundations for very small structures if the parent rock is satisfactory.

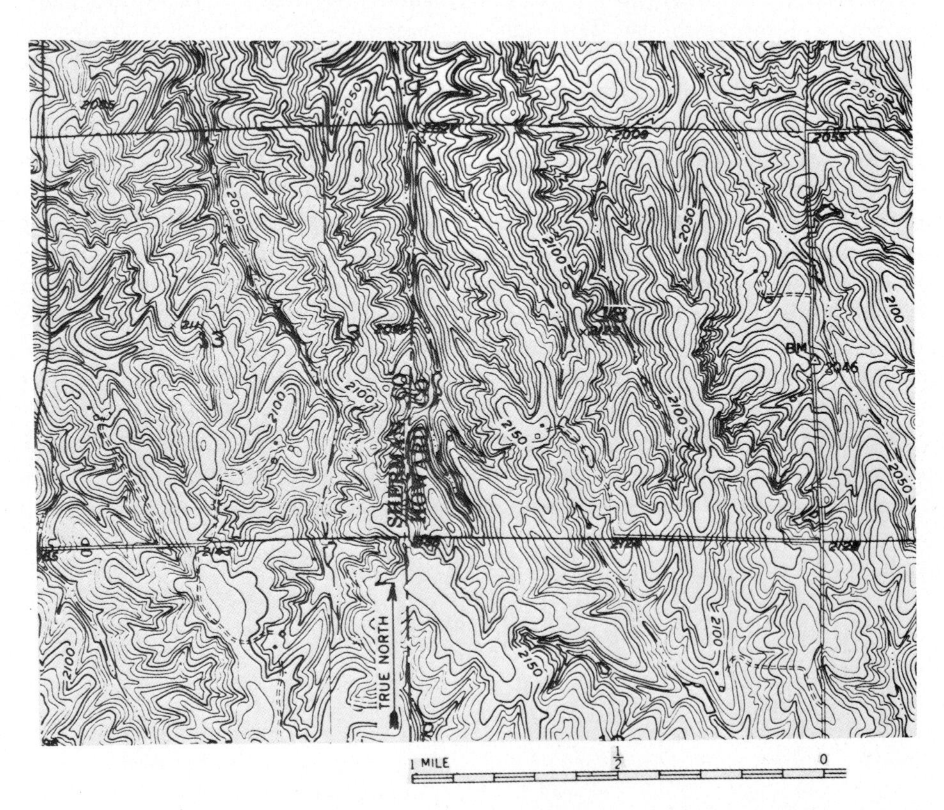

Figure 5-31.—Aerial view and topography of loess. Identified by smooth silt ridges; usually parallel, right-angle drainage patterns; and steep-sided, flat-bottomed gullies and streams. (Photograph by U.S. Commodity Stabilization Service). PX–D–16263.

Figure 5-32.—A 90-foot nearly vertical cut in a loess formation in Nebraska. GE–144–11.

G. GEOPHYSICAL EXPLORATION METHODS

5.29. *General.*—Geophysical surveys have been used for civil engineering investigations since the late 1920's, when seismic and electrical resistivity surveys were used for dam siting studies. A seismic survey was performed in the 1950's in St. Peter's Basilica to locate buried catacombs before a renovation project. With the advent of the nuclear power industry, detailed siting investigations have been necessary. Part of these investigations have been performed by geophysical studies. The initial geophysical surveys performed for nuclear powerplant sites attracted the attention of the civil engineering community and the Nuclear Regulatory Commission, to the extent that geophysical surveys are now required by law for these types of investigations.

A direct outgrowth of such uses has been the wider acceptance of geophysical surveys by the civil engineering community. Geophysical surveys are now used in an almost routine manner to complement engineering geology investigations and to provide information on site parameters (e.g., in place dynamic properties, cathodic protection values, depth to bedrock) that in some instances are not obtainable by other methods. Nevertheless, where some site parameters are obtainable by other means (e.g., laboratory testing), the values derived from geophysical surveys are still useful for checking. Figure 5-33 presents an idea of the importance of different geophysical methods used in civil engineering.

All geophysical techniques are based on the detection of contrasts in different physical properties of materials. If such contrasts do not exist, geophysical methods will not function. These contrasts range from those in the acoustic velocities to contrasts in the electrical properties of materials. Seismic methods, both reflection and refraction, depend on the contrast in the compressional or shear-wave velocities of different materials. Electrical methods depend on contrasts in electrical resistivities. Contrasts in the unit weights of different materials permit gravity surveys to be used in certain types of investigations. Contrast in magnetic susceptibilities of materials permit magnetic surveying to be used in other investigations. Finally, contrasts in the magnitude of the naturally existing electric current within the earth can be detected by SP (self-potential) surveys.

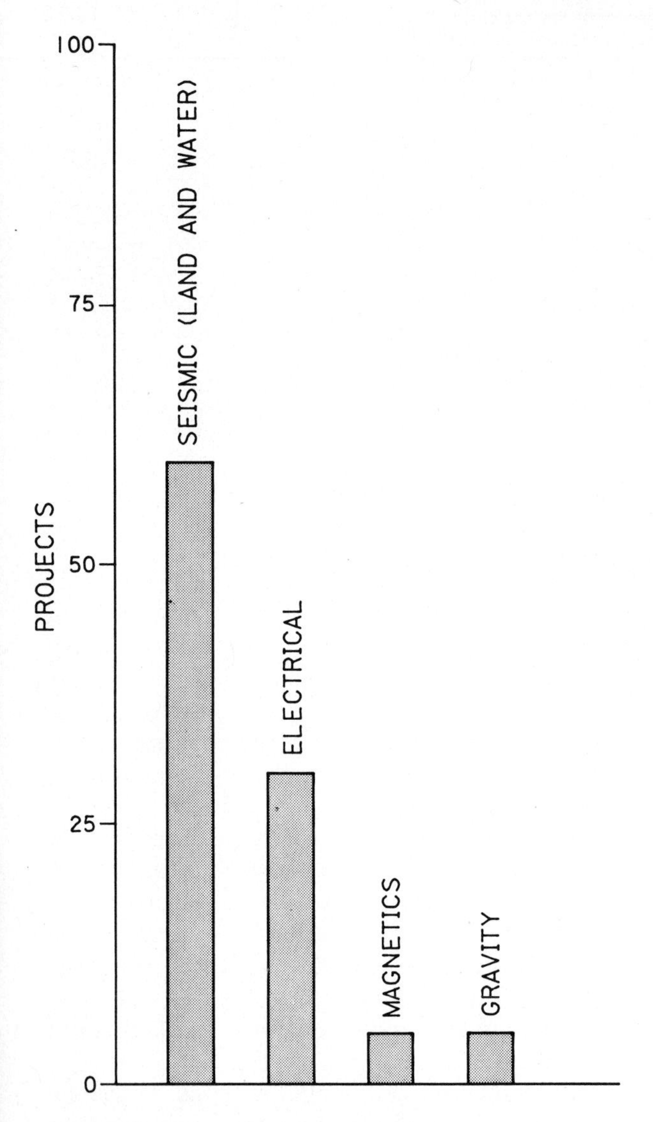

Figure 5-33.—Importance of geophysical methods in civil engineering. (For 100 projects).

Based on the detection and measurement of these contrasts, geophysical surveys can be designed to assist engineering geologists and engineers involved in geotechnical investigations. Seismic refraction surveys are used to determine depths to bedrock and to provide information on the compressional and shear-wave velocities of the surficial deposits overlying bedrock. This velocity information can also be used to calculate the inplace dynamic properties of these units. Electrical resistivity surveys can also be used to determine the depth to bedrock (should an acoustic velocity contrast not exist) and the electrical properties of the bedrock and the surficial deposits. However, resistivity surveys do not provide information on the dynamic properties of these units. Resistivity surveys have proven useful in delineating areas of contamination within soils and rock, and in delineating aquifers. Gravity and magnetic surveys are not used as often as seismic and resistivity surveys in geotechnical investigations, but these surveys have been used to locate buried utilities (magnetics) and to determine the success of grouting programs (gravity). Self-potential surveys have been used to map leakage from dams and reservoirs.

Geophysical surveys can be used in a number of geotechnical investigations. With a basic understanding of the geophysical methods available and of the engineering problems to be solved, useful geophysical programs can be designed for geotechnical investigations.

Geophysical surveys provide indirect information to determine characteristics of subsurface materials. In this sense, it is important that the results of geophysical surveys be integrated with the results of direct observations and investigations. Only then can correct interpretation of the geophysical surveys be made. Each type of geophysical survey has its capabilities and its limitations (a discussion of which is included in the following sections). Perhaps the biggest limitation is the use of personnel unfamiliar with geophysical methods to plan, perform, and interpret the results of geophysical surveys. In some cases, this limitation can be overcome, and in some cases, nonskilled personnel can perform the surveys in the field.

5.30. *Surface Geophysical Techniques.*—A brief description of available types of geophysical techniques is presented in the following paragraphs.

Each description includes the applications and equipment required for each type of survey.

(a) *Seismic Refraction Surveys.*—Seismic refraction surveys are performed to determine the compressional-wave velocities of materials from the ground surface down to a specified depth. For most engineering surveys, the maximum depth of investigation is specified by the nature of the project. In many cases, the objective of a seismic refraction survey is to determine the configuration of the bedrock surface and the compressional-wave velocities in the surficial deposits. Bedrock may be defined in terms of compressional-wave velocity. The information obtained from a seismic refraction survey can be used to compute the depths to various subsurface layers and the configurations of those layers. The thickness of the layers and the velocity contrasts between the layers govern the effectiveness of a seismic refraction survey. These parameters also govern the accuracy of the resulting data. Seismic refraction surveys will not define all compressional-wave velocities or all subsurface layers.

(1) *Applications.*—Seismic refraction surveys have been used in many types of exploration programs and geotechnical investigations. Seismic refraction surveys are routinely used in foundation studies for construction projects and in siting studies, fault investigations, dam safety analyses, tunnel alignment studies, and rippability studies.

(2) *Equipment.*—The basic equipment used for seismic refraction work consists of a seismic amplifier, a recorder (oscillograph or an oscilloscope) and a transducer (geophone). Depending on the scope of work, a single channel (one geophone) to a multichannel system may be required.

Most equipment manufactured since 1972 uses signal-enhancement electronics. This technique allows the stacking of repeatable energy from the seismic energy source to eliminate the unwanted affects of ambient noise. For most types of engineering investigation, 1- to 24-channel equipment is sufficient. For large-scale operations requiring greater depths of investigation, systems of 48 to 1,024 channels can be used. The larger channel systems require more personnel for field operations and are not as portable for field operations.

Small geophones are used to detect the seismic energy. These geophones are available in many different frequencies, and the frequency selected for a particular survey will depend on the objectives of that survey. The normal geophone frequency used in most seismic refraction work is 14 hertz (c/s). The geophones are connected to the seismic amplifier by means of a land cable. For multichannel systems, the geophones are normally connected to one cable at different connecting points, called (takeouts), which can be built into the cable at different intervals, depending on the spacing required. In normal practice, the takeout spacing is specified to the manufacturer when ordering the cable, and the spacing is usually constant throughout the cable. For an engineering-type seismic refraction survey, no more than 12 to 24 geophones are normally used per cable.

Other equipment used for seismic refraction surveying may include a blasting machine to detonate explosives, a magnetic tape recorder to record the seismic data for computer processing, two-way radios, surveying equipment to provide topographic control along the geophone alignment, and miscellaneous reels for the geophone and blasting cables.

(b) *Seismic Reflection Surveys.*—Seismic reflection surveys provide information on the geological structure within the earth. They do not provide as accurate information on compressional-wave velocities as seismic refraction surveys. Seismic reflection surveys have been used for engineering investigations. The information obtained from seismic reflection surveys can be used to define the geometry of subsurface layers and, thereby, provide information on faulting.

(1) *Applications.*—High-resolution seismic reflection surveys have been used in a large number of engineering investigations to provide definitive information on the locations and types of faults and the locations of buried channels. In some cases where it is not practical to use seismic refraction surveys, seismic reflection surveys have been used.

Shallow, high-resolution seismic reflection surveys are playing an increasingly important role in engineering investigations. Much of the necessary equipment is portable, and with the advent of small computers, data processing routines can be easily handled. When used correctly, seismic reflection surveys can provide certain data that seismic refraction surveys cannot, i.e., velocity reversal information. However, compressional-wave velocity information derived from reflection surveys may not be as accurate as that from refraction surveys. The compressional-wave velocities needed for the analysis of seismic reflection survey data can be obtained from computer analysis of the reflection records themselves, from seismic refraction surveys, uphole velocity surveys, and from sonic logs.

Seismic reflection surveys have been used since the 1920's for oil exploration. With the advent of CDP (common depth point) shooting, computer processing techniques and the digitization of the field data, seismic reflection surveys now dominate the exploration methods for oil. Seismic reflection surveys are now being used in the geotechnical field, providing high resolution data on subsurface layering, and geological structure. These surveys have been used for siting studies for a number of large structures, including nuclear powerplants, tunnel routing studies, mine planning studies, and fault studies.

(2) *Equipment.*—The basic equipment used for seismic reflection surveys is very similar to that used for seismic refraction surveys. In some cases, the equipment may be identical. For civil engineering investigations and ground-water studies, small portable equipment of up to 24 channels may suffice.

Almost all seismic reflection data are recorded on magnetic tape, such that the field data can be directly input into computer systems for direct processing. Tape transport systems may require air-conditioning for stability when working in hot areas. This is usually accomplished by mounting the total equipment system in a camper-type housing on a truck body. Smaller, portable reflection systems subjected to direct environmental contact should be protected against direct sunlight, heat, humidity, cold, and dust. With proper care, these smaller systems will function as well as the larger, truck-mounted, petroleum exploration systems.

The same type of geophones are used in reflection surveying as in refraction surveying. Based on the design of the seismic reflection spread, a group of geophones may be used at a single station to filter out unwanted noise and waves. The output of this group of geophones is summed and used as a single geophone. As an example, a land cable with 12 takeouts may be used to record the responses of 12 groups of geophones, each of which contains 6 geophones.

Land cables used in large-scale reflection operations may differ from those used in small-scale reflection or refraction operations. Whereas standard land cables normally contain 12 takeouts, special reflection cables (data cables) may only contain 2 or 3 takeouts. A series of these data cables can be connected to each other through special junction plugs. In addition to transmitting the geophone data to the amplifiers, the positions of the geophones on these cables can be changed by use of a roll-along switch. The use of this switch allows the instrument operator to record a large number of channels (geophones) and automatically advance the geophone positions along the cables in preparation for the next recording. This, of course, assumes that a sufficient number of geophones (groups) have been laid out on the ground and connected to the data cables.

Another piece of equipment used in seismic reflection surveying is a blasting machine to detonate explosives or vibrators (small, portable, or truck-mounted) to act as the energy source. The use of vibrators requires a correlator to correlate the input signal of the seismic source with the geophone response. Most of the seismic energy sources are detonated or activated by a two-way radio system.

(c) *Shear-Wave Surveys.*—Shear waves travel through a medium at a slower velocity than compressional waves. Therefore, shear-wave arrivals occur after compressional-wave arrivals on seismograms, or they are recorded as secondary arrivals. Other types of secondary arrivals are due to reflections, combinations of reflections and refractions, and surface waves. To identify shear-wave arrivals, special surveys (field techniques) are used. These surveys are designed to suppress compressional waves and unwanted secondary arrivals and to enhance shear-wave arrivals.

(1) *Applications.*—In engineering investigations shear-wave velocities are important because they can provide information on the inplace dynamic properties of a material. The relationship between compressional-wave velocity, shear-wave velocity, unit weight, and the inplace dynamic properties of a material is shown on figure 5-34. The compressional-wave velocity can be determined from refraction surveys, the shear-wave velocity from shear-wave surveys, and the unit weight from borehole geophysics or laboratory testing.

Shear-wave surveys are also used for exploration surveys for both engineering and oil and gas investigations. Because shear waves are slower than compressional waves, shear-wave surveys can sometimes provide better resolution of subsurface conditions than compressional-wave surveys (for reflections).

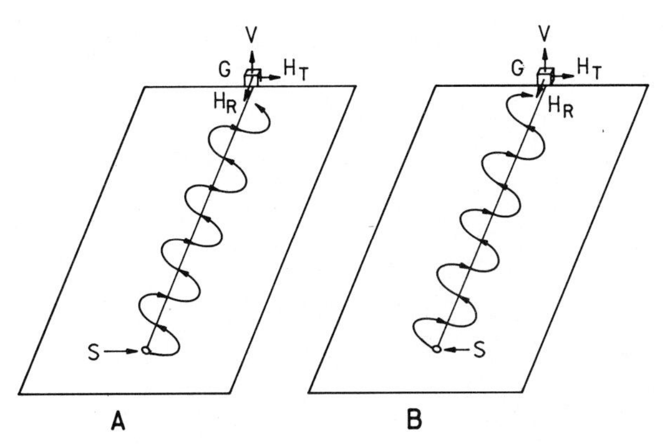

SH = Shear wave
S = Shotpoint
G = Geophone
V = Vertical component
H_R = Horizontal radial component
H_T = Horizontal transverse component

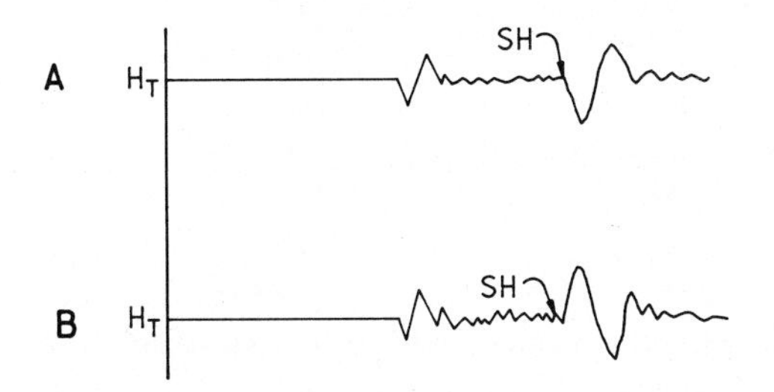

Figure 5-34.—Seismograph setup and readings. 103–D–1866.

(2) *Equipment.*—The equipment used in seismic refraction and reflection surveying can also be used in shear-wave refraction and reflection surveying. However, horizontally oriented geophones are used to record shear-wave arrivals. These geophones have a lower natural frequency than those geophones used in normal refraction-reflection surveying.

(d) *Surface Waves.*—Surface-wave surveys are designed to produce and record surface waves and their characteristics. Surface waves, which travel along the boundaries between different materials, are the slowest seismic waves. Because there are different types of surface waves, not only must the waves be recorded, but their characteristics must also be determined. Normally, surface waves are filtered out of seismic data or ignored. The term "ground roll" in the oil exploration industry denotes surface waves. Special care should be taken in seismic reflection surveys to filter out surface waves, otherwise they can interfere with desired reflections.

Surface waves are created by the constructive and destructive interference of refracted and reflected seismic waves. In addition to having the slowest velocities, surface waves have the lowest frequencies and the highest amplitudes of all seismic waves.

Surface waves that travel along the boundaries within a body are called Stonley waves. Other types of surface waves are Rayleigh waves, hydrodynamic waves, and Love waves. These surface waves and their characteristic motions are shown on figure 5-35.

(1) *Applications.*—The principal application of shear-wave surveying, for geotechnical investigations, is to determine the type and characteristics of surface waves that can exist at a given site. This information is useful for determining preferred site frequencies; and for earthquake design analysis.

(2) *Equipment.*—The cables and amplifiers used in normal refraction surveying can also be used in surface-wave surveying. Normally, special geophones are used, when available. These geophones contain three components: vertical, horizontal transverse, and horizontal radial (transverse and radial signify the orientation of the geophone in respect to the source of seismic energy). Surface-wave geophones have lower frequencies (from 1 to 5 Hz) than normal refraction-reflection geophones. If such geophones are not available, normal refraction-reflection geophones may be used, but special care must be taken. Vertical geophones can be used as the vertical component, and horizontal geophones (such as those used in shear-wave surveying) can be used for both radial and transverse components.

(e) *Vibration Surveys.*—Vibration surveys measure the vibrational levels produced by mechanical or explosive sources. Once these levels are determined, procedures can be designed to reduce the possibility of vibrational damages.

(1) *Applications.*—Vibrational surveys have been performed in conjunction with quarrying and mining operations, during excavations, to measure the effects of traffic on sensitive equipment, and to measure the effects of aircraft (sonic vibrations) on urban areas and on historic buildings.

Many manufacturing and research facilities contain extremely sensitive equipment with specific vibration tolerances. In the event of nearby construction, vibration surveys can be useful in determining the exact limits of allowable source vibrations and in designing procedures to both reduce the vibrational levels and maintain construction progress. The same type of vibration survey can be used in quarrying and in mining operations to reduce the vibrational levels and yet maintain rock breakage and fragmentation.

(2) *Equipment.*—Several firms manufacture equipment designed specifically for vibration surveys. Most of this equipment is similar, in that it contains a special geophone, an amplifier, and a paper recorder, and may have an optional magnetic tape recorder and a sound meter. The geophones are three-component, low frequency geophones, similar to (or the same as) those used in surface-wave surveys. Most equipment can record ground motion in terms of particle displacement, velocity, or acceleration. Some equipment only records on magnetic tape, which then must be sent to the manufacturer for interpretation.

(f) *Electrical-Resistivity Profiling Surveys.*—Electrical-resistivity profiling is based on the measurement of lateral changes in the electrical properties of subsurface materials. The electrical resistivity of any material depends on its porosity and the salinity of the water in the pore spaces. Although the electrical resistivity of a material may not be diagnostic of that material, certain materials can be classified as having specific ranges of electrical resistivities. In all electrical-resistivity surveying techniques, an electrical current of known intensity is transmitted into the ground through two (or more) electrodes. The separation between these electrodes depends on the type of surveying being performed and the required depth of investigation. The potential voltage of the electrical field resulting from the application of the current is measured between two (or more) other electrodes at various locations. Because the current is known, and the potential can be measured, the apparent resistivity can be calculated.

(1) *Applications.*—Electrical-resistivity profiling is used to detect lateral changes in the electrical properties of subsurface material, usually to a specified depth. This technique has been used to map the lateral extent of sand and gravel deposits, to provide information for cathodic protection of underground utilities, to map the lateral extent of contamination plumes (in toxic waste studies), and in fault exploration studies.

(2) *Equipment.*—Most electrical-resistivity surveying equipment consists of a current transmitter, a receiver (to measure the resulting potential), two (or more) current electrodes and two (or more) potential electrodes. Two types of current transmitters are available for use: direct current and alternating current transmitters. Direct-current transmitters are powered by dry cell or ni-cad battery systems and are limited in their output; however, they are very portable for field work. Alternating-current transmitters have a more powerful output range and, therefore, can penetrate to greater depths. However, they are not very portable, because the power source requires a generator. Recent innovations in transmitter design have included the use of pulsing direct current to the current electrodes. This system, in effect, acts as a signal-enhancement source.

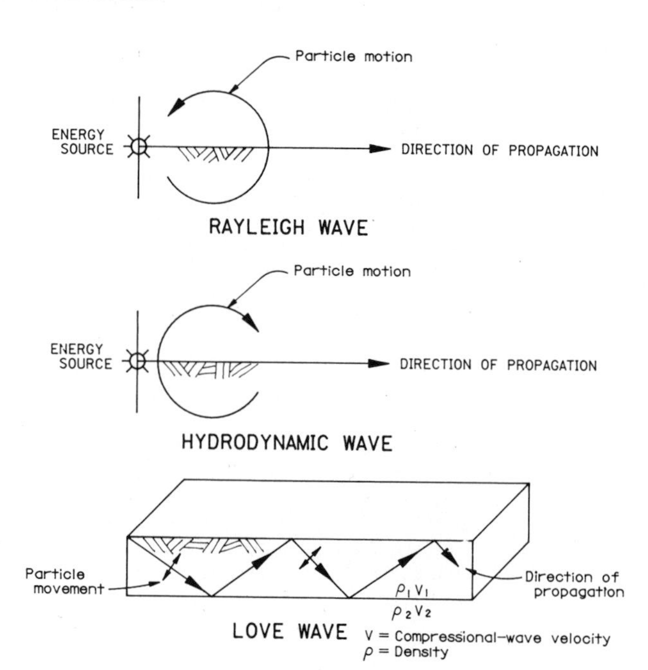

Figure 5-35.—Types of surface waves. 103-D-1867.

Most current and potential electrodes are metallic, usually stainless or copper-clad steel. Where natural earth currents, or electrochemical reactions affect the potential electrodes, nonpolarizable electrodes must be used to measure the potentials resulting from the input of current. These nonpolarizable electrodes consist of a plastic or porcelain container with an unglazed porous bottom. The container is filled with a metallic salt solution that is in contact with a rod of the same metal. Copper sulfate salt in solution is commonly used with a copper rod.

The electrodes are connected to the transmitter and receiver by cables, which are usually contained on small portable reels.

(g) *Electrical-Resistivity Soundings.*—Electrical-resistivity sounding is based on the measurement of vertical changes in the electrical properties of subsurface materials. In contrast to resistivity profiling, in which the electrode separation is fixed, the electrode spacing used for resistivity sounding is variable, while the center point of the electrode array remains constant. The depth of investigation increases in a general sense as the electrode spacing increases, thus resistivity soundings are used to investigate variations of resistivity with depth.

(1) *Applications.*—Electrical-resistivity soundings, often referred to as VES (vertical electrical soundings), are commonly used for aquifer and aquaclude delineation in ground-water investigations. They have been used for bedrock delineation studies, where there may not be enough contrast in velocity to permit seismic surveying.

(2) *Equipment.*—The equipment used in resistivity sounding is identical to the equipment used in electrical-resistivity profiling. For shallow investigations a d-c (direct current) transmitter is normally sufficient; whereas, for deeper investigations an a-c (alternating current) transmitter may be required.

(h) *Electrical-Resistivity, Dipole-Dipole Surveying.*—Dipole-dipole surveying refers to the electrode array orientation, where the pair of potential electrodes may have any position with respect to the pair of current electrodes. When the current and potential electrodes are positioned along the same line, the array is referred to as an axial dipole array (fig. 5-36). The current electrodes are separated from the potential electrodes by an interval, *n*, which is some multiple of the current and potential electrode separation. Normally, the separation of the current and potential electrodes will be equal. Dipole-dipole arrays are used to determine both the lateral and vertical changes in electrical properties of the subsurface materials with one electrode array.

(1) *Applications.*—The dipole-dipole array has limited applications in engineering and ground-water geophysics. This type of electrode array has been used primarily in mineral and geothermal exploration. It has, however, been applied to studies for the delineation of abandoned mines, mapping of salt-fresh water interfaces, and mapping of buried stream channels.

(2) *Equipment.*—The equipment used in dipole-dipole surveying is mostly identical to that used in other types of resistivity surveying. However, because the current and potential electrodes are separated, it is preferable to have the transmitter and receiver as individual units. Fewer cables are required than for other types of resistivity surveyings, because the only cables needed are for the connections between the current electrodes and between the potential electrodes. Because the distance sep-

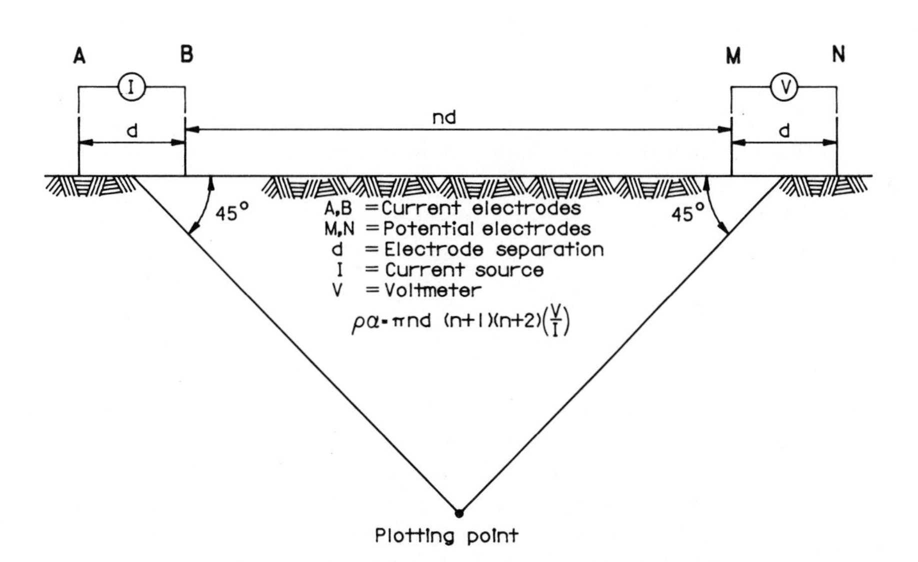

Figure 5-36.—Dipole-dipole resistivity array. 103–D–1868.

arating the current and potential electrodes may be large, dipole-dipole surveying normally requires more transmitter power than either resistivity soundings or profiling surveys, therefore, a generator may be required for the transmitter.

(i) *Electromagnetic-Conductivity Profiling Surveys.*—EM (Electromagnetic) surveying uses time-varying, low-frequency electromagnetic fields induced into the earth. Basically, a transmitter, receiver, and buried conductor are coupled by electrical circuitry through electromagnetic induction. The characteristics of electromagnetic-wave propagation and attenuation at a site can permit an interpretation of the electrical conductivities of the subsurface materials. Because electrical conductivity is the reciprocal of electrical resistivity, electromagnetic surveys are also used to provide resistivity information on subsurface materials. Electromagnetic-conductivity profiling surveys are specifically used to determine lateral changes in the conductivity of the subsurface materials.

(1) *Applications.*—EM surveys have also been used recently in engineering and ground-water investigations. Furthermore, they have been used on occasion to locate buried pipes and cables.

(2) *Equipment.*—The EM survey technique requires sophisticated equipment, which includes a transmitting coil that induces a current into the ground. The receiving coil senses the magnetic field generated by the induced current and the primary field generated by the transmitter. Under certain constraints, the ratio of the induced secondary field to the primary field is linearly proportional to the earth conductivity.

There are two types of systems: fixed-coil spacing and variable-coil spacing. The coil spacing determines the effective depth of investigation. The fixed-spacing equipment can be operated by a single person, but because of the relatively small coil, its spacing is only useful for shallow surveys. Other equipment can be used at different spacings and, therefore, can be used to investigate materials at various depths. The depths, however, are limited to a preselected range that is based on coil-tuning restrictions and other conditions that must be met to maintain a linear relationship with the earth's conductivity field.

(j) *Electromagnetic-Conductivity Sounding Surveys.*—The basic principles involved in EM surveying have been discussed in the previous paragraphs. Electromagnetic sounding surveys are used to determine vertical changes in the conductivity of surface materials.

(1) *Applications.*—Electromagnetic sounding surveys have been applied to delineate areas of permafrost, to locate gravel deposits, to map bedrock topography, and to provide general geologic information. The EM sounding and profiling surveys have also been applied to fault studies.

(2) *Equipment.*—The equipment used in EM sounding surveys is the same as that used in EM profiling surveys. For shallow investigations, less sophisticated equipment is required than for deeper investigations.

(k) *Ground-Probing Radar.*—Ground-probing radar surveys have the same general characteristics as seismic surveys. However, the depth of investigation with radar is much more shallow than that of a seismic survey. This disadvantage is partially offset, however, by the much greater size-resolution of radar techniques.

(1) *Applications.*—Ground-probing radar surveys can be used for a variety of very shallow engineering applications, including locating pipes or other buried objects, high-resolution mapping of near-surface geology, locating near-surface cavities, and locating and determining the extent of piping caused by sink-hole activity and leakage in dams.

These applications are limited, however, by the very small depth of penetration usually possible with the very high frequencies involved in radar. Silts, clays, salts, saline water, the water table, and any other conductive materials in the subsurface will severely restrict or even prevent any further penetration of the subsurface by the radar pulses.

(2) *Equipment.*—The equipment for ground-probing radar is manufactured by only two or three companies at this time, and only a few contractors offer these services. Therefore, the present sources for equipment and contract services are limited.

The equipment itself consists of an antenna/receiver sled, a control/signal processor unit, a strip-chart recorder, a power supply, and various accessories, such as a tape recorder and special signal analyzers. This equipment would normally be operated from a vehicle, except for the antenna/receiver sled, which can be either towed behind the vehicle or pulled by hand. A schematic diagram of radar operations is shown on figure 5-37.

(l) *Self-Potential Surveying.*—SP (Self potential), also called spontaneous potential or natural potential, is the natural electrical potential within the earth. This potential arises from a number of causes, which can be broadly classified into two groups (excluding manmade causes):

- Mineralization potentials, which are primarily the results of chemical concentration cells formed when conductive mineral deposits, such as graphite or sulfide, are intersected by the water table.
- Background potentials, which are primarily the result of (1) two electrolytes of different concentration in contact with each other, (2) electrolytes flowing through a capillary system or porous media, (3) an electrolyte in contact with a solid, and (4) electromagnetically induced telluric currents.

Mineralization potentials are almost always negative and may have values up to several hundred millivolts. Background potentials can be either positive or negative, and usually have values of less than 100 millivolts.

The background potentials developed by electrolytes flowing through a capillary system or porous media (called electro-filtration or streaming potentials) are used for the study of seepage. As water flows through a capillary system, it collects and transports positive ions from the surrounding materials. These positive ions accumulate at the exit point of the capillary, leaving a net positive charge. The untransported negative ions accumulate at the entry point of the capillary, leaving a net negative charge. If the streaming potentials developed by this process are large enough to measure, the entry point and the exit point of concentrated seepage zones may be determined from their respective negative and positive self-potential anomalies.

(1) *Applications.*—In engineering applications, self-potential surveys have been used to map leakage paths from dams, both in the reservoir area and along the crest, toe, and abutments. Self-potential surveying has also been used to map leaks from canals and from buried pipelines. Detachment walls and lateral limits of some landslide masses have been mapped with self-potential surveys. Self-potential surveying may play an important role in contaminated waste studies (contaminant-plume mapping) and in monitoring leakage from hazardous waste sites and dams.

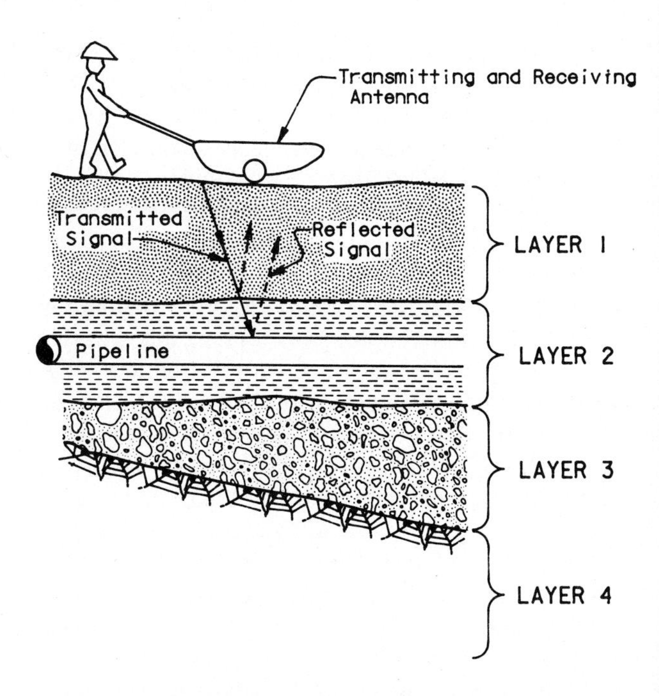

Figure 5-37.—Schematic diagram of ground-penetrating radar. 103–D–1869.

(2) *Equipment.*—The basic piece of equipment required for self-potential surveying is a voltmeter. Analog voltmeters can be used, but because very small potentials are being sought, a digital voltmeter or multimeter is preferable. Self potentials are detected by the use of two nonpolarizable electrodes embedded in soil or water. Nonpolarizable electrodes are used to preclude the development of electrode potentials, which can be larger than the self potentials sought. The two nonpolarizable electrodes are connected to the voltmeter (multimeter) by a single-conductor, jacketed cable. Theoretically this cable may be any length, however, because cable resistance must be taken into account, the length of cable used normally varies from 1,000 to 2,000 feet.

H. SUBSURFACE EXPLORATORY METHODS

5.31. *Accessible Exploratory Methods.*—Accessible test pits, large diameter borings, trenches, and tunnel drifts are exploration methods that can provide the most accurate and complete information possible for subsurface material investigations. These methods are recommended for foundation explorations in lieu of sole reliance on information obtained from exploratory drilling methods. They are subject to economic considerations, structural design and safety considerations, and the complexity of the subsurface geologic structure.

(a) *Test Pits.*—Test pits are used to provide personnel access for visual examination, logging, sampling, and testing of earth foundations and construction materials. They are most commonly used to facilitate sampling and making quantitative computations of potential sources for concrete aggregates, or for performing inplace soil tests. The most economical method of excavating a test pit is by backhoe or bulldozer. The depth by either method is generally limited to a maximum of 20 feet or to the water table. Dozers and backhoes are often used together to exceed 20 feet when the water table is sufficiently deep. By excavating test pits with a backhoe in the bottom of dozer trenches, depths of 30 feet or more can be reached. All open test pit excavations should be sloped to the angle of repose from the bottom of the pit, but never less than a slope of 0.75:1, in accordance with requirements in the *USBR Construction Safety Standards* [2].

(b) *Large-Diameter Borings.*—Caisson auger rigs using large-diameter discs or buckets can be used when accessible explorations are required to be deeper than 20 feet. Depths of over 100 feet have been achieved using this method. Wall support must be provided to the total depth. Typical wall support for large-diameter borings may consist of welded steel casing installed after the boring is completed or preformed steel liner plate segments bolted together as the boring progresses. Personnel access within a drilled caison hole may be provided by the use of an elevator platform rigging with power from a crane hoist, or by notched safety rail ladder using an approved grab-ring safety belt. Work may be performed at any depth of the drilled caison boring through the use of steel platform decking attached to the steel wall support, from a steel scaffolding, or from an elevator platform.

Access for material logging or sample collection behind a steel-encased caisson hole may be accomplished by the use of acetylene torches to cut and remove randomly spaced access openings around the casing circumference or by the removal of bolted liner plate segments to expose the material. Sufficient ventilation must be maintained at all times for personnel working within a drilled test pit; radio communication to surface personnel should also be maintained. Water within a drilled excavation may be removed by an electric or air-powered pump with a discharge conduit to the surface. Dewatering may have to be by stage pumping, using several holding reservoirs and additional pumps as required to lift the water from the test pit to the surface.

Both surface excavated test pits and drilled explorations are excellent exploration methods to achieve an accurate classification of the subsurface material, expose natural fissures or fault zones, obtain undisturbed hand-cut samples, and conduct inplace soil or rock tests.

For safety, all surface excavated test pits left open for inspection should be enclosed within protective fencing and drilled explorations should be provided with locked protective covers and barricades.

(c) *Trenches.*—Test trenches are used to provide access for visual examination of a continuous exposure of the subsurface material along a given line or section. In general, they serve the same purpose as the open test pits (logging, mapping, sampling, inplace testing, etc.), but have the added advantage of disclosing the continuity or character of particular strata. Test trenching is commonly used for seismotectonic studies of material displacement through a natural fault zone. For these studies, the trench is usually excavated perpendicular to the fault line to reveal the vertical displacement of material on both sides of the fault (see fig. 5-38).

Trenches are best suited for shallow exploration. They should usually be at least 3 feet wide and not more than 15 feet deep. Trench jacks, breast boards, or interwoven wire fabric must be installed in all trenches excavated over 5 feet deep. The maximum open interval between any breast board or jack should not exceed 3 feet on center.

Trenches excavated normal to moderately steep slopes have been used successfully in explorations requiring a greater depth than the 15-foot safety limitation. The slope of the natural terrain enables personnel access to greater depths while maintaining the excavated depth at 15 feet. A slope trench may be excavated by a bulldozer, ditching machine, or backhoe from the top to the bottom of the slope to expose representative undisturbed strata or to expose natural fault zones. The profile exposed by test trenches may represent the entire depth of significant strata in an abutment of a dam; however, their shallow depth may limit exploration to the

Figure 5-38.—Trench excavation showing hydraulic trench jack shoring. Trench 1, Pyramid Lake, Nevada (October 1983). P801–D–81042.

upper weathered zone of foundations. The exposed banks of a river channel or road cuts can provide much information for the subsurface exploration program. Exposed and weathered surface material may be removed by hand methods, with the use of a slope grading machine equipped with boom extension and bucket, or with a dragline.

(d) *Tunnels.*—Tunnels and drifts are considered to be the best but most expensive method of exploring foundation or abutment rock formations for structural design studies. Exploratory tunnels and drifts are generally excavated in a horseshoe shape approximately 5 feet wide by 7 feet high. Rock bolts, steel sets, and lagging should follow excavation of the tunnel heading as close as practicable through unstable or blocky rock structure.

Controlled blasting techniques with timed delays should be used to minimize rock fracture beyond the tunnel or drift alignment. A typical controlled explosive blast would involve pulling the center wedge from the heading face instantly, followed by the explosion of time delay charges placed in the following order: invert, ribs, and crown. All tunnel construction safety practices must be throughly adhered to including washing down the tunnel or drift face and muck pile, checking for and detonating misfires, extending air ventilation duct lines, barring loose rock, rock bolting, etc.

Logging and mapping operations should proceed concurrently with excavation operations. Locations for underground core-drill operations or rock mechanics inplace testing should be selected during the tunnel progression so that sections of the tunnel or drift can be enlarged if necessary to accommodate drills or test equipment. Setup of core drills or testing equipment should be scheduled to follow the completion of tunneling activities because of the limited available work area.

5.32. *Nonaccessible Exploratory Methods.*— Cone penetrometer, standard penetration, auger drilling, rotary drilling, and core drilling are the usual nonaccessable exploratory methods. Of these methods, auger drilling, rotary drilling, and core drilling are the most common methods used for subsurface explorations. However, it must be emphasized that sole reliance on drilling operations to provide accurate and reliable geologic interpretations of a complex geologic structure is a gamble that may prove to be extremely costly. The complexity of the geologic structure should be determined before hand. Sometimes, the complexity of the subsurface structure can be determined from the drilling of the first two holes, which are located relatively close to each other (50 to 100 ft) along a floodplain or structure axis alignment. If there is a drastic change in the classification, composition, or structure of the material recovered from sampling or coring operations, and correlation of the materials cannot be projected between the two holes, a decision on the type of exploration method to be used for the rest of the program should be made.

Economics and depth requirements are the principal reasons for performing extensive drilling programs in lieu of constructing accessible trenches or tunnels into a complex geologic structure. If drilling is considered the only feasible method of conducting subsurface explorations, the following considerations should be given priority in the plan for the rest of the exploration program:

(1) All relevant geologic information should be assembled and used for the selection of strategic drilling locations so that an optimum amount of subsurface information can be obtained from a minimum number of drilling locations.

(2) The type of exploration drilling, inplace testing, sampling, or coring necessary to produce pertinent and valid information should be decided upon.

(3) The type of drilling rig that is capable of accomplishing the exploration requirements should be determined.

(4) Complete and concise drilling contract specifications should be developed, if the work cannot be accomplished in-house. The contract award should be based equally upon the contractor's previously demonstrated professional skills to successfully achieve similar exploration drilling requirements and the contract bid price.

Although drilling may be accomplished to some degree of success using manual methods (hand augers, tripod assemblies, and hand-crank hoist systems), many factors (equipment technology, economics, depth requirements, type of sample needs, and the need for accurate subsurface information) have made manual exploration methods obsolete. The following paragraphs identify the various types of mechanical power-driven drilling equipment available and define the most efficient use and equipment capability of each type of drilling unit.

(a) *Cone-Penetrometer Testing.*—A method of exploration that is gaining widespread use in the United States is the cone-penetrometer test (sometimes referred to as the "Dutch Cone Test"). The cone penetrometer consists of a tip and sleeve assembly that is pushed into the ground at a controlled rate. Soil resistance acting on the tip and sleeve are monitored on the surface either mechanically or electrically. If monitored electrically, other parameters such as inclination, and pore-water pressure can also be measured. The device can be operated off a conventional drill rig or can be self-contained on a truck. From the test data, estimates can be made of soil type, inplace unit weight, shear strength, and compressibility. The test is relatively quick to conduct, and although a soil sample is not obtained, when used with conventional drilling and sampling techniques, soil types and profiles in foundations and borrow areas can be rapidly delineated. A mechanical cone-penetrometer apparatus is shown on figure 5-39.

A self-contained, truck-mounted electrical cone-penetration apparatus is shown on figure 5-40. An example of output data from an electrical cone penetrometer is shown on figure 5-41. A more detailed description of the cone penetrometer test is given in USBR 7020 and 7021, Performing Cone Penetration Testing of Soils—Mechanical and Electrical Methods, in the Bureau's *Earth Manual* [7].

(b) *Standard Penetration Testing.*—This is a standardized procedure for taking subsurface soil samples with a split-barrel penetration sampler, and at the same time, measuring the inplace strength, firmness, and denseness of the foundation. The split-barrel penetration sampler is a thick-walled sampler, 2 inches o.d. (outside diam-

Figure 5-39.—Cone penetrometer testing using a conventional drill rig.

Figure 5-40.—Self-contained, truck-mounted, electrical cone-penetration apparatus.

eter), that collects a core sample 1⅜ inches in diameter. The barrel can be separated for examination and removal of the sample (figs. 5-42 and 5-43), and the resistance to penetration can be measured in terms of the number of blows that a 140-pound hammer dropping 30 inches takes to drive the sampler 12 inches (fig. 5-44). In performing this test it is essential that a standardized procedure be used and that information on soil type, water content, and penetration resistance be recorded. Split-barrel samplers other than 2 inches in outside diameter may be used; however, all penetration records made with those samplers should be conspicuously marked with the size of sampler used.

Penetration tests should be made continuously in exploring foundations for dams, except where the resistance of the soil is too great. Any loss of circulation in drilling fluid during the advancing of holes should be noted and recorded on the log. When a casing is used, it should not proceed in advance of the sampling operation. Complete ground-water information should be obtained, including ground-water levels and elevations at which water was lost or water under pressure was encountered. Ground-water levels should be measured before and after the casing is pulled.

Information on sampling and logging of standard penetration holes is given in parts I and J of this chapter, respectively. The penetration resistance values should be recorded and plotted on a log similar to that shown on figure 5-67. The significance of the penetration records in the design of foundations for small dams is discussed in sections 6.12 and 6.13. A more detailed description of the standard penetration test is given in test designation USBR 7015, Performing Penetration Resistance Testing and Sampling of Soil, in the Bureau's *Earth Manual* [7].

(c) *Auger Drilling.*—Auger drills are power drills that are designed for high rotational torque at low

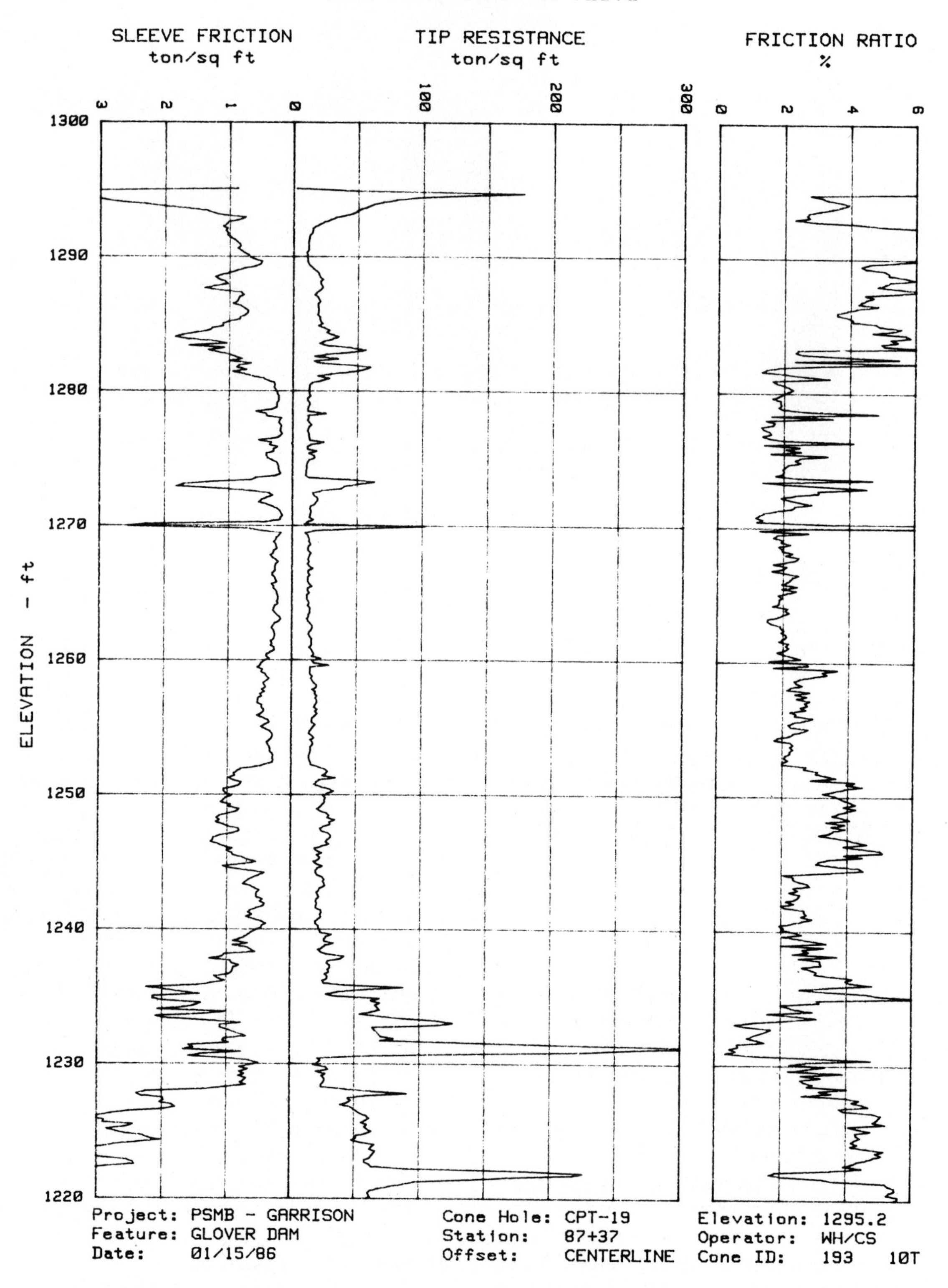

Figure 5-41.—Example of output data from an electrical cone penetrometer. 103-D-1870.

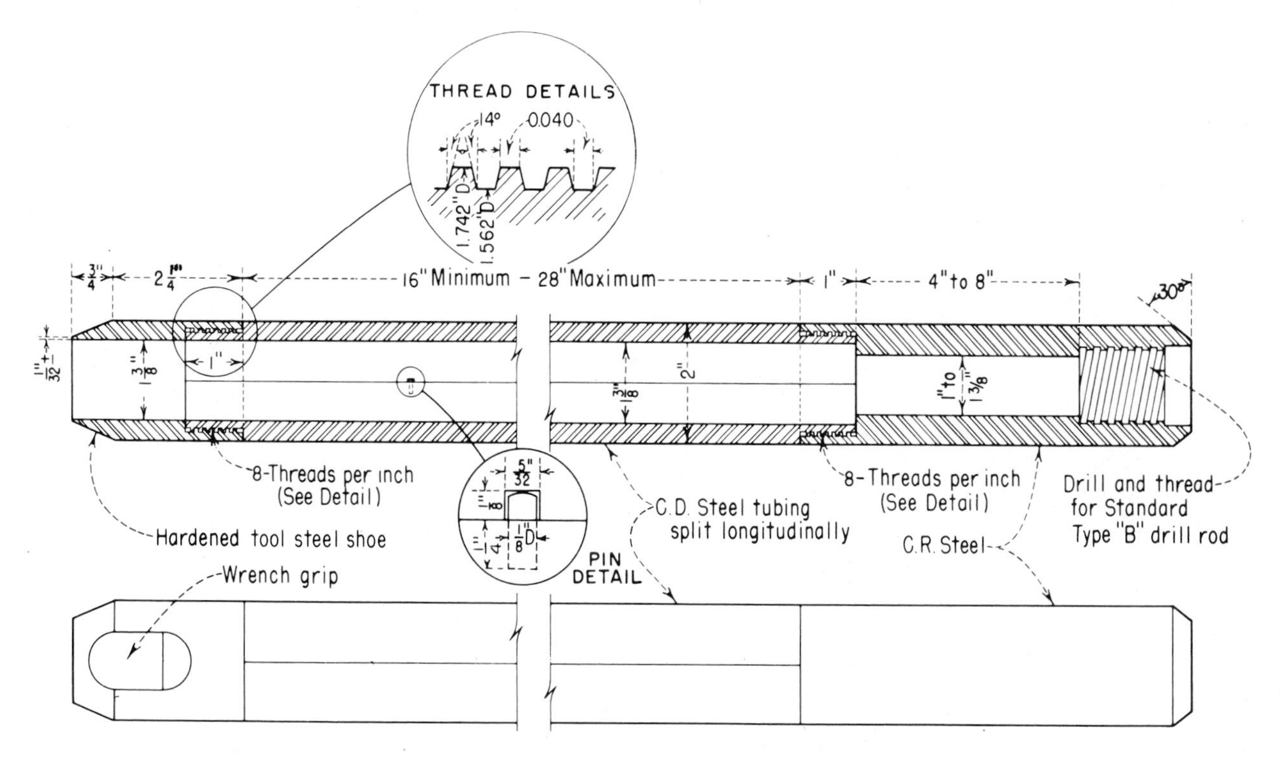

Figure 5-42.—Standard split-barrel sampler. 101–D–169.

Figure 5-43.—Disassembled split-barrel sampler. 288–D–2933.

revolutions per minute as required to drill and collect subsurface soil samples of surfical deposits. Drill cuttings and soil samples are removed by the mechanical rotation of the auger tools without the use of circulation media, thus the requirement for the high torque capability of the drill. Multipurpose auger drills are available that are capable of auger, rotary, or core operations; however, the intent of this section is to individually describe and explain the general use for each of the four distinct types of auger-drilling operations used in subsurface explorations:

- Continuous-flight auger drilling
- Hollow-stem auger drilling
- Disk auger drilling
- Bucket drilling

(1) *Continuous-Flight Augers.*—Continuous-flight auger drilling often provides the simplest and most economical method of subsurface exploration and sampling of surfical deposits in a disturbed condition. Flight augers consist of a center rotational drive shaft with spiral-shaped steel flights welded around the outside circumference of the drive shaft. As each auger section is drilled into the ground, another section is added with an identical spiral flight that is manufactured to match the in-hole auger. The joining of each matched auger section results in a continuous spiral flight from the bottom of the hole to the surface. The rotation of the auger causes the drill cuttings to move upward along the spiral flights, so that samples can be collected at the hole collar. Figure 5-45 shows a continuous-flight auger drilling operation.

Flight augers are manufactured in a wide range of diameters from 2 inches to greater than 24 inches. The most common diameter used for obtaining dis-

Figure 5-44.—Making a standard penetration test using a drill rig. PX-D-34356.

Figure 5-45.—Continuous-flight auger mounted on an all-terrain carrier. D-1635-11.

turbed samples of overburden is 6 inches. Drill depths are normally limited by the torque capability of the drill, the ground-water table, cobble strata, caliche zones, or bedrock.

Continuous-flight auger drilling is an economical and highly productive method used to determine the depth of shallow (100 ft or less) water tables. Another common and efficient use of flight augers is to define borrow area boundaries and depths. Borrow area investigations are conducted by augering holes on a grid pattern to define borrow boundaries and to estimate quantities of usable material. Flight augers are especially beneficial in collecting composite samples of mixed strata material to establish a borrow depth for excavation by belt-loader equipment. Composite samples are collected by advancing the auger boring to the depth capability of the belt-loader. Hole advancement is accomplished by turning the auger at a low, high-torque r/min (revolutions per minute) while adding downpressure for penetration to the depth capability of the belt-loader. At the end of the penetration interval, the auger is turned at a higher r/min without further advancement to collect a composite sample of the material augered through. After the hole is thoroughly cleaned, the material is mixed for a representative composite sample, and sacked according to requirements for laboratory testing. The hole is then deepened to sample a second depth.

Although the above procedure for collecting composite samples of mixed material strata is efficient, it may not result in an accurate representative sample of the material being drilled. This is because of the mixing of the augered material with the side wall material drilled through. In addition, auger borings into a noncohesive loose sand stratum can result in a sample with a greater volume of sand than the volume of sand that would be obtained from a borehole having an equal diameter throughout the hole depth. Therefore, if there is evidence of material contamination, or too much material is recovered from any auger penetration interval, a hollow-stem auger with an inner barrel wireline system or a continuous sampler system should be used in lieu of a continuous-flight auger.

Other beneficial and efficient uses of flight auger drilling include:

- Determination of shallow bedrock depths. It is especially advantageous for estimating overburden excavation volume required to expose potential rockfill or riprap sources. Confirmation of potential rock quality and usable volume can be determined from core drilling exploration methods.
- Drilling through cohesive soils for the installation of well points to monitor water table fluctuation. This is recommended for use only through cohesive soil strata that can be completely removed from the auger hole to leave a clean, full-size open hole for the well point installation and placement of backfill material.
- Determination of overburden depth to potential sand and gravel deposits for concrete aggregate processing. This would be used to estimate the volume of overburden excavation required to expose the sand/gravel deposit. Confirmation of potential concrete aggregate quality and usable volume could be determined from open pit excavation or from the use of a bucket drill.

(2) *Hollow-Stem Augers.*—Hollow-stem auger drilling can provide an efficient and economical method of subsurface exploration, in place testing, and sampling of overburden material in an undisturbed condition. Hollow-stem augers are manufactured similar to flight augers with spiral shaped steel flights welded around the outside circumference of a center rotational drive shaft. The difference between flight augers and hollow-stem augers involves the design of the center drive shaft. The continuous-flight auger drive shaft consists of a steel tube with closed end sections for solid pin connections to adjacent auger sections. However, the hollow-stem auger drive shaft consists of a hollow steel tube throughout the total length with threaded or cap-screw connections for coupling to adjacent auger sections. The advantages of hollow-stem auger drilling over continuous-flight auger drilling are:

- Undisturbed sampling tools and inplace testing equipment can be lowered and operated through the hollow-stem without removal of the in-hole auger.
- Unstable soils and water zones can be drilled through and cased by the hollow-stem auger to inhibit caving or infiltration into adjacent soil strata.
- Instruments and ground behavior monitoring equipment can be installed and backfilled through the hollow-stem.
- Removal of samples through the hollow-stem eliminates contamination from upper-strata material.

- Rotary drilling or core drilling operations may use the hollow-stem as casing to advance the hole beyond auger drilling capabilities.

In addition to the advantages previously listed, the hollow-stem auger can be operated to function as a continuous-flight auger. This is accomplished with the use of a plug bit within the center tube of the lead auger, as shown on figure 5-46. The bit can be retracted at any time for further undisturbed sampling or inplace testing without removing the auger tools.

Before the early 1980's, undisturbed sampling with hollow-stem augers was accomplished by removing the lead auger plug bit and lowering conventional soil samplers, thinwall push tubes, or penetration resistance samplers to the hole bottom. The sample quality was generally satisfactory, but this procedure was inefficient, especially during the changeover from dry auger drilling to the preparation and use of circulation fluids necessary to remove drill cuttings during sampling operations with rotary soil samplers. Auger manufacturers solved this problem with the development of soil sampling tools that recover undisturbed soil samples simultaneous with the advancement of the hollow-stem auger and without the need for drill fluids. This development has resulted in an improved method to recover quality undistrubed soil samples of surficial deposits more efficiently and economically than any other method.

Hollow-stem augers are commonly manufactured in 5-foot lengths and with sufficient inside clearance to pass sampling or inplace testing tools from 2 to 7 inches in diameter. The spiral flights are generally sized to auger a hole 4 to 5 inches larger than the inside diameter of the center tube. Drill depths are normally limited by the rotational torque capability of the drill, cobble strata, caliche zones, or bedrock.

(3) *Disk Augers.*—Disk auger drilling can be an economical method of drilling large-diameter holes for disturbed sampling or of installing the large-diameter castings for accessible explorations. A disk auger has spiral-shaped flights that are similar in design to a flight auger; however, it is used as a single-length tool rather than being coupled to adjoining sections. Rotational power is provided by a square or hexagonal drive shaft (Kelly bar). Drill cuttings are retained by the upper disk flight and are removed by hoisting the disk auger from the hole after every 3 to 5 feet of penetration.

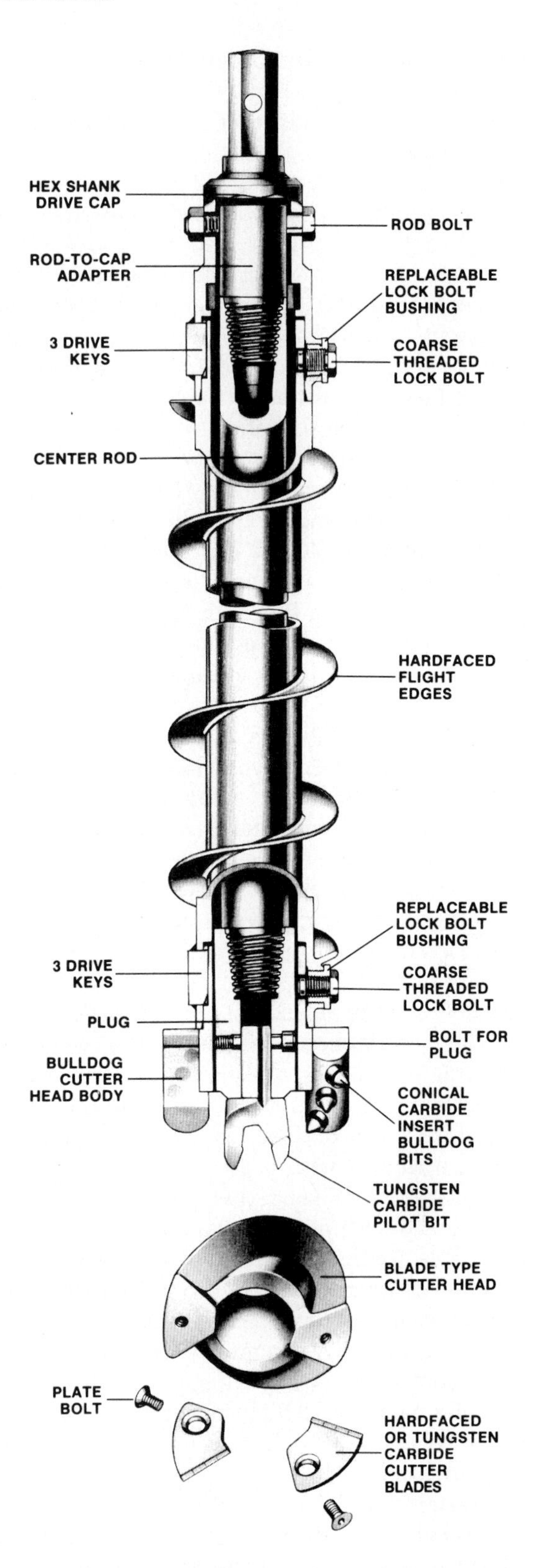

Figure 5-46.—Hollow-stem auger with center plug. D-1635-14.

Hole diameters can range from 12 to 120 inches, and the larger disk auger rigs can drill to 120 feet or more using telescoping Kelly drive bars. Unless a casing is used, disk auger capabilities are generally limited by cobble or boulder strata, saturated flowing sands, or ground-water tables. Weathered or "soft" rock formations can be drilled effectively with a disk auger equipped with wedge-shaped "ripper" teeth (fig. 5-47). Concrete and "hard" rock can be drilled by disk augers equipped with conical, tungsten-carbide tipped teeth.

In addition to the drilling and installation of deep accessible explorations, disk augers are used to recover large-volume samples from specific subsurface material strata. They may also be used to drill and install perforated casing or well screens for ground-water monitoring systems. The most frequent use of disk augers is for the drilling of caissons for the building construction industry.

(4) *Bucket Drills.*—Bucket drills, occasionally misnamed "bucket augers," are used to drill large-diameter borings for disturbed sampling of overburden soil and gravel material. The bucket is designed as a large-diameter hollow steel drum, usually 3 to 4 feet long, that is rotated by a square or hexagonal drive (Kelly bar) connected to a steel yoke at the top of the bucket. The bottom of the bucket is designed with a hinged and lockable steel cutter plate equipped with wedge shaped ripper teeth. The cutter plate is mechanically locked during the rotational drilling operation and has a 9- to 12-inch bottom opening through which drill cuttings are forced and collected in the bucket. After a 3- to 4-foot drilling penetration, the bucket is hoisted out of the drill hole, attached to a side jib boom, and moved off the hole for the discharge of the cuttings. The cuttings are then discharged by a mechanical release of the hinged cutter plate or by opening one side of the bucket, which may be designed with hinges. The drilling operation is continued by locking the cutter plate or the hinged side panel of the bucket before lowering the bucket to the hole bottom.

Hole diameters can range from 12 to 84 inches in diameter using a standard bucket. A reamer arm extension, equipped with ripper teeth, can be attached to the bucket drive yoke for over-reaming the hole to 120 inches in diameter using special crane-attached bucket drills. When using over-reaming bar extensions, drill cuttings enter the bucket from the bottom cutter plate during rotary penetration. Cuttings also fall into the top of the bucket as a result of the rotational cutting action of the over-reamer.

Figure 5-47.—Large disk auger with ripper teeth. D-1635-18.

Bucket drill capabilities are generally limited by saturated sands, boulders, caliche, or the ground-water table unless casing is used. Weathered or "soft" rock formations can be effectively penetrated with bucket drills. The larger crane-attached bucket drills have achieved depths of 190 feet using telescoping Kelly drive bars and crane drawworks hoist systems.

Bucket drills are used in the construction industry for boring caisson holes. They have proved extremely beneficial in performing subsurface investigations into sand and gravel deposits for concrete aggregate investigations. They may also be used to drill and collect intermixed gravel and cobble samples up to approximately 8 inches in diameter. Bucket drills can be an effective method of drilling deep accessible explorations. Figure 5-48 shows a bucket drill in operation.

(d) *Rotary Drilling.*—Rotary drills are power drills designed for medium rotational torque at variable rotational speeds from low (approximately 100 r/min) for hole penetration using tri-cone rock bits or carbide-tipped drag bits to medium-high (approximately 800 r/min) for undisturbed soil sampling or rock core drilling with core barrels.

All rotary drills are equipped with high-pressure fluid injection pumps or air compressors to circulate drill media. This media, which may consist of water, drill mud, compressed air, or air-foam, is used to cool and lubricate the cutting bits and to hold the drill cuttings in suspension for circulation to the top of the hole.

Seven distinctively different types of rotary drills are used in subsurface explorations:

- Rotary-table drills
- Top-head drive drills
- Hollow-spindle drills
- Fluted Kelly drills
- Reverse-circulation (rotary and percussion) drills
- Top-head drive with percussion casing hammer drills
- Horizontal rotary drills

The following paragraphs describe each type of rotary drill and explain the most beneficial use for which each drill has been designed. In addition, although it is not classified as a rotary drill, the operation and use of the churn/cable-tool drill is described.

(1) *Rotary-Table Drills.*—Rotary drills were initially developed for the petroleum industry as a stationary-plant, heavy-duty drill machine using a large rotational table mechanism to provide rotary power to a rigid tabular string of rods with a bit attached. Hole penetration is accomplished by the use of heavy, weighted drill collars coupled to the drill rod and high-pressure pumps that discharge circulation fluid through small jet ports in the bit. The weight, butting action of the rotary bit, and high-pressure jetting action of the circulation media all combine to rapidly advance the drill hole through all types of surfical deposits and bedrock. Although this type of drill has proved extremely effective for the petroleum industry (it rapidly advances boreholes to deep "paysands"), it is not designed to perform relatively shallow subsurface investigations. This type of a drilling operation would be cost-prohibitive in shallow exploration work and would result in very poor core quality in low-strength rock.

A smaller version of the rotary-table drill was developed by drilling manufacturers to perform shallow explorations and water well drilling. These are generally truck-mounted rigs with a chain- or gear-driven rotary table. The use of smaller, lower pressure pumps with bypass systems provides better control over the injection of downhole fluid pressure that could easily erode or fracture the rock. Mechanical chain pulldowns were added to eliminate the use of heavy drill collars for more precise control over the bit pressure. However, a drill with a mechanical chain pulldown is not designed with the precision control features necessary to recover quality core samples of soil or laminated hard to

Figure 5-48.—Bucket drill rig in drilling position with a 24-foot triple Kelly and 36-inch bucket. D-1635-20.

soft rock. This type of a rotary-table drill is primarily used in the water well industry and could be beneficial to the subsurface exploration industry as a method to install ground-water monitoring systems.

Rotary-table drills can drill holes with diameters from 6 to 24 inches. Depth capabilities can range from 2,500 feet to greater than 10,000 feet.

(2) *Top-Head Drive Drills.*—The top-head drive drill was developed to provide greater operator control over the drilling operation. This is accomplished through the use of variable-speed hydraulic pumps and motors for the rotational speed and control of bit pressure. The incorporation of hydraulic systems into drilling machinery has vastly improved drilling capabilities, performance, and reliability, with less down time for costly repairs. A skilled operator can control even the largest top-head drive drill with precision by monitoring the drill-head hydraulic pressure (indicating bit torque resistance); by monitoring the drill media circulation pressure (indicating open-hole, blocked-hole, open-bit, or plugged-bit condition); and by controlling the applied hydraulic pulldown pressure, making it compatible with the bit pressure required to drill the formation at a constant and efficient rate of penetration. In addition to the capability to apply controlled hydraulic down pressure (crowd pressure), the new top-head drive drill rigs are equipped with "float" controls, which provide gravity pulldown pressure equal to the weight of the drill head and in-hole drill tools, and with "hold-back" controls, which apply a back pressure to the gravity down pressure to reduce the applied weight at the bit. All of these features have made the top-head drive rotary drill one of the most advanced drilling units for quality subsurface explorations.

Top-head drive rotary drills are generally long-stroke drills capable of continually penetrating 10 to 30 feet without requiring additional rods or "re-chucking". Conventional drilling for the advancement of boreholes to specific depths is normally accomplished with the use of 2⅜- to 5½-inch o.d. rods. For drilling stability, maintenance of hole alignment, and thorough circulation of drill cuttings out of the hole, the drill rod diameter should not be less than one-half that of the cutting bit. A drill rod/bit combination of a 4½-inch-o.d. rod and an 8-inch-diameter bit results in an annulus of 1¾ inches between the rod and hole wall. This annulus is sufficient for the thorough removal of all drill cuttings by high-velocity circulation media flow while minimum pump pressure is maintained. For holes larger than 8 inches in diameter, centralizers or stabilizers manufactured approximately 1 inch smaller in diameter than the bit, should be added to the drill rod string on approximately 30-foot centers. These stabilize the drill string and aid the removal of drill cuttings from the hole through the reduced annulus area.

Downhole percussion hammers are commonly used with top-head drive drills for rapid penetration through hard materials and to maintain a better drill-hole alignment than can be achieved with the use of tricone rock bits.

Tricone rock bits are generally rotated 3 to 4 times faster than a downhole hammer, but have a tendency to drift off alignment when one or more cutting cones contact the edge of a boulder or other obstruction. Downhole hammers are operated with air or an air-foam mix and are generally rotated between 12 and 20 r/min. The bit is slightly concave and embedded with rounded tungsten-carbide buttons that chip away at the rock with rapid in-out percussion impact blows. The slow rotation and direct impact hit of the single piece button bit can result in the control of a truer hole alignment than with the use of a 3-roller tricone bit.

In subsurface exploration programs, top-head drive drills are commonly used to drill for and install ground-water monitoring systems, structural-behavior monitoring instruments, geothermal investigations, waste injection wells, and to recover large-diameter surficial deposit or rock core samples. When continuous cores are required, a large-diameter wireline system should be used to maintain efficiency and eliminate the need to remove all rods from the hole for core recovery. In all coring operations using air-foam circulation media, the outside diameter of the core bit must be sized to drill a hole not less than ⅞-inch larger in diameter than the outside diameter of the drill rod. Water or low-viscosity mud circulation could be accomplished with a core bit at least ½-inch larger in diameter than the outside diameter of the rod.

Hole diameters using top-head drive drills generally range from 6 to 24 inches; depth capabilities may range from 1,500 to more than 5,000 feet. Figure 5-49 shows a top-head drive drill with head in mast.

(3) *Hollow-Spindle Drills.*—The hollow spindle drill is a multiple-use drill developed to provide a

Figure 5-49.—Top-head drive drill with head in mast for drilling. P801–D–81043.

method of quick changeover from auger drilling to rotary or core drilling operations. Basically, the hollow spindle provides the rotary drive power, pulldown, and retract to the specific drill tools being used. Unlike other rotary drills designed to drill only with tubular-shaped drill rods or heavy-duty Kelly bars, the hollow-spindle drillhead has been designed for the attachment of a flight auger or hollow-stem auger drive head, of manual or hydraulically activated chuck assemblies to clamp tubular-shaped drill rods, or of automatic chuck assemblies for clamping and drilling with fluted Kelly drive bars.

Another advantage of a hollow-spindle drill is that the spindle opening provides access for the passage of smaller sampling tools or of inplace testing tools through the larger diameter drill rod or the hollow-stem auger without having to disassemble major equipment. This is especially advantageous in wireline core drilling or penetration resistance testing operations.

Hollow-spindle drills are manufactured either with variable-speed hydraulic drillheads or mechanically driven drillheads powered by a multiple rotary-speed transmission. The pulldown feed rate and retraction is hydraulically controlled and can be automatically set to maintain a constant rate of feed and pressure on the drill bit. Hollow-spindle drills are manufactured with the capability to continuously drill 6 to 11 feet in a single feed stroke without having to add drill rods or rechuck to achieve additional depth.

A wide variety of sampling and inplace testing operations can be achieved with a hollow-spindle drill. Disturbed samples can be obtained by flight auger drilling. Undisturbed samples can be obtained with the use of 3- to 5-inch thinwall push tubes or soil samplers that are designed to lock within the hollow-stem auger and simultaneously recover a soil core sample with the advancement of the hollow-stem auger. Large-diameter undisturbed soil samples (4- to 6-inch diameter) can be recovered using drill mud or air-foam circulation media and conventional soil-sampling core barrels. The hollow-spindle design also permits fixed-piston sampling of noncohesive sands or of saturated soils with sampling tools that require an inner rod within the drill rod. Rock coring operations can be performed using wireline systems or conventional core barrels with water, air, or air-foam circulation media.

Inplace testing can be conducted within the hollow-stem auger without a major changeover of equipment. The specific inplace tests that can be efficiently conducted with a hollow-spindle drill are vane shear, penetration resistance, and hydraulic Dutch-cone testing.

Holes using hollow-spindle drills generally do not exceed 8 inches in diameter. Depth capabilities vary: approximately 150 feet through surficial deposits with a hollow-stem auger, 200 feet through surficial deposits with a flight auger, 800 feet through surficial deposits and bedrock with a 6-inch-diameter rotary bit, and up to 1,000 feet through bed rock with a 3-inch-diameter wireline coring system.

(4) *Fluted Kelly Drills.*—A rotary drill that is equipped with a fluted Kelly rod is designed to con-

tinuously drill 10 to 30 feet (continuous drill length depends on the length of the Kelly rod) without having to add additional drill rods. The Kelly rod is a thick-walled tubular steel rod that has 3 or 4 semicircular grooves milled on equally spaced centers into the outer wall of the rod and parallel to the axis of the rod. The milled grooves (flutes) run continuously along the total length of the Kelly rod except through the upper and lower tool joint connections.

Drills equipped with fluted Kelly rods are generally designed to supply rotational power to the Kelly rod through the combined use of a stationary drillhead and rotary quill. The quill is equipped with an automatic pulldown and Kelly drive bushing to apply downward pressure and rotational drive to the Kelly rod. The Kelly drive bushing contains hardened steel pins sized to fit into the rod flutes for rotational drive power to the Kelly rod. While rotational torque is being applied by the drive bushing pins within the flute grooves, the Kelly rod has an unrestricted up or down movement throughout the total length of the flutes. Hole advancement is accomplished by engaging the automatic pulldown to clamp and apply hydraulically controlled down pressure to the Kelly rod. It is also common practice to disengage the automatic pulldown, in relatively easy drilling material, and let the weight of the total drill string (Kelly rod, attached drill rods, and bit) advance the hole with hold-back control maintained by controlled braking of the drawworks hoist cable attached to the top of the Kelly rod.

Fluted Kelly drills are commonly used in subsurface exploration programs to bore 6- to 8-inch-diameter holes through surficial deposits and bedrock, to set casing, and to recover large-diameter (4- to 6-inch) undisturbed soil or rock cores with conventional core barrels. Drill mud or air-foam is generally used to remove cuttings. A fluted Kelly drill is not considered efficient for exploration programs that require continuous core recovery because they are generally not equipped for wireline core operations. This limitation significantly reduces coring production because all rods and the core barrel must be removed from the hole after each core run.

Fluted Kelly drills are best used in the drilling and installation of water observation wells. Hole sizes may be drilled to 12 inches diameter and to depths ranging from 1,000 to 1,500 feet. Figure 5-50 shows a fluted Kelly drill setup.

Figure 5-50.—Fluted Kelly drill setup. Automatic pull-down chuck assembly and breakout table. P801-D-81044.

(5) *Reverse-Circulation (Rotary and Percussion) Drills.*—A reverse-circulation drill is a specialized rotary or percussion drill that uses a double-walled tubular drill rod. The circulation drilling media, compressed air or air-foam, is forced downhole through the annulus between the inner and outer rod wall. For a reverse-circulation rotary drill, the circulation media is ejected near the tool joint connection between the rotary bit and the center rod. The media circulates around the outside face of the bit to cool the bit and move the drill cuttings upward through a center opening in the bit. The cuttings are forced up the center tube to a discharge point at the hole collar. For a reverse-circulation

percussion drill, the circulation media is ejected just above the drive shoe on the outer rod. The media forces the movement of drill cuttings that have entered the drive shoe upward through the center tube to a discharge point at the hole collar.

The reverse-circulation rotary drill uses a hydraulically powered top-head drive drillhead and hydraulic pulldown/retract system. This drill is especially beneficial for drilling through loss circulation zones (loose sands, voids, etc.), for recovering uncontaminated disturbed samples, and for testing water aquifier yield. Drill depths to 1,000 feet can be achieved using a dual-wall drill rod with an outside diameter of 5½ inches and a center tube inside diameter of 3¼ inches.

The reverse-circulation percussion drill uses an air-or diesel-powered pile drive hammer to drive dual-wall drive pipe sizes ranging from 5½ inches o.d. by 3¼ inches center tube diameter to 24 inches o.d. by 12 inches center tube i.d. Depth capabilities range from 50 feet (with the 24-inch-o.d. drive pipe) to 350 feet (with the 5½-inch-o.d. drive pipe). This drill is especially good for drilling gravel to boulder-size material and for recovering uncontaminated disturbed samples of sand, gravel, and cobble-size material.

Another advantage of a reverse-circulation percussion drill and dual-wall drive pipe is that the drive pipe can be used as a temporary casing through coarse aggregate deposits. Smaller drills can then be set over the casing to conduct coring operations or inplace tests or to install subsurface instrumentation systems.

(6) *Top-Head Drive with Percussion Casing Hammer Drills.*—A top-head drive rotary drill equipped with an automatic casing hammer has given a new dimension to the expanded capabilities of rotary drilling. The drill is essentially the same as the conventional top-head drive drill previously described. The addition of an automatic casing driver gives additional capabilities to the drilling equipment to simultaneously advance the casing during rotary drilling operations. This is especially advantageous during rotary drilling operations through materials susceptible to caving or squeezing such as sand-cobble-boulder strata, saturated sands, and soft saturated silts and clays subject to squeezing.

Before the development of automatic casing drivers, the material subject to caving had to be drilled through, followed by the removal of all rods and the drill bit from the hole. The casing would then be driven to refusal with the use of a rope catline and mechanical cathead to hoist and drop a heavy, weighted drive hammer to impact on a steel anvil installed on the top of the casing. More often than not, driving refusal would only be to the top of cave material that had previously been drilled. This procedure would then be followed by the redrilling of the caved material, removing rods, repeating casing driving attempts, etc. This unfortunate but common situation has often resulted in significant losses in production, money, and damaged equipment for many drilling contractors.

Automatic casing drivers are designed for use only with top-head drive rotary drills. The casing driver is designed with a circular opening through the center of the driver assembly for the rotation of drill rods through the casing. This permits simultaneous drilling advancement with casing advancement. As the casing driver lowers during the percussion driving of the casing, the drillhead lowers to ream a pilot hole for the casing drive shoe and to remove cuttings from within the casing.

Casing drivers are powered by compressed air. This actuates the driving ram, which is designed to impact the casing drive anvil with a driving energy ranging from 1,300 foot-pounds, for the smaller drivers, to 7,400 foot-pounds, for the larger drivers. The circulation media for the removal of cuttings is compressed air or air-foam. The cuttings travel upward through the casing to a discharge spout that is a component of the casing driver.

The efficiency of simultaneous rotary drilling with a downhole hammer and installation of a 10-inch-o.d. casing through 180 feet of homogeneous cobble (6- to 12-inch) material was recently demonstrated at El Vado Dam, New Mexico. Two 180-foot deep holes through the cobble embankment were drilled and cased in 20 hours production time. After the installation of a well screen and backfill material through the casing in each hole, the casing was removed from both holes in 14 hours production time. Removal of the casing is accomplished by the capability of the casing driver to drive upward for impact against a pulling bar anvil positioned in the top of the driver assembly. The bottom of the pulling bar, opposite the upward-drive anvil, is connected to an adaptor "sub" for attachment to each section of casing.

One of the greatest benefits derived from the use of a rotary drill equipped with a casing driver is minimizing the possibility of creating a hydraulic fracture in earth embankment dams during drilling operations. After the 1976 failure of Teton Dam in eastern Idaho, top priority was placed on the installation of dam safety monitoring instrumentation into existing embankment dams. However, it was soon discovered that conventional rotary drill rigs, using mud, water, or air circulation media, could create severe problems during embankment drilling. The high priority given to the program created a sense of urgency to drill and install dam safety monitoring instrumentation as quickly as possible. Problems soon surfaced when uncased drill holes were advanced through zones of some embankments. These zones were subject to squeezing or caving and would sometimes result in blockage above the drill bits, restricting the return circulation. Failure to maintain an open hole could result in a sudden increase of the circulation media pressure, which could, in turn, cause hydraulic fracturing of the embankment.

In 1982, the Bureau of Reclamation developed a method for rotary drilling through embankments with high-pressure, compressed-air-foam circulation media that has practically eliminated the danger of hydraulic fracture. Simultaneous rotary drilling/casing driving operations are performed using an air-actuated casing driver capable of delivering 7,400 foot-pounds of driving energy per impact blow at 75 blows per minute. Special high-strength threaded casing, with inside diameters of 6 and 8 inches, has repeatedly been driven to depths of 400 feet through earth embankments and removed after instrumentation installation. The high-pressure air-foam circulation media is contained within the open casing by advancing the casing drive shoe 6 to 8 inches ahead of the rotary bit. This procedure ensures containment of the circulation media pressure within the casing by the formation of a compacted soil plug within the drive shoe. When cobbles or boulder-size materials are encountered, the bit or downhole hammer is lowered to 3 inches below the drive shoe to continue casing advancement to bedrock. The accumulation of cuttings along the inner wall of the casing is inhibited by continuous monitoring of the air-foam injection pressure and by back reaming through the casing after every 5 feet of penetration.

After completion of the borehole to the planned depth, the instruments and backfill material are installed within the casing. After the placement of backfill to a height of approximately 30 feet above the hole bottom, 10 to 20 feet of casing is removed followed by a continuation of the backfilling operation. This procedure leaves the upper part of the backfill within the casing at all times to prevent the cave material from damaging the instrument or contaminating the backfill. The percussive blows of the casing driver contributes to a thorough consolidation of the backfill material by vibration of the casing during the removal operation.

(7) *Horizontal Rotary Drills.*—Horizontal rotary drills were initially developed in the 1960's for the installation of perforated or slotted pipe drains into water-saturated landslide areas for stabilization purposes. The success of this innovative idea resulted in the development of an industry involved in the manufacture of specialized drilling and slotted PVC drainpipe. Horizontal rotary drills are crawler tractor-mounted for all-terrain mobility and are designed with adequate weight distribution for stability to provide the required horizontal thrust. The track carrier power unit provides the mechanical tracking power for the tractor and the total hydraulic power for the drill unit. The rotary drillhead is positioned on a box-beam slide attached to the side of the tractor. The slide is equipped for movement, with the use of hydraulic cylinders, to result in drilling capabilities at any angle from vertical to 45° above horizontal. Drilling is continuous throughout a 10-foot travel length of the drillhead over a smooth plane surface of the beam slide. Forward thrust and retract of the drillhead is hydraulically controlled through the combined use of a hydraulic ram, equipped with wire rope sheave wheels, and a cable (wire rope) attached to the drillhead.

Drilling is accomplished by using a custom-sized drill rod, 2¼ inches i.d. by 3 inches o.d., or 4½ inches i.d. by 5 inches o.d. The smaller rod is used to install 2-inch diameter slotted PVC drainpipe; the larger rod is used to install up to 4-inch-diameter drainpipe, piezometers, or slope inclinometer casing. Special carbide tipped drag bits or tricone bits are locked to a drill sub on the lead rod that is manufactured with two J-shaped slots milled into opposite side walls of the drill sub body. The bit shank (threaded tool joint connection of the bit body) is welded to a tubular steel sleeve that is milled with an inside diameter slightly larger than the outside diameter of the J-slotted drill sub. A hardened steel pin is welded across the inside diameter of the bit sleeve for locking into the J slots of the sub. The bit is attached for drilling by pushing the bit sleeve over the drill sub to bottom contact of the hardened pin into the J slot, and locked by one-quarter turn to the opposite direction of the drilling rotation. Figure 5-51 shows an Aardvark Model 500 horizontal drill in operation.

The most successful landslide stabilization programs evolve from good preplanning to analyze the hydrogeologic system. This is accomplished by drilling several vertical water observation wells upslope from the toe of the slide to determine the drilling angle required to intercept the water influence zone for dewatering through drain installation. Drilling setup locations are established at the toe of the slide and at strategic elevations upslope from the toe (the number of locations depends on the area and vertical rise of the landslide). The horizontal rotary drill is then set on location and the drill slide beam is elevated and locked on the interception angle.

Drilling for landslide drain installations is performed using water as the circulation media to remove cuttings. Horizontal or angle drilling into slide zones is generally a high-production operation (average drilling penetration rate is 8 to 10 ft/min) primarily because of the saturated and loose condition of the material. The drill can drill to 800-foot depths using a 4½-inch bit for the 3-inch-o.d. drill rod, and to 500-foot depths using a 6½-inch bit for the 5-inch-o.d. drill rod. Most of the drain installations are drilled in a fan pattern through the slide material.

After the completion of the hole to the designed depth, the drillhead is unthreaded from the drill rod, and slotted PVC drain pipe is installed within the drill rod to contact with the drill bit. A one-way check valve assembly, positioned behind the discharge ports of the bit, inhibits the entrance of ground water or drill cuttings into the rod during the installation of the drain pipe. The drain pipe installation into the drill rod is measured to equal total hole depth plus 3 feet to ensure the water discharge point is outside the hole collar. The drillhead is power threaded onto the drill rod containing the slotted drain pipe, and an additional 1 to 1½ feet of drilling penetration is made without the use of circulation media. This operation forces dry cuttings to plug and seize the drill bit so that it can be ejected from the drill rod. After the dry drilling, water is pumped into the drill rod to approximately

Figure 5-51.—Horizontal rotary drill. Aardvark Model 500 drill with adjustable box-beam slide, crawler-tractor mounted. P126-100-4001.

300 lb/in^2 pressure behind the plugged bit. A reverse rotation on the drill rod unlocks the expendable bit from the J-slotted drill sub. This is followed by a rapid (high-power) pullback on the drill rod while monitoring the pump pressure for indication of a sudden pressure drop. The pressure drop confirms bit drop off, which is immediately followed by rapid withdrawal of the drill rods. As the rods are withdrawn, the drain pipe is maintained in the hole (against the expendable bit) by continuing to inject water against a floating piston device seated against the outlet end of the drain pipe. This floating piston maintains pressure on the drain pipe to prevent withdrawal of the drain during rod removal. After all rods are removed, the drain discharge is plumbed into a manifold pipe assembly and conduit to direct the water away from the slide zone.

Leaving a bit in the hole generally creates some concern over wasting a drill bit that could be used for additional drilling operations. The cost is insignificant compared with the cost of removing all drill rods, saving the bit, and attempting to install drain pipe in a hole that has collapsed.

In addition to drilling for drain installations into

water-saturated landslides, horizontal rotary drills have proven extremely efficient and effective for use in performing the other types of subsurface work listed below.

a. Core Drilling for Tunnel Alignment Geology.—A river diversion tunnel alignment at Buttes Damsite, Arizona, was horizontally core drilled to a depth of 927 feet using a horizontal rotary drill and NWD-3 core-barrel assembly. Core recovery was 98.9 percent. The production rate was good at an average of 26 feet per shift; however,the addition of a pump-in wireline core barrel would have the potential to triple the conventional core-barrel production.

b. Slope Inclinometer Casing Installation.—The most productive and efficient method known for the drilling, installation, and grouting of inclinometer casing is with the use of a horizontal rotary drill. The drill can be track-walked under its own power to difficult access sites. The inclinometer hole can be drilled with a 6¼-inch expandable bit and a 4¼-inch-i.d. drill rod. The inclinometer casing can be installed to the hole bottom through the large-diameter drill rod. After the release of the expandable bit, the annulus between the hole wall and inclinometer casing can be homogeneously grouted by pumping through the drill rod. When the grout fills to the hole collar, the drill rod can be removed from the hole to complete the inclinometer casing installation. After completion, a water-injection pipe should be lowered to the bottom of the casing installation for clean water circulation and removal of any grout that may have entered the inclinometer casing joints.

c. Piezometer Installation.—The drilling and installation procedure is the same as that described for an inclinometer casing. However, the backfilling procedure is changed to be compatible with the type of backfill material used. Generally, a uniformly graded clean sand is placed around the piezometer tip or to a specified height above the slot openings of a well screen. This can be accomplished by placing in the drill rod a measured volume of backfill material that is 1 to 2 feet greater than the volume required to fill the hole after removal of a single drill rod. The drillhead is then threaded onto the collar rod, and one rod is removed while clean water is simultaneously pumped and rotating slowly to force the backfill out of the rod. This procedure leaves 1 to 2 feet of material in the bottom rod that protects the piezometer from an open hole condition and possible caving. The backfill and rod removal procedure is repeated in like increments to completion of the hole.

d. Settlement-Plate Monitoring Systems.—Choke Canyon Dam, Texas, was constructed with 1-yd^2 steel settlement plates embedded at the interface between the embankment and compacted overburden material just below the embankment. After the completion of the embankment construction, a horizontal rotary drill was set on the 3:1 downstream slope face to drill and install a steel reinforcement measurement rod to contact on the plate for survey monitoring of the embankment settlement. Drilling was conducted using a 3-inch-o.d. rod and a 4¼-inch drag bit with water circulation media. The plates were located at 6 separate stations along the embankment to an average depth of 140 feet. After the bit contacted each plate, the rods were pulled and the bit removed. The second drill phase was conducted with an open drill sub on the lead rod to contact the steel plate. The 2-inch casing pipe was lowered through the drill pipe to plate contact. A bentonite seal was injected to the bottom of the hole during the removal of a 10-foot rod section. The bentonite was used to seal the casing to inhibit grout intrusion. The installation was completed by filling the annulus between the casing and hole wall with grout from the top of the bentonite seal to the hole collar. After removal of all drill rods from the hole and initial grout set, a reinforced steel rod was installed through the casing to plate contact. The top of the steel rod is survey checked to monitor embankment settlement.

(8) *Churn/Cable-Tool Drills.*—Although incapable of performing rotary drilling operations, the churn drill, or cable-tool, is widely used in lieu of or in combination with rotary or core drills. The churn/cable-tool drilling operational procedure is one of the oldest known methods of boring holes, and continues to be one of the principal methods used to drill water wells. The drilling is performed by raising and dropping a heavy string of tools led by a blunt-edge chisel bit. The tools are attached to a steel cable that is alternately raised and released for free-fall by a powered drum assembly. The cable is suspended from a sheave assembly mounted on an oscillating beam that absorbs the shock load created by the quick release of load on the taut cable upon impact of the drill tools. The impact of the blunt-edge chisel pulverizes soil and rock material as the borehole is advanced. The cut-

tings are suspended in a slurry that is injected into the borehole. After each 10- to 20-foot penetration, the cable tools are hoisted out of the hole, and a cylindrical bailer equipped with a bottom check valve is lowered into the hole to remove the slurry. This process is repeated to the total hole depth.

A sampling barrel can also be attached in place of the blunt-edge chisel bit. In this mode, the churn/cable-tool drill can be used to sample and to advance the hole without the use of water and the resulting muddy hole. The sampler mode has been used to advantage in sampling glacial terrains where great thicknesses of heterogeneous surfical deposits overlie bedrock. The sampler mode of churn/cable-tool drilling has also been used to advantage for sampling and instrumentation of dam embankments. The Bureau of Reclamation has had little experience with this mode of sampling; however, the potential uses for this older technology are great.

The churn/cable-tool drill is often used to drill and drive casing pipe through cobble-laden or fractured overburden material for core drilling of the deeper formation material with diamond-core drills. When true vertical hole alignment is critical, the churn/cable-tool drilling method is the most reliable method known. The churn/cable-tool drill has been used successfully by the petroleum industry to drill 15-inch-diameter holes to depths of 7,000 feet. The simplicity of the equipment makes churn/cable-tool drilling operations the least expensive method known for boring holes.

(e) *Core Drilling.*—Core drills are power rotary drills designed to drill and recover cylindrical cores of rock material. Most core drilling equipment is designed with gear or hydraulically driven variable-speed rotary drill heads capable of producing up to 1,800 r/min (fig. 5-52). Average core-diameter capability with these drills ranges from ¾ inch to 3⅜ inches and to depths of 1,000 feet. Larger-diameter coring operations (4 to 6 inches) are usually performed with the use of rotary drills (described in sec. 5-32(d)) and cores to 6 feet in diameter can be drilled and recovered with the use of a shot/calyx drill.

There has been a general misconception that coring operations with diamond core bits must be performed at the highest rotary speed, regardless of core size, to be efficient. However, this type of an operational procedure usually results in a shortened bit life, poor penetration rate, and excessive vibration that results in broken cores or premature core blockage.

Diamond-core drilling can be compared to the use of drill presses or center-bore lathes in a machine shop. A small-diameter drill bit has to be rotated at high speed with minimum pressure applied to the bit, while a large diameter drill bit has to be rotated at a low rate of speed with significant pressure on the bit. Any variation from this procedure results in bit chatter, dulled drill bits, and poor penetration rate. The same thing happens in a core drilling operation. The rotational speed and "crowd" pressure must be compatible with the type and hardness of rock being drilled to achieve a smooth and steady rate of penetration throughout the core length. Any variation results in the loss of extremely expensive core bits, poor production, and poor quality core recovery.

All core drills are equipped with pumps or com-

Figure 5-52.—Diamond-core drill rig used in exploration of a dam foundation. E-2255-4NA.

pressors for drill media circulation with the use of water, drilling mud, air, or air-foam to cool and lubricate the coring bits and to circulate the drill cuttings to the top of the hole. Most core drills are equipped with a mast assembly, powered hoist assembly for hoisting heavy loads and, sometimes, a wireline hoist assembly for hoisting or lowering a wireline core barrel through the drill rods.

Although some core rigs have been manufactured with gear or chain pulldown/retract systems, precise control over bit pressure can best be accomplished with the use of a hydraulic pulldown/retreat system. The hydraulic system must have a precision regulator control to set and maintain the desired pressure on the bit. Deep-hole rigs should be equipped with a holdback control to apply hydraulic back pressure to the weight of the drill tools.

There are many variations in the design of drill rigs and mountings for drills that are manufactured specifically for coring. However, there are only two basic types, in addition to the coring capabilities of rotary rigs described in sec. 5.32(d). They are conventional or wireline core drills, for drilling and recovery of cores up to 3⅜ inches in diameter, and shot/calyx core drills for drilling and recovery of cores to 6 feet in diameter.

The following paragraphs describe each type of core drill and its most beneficial use.

(1) *Conventional and Wireline Core Drills.*—Conventional and wireline core drills are capable of high-speed rotary core drilling (up to 1,800 r/min) for the recovery of relatively small-diameter cores ranging from ¾ inch to 8 inches in diameter; however, wireline core recovery is limited to 3⅜ inches in diameter. Conventional core drilling is performed with the use of standard rotary drill rods to which a core barrel is attached. After each core run, all rods and core barrel must be removed from the hole to recover the core. A wireline core drill uses large-i.d. drill rods through which an inner core-barrel assembly is lowered by wireline cable and locked into a latch mechanism in the lead rod. After each core run, an "overshot" tool is lowered by wireline to unlock and retrieve the inner-barrel assembly for core recovery.

Conventional core drilling is usually limited to relatively shallow coring depths, or when intermittent core runs are separated by intervals of hole advancement by rock bitting. However, the non-recovery advancement of boreholes between coring intervals can also be achieved with a wireline system by removing the inner core barrel and lowering a rock bit, designed with a wireline latching mechanism, into the wireline drill rod.

Other advantages of wireline core drilling over conventional core drilling include the following:

- Production.—Wireline core drilling is three to four times faster.
- Hole Protection.—The larger drill rod functions as a casing to protect the hole at all times from cave material or squeeze zones.
- Drilling Stabilization.—The wireline drill rod helps to eliminate rod vibration and rotational whipping action by minimizing the open hole annulus between the outside of the rod and the hole wall.
- Extended Bit Life.—The only time wireline rods must be removed from a core hole is to replace a worn core bit. Rod trips in and out of a core hole, as with conventional core drilling operations, reduces bit life because the outside diameter gauge stones (diamonds) on the bit are in contact with abrasive rock formations during rod "tripping" operations. This is especially true during angle or horizontal hole coring operations. In addition, removal of rods from the hole may cause rock fragments to loosen and fall or wedge in the hole. As a result, reaming through the fallout material is necessary while the rods are lowered to the hole bottom.
- Water Permeability Testing.—Water testing through a wireline rod can be accomplished by hoisting the rod approximately 3 feet above the bottom of the hole, then lowering a wireline packer unit through the bit for expansion and seal against the hole wall. Conventional core-drill operations would require the removal of all rods and core barrel before setting the packer at the zone to be tested.

Some core drills are designed with angle-drilling capabilities, including up-hole drilling with underground drills used in the tunneling and mining industry. Angle hole drills are generally small in size and can be quickly disassembled for moving by helicopter or other means into areas of rough terrain. Core drills can be mounted on motorized carriers, trailers, skids, or stiff-leg columns for underground operations.

Core drills have limited capabilities for drilling through gravels, cobbles, or any surficial material that requires significant rotary torque power. Casing generally has to be set through surficial materials to preclude hole caving and the loss of circulation. Core drill depth capabilities are limited mainly by the hoisting capacity of the mast and drawworks and by the ability to maintain a clean hole free of cuttings.

(2) *Shot, or Calyx, Drills.*—A shot drill, also called a calyx drill, is a large rotary drill that is primarily used for large-diameter (4-inch to 6-foot) rock or concrete core-drilling operations. After the development and use of industrial diamond-core bits, the shot, or calyx, drill has become almost obsolete in the United States, but is still being used in some European and Asian countries. The primary differences between a shot/calyx drill and rotary core drills previously discussed are the tools and methods used to perform core-drilling operations. Coring is performed by using a coring bit that is a flat-face steel cylinder with one or two diagonal slots cut in the bottom edge. As the bit and core barrel are rotated, small quantities of hardened steel shot (also called adamantine shot, buckshot, chilled shot, or corundum shot) are fed at intervals into the drill-rod water injection system. The water circulation media flows through the core barrel around the bit face for cooling and return circulation of cuttings, leaving the heavier steel shot on the hole bottom. The rotating core barrel creates a vortex at the bit, resulting in the movement of the steel shot under the flat face of the bit. As the core bit rotates, the steel shot aids in coring penetration by an abrasive cutting action on the rock.

A steel tube called a calyx barrel is attached to the upper (head) end of the core barrel. The outside diameter of the calyx barrel is the same as that of the core barrel; the calyx barrel serves as a stabilizing guide rod for the core barrel. The top end of the calyx barrel is open except for a steel yoke welded across the inside diameter of the barrel to a steel ring encircling the drill rod. In addition to functioning as a stabilizer for the core barrel, the calyx barrel functions as a bucket to catch and contain drill cuttings too heavy for circulation out of the hole by the drill water. Cores are removed by hoisting all rods and the core barrel out of the hole with the use of a cable drawworks system.

The depth limitation for a shot/calyx drill depends on the mast and drawworks hoist capacity and the capability to maintain a clean open hole. Although smaller diameter cores can be drilled with a shot/calyx drill, only jobs requiring large-diameter (3- to 6-foot) cores would be comparably priced and efficient for diamond and for shot drilling.

I. SAMPLING METHODS

5.33. *General.*—Sampling has many purposes for the foundations and construction materials of small dams. Samples are required to accurately identify and classify soil or rock. Samples are essential for obtaining information on inplace unit weight and moisture determinations, for performing laboratory tests on earth and rock materials, for testing potential concrete sand and aggregate deposits, for designing concrete mixes, and for testing potential riprap sources. To a large degree, information obtained from the laboratory testing of samples is used to finalize the design of foundations, and to select the construction materials to be used in earth and concrete dams.

The importance of obtaining representative samples cannot be overemphasized. Samples that are not truly representative of the subsurface inplace conditions can result in erroneous conclusions and can contribute to an unsafe or poorly designed dam or appurtenant structure. Sample recovery requires considerable care to avoid altering the variations in natural deposits of subsurface materials. Representative samples are relatively easy to secure from accessible trenches, test pits, or tunnels because the inplace material can be visually inspected to determine the best method of hand sampling. Boreholes, however, do not permit a visual inspection of the material. Therefore, it is more difficult to recover representative samples.

Samples are broadly classified as either disturbed or undisturbed. Disturbed samples are those for which no effort is made to maintain the inplace condition of the soil or rock. Conversely, undisturbed samples require significant care and experience to maintain as much of the inplace condition of the material as possible. Nevertheless, there is no such thing as a true undisturbed soil or rock sample because the removal of the sample from the natural confining pressure of the adjacent material affects the inplace characteristics of the sample.

The following paragraphs describe both hand and mechanical sampling methods commonly used for the recovery of disturbed and undisturbed subsurface samples.

5.34. *Disturbed Samples (Hand-Sampling Methods).*—Hand samples are usually taken from accessible excavations, from existing stockpiles and windrows, or from shallow hand auger borings. The following paragraphs describe the various methods of obtaining samples from these sources.

(a) *Accessible Test Pits, Trenches and Large-Diameter Borings.*—Obtaining disturbed hand samples from accessible test pits or trenches (including road cut and river bank deposits) can be accomplished in the following manner. An area of sidewall of the test pit, trench, or open cut should be trimmed to remove all weathered or mixed material. The exposed strata should then be examined for changes in gradation, natural water content, plasticity, uniformity, etc., then a representative area should be selected for sampling. Either individual or composite samples can be obtained by trenching down the vertical face of a pit, trench, or cut bank with a cut of uniform cross section and depth. The soil can be collected on a quartering cloth spread below the trench. The minimum cross section of the sampling trench should be at least four times the dimension of the largest gravel size included in the soil.

In taking individual samples it is important that enough representative material is obtained from the stratum and that extraneous material is not included. For composite samples, a vertical trench is cut through all strata above any desired elevation.

If the material sampled is a gravelly soil that contains large percentages (about 25 percent or more of total material) of particles 3 inches or larger, it is usually advantageous to take representative parts of the excavated material (such as every fifth or tenth bucketful) rather than to trim the sample from the inplace sidewall of the excavation.

The testing size requirements for disturbed samples are listed in table 5-6. When the samples are larger than required for testing, they may be reduced by quartering. This is done by piling the total sample in the shape of a cone on a canvas tarpaulin. Each shovelful should be dropped on the center of the cone and allowed to run down equally in all directions. The material in the cone is then spread out in a circular manner by walking around the pile and gradually widening the circle with a shovel until a uniform thickness of material has been spread across the canvas surface. The spread sample is then quartered. Two opposite quarters are discarded, and the material in the remaining two quarters is mixed again by shoveling the material into another conical pile, taking alternate shovelfuls from each of the two quarters. The process of piling, spreading, and discarding two quarters is continued until the sample is reduced to the desired size.

(b) *Stockpiles and Windrows.*—When sampling stockpiles or windrows, care must be taken to ensure that the samples are not selected from segregated areas. The amount of segregation in materials depends on the gradation of the material and on the methods and equipment used for stockpiling. Even with good control, the outer surface and fringes of a stockpile are likely to have some segregation, particularly if the slopes are steep and the material contains a significant amount of gravel or coarse sand. Representative samples from stockpiles can be obtained by combining and mixing small samples taken from several small test pits or auger holes distributed over the pile. A windrow of soil is best sampled by taking all the material from a narrow cut transverse to the windrow. Samples from either stockpiles or windrows should be fairly large originally, and they should be thoroughly mixed before they are quartered down to the size desired for testing.

(c) *Hand-Auger Borings.*—Small auger holes cannot be sampled and logged as accurately as an open trench or a test pit because they are inaccessible for visual inspection of the total profile and for selection of representative strata. Small hand augers (4-inches in diameter or smaller) can be used to collect samples that are adequate for soil classification, but do not provide enough material for testing material properties (fig. 5-53). As the auger hole is advanced, the soil should be deposited in individual stockpiles to form an orderly depth sequence of removed material. In preparing an individual sample from an auger hole, consecutive piles of the same type of soil should be combined to form a representative sample. All or equal parts from each of the appropriate stockpiles should be mixed to form the desired sample size for each stratum (fig. 5-54).

(d) *Concrete Aggregate Sources.*—Disturbed samples of concrete aggregate materials can be obtained from test pits, trenches, and cased auger holes. Because the gradation of concrete aggregate is of great importance, a portable screening apparatus is sometimes used to determine the individual

Table 5-6.—Identification and sizes of samples.

Purpose of material	Sample size	Remarks[1]
Individual and composite samples of disturbed earth materials for classification and laboratory compaction tests	Sufficient material, all passing the 3-inch sieve, to yield 75 pounds passing the No. 4 sieve	Include information relative to the percentage by volume 3 inches to 5 inches and plus 5 inches
Soil-rock permeability tests	300 pounds passing a 3-inch sieve	Air dried
Relative density test	150 pounds passing a 3-inch sieve	Air dried
Moisture samples, inspection samples of soil, soil samples for sulfate determination (reaction with concrete)	Sealed pint quart jar (full)	Individual inspection samples should represent range of moisture and type of materials
Concrete aggregate	600 pounds of pit-run sand and gravel; If screened: 200 pounds of sand, 200 pounds of No. 4 to ¾ inch size, and 100 pounds of each of the other sizes produced; 400 pounds of quarry rock proposed for crushed aggregate	For commercial sources, include data on ownership-plant and service history of concrete made from aggregates
Riprap	600 pounds, which represents proportionally the quality range from poor to medium to best as found at the source	Method of excavation used, location of pit and quarry
Inplace unit weight and water content of fine-grained soils above water table	8- to 12-inch cubes or cylinders	Sealed in suitable container

[1]For identification on sample tags, give project name, feature, area designation, hole number, and depth of sample.

size percentages of the samples in the field. This provides an indication of the processing operations that will be required. Whenever facilities are available, representative samples of the aggregate should be tested in the laboratory to determine the physical and chemical properties of the material. In the absence of facilities for laboratory tests, examination of the aggregate by an experienced petrographer will aid considerably in estimating its physical and chemical soundness. Information on the durability and strength record of an aggregate in concrete can be obtained by designing and breaking test cylinders of trial concrete mixes. This test procedure is of great value in appraising the potential source of concrete aggregate and should be used whenever possible. Laboratory tests on concrete aggregate are discussed in part K (sec. 5.50).

(e) *Riprap Sources.*—The quality and durability of rock for riprap can be judged by geologic field conditions, physical properties tests, petrographic examination, and the service record of the material. Because riprap requirements include obtaining proper sizes of rock fragments, quality tests made in the laboratory must be supplemented by data obtained during field examination and by the results of blasting tests in proposed quarry sites. The importance of obtaining representative samples of each type of material in a proposed riprap source must be emphasized. If there is more than one type of material in a source, separate samples representing each material proposed for use should be obtained. Samples of intervening layers of soil, shale, or other soft rock that is obviously unsuitable for riprap is not required, but full descriptions of these materials should be recorded on the logs and in a report of the investigation.

Samples can be obtained by blasting down an open face of the sidewall of a test pit, trench, or exposed ledge to obtain unweathered fragments representing each type of material as it will be quarried and used in riprap. Sampling of the exposed weathered rock should not be conducted for laboratory

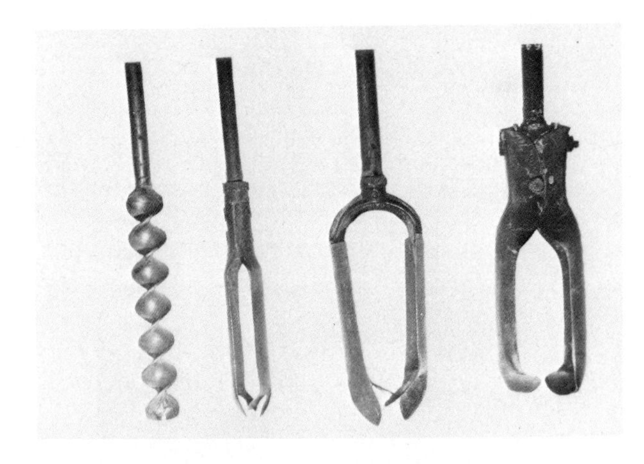

Figure 5-53.—Types of hand augers; 2-inch helical; 2- and 6-inch Iwan; and 6-inch Fenn (adjustable). PX-D-16998.

Figure 5-54.—Auger sampling. PX-D-16331.

testing because the test values will not be representative of the natural rock condition. Figure 5-55 shows the blasting operation at a rock ledge riprap source for Stampede Dam, California, and the resulting riprap material.

Large fields of boulders are sometimes proposed as sources of riprap. However, the production of riprap from boulder fields is always a costly process and should be considered only when quarried materials are not available. Moreover, field boulders usually do not have the angularity and interlocking properties of quarried riprap. Sampling of boulder sources should include breaking large boulders to obtain samples of fragments similar to those likely to result from construction operations. Talus slopes should be sampled only if the talus itself is proposed for use as riprap. Samples of talus material generally do not represent the material obtainable from the solid rock ledge above the talus slope because the talus fragments are generally weathered or altered.

5.35. *Disturbed Samples (Mechanical Sampling Methods).*—Generally, disturbed samples are obtained from drilled holes; however, samples can be obtained through the use of construction excavation equipment (backhoes, draglines, trenchers, dozers, etc.) when the samples are required primarily for identification or for making volume computations of usable material. Samples obtained in this manner are generally unsuitable for use in laboratory testing because of the heavy mixing of material that occurs during the excavation process. Heavy excavation equipment is best used to excavate an accessible test pit or trench. Individual material stratum can then be sampled by hand methods to avoid contamination from adjacent materials.

(a) *Power Auger Drills.*—One of the most common methods of obtaining subsurface disturbed samples is by using power auger drills. Continuous-flight auger drilling can be used to obtain disturbed samples of borrow area materials. After each selected interval, or material change, the soil sample cuttings travel up the spiral flight to the collar of the hole for collection of the sample. However, the cuttings moving upward along the flight can loosen and mix with previously drilled material. If contamination or mixing with other soil material is undesirable, a hollow-stem auger with an internal sampling system should be used.

Disk augers are commonly used to recover disturbed samples of soil and moderately coarse-grained material. After each penetration, the disk should be removed from the hole with the disturbed sample cuttings retained on the top of the disk. Collection of the sample can then be made at the hole collar followed by repeated drilling intervals.

Bucket drills are suitable for the recovery of disturbed samples of coarse-grained soils, sands, and gravel deposits. During each drilling interval, the sample cuttings enter the cylindrically shaped

(A) INITIAL BLAST.

(B) RESULTS OF BLAST.

Figure 5-55.—Blasting a rock ledge at the riprap source for Stampede Dam, California. The rock is basalt having a specific gravity of 2.6. P949–235–432NA, P949–235–436NA.

bucket through the bottom cutter block. Removal and collection of samples is then accomplished by hoisting the bucket from the hole and releasing the hinged bottom plate or side of the bucket.

(b) *Reverse-Circulation Drills.*—The reverse-circulation drills are advantageous to use in the recovery of sand, gravel, and cobble-size disturbed samples. However, this sampling method is relatively expensive and is not used for borrow area investigations. This process involves using a double-walled drill stem and compressed air to circulate the cuttings for collection at the hole collar. Compressed air is pumped down the annulus between the inner and outer walls of the double-walled drill rod, and cuttings are forced upward through the center rod as the drilling progresses. Collection of the cuttings is made at the discharge spout of a special funnel-shaped cyclone assembly that is designed to disperse the compressed air and deposit the cuttings in the order drilled through. This method of disturbed sampling is considered to be the most reliable to produce a noncontaminated sample because the drill stem seals previously drilled material zones.

5.36. *Protection and Preparation of Disturbed Samples for Shipping.*—The sizes of samples required depends on the nature of the laboratory tests. Table 5-6 gives suggested sample sizes and the information required on a sample identification tag. Disturbed samples of 75 pounds or more should be placed in bags or other suitable containers that will prevent the loss of moisture and the fine fraction of the soil. Samples of silt and clay that are proposed for laboratory testing for use as borrow material should be protected against drying by placement in waterproof bags or other suitable containers. Samples of sands and gravels should be shipped in closely woven bags and air dried before they are placed in the bags. When the sack samples are shipped by public carrier, they should be double sacked. It is recommended that those samples not tested be stored for possible future examination and testing until the dam is complete and in operation for 5 years.

5.37. *Undisturbed Hand-Sampling Methods.*—Undisturbed samples in the form of cubes, cylinders, or irregularly shaped samples can be obtained from strata exposed in the sides or bottoms of open excavations, test pits, trenches, and large-diameter auger holes. Such samples are useful for determining inplace unit weight and moisture content, and for other laboratory tests.

(a) *Procedures for Obtaining Hand-Cut Samples.*—Figures 5-56 and 5-57 show procedures commonly used in hand-cut block sampling. Cutting and trimming samples to the desired size and shape requires extreme care, particularly when working with easily disturbed soft or brittle materials. The appropriate cutting tool should be used to prevent disturbance and cracking of the sample. Soft, plastic soils require thin, sharp knives. Sometimes a thin piano wire is advantageous.

A faster and more economical method of obtaining undisturbed block samples can be accomplished with the use of chain saws equipped with specially fabricated carbide-tipped chains to cut block samples of fine-grained material and soft rock (fig. 5-58).

In dry climates, moist cloths should be used to inhibit drying of the sample. After the sample is cut and trimmed to the desired size and shape, it should be wrapped with a layer of cheesecloth and painted with melted, microcrystalline, sealing wax. Rubbing the partially cooled wax surface with the bare hands helps seal the pores in the wax. These operations constitute one layer of protection, and at least two additional layers of cloth and wax should be applied.

(b) *Protection and Shipping Preparation for Hand-Cut Undisturbed Samples.*—A firmly constructed wood box with the top and bottom panels removed should be placed over the sample before it is cut from the parent material and lifted for removal. The annular space between the sample and the walls should be packed with moist sawdust or similar packing material. The top cover of the box should then be placed over the packing material. After removal, the bottom side of the specimen should be covered with the same number of layers of cloth and wax as the other surfaces, and the bottom of the box should be placed over the packing material.

Samples may vary in size; the most common are 6- or 12-inch cubes. In addition, cylindrical samples 6 to 8 inches in diameter and 6 to 12 inches long are frequently obtained in metal cylinders used to confine the sample for shipping. Otherwise, the same trimming and sealing procedures described above for boxed samples apply.

5.38. *Undisturbed Mechanical Sampling Methods.*—Soil samplers used by the Bureau of Reclamation are designed to obtain relatively undisturbed samples of soils ranging from saturated, noncohesive soils to hard shale or siltstone. Each

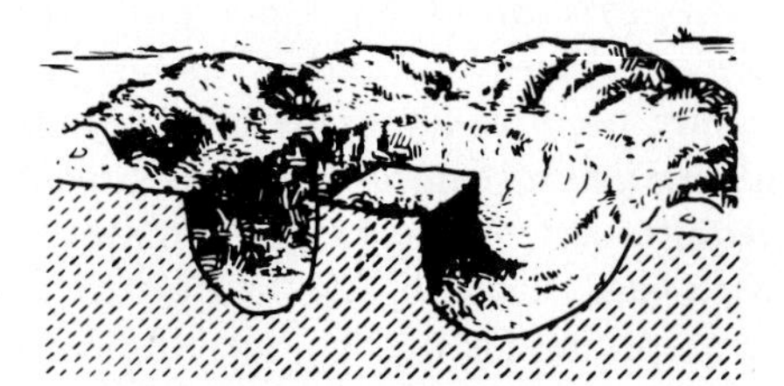

1. **Smooth ground surface and mark outline of sample.**
2. **Carefully excavate trench around sample.**

3. **Deepen excavation and trim sides of sample to desired size with knife.**

4. **Cut sample from parent stratum, or encase sample in box before cutting if sample is easily disturbed.**

(A)

1. **Carefully smooth face surface and mark outline of sample.**

2. **Carefully excavate around and in back of sample. Shape sample roughly with knife.**

3. **Cut sample and carefully remove from hole, or encase sample in box before cutting if sample is easily disturbed.**

(B)

Figure 5-56.—Initial steps to obtain a hand-cut undisturbed block sample. From (A) bottom of test pit or level surface, (B) cut bank or side of test pit. PX–D–4788.

soil type dictates the use of a different type of sampling equipment to effectively recover quality samples. The following paragraphs describe the soil condition and the type of sampler best suited for good sample recovery.

(a) *Soft, Saturated Cohesive or Noncohesive Soils.*—Soils found near or below the water table are generally soft and saturated. This type of soil can be easily disturbed from its natural condition by sampling. The saturated condition of the soil acts as a lubricant, and the sample can tear apart or completely fall from the sampling equipment as it is being retrieved. For these reasons, specialized fixed-piston samplers must be used to obtain such a sample in as undisturbed a condition as possible.

The principal of operation of a fixed-piston sampler is to obtain a sample within a thin-wall cylindrical tube by driving the tube into the soil with an even and uninterrupted hydraulic thrust. The sample is held within the tube during removal from the

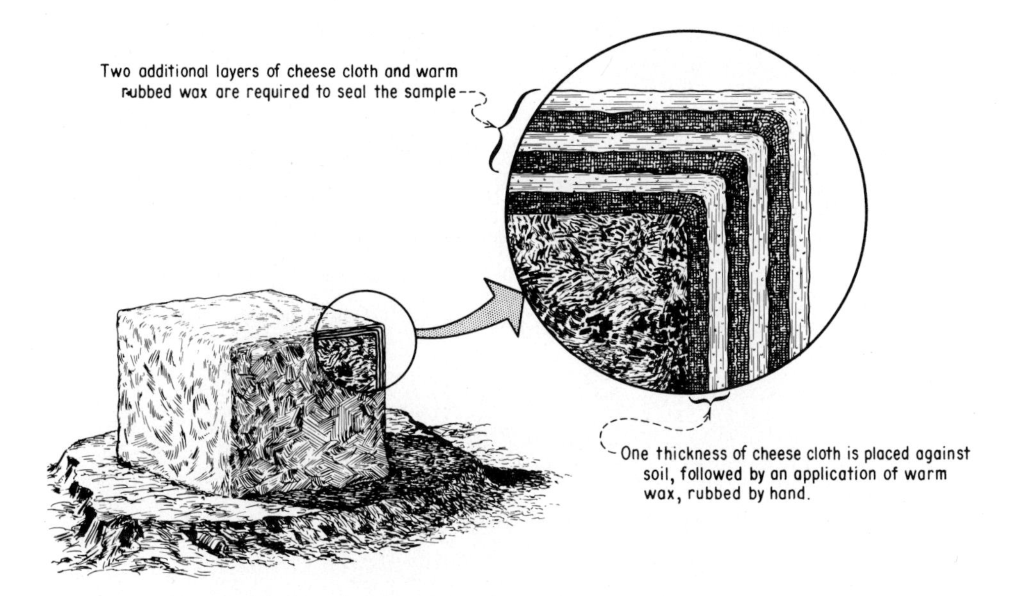

Figure 5-57.—Final steps to obtain a hand-cut undisturbed block sample. PX–D–4783.

drill hole by a vacuum created by a locked piston, which is an integral part of the sampler.

Three types of fixed-piston samplers are used in the recovery of soft, saturated soils in the Bureau of Reclamation. With the Hvorslev sampler and the Butters sampler, the piston is held stationary while the sample tube is pushed into the soil by a piston-rod extension connected to the upper part of the mast. These samplers require a drill rig with a hollow spindle. The third type, the Osterberg sampler, has a piston that is attached to the head of the sampler. Sample recovery is accomplished by pumping hydraulic pressure down the drill rod to push the thinwall sample tube into the soil. A fluid by-pass system manufactured into the sampler stops the penetration of the sampler tube at 30 inches.

Figure 5-58.—Chain saw equipped with carbide-tipped blade being used to cut block sample.

The sample is removed from the borehole by removing all rods and the sampler from the hole.

(b) *Soft to Moderately Firm Cohesive Soils.*—Soft to moderately firm cohesive soils found in surficial deposits above the water table can be sampled in as undisturbed a condition as possible with the use of relatively simple sampling methods. The sampling equipment used in the Bureau of Reclamation for this type of soil includes the thin-wall drive sampler and the hollow-stem auger sampler. The following paragraphs discuss each sampler and the operational procedures necessary to ensure the recovery of a quality representative soil sample.

(1) *Thin-Wall Drive Samplers.*—Thin-wall drive samplers were developed primarily for obtaining undisturbed soil core samples of soft to moderately firm cohesive soils. The sampler consists of a thin-wall metal tube attached to a sampler head containing a ball check valve. The principal of operation is to push the sampler without rotation into the soil at a controlled penetration rate and pressure. The sample is held in the tube primarily by a soil cohesion bond to the inner tube, assisted by a partial vacuum created by the ball check valve in the sampler head.

The Bureau of Reclamation commonly uses thin-wall sampling equipment designed to recover either 3- or 5-inch-diameter soil cores. The size requirements depend primarily upon the use of the sample. For moisture-unit weight determinations, a 3-inch sample will suffice. However, for most laboratory testing, a 5-inch sample is required. Laboratory testing requires that the sample be contained in a thin metal sleeve rather than in the heavier thin-wall tube. For this requirement, a special 5-inch thin-wall tube was developed with external threads to which a cutting bit is attached. The bit is designed with an internal recess that supports the bottom edge of a sheet metal sleeve contained within the thin-wall sampling tube.

(2) *Hollow-Stem Auger Samplers.*—Three types of sampling operations for the recovery of soft to moderately firm cohesive soils are available with the use of hollow-stem augers.

The first type of sampling operation is accomplished by drilling to the sampling depth with a hollow-stem auger equipped with a center plug bit. The plug bit is attached to drill rods positioned within the hollow-stem auger. At the sampling depth, the drill rods and plug bit are removed, and a thin-wall drive sampler is lowered to the bottom of the hole. After the sample is recovered, the plug bit is replaced, and augering continues to the next sampling depth.

A second type of hollow-stem auger sampling operation involves a wireline latch system to lock the plug bit and soil sampler within the lead hollow-stem auger. After the auger has advanced to the sampling depth, an overshot assembly is lowered by wireline to unlock and latch onto the plug bit for removal from the hole. A thin-wall sampler with a head bearing assembly is then lowered by wireline and locked within the lead auger section. Sampling is accomplished by continued auger rotation and penetration, which allows the center core material to enter the thin wall sampler. The head bearing assembly on the sampler allows the sample tube to remain stationary while the auger is rotating. At the end of the sample run, the overshot is lowered by wireline to release the sampler lock mechanism, latch onto the sampler, and remove it with the soil sample from the hole.

The third and most recently developed hollow-stem auger sampling system involves the use of rods to lower, hold, and hoist a continuous sampler unit designed to recover samples during auger penetration. This system positively eliminates rotation of the sampler as the auger rotates. It is considered the best mechanical sampling system available for the recovery of undisturbed soil samples by hollow-stem auger.

The stability of any sampling tool is critical to the recovery of representative undisturbed samples. With hollow-stem augers, the inner barrel or sample tube that receives the soil core must prevent rotation as the soil enters the sampler. A sampler with a head bearing assembly can rotate if cuttings are allowed to accumulate in the annulus between the outer rotating auger and the inner sample barrel. To eliminate any chance of movement, the continuous sampler system is rigidly connected to rods that extend up the hollow-stem auger to a yoke located above the rotating auger drillhead. The auger is then allowed to rotate for drilling penetration, and the sampler within the auger is held stationary to prevent rotation as the soil core enters the sample tube.

To recover a sample from the continuous sampler system, all sampler connecting rods and the sampler are removed from the auger to retrieve the soil core. This is followed by lowering the sampling unit to the hole bottom for the continuation of sampling operations.

(c) *Medium to Hard Soils and Shales.*—Medium to hard soils and shales located both above and below the water table can usually be sampled in an undisturbed condition by the use of double-tubed coring barrels. The three types of core barrels commonly used in the Bureau of Reclamation are the Pitcher sampler, Denison core barrel, and DCDMA (Diamond Core Drill Manufacturers Association) series 4- by 5½-inch and 6- by 7¾-inch core barrels. The DCDMA series barrels can be converted to perform diamond coring for rock sampling. The following paragraphs discuss each sampler and the procedures necessary to ensure the recovery of a quality representative soil sample.

(1) *Pitcher Sampler.*—The Pitcher sampler was developed primarily for obtaining undisturbed soil core samples of medium to hard soils and shales. One advantage of using the Pitcher sampler over other types of soil core barrels is that it has a spring-loaded inner barrel, which permits the trimming shoe to protrude or retract with changes in soil firmness. In extremely firm soils, the spring compresses until the cutting edge of the inner barrel shoe is flush with the crest of the outer barrel cutting teeth. In soft soils, the spring extends and the inner barrel shoe protrudes below the outer barrel bit, preventing damage to the sample by the drilling fluid and the drilling action.

Although the Pitcher sampler is available in various sizes for obtaining cores from 3 to 6 inches in diameter, the Bureau's laboratory requirements normally dictate 6-inch core recovery; therefore, a 6- by 7¾-inch Pitcher sampler is used. This sampler was designed to use 6-inch thin-wall tubes as the inner barrel. The soil core is normally contained within the thin-wall tube, and a new tube is normally attached to the sampler for each sampling run. However, the Bureau of Reclamation has changed the inner barrel configuration to one that contains sheet metal liners for the soil core, rather than thinwall tubes. The modified inner barrel is threaded for attachment of a trimming shoe with a recess milled to contain the sheet metal liner. The metal liners are preferred for laboratory testing because they are more easily opened, and because it is easier to remove the core and, therefore, eliminate possible damage to the core.

(2) *Denison Sampler.*—The Denison sampler was developed to obtain large-diameter undisturbed cores of cohesive soils and shales that have medium to hard consistency. Although many consider it an extremely reliable sampling barrel (occasionally cores of noncohesive sands and silts have been obtained with the Denison sampler), others consider

it outdated and believe it should be replaced with the Pitcher sampler or the new large-diameter series sampling barrels (6 by 7¾ inches). All of the arguments against the Denison sampling barrel arise from the problem of having to manually adjust the position relationship between the outer barrel cutting bit and the inner barrel trimming shoe according to the consistency of the soil. The required settings must be determined by the operator before each sampling run. The settings are achieved by interchanging varied lengths of outer barrel cutting bits to conform with the type and consistency of the soil. The proper cutting bit for various soil consistencies is selected as described below.

- Soft soil samples can be obtained with a short cutting bit attached to the outer barrel so that the inner barrel trimming shoe protrudes approximately 3 inches beyond the bit. The shoe acts as a stationary drive sampler, trims and slides over the sample, and protects the core from drill-fluid erosion or contamination.
- Firm soil samples can be obtained by attaching a cutting bit having a length that will position the crown of the bit teeth approximately flush with the inner barrel shoe trimming edge. With this setting, the bit teeth cut the core simultaneously with the trimming of the core by the shoe. The shoe continues to provide some protection to the sample from the drill fluid because most of the fluid circulates between the teeth openings rather than through the crown area.
- Hard soil samples are obtained by attaching a cutting bit having a length that will position the teeth approximately 1 to 2 inches below the trimming shoe. This setting is intended only for nonerodible soils because the entire sample is subjected to drill fluid circulation before it is contained within the trimming shoe.

(3) *Large-Diameter Hi-Recovery Core Barrels.*—The increased demand for large diameter soil samples for laboratory testing became obvious to manufacturers of conventional rock coring equipment in the late 1960's. To compete successfully with strictly soil-sampling core barrels (e.g., Denison and Pitcher core barrels), the DCDMA developed standards for a large-diameter core barrel with the versatility to sample both soil and rock cores. These core barrels have a variety of interchangeable parts that are used to convert the basic rock core barrel so that it is able to core medium to hard soils and shales, fragmentary rock, rock with soil lenses, and homogeneous rock.

Some of the interchangeable parts and their functions are as follows:

- A clay bit with face extension to trim and advance over the softer clay soils and protect the core from drill-fluid erosion
- A spring-loaded inner barrel to protrude in front of the core barrel for soft soils and retract into the core barrel for harder soils
- A split inner barrel for coring shales, soft rock, fragmented rock, and lensed rock
- A single-tube inner barrel for coring homogeneous hard rock

The Bureau of Reclamation has successfully used both the 4- by 5½-inch core barrel and the 6- by 7¾-inch core barrel, depending upon the size requirements of the laboratory. A metal liner should be inserted inside the inner barrel to contain and seal the core sample for shipment to the laboratory.

5.39. *Rock Coring Methods.*—Rotary drilling and sampling methods may be used for both hard and soft bedrock. Core barrels can obtain cores from ¾ to 6 inches in diameter. There are three principal types of core barrels: (1) single-tube, (2) double-tube, and (3) triple-tube.

The single-tube core barrel which has the simplest design, consists of a core barrel head, a core barrel, and an attached coring bit that cuts an annular groove that permits passage of drilling fluid pumped through the drill rod. This design exposes the core to drilling fluid over its entire length, which results in serious core erosion of the unconsolidated or weakly cemented materials. Therefore, the single tube core barrel is no loner used except in unusual situations, such as in concrete sampling and in the use of "packsack-type" one-man drills.

The double-tube core barrel (fig. 5-59), preferably with a split inner tube in addition to the outer rotating barrel, provides an inner stationary barrel that protects the core from the drilling fluid and reduces the torsional forces transmitted to the core. The double-tube barrel is used to sample most rock, and may be used to obtain cores in hard, brittle, or poorly cemented materials, such as shale and siltstone or cores of soft, partially consolidated or weakly cemented soils. For these materials, hard metal drill bits are used. Many of the double-tube core barrels have been slightly modified to allow a sample liner to be inserted in the inner barrel. This modification allows the liner to serve as a shipping

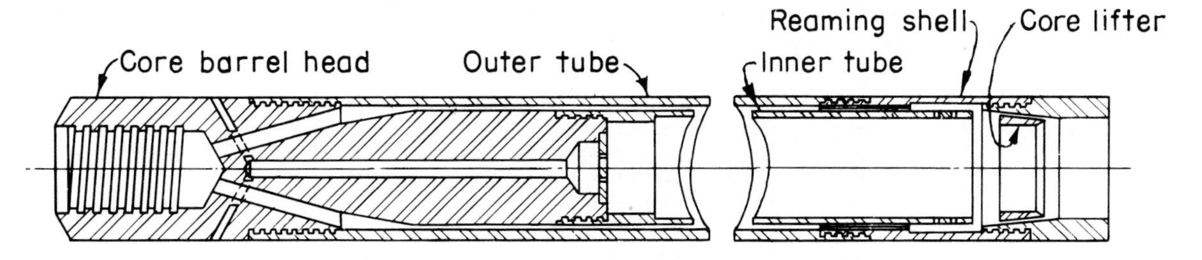

Figure 5-59.—Double-tube core barrel used for obtaining samples of rock. 288–D–2514.

container for the core and eliminates the possibility of damaging the core when removing it from the inner barrel.

The triple-tube core barrel has been designed with a rotating outer barrel, stationary inner barrel, and a split liner inside the inner barrel to accept the core sample. Plastic or metal sample containers may be used in lieu of the split liner for shipping purposes.

Core samplers also have been designed with a spring-loaded retractable inner barrel, which enables the same type of core barrel to be used for coring either soil or rock. The retractable inner barrel and soil-coring bits are replaced with a standard inner barrel and diamond bits for rock coring. As the cores are removed from the core barrels, they are placed in core boxes and logged.

A more complete explanation of single-, double-, and triple-tube samplers and their uses is given in Test Designation USBR 7105 in the Bureau's *Earth Manual* [7].

The DCDMA (Diamond Core Drill Manufacturers Association), which is composed of members from the United States and Canada, has established dimensional standards for a series of nesting casings with corresponding sizes for bits and drill rods. The DCDMA standards for core-drill bits, casings, and drill rods are shown on figures 5-60 through 5-64.

The size combination is such that HX core-barrel bits will pass through flush-coupled HX casing (flush-coupled casing is denoted by the group letter X) and will drill a hole large enough to admit flush-coupled NX casing (the next smaller size) and so on to the RX size. Flush-joint casing, denoted by group letter W, is such that ¾- by 6-inch (nominal) core-barrel bits will pass through ZW casing and will drill a hole large enough to admit flush-jointed UW casing (next smaller size) and so on to the RW size.

J. LOGGING EXPLORATIONS

5.40. ***Identification of Holes.***—To ensure completeness of the exploration record and to eliminate confusion, test holes should be numbered in the order they are drilled, and the numbering series should be continuous through the various stages of investigation. If a hole is planned and programed, it is preferable to maintain the hole number in the record as "not drilled" with an explanatory note rather than to use the hole number elsewhere. When explorations cover several areas, such as alternative damsites or different borrow areas, a new series of numbers or suffixes for each damsite or borrow area should be used.

Exploration numbers should be prefixed with a 2- or 3-letter designation to describe the type of exploration. The letter designations used frequently are listed below with the types of explorations they identify.

DH	Drillhole
AH	Auger hole (hand)
AP	Auger hole (power)
CH	Churn-drill hole
PR	Penetration-resistance hole
VT	Vane test
DS	Dutch Cone
TP	Test pit
DT	Dozer trench
BHT	Backhoe trench
SPT	Standard penetration-resistance test hole
PT	Pitcher
DN	Denison
OW	Observation well

THREE LETTER NAMES		
FIRST LETTER	SECOND LETTER	THIRD LETTER
HOLE SIZE	GROUP	DESIGN
Casing, core barrel, diamond bit, reaming shell and drill rods designed to be used together for drilling an approximate hole size.	Key diameters standardized on an integrated group basis for progressively reducing hole size with nesting casings.	The standardization of other dimensions, including thread characteristics, to permit interchangeability of parts made by different manufacturers.
Letter / Inches / Millimeters R / 1 / 25 E / $1\frac{1}{2}$ / 40 A / 2 / 50 B / $2\frac{1}{2}$ / 65 N / 3 / 75 K / $3\frac{1}{2}$ / 90 H / 4 / 100 P / 5 / 125 S / 6 / 150 U / 7 / 175 Z / 8 / 200	Letters X and W are synonymous when used as the GROUP (second) letter. Any DCDMA standard tool with an X or W as the GROUP letter belongs in that DCDMA integrated group of tools designed using nesting casings and tools of sufficient strength to reach greater depths with minimum reductions in core diameter.	The DESIGN (third) letter designates the specific design of that particular tool. It does not indicate a type of design.

TWO LETTER NAMES	
FIRST LETTER	SECOND LETTER
HOLE SIZE	GROUP AND DESIGN
Approximate hole size, same as in 3-letter names.	GROUP standardization of key diameters for group integration and DESIGN standardization of other dimensions affecting interchangeability.

Figure 5-60.—Nomenclature for diamond-core drill equipment. (Diamond Core Drill Manufacturers Association). 288–D–2887.

5.41. ***Log Forms.***—A log is a written record of the data on the materials and conditions encountered in each exploration. It provides the fundamental facts on which all subsequent conclusions are based, such as need for additional exploration or testing, feasibility of the site, design treatment required, cost of construction, method of construction, and evaluation of structure performance. A log may present pertinent and important information that is used over a period of years; it may be needed to delineate accurately a change of conditions with the passage of time; it may form an important part of contract documents; and it may serve as evidence in a court of law. Each log, therefore, should be accurate, clear, and complete. Log forms are used to record and provide the required information. Examples of logs for three types of exploratory holes are:

- Geologic log of a drill hole (fig. 5-65).—This form is suitable for all types of core borings.
- Log of test pit or auger hole (fig. 5-66).—This form is suitable for all types (but primarily in surficial deposits) of exploratory holes that produce complete but disturbed samples.,
- Penetration-resistance log (fig. 5-67).—This form can be used for exploratory holes that test the inplace soil conditions.

Records of tunnels, shafts and large trenches are best presented on drawings and dam sheets; these drawings should also contain the pertinent information outlined on figure 5-65. Test pits and smaller trenches require separate logs.

The headings on the log forms provide spaces for identifying information such as project, feature, hole number, location, elevation, dates started and completed, and the name of the logger.

The body of the log forms are divided into a series of columns covering the various kinds of information required according to the type of exploration.

When logging surficial deposits, every stratum of

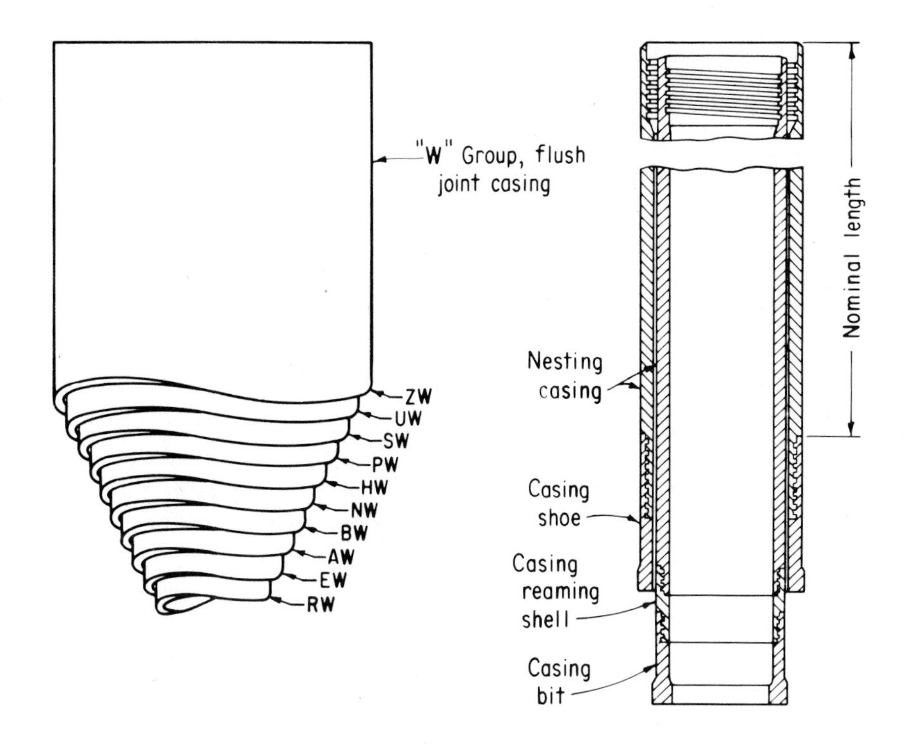

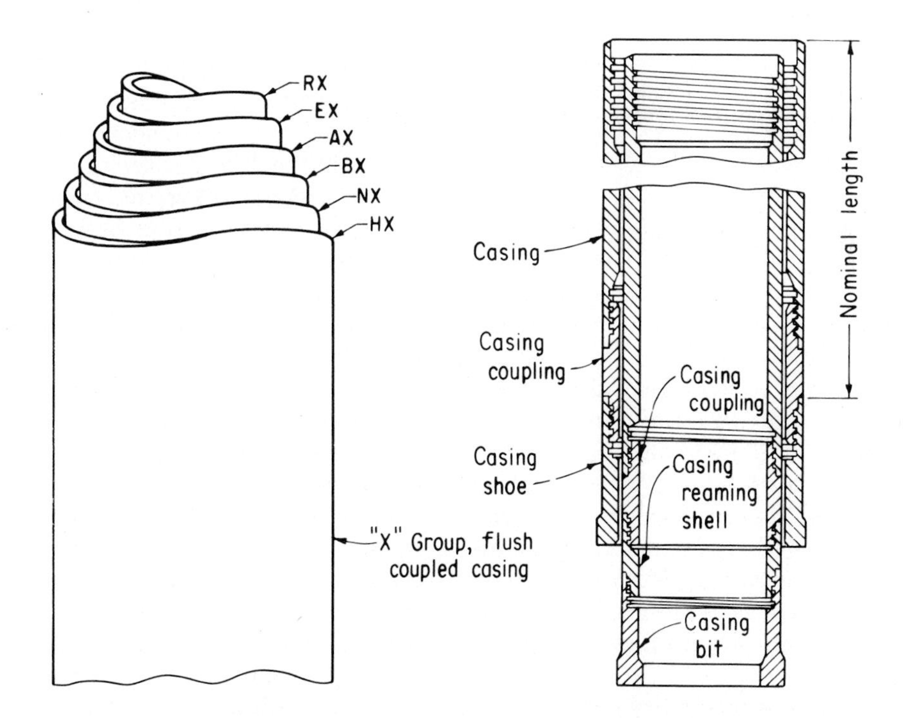

Note: Use of casing shoe allows nesting; use of casing bit does not.

Figure 5-61.—Size variations for core-drill casing. (Diamond Core Drill Manufacturers Association). 288–D–2888.

Size Designations: Casing; Casing coupling; Casing bits; Core barrel bits	Size Designations: Rod; Rod couplings	Casing O. D., inches	Casing coupling: O. D., inches	Casing coupling: I. D., inches	Casing bit, O. D., inches	Core barrel bit O. D., inches*	Drill rod O.D., inches	Approximate core diameter: Normal, inches	Approximate core diameter: Thinwall, inches
RX	RW	1.437	1.437	1.188	1.485	1.160	1.094	—	.735
EX	E	1.812	1.812	1.500	1.875	1.470	1.313	.845	.905
AX	A	2.250	2.250	1.906	2.345	1.875	1.625	1.185	1.281
BX	B	2.875	2.875	2.375	2.965	2.345	1.906	1.655	1.750
NX	N	3.500	3.500	3.000	3.615	2.965	2.375	2.155	2.313
HX	HW	4.500	4.500	3.938	4.625	3.890	3.500	3.000	3.187
RW	RW	1.437	Flush joint	No coupling	1.485	1.160	1.094	—	.735
EW	EW	1.812			1.875	1.470	1.375	.845	.905
AW	AW	2.250			2.345	1.875	1.750	1.185	1.281
BW	BW	2.875			2.965	2.345	2.125	1.655	1.750
NW	NW	3.500			3.615	2.965	2.625	2.155	2.313
HW	HW	4.500			4.625	3.890	3.500	3.000	3.187
PW	—	5.500			5.650	—	—	—	—
SW	—	6.625			6.790	—	—	—	—
UW	—	7.625			7.800	—	—	—	—
ZW	—	8.625			8.810	—	—	—	—
—	AX [1]	—	—	—	—	1.875	1.750	1.000	—
—	BX [1]	—	—	—	—	2.345	2.250	1.437	—
—	NX [1]	—	—	—	—	2.965	2.813	1.937	—

* For hole diameter approximation, assume $\frac{1}{32}$ inch larger than core barrel bit.

[1] Wire line size designation, drill rod only, serves as both casing and drill rod. Wire line core bit, and core diameters vary slightly according to manufacturer.

Figure 5-62.—Nominal dimensions for drill casings and accessories. (Diamond Core Drill Manufacturers Association). 288–D–2889.

Coring bit size	Nominal *: O.D.	Nominal *: I.D.	Set size *: O.D.	Set size *: I.D.
RWT	$1\frac{5}{32}$	$\frac{3}{4}$	1.160	.735
EWT	$1\frac{1}{2}$	$\frac{29}{32}$	1.470	.905
EX, EXL, EWG, EWM	$1\frac{1}{2}$	$\frac{13}{16}$	1.470	.845
AWT	$1\frac{7}{8}$	$1\frac{9}{32}$	1.875	1.281
AX, AXL, AWG, AWM	$1\frac{7}{8}$	$1\frac{3}{16}$	1.875	1.185
BWT	$2\frac{3}{8}$	$1\frac{3}{4}$	2.345	1.750
BX, BXL, BWG, BWM	$2\frac{3}{8}$	$1\frac{5}{8}$	2.345	1.655
NWT	3	$2\frac{5}{16}$	2.965	2.313
NX, NXL, NWG, NWM	3	$2\frac{1}{8}$	2.965	2.155
HWT	$3\frac{29}{32}$	$3\frac{3}{16}$	3.889	3.187
HWG	$3\frac{29}{32}$	3	3.889	3.000
$2\frac{3}{4} \times 3\frac{7}{8}$	$3\frac{7}{8}$	$2\frac{3}{4}$	3.840	2.690
$4 \times 5\frac{1}{2}$	$5\frac{1}{2}$	4	5.435	3.970
$6 \times 7\frac{3}{4}$	$7\frac{3}{4}$	6	7.655	5.970
AX Wire line [1]	$1\frac{7}{8}$	1	1.875	1.000
BX Wire line [1]	$2\frac{3}{8}$	$1\frac{7}{16}$	2.345	1.437
NX Wire line [1]	3	$1\frac{15}{16}$	2.965	1.937

* All dimensions are in inches; to convert to millimeters, multiply by 25.4.

[1] Wire line dimensions and designations may vary according to manufacturer.

Figure 5-63.—Standard coring-bit sizes. (Diamond Core Drill Manufacturers Association). 288–D–2890.

material that is substantially different in composition from either the overlying or the underlying strata should be located by depth interval, separately classified, and described in the body of the log. In explorations other than those for structural foundations, thin layers or lenses of different material in a relatively uniform stratum of material should be described, but need not be separately classified on the log; for example, "a 1-inch-thick discontinuous lens of fine sand occurs at 7-foot depth." However, logs of foundation explorations for structures should indicate the location by depth of all lenses and layers of material and include the classification in addition to a detailed description of the material.

Machine-excavated test pits or test trenches may require more than one log to adequately describe the variations in materials found in different portions of the pit or trench. The initial log of such pits or trenches should describe a vertical section at the deepest part of the excavation and is usually taken at the center of one wall of the pit or trench. If this one log does not adequately describe the variations in the different strata exposed by the pit or trench, additional logs for other locations within the test excavation should be prepared to give a true representation of all strata encountered in the test pit or trench. In long trenches, at least one log should be prepared for each 50 feet of trench wall, regardless of the uniformity of the material or strata. A geologic section of one or both walls of test trenches is desirable and may be required to describe variations in strata and material between log locations. When more than one log is needed to describe the material in an exploratory pit or trench, coordinate location and ground surface elevation should be given for each point for which a log is prepared. A plan geologic map and geologic sections should be prepared for large trenches.

5.42. *Information on Log Forms.*—A log should always contain information on the size of the hole and on the type of equipment used for boring or excavating the hole. This should include the kind of drilling bit used on drill holes and a description of either the excavation equipment (or type of au-

Size designation	Remarks	Rod and coupling O.D.	Rod I.D.	Coupling I.D.	Threads per inch
E	Old standard still in use on many projects	1.313	.844	.438	3
A		1.625	1.266	.563	3
B		1.906	1.406	.625	5
N		2.375	2.000	1.000	4
RW	Present standard	1.094	.719	.406	4
EW		1.375	1.000	.437	3
AW		1.718	1.344	.625	3
BW		2.125	1.750	.750	3
NW		2.625	2.250	1.375	3
HW		3.500	3.062	2.375	3
KWY	Tapered thread (A.P.I.)	2.875	2.312	1.375	4
HWY		3.500	2.875	1.750	4
AQ	Wire line drill rods 1/ Taper thread	1.750	1.375	—	4
BQ		2.188	1.813	—	3
NQ		2.750	2.375	—	3
HQ		3.500	3.063	—	3
PQ		4.500 / 4.625 2/	4.063	4.063	3

1/ Wire line drill rod dimensions and designations may vary according to manufacturer.

2/ For PQ size designation, rod O.D. = 4.500 inches and coupling O.D. = 4.625 inches.

Figure 5-64.—Standard drill-rod sizes. (Diamond Core Drill Manufacturers Association). 288-D-2891.

ger) used or the method of excavating test pits or trenches. The location from which samples are collected should be indicated on the logs, and the amount of core material recovered should be expressed as a percentage of each length of penetration of the barrel. The logs should also show the extent and the method of support used as the hole is deepened, such as the size and depth of casing, the location and extent of grouting, the type of drilling mud, or the type of shoring in test pits or trenches. Caving or squeezing material also should be noted.

Information on the presence or absence of water levels and comments on the reliablility of these data should be recorded on all logs. The date measurements are made should also be recorded, since water levels fluctuate seasonally. Water levels should be recorded periodically as the test hole is deepened from the time water is first encountered. Upon completion of drilling, the hole should be bailed and allowed to recover overnight to obtain a more accurate level measurement. Perched water tables and water under artesian pressure are important to note. The extent of water-bearing members should be noted, and areas where water is lost as the boring proceeds should be reported. The log should contain information on the water tests made at intervals, as described in section 5.46. Because it may be desirable to maintain periodic records of water level fluctuations in drilled holes, it should be determined whether this is required before abandoning and plugging the exploratory hole.

Where cobbles and boulders are encountered in explorations for sources of embankment materials, it is important to determine their percentage by volume. The log form for a test pit or auger hole (fig. 5-66) includes a method for obtaining the percentage by volume of 3- to 5-inch rock and of rock over 5 inches in diameter. The method involves weighing the rock, converting this weight to solid volume of rock, and measuring the volume of hole containing the rock. This determination can be made either on the total volume of stratum excavated or on a representative portion of the stratum by the use of a sampling trench, which is described in section 5.34(a).

For test holes and pits, a statement giving the reason for stopping the hole should be made under "Remarks" in the log. For all other types of bore holes, a statement should be made at the end of the log that the work was completed as required, or a statement explaining why the hole was abandoned.

The data required for geologic logs of drill holes (fig. 5-65) include adequate descriptions of surficial deposits and bedrock encountered, a detailed summary of drilling methods and conditions, and the recording of appropriate physical characteristics and indexes to ensure that adequate engineering data are available for geologic interpretation and design analyses. The log form is divided into three basic sections: drilling notes (in the left column); indexes, notes, and water tests (center column); and classification and physical conditions (right column). The data required for each column of the geologic log of a drill hole (fig. 5-65) are described below.

(a) *Drilling Notes Column.*—Comments in this column should come from geologists' notes and from information on the drillers' Daily Drill Reports.

Drill Site: General physical description of the location of the drill hole. If possible, provide location information based on offset and stationing of the feature.

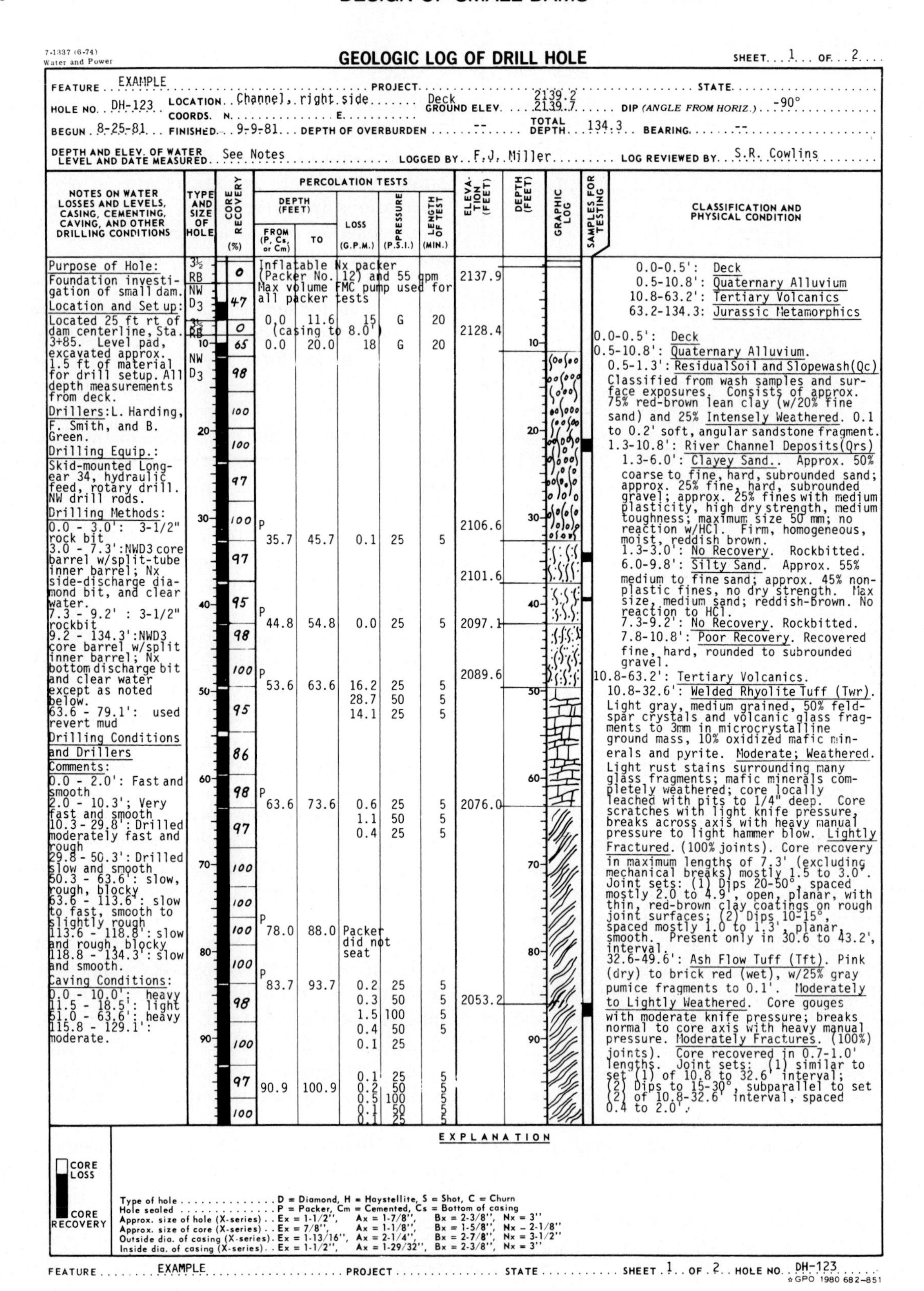

7-1337 (6-74)
Water and Power

GEOLOGIC LOG OF DRILL HOLE

SHEET 1 OF 2

FEATURE: EXAMPLE PROJECT: STATE:
HOLE NO.: DH-123 LOCATION: Channel, right side GROUND ELEV.: Deck 2139.2, 2139.7 DIP (ANGLE FROM HORIZ.): -90°
COORDS. N. E.
BEGUN: 8-25-81 FINISHED: 9-9-81 DEPTH OF OVERBURDEN: -- TOTAL DEPTH: 134.3 BEARING: --
DEPTH AND ELEV. OF WATER LEVEL AND DATE MEASURED: See Notes LOGGED BY: F.J. Miller LOG REVIEWED BY: S.R. Cowlins

NOTES ON WATER LOSSES AND LEVELS, CASING, CEMENTING, CAVING, AND OTHER DRILLING CONDITIONS

Purpose of Hole:
Foundation investigation of small dam.
Location and Set up:
Located 25 ft rt of dam centerline, Sta. 3+85. Level pad, excavated approx. 1.5 ft of material for drill setup. All depth measurements from deck.
Drillers: L. Harding, F. Smith, and B. Green.
Drilling Equip.:
Skid-mounted Longear 34, hydraulic feed, rotary drill. NW drill rods.
Drilling Methods:
0.0 - 3.0': 3-1/2" rock bit
3.0 - 7.3': NWD3 core barrel w/split-tube inner barrel; Nx side-discharge diamond bit, and clear water.
7.3 - 9.2' : 3-1/2" rockbit
9.2 - 134.3': NWD3 core barrel w/split inner barrel; Nx bottom discharge bit and clear water except as noted below.
63.6 - 79.1': used revert mud
Drilling Conditions and Drillers Comments:
0.0 - 2.0': Fast and smooth
2.0 - 10.3'; Very fast and smooth
10.3 - 29.8': Drilled moderately fast and rough
29.8 - 50.3': Drilled slow and smooth
50.3 - 63.6': slow, rough, blocky
63.6 - 113.6': slow to fast, smooth to slightly rough
113.6 - 118.8': slow and rough, blocky
118.8 - 134.3': slow and smooth.
Caving Conditions:
0.0 - 10.0': heavy
11.5 - 18.5': light
51.0 - 63.6': heavy
115.8 - 129.1': moderate.

TYPE AND SIZE OF HOLE: 3½ RB; NW D3; 3½ RB; NW D3

CORE RECOVERY (%): 0, 47, 0, 65, 98, 100, 100, 97, 100, 97, 95, 98, 100, 95, 86, 98, 97, 100, 100, 100, 100, 98, 100, 97, 100

PERCOLATION TESTS

Inflatable Nx packer (Packer No. 12) and 55 gpm Max volume FMC pump used for all packer tests

Depth (feet) From (P, Cs, or Cm)	To	Loss (G.P.M.)	Pressure (P.S.I.)	Length of test (min.)	Elevation (feet)
					2137.9
0.0	11.6	15	G	20	
(casing to 8.0')					2128.4
0.0	20.0	18	G	20	
P 35.7	45.7	0.1	25	5	2106.6
					2101.6
P 44.8	54.8	0.0	25	5	2097.1
P 53.6	63.6	16.2	25	5	2089.6
		28.7	50	5	
		14.1	25	5	
P 63.6	73.6	0.6	25	5	2076.0
		1.1	50	5	
		0.4	25	5	
P 78.0	88.0	Packer did not seat			
P 83.7	93.7	0.2	25	5	
		0.3	50	5	2053.2
		1.5	100	5	
		0.4	50	5	
		0.1	25		
90.9	100.9	0.1	25	5	
		0.2	50	5	
		0.5	100	5	
		0.1	50	5	
		0.1	25	5	

DEPTH (FEET): 10, 20, 30, 40, 50, 60, 70, 80, 90

GRAPHIC LOG — **SAMPLES FOR TESTING**

CLASSIFICATION AND PHYSICAL CONDITION

0.0-0.5': Deck
0.5-10.8': Quaternary Alluvium
10.8-63.2': Tertiary Volcanics
63.2-134.3: Jurassic Metamorphics

0.0-0.5': Deck
0.5-10.8': Quaternary Alluvium.
0.5-1.3': Residual Soil and Slopewash (Qc). Classified from wash samples and surface exposures. Consists of approx. 75% red-brown lean clay (w/20% fine sand) and 25% Intensely Weathered. 0.1 to 0.2' soft, angular sandstone fragment.
1.3-10.8': River Channel Deposits (Qrs)
1.3-6.0': Clayey Sand.. Approx. 50% coarse to fine, hard, subrounded sand; approx. 25% fine, hard, subrounded gravel; approx. 25% fines with medium plasticity, high dry strength, medium toughness; maximum size 50 mm; no reaction w/HCl. Firm, homogeneous, moist, reddish brown.
1.3-3.0': No Recovery. Rockbitted.
6.0-9.8': Silty Sand. Approx. 55% medium to fine sand; approx. 45% nonplastic fines, no dry strength. Max size, medium sand; reddish-brown. No reaction to HCl.
7.3-9.2': No Recovery. Rockbitted.
7.8-10.8': Poor Recovery. Recovered fine, hard, rounded to subrounded gravel.
10.8-63.2': Tertiary Volcanics.
10.8-32.6': Welded Rhyolite Tuff (Twr). Light gray, medium grained, 50% feldspar crystals and volcanic glass fragments to 3mm in microcrystalline ground mass, 10% oxidized mafic minerals and pyrite. Moderate; Weathered. Light rust stains surrounding many glass fragments; mafic minerals completely weathered; core locally leached with pits to 1/4" deep. Core scratches with light knife pressure, breaks across axis with heavy manual pressure to light hammer blow. Lightly Fractured. (100% joints). Core recovery in maximum lengths of 7.3' (excluding mechanical breaks) mostly 1.5 to 3.0'. Joint sets: (1) Dips 20-50°, spaced mostly 2.0 to 4.9', open, planar, with thin, red-brown clay coatings on rough joint surfaces; (2) Dips 10-15°, spaced mostly 1.0 to 1.3', planar, smooth. Present only in 30.6 to 43.2', interval.
32.6-49.6': Ash Flow Tuff (Tft). Pink (dry) to brick red (wet), w/25% gray pumice fragments to 0.1'. Moderately to Lightly Weathered. Core gouges with moderate knife pressure; breaks normal to core axis with heavy manual pressure. Moderately Fractures. (100%) joints). Core recovered in 0.7-1.0' lengths. Joint sets: (1) similar to set (1) of 10.8 to 32.6' interval; (2) Dips to 15-30°, subparallel to set (2) of 10.8-32.6' interval, spaced 0.4 to 2.0'.

EXPLANATION

CORE LOSS
CORE RECOVERY

Type of hole . . . . . D = Diamond, H = Haystellite, S = Shot, C = Churn
Hole sealed . . . . . P = Packer, Cm = Cemented, Cs = Bottom of casing
Approx. size of hole (X-series) . . Ex = 1-1/2", Ax = 1-7/8", Bx = 2-3/8", Nx = 3"
Approx. size of core (X-series) . . Ex = 7/8", Ax = 1-1/8", Bx = 1-5/8", Nx – 2-1/8"
Outside dia. of casing (X-series). Ex = 1-13/16", Ax = 2-1/4", Bx = 2-7/8", Nx = 3-1/2"
Inside dia. of casing (X-series). . Ex = 1-1/2", Ax = 1-29/32", Bx = 2-3/8", Nx = 3"

FEATURE: EXAMPLE PROJECT: STATE: SHEET 1 OF 2 HOLE NO. DH-123

☆GPO 1980 682–851

Figure 5-65.—Example geologic log of a drill hole. (Sheet 1 of 2).

7-1337 (6-74)
Water and Power

GEOLOGIC LOG OF DRILL HOLE

SHEET 2 OF 2

FEATURE EXAMPLE PROJECT .... STATE ....

HOLE NO. DH-123 LOCATION .... COORDS. N. .... E. .... GROUND ELEV. .... DIP (ANGLE FROM HORIZ.) ....

BEGUN .... FINISHED .... DEPTH OF OVERBURDEN .... TOTAL DEPTH .... BEARING ....

DEPTH AND ELEV. OF WATER LEVEL AND DATE MEASURED .... LOGGED BY .... LOG REVIEWED BY ....

NOTES ON WATER LOSSES AND LEVELS, CASING, CEMENTING, CAVING, AND OTHER DRILLING CONDITIONS

Casing and Cementing Record

Size	Casing Depth	Interval Drilled
4"	0.0	0.0-5.2'
4"	5.0	5.2-9.2'
NxCs	8.0	9.2-10.8'
NxCs	10.0	10.8-15.6'
NxCs	23.0	23.8-63.5'
NxCs	48.0	63.5-80.0'
CM cemented 46.5' to 63.5'		80.0 - 134.3'

Drilling Fluid Color and Return

Interval Drilled	Color	% Return
0.0-5.2'	red-brown	0.25
5.2-8.0'	red-brown	40
8.0-9.5'	--	0
9.5-23.5	gray	0-15
23.5-29.5'	gray to red-gray	90
59.5-63.5'	gray	50
53.5-80.0'	revert, blue	80
80.0-134.3'	gray to greenish gray	90

Depths to Water During Drilling & Water Level

Date	Depth Water	Depth Hole
8-26-81	5.0	15.6
8-27-81	7.9	32.6
8-28-81	4.5	50.0
8-29-81	53.1	68.0
9-02-81	89.2	92.7*
9-03-81	107.6-	105.8*
9-04-81	109.8-	117.0*
9-05-81	110.2-	130.0*
9-08-81	107.6-	134.3
9-10-81	105.4-	134.3
10-1-81	103.2-	134.3
11-12-81	101.6-	134.3
7-09-82	104.8-	134.3

*Hole bailed at end of shift

Time Required to Complete Hole: 118 hrs. includes 13 hrs. mobilization and 5 hrs. downtime due to pump failure.

Hole Completion: Left 48.0' NxCs in hole; hole capped for water-level readings. Hole reached pre-determined depth.

TYPE AND SIZE OF HOLE: NWD

CORE RECOVERY (%): 98, 100, 100, 95, 98, 89, 100, 100

PERCOLATION TESTS

Depth (feet) From (P, Cs, or Cm)	To	Loss (G.P.M.)	Pressure (P.S.I.)	Length of Test (Min.)
P 100.4	110.4	0.1	25	5
		0.2	50	5
		0.3	100	5
		0.1	50	5
		0.0	25	5
P 107.0	117.0	0.0	25	5
		0.0	50	5
		0.1	100	5
P 116.0	126.0	0.3	25	5
		1.9	50	5
		3.2	100	10
		2.1	50	5
		0.2	25	5
P 124.3	134.3	0.1	25	5
		0.1	50	5
		0.3	100	5
		0.1	25	5

ELEVATION (FEET): 2022.0, 2018.4, 2014.1, 2004.9

DEPTH (FEET): 110, 120, 130

CLASSIFICATION AND PHYSICAL CONDITION

37.6-42.1': Altered Ash Flow Tuff. Reddish-brown. Fragments can be broken from core with light to moderate manual pressure, pumice fragments powder w/light finger pressure. Very Intensely Fractures. Core recovered in lengths to 0.5', mostly fragments to 0.2' core segments. Thin discontinuous brown clay films on all joint surfaces.

49.6-63.2': Basalt(Tb). Gray to black. Moderately to lightly vesicular, vesicles decrease with depth. Most vesicles 1/16 to 1/2", largest 5/8" across; coated or filled with soft clay. Lightly Weathered. Core scratches with moderate knife pressure, and breaks 60 to 90° to core axis with moderate hammer blow. Moderately Fractured. Recovered mostly as 0.5 to 1.3' lengths; maximum 2.3'. Joint sets: (1) Dips 85 to 90°, 2 fractures cross core axis at 53.6' and 61.2', irregular surfaces with oxide stains; (2) Dips 0 to 30°, spaced 0.5-2.9', irregular rough surfaces, with thin, discontinuous clay coatings.

50.3-51.4': Intensely Fractures.

59.2-63.2': (100% joints). Core recovered as 0.2 to 0.3' lengths, maximum length 0.5'; joints dip 10 to 35°; spaced 0.2 to 0.4' irregular, rough surfaces, joints open and filled with up to 1/4" of buff colored clay.

63.2-134.3': Jurassic Metamorphic Rock

63.2-134.3': Amphibolite Schist (Jam) Dark green to greenish gray, fine-grained, schistose to subschistose, composed chiefly of hornblende and quartz with calcite veinlets to 3/4" along schistosity and epidote stringers throughout.

63.2-122.3': Lightly Weathered. Red-brown oxidation stains on most discontinuities. Core breaks along schistosity with moderate to heavy hammer blow, scratches w/heavy knife pressure.

Moderately Fractured. (60% joints, 40% cleavage) except as noted below. Core recovered in lengths to 1.8', mostly 0.6 to 1.3'. Cleavage dips 65° spaced 0.8 to 1.9'. Two joint sets noted: (1) Dips 15-30°, spaced 0.7 to 2.0', smooth, coated with oxides of Fe and Mn; (2) Dips 5-10°, normal to set (1), spaced 0.4 to 2.5', most surfaces smooth, locally minor slickensides.

87.2-101.2': Lightly Fractured. (50% joints, 50% cleavage). Core recovered in lengths to 2.9', mostly 1.6 to 2.1'.

113.2-117.2': Intensely Fractured. (80% joint, 20% cleavage). Core recovered in lengths to 0.7', mostly 0.3 to 0.4'.

CONTINUED IN CENTER COLUMN.

CLASSIFICATION AND PHYSICAL CONDITION CONT'D

117.2-120.8': Dike. Light gray, fine-grained. Upper contact welded, dips 28°, lower contact broken, dips 35°: Lightly Weathered. Solution pitting to 1/8". Core breaks with moderate hammer blow. Intensely to Moderately Fractured. (100% joints). Joints are randomly oriented and spaced; surfaces are irregular and rough; no sets discernible. Recovered mostly as 0.3 to 0.7' core lengths.

122.3-134.3: Fresh. No oxidation on discontinuities. Core breaks along schistosity or across axis with heavy hammer blow; scratches with heavy knife pressure. Lightly Fractured, except as noted below (65% joints, 35% cleavage). Recovered in lengths to 4.2', mostly 1.6 to 2.7'. Cleavage dips 65 to 70°; spaced 1.5 to 4.5'. Joint sets noted: (1) Dips 15-35°, spaced 1.5 to 5.3', most surfaces smooth, planar; (2) Dips 10-25°, normal to set (1), spaced 2.0 to 6.5', most surfaces planar & smooth, about 5% with minor slickensides, 10% healed by Qtz-cal.

123.4-127.7': Intensely Fractured. (50% joints 50% cleavage). Recovered in lengths to 0.6', mostly 0.3 to 0.4'.

125.1-125.8': Shear Zone. 0.5' thick. No Recovery. 125.1-125.3'. Upper contact (?); lower contact dips 62-67° (subparallel to schistosity). Consists of 70% green, moist, soft clay gouge and 30% 1/16 to 1/4" platy, slickensided, amphibolite fragments. Lower 1/2" of shear is healed by quartz calcite. Fragments break with heavy finger pressure.

CORE LOSS / CORE RECOVERY

Type of hole .... D = Diamond, H = Haystellite, S = Shot, C = Churn
Hole sealed .... P = Packer, Cm = Cemented, Cs = Bottom of casing
Approx. size of hole (X-series) .. Ex = 1-1/2", Ax = 1-7/8", Bx = 2-3/8", Nx = 3"
Approx. size of core (X-series) .. Ex = 7/8", Ax = 1-1/8", Bx = 1-5/8", Nx = 2-1/8"
Outside dia. of casing (X-series) . Ex = 1-13/16", Ax = 2-1/4", Bx = 2-7/8", Nx = 3-1/2"
Inside dia. of casing (X-series) . Ex = 1-1/2", Ax = 1-29/32", Bx = 2-3/8", Nx = 3"

FEATURE EXAMPLE PROJECT .... STATE .... SHEET 2 OF 2 HOLE NO. DH-123

☆GPO 1980 682-851

Figure 5-65.—Example geologic log of a drill hole. (Sheet 2 of 2).

7-1336-A (1-86) Bureau of Reclamation	LOG OF TEST PIT OR AUGER HOLE	HOLE NO. TP-103a

FEATURE Whatsit Dam — PROJECT Dohicky Central
AREA DESIGNATION Spillway Foundation — GROUND ELEVATION 1234.7 ft
COORDINATES N 1111 E 2222 — METHOD OF EXPLORATION backhoe
APPROXIMATE DIMENSIONS 8 by 12 ft — LOGGED BY A. Purson
DEPTH WATER ENCOUNTERED 1/ none DATE ____ — DATE(S) LOGGED 1-25 to 1-26, 1986

CLASSIFICATION GROUP SYMBOL (describe sample taken)	CLASSIFICATION AND DESCRIPTION OF MATERIAL SEE USBR 5000, 5005	% PLUS 3 in (BY VOLUME) 3 - 5 in	5 - 12 in	PLUS 12 in
CL three sack samples 4.2 ft	0.0 to 4.2 ft LEAN CLAY: About 90% fines with medium plasticity, high dry strength, medium toughness; about 10% predominantly fine sand; maximum size, medium sand; strong reaction with HCl. IN-PLACE CONDITION: Soft, homogeneous, wet, brown. Three 50-lbm sack samples taken from 12-inch-wide sampling trench for entire interval on north side of test pit. Samples mixed and quartered.			
(SC)g block sample 9.8 ft	4.2 to 9.8 ft CLAYEY SAND WITH GRAVEL: About 50% coarse to fine, hard, subangular to subrounded sand; about 25% fine, hard, subangular to subrounded gravel; about 25% fines with medium plasticity, high dry strength, medium toughness; maximum size, 20 mm; weak reaction with HCl. IN-PLACE CONDITION: Firm, homogeneous except for occasional lenses of clean fine sand 1/4 inch to 1 inch thick, moist, reddish-brown. 12- by 12-inch block sample taken at 6.0 to 7.0 ft depth, at center of south side of test pit.			

REMARKS: Excavated with Yonka 67Z backhoe

Observation well installed

Date	Depth to water
1-31-86	7.4 ft
4-13-86	4.2 ft
8-28-86	9.7 ft

1/ Report to nearest 0.1 foot

GPO 849-366

Figure 5-66.—Example log of test pit or auger hole.

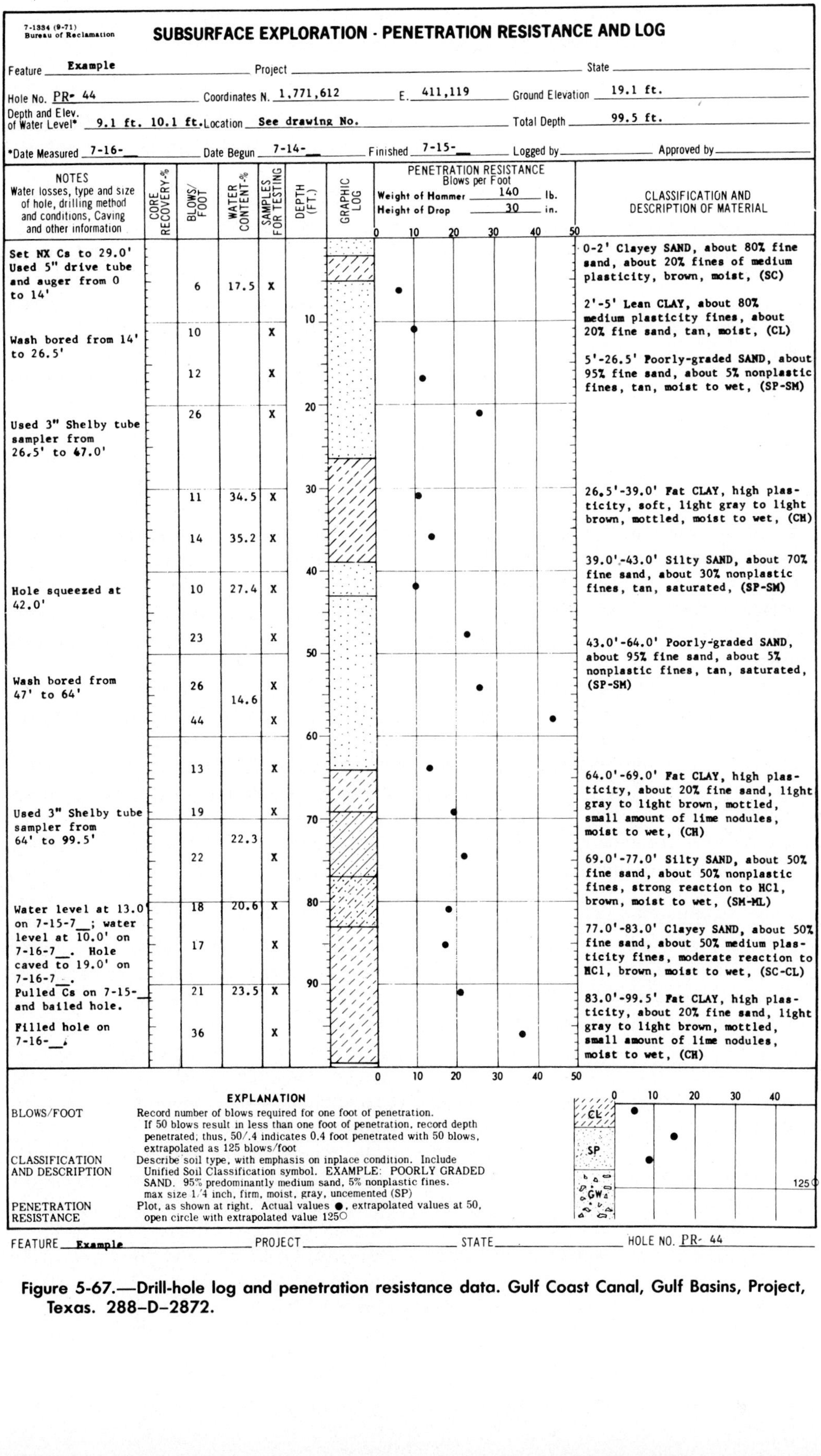

7-1334 (9-71)
Bureau of Reclamation

SUBSURFACE EXPLORATION - PENETRATION RESISTANCE AND LOG

Feature **Example** Project ______ State ______

Hole No. PR- 44 Coordinates N. 1,771,612 E. 411,119 Ground Elevation 19.1 ft.

Depth and Elev. of Water Level* 9.1 ft. 10.1 ft. Location See drawing No. ______ Total Depth 99.5 ft.

*Date Measured 7-16-__ Date Begun 7-14-__ Finished 7-15-__ Logged by ______ Approved by ______

PENETRATION RESISTANCE Blows per Foot — Weight of Hammer 140 lb. Height of Drop 30 in.

NOTES (Water losses, type and size of hole, drilling method and conditions, Caving and other information)

Set NX Cs to 29.0'. Used 5" drive tube and auger from 0 to 14'

Wash bored from 14' to 26.5'

Used 3" Shelby tube sampler from 26.5' to 47.0'

Hole squeezed at 42.0'

Wash bored from 47' to 64'

Used 3" Shelby tube sampler from 64' to 99.5'

Water level at 13.0' on 7-15-7__; water level at 10.0' on 7-16-7__. Hole caved to 19.0' on 7-16-7__.

Pulled Cs on 7-15-__ and bailed hole.

Filled hole on 7-16-__.

CORE RECOVERY-%	BLOWS/FOOT	WATER CONTENT-%	SAMPLES FOR TESTING
	6	17.5	X
	10		X
	12		X
	26		X
	11	34.5	X
	14	35.2	X
	10	27.4	X
	23		X
	26	14.6	X
	44		X
	13		X
	19		X
		22.3	
	22		X
	18	20.6	X
	17		X
	21	23.5	X
	36		X

DEPTH (FT.): 10, 20, 30, 40, 50, 60, 70, 80, 90

Penetration resistance scale: 0 10 20 30 40 50

CLASSIFICATION AND DESCRIPTION OF MATERIAL

0-2' Clayey SAND, about 80% fine sand, about 20% fines of medium plasticity, brown, moist, (SC)

2'-5' Lean CLAY, about 80% medium plasticity fines, about 20% fine sand, tan, moist, (CL)

5'-26.5' Poorly-graded SAND, about 95% fine sand, about 5% nonplastic fines, tan, moist to wet, (SP-SM)

26.5'-39.0' Fat CLAY, high plasticity, soft, light gray to light brown, mottled, moist to wet, (CH)

39.0'-43.0' Silty SAND, about 70% fine sand, about 30% nonplastic fines, tan, saturated, (SP-SM)

43.0'-64.0' Poorly-graded SAND, about 95% fine sand, about 5% nonplastic fines, tan, saturated, (SP-SM)

64.0'-69.0' Fat CLAY, high plasticity, about 20% fine sand, light gray to light brown, mottled, small amount of lime nodules, moist to wet, (CH)

69.0'-77.0' Silty SAND, about 50% fine sand, about 50% nonplastic fines, strong reaction to HCl, brown, moist to wet, (SM-ML)

77.0'-83.0' Clayey SAND, about 50% fine sand, about 50% medium plasticity fines, moderate reaction to HCl, brown, moist to wet, (SC-CL)

83.0'-99.5' Fat CLAY, high plasticity, about 20% fine sand, light gray to light brown, mottled, small amount of lime nodules, moist to wet, (CH)

EXPLANATION

BLOWS/FOOT — Record number of blows required for one foot of penetration. If 50 blows result in less than one foot of penetration, record depth penetrated; thus, 50/.4 indicates 0.4 foot penetrated with 50 blows, extrapolated as 125 blows/foot

CLASSIFICATION AND DESCRIPTION — Describe soil type, with emphasis on inplace condition. Include Unified Soil Classification symbol. EXAMPLE: POORLY GRADED SAND. 95% predominantly medium sand, 5% nonplastic fines. max size 1/4 inch, firm, moist, gray, uncemented (SP)

PENETRATION RESISTANCE — Plot, as shown at right. Actual values ●, extrapolated values at 50, open circle with extrapolated value 125○

(Example chart: CL, SP, GW; scale 0 10 20 30 40; 125○)

FEATURE Example PROJECT ______ STATE ______ HOLE NO. PR- 44

Figure 5-67.—Drill-hole log and penetration resistance data. Gulf Coast Canal, Gulf Basins, Project, Texas. 288-D-2872.

Purpose of Hole: Reason for drilling the hole, for example: "dam foundation investigation," "materials investigation," or " sampling for testing."

Drill Equipment:
- Drill rig (make and model)
- Core barrels (type, size)
- Bits (type, size)
- Drill rods (type, size)
- Spacers (type)
- Water-test equipment (rod size, transducer)
- Packers (type)

Drillers: Names

Drill Fluid: Type and where used (including drill-fluid additives)

Drilling Fluid Return:
- Interval
- Percent return

Drill-Fluid Return Color:
- Interval
- Color

Drilling Methods: Synopsis of drilling procedures used through the various intervals of the hole.

Drilling Conditions and Drillers' Comments: Record, by interval, the relative speed at which the bit penetrates the rock and the action of the drill during this process (e.g., "105.6-107.9: drilled slowly, very blocky, hole advance 15 minutes per foot"). Changes in drilling conditions may indicate differences in lithology, weathering, or fracture density. Record locations and amounts of explosives used for blasting to help advance the hole. Any other comments relative to ease or difficulty of advancing or maintaining the hole (provide locations).

Caving Conditions: Record intervals of cave with appropriate remarks about the relative amount of caving. Intervals should be noted where the caving occurs, not the depth of the hole.

Cement Record: Record all intervals cemented and whether some intervals were cemented more than once. This may be combined with the casing record if one or the other is short.

Borehole Survey Data: If obtained.

Water-Level Data: Notes on location, water quantities, and pressures from artesian flows.

Hole Completion: How hole was completed or backfilled; if jetting, washing, or bailing was used; depth of casing left in hole, or whether casing was pulled. Location and type of piezometers; location, sizes, and types of slotted pipes (including size and spacing of slots) or piezometer risers. Type and depth of backfill or depths of concrete and bentonite plugs; location of isolated intervals; elevation of tops of risers.

Reason for Hole Termination: Whether hole reached predetermined depth or the reason why it was stopped before reaching predetermined depth.

Estimated Drilling Time:
- Setup time
- Drilling time
- Downtime

(b) *Center Column.*—The subcolumns within the center column are generally self explanatory. These columns may be modified, or new columns added to the existing log form to record appropriate indexes or special conditions.

Percolation Tests: Record the general information of the tests. Additional data may be recorded on "water testing" log forms or drillers' reports.

Type and Size of Hole, Elevation, and *Depth*: These columns are self-explanatory.

Core Recovery: Record percent of recovery by run (this does not necessarily require a visual graph). The core recovery for each run should be carefully noted by the driller on the Daily Drill Reports. However, this column should be the record of those measurements prepared by the geologist during logging.

Hole Completion: This column may be added. It is a graphic portrayal of how the hole was completed. An explanation of the graphics can be put in the bottom midsection of the log form, provided in report narratives, or explained on note drawings.

RQD (Rock Quality Designation): Should be reported by core run. This column is considered necessary for all underground structures and is recommended for most logs of N-size holes.

Lithologic Log: An orographic column helps to quickly visualize the geologic conditions. Appropriate symbols may be used for correlation of tests and shear zones, water levels, weathering and fracturing.

Samples for Testing: Should include locations of samples obtained for testing and can later have actual sample results inserted in the column, if the column is enlarged.

(c) *Classification and Physical Conditions Column.*—All data presented should be divided into main headings with several sets of first, second, and third order subheadings. Main headings may be "Surficial Deposits," and "Bedrock Units," or they may be "Differentiation of Weathering" or "Lithologies." Descriptions of bedrock cores and bedrock data required for this column are discussed in section 5.44.

5.43. *Description of Soils.*—The logger should be able to identify and record soils according to the USCS. The description of a soil in a log should include its group name, followed by pertinent descriptive data, as listed in table 5-7. After the soil is described, it should be identified with the appropriate soil classification group by letter symbols. These group symbols represent various soils having certain common characteristics; therefore, by themselves that may not be sufficient to describe a particular soil. Borderline classifications (two sets of symbols separated by a slash) should be used when the soil does not fall clearly into one of the groups, but has strong characteristics of both groups. (See sec. 5.16, sec. 5.17, and fig. 5-12 for more detailed discussions of soil classification.)

Identification and classification of soils in exploration logs should be based on visual examination and manual tests. Laboratory tests may be used to verify field classifications; however, laboratory results should be described in a separate, subordinate paragraph.

Soils for small dams may be investigated as (1) borrow materials for embankments or for backfill, or (2) foundations for the dam and appurtenant structures. The soil features that should be de-

Table 5-7.—Checklist for description of soils.

1. Group name
2. Group symbol
3. Percent, by volume, of cobbles and boulders
4. Percent, by dry weight, of gravel, sand, and fines
5. Particle-size range:
   - Gravel - fine, coarse
   - Sand - fine, medium, coarse
6. Particle angularity:
   angular subangular subrounded rounded
7. Particle shape:
   flat elongated flat and elongated
8. Hardness of coarse grains
9. Maximum particle size or dimension
10. Plasticity of fines: nonplastic low medium high
11. Dry Strength: none low medium high very high
12. Dilatancy: none slow rapid
13. Toughness: low medium high
14. Color (in moist condition)
15. Odor - mention only if organic or unusual
16. Moisture: dry moist wet
17. Reaction with HCl: none weak strong

For intact samples:

18. Consistency: very soft soft firm hard very hard
19. Natural density: loose dense
20. Structure: stratified laminated fissured slickensided block lensed
21. Cementation: weak moderate strong
22. Geologic interpretation
23. Additional comments:
   - Presence of roots or root holes
   - Presence of mica, gypsum, etc.
   - Surface coatings on coarse-grained particles
   - Caving or sloughing of auger hole on side of pit or trench
   - Difficulty in augering
   - Etc.

scribed depend on which of these categories is involved. For many structures, large quantities of soil must be excavated to reach a desired foundation. In the interests of economy, maximum use of this excavated material should always be made in the construction of embankments and for backfill. A foundation area, therefore, often becomes a source of materials, and soil investigations must take this dual purpose into account. Descriptions of soils or of weathered bedrock encountered in such explorations should contain the essential information required both for borrow materials and for foundation soils.

Soils and weathered bedrock that are potential sources of borrow material for embankments must be described adequately in the log of the exploratory test pit or auger hole. Because these materials are destined to be disturbed by excavation, transportation, and compaction in the fill, their structure is less important than the amount and characteristics of their soil constituents. However, recording their natural water condition is important. Very dry borrow materials require the addition of large amounts of moisture for compaction control, and wet borrow materials containing appreciable fines may require extensive processing and drying to be usable. For simplicity, the natural moisture content of borrow materials should be reported as either "dry," "moist," or "wet." Borrow investigation holes are logged to indicate divisions between soils of different classification groups. However, within the same soil group significant changes in moisture should be logged.

When soils are being explored as foundations for dams and appurtenant structures, their natural structure, compactness, and moisture content are of paramount importance. Logs of foundation explorations, therefore, must emphasize the inplace condition of a soil in addition to describing its constituents. The natural state of foundation soils is significant because bearing capacity and settlement under load vary with the consistency or compactness of the soil. Therefore, information that a clay soil is hard and dry, or soft and moist, is important. Changes in consistency of foundation soils caused by moisture changes under operating conditions must be considered in the design. Correct classification is needed so that the effect of these moisture changes on foundation properties can be predicted. The inclusion of the geologic interpretations such as loess, caliche, etc., in addition to the soil classification name may be helpful in identifying inplace conditions.

Table 5-8 lists the data needed to describe soils for borrow material and for foundations. Examples of soil descriptions are given on the soil classification chart (fig. 5-12) and on the example log forms (figs. 5-65, 5-66, and 5-67).

5.44. *Description of Rock Cores.*—The ability of a foundation to support the loads imposed by various structures depends primarily on the deformability, stability, and ground-water conditions of the foundation materials. Judgment and intuition alone are not adequate for the safe design of dams. It has become imperative to properly develop geologic design data because recent advancements in soil and rock mechanics and new analytical procedures enable engineers to assess more conditions

Table 5-8.—Description of soils.

Items of descriptive data	Borrow		Foundation	
	Coarse-grained soils	Fine-grained soils	Coarse-grained soils	Fine-grained soils
Group name (as shown in soil classification chart, fig. 5-12)	R[1]	R	R	R
Approximate percentages of gravel and sand	D	D	D	D
Maximum size of particles (including cobbles and boulders)	R	D	D	D
Shape of the coarse grains—angularity	D	-	D	-
Surface condition of the coarse grains—coatings	D	-	-	-
Hardness of the coarse grains—possible breakdown into smaller sizes	D	-	D	-
Color (in moist condition for fine-grained soils and fraction of fines in coarse-grained soils)	D	D	D	D
Moisture (dry, moist, wet)	R	R	R	R
Organic content	D	D	D	D
Plasticity—degree (nonplastic, low, medium, high) and dilatancy, dry strength, and toughness for fine-grained soils and of the fine-grained fraction in coarse-grained soils	D	R	R	R
Structure (stratification, lenses and seams, laminations, giving dip and strike and thickness of layer; honeycomb, flocculent, root holes, etc.)	-	-	R	R
Cementation—type	R	D	R	R
Consistency in undisturbed and remolded states (clays only)	-	-	-	R
Local or geologic name	D	D	R	R
Group symbol	R	R	R	R

[1] R = Information *required* on all logs.
D = Information *desired* on all logs.

analytically than previously possible. To incorporate these new techniques, foundation data reported in geologic logs must be not only accurate and concise, but also quantified as much as possible.

(a) *Objectives of Geologic Logging.*—The basic objective of describing a core is to provide a concise record of its important geologic and physical characteristics of engineering significance. The Bureau of Reclamation has adopted recognized indexes, standardized descriptors and, when required, quantified numeric descriptors for physical properties to ensure that these data are recorded uniformly, consistently, and accurately. The descriptions should be prepared by an engineering geologist. An experienced logger may describe seemingly minor features or conditions that he/she knows have engineering significance, and exclude petrologic features or geologic conditions having only minor or academic interest. Adequate descriptions of rock core can be prepared solely through visual or "hand specimen" examination of the core with the aid of simple field tests. Detailed microscopic or laboratory testing to define rock type or mineralogy is generally necessary only in special cases. Figure 5-68 shows how core obtained from a borehole are arranged for logging.

(b) *Data Required for Geologic Logs of Drill Holes.*—The purpose of drilling and logging is to secure evidence of the inplace condition of the rock mass. Therefore, any core condition, damage, or core loss caused by the type of bit, barrel, or other equipment used, or caused by using the improper equipment or techniques in the drilling process should be ascertained. Such factors may have a marked effect on the amount and condition of the core recovered, particularly in soft, friable, weathered or intensely fractured rock masses, or in zones of shearing. Geologic logs require both the adequate description of materials, and a detailed summary of drilling equipment, methods, and conditions that may provide significant engineering data or be useful for geologic interpretations (see sec. 5.42).

Descriptions of surficial deposits recovered from drill holes and recorded on geologic logs (e.g., slopewash, alluvium, colluvium, and residual soil) are normally described using the USCS where reasonably good samples are obtained. If samples cannot be obtained, descriptive terms of the cuttings, return drill-water color, drilling characteristics, and correlation to surface exposures must be used. It is necessary always to record what is being decribed—samples or cuttings. Uniformity of descriptions for all exploration logs and reports is desirable, and descriptors for physical characteristics such as compactness, consistency, and structure should conform to those of the guidelines established for the USCS. The geologic unit name and age, when known, also should be provided (e.g., "Quaternary basin fill," "Recent stream channel deposits," "Quaternary alluvium," and "Quaternary colluvium").

Descriptions of bedrock should include a typical name based on general lithologic characteristics followed by data on structural features and physical conditions. Bedrock or lithologic units should be delineated and identified not only by the general rock types provided in part E of this chapter, but also by any special geologic, mineralogic, or physical features with engineering significance or relevance to the interpretation of the subsurface conditions. Bedrock descriptions should include the data listed in the following subsections.

(1) *General Description.*—A general description of each lithologic unit should be provided. This should include notes on composition, grain size, shape, texture, color of fresh and altered or weathered surfaces, cementation, structure, foliation, and banding or schistosity and their orientation. More detailed descriptions are normally provided in geologic reports, thereby permitting briefer logs.

(2) *Hardness and Strength.*—The hardness and strength of rock masses primarily are related to individual rock types, but also may be modified by weathering or alteration. Combined with hardness-strength descriptors, weathering may be the primary criterion for determining the depth of excavation, cut-slope design, and use of excavated materials. Large differences in hardness are more important than very subtle or localized differences.

(3) *Structural Features.*—Structural features (discontinuities) in rock masses in the form of planes or surfaces of separation include cleavage, bedding-plane partings, fractures, joints, and zones of crushing or shearing. Because these features control or significantly influence the behavior of the rock mass such as strength, deformation, and permeability, they must be described in detail. There are several indexes and at least three types of data that are useful to evaluate structural features; these are fracture density or intensity, de-

Figure 5-68.—Logging of core obtained from rotary drilling. P1222–142–2198.

scriptions of fractures, and descriptions of shear and fault zones.

a. *Fracture Density.*—Fracture density is based on the spacing of all naturally occurring breaks in the recovered core (core recovery lengths), excluding mechanical breaks and shear or fault zones. Maximum and minimum lengths and a range or the average length of recovered core should be recorded. These fracture spacings always should be described in physical measurements, but descriptive terms relating to these measurements are convenient and help communicate the characteristics of the rock mass. It is usually helpful to provide a percentage of the types of discontinuities.

b. *Fracture Descriptions.*—Fractures or joints should be categorized into sets based on similar orientations, and each set should be described. Physical measurements, such as orientation (inclination or dip) in drill holes, spacing or frequency where applicable, and persistence or continuity, should be recorded. In addition, the following characteristics should be described: the composition, thickness, and hardness of fillings or coatings; the character of surfaces (smooth or rough); waviness; healing; and whether the fracture is open or tight. In drill cores, the average spacing between fractures should be measured along the centerline of the core or, when a set can be distinguished (parallel or subparallel joints), true spacing should be measured normal to the fracture surfaces.

c. *Descriptions of Faults and Shear Zones.*—Faults and shear zones should be described in detail, including data such as percentage of the various components (gouge, rock fragments, quartz or calcite veinlets) and the relationship of these components to each other. The gouge color, moisture, consistency, and composition; and the fragment or breccia sizes, shapes, surface features, lithology, and strengths should be recorded. The depths, dip or inclination and true thickness (measured normal to the shear or fault contacts) also must be determined, if possible, along with healing, strength, and other associated features.

(4) *Core Loss.*—Intervals of core loss and the reasons for the losses should be recorded. All cores should be measured by the logger (using the midpoint of core ends), and gains and losses should be transferred to adjacent runs to cancel each other out. Unaccountable losses or gains determined from the driller's report should be reconciled, and the location of the loss or gain determined. Inaccurate driller's measurements and locations where portions of the previously drilled run was left in the hole (pulled off of, or fell back in and redrilled) can be determined by examining the end and beginning of adjacent core runs to see whether they fit together or show signs of having been redrilled.

Where losses occur, examining the core to determine the reason for the loss is critical. Drill-water losses and color, or changes in the drilling conditions noted by the driller may suggest the reason for the core loss. Poor drilling methods, mismeasurement, or geologic conditions noted by the driller may also suggest the reason for the core loss. Poor drilling methods mismeasurement, or geologic conditions responsible for the losses usually can be recognized by an experienced logger. When a portion of a shear zone is interpreted to have been lost during drilling, the unrecovered portion should be described as part of the shear zone, and the loss used in determining its thickness.

K. FIELD AND LABORATORY TESTS

5.45. *General.*—There are a great variety of field and laboratory tests that have been used for the design of dams. However, only fundamental field test procedures are described herein. In addition to the standard penetration test, described in section 5.32(b), three other field tests that obtain values for the natural ground are applicable in foundation explorations: (1) permeability tests, (2) inplace unit weight tests, and (3) vane shear tests. The inplace unit weight test is used also in borrow areas to determine the shrinkage between excavation and embankment volumes.

The laboratory tests on soils discussed herein are limited to those required to verify soii classifications, or to determine compaction characteristics for comparison with design assumptions made from data in table 5-1 (sec. 5.18), or for correlation with construction control tests given in appendix E. The descriptions of the tests are intended to furnish a general knowledge of their scope. For detailed test procedures refer to the Bureau of Reclamation's *Earth Manual* [7].

The laboratory tests on the quality of riprap and concrete aggregate, commonly used in specifications for these materials, are described to afford an understanding of the significance of those tests. Details of the test procedures can be found in the Bureau of Reclamation's *Concrete Manual* [9].

5.46. *Field Permeability Tests.*—(a) *General.*—Approximate values for the permeability of individual strata can be obtained through water testing in drill holes. The reliability of the values obtained depends on the homogeneity of the stratum tested and on certain restrictions of the mathematical formulas used. However, if reasonable care is exercised in adhering to the recommended procedures, useful results can be obtained during ordinary drilling operations. Using the more precise methods of determining permeability (by pumping from wells and measuring drawdown of the water table in a series of observation holes or by pump-in tests using large-diameter perforated casing) is generally unnecessary for the design of small dams.

The bore hole permeability tests described below are of the pump-in type; that is, they are based on measuring the amount of water accepted by the ground through the open bottom of a pipe or through an uncased section of the hole. These tests become invalid and may be grossly misleading unless clear water is used. The presence of even small amounts of silt or clay in the added water will plug up the test section and yield permeability results that are too low. By means of a settling tank or a filter, efforts should be made to ensure that only clear water is used. It is desirable for the temperature of the added water to be higher than the ground-water temperature to prevent the creation of air bubbles in the ground, which may greatly reduce the acceptance of water.

(b) *Open-End Tests.*—Figure 5-69 (A) and (B) show a test made through the open end of a pipe casing that has been sunk to the desired depth and has been carefully cleaned out to the bottom of the casing. When the hole extends below the ground-water table, it is recommended that the hole be kept filled with water during cleaning and especially during the withdrawal of tools to avoid squeezing of soil into the bottom of the pipe. After the hole is cleaned to the proper depth, the test is begun by adding clear water through a metering system to maintain gravity flow at a constant head. In tests above the water table (fig. 5-69 (B)) a stable, constant level is rarely obtained, and a surging of the level within a few tenths of a foot at a constant rate of flow for approximately 5 minutes is considered satisfactory.

If it is desirable to apply pressure to the water entering the hole, the pressure, in units of head, is added to the gravity head, as shown on figure 5-69 (C) and (D). Measurements of constant head, constant rate of flow into the hole, size of casing pipe, and elevations of top and bottom of the casing are recorded. The permeability is obtained from the following relationship:

$$K = \frac{Q}{5.5rH} \tag{2}$$

where:

K = permeability,
Q = constant rate of flow into the hole,
r = internal radius of casing, and
H = differential head of water.

Any consistent set of units may be used. For convenience, equation (2) may be written:

$$K = C_1 \frac{Q}{H}$$

where K is in feet per year, Q is in gallons per minute, H is in feet, and values of C_1 vary with the size of casing as follows:

Size of casing	***EX***	***AX***	***BX***	***NX***
C_1	204,000	160,000	129,000	102,000

The value of H for gravity tests made below the water table is the difference in feet between the level

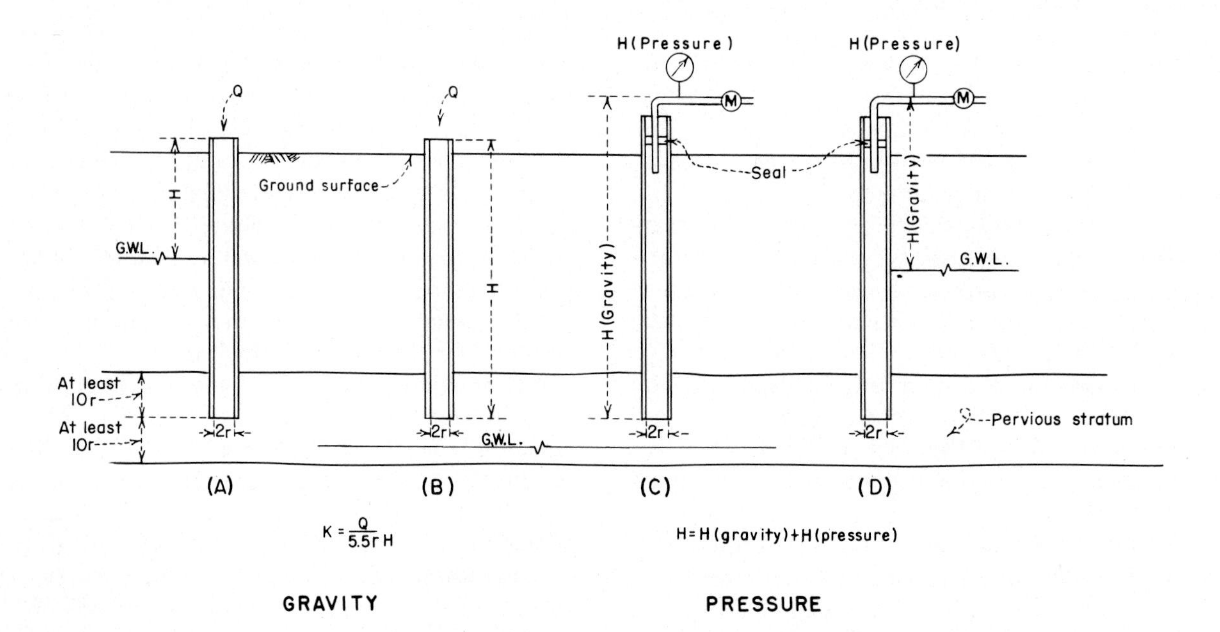

Figure 5-69.—An open-end pipe test for soil permeability that can be made in the field. 288–D–2476.

of water in the casing and the ground-water level. For tests above water table, H is the depth of water in the hole. For pressure tests, the applied pressure in feet of water (1 lb/in^2 = 2.31 ft of head) is added to the gravity head to obtain H.

For the example shown on figure 5-69 (A):
Given:

NX casing,
Q = 10.1 gal/min, and
H = 21.4 feet;

then:

$$K = C_1\frac{Q}{H} = \frac{(102{,}000)(10.1)}{21.4} = 48{,}100 \text{ ft/yr.}$$

For the example shown on figure 5-69(D):
Given:

NX casing,
Q = 7 gal/min,
H (gravity) = 24.6 feet, and
H (pressure) = 5 lb/in^2 = 5 (2.31) = 11.6 feet of water;

then:

$$H = 24.6 + 11.6 = 36.2 \text{ feet, and}$$

$$K = C_1\frac{Q}{H} = \frac{(102{,}000)(7)}{36.2} = 19{,}700 \text{ ft/yr.}$$

(c) *Packer Tests.*—Figure 5-70 shows a permeability test made in a portion of a drill hole below the casing. This test can be made both above and below the water table, provided the hole will remain open. It is commonly used for pressure testing of bedrock using packers, but it can be used in unconsolidated materials where a top packer is placed at the base of the casing. If the packer is placed inside the casing, measures must be taken to properly seal the annular space between the casing and the drill hole wall to prevent water under pressure from escaping. Even if these measures are taken to seal the casing, the value of the test is questionable because there is no sure way of knowing if the annular seal is effective.

The formulas for this test are:

$$K = \frac{Q}{2\pi LH}\log_e\frac{L}{r} \quad (\text{where } L \le 10r) \qquad (3)$$

$$K = \frac{Q}{2\pi LH}\sinh^{-1}\frac{L}{2r} \quad (\text{where } 10r > L \ge r) \qquad (4)$$

where:

K = permeability,
Q = constant rate of flow into the hole,
L = length of the portion of the hole tested,
H = differential head of water,
r = radius of hole tested,
$\log_e$ = natural logarithm, and
$\sinh^{-1}$ = inverse hyperbolic sine.

Formulas (3) and (4) are most valid when the thickness of the stratum tested is at least $5L$. They are considered to be more accurate for tests below the water table than above it.

For convenience, the formulas (3) and (4) may be written:

$$K = C_p\frac{Q}{H} \qquad (5)$$

where K is in feet per year, Q is in gallons per minute, and C_p is determined from table 5-9. Where the test length is below the water table, H is the distance in feet from the water table to the swivel plus applied pressure in feet of water. Where the test length is above the water table, H is the distance in feet from the center of the length tested to the swivel plus the applied pressure in feet of water. For gravity tests (no applied pressure), measurements for H are made to the water level inside the casing (usually the level of the ground).

Values of C_p are given in table 5-9 for various lengths of test section and hole diameters.

The usual procedure for the packer-type of permeability test in rock is to drill the hole, remove the core barrel or other tool, seat the packer, make the test, remove the packer, drill the hole deeper, set the packer again to test the newly drilled section, and repeat the tests (see fig. 5-70 (A)). If the hole stands without casing, a common procedure is to drill it to final depth, fill it with water, surge it, and bail it out. Then set two packers on pipe or drill stem, as shown on figure 5-70 (C) and (D). The length of packer when expanded should be at least five times the diameter of the hole. The bottom of the pipe holding the packer must be plugged, and its perforated portion must be between the packers. In testing between two packers, it is desirable to

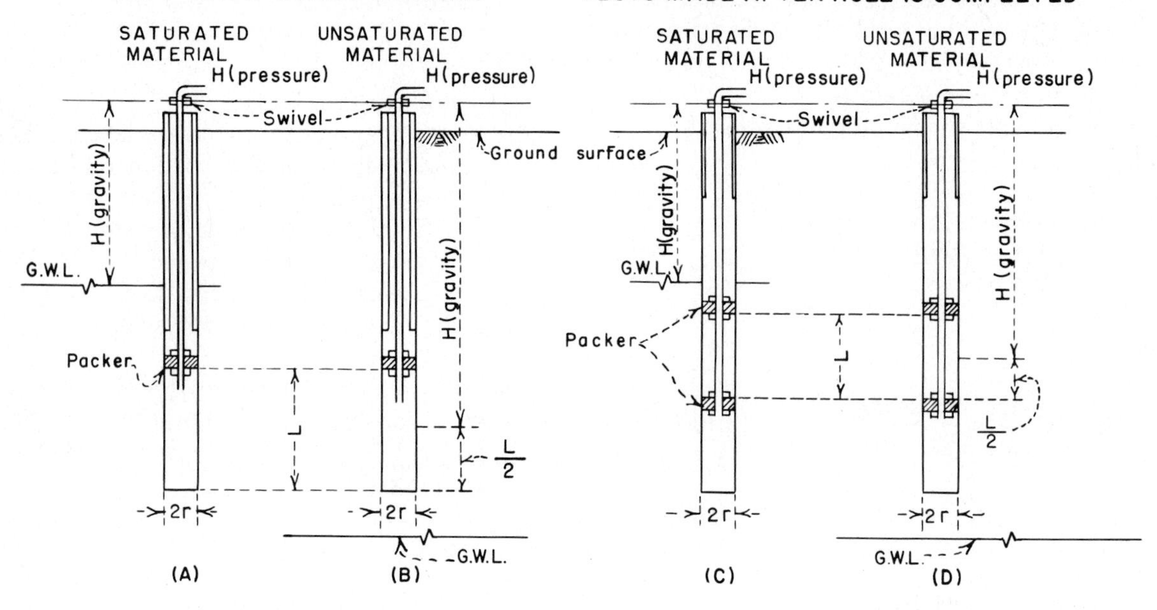

Figure 5-70.—Packer test for rock permeability. 288–D–2477.

start from the bottom of the hole and work upward.

For the example on figure 5-70(A):

Given:

NX casing set to a depth of 5 feet,
Q = 2.2 gal/min,
L = 1 foot,
H (gravity) = distance from ground-water level to swivel = 3.5 feet,
H (pressure) = 5 lb/in² = 5(2.31) = 11.55 feet of water,
$H = H$ (gravity) + H (pressure) = 15.1 feet, and
C_p = 23,300, from table 5-9;

then:

$$K = C_p \frac{Q}{H} = \frac{(23{,}300)(2.2)}{15.1} = 3{,}400 \text{ ft/yr.}$$

5.47. *Inplace Unit Weight Tests (Sand Replacement Method).*—This method is used to determine the inplace unit weight in a foundaiton, a borrow area, or a compacted embankment by excavating a hole from the horizontal surface, weighing the material excavated, and determining the volume of the hole by filling it with calibrated sand. A moisture content determination on a sample of the excavated soil enables the dry unit weight of the ground to be calculated. Various devices using balloons and water or oil unit weight devices have been used to measure the volume of the hole, but the sand method is the most common.

About 100 pounds of clean, air-dry, uniform sand passing the No. 16 sieve and retained on the No. 30 sieve has been found to be satisfactory. The sand is calibrated by pouring it into a cylindrical container of known volume, determining its mass and calculating its unit weight.

At the location to be tested, all loose soil is removed from an area 18 to 24 inches square and the surface is leveled. A working platform supported at least 3 feet from the edge of the test hole should be provided when excavating in soils that may deform and change the dimensions of the hole as a result of the weight of the operator. An 8-inch-diameter hole 12 to 14 inches deep is satisfactory for cohesive soils that contain little or no gravel. A hole about 12 inches in diameter at the surface, tapering down to about 6 inches at a depth of 12 to 14 inches, is needed for gravelly soils.

Table 5-9.—Values of C_p for permeability computations.

Length of test section in feet, L	Diameter of test hole			
	EX	AX	BX	NX
1	31,000	28,500	25,800	23,300
2	19,400	18,100	16,800	15,300
3	14,400	13,600	12,700	11,800
4	11,600	11,000	10,300	9,700
5	9,800	9,300	8,800	8,200
6	8,500	8,100	7,600	7,200
7	7,500	7,200	6,800	6,400
8	6,800	6,500	6,100	5,800
9	6,200	5,900	5,600	5,300
10	5,700	5,400	5,200	4,900
15	4,100	3,900	3,700	3,600
20	3,200	3,100	3,000	2,800

Figure 5-71.—Determining inplace unit weight by replacing soil with a sand of known unit weight.

A template with the proper size hole is placed on the ground, and the excavation is carefully made with an auger or other handtools. All material taken from the hole is placed in an airtight container for subsequent mass and moisture determinations. To avoid loss of moisture, the cover should be kept on the container except when in use. In hot, dry climates a shade for the test area and a moist cloth over the container should be provided. A plastic bag should be inserted in the container to hold the soil removed, and it should be sealed to prevent moisture loss.

The volume of the hole is determined by carefully filling it with calibrated sand using the sand cone device shown on figure 5-71. The mass of sand used to fill the hole is determined by subtracting the final mass of sand and container (plus the calculated mass of sand occupying the small space in the template) from the initial mass. The volume of the sand (and of the hole) is calculated from the known unit weight of the calibrated sand.

The inplace wet unit weight of the soil is the weight of the soil removed from the hole divided by the volume of the hole. For soils containing no gravel, a representative moisture sample is taken, and the moisture content is determined (see sec. 5.49(b) for moisture content test). The inplace dry unit weight is then calculated.

For soils containing gravel sizes, the wet unit weight of the total material is determined as described above. In the laboratory the gravel particles are separated from the soil, and their mass and solid volume are determined and subtracted from the total mass of material and the volume of the hole, respectively, to obtain the wet unit weight of the minus No. 4 fraction of the soil. This is converted to dry unit weight by a moisture content determination. The field and laboratory procedures used for inplace unit weight tests are shown on figure 5-72.

Further information on determining the inplace unit weight of soils may be found in test designations USBR 7205, 7206, 7215, 7216, 7220, 7221, and 7230 of the Bureau's *Earth Manual* [7].

5.48. *Vane Shear Test.*—The vane shear test is an inplace test to determine the undrained shear strength of a saturated cohesive soil. The vane consists of four rectangular, thin metal elements of equal area, which are rigidly attached to a rod. The vane is inserted into a previously undisturbed zone of cohesive soil, usually through a borehole. A torque is applied to the rod from the ground surface. The torque on the rod is then increased until shear failure occurs along a cylindrical element of soil defined by the height and diameter of the vane. The undrained shear strength of the soil is computed from the measured torque and the surface area of the cylindrical element.

A more detailed description of the vane shear test is given in USBR 7115, Performing Field Vane Shear Testing, in the *Earth Manual*[7].

5.49. *Laboratory Tests on Soils.*—

(a) *Gradation.*—The gradation or grain-size analysis of soils is done by a combination of sieving and wet analysis. A representative sample of the soil is dried, weighed, and screened on a U.S. standard No. 4 screen to remove the gravel. The gravel

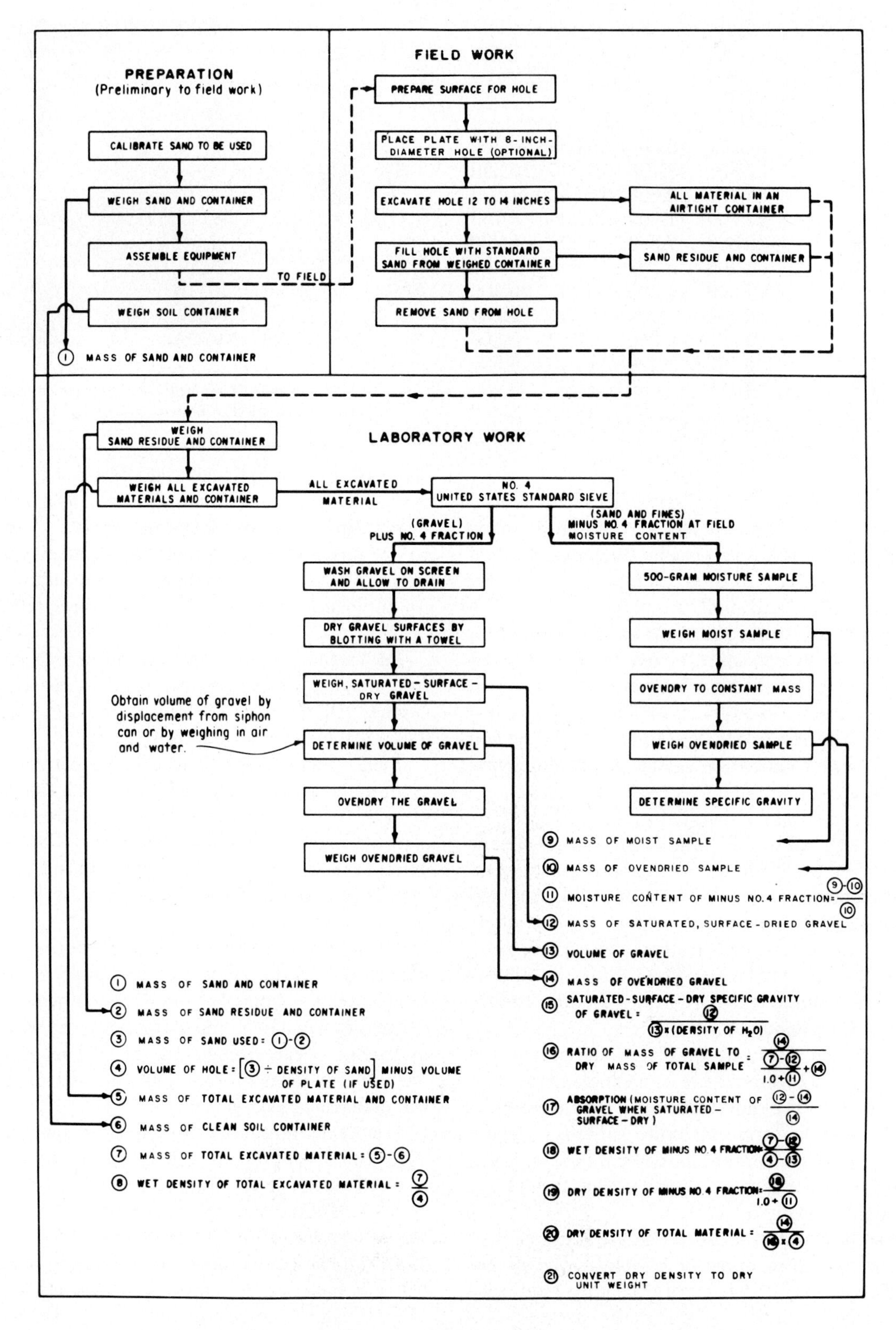

Figure 5-72.—Procedure for inplace unit weight test. 101–D–285.

is then passed through a series of screens to determine the amounts larger than 3 inches, 1½ inches, ¾ inch, ⅜ inch, and ¼ inch. An ovendried sample of the minus No. 4 material is used for the remainder of the test. One hundred grams of soil for sands (50 grams for silts and clays) are carefully weighed out and treated with 125 mL of a 4-percent solution of sodium hexametaphosphate and distilled water to separate the fine grains. After letting the mixture stand for at least 18 hours, it should be dispersed by thorough mixing in a blender, then transferred to a 1,000-mL graduated cylinder. Exactly 1,000 mL of distilled water is added and mixed in.

The cylinder containing the mixture is placed on a table, and a stopwatch is started. A soil hydrometer is placed in the mixture and readings are made at 1, 4, 19, and 60 minutes (and at 7 hours 15 minutes when clays are involved). The hydrometer is of the Bouyoucos type, which is calibrated in grams per liter at 20 °C, and its readings are corrected for the meniscus error (the top of the meniscus is read during the test), for difference in temperature from 20 °C, and for the amount of deflocculating agent used. On completion of the 1-hour or the 7-hour 15-minute reading, the mixture is washed on a No. 200 U.S. standard sieve and the retained fraction is dried and separated on the Nos. 8, 16, 30, 50, 100, and 200 standard sieves. Fifteen minutes of shaking in a power sieve shaker is usually done, then the residue on each screen is weighed. This procedure is explained in greater detail in test designations USBR 5325, 5330, 5335, and 5345 of the *Earth Manual* [7]. Figure 5-73 is an example of a resulting gradation analysis curve.

(b) *Moisture Content.*—The moisture content of a soil is defined as the mass of water it contains divided by the mass of dry soil. The procedure involves determining the mass of a sample of moist soil and its container then drying it in an oven at 10 °C to constant mass. The time required to attain constant mass varies for different soils, from a few hours for sandy soils to several days for very fat clays. About 16 hours should be the minimum time used. The dried sample and container should be placed in a desiccator to cool to room temperature before weighing. The moisture content is calculated as the difference between the initial and final masses of the soil with container, divided by the difference between the mass of the dry soil with container and the mass of the container alone. To ensure accuracy, the following minimum masses of moisture content samples are recommended:

Size of soil particles	*Minimum mass of sample, grams*
Minus No. 4	500
Minus ⅜ inch	1,000
Minus ¾ inch	2,000
Minus 1½ inches	3,000
No. 4 to 3-inch gravel	≥3,000

The sample for the No. 4 to 3-inch gravel should be large enough to get a representative sample of the material up to the 3-inch size.

Further information on determing the moisture content of soils may be found in test designations USBR 5300, 5305, 5310, and 5315 in the Bureau's *Earth Manual* [7].

(c) *Atterberg Limits.*—To obtain the liquid limit of a soil, the fraction passing the No. 40 sieve is mixed with water to a puttylike consistency and placed in a brass cup, as shown on figure 5-9. It is leveled off to a depth of 1 centimeter and divided by a grooving tool, as shown on the figure. The crank is turned two rotations per second until the two sides of the sample come in contact at the bottom of the groove for a distance of ½ inch along the groove; the number of blows is then recorded. The moisture content of the soil is then determined. The test is repeated with added water or with less water until a result of 25 blows is bracketed; that is, test results above and below 25 blows are obtained. A flow curve is then plotted on a semilogarithmic graph with the number of blows on the logarithmic scale against the moisture content on the arithmetic scale. The moisture content corresponding to the 25-blow value is the liquid limit. Detailed procedures for this test and the one-point liquid limit method are given in USBR 5350 and 5355 in the *Earth Manual* [7].

The plastic limit is the lowest moisture content expressed as a percentage of the mass of ovendried soil at which the soil can be rolled into threads ⅛ inch in diameter without the thread breaking into pieces. To determine the plastic limit, about 15 grams of the minus No. 40 fraction of a soil are mixed with enough water to obtain a plastic material and shaped into a ball. The soil is then rolled between the palm of the hand and a ground glass plate to form the soil into a thread ⅛ inch in diameter. It is then reformed into a ball, kneaded and rolled out again. This procedure is continued until the soil crumbles when the thread becomes ⅛ inch

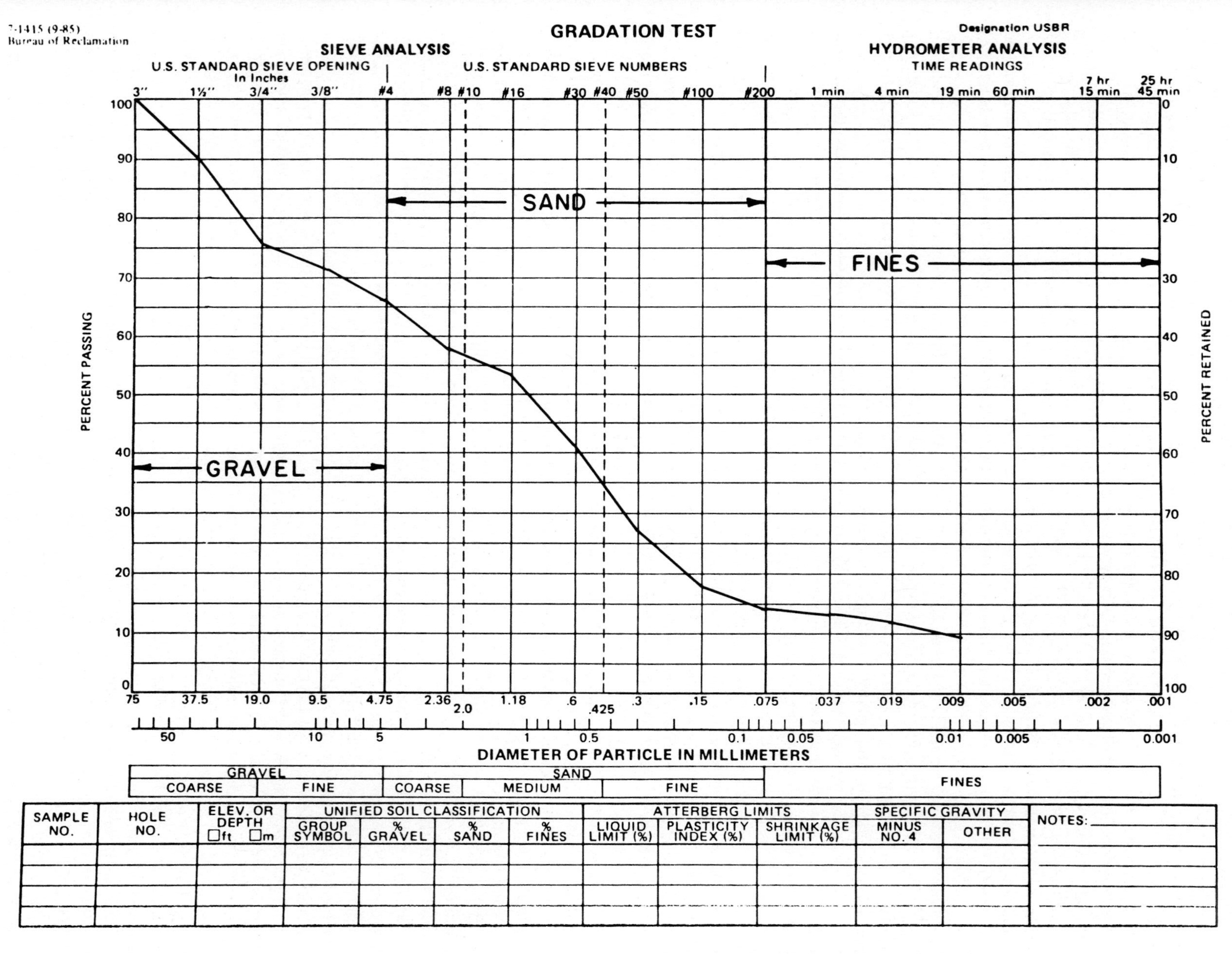

Figure 5-73.—Example gradation analysis curves.

and cannot be reformed. The moisture content determined for this condition is the plastic limit. Figure 5-10 shows the test for the plastic limit. The plasticity index of a soil is the difference between its liquid limit and plastic limit. Detailed test procedures are given in USBR 5360 in the *Earth Manual* [7].

(d) *Specific Gravity.*—Specific gravity is defined as the ratio of the mass in air of a given volume of material to the mass in air of an equal volume of distilled water at a stated temperature. The minus No. 4 fraction of soil is commonly tested for specific gravity by the flask method, as described in USBR 5320 in the Bureau's *Earth Manual* [7]. In this method, a 250-mL, long-necked flask is calibrated for volume at several temperatures. Then, 100 grams of ovendried minus No. 4 material is washed into the calibrated flask with distilled water. With the water level well below the neck of the flask, a vacuum is applied to the mixture; this boils the entrapped air from the mixture. When the air has been virtually exhausted, distilled water is added to bring the volume to exactly the calibrated volume of the flask, and the vacuum is applied again. When all the air has been removed, the mass of the flask and its contents is determined, and the temperature of the mixture is determined. The volume of the 100 grams of dried soil is determined from the data obtained, and the specific gravity of the soil is then computed.

To determine the specific gravity of gravel and cobbles, the material is immersed in water for a period of 24 hours and then blotted with a towel. This is the saturated surface-dry condition. It is then weighed and carefully placed in a filled siphon can, from which the volume of water it displaces is measured. The bulk specific gravity on a saturated surface-dry basis is the mass of the sample divided by the volume of water displaced. The bulk specific gravity on an oven-dry basis is the oven-dry mass of the material divided by the volume displaced by the saturated surface-dry material. This procedure is described in detail in test designation USBR 5320 in the *Earth Manual* [7]. See section 5.50(a) for another method of specific gravity determination.

(e) *Laboratory Compaction.*—The laboratory maximum dry unit weight of a soil is the greatest dry unit weight obtainable by the method to be described. The optimum moisture content of the soil is the moisture content at this condition. This method is described in detail in USBR 5500 in the *Earth Manual* [7]. For this test, water is added to about 35 pounds of the minus No. 4 fraction of the soil until its consistency is such that it barely adheres when squeezed firmly in the hand. A sample of the soil is compacted in a 1/20-ft^3 (0.05-ft^3) compaction mold (with collar attached) in 3 equal lifts by 25 uniformly distributed blows per lift with a tamping rod having a mass of 5.5 pounds dropped freely from 18 inches above each lift. The third compacted lift should extend slightly into the collar section. The collar is then removed, and the soil is trimmed to the top of the mold with a straightedge trimmer. The soil and mold are then weighed. The moisture content of the compacted specimen is determined from a sample taken near its center. This procedure is repeated at least five times using new soil for each specimen and increasing the water added until the resulting compacted wet mass decreases.

The compaction mold used by the Bureau of Reclamation is 1/20-ft^3 (0.05-ft^3) in volume. Using the procedure described above, this mold results in a compactive effort of 12,375 ft-lb/ft^3 of soil. ASTM D 698 and the standard AASHTO methods use the same compactive effort, 12,375 ft-lb/ft^3, and identical procedures, except that a 1/30-ft^3 (0.033-ft^3) cylinder is used and the free drop is 12 inches instead of 18 inches.

The penetration resistance of the compacted soil for points along the compaction curve, as shown on figure 5-74 and described in test designation USBR 5505 in the *Earth Manual* [7], can be obtained by forcing the Proctor needle into each compacted specimen and determining the penetration resistance in pounds per square inch. This method has been used extensively for moisture control of compacted fills. However, the rapid method of compaction control described in test designation USBR 7240 of the *Earth Manual* [7] is believed to be a more accurate method that should replace the Proctor needle for that purpose.

(f) *Relative Density.*—Relative density is defined as the state of compactness of a soil with respect to the loosest and densest states at which it can be placed by specific laboratory procedures. This test is applicable to cohesionless materials that do not have well-defined laboratory compaction curves. The minimum index unit weight (zero percent relative density) is obtained by carefully placing dried soil in a container of known size, usually 0.1 to 0.5 ft^3. About 1 inch free fall is permitted

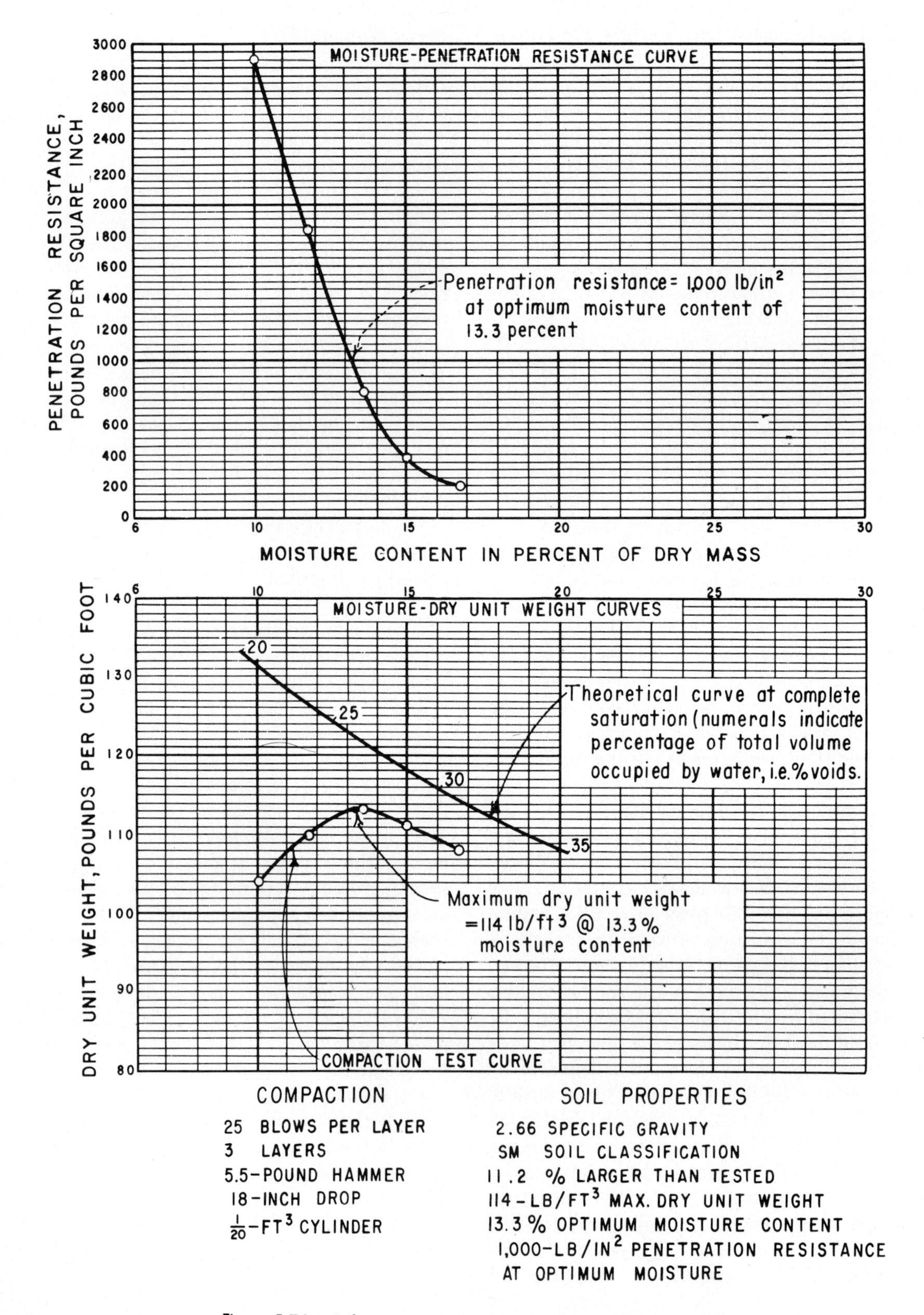

Figure 5-74.—Laboratory compaction test curves. 288-D-2478.

for material smaller than ⅜-inch maximum size; material larger than the ⅜-inch size should be placed with a scoop. The excess soil is carefully trimmed level to the top and the full container is weighed.

Two methods can be used to obtain the maximum index unit weight (100 percent relative density). In one method the soil is thoroughly saturated and placed slowly into the container while the attached vibrator is operating. After the container is filled, the vibrator continues operating. The material in the container is then weighed, emptied into a pan, dried, and weighed again. For the other method the soil and container used in the minimum index unit weight test is vibrated, the reduced volume caused by the vibration is measured, and the maximum index unit weight is calculated. Both methods should be tried to see which results in the highest maximum index unit weight.

Test designations USBR 5530 and 5525 in the *Earth Manual* [7] explains this procedure in detail. Test designation USBR 7250 in [7] explains the method for determining the relative density of cohesionless soil.

5.50. *Laboratory Tests on Riprap and Concrete Aggregate.*—(a) *Specific Gravity and Absorption.*—The specific gravity of sand for concrete aggregate can be determined on an SSD (saturated-surface-dry) sample in a manner similar to that given for soil in section 5.49(d). The specific gravity of coarse aggregates and riprap (crushed to 1½-inch maximum size) is determined by washing the sample to remove dust and other coatings from the surface of the particles, drying to a constant mass, immersing in water at room temperature for 24 hours, blotting with a towel, and weighing. After weighing, the material is placed in a wire basket and is weighed again in water having a temperature of 23 °C. The sample is then dried to a constant mass in an oven, cooled to room temperature, and weighed again. If A is the mass in grams of the ovendried sample in air, B the mass in grams of the SSD sample in air, and C the mass in grams of the sample in water, then the specific gravity on a dry basis equals $A/(B-C)$; the specific gravity on an SSD basis equals $B/(B-C)$; and the absorption equals $(B-A)/A$ on a dry basis and $(B-A)/B$ on an SSD basis. Absorption is usually expressed as a percentage. ASTM C 127-68 describes detailed procedures for these tests.

(b) *Abrasion.*—This test determines the abrasion resistance of crushed rock and natural and crushed gravel. The Los Angeles abrasion machine is used. It consists of a hollow steel cylinder closed at both ends, having a diameter of 28 inches and a length of 20 inches.

The abrasive charge consists of cast iron or steel spheres approximately 1⅞ inches in diameter. Twelve spheres are used for an "A" grading (maximum size of particle is 1½ inches), 11 for a "B" grading (¾ inch maximum), 8 for a "C" grading (⅜ inch maximum), and 6 for a "D" grading (No. 4 sieve maximum).

The test sample of 5,000 grams and the proper abrasive charge are placed in the Los Angeles abrasion testing machine, and the machine is rotated for 100 revolutions at a speed of from 30 to 33 r/min. The material is then removed from the machine, sieved through a No. 12 screen, and the material retained on the screen is weighed. The entire sample including the dust of abrasion is returned to the testing machine; the machine is rotated an additional 400 revolutions; and the screening and weighing are repeated. The differences between the original mass of the test sample and the mass of the material retained on the screen at 100 and 500 revolutions are expressed as percentages of the original mass of the test sample. These values are reported as percentages of wear. ASTM C 131-69 describes detailed procedures for this test.

(c) *Soundness.*—The most commonly used soundness test is the sodium sulfate test. The results of this test are used as an indication of the ability of aggregate and riprap to resist weathering. A carefully prepared saturated solution of sodium sulfate is kept at a temperature of 21 °C. After washing and drying in an oven, the material to be tested is seived to provide a specified gradation, usually from 1½ inches to the No. 50 sieve size. Specified masses of the various fractions of the material are placed in separate containers resistant to the action of the solution, and sufficient sodium sulfate solution is poured into the containers to cover the samples. The material is permitted to soak for at least 16 hours but no more than 18 hours, during which the temperature is maintained at 21 °C.

After the immersion period, the samples are removed from the solution and dried to a constant mass (about 4 hours) at a temperature of 105 to 110 °C. After drying, the sample fractions are cooled to room temperature and the process is repeated. At the end of five cycles, the test sample is inspected and records made of the observation. Each fraction is then washed thoroughly, to remove the sodium sulfate from the material, dried, and cooled. Each fraction is screened and the quantities of material retained are weighed. The weighed average loss for each fraction is computed and reported. ASTM C 88-69 describes the detailed procedure for this test.

L. BIBLIOGRAPHY

5.51. *Bibliography.*

[1] *Soil Survey Manual*, U.S. Department of Agriculture, Handbook No. 18, 1951.

[2] *Construction Safety Standards*, rev., Bureau of Reclamation, Denver, CO, 1987.

[3] Travis, R. B., *Quarterly School of Mines*, vol. 50, No. 1, January 1955.

[4] Fisher, R. V., "Rocks Composed of Volcanic Fragments and their Classification," *Earth Science Review*, vol. 1, No. 4, pp. 287-298, 1966.

[5] Williams, H., and A. R. McBirney, *Volcanology*, Freeman and Cooper, San Franciso, CA, 1979.

[6] *Engineering Geology Manual*, Bureau of Reclamation, (in publication) 1986.

[7] *Earth Manual*, vol. 2, "Test Designations," Bureau of Reclamation, Denver, CO, 1987.

[8] *Ground Water Manual*, rev. reprint, Bureau of Reclamation, 480 pp., Denver, CO, 1981.

[9] *Concrete Manual*, vol. 2, "Test Designations," Bureau of Reclamation, Denver, CO, 1987.

Attewell, P. B. and I. W. Farmer, *Principals of Engineering Geology*, 2d ed., Chapman and Hall, London, 1981.

Bates R. L., and J. A. Jackson, *Glossary of Geology*, 2d ed., American Geological Institute, Falls Church, VA, 1980.

Davenport, G. C., L. M. Hadley, and J. A. Randall, "The Use of Seismic Refraction and Self-Potential Surveys to Evaluate Existing Embankments," paper presented at Rocky Mt. regional AIME meeting, Vail, CO, August 3-5, 1983.

Griffiths, D. H., and R. F. King, *Applied Geophysics for Engineers and Geologists*, Pergamon Press, New York, NY, 1965.

Heiland, C. A., *Geophysical Exploration*, Hafner, New York, NY, 1968.

Hunt, Roy E., *Geotechnical Engineering Investigations Manual*, McGraw-Hill Book Co., 1983.

Keller, G., and F. Frischknecht, *Electrical Methods in Geophysical Prospecting*, Pergamon Press, New York, NY, 1966.

Leet, L. Don, *Earth Waves*, John Wiley and Sons, New York, NY, 1950.

Leggett, Robert F., *Geology and Engineering*, McGraw-Hill Book Co.

Leggett, Robert F., and Paul F. Karrow, *Geology and Civil Engineering*, McGraw-Hill Book Co., 1983.

Meiser, P., "A Method for Quantitative Interpretation of Self-Potential Measurements," *Geophysical Prospecting*, vol. 10, No. 2, pp. 203-218, 1962.

Mooney, Harold M., and W. W. Wetzedl, *The Potentials About a Point Electrode and Apparent Resistivity Curves for a Two-, Three-, and Four-Layered Earth*, University of Minnesota Press, Minneapolis, MN, 1965.

Nettleton, L. L., "Elementary Gravity and Magnetics for Geologists and Seismologists," Society of Exploration Geophysicists Monograph No. 1, 1971.

Soske, Joshua L., "The Blind Zone Problem in Engineering Geophysics," *Geophysics*, vol. 24, pp. 359-365, 1958.

"Bituminous Minerals for Highway Construction and Roofing; Soils; Peats, Mosses, and Humus; Skid Resistance," American Society for Testing and Materials, 1970 Annual Book of ASTM Standards, pt. 11, 982 pp. April 1970.

Bureau of Reclamation, *Reclamation Instructions*, Series 10, par. 7, p. 115, May 5, 1980.

Bureau of Reclamation, *Reclamation Instructions*, Series 510, par. 7s, pp. 511-515, September 30, 1982.

"Concrete and Mineral Aggregates," American Society for Testing and Materials, 1970 Annual Book of ASTM Standards, pt. 10, 620 pp., November 1970.

Department of Agriculture, *Soil Taxonomy*, Agriculture Handbook No. 436, December 1975.

Chapter 6

Earthfill Dams

A. INTRODUCTION

6.1. *Origin and Development.*—Earthfill dams have been used since the early days of civilization to store water for irrigation. This is attested both by history and by the remnants of ancient structures. Some of the structures built in antiquity were very large. An earthfill dam completed in Ceylon in 504 B.C. [1][1] was 11 miles long, 70 feet high, and contained about 17,000,000 yd^3 of embankment. Today, as in the past, the earthfill dam continues to be the most common type of dam, principally because its construction involves using materials in their natural state with little processing.

Until modern times, all earthfill dams were designed by empirical methods, and engineering literature is filled with accounts of failures [2]. These failures brought on the realization that empirical methods must be replaced by rational engineering procedures for both the design and construction of earthfill dams. One of the first to suggest that the slopes for earthfill dams be selected on that basis was Bassell in 1907 [3]. However, little progress was made on the development of rational design procedures until the 1930's. The rapid advancement of the science of soil mechanics since that time has resulted in the development of greatly improved procedures for the design of earthfill dams. These procedures include (1) thorough preconstruction investigations of foundation conditions and of construction materials, (2) application of engineering skill and technique to design, (3) carefully planned and controlled methods of construction, and (4) carefully planned and designed instrumentation and monitoring systems. Threaded throughout the plan, design, construct, operate, and maintain process is the philosophy that the design is not complete until the dam is accomplishing its purpose and has proved itself safe through several cycles of operation.

Earthfill dams have now (1987) been constructed to heights approaching 1,000 feet above their foundations, and hundreds of large rolled earthfill dams have been constructed in the past 40 years with a very good success record. Failures of small earthfill dams, however, occur more often. Though some of these failures are probably the result of improper design, many are caused by careless construction. Proper construction methods include adequate foundation preparation and the proper placement of materials in the dam embankment—with the necessary degree of compaction and under established testing and control procedures.

The design of an earthfill dam must be realistic. It should reflect the actual foundation conditions at the site and the materials available for embankment construction. It should not be patterned after a successful design used at a site with different conditions or materials, or even at a site with similar conditions. It should be designed for its specific site geology.

6.2. *Scope of Discussion.*—This discussion is limited to design procedures for earthfill dams of the rolled-fill type of construction, as defined in section 6.3. This type of construction is now being used almost exclusively for the construction of earthfill dams. Semihydraulic or hydraulic fills are seldom, if ever, used.

The information presented in this chapter is generally applicable to the design of any earthfill dam. However, there are some empirical procedures presented that are strictly for the design of small dams, in straightforward geologic settings using trouble-free embankment materials. A "small" dam is one whose maximum height above the lowest point in the original streambed does not exceed about 50 feet and whose volume is not so great that significant economical advantage would be obtained by using the more precise design methods usually reserved for large dams. A low dam cannot be considered

[1] Numbers in brackets refer to entries in the bibliography (sec. 6.28).

Figure 6-1.—Upstream face of dam and fishscreened inlet structure. Crane Prairie Dam on the Deschutes River in Oregon.

small if its volume exceeds say, 1 million yd^3. Figures 6-1 and 4-1 show typical small dams constructed by the Bureau (Bureau of Reclamation). Crane Prairie Dam, which was completed in 1940, has a height of 31 feet and contains 29,700 yd^3 of fill. Crescent Lake Dam, which was completed in 1956, has a height of 22 feet and contains 16,800 yd^3 of fill. The maximum sections of these dams are shown on figures 6-64 and 6-65, respectively.

Figures 6-2 and 6-3 show dams constructed by the Bureau that are at the upper limit of height for the use of the empirical procedures presented in this chapter. In fact, Fruitgrowers Dam (fig. 6-2) is slightly above the height limit. It has a maximum height of 55 feet and a volume of 135,500 yd^3, but is included herein as a matter of interest. Irrigation at this site dates back to 1898. The dam shown on figure 6-2 was constructed in 1939, downstream from the original structure, which was breached in June 1937 to forestall failure. Fruitgrowers Dam was modified in 1986, to replace a damaged spillway and to increase flood bypass capacity and earthquake resistance. A maximum section of Fruitgrowers Dam is shown on figure 6-68. Many dams, small and large, are being modified to bring their capabilities up to modern-day requirements, especially in the area of flood capacity and earthquake resistance. Shadow Mountain Dam (fig. 6-3) is a 50-foot-high structure containing 168,000 yd^3 of embankment, which was completed in 1946. Its maximum section is shown in figure 6-79.

The design procedures presented in this text are not sufficiently detailed to permit their sole use for the design of dams where complicated conditions such as exceedingly soft, exceedingly pervious, highly fractured, or collapsible soil foundations are involved. The design procedures are also inappropriate where the nature of the only soil available for construction of the embankment is unusual. In this category are dispersive soils, soils with high plasticity, with low maximum unit weight, and with very high natural water content that cannot be reduced by drainage. These conditions require that an engineer specializing in earthfill dam design direct the investigations, determine the laboratory testing program, interpret the laboratory test results, and supervise the preparation of the design and specifications.

6.3. *Selection of Type of Earthfill Dam.*—

(a) *General.*—The selection of the type of dam (earthfill, rockfill, concrete gravity, or a combination of these) is discussed in chapter 4. When the procedure leads to the selection of an earthfill dam, another decision must be made; that is, the type of earthfill dam.

The scope of this text includes only the rolled-fill type of earthfill dam. For this type, the major portion of the embankment is constructed in successive, mechanically compacted layers. The material from borrow pits and that suitable from

Figure 6-2.—Fruitgrowers Dam, an earthfill storage dam at an offstream location in Colorado.

required excavations for the dam and other structures is delivered to the embankment, usually by trucks or scrapers. It is then spread by motor graders or bulldozers and sprinkled, if necessary, to form lifts of limited thickness having the proper moisture content. These lifts are then thoroughly compacted and bonded with the preceding layer by means of power rollers of the proper design and weight. Rolled-fill dams consist of three types: diaphragm, homogeneous, and zoned.

(b) *Diaphragm Type.*—For this type of section, most of the embankment is constructed of pervious (permeable) material (sand, gravel, or rock), and a thin diaphragm of impermeable material is provided to form the water barrier. The position of this impervious diaphragm may vary from a blanket on the upstream face to a central vertical core. The diaphragm may consist of earth, portland cement concrete, bituminous concrete, or other material. An earth blanket or core is considered a diaphragm if its horizontal thickness at any elevation is less than 10 feet or its thickness at any elevation is less than the height of the embankment above that elevation. If the impervious earth zone equals or exceeds these thicknesses, the design is considered a zoned embankment type. Design and construction of diaphragm-type dams must be approached with care.

Although successful dams have been constructed with internal (or buried) diaphragms, this type of construction is not recommended for structures within the scope of this text. All internal diaphragms, including those constructed of earth or rigid materials such as concrete, have a potential for cracking caused by differential movements induced by embankment consolidation, fluctuating reservoir levels, and non-uniform foundation settlement. The construction of an internal earth diaphragm with the necessary filters requires a higher degree of precision and closer control than that normally used for small dams. Internal diaphragms made of rigid material such as concrete also have the disadvantage of not being readily available for inspection or emergency repair if they are ruptured by settlement of the dam or its foundation.

An earth blanket on the upstream slope of an otherwise pervious dam is not recommended because of the expense and the difficulty of constructing suitable filters. Furthermore, because the earth blanket must be protected from erosion by wave action, it must be buried and therefore, is not readily available for inspection or repair. If the supply of impermeable soil is so limited that a zoned embankment dam cannot be constructed, a diaphragm of manufactured material placed on the upstream slope of an otherwise pervious embankment is recommended for small dams. The design of suitable impervious pavings is discussed in chapter 7.

If most of the material in a diaphragm-type dam is rock, the dam is classified as a rockfill dam. The design of rockfill dams is discussed in chapter 7.

(c) *Homogeneous Type.*—A purely homogeneous dam is composed of only one kind of material (exclusive of the slope protection). The material used in such a dam must be sufficiently impervious to provide an adequate water barrier, and the slopes

Figure 6-3.—Shadow Mountain Dam, an earthfill structure on the Colorado River in Colorado. Constructed as part of a large transmountain diversion scheme. SM–175–CBT.

must be relatively flat for stability. To avoid sloughing, the upstream slope must be relatively flat if rapid drawdown of the reservoir after long-term storage is anticipated. The downstream slope must also be relatively flat to provide a slope stable enough to resist sloughing when saturated to a high level. For a completely homogeneous section, it is inevitable that seepage will emerge on the downstream slope regardless of its flatness and the impermeability of the soil if the reservoir level is maintained for long enough. The downstream slope eventually will be affected by seepage to a height of roughly one-third the depth of the reservoir pool [4], as shown on figure 6-4.

Although formerly very common in the design of small dams, the completely homogeneous section has been replaced by a modified homogeneous section in which small amounts of carefully placed pervious materials control the action of seepage so as to permit much steeper slopes. The effect of drainage at the downstream toe of the embankment is shown on figures 6-5(A) and 6-5(B).

Large rock toes may be provided for drainage (fig. 6-5(A)), or, if suitably graded materials are available, a horizontal drainage blanket (fig. 6-5(B)) may be used. The drainage and filter layers must be designed to meet filter requirements with surrounding fill or foundation materials (see sec. 6.10(i)). Recently, to avoid construction defects such as loose lifts, poor bond between lifts, inadvertent pervious layers, desiccation, and dispersive soils, inclined filter drains in combination with a horizontal drainage blanket have become almost standard. Figure 6-5(C) illustrates the control of seepage with an inclined chimney drain and horizontal drainage blanket. Another method of providing drainage has been the installation of pipe drains. These are recommended for small dams only when used in conjunction with a horizontal drainage blanket or pervious zones. Reliance should not be placed solely upon pipe drains because the pipes can clog as the result of improper filters, root growth, or deterioration.

Because drainage modifications to a homogeneous section provide a greatly improved design, the fully homogeneous section should seldom be used.

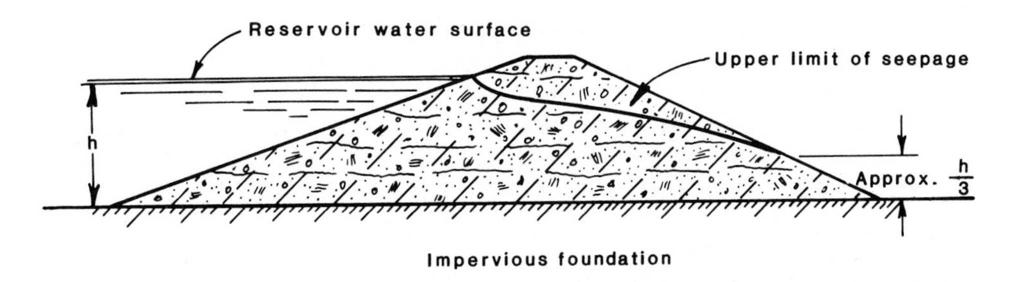

Figure 6-4.—Seepage through a completely homogeneous dam. 288-D-2479.

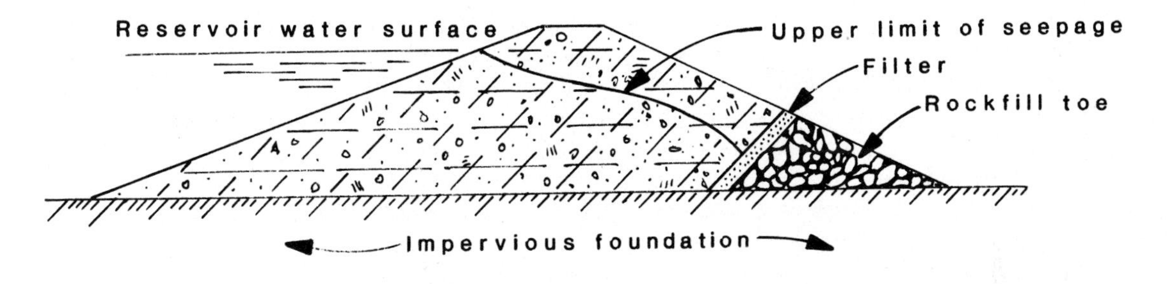

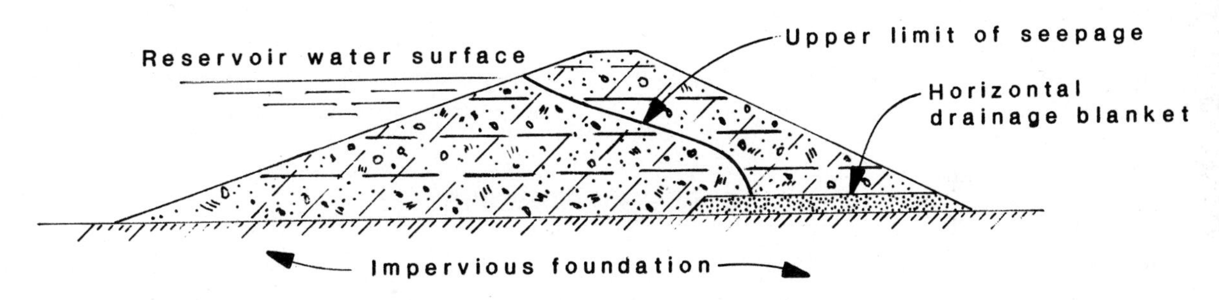

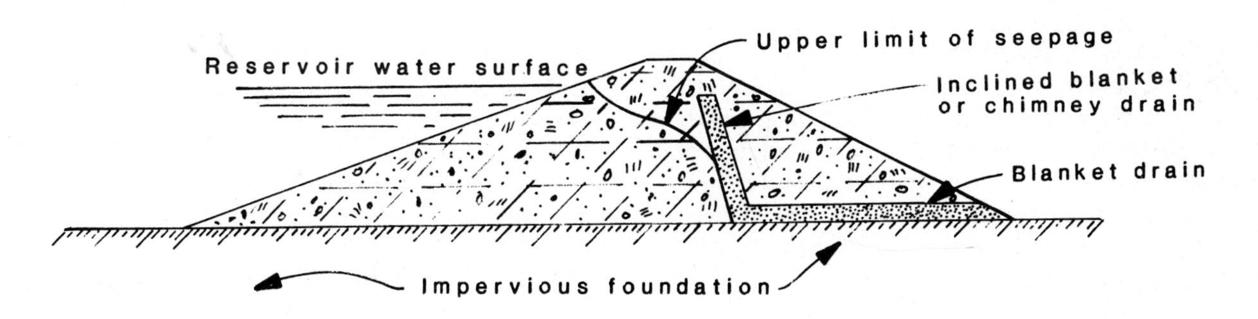

Figure 6-5.—Seepage through modified homogeneous dams. 103-D-1827.

Filtering and drainage should normally be provided. A homogeneous (or modified homogeneous) dam is recommended in localities where readily available soils show little variation in permeability, and soils of contrasting permeabilities are available only in minor amounts or at considerably greater cost.

A homogeneous section should never be used if the available materials are dispersive, erodible such as silts and fine sands, or subject to moderate to severe desiccation. Soils should always be tested for these characteristics. Where these characteristics exist, the advice of an experienced earthfill dam designer is recommended.

(d) *Zoned Embankment Type.*—The most common type of a rolled earthfill dam section is that in which a central impervious core is flanked by zones of materials considerably more pervious, called shells. These pervious zones or shells enclose, support, and protect the impervious core; the upstream pervious zone affords stability against rapid drawdown; and the downstream pervious zone acts as a drain to control seepage and lower the phreatic surface. In many cases, a filter between the impervious zone and downstream shell and a drainage layer beneath the downstream shell are necessary. These filter-drainage layers must meet filter criteria with adjacent fill and foundation materials. They are sometimes multilayered for capacity requirements.

In any case, filter criteria given in section 6.10(i) must be met between the impervious zone and the downstream shell and between the shell and the foundation. For most effective control of through seepage and drawdown seepage, the permeability should progressively increase from the center of the dam out toward each slope.

The pervious zones may consist of sand, gravel, cobbles, rock, or mixtures of these materials. For purposes of this text, the dam is considered to be a zoned embankment if the horizontal width of the impervious zone at any elevation equals or exceeds the height of embankment above that elevation in the dam and is at least 10 feet. The maximum width of the impervious zone will be controlled by stability and seepage criteria and by the availability of material. A dam with an impervious core of moderate width composed of strong material and with pervious outer shells may have relatively steep outer slopes, limited only by the strength of the foundation, the stability of the embankment itself, and maintenance considerations. Conditions that tend to increase stability may be decisive in the choice of a section even if a longer haul is necessary to obtain required embankment materials.

If a variety of soils are readily available, the type of earthfill dam chosen should always be the zoned embankment because its inherent advantages will lead to more economical construction.

B. DESIGN PRINCIPLES

6.4. *Design Data.*—The data required for the design of an earthfill dam are discussed in the various chapters of this manual, and the investigation of foundations and sources of construction materials are described in chapter 5. The required detail and the accuracy of the data are governed by the nature of the project and the immediate purpose of the design; that is, whether the design is for a cost estimate to determine project feasibility, whether the design is for construction, or whether some other purpose is to be served. The extent of investigations of foundations and sources of construction material are also governed by the complexity of the situation.

6.5. *Design Criteria.*—The basic principle of design is to produce a satisfactory, functional structure at a minimum total cost. Consideration must be given to maintenance requirements so that savings achieved in the initial cost of construction do not result in excessive maintenance costs. Maintenance costs vary with the provisions of upstream and downstream slope protection, drainage features, and the type of appurtenant structures and mechanical equipment. To achieve minimum cost, the dam must be designed for maximum use of the most economical materials available, including materials excavated for its foundations and for appurtenant structures.

An earthfill dam must be safe and stable during all phases of the construction and the operation of the reservoir. To accomplish this, the following criteria must be met:

(a) The embankment, foundation, abutments, and reservoir rim must be stable and must not develop unacceptable deformations under all loading conditions brought about by construction of the embankment, reservoir operation, and earthquake.

(b) Seepage flow through the embankment, foundation, abutments, and reservoir rim must be controlled to prevent excessive uplift pressures; piping; instability; sloughing; removal of material by solutioning; or erosion of material into cracks, joints, or cavities. The amount of water lost through seepage must be controlled so that it does not interfere with planned project functions.

(c) The reservoir rim must be stable under all operating conditions to prevent the triggering of a landslide into the reservoir that could cause a large wave to overtop the dam.

(d) The embankment must be safe against overtopping or encroachment of freeboard during occurrence of the IDF (inflow design flood) by the provision of sufficient spillway and outlet works capacity.

(e) Freeboard must be sufficient to prevent overtopping by waves.

(f) Camber should be sufficient to allow for settlement of the foundation and embankment, but not included as part of the freeboard.

(g) The upstream slope must be protected against wave erosion, and the crest and downstream slope must be protected against wind and rain erosion.

An earthfill dam designed to meet the above criteria will prove permanently safe, provided proper construction methods and control are achieved. The design procedure to meet the requirements of criterion (d) above is discussed in chapters 9 and 10. Methods for satisfying other criteria for earthfill dams, subject to the limitations in scope described in section 6.2, will be discussed in this chapter. The applicability of the procedures to a specific case depends upon the purpose of the design, the size and importance of the structure, and the complexity of the problems.

C. FOUNDATION DESIGN

6.6. *General.*—The term "foundation" as used herein includes both the valley floor and the abutments. The essential requirements of a foundation for an earthfill dam are that it provide stable support for the embankment under all conditions of saturation and loading, and that it provide sufficient resistance to seepage to prevent excessive loss of water.

Although the foundation is not actually designed, certain provisions for treatment are made in designs to ensure that the essential requirements are met. No two foundations are exactly alike; each foundation presents its own separate and distinct problems requiring corresponding special treatment and preparation. Various methods of stabilization of weak foundations, reduction of seepage in pervious foundations, and types and locations of devices for the interception of underseepage must depend upon and be adapted to local conditions. The importance of adequate foundation treatment is emphasized by the fact that approximately 40 percent of all earthfill dam accidents and 12 percent of all failures are attributed to foundation failures.

Theoretical solutions based on principles of soil mechanics can be made for problems involving pervious or weak foundations. Most of these solutions are relatively complex and they may be relied upon only to the degree that the actual permeabilities in various directions or the strength of the foundation can be determined by expensive, detailed field and laboratory testing. Ordinarily, extensive exploration of this nature and complex theoretical designs are not required for small dams. For these structures, it is usually more economical to design foundations empirically, deliberately striving for substantial safety factors. The savings in construction costs that can be achieved by more precise design ordinarily do not warrant the cost of the additional exploration, testing, and engineering involved. There are foundations, however, where conditions are so unusual that empirical methods cannot be relied upon to produce a design with an adequate safety factor. Such conditions require the services of an engineer specializing in the field of earthfill dam design and are beyond the scope of this text.

Because different treatments are appropriate for different conditions, foundations are grouped into three main classes according to their predominant characteristics:

1. Foundations of rock
2. Foundations of coarse-grained material (sand and gravel)
3. Foundations of fine-grained material (silt and clay)

Foundations, which originate from various

sources, such as river alluvium, glacial outwash, talus, and other processes of erosion, disintegration, and deposition, are characterized by infinite variations in the combinations, structural arrangement, and physical characteristics of their constituent materials. The deposits may be roughly stratified, containing layers of clay, silt, fine sand and gravel, or they may consist of lenticular masses of the same material without any regularity of occurrence and of varying extent and thickness. Nevertheless, the character of a foundation, as revealed by exploration, can usually be safely generalized for the design of small dams to fit into one of the classes given above, and once the class is determined the nature of the problem requiring treatment will be evident. Ordinarily, coarse-grained, pervious foundations present no difficulties in the matter of settlement or stability for a small dam; conversely, fine-grained, weak foundations subject to settlement or displacement usually present no seepage problems.

The special treatments required for the different types of foundations listed above are discussed in this chapter. If the foundation material is impervious and comparable with the compacted em bankment material in structural charactertistics, little foundation treatment is required. *The minimum treatment for any foundation* is stripping the foundation area to remove sod, topsoil with high content of organic matter, and other unsuitable material that can be disposed of by open excavation. In many cases where the overburden is comparatively shallow, the entire foundation is stripped to bedrock. *In all soil foundations in which a cutoff trench or partial cutoff trench (see sec. 6.10) is not used, a key trench should be provided.* The top several feet of the soil foundation invariably lack the density of the underlying soil because of frost action, surface runoff, wind, or other cause. This layer should be penetrated by the key trench to allow inspection and to ensure cutoff by the impervious zone of the embankment through this questionable zone. A bottom width of 20 feet for the key trench is usually sufficient.

The foundation at any particular site usually consists of a combination of the three main types of foundations listed above. For example, the stream portion often is a sand-gravel foundation, while the abutments are rock that is exposed on the steep slopes and mantled by deep deposits of clay or silt on the gentle slopes. Therefore, the design of any dam may involve a variety of foundation design problems.

6.7. *Rock Foundations.*—Rock foundations are generally considered to be the more competent type of foundation and usually do not present any problem for small dams. Even foundations of weaker rock are generally preferred over soil foundations. The selection of a rock foundation is undoubtedly justified where the rock mass is generally homogeneous and competent throughout zones of the foundation that will be affected by the dam and reservoir. However, damsites with good rock foundations are becoming increasingly rare. Designers are being forced to use foundations that are far from ideal because of the growth and shifting of population centers that cause increased emphasis on water conservation for domestic, agricultural, and industrial use in new locations. Rock foundations should be carefully investigated to ensure that they are adequately competent. If there is any doubt, an experienced earth dam designer should be consulted.

Foundation rock surfaces against which fill is to be placed must be properly treated to ensure that fractures, fault zones, steep faces, rough areas, weathered zones, etc., do not lead to seepage and piping in the interface zone between foundation and fill. Treatment of deficient foundation zones is especially critical for the areas beneath the impervious core and the filter and drainage zones immediately downstream of the impervious zone. More explicit foundation surface treatment requirements are presented in chapter 3 of USBR Design Standard No. 13.

6.8. *Methods of Treating Rock Foundations.*—Rock foundations should be carefully investigated to determine their permeability. If erosive leakage, excessive uplift pressure, or high water losses can occur through joints, fissures, crevices, permeable strata, or along fault planes, consideration should be given to grouting the foundation. Whether or not a foundation should be grouted should be determined by examining the site geology and by analyzing the water losses through foundation exploration holes. A great deal of experience is required to make this decision because every foundation is unique. Moreover, there may be more effective or economical methods of controlling seepage or leakage than grouting. The advice of an experienced designer should be sought when questionable conditions exist.

Ordinarily, the design and estimate for a storage dam should provide for foundation grouting. On the other hand, grouting of rock foundations is not generally required for small detention dams or for extremely low diversion and storage dams.

Foundation grouting is a process of injecting under pressure a fluid sealing material into the underlying formations through specially drilled holes to seal off or fill joints, fractures, fissures, bedding planes, cavities, or other openings. Unless the geologic conditions dictate otherwise, the foundation should be grouted to a depth below the surface of the rock equal to the reservoir head above the surface of the rock.

The grouting of a dam foundation is usually performed along a single line of grout holes spaced 10 to 20 feet on center. This creates some tightening deep in the foundation and some reduction in permeability. However, multiple lines of grout holes are necessary when severely fractured or highly permeable rock is encountered. Only multiple-line curtains improve the degree of reliability, but even then results are speculative because it is impossible to thoroughly grout all fractures or pores in the foundation. A grout curtain should not be relied on as the single provision to reduce seepage and related uplift pressures so that downstream seepage control features are reduced or eliminated. The grout curtain used on the abutment of Granby Dam in Colorado is shown on figure 6-6.

In cases where large zones of fractured rock lie at the foundation contact or where the zone of broken rock within a fault has great width, it may be possible to grout the zone by grouting to a shallow depth, usually 10 to 30 feet, by using a grid pattern. This type of grouting is referred to as "blanket grouting." It reduces leakage in the fractured zone and provides a more firm foundation for the dam. In most cases, the foundation directly beneath the impervious zone requires some blanket grouting.

Foundation grouting is generally performed with

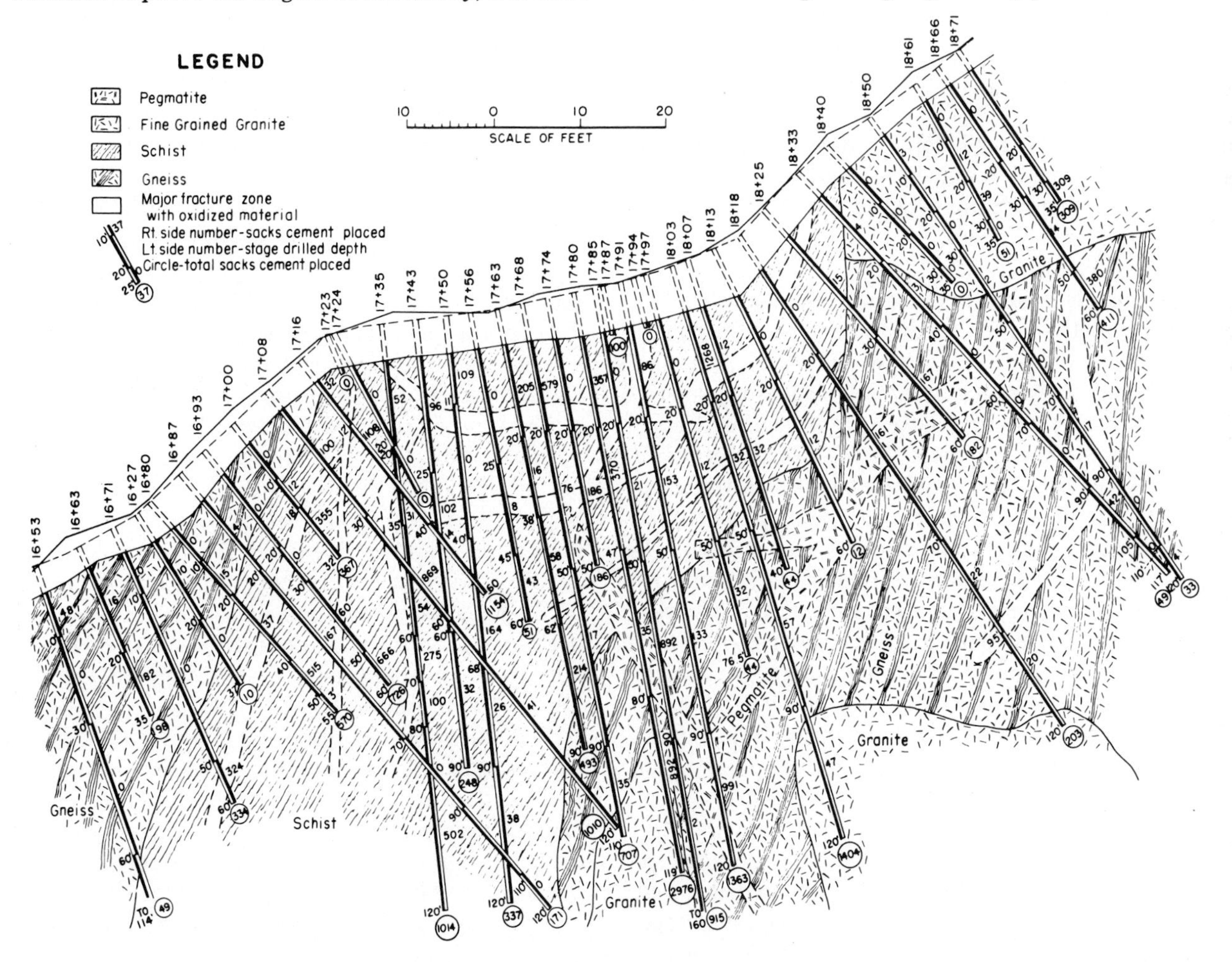

Figure 6-6.—Grout curtain used on the abutment of Granby Dam, Colorado. 101–D–245.

a mixture of cement and water, starting with a ratio of 5:1. If considerable "take" in a hole is experienced, the grout mixture is progressively thickened. Grout mixes usually vary between 10:1 and 0.8:1. If the grout take is excessive, sand is added to give the gout additional bulk. In some cases, bentonite is combined with the sand in small quantities, about 2 percent by weight of the cement, to obtain a more pumpable grout mix and some expansion of the grout. A suggested gradation of sand that is used for grouting on Bureau projects is given in the tabulation below.

Sieve size, No.	*Cumulative percent, by weight retained on screen*
8	0
16	0 to 5
30	15 to 40
50	50 to 80
100	70 to 90
200	95 to 100

Where the grout hole continues to take a large quantity of grout, it may be advantageous to require intermittent pumping, waiting up to 24 hours between pumping periods to allow grout in the foundation to set.

Grouting is usually performed by one of the following methods: (1) staging-down, or (2) staging-up.

Grouting by the staging-down method consists of drilling the grout hole to a predetermined depth, washing the hole, pressure testing it with water, and then grouting. After grouting but before the grout in the hole has set, the grout is washed out of the hole and drilling for the second stage is begun. In the second and succeeding stages, the same sequence of operations is used, except that a packer is sealed near the bottom of the previously grouted stage. In this manner, subsequent stages are grouted until the entire length of the hole has been grouted. This method is useful when drill-hole caving occurs, when the upper layers of the foundation are extensively cracked, or when the hole suddenly loses drill water.

When grouting by the staging-up method, the entire length of the hole is drilled, the hole washed, and a packer attached to the end of the grout supply pipe, which is then lowered and seated at a predetermined distance above the bottom of the hole. Then grouting is performed at the required pressure. The grout pipe and packer are withdrawn to the next stage and the grouting is repeated. This upward staging continues until the entire hole is grouted.

Grout holes are usually drilled with the commercial standard EX (approximately 1½-inch diameter) drill size, and a grout nipple is used to introduce the grout into the foundation. The grout nipple is usually a 2-inch-diameter pipe from 18 inches to 5 feet long (depending on rock conditions) that is anchored into the rock by cement grout, oakum, or other suitable calking material to facilitate drilling and grouting. The different drilling methods include air and water percussion and air and water rotary (plug or core bit). The primary concern when choosing a grout-hole drilling method is plugging fractures with cuttings. The drilling method should be chosen on the basis of the geologic conditions determined from data obtained during the design explorations.

Packers are devices that seal off drill holes at any elevation to permit grouting of a selected stage below the packer. The four types of packers most commonly used are shown on figure 6-7 and 6-8. The leather-cup packer (fig. 6-7(A)) seals when the grout forces the cups outward against the drill-hole wall; it is most commonly used in hard rock. The mechanical packer (fig. 6-7(B)) requires a double-pipe arrangement; it is seated against the drill-hole wall by compressing the annular rubber sleeve at the bottom of the packer pipe by tightening the nut at the top of the pipe; this type of packer is more suitable than the leather-cup packer in slightly oversized holes. The pneumatic packer (fig. 6-8(C)) is expanded by compressed air or inert gas; it is used in poor rock where the drill holes may be considerably oversized. The cone-type packer (fig. 6-8(D)) is seated when grout forces the annular rubber sleeve upward on the cone; it is used in relatively hard rock. Photographs of the four types of packers are shown on figure 6-9.

A great variety of grouting equipment is available. In general, the equipment consists of a grout mixer, grout agitator, grout pump, and a pipe and/or hose system for circulating the grout. The circulating line and manifold system allows grouting pressures to be controlled at the collar of the hole. Figure 6-10 illustrates the circulating-type grout system and the equipment generally used for grouting.

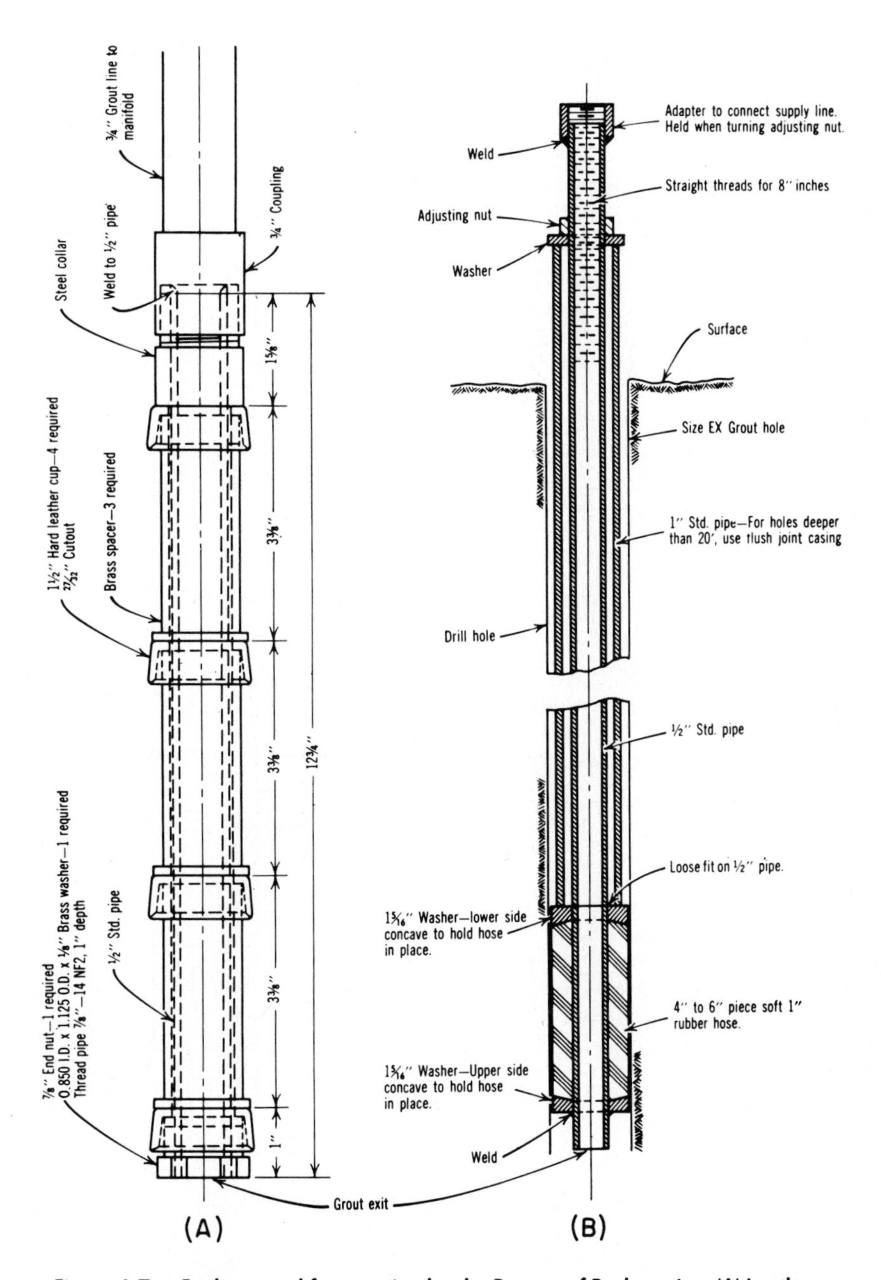

Figure 6-7.—Packers used for grouting by the Bureau of Reclamation: (A) Leather-cup, (B) Mechanical. 288–D–2873.

Grout is usually pumped with a duplex piston-type pump or a helical-screw rotor-type pump; a standby grout pump should always be required for the grout plant. Piston-type pumps require devices to smooth the pressure pulsations that occur at various phases of the stroke. Figure 6-11 shows the grout plant used at Ruedi Dam, Colorado.

Grouting pressures are influenced by the following factors:

- Type of rock
- Degree to which rock is fractured
- Jointing system within the rock
- Stratification of rock
- Depth of zone being grouted
- Location of hole being grouted
- Weight of overlying material at time of grouting

The maximum grouting pressure should be such

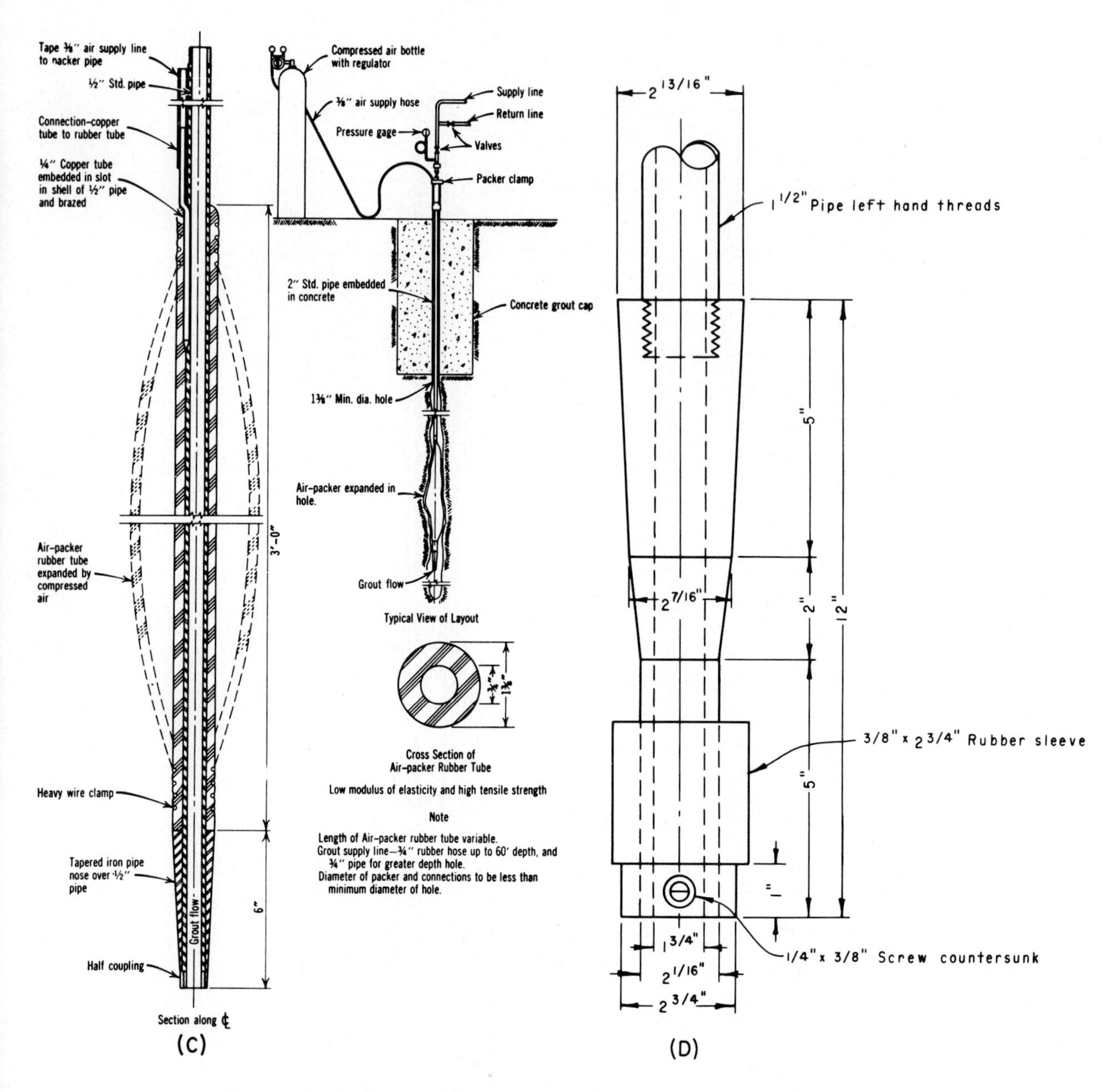

Figure 6-8.—Packers used for grouting by the Bureau of Reclamation: (C) Pneumatic, (D) Cone-type. 288–D–2874.

that rock fracture or uplift will not occur. Excessive pressures may weaken the rock strata by fracture, or may rupture a portion of the grout curtain already constructed, and result in increased permeability. Maximum pressures are difficult to determine because each foundation has a unique rock joint pattern and stratification, which is usually found by trial at the actual time of foundation grouting or by performing grouting tests before foundation treatment.

Unless other criteria are established, 1-lb/in^2 per foot of depth measured from the surface of the foundation to the center of the zone being grouted may be used as the initial grouting pressure. Variations may be determined by observing the grout take. Current Bureau of Reclamation requirements for termination of grouting are presented in section G.60.

Grout should usually be introduced into the foundation through grout nipples set directly in the

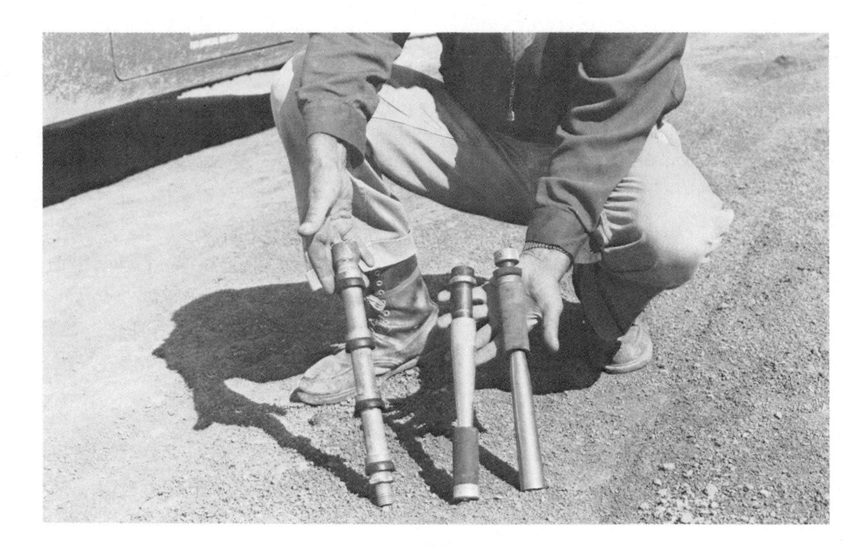

(A) P805-236-1594

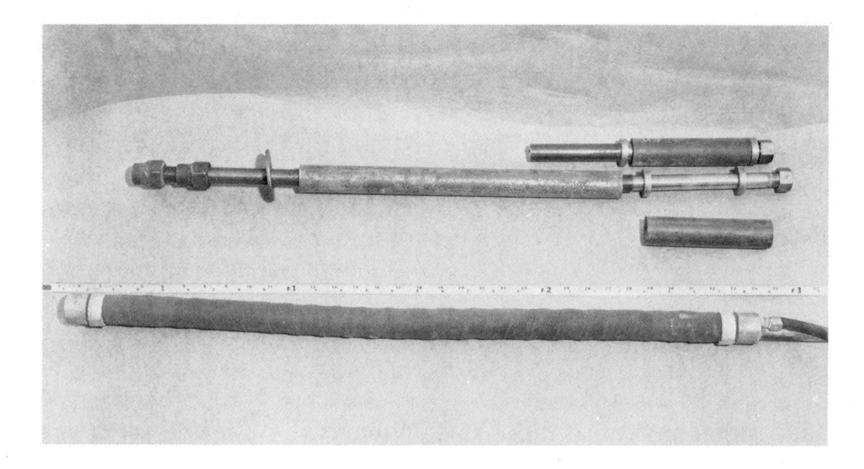

(B) P557-420-3459

Figure 6-9.—Types of grout hole packers used by the Bureau of Reclamation.(A) From left to right: leather-cup and cone-type, (B) From top to bottom: mechanical and pneumatic.

rock. Bedrock found to be badly jointed or broken below its surface may require a concrete group cap to facilitate grouting. However, use of a permanent grout cap can usually be avoided by leaving the foundation high and grouting through temporary grouted or concreted nipples or concrete caps. The use of grout caps under earth dams should be avoided because of the difficulty in sealing between them and the foundation rock and the possibility of cracking in the grout cap creating high seepage gradients. If a grout cap is used, it generally is a concrete-filled trench excavated from 3 to 8 feet into the bedrock, depending on the extent of broken rock; the trench is usually at least 3 feet wide to facilitate construction. The advantages and disadvantages of grout caps are shown in the following tabulations:

Grout cap

Advantages	*Disadvantages*
Good anchorage for nipples	Increased costs associated with excavation and concrete
Forms near-surface seepage barrier of zone 1 contact (critical where filters, slush grouting, dental concrete, and blanket grouting are absent)	Creates potential for high gradient at contact with zone 1
May allow use of shorter nipples for near-surface grouting	Creates the need for special compaction, particularly where rock deteriorates near the cap
Provides good work platform for drilling and grouting	Excavation for the cap may disturb (damage) foundation
Provides control for heave monitoring and inspection	Interferes with final foundation cleanup

No grout cap

Advantages	*Disadvantages*
Less excavation and concrete, therefore, less cost	Longer nipples may be required for anchorage
Encourages the use of multiple-row grout curtains	In some cases, nipples may require concrete anchorage (removed during foundation cleanup)
Potential for high seepage gradient is not created	No concrete seepage cutoff is provided along the zone 1 contact
Less special compaction	Working platform for drilling and grouting is not provided
Easier foundation cleanup	
Does not result in foundation damage	
In soft or friable rock, foundation is left high, and only one final foundation cleanup is required	

Grout pipes (nipples) are normally embedded at 10-foot centers in the foundation rock or grout cap, if used, during the concrete placement. Excavation for any grout cap must be carefully performed so that rock adjacent to the trench is not shattered. Figure 6-12 shows the construction of a typical grout cap at Navajo Dam, New Mexico.

When grouting foundations in which the surface rock is broken or jointed, grout often rises to the surface through these cracks and prevents complete grouting. The cracks or seams through which grout rises to the surface should be caulked to prevent excessive leakage. Caulking can be done with wooden wedges, cement grout, or burlap. The grout pumped into the foundation may also be allowed to set within the cracks.

If it is highly probable that the foundation will require extensive grouting, a preliminary test program may be desirable. Such test programs furnish specific data with which the final grouting program may be carefully planned. Test grouting programs can eliminate expensive delays caused by large grout overruns and should expedite the completion of the job.

Specifications for the performance of foundation grouting and for the excavation of the grout cap are included in sections G.56 through G.60. If an extensive grouting program is contemplated, an engineer experienced in this type of work should be consulted. For additional information see [5, 6, 7, 8, 9].

At one time, concrete cutoff walls were constructed to intercept seepage along the contact of the embankment with the rock foundation. But these walls are expensive and prone to cracking, and their usefulness is questionable. They are not recommended for the earthfill dams discussed herein. However, in unusual cases where the bedrock is very smooth, a cutoff wall may be warranted.

In some very pervious rock foundations or those containing soluble zones or layers, such as limestone or gypsum, it may be appropriate to provide cutoffs through pervious zones to control seepage. Cutoffs are also sometimes advisable through upper zones of weathered or broken foundation rock. Shallow cutoffs are usually provided by earthfilled cutoffs with sloping sides. Where deep cutoffs are required, thin foundation cutoffs such as a concrete diaphragm wall may be more economical. USBR Embankment Dams Design Standards No. 13, chapter 16, discusses foundation cutoff walls.

All loose and overhanging rock must be removed from the abutments; rock slopes should not be steeper than 0.5:1 (horizontal to vertical) and preferably flatter. Where flattening the rock slopes or overhangs is not practicable, the slopes may be shaped by the use of dental concrete.

If the bedrock is a shale that slakes in air, it may be necessary to excavate several feet into bedrock to remove the surface disintegration just before placement of the embankment; in more durable rock types, little excavation into the bedrock (other than for a grout cap) is usually necessary. Fractured rock should be treated by slush grouting (see sec. G.61). USBR Design Standards No. 13, chapter 3, discusses foundation surface treatment in detail. A sample specification for construction on a shale foundation subject to slaking is included in appendix G.

In most instances, bedrock is mantled by overburden of various types and thicknesses. The foun-

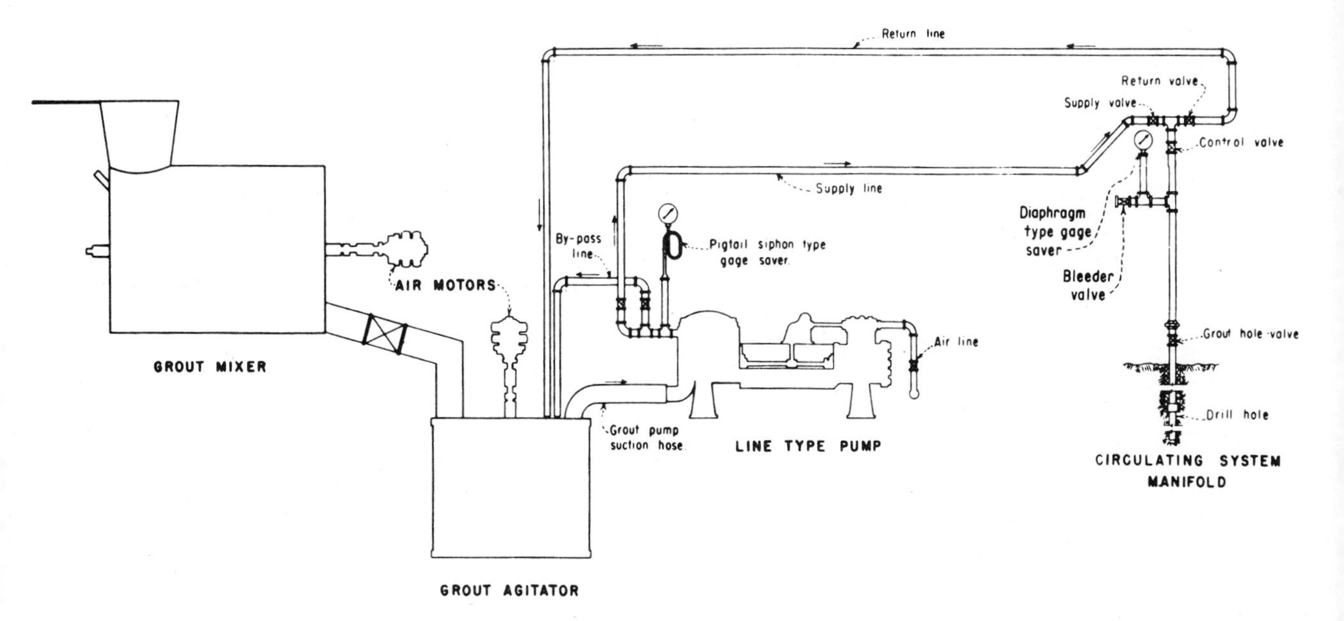

Figure 6-10.—Circulating grouting system. 288–D–2866.

Figure 6-11.—Grouting plant used at Ruedi Dam, Colorado. P382–706–1134NA.

Figure 6-12.—Placing concrete grout cap at Navajo Dam, New Mexico. The 2-inch-diameter grout nipples are fixed at 10-foot intervals. 711-422-250.

dation design then depends on the nature and depth of the overburden as described in succeeding section. The above discussion is applicable not only to exposed rock foundations, but also to bedrock reached by trenching through the overburden.

Filters and drains are the most important features for collecting and controlling seepage through rock foundations. Even though a rock foundation may be grouted and cutoffs provided, appropriate filters and drainage are still necessary to collect seepage and reduce uplift pressures in the area downstream of the impervious zone. This is a necessary design measure that precludes unforeseen events such as foundation fracturing caused by earthquakes or construction deficiencies that may occur in grout curtains and cutoffs. Drainage blankets, toe drains, toe trenches, and relief wells should be used individually or in combination as necessary to control seepage. USBR Design Standards No. 13, chapters 5 and 8, cover the design of these features.

6.9. *Sand and Gravel Foundations.*—

(a) *General.*—Often the foundations for dams consist of recent alluvial deposits composed of relatively pervious sands and gravels overlying impervious geologic formations. The pervious materials may range from fine sand to openwork gravels, but more often they consist of stratified heterogeneous mixtures. Generally, sand and gravel foundations have sufficient strength to adequately support loads induced by the embankment and reservoir, but this must be verified by adequate exploration, testing, and analyses. Knowledge of the geologic deposition process can help determine the potential occurrence of low strength zones.

Two basic problems are found in pervious foundations; one pertains to the amount of underseepage, and the other is concerned with the forces exerted by the seepage. The type and extent of treatment justified to decrease the amount of seepage should be determined by the purpose of the dam, the streamflow yield in relation to the reservoir conservation capacity, and the necessity for making constant reservoir releases to serve senior water rights or to maintain a live stream for fish or for other conservation purposes. Loss of water through underseepage may be of economic concern for a storage dam but of little consequence for a detention dam. Economic studies of the value of the water and the cost of limiting the amount of underseepage are required in some instances to determine the extent of treatment. However, adequate measures must be taken to ensure the safety of the dam against failure caused by piping, regardless of the economic value of the seepage.

A special problem may exist in foundations consisting of low density sands and gravels. The loose structure of saturated sands and gravels is subject to collapse under the action of a dynamic load. Although the loose sand may support sizable static loads through point-to-point contact of the sand grains, a vibration or shock may cause the grains to try to readjust into a more dense structure. Because drainage cannot take place instantaneously, part of the static load formerly carried by the sand grains is then transferred temporarily to the water, and the effective strength of the foundation may be greatly reduced, possibly leading to failure. USBR Design Standards No. 13, chapter 13, covers seismic design and analyses.

Foundations consisting of cohesionless sand of low density are suspect, and special investigations should be made to determine required remedial treatment. If the relative density of the foundation is less than 50 percent, the approximate magnitude of the relative density of a cohesionless sand foundation can be determined from the results of standard penetration tests described in section 5.32(b). The number of blows per foot is related to the relative density, but is affected by the depth of the test and, to some extent, by the location of the water table. The following tabulation gives average standard penetration resistance values for 50 percent relative density irrespective of the water table, based on research by the Bureau [10].

Effective overburden pressure

Overburden pressure,[1] *lb/in*^{2}	*Number of blows per foot*
0	4
20	12
40	17

[1]Based on submerged unit weight.

Special studies in triaxial shear on undisturbed samples may be required for foundations of cohesionless sand indicated to be below 50 percent relative density. Such studies are beyond the scope of this text, and the advice of specialists in dam design should be obtained.

(b) *Amount of Underseepage.*—To estimate the volume of underseepage that may be expected, it is necessary to determine the coefficient of permeability of the pervious foundation. This coefficient is a function of the size and gradation of the coarse particles, of the amount of fines, and of the density of the mixture. Three general field test methods are used to determine the coefficient of permeability of foundations: (1) pump-out tests, in which water is pumped from a well at a constant rate and the drawdown of the water table observed in wells placed on radial lines at various distances from the pumped well; (2) tests conducted by observation of the velocity of flow as measured by the rate of travel of a dye or electrolyte from the point of injection to an observation well; and (3) pump-in tests, in which water is pumped into a drill hole or test pit and the rate of seepage observed under a given head. Various laboratory test methods are also used to determine the coefficient of permeability, such as permeability and settlement tests, one-dimensional consolidation test, and falling head and constant head permeability tests. Most of these tests methods are covered in the Bureau's *Earth Manual*[11] and *Ground Water Manual*[12]. Seepage analyses and control are covered in chapters 5 and 8 of USBR Embankment Dam Design Standards No. 13.

The pump-out tests are relatively expensive, but in results are more dependable than other methods. The rate-of-travel methods is costly and difficult to interpret. The pump-in tests are economical for small dams because they can be accomplished in conjunction with the usual exploratory drilling; however, the results can be considered as only approximations. Another advantage to the pump-in tests in drill holes (see ch. 5) is that the permeability of various layers is more easily tested.

Upon determination of the coefficient of permeability of the foundation, a rough approximation of the amount of underseepage may be made by use of Darcy's formula:

$$Q = kiA \tag{1}$$

where:

Q = discharge volume per unit of time,
k = coefficient of permeability for the foundation; i.e., discharge through a unit area at unit hydraulic gradient,
i = hydraulic gradient = h/L = difference in head divided by length of path, and
A = gross area of foundation through which flow takes place.

The underseepage for the example shown on figure 6-13 is as follows:

k = 25,000 ft/yr = 0.00079 ft/s
h = El. 210 − El. 175 = 35 feet
L = 165 feet
$i = h/L$ = 35/165 = 0.212

Depth of foundation, d = El. 170 − El.100 = 70 feet.

For a width of 1 foot, A = (70)(1) = 70 ft^2. Q per foot of width = (0.00079)(0.212)70 = 0.012 ft^3/s.

For foundation width of 100 feet, Q = 1.2 ft^3/s; for foundation width of 1,000 feet, Q = 12 ft^3/s.

The accuracy of the amount of underseepage as determined by Darcy's formula, equation (1), depends on the homogeneity of the foundation and the accuracy with which the coefficient of permeability is determined. The results should be considered as an indication only of the order of magnitude of seepage in the evaluation of water loss from a project-use viewpoint.

If the foundation is stratified (as is usually the case), the vertical permeability will be much less than the horizontal permeability, and permeable layers at depth will not be fully effective in trans-

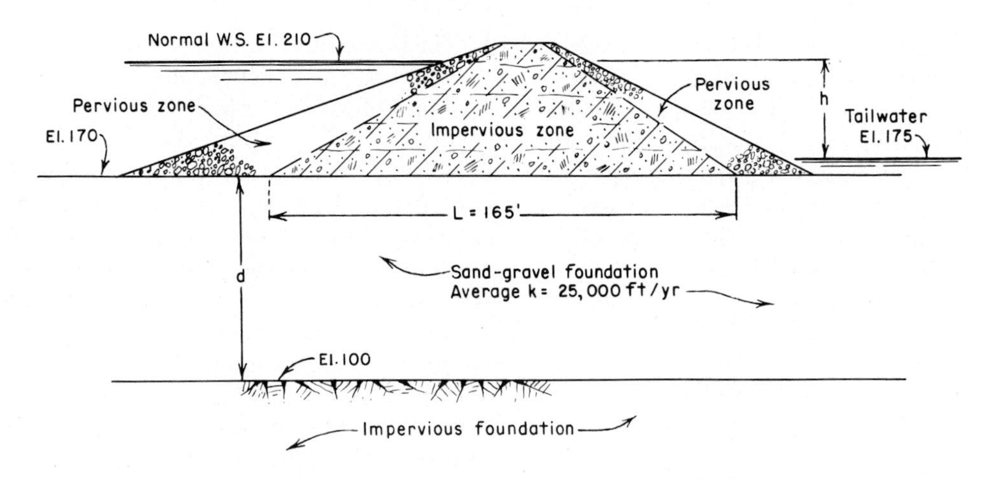

Figure 6-13.—Example computation of seepage by Darcy's formula. 288–D–2481.

mitting underseepage. The quantity of seepage as determined by equation (1) will be liberal if an average coefficient of permeability of the various layers, obtained by weighting each coefficient by the thickness of the layer, is used in the computations.

(c) *Seepage Forces.*—The flow of water through a pervious foundation produces seepage forces as a result of the friction between the percolating water and the walls of the pores of the soil through which it flows. This friction is similar to that developed by water flowing through a pipe. Figure 6-14 shows the flow path of an infinitesimal element of water through the pervious foundation of a dam. The water percolating downward at the upstream toe of the dam adds the initial seepage force, F_1,to the submerged weight, of the soil, W_5, to produce the resultant body force, R_1. As the water continues on the seepage path, it continues to exert seepage forces in the direction of flow, which are proportional to the friction loss per unit of distance. When the cross-sectional area through which flow takes place is restricted, as under a dam, the velocity of the seepage for a given flow is increased. This increase in velocity is accompanied by an increase in friction loss, and the seepage force is correspondingly increased. This increase in seepage force is represented on figure 6-14 by larger vectors for F_2 and F_3 than for F_1 and F_4. As the water percolates upward at the downstream toe of the dam, the seepage force tends to lift the soil, reducing the effective weight to R_4. If F_4 exceeds W_5, the resultant would be acting upward and the soil could be carried our or "piped out."

If the foundation materials are similar throughout, the erosion could progress backwards along the flow line until a "pipe" is formed to the reservoir, allowing rapid escape of reservoir storage and subsequent failure of the dam. Experience has shown that this action can occur rapidly or can be slow and cumulative with final failure occuring months or even years later. If a more impervious layer at the surface overlies a pervious foundation, sudden upheaval of the foundation at the downstream toe of the dam can occur. Some engineers [13] refer to the former type as piping failure, and the latter type [14] as a "blowout." This does not mean that initial piping will always result in failure. If the foundation soil is nonuniform, fine material may be carried away, leaving the coarse material structural matrix intact and resulting in a stable but more pervious foundation. It is always difficult to determine whether piping will result in failure or will produce an eventual stabilization; therefore, it is advisable to design the structure so that piping will not occur.

The magnitude of the seepage forces throughout the foundation and at the downstream toe of the dam, where piping usually begins, depends on the pressure gradient driving the seepage water. Relatively impervious foundations are not usually susceptible to piping because impervious soil offers a greater resistance to seepage forces and, consequently, to displacement. This is due to particle cohesion and the low velocity of flow as water exits at the toe. Pervious foundations, on the other hand, permit higher flow velocity and are usually cohesinless, offering less resistance to seepage forces. In such instances, the design must include measures to prevent seepage forces from heaving [13] or removing soil from the downstream toe of the dam.

Another type of piping failure is due to internal

erosion from springs that start near the downstream toe and proceed upstream along the base of the dam, the walls of a conduit, a bedding plane in the foundation, an especially pervious stratum, or other weakness that permits a concentration of seepage to reach the area downstream from the dam without high friction losses. This type of failure is termed by some engineers [13] as "failure by subsurface erosion."

The phenomenon known as "blowout" [14] is a type of failure usually associated with a confining layer at the downstream surface that results in uplift seepage forces that rupture the confining layer. This initial eruption may lead to complete failure if the resulting increase in velocity is large enough to erode the remaining foundation by piping.

The magnitude and distribution of the seepage forces in a foundation can be obtained from a flow net, which is a graphical representation of the paths of percolation and lines of equal potential (lines drawn through points of equal total head) in subsurface flow. It consists of flow lines and equipotential lines superimposed on a cross section of the foundation. Although the two families of curves may in simple cases be derived mathematically, the graphical solution is more commonly used. The method of applying the flow net to the solution of problems involving subsurface flow is presented in many publications [15, 16, 17, 18].

Analysis of seepage pressures and of the safety of the foundation against piping by the flow net method has some serious limitations. It takes considerable experience to construct an accurate flow net, especially where foundations are stratified and where drains or partial cutoffs are installed. The coefficients of permeability for each stratum and lens (and in different directions) are required. Experience has shown that the grain size and gradation of the foundation material have an important bearing on piping failures and that piping failures often occur after the dam has been in service for some time. Therefore, it appears that many failures caused by piping are of the subsurface erosion type as a result of seepage following minor geological weakness. This type of failure cannot be analyzed by flow nets or other theoretical methods.

The foundation designs given in the remainder of this chapter are based upon the same theoretical principles used in the design of major structures; however, the procedures have been simplified so they may be applied to small dams by those who are not specialists in the field of earthfill dam design. Nevertheless, some experience in this field is recommended. These procedures are for relatively straightforward geologic conditions. If the geology is not straightforward, an experienced earthfill dam designer should be consulted.

6.10. *Methods of Treating Sand and Gravel Foundations.*—(a) *General.*—Various methods of seepage and percolation control can be used, depending on the requirements for preventing uneconomical loss of water and the nature of the foundation in regard to stability from seepage

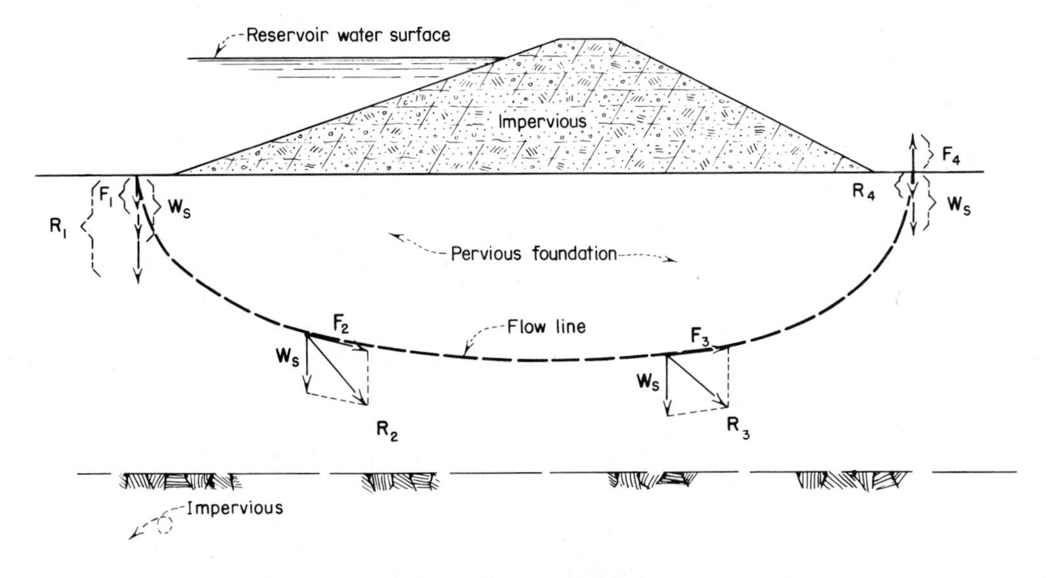

Figure 6-14.—Seepage force components. 288–D–2482.

forces. Cutoff trenches, sheet piling, mixed-in-place concrete pile curtains, slurry trenches, grouting of alluvium, or combinations of these methods have been used to reduce the flow and to control seepage forces. Blankets of impervious material, extending upstream from the toe of the dam and possibly covering all or part of the abutments, are frequently used for the same purpose. Horizontal drainage blankets may be incorporated in the downstream toe of a dam or used to blanket the area immediately downstream from the toe of the dam through which percolating water may escape under an appreciable head. The purpose of these blankets is to permit free flow and dissipation of pressure without disruption of the foundation structure and loss of fine soil particles. Pressure-relief wells are used to relieve pressure in pervious layers or zones deeper in the foundation before the pressures are transmitted to the downstream toe area.

The details of these various devices together with an appraisal of effectiveness are contained in this section. The application of the various devices to the design of pervious foundations is included in section 6.11.

(b) *Cutoff Trenches.*—These may be classified into two general types: sloping-side cutoff trenches and vertical-side cutoff trenches. Sloping-side cutoff trenches are excavated by shovels, draglines, or scrapers and are backfilled with impervious materials that are compacted in the same manner as the impervious zone of the embankment. Vertical-side cutoff trenches may be excavated in open cut by hand, by trenching machine, or by stopping where it is necessary to remove and replace breccia or debris in fault zones. Ordinarily, vertical-side trenches are not economical because of the cost of the hand labor involved in placing and compacting the backfill material.

The cutoff trench should be located at or upstream from the centerline of the crest of the dam, but not beyond a point where the cover of impervious embankment above the trench cannot provide resistance to percolation at least equal to that offered by the trench itself. The centerline of the cutoff trench should be parallel to the centerline of the dam across the canyon bottom or valley floor, but it should converge toward the centerline of the dam as it is carried up the abutments to maintain the required embankment cover.

Whenever economically possible, seepage through a pervious foundation should be cut off by a trench extending to bedrock or other impervious stratum. This is the most positive means of controlling the amount of seepage and ensuring that no difficulty will be encountered by piping through the foundation or by uplift pressures at the downstream toe.

Figure 6-15 shows the cutoff trench excavation and backfill at Great Cut Dike, part of McPhee Reservoir in southeast Colorado. Dental concrete and a filter zone were used to prevent piping of zone 1 into fractured rock. These features can be seen in the photograph. Figure 6-16 shows placement of compacted fill in the cutoff trench at Sugar Loaf Dam in Colorado; construction of the outlet works gate chamber is shown in the middle background.

To provide a sufficient thickness of impermeable material and an adequate contact with the rock or other impervious foundation stratum, the bottom width of the cutoff trench should increase with an increase in reservoir head. However, the cutoff trench bottom width may be decreased as the depth of the trench increases because the seepage force at the foundation contact will decrease (caused by loss of head as the water travels vertically through the foundation) as the depth increases. An adequate width for the cutoff trench of a small dam may be determined by the formula:

$$w = h - d \tag{2}$$

where:

w = bottom of width of cutoff trench,
h = reservoir head above ground surface, and
d = depth of cutoff trench excavation below ground surface.

A minimum bottom width of 20 feet should be provided so that excavating and compacting equipment can operate efficiently in trenches, which must be unwatered by well points or sump pumps if they are below the water table.

(c) *Partial Cutoff Trenches.*—Darcy's formula for seepage, equation (1), indicates that the amount of seepage is directly proportional to the cross-sectional area of the foundation. It might be concluded from this that the amount of seepage could be reduced 50 percent by extending the impervious zone on figure 6-13 into the ground so that the depth of the pervious foundation is reduced from 70 to 35 feet; however, this is not the case. The action of a partial cutoff is similar to that of an obstruction in a pipe—the flow is reduced because of the loss of head caused by the obstruction, but the reduction in flow is not directly proportional to the reduction

Figure 6-15.—Cutoff trench excavation and backfill. Great Cut Dike, Dolores Project, Colorado. CN71–438–10903NA.

in the area of the pipe. Experiments by Turnbull and by Creager on homogeneous isotropic pervious foundations have demonstrated that a cutoff extending 50 percent of the distance to the impervious stratum will reduce the seepage by only 25 percent; an 80-percent cutoff penetration is required to reduce the seepage 50 percent [19].

A partial cutoff trench may be effective in a stratified foundation by intercepting the more pervious layers in the foundation and by substantially increasing the vertical path the seepage must take. Reliance cannot be placed upon a partial cutoff trench in this situation unless extensive subsurface exploration has verified that the more impervious layers are continuous. Pervious foundations also may consist of an impervious foundation stratum of considerable thickness sandwiched between upper and lower pervious layers. A partial cutoff extending to such an impervious layer would cut off only the upper pervious layer. This would be effective if the thicknesses of the impervious and upper pervious layers are sufficient to resist the seepage pressures in the lower pervious layers near the downstream toe so that blowouts do not occur.

(d) *Sheet Piling Cutoffs.*—Steel sheet piling is relatively expensive, and experience [6, 20, 21, 27] has shown that leakage through the interlocks between the individual sheets is considerable. Never-

Figure 6-16.—Placement of compacted fill in the cutoff trench. Sugar Loaf Dam, Colorado. Construction of the outlet works gate chamber can be seen in the middle background. P382–706–2578.

theless, sheet piling is still used occasionally in combination with a partial cutoff trench to increase the depth of the cutoff. Under certain conditions it is also used in lieu of a cutoff trench. The sheet piling should be steel because of its high strength. Sheet piling cutoffs are practically limited to use in foundations of silt, sand, and fine gravel. Where cobbles or boulders are present, or where the material is highly resistant to penetration, driving or jetting becomes difficult and costly, and it is highly doubtful that an effective cutoff can be obtained because of the tendency of the piling to wander and become damaged by breaks in the interlocks or tearing of the steel. A heavy structural section with strong interlocks should be used if the foundation contains gravel.

It is not practicable to drive sheet piling so that it is watertight. Under the best conditions, including the use of compound to seal the interlocks and good contact of the bottom of the piling with an impervious foundation, it can be expected that the piling will be only 80 to 90 percent effective in preventing seepage. With poor workmanship, or if the piles cannot be seated in an impervious stratum, they will not be more than 50 percent effective and may be much less.

(e) *Cement-Bound and Jet-Grouted Curtain Cutoffs.*—The mixed-inplace cement-bound curtain is another means of establishing a cutoff in pervious foundations. It has been used in the construction of Slaterville Diversion Dam near Ogden, Utah; Putah Diversion Dam near Sacramento, California; and Lower Two Medicine Dam in Montana.

The curtain is constructed by successively overlapping individual piles. Each mixed-in-place pile consists of a column of soil intimately mixed with mortar to form a pilelike structure within the soil. Such a pile is constructed by injecting mortar through a vertical rotating hollow shaft, the lower end of which is equipped with a mixing head for combining the soil with the mortar as the latter is injected. The mortar is introduced into soil that has been loosened by the mixing head as the bit is simultaneously rotated and advanced into, or withdrawn from, the soil. The piles may be reinforced as required. Photographs showing the mixing operation for a single pile and a finished cutoff wall are shown on figure 6-17(A) and (B).

Patents on the methods and some of the materials used in construction of the mixed-in-place pile are held by Intrusion-Prepakt, Inc., Cleveland, Ohio.

The manufacturer's literature [22] states that use of a 15-inch mixing head at 14-inch centers produced piles averaging 18 inches in diameter with a minimum cross-sectional thickness of 15 inches. The maximum depth was listed as 58 feet.

(A) Mixing operation. (Intrusion-Prepakt Co.). 288–D–2875.

(B) Finished wall. (Intrustion-Prepakt Co.). 288–D–2876.

Figure 6-17.—Cement-bound curtain cutoff.

The mixed-in-place process is designed for use in granular soils, including silt, sand, and gravel. But it is not recommended for predominantly clayey materials and is not capable of handling cobbles and boulders. Sample specifications are given in appendix G.

Recently, a very similar process called jet grouting has been developed. Jet grouting depends on very high pressure jets (3,000 to 10,000 lb/in^2) rather than a mixing head to mix the soil and grout. There are also other versions of these processes, and along with development of better machinery, more effective cutoffs can be constructed to greater depths.

(f) *Slurry Trench Cutoffs.*—An effective method of constructing positive cutoffs when wet conditions or deep cutoffs in alluvial valleys make conventional construction methods uneconomical is the slurry trench method.

The technique was adapted from well drilling methods used by the oil industry. Bentonite clay suspensions are used to support holes cut in soft soils. The slurry trench method uses a water-bentonite slurry to seal and support the trench wall during the excavation process. The sequence of construction operations for a slurry trench is shown on figure 6-18. Vertical-sided trenches, usually from 3 to 10 feet wide, are excavated with either draglines, clamshells, backhoes, or trenching machines. Figure 6-19 shows excavation of a slurry trench using a dragline at the Corps of Engineers' West Point Dam. As material is excavated, the bentonite slurry is pumped into the trench; care is taken to keep the slurry elevation constant and above the water table to avoid caving. Upon introduction to the trench, the slurry weighs more than water. Because the slurry tends to flow out of the trench, a relatively thin, impermeable filter cake develops. Hydrostatic pressure on this impermeable filter cake reduces caving and sloughing and provides overall stability. In the case of a soil-bentonite backfilled cutoff wall, the excavated material is stockpiled near the trench, and excess slurry is allowed to drain back into the trench. Backfill material that satisfies the gradation requirements of the design is placed back into the trench, with the filter cake to form an essentially impermeable barrier.

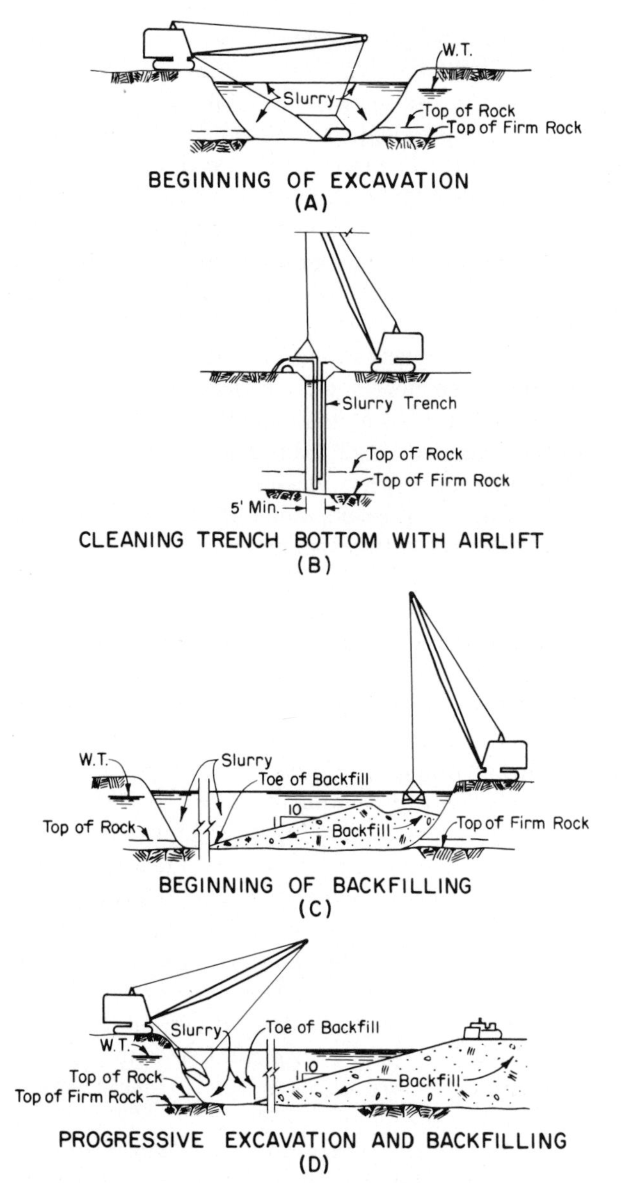

Figure 6-18.—Sequence of operations for the construction of a slurry trench. (U.S. Army Corps of Engineers). 288–D–2783.

The slurry is usually made by mixing bentonite, a clay having a high content of the mineral montmorillonite, and water. Generally, naturally pure premium-grade Wyoming-type sodium cation base montmorillonite is specified because of its small particle size and high swelling characteristics. After the slurry is mixed with water and allowed to hydrate, it forms a dispersed suspension that is denser and more viscous than water. The slurry is thixotropic, which means that left undisturbed, the suspension develops shear or gel strength, but fluidizes when agitated [23, 24]. The density and the hydrostatic pressure the slurry exerts increase as a result of the suspension of clay, silt, and sand particles during the excavation process.

Figure 6-19.—Excavation of a slurry trench. (U.S. Army Corps of Engineers). 288–D–2894.

Bentonite used for slurry trench construction is required to meet the standards described in section 3, API Standard 13A, "Specifications for Oil-Well Drilling Fluid Materials," Eighth Edition, March 1981 (supplemented May 1982).

Bentonite-water slurries for trench excavations are designed to perform several functions: (1) prevent seepage into the foundation by the formation of a filter cake, (2) suspend clay, silt, and fine-to-medium-sized sand particles during excavation, and (3) provide hydrostatic pressure to the face of the excavation. These functions are accomplished by the design and either the direct or indirect control of one or more of the slurry properties. Those properties, which include bentonite concentration, density, viscosity, shear strength, filtration loss, sand content, and pH, are measured according to procedures outlined by the American Pipe Institute's API Code 13B, "Standard Procedures for Testing Drilling Fluids," Ninth Edition (May 1982).

Slurry densities generally range from 65 to 90 lb/ft^3. Freshly mixed and fully hydrated slurry entering the trench usually has a density between 63 to 68 lbs/ft^3. As clay, silt, and sand are suspended in the slurry during excavation, the density increases. Densities ranging from 70 to 80 lb/ft^3 are generally sufficient to maintain stability for most construction applications. Densities greater than 90 lb/ft^3 can prevent the backfill from fully displacing the slurry when it is placed in the trench and should be desanded.

The viscosity of the slurry can vary considerably as a result of changes in bentonite concentrations, in the sand content, and in the concentration and type of additive. The slurry viscosity limits the penetration of slurry into the in situ soil structure before formation of the filter cake, but is not so great as to reduce the pumpability of the slurry. The viscosity also helps control the rate at which suspended particles exceeding the gel strength settle during the excavation. The gel or shear strength of the slurry controls the size of the silt and sand particles that can be maintained in suspension without settling.

The filtration loss is an indicator of the quality of filter cake a slurry can develop. A filter cake that is continually destroyed by excavating equipment is required to form quickly and compactly, preventing excessive seepage and filtration losses.

The slurry pH is monitored for changes that may destabilize its gel strength and its ability to form an adequate filter cake. Changes in the pH, outside a range of 7 to 12, can cause reduction in viscosity and gel strength.

(1) *Location and Dimensions.*—The location and dimensions of a slurry trench should satisfy the specific requirements of the site. The cutoff may be placed at any location beneath the dam upstream of the centerline of the impervious core, but the optimum location depends upon the type and location of the core, the depth of impervious stratum along the foundation, variations in foundation material, construction sequence, diversion requirements, and reservoir operation. Therefore, different consideration are required at each site.

Central trench locations have the disadvantage of inaccessibility if future modification or rehabilitation is required. For this reason, some designers favor placing the slurry trench upstream of the dam and connecting it to the core by an impervious blanket, even though reservoir dewatering is required to gain access to the slurry trench.

(2) *Transitions.*—Transitions are necessary between the slurry backfill and the impervious core material to compensate for the effect of differential settlement between the backfill material and the foundation. The transition is accomplished by simply making the trench wider at the top than at the bottom, usually by sloping the walls of the trench. This allows settlement of the core with the slurry backfill, reducing the tendency of the core and slurry wall to separate. It also provides a greater width for the core to adjust to settlement, reducing the tendency of cracking within the core.

(3) *Backfill.*—Slurry trench backfill is selected to reduce or stop foundation seepage. Two types of backfill commonly used are soil-bentonite and cement-bentonite.

Soil-bentonite backfill is designed to provide the desired reduction in permeability and resist the movement of backfill fines caused by the hydraulic gradients that develop across the trench. The backfill is often made by mixing the material excavated from the trench with clay, silt, sand, and/or gravel, as necessary to meet design requirements. A well-graded material with approximately 15 to 20 percent clay and silt sized particles is an excellent backfill because of its low permeability. The backfill is thoroughly mixed with slurry taken from the trench until a mixture with a consistency similar to that of concrete with a 3- to 6-inch slump is obtained.

The backfill is placed at the bottom of the trench by clamshell bucket to prevent it from segregating. Backfill is placed until it develops a slope of about 10:1 that extends from the trench bottom to the surface of the trench, as shown on figure 6-18(C). Additional backfill is bulldozed in and the trench is filled as shown on figure 6-18(D).

Cement-bentonite backfill is made by mixing cement with bentonite slurry. After mixing, the cement-bentonite backfill is pumped to the trench where it provides stability during the excavation and hardens into an impermeable cutoff wall. While curing, the backfill gains strength yet remains elastic enough to deform without cracking.

Before placing soil-bentonite or cement-bentonite backfill in the trench, the depth of the trench should be measured and samples taken to ensure that the bottom of the trench is keyed into the proper foundation material. The trench bottom is cleaned by an airlift system to remove any wall slough or sand settling from the slurry, which is shown on figures 6-18(B) and 6-20.

The use of a slurry trench should be reviewed carefully when cobbles, boulders, or large blocks of rock exist in the lower portions of the trench. In stratified foundations, extreme care must be taken to ensure that the bottom of the trench contacts the impervious layer on which the backfill material will rest. Cases have been reported of one of the harder stratifications being mistaken for the trench bottom, which was only detected later by coring. This care necessitates a great delay of additional construction time and expense, but can be avoided by frequent sounding operations on the trench bottom and prior foundation investigation. For additional information concerning slurry trenches, the reader is referred to the references at the end of the chapter. USBR Design Standards No. 13, chapter 16, should also be referred to for construction of slurry walls.

Table 6-1, adapted from Jones [23], presents a general description of the materials through which slurry trenches have been constructed, the trench widths used, and the hydraulic head for existing or proposed structures.

(g) *Grouting.*—Various materials have been used in attempts to develop grouting procedures that improve the stability and impermeability of pervious overburden foundation. These materials have been injected to act as a binder and to fill the voids.

Figure 6-20.—Airlifting sand from bottom of slurry trench. (U.S. Army Corps of Engineers). 288–D–2895.

Among these materials have been cement, asphalt, clay, and various chemicals.

Cement grouting cannot be successful in very fine granular materials because of the comparatively large particle size of the cement, which limits the penetration. However, coarse alluvial material has been successfully grouted in a number of cases using cement or cement-clay grouts. Asphalt grouting is also limited by the particle size. The value of clay grouting is doubtful because the clay is easily carried away by seepage forces. Chemical grouts have about the same viscosity as water and can be injected into pervious soils. However, chemical grouts are too expensive for general use in grouting pervious overburden foundations.

Despite the disadvantages enumerated above, grouting procedures that improve the impermeability of pervious overburden materials have been developed. Using these procedures, several dams have been built at sites that would have been considered impossible or uneconomical using other methods. Commonly, a cutoff curtain in overburden consists of several rows of grout holes, in which the outer rows of holes are grouted with cement, clay, and cement-clay grouts, and one or more of the inner rows are grouted with a chemical grout.

Overburden grouting is a costly process, the injection techniques are complex, and the selection of the grout and appropriate techniques requires considerable field exploration and laboratory and field testing. Furthermore, the results of the injection process are difficult to evaluate. For these reasons, overburden grouting is not considered an appropriate treatment for the foundations of small dams within the scope of this text. For information on this subject, the reader is referred to [25].

(h) *Upstream Blankets.*—The path of percolation in pervious foundations can be increased by the construction of a blanket of impervious material connecting with the impervious zone of the dam and extending upstream from the toe. Blankets are commonly used when cutoffs to bedrock or to an impervious layer are not practicable because of excessive depth; they are also used in conjunction with partial cutoff trenches. The topography just upstream from the dam and the availability of impervious materials are important factors in deciding on the use of blankets. The blanket is generally used for a stream channel or valley floor of sand and gravel, but may also be required for portions of the abutments.

Table 6-1.—Comparison of slurry trench cutoffs[1].

Project	Foundation material	Trench width	Maximum head	Remarks
Kennewick Levee, McNary Dam Project, Columbia River, Washington State Owner: Corps of Engineers	Sandy or silty gravels with zones of open gravel; k = 0.4 cm/s (0.41×10^6 ft/yr)	6 ft Central core	15 ft	Constructed in 1952; maximum depth = 22 ft
Wanapum Dam, Columbia River, Washington State, Owner: Public Utility District No. 2 of Grant County	Sandy gravels and gravelly sands underlain by open-work gravels; k (open gravels)=2.5 cm/s (2.6×10^6 ft/yr), average k = 1 cm/s (1.03x10^6 ft/yr)	10 ft Central core	88.5 ft	Preconstruction test trench, pump-out and laboratory piping tests; grouting beneath trench; construction in 1959-62; maximum depth of cutoff = 190 ft
Mangla Closure Dam, Mangla Dam Project, Jhelum River, West Pakistan Owner: West Pakistan Water and Power Development Authority	Sandy gravel with cobbles and boulders; gap graded in range of fine gravel and coarse sand; k = 0.4 cm/s (0.41×10^6 ft/yr)	10 ft Central core	230 ft Construction condition only	Constructed in 1964; maximum depth = 22 ft
Duncan Lake Dam, Duncan River, British Columbia, Canada Owner: British Columbia Hydro and Power Authority	Surface zone of sands and gravels over zone of silt to fine silty sand with some silty clay; k (surface zone) = 1 cm/s (1.03×10^6 ft/yr)	10 ft Upstream berm	102 ft Short term	Constructed in 1965-66; maximum depth = 60 ft
West Point Dam, Chattahoochee River, States of Georgia and Alabama Owner: Corps of Engineers	Upper stratum of alluvial soil, alternating layers of clay, silt, sand, and gravel varies from k=1.8×10^{-2} to 3.5×10^{-5} cm/s (18,600 to 36 ft/yr); lower stratum of residual soil brown silty sand; k = 0.6×10^{-5} cm/s (6 ft/yr)	5 ft Upstream blanket	61 ft	Constructed in 1966; maximum depth = 60 ft; grouting in sound rock below the trench; maximum depth of cutoff=100 ft
Saylorville Dam, Des Moines River, Iowa Owner: Corps of Engineers	Surface zone of impervious alluvial sandy clay; pervious zone, medium to fine sand and gravelly coarse to fine sand; average k (gravelly sand) = 0.15 cm/s (0.16×10^6 ft/yr)	8 ft Upstream berm	93 ft Short term	Dam under construction; construction of cutoff scheduled for 1969[2]; maximum depth=approx. 60 ft

Table 6-1.—Comparison of slurry trench cutoffs.—Continued

Project	Foundation material	Trench width	Maximum head	Remarks
Prokopondo Project (Quarry A Cofferdam), Suriname River, Suriname, S.A. Owner: Suriname Aluminum Co.	Uniform fine to coarse sand with some gravel; D_{10}= 0.1 mm	5 ft	40 ft	Constructed in 1959; maximum depth = 15 ft
Wells Dam, Columbia River, Washington State Owner: Public Utility District No. 1 of Douglas County	Pervious gravels	8 ft Central core	70 ft	Constructed in 1964; maximum depth >80 ft
Yards Creek Lower Reservoir, New Jersey Owner: Public Service Electric and Gas Co., Jersey Central Power and Light, New Jersey Power and Light Co.	Sands, gravels, cobbles, and boulders	8 ft Central core	55 ft	Constructed in 1964; maximum depth = 40 ft
Camanche Dam-Dike 2, Mokelumne River, California Owner: East Bay Municipal Utility District	Alluvial deposit with upper stratum of clayey silts, silts and clayey sands, and a lower stratum of poorly graded medium to fine sand over a thin zone of well-graded gravel; average $k = 7.5\times10^{-3}$ cm/s (7,760 ft/yr)	8 ft	135 ft	Constructed in 1966; maximum depth = 95 ft; maximum head on dam = 45 ft; head on trench depends on groundwater level downstream
Calamus Dam–Pick-Sloan Missouri Basin Program, Nebraska Owner: Bureau of Reclamation	Dune sands and underlying interbedded alluvial sands and gravels; maximum k = 0.14 cm/s (0.14×10^6 ft/yr)	5 ft Where fully penetrating; 3 ft Where partially penetrating; Upstream blanket	73 ft	Constructed in 1982-84; maximum depth = 115 ft; fully penetrating for 4,000-ft length, partially; penetrating (50 ft) for 3,000-ft length

[1]Adapted from table 1 of [23].
[2]Construction postponed until 1972.

Figures 6-21 and 6-22 show an abutment blanket that was constructed during the rehabilitation of Ochoco Dam by the Bureau of Reclamation in 1949. The purpose of this blanket was to reduce the seepage through the landslide debris, which forms the right abutment. It was successful because it reduced the seepage at full reservoir level from 28 to 12 ft³/s.

The blanket is continuous from the impervious zone of the dam, and it extends about 400 feet upstream. The abutment was dressed smooth to receive the blanket, which extends from the reservoir floor to an elevation 53 feet above. The blanket was constructed 5 feet thick, normal to the approximate 3:1 abutment slope. It is protected from erosion by 2 feet of riprap on 12 inches of bedding. Figure 6-21 shows the earthfill blanket complete and the beginning of riprap placement. Figure 6-22 shows a general view of the upstream face of the dam and the right abutment blanket completed.

Natural impervious blankets sometimes help reduce seepage and related pressures. Areas of the foundation that are covered by a natural impervious blanket should be stripped of vegetation, defective places should be repaired, and the entire surface of the natural blanket should be rolled to seal root holes and other openings. Stripping a natural blanket upstream from the dam to secure impervious soil for the construction of the dam should be avoided when possible. The normal procedure is to avoid excavating a natural impervious blanket within 200 to 400 feet upstream of the toe of the dam. The natural blanket is an added benefit, but should not be relied on for seepage control.

Although blankets may be designed by theoretical means [26], a simplified approach may be used for small dams. A suitable blanket thickness for small dams is 10 percent of the depth of the reservoir above the blanket but not less than 3 feet. This calculation is for blankets made from materials suitable for the construction of the impervious zone of an earthfill dam and compacted accordingly.

A blanket must meet filter criteria with the foundation material on which it is placed. If it does not, then a proper filter must be provided between the blanket and its foundation. See section 6.10(i) for filter criteria.

The length of the blanket should be governed by the desired reduction in the amount of underseepage. From an examination of equation (1) and figure 6-13, it is apparent that the amount of seepage is inversely proportional to the length of the path (for homogeneous isotropic foundations). Therefore, the blanket should be extended so that the seepage loss is reduced to the amount that can be tolerated from a project-use standpoint.

An upstream blanket should not be relied upon to reduce the seepage forces in the foundation enough to preclude piping failures. Although, theoretically, an upstream blanket would accomplish this purpose in a homogeneous foundation, the natural stratification that occurs in almost every alluvial foundation allows high pressures to exist in one or more foundation strata at the downstream toe of the dam. Horizontal drainage blankets or pressure-relief devices (drains or wells) should always be provided for a dam on a pervious foundation when a complete cutoff trench cannot be secured.

(i) *Downstream Embankment Zones for Pervious Foundations.*—The downstream sections of dams on pervious foundations must be constructed to perform the following functions:

- Relieve the uplift pressure from seepage
- Readily permit discharge of seepage water from the foundation
- Prevent piping of the fines from the embankment and from the foundation
- Provide sufficient weight to prevent uplift
- Adequately convey the total amount of seepage to the downstream channel

These functions are accomplished by providing:

- Extended downstream zones to lengthen seepage paths
- Zones so thick that their weight will prevent uplift
- Pervious downstream shells or horizontal drainage blankets that meet filter requirements to allow water to percolate from the foundation, but that prevent piping
- Toe drains with sufficient capacity to convey the accumulated seepage water back to the stream channel

Downstream zones incorporating either pervious shells, horizontal and inclined drainage blankets, toe drains, or combinations thereof should be used in the design of earthfill dams on relatively homogeneous pervious foundations without positive cutoff trenches. They may also be used on relatively homogeneous pervious foundations that are overlain by thin impervious layers: The pervious shell will supply weight to stabilize the foundation and will also effectively relieve pressures that may break

Figure 6-21.—Right abutment blanket construction at Ochoco Dam. On a tributary of the Crooked River in Oregon.

Figure 6-22.—Upstream slope of Ochoco Dam.

through the impervious layer. A horizontal drainage blanket meeting filter requirements may be required to prevent piping. Pervious foundations covered by impervious layers may also involve trenches backfilled with filter drain material or pressure-relief wells to reduce the uplift pressure and control seepage (see secs. 6.10(j) and (k)).

The required length of the downstream pervious zone can be determined theoretically by means of the flow net (sec. 6.9(c)), provided the ratio of the horizontal to the vertical permeability of the foundation is determined by the procedure known as transformed sections. This method of dealing with anisotropy in permeable foundations is discussed by Terzaghi and Peck [27] and Cedergren [18]. The method demonstrates that the larger the ratio of horizontal to vertical permeabilities, the farther downstream the seepage emerges from the toe of the impervious zone of the dam, and the longer the embankment required downstream.

Because of the difficulty or limitation in using flow nets to design small dams with relatively meager foundation exploration, design criteria are presented in this text to determine the lengths of downstream pervious zones. For small dams, it is recommended that the length of the downstream pervious zone equal three times the height of the dam, as shown on figure 6-23.

Figure 6-23 shows the typical downstream zoning used with exposed pervious foundations; that is, those not overlain by impervious material. Covered pervious foundations are discussed in section 6.11(e). Each method shown consists of an extended downstream section that lengthens the seepage path. In (A) and (B) of figure 6-23, the requirement for drainage is provided by the overlying pervious shell. This pervious shell should be designed to prevent piping from the foundation and impervious zone. However, if the shell material is such that it cannot prevent piping, a horizontal drainage blanket similar to that shown on figure 6-23(C) and an inclined drainage blanket, both designed to meet filter requirements, should be used. For homogeneous embankments or where the material permeability of the downstream zone is questionable, horizontal drainage blankets designed to prevent piping should be used. Furthermore, experience has shown that seepage through an impervious zone sometimes remains higher than would be predicted by procedures such as a flow net because of poor bond between lifts, inadvertent loose lifts, cracking caused by differential settlement, desiccation cracks, etc. Therefore, an inclined drainage blanket, as shown on figure 6-5(C), is often used and recently has become almost standard. These drainage blankets must have sufficient capacity to conduct all of the seepage from the embankment and the foundation to the toe drains. Horizontal drainage blankets used (and inclined drainage blankets, if used) with homogeneous embankments convert them to the modified homogeneous type of dam with the resultant advantages described in section 6.3.

Figure 6-23(A) illustrates the recommended minimum length and vertical thickness of the downstream section of a zoned embankment using the recommended minimum impervious core (minimum core B, fig. 6-43) for a dam constructed on a pervious foundation without a positive cutoff

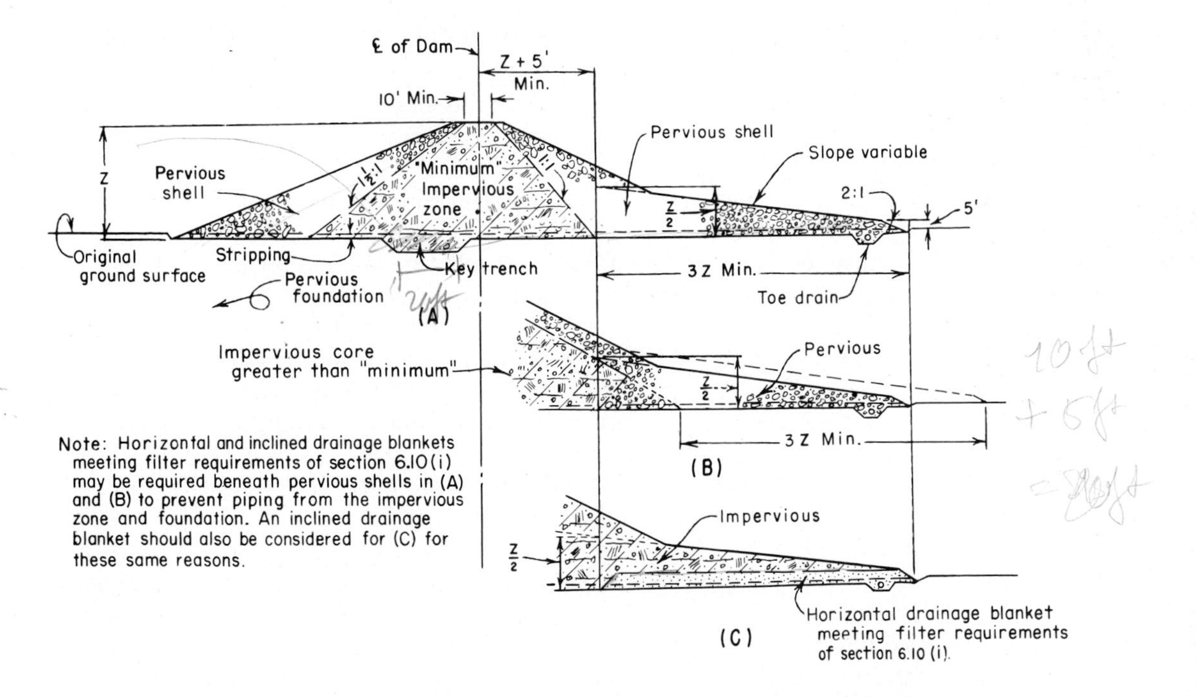

Figure 6-23.—Downstream embankment sections for pervious foundations. 288–D–2483.

trench. Figure 6-23(B) illustrates the recommended design for a zoned dam with an impervious core larger than minimum core B. The reverse slope of the impervious core (fig. 6-23(B)) is used to:

(1) Reduce the length of the downstream pervious shell.
(2) Facilitate construction of the downstream pervious shell if material excavated from the cutoff trench is used.
(3) Reduce the volume of embankment, as shown on figure 6-23(B).

The dashed outline on figure 6-23(B) indicates the drainage blanket that would be required if the reverse slope were not used.

The horizontal drainage blanket shown on figure 6-23 and an inclined drainage blanket, if used, must satisfy three requirements:

(1) Gradation must be such that particles of soil from the foundation and the upstream and overlying embankment are prevented from entering the filter and clogging it.
(2) Capacity of the filter must be such that it adequately handles the total seepage flow from both the foundation and the embankment.
(3) Permeability must be great enough to provide easy access of seepage water to reduce seepage uplift forces.

Requirements for gradation and permeability are closely related and are discussed below.

A minimum drainage blanket thickness of 3 feet is suggested to provide unquestionable capacity for seepage flows.

Multilayer filters for small earthfill dams should, in general, be avoided; they are more efficient but add to the cost of filter construction. In cases where large seepage quantities must be handled, it has been demonstrated [28] that multilayer filters can provide an economical solution.

If the overlying pervious zones in (A) and (B) of figure 6-23 are sand-gravel similar in gradation to the sand-gravel of the foundation and they meet filter requirements with zone 1 and the foundation, there is no danger of flushing particles from the impervious zone or foundation into the pervious shells of the embankment, and no special filters are required. Otherwise, a filter must be provided so that the finer foundation or impervious material is not carried into the voids of larger materials.

The rational approach to the design of filters is generally credited to Terzaghi [29]. Considerable experimentation has been performed by the Corps of Engineers [30] and the Bureau of Reclamation [31]. Several somewhat different sets of criteria are given by these authorities. The following limits are recommended to satisfy filter stability criteria and to provide ample increase in permeability between base and filter. These criteria are satisfactory for use with filters of either natural sand and gravel or crushed rock and for filter gradations that are either uniform or graded:

(1) $\dfrac{D_{15} \text{ of the filter}}{D_{15} \text{ of base material}} \geq 5$, provided that the filter does not contain more than 5 percent of material finer than 0.074 mm (No. 200 sieve) after compaction.

(2) $\dfrac{D_{15} \text{ of the filter}}{D_{85} \text{ of base material}} \leq 5.$

(3) $\dfrac{D_{85} \text{ of the filter}}{\text{Maximum opening of pipe drain}} \geq 2.$

(4) Generally, the filter should be uniformly graded to provide adequate permeability and prevent segregation during processing, handling, and placing.

In the foregoing, D_{15} is the size at which 15 percent of the total soil particles are smaller; the percentage is by weight as determined by mechanical analysis. The D_{85} size is that at which 85 percent of the total soil particles are smaller. If more than one filter layer is required, the same criteria are followed; the finer filter is considered as the base material for selection of the gradation of the coarser filter.

In addition to the limiting ratios established for adequate filter design, the 3-inch particle size should be the largest in a filter to minimize segregation and the bridging of large particles during placement of filter materials. In designing filters for base materials containing gravel particles (broadly graded materials), the base material should be analyzed on the basis of the gradation of the fraction smaller than No. 4.

It is important to compact filter material to the same density required for sand-gravel zones in embankments (see appendix G). Filter materials must be placed carefully to avoid segregation. A uniformly graded filter is advantageous in preventing segregation. The construction of thin filter layers requires proper planning and adequate inspection during placement. In many cases, the concrete sand used in the spillway, outlet works, or appurtenant structures may also be used as filter material. This reduces costs by eliminating any special blending requirements. A more complete discussion of filter criteria is given in USBR Design Standards No. 13, chapter 5.

The following is an example (see fig. 6-24) of a typical design that would be applicable for filters such as those shown around the toe drain on figure 6-25.

Example

Required:

Gradation limits of filter materials

Given:

Gradation range of base soil shown on figure 6-24 with D_{15max} = 0.03 mm and D_{85min} = 0.10 mm

Openings in drainpipe = ¼ inch

Solution:

(1) Lower limit of D_{15} of filter = 5 × 0.03 = 0.15 mm

(2) Upper limit of D_{15} of filter = 5 × 0.10 = 0.50 mm

To meet criteria (1), (2), and (4), sand shown as F_1 on figure 6-24 was selected. For F_1, D_{15} ranges between 0.15 and 0.50 millimeter. This material is too fine to place adjacent to a pipe with ¼-inch openings because the requirement is for D_{85} of the filter to be at least 2(¼) = 0.5 inch; hence, a second filter layer of gravel is required.

(3) Lower limit of D_{15} of gravel = 5(0.50) = 2.5 mm

(4) Upper limit of D_{15} of gravel = 5(1.0) = 5 mm

(5) Lower limit of D_{85} of gravel = 2(¼) = 0.5 inch = 13 mm

To meet criteria (1), (2), (3), and (4), the gravel shown as F_2 on figure 6-24 was selected.

(j) *Toe Drains and Drainage Trenches.*—Toe drains are commonly installed along the downstream toes of dams in conjunction with horizontal drainage blankets in the position shown on figure 6-23. Beginning with smaller diameter drains laid along the abutment sections, the drains are progressively increased in size, and maximum diameter drains are placed across the canyon floor. The purpose of these drains is to collect the seepage discharging from the embankment and foundation and convey it to an outfall pipe that discharges either into the spillway or outlet works stilling basin or into the river channel below the dam. Pipes, rather than French drains, are used to ensure adequate capacity to carry seepage flows. Toe drains are also used on impervious foundations to ensure that any seepage that may come through the foundation or the embankment is collected and to ensure that enough of the ground water is kept below the surface to avoid unsightly boggy areas below the dam.

The toe drains pipes may be made of any material that has adequate durability and strength. Perforated or slotted pipe should be used instead of pipe laid with open joints. The drainpipes should be placed in trenches at a sufficient depth to ensure effective interception of the seepage flow. The minimum depth of the trench is normally about 4 feet; the maximum depth is that required to maintain a reasonably uniform gradient although the ground surface may undulate. The bottom width of the trench is 3 to 4 feet, depending on the size of the drainpipe. The minimum pipe diameter recommended for small dams is 6 inches; however, diameters up to 18 inches may be required for long reaches at flat gradients. Manholes should be provided at a spacing that allows adequate access for inspection and maintenance. The pipe should be located such that access for repairs does not adversely affect the embankment. The drainpipe should be surrounded by a properly designed filter to prevent clogging of the drains by inwash of fine material or piping of foundation material into the drainage system. Two-layer filters are often required; the layer in contact with the pipe must have particles large enough that material will not enter or clog the perforations in the pipe.

The filter in contact with the toe drain must satisfy criterion (3) of section 6.10(i). This criterion requires that the D_{85} size of the filter be equal to or greater than twice the size of the maximum opening in the pipe. The other design criteria ((1), (2), and (4)) that the filters must satisfy are given in section 6.10(i). Figure 6-25 shows typical toe drain installation details used in most Bureau of Reclamation dams. Figure 6-26 shows construction of the toe drain at Calamus Dam in Nebraska.

Drainage trenches are normally used when pervious foundations are overlaid by a thin impervious layer. A drainage trench is simply an excavated trench backfilled with permeable material that penetrates the impervious layer and relieves the uplift

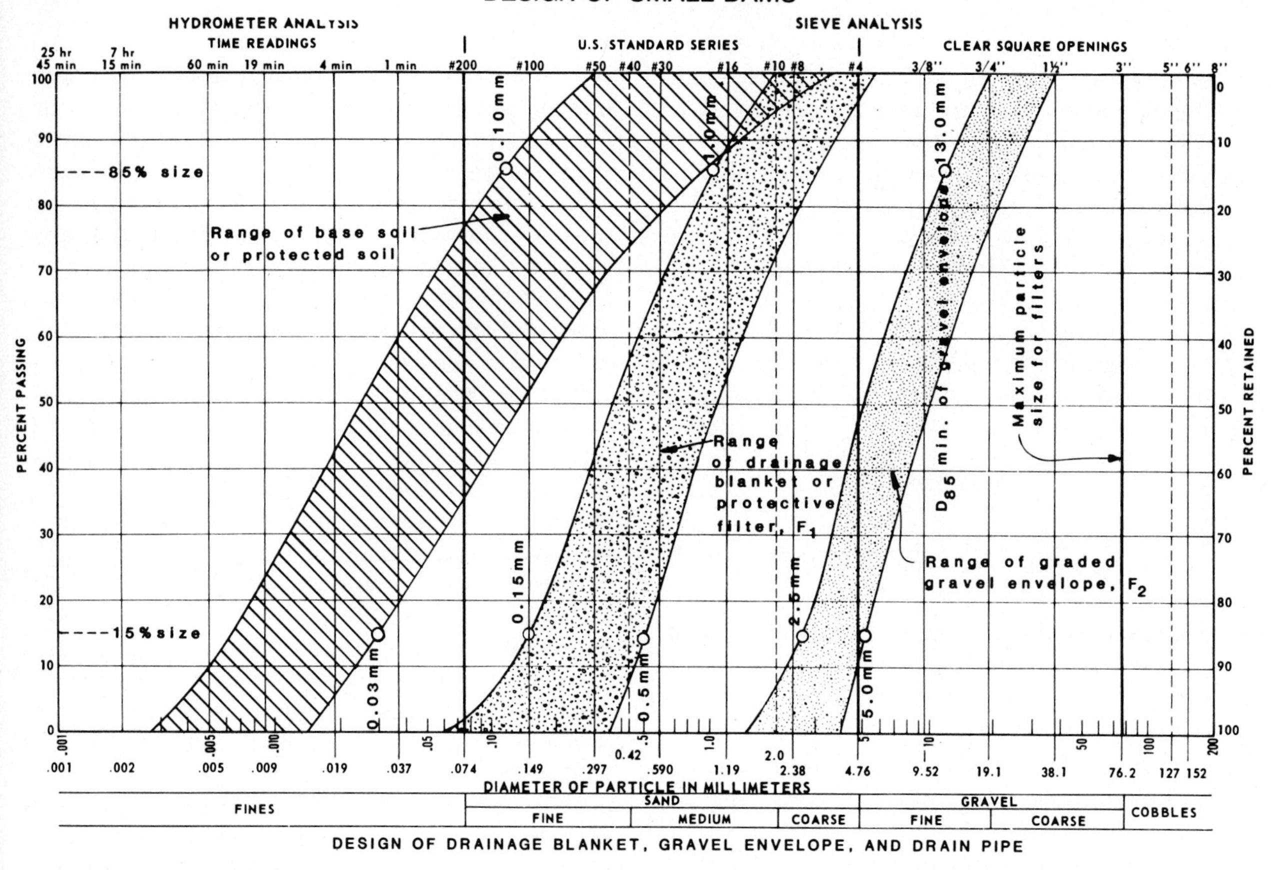

FOR DRAINAGE BLANKET, F_1

$5D_{15}\,\text{base} \leq D_{15}F_1 \leq 5D_{85}\,\text{base}$

$5 \times 0.03\,\text{mm} \leq D_{15}F_1 \leq 5 \times 0.10\,\text{mm}$

$0.15\,\text{mm} \leq D_{15}F_1 \leq 0.50\,\text{mm}$

$1.5 \leq Cu$ (coeficient of uniformity) ≤ 8

$Cu = \frac{D60}{D10} = \frac{0.45\,\text{mm}}{0.12\,\text{mm}} = 4$

$1.5 \leq 4 \leq 8$, ok

FOR GRAVEL ENVELOPE, F_2

$5D_{15}F_1 \leq D_{15}F_2 \leq 5D_{85}F_1$

$5 \times 0.5\,\text{mm} \leq D_{15}F_2 \leq 5 \times 1.0\,\text{mm}$

$2.5\,\text{mm} \leq D_{15}F_2 \leq 5\,\text{mm}$

$1.5 \leq Cu \leq 8$

$Cu = \frac{D60}{D10} = \frac{6.5}{2.3} = 3$

$1.5 \leq 3 \leq 8$, ok

FOR DRAIN PIPE WITH 1/4-inch SLOTS

$D_{85}F_2 > 2\times$ slot width or ϕ of perforation

$D_{85}F_2 > 2 \times \frac{1}{4}\,\text{in.} \times 25.4\,\text{mm/in.}$

$D_{85}F_2 > 13\,\text{mm}$

SEGREGATION:

Maximum size filter < 3in.

Figure 6-24.—Typical filter design. 103–D–1828.

pressures in the underlying pervious stratum. Drainpipes are generally installed in the bottom of the trench, and material satisfying the filter criteria ((1), (2), (3), and (4)) of section 6.10(i) is used as backfill.

A drainage trench usually is not effective if the underlying pervious foundation is stratified because it will relieve uplift pressures only in the uppermost pervious stratum. More effective drainage of stratified foundations can be accomplished by pressure-relief wells.

(k) *Pressure-Relief Wells.*—For many low dams on pervious foundations overlain by an impervious stratum, the thickness of the top impervious layer precludes piping, either of the blowout or internal-erosion type. Theoretically, piping occurs when the fluid (uplift) pressure at some level in the foundation near the downstream toe reaches the pressure exerted by the combined weight of soil and water above it. For the usual condition of tailwater at the ground surface, the uplift pressure (in feet of water) at the point in question equals the depth, d, of the point below ground plus the reservoir pressure head minus the head lost in seepage through the foundation to that point. The pressure exerted by the weight of soil and water above this point is the saturated unit weight of the soil times the depth to the point. If the thickness of the impervious layer is equal to the reservoir head, h, the uplift pressure beneath the layer cannot exceed the weight of the layer. This is so because the saturated weight of soil equals approximately twice the weight of water, and for $h = d$:

$$(2\gamma_{\omega})\,(d)(1) = (h + d)\gamma_{\omega} \tag{3}$$

or pressure exerted by saturated weight equals uplift pressure.

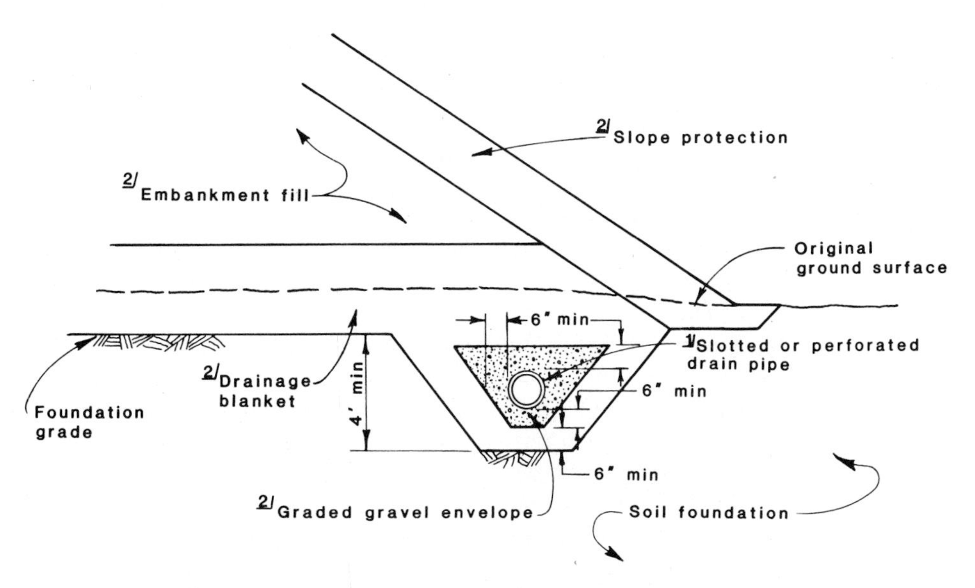

[1] There are many suitable drain pipes on the market. The requirements are adequate durability and strength. Pipe laid with open joints should not be used. Slots or perforations should meet criteria given in section 6.10(i).

[2] Should meet filter criteria, given in section 6.10(i), with adjacent material.

Figure 6-25.—Typical toe drain installation. 103–D–1829.

Figure 6-26.—Toe drain construction at Calamus Dam, Nebraska. P801–D–81041.

Actually, there is always appreciable loss of reservoir head because of resistance of the soil to seepage; hence, the value of h in the right side of equation (3) is too large, and the uplift pressure will be smaller than the pressure exerted by the overlying weight. Therefore, if the thickness of the top impervious stratum is equal to the reservoir head, it may be considered that an appreciable safety factor against piping is assured. In this situation, no further treatment of the foundation is required. However, if the thickness of the top impervious stratum is less than the reservoir head, some preventive treatment is recommended. If the top impervious stratum is less than h, but is too thick for treatment by drainage trenches, or if the pervious foundation is stratified, pressure-relief wells are required.

The primary requirements for a pressure-relief well system are:

(1) The wells should extend deep enough into the pervious foundation underlying the impervious top layer so that the combined thickness of the impervious layer and drained material is sufficient to provide stability against underlying unrelieved pressures. Depths of wells equal to the height of the dam are usually satisfactory.
(2) The wells must be spaced to intercept the seepage and reduce the uplift pressures between wells to acceptable limits.
(3) The wells must offer little resistance to the infiltration of seepage and the discharge thereof.
(4) The wells must be designed so that they will not become ineffective as a result of clogging or corrosion.

The Corps of Engineers has conducted extensive research programs on the design and installation of relief wells. The results of these studies have been published in a number of excellent papers [32, 33, 34, 35]. The reader is advised to consult these references for theoretical design methods.

Well spacing usually must be based on judgment because of the lack of detailed information regarding the foundations of small dams. This is an acceptable procedure provided plans are made to install additional wells after the dam is constructed at the first sign of excessive pressures. When the pervious strata have high rates of permeability, there will be more water at the downstream toe of the dam than when the permeability rates are lower. Suggested well spacing is approximately 25 feet for the most pervious foundations and 100 feet for less pervious foundations.

Experiments have shown that, in general, the well diameter should not be less than 6 inches, so that there will be little head loss for infiltrating seepage. It is recommended that a minimum thickness of 6 inches of filter, which meets the criteria previously established (sec. 6.10(i)), be provided between the well screens and the foundation, and that the ratio of the D_{85} size of the filter to the screen opening be greater than 2.0.

Examples of pressure-relief wells are shown on figure 6-27. Figure 6-27(A) shows the type of pressure-relief well used by the Bureau of Reclamation to reduce seepage pressures at Red Willow Dam in Nebraska. The 4-inch stainless steel well screen is surrounded by a minimum of 6 inches of filter material and sealed at the top with an impervious clay-silt mixture to prevent water from rising along the outside of the pipe. The 42-inch precast concrete pipe inspection well allows easy examination of the well and adequate working space for any maintenance required. The relief water is dissipated through the 8-inch outflow pipe to a collector drain along the downstream toe of the dam.

Figure 6-27(B) shows a pressure-relief well developed by the Corps of Engineers [34, 35] for use in alluvium adjacent to Mississippi River levees. The well consists of a wood screen, wood riser pipe, gravel filter, sand backfill, and a concrete backfill seal near the ground surface. Today, a stainless steel, plastic, or fiberglass riser and screen would be used instead of wood, but the figure adequately illustrates the components of a relief well. The inside diameter of the riser and screen is 8 inches and the screen slots are 3/16 inch wide and 3¼ inches long; the bottom of the pipe is closed with a wood plug. Heavily galvanized, 6-gauge winding wire at 3-inch spacings was used to band the pipe. A reverse rotary method of drilling the holes was used. This method is excellent for installing these wells because the material is removed through a suction pipe, which helps prevent sealing of the pervious strata. The walls of the hole are supported by hydrostatic forces acting against a thin film of fine-grained soil on the walls, created by maintaining a head of water in the hole several feet above the ground-water table. Additional information con-

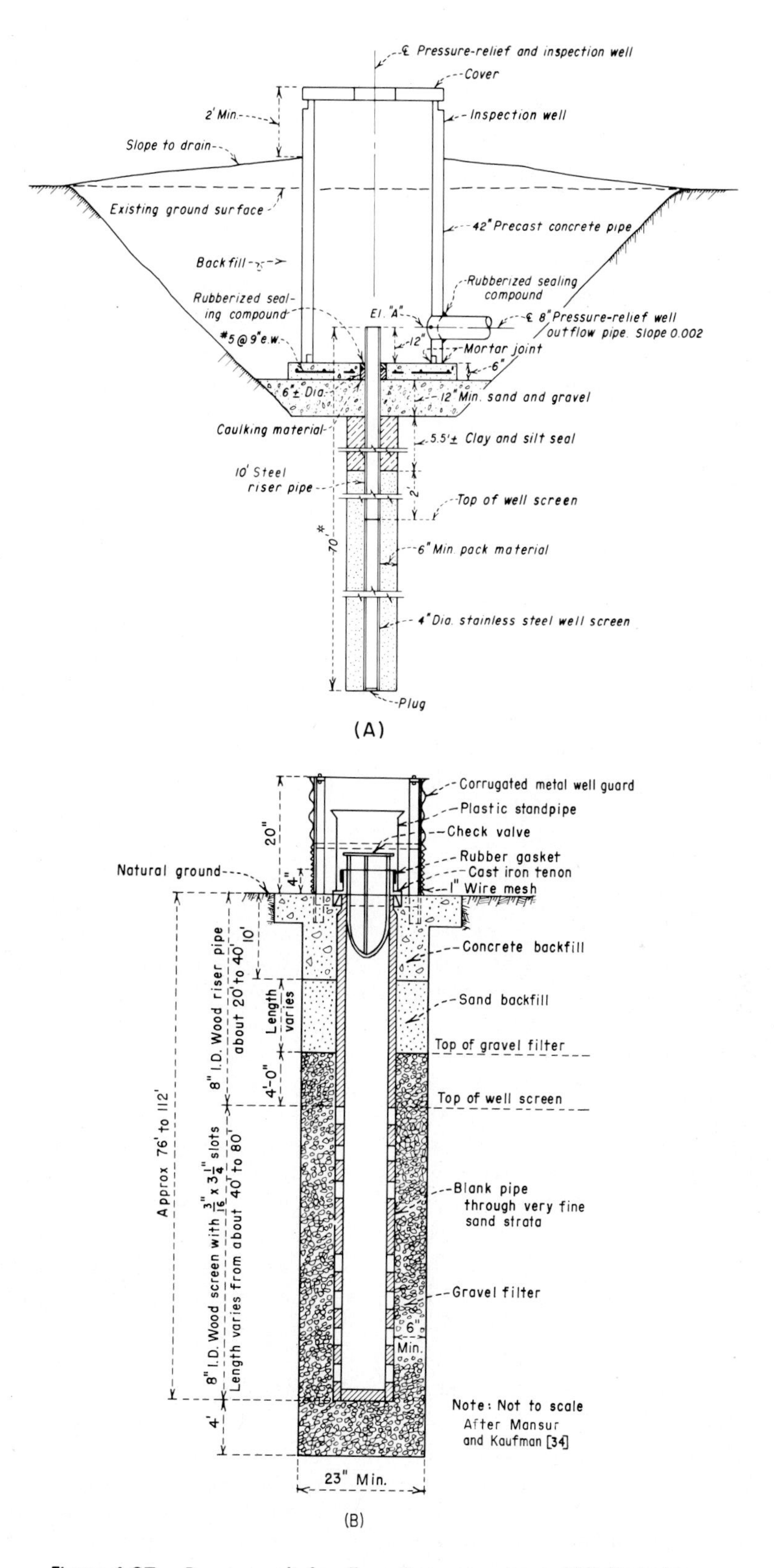

Figure 6-27.—Pressure-relief wells and appurtenances. 288–D–2485.

cerning well construction procedure is contained in [35].

Another method of installing a pressure-relief well requires lowering a casing of appropriate size to the required depth and washing out the soil inside the casing. The assembled well pipe, consisting of the screen and riser, is lowered in the casing and properly aligned. The filter is then placed in 6- to 8-inch layers and the casing withdrawn a like amount. This process is repeated until the filter is several feet above the top of the screen section. Above this point, impervious backfill or concrete is placed to prevent leakage along the outside of the pipe. After installation, the wells should be cleaned out and pumped or surged to remove any fine soil immediately adjacent. Pressure-relief wells should be inspected periodically and cleaned by surging, if necessary.

Relief wells, like other drainage systems, have some limitations. Too great a volume of seepage may require an excessive number of wells. In such cases, upstream impervious blanketing of the areas, which allows reservoir water to enter the pervious layers, may be used to reduce the amount of seepage.

The design and installation of pressure-relief wells demands specialized knowledge, skill, and the highest quality of construction inspection to ensure satisfactory performance. These wells also require postconstruction supervision and maintenance. Therefore, the need to use pressure relief wells should be carefully considered. The use of a pressure relief well system should be compared with the adequacy of simpler, more maintenance-free systems before deciding to use them.

6.11. *Designs for Sand and Gravel Foundations.*—(a) *General.*—Criteria (b) for the design of earthfill dams, presented in section 6.5, requires that the flow of seepage through the foundation and abutments be controlled so that no internal erosion occurs and there is no sloughing in the area where the seepage emerges. This criterion also requires that the amount of water lost through seepage be controlled so that it does not interfere with planned project functions. Section 6.6 discusses the basis used for designing foundations for small dams, which requires a generalization of the nature of the foundation in lieu of detailed explorations and the establishment of less theoretical design procedures than those used for major structures. Section 6.6 also cautions against the use of these design procedures for unusual conditions where procedures based largely on judgment and experience are not appropriate.

The purpose of this section is to show the application of methods of foundation treatment to specific instances. For purposes of discussion, pervious foundations are divided into the following cases:

Case 1: Exposed pervious foundations

Case 2: Covered pervious foundations—the pervious foundation is overlain by an impervious layer that may vary in thickness from a few feet to hundreds of feet.

In both of these cases, the pervious foundation may be relatively homogeneous, or it may be strongly stratified with less pervious layers so that the horizontal permeability will be many times greater than the vertical permeability. Stratification will influence selection of the appropriate foundation treatment method.

The treatment of Case 2: covered pervious foundations, is influenced by the thickness of the impervious top layer. The following three conditions, based upon the thickness of the top impervious layer, are considered:

(1) Impervious layer has a thickness of 3 feet or less: It should be assumed that the layer will be largely ineffective as a blanket in preventing seepage because thin surface strata usually lack the density required for impermeability and because they commonly have a large number of openings through them. There also exists the possibility that construction operations near the dam may penetrate the layer or that, while filling the reservoir, unequalized hydrostatic pressure on the surface of the blanket may puncture it. Therefore, a very thin impervious top layer such as this is considered to have little effect on the imperviousness of the foundation. Drainage trenches or pressure-relief wells near the downstream toe may be necessary to penetrate continuous layers and relieve uplift pressure.

(2) Impervious layer has a thickness greater than 3 feet but less than the reservoir head: This type of foundation condition is usually treated by using drainage trenches or pressure-relief wells near the downstream toe to penetrate the impervious layer and relieve the uplift pressures. In the upstream reservoir areas near the dam, the natural blan-

keting of the impervious layer may reduce seepage. If this is relied upon, the adequacy of the natural blanket should be carefully evaluated.

(3) Impervious layer thickness is greater than the reservoir head: It can be assumed here that there will be no major problems involved so far as seepage or seepage forces are concerned. This is demonstrated by equation (3) in section 6.10(k).

The treatment of impervious foundations of silt and clay is discussed in section 6.12.

(b) *Case 1: Exposed Pervious Foundations (Shallow Depth).*—The foundation treatment for an exposed pervious foundation of shallow[2] depth is shown on figure 6-28(A). A cutoff trench excavated to the impervious stratum, called a positive cutoff, should always be used because it is the most "positive" means of avoiding excessive seepage losses and piping. If the stratum is rock, grouting may be required to control the seepage. A horizontal drainage blanket is not necessary if the shallow pervious foundation can act as a filter and provide adequate drainage capacity. For example, if the downstream portion of the embankment is sand and gravel similar in gradation to the foundation, the horizontal drainage blanket shown on figure 6-28(A) may not be necessary. Horizontal drainage blankets meeting filter requirements are generally used when the following conditions exist:

(1) The embankment is homogeneous or the downstream shell is rockfill.
(2) The perviousness of the foundation is questionable.
(3) The possibility of piping exists, either from the embankment into the foundation or from the foundation into the downstream zone of the embankment.
(4) The foundation is stratified.

A filter may also be necessary against the downstream slope of the cutoff trench and impervious zone to prevent piping.

If the downstream portion of the embankment is rockfill, a horizontal drainage blanket should be used to prevent piping from the foundation. It should extend from the downstream slope of the dam to the impervious zone, as shown on figure 6-28(A). If the embankment is homogeneous, a horizontal drainage blanket should be provided because it ensures that the seepage line (phreatic line) through the embankment will be drawn down and the stability of the section increased; however, the blanket need not extend upstream closer to the centerline of the dam than a distance of $Z + 5$ feet. Section 6.18(d) discusses the extent of the filter required for a homogeneous embankment. Toe drains should be installed to carry away the excess seepage and to keep the downstream toe of the dam dry.

If a shallow foundation is stratified, similar to that shown on figure 6-29, a positive cutoff trench should be constructed. Horizontal drainage blankets are beneficial for stratified foundations, especially if the top layer is impervious or of doubtful permeability. As stated above, grouting may be required if the base stratum is rock of high permeability. Deeply stratified foundations are discussed in section 6.11(d).

When conditions such as lack of impervious material, short construction seasons, wet climates, and high dewatering costs prevent the use of a trench-type cutoff, other methods of constructing an impermeable barrier may be used. These methods include sheet piling, alluvial grouting, cement-bound or jet-grouted curtain cutoffs, a concrete cutoff wall, and a slurry trench. If one of these methods is used, an experienced dam designer should be consulted.

(c) *Case 1: Exposed Pervious Foundations (Intermediate Depth).*—A foundation is considered to be of intermediate depth when the distance to the impervious layer is too great for a cutoff trench, but can be economically reached by another type of positive cutoff. Whether or not a positive cutoff is economical depends heavily on three items:

(1) The effect of underseepage on the stability of the embankment
(2) The economic value of the water lost by underseepage
(3) Whether or not treatment of the foundation as if it were a Case 1 (exposed pervious foundation of great depth) (sec. 6.11(d)) is more economical

If it is decided that treatment as an intermediate depth foundation is required, the following methods of constructing a positive cutoff are available:

- Sheet piling
- Cement-bound or jet-grouted curtain cutoff
- Slurry trench
- Alluvial grouting
- Concrete cutoff wall

[2]The term shallow usually implies a depth approximately equal to or less than the height of the dam. This informal definition breaks down when dam heights exceed about 50 feet.

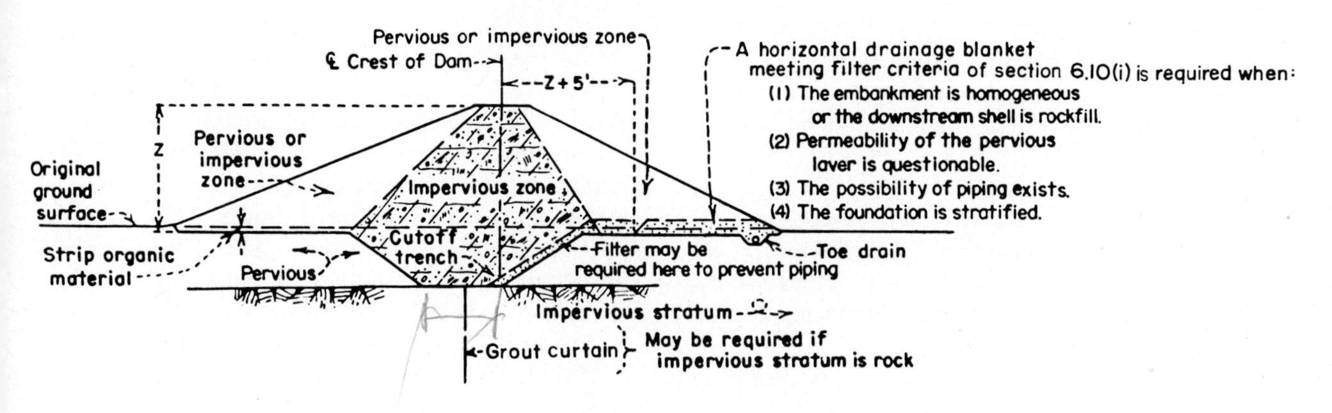

(A) SHALLOW PERVIOUS FOUNDATION

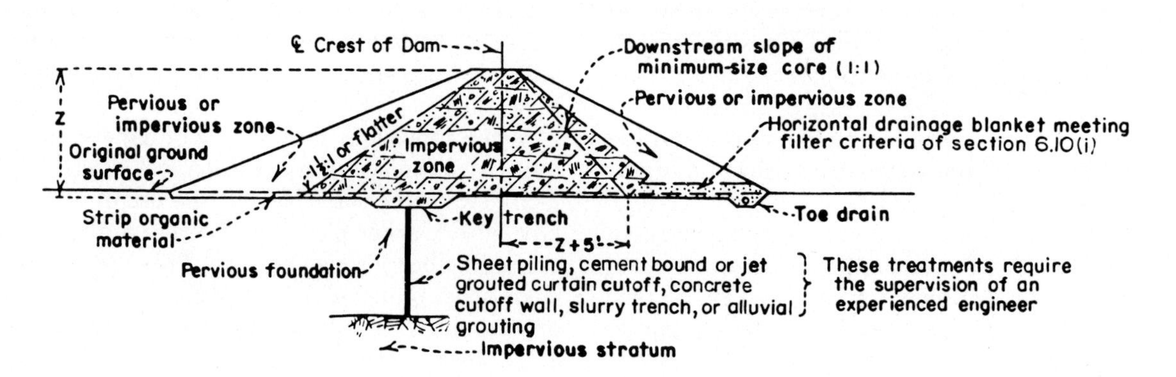

(B) INTERMEDIATE DEPTH OF PERVIOUS FOUNDATION

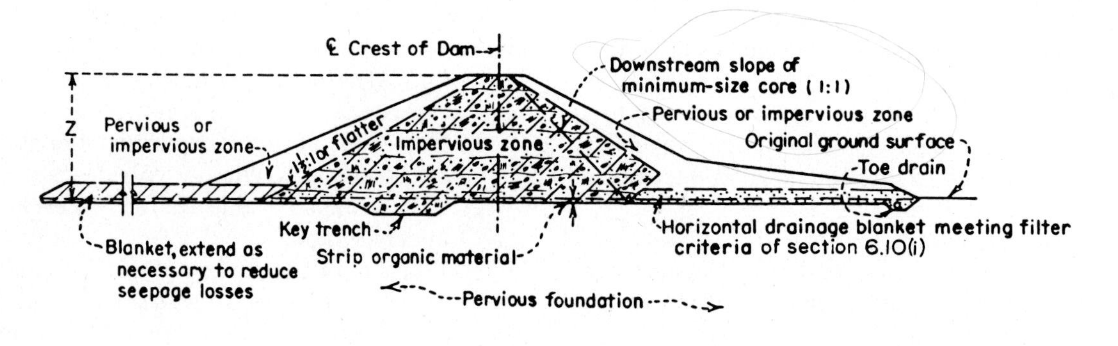

(C) DEEP PERVIOUS FOUNDATION

NOTE: Filter criteria given in section 6.10(i) applies between the impervious zone and any downsteam zone or a properly designed filter must be provided on (A),(B) and (C).

Figure 6-28.—Treatment of Case 1: exposed pervious foundations. 288-D-2486.

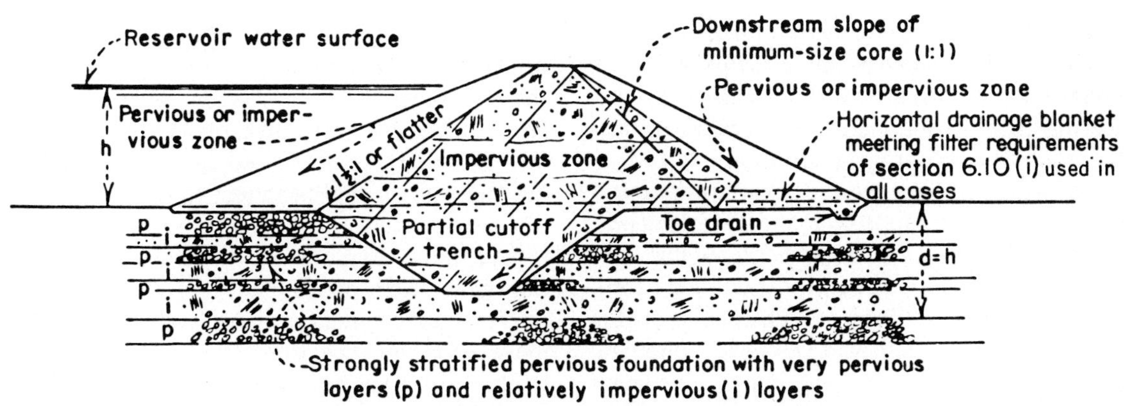

Figure 6-29.—Treatment of stratified foundations. 288–D–2487.

If one of these methods is used, an experienced engineer should supervise the design and construction of the entire dam. Minimum core B, for zoned dams on deep pervious foundations (see fig. 6-43), is the smallest impervious core recommended with this type of foundation treatment. Treatment of the intermediate depth foundation is shown on figure 6-28(B). As noted in section 6.11(b), these treatments may also be required when excessively wet climates, short construction seasons, shortages of impervious material for upstream blanket construction, etc., prevent the use of a positive cutoff trench.

(d) *Case 1: Exposed Pervious Foundations (Great Depth)*.—The problem in dealing with deep pervious foundations is to determine the ratio of horizontal to vertical permeability. If this can be done, an accurate flow net can be constructed, correct seepage quantities determined, and appropriate drainage measures taken. Because this ratio is difficult to determine, general assumptions must be made regarding the homogeneity of the pervious layer. Contingency plans must be made in case the horizontal permeability is much greater than expected or the foundation contains thin layers whose permeability is much greater than the average.

The general treatment for a pervious foundation that is too deep to permit a positive cutoff is shown on figure 6-28(C). The upstream blanket is provided to lengthen the seepage path and reduce the total quantity of seepage to acceptable limits. If an upstream pervious zone is used in the embankment, the blanket should extend beneath this zone so that it forms a continuation of the impervious core.

The smallest impervious zone recommended for use with zoned embankments on deep pervious foundations is minimum core B, shown on figure 6-43. The key trench is used to intercept any critical areas of the foundation and should be located upstream from the centerline of the crest of the dam.

To avoid foundation stability problems caused by seepage, an adequate thickness of pervious or impervious material must be maintained over the pervious foundation across the valley floor. Suggested dimensions for the length and cover requirements for the downstream section are shown on figure 6-23. Several sections should be taken along the centerline of the embankment to ensure that adequate material is provided for the most critical section.

If a homogeneous section is used, a horizontal drainage blanket is needed to handle seepage from the foundation and to reduce the height of the phreatic line in the embankment. A horizontal drainage blanket should also be used with a downstream pervious zone when the possibility of piping from the foundation exists. The drainage blanket should meet the filter criteria presented in section 6.10(i).

Toe drains are used to collect seepage, convey it to the downstream channel, and prevent wet areas at the downstream toe.

If the permeability is great enough to cause extensive seepage, ponding, or sand boils at the downstream toe, then drainage trenches, pressure-relief wells, extension of the downstream toe of the dam, or blanketing the downstream area with pervious fill meeting filter criteria given in section 6.10(i) may be required to control the situation.

In deep stratified foundations, a different treatment is required. This type of foundation consists of alternating layers of relatively pervious and impervious material and is generally treated by constructing a partial cutoff trench. The depth of the partial cutoff must be such that the total combined depth of the cutoff trench and the impervious layer upon which it rests is not less than the reservoir head. Typical embankment and foundation treatment for stratified foundations is shown on figure 6-29. On this figure, d must be equal to or greater than h. (Note that d is the depth to the uppermost pervious layer that is not cut off. It is not the depth of the partial cutoff trench.) If this requirement is met, the foundation should be stable against seepage pressures that may exist in the uppermost pervious layer that is not cut off (see eq. (3)).

A horizontal drainage blanket meeting filter requirements should be used with stratified foundations in case the downstream embankment zone is impervious or if piping requirements are not met by an overlying pervious layer. Toe drains should also be used. Additional drainage measures, such as the use of pressure-relief wells, may be required if high uplift pressures exist below the downstream toe and are not detected until reservoir filling.

(e) *Case 2: Covered Pervious Foundations.*—In the case of pervious foundation covered by an impervious layer, the type of treatment depends on the thickness and imperviousness of the layer covering the pervious zone and on the permeability of the underlying pervious layer.

If the overlying layer is equal to or less than a few feet thick (say 3 ft), its effect is generally ignored because of thickness variations near the damsite and the possibility of a puncture during construction of the dam or a blowout after filling. In this case, the foundation should be designed as a Case 1: exposed pervious foundation, either shallow (sec. 6.11(b)) or deep (sec. 6.11(d)).

An overlying impervious layer having a thickness greater than 3 feet and less than the hydraulic head may be assumed to act as an upstream impervious blanket if the thickness, continuity, impervious qualities, and upstream distance of the natural deposit have been carefully checked. It is usually necessary to compact the impervious layer with a heavy roller. If it is not possible to adequately evaluate the suitability of the upstream covering, it should be assumed that the natural blanket is not extensive enough or impermeable enough to prevent seepage or cause substantial head loss to the water entering the pervious layer. Provisions should be made to relieve uplift pressures at the downstream toe and to remove the seepage.

If the underlying pervious layer is relatively homogeneous and the top impervious layer is relatively thin, the top layer should be completely penetrated by a drainage trench, as shown on figure 6-30. This will relieve the uplift pressures that develop beneath the impervious layer. Additional drainage trenches may be required after construction if excessive uplift pressures still exist or if seepage quantities are large. When the overlying impervious layer is too deep to penetrate economically with a drainage trench, pressure-relief wells (sec. 6.10(k)) should be used along the downstream toe, as shown on figure 6-30(B). The correct spacing of relief wells is difficult to determine, primarily because of the inaccuracy in estimating the permeability of the strata. Wells are usually spaced from 50 to 100 feet apart for the initial design, and then additional wells are installed if postconstruction seepage analysis requires them.

When the dam embankment is homogeneous or when the downstream zone has questionable permeability, a horizontal drainage blanket is constructed as shown on figure 6-30. This is done to (1) lower the height of the seepage line through the embankment, (2) provide adequate embankment drainage, and (3) eliminate piping from the embankment. The blankets should extend from the downstream toe to within a distance of $Z + 5$ feet from the centerline.

Stratified foundations should be treated as discussed in sections 6.11(b) and (c) and as shown on figure 6-29.

(f) *Summary of Pervious Foundation Treatments.*—Table 6-2 is a summary of recommended treatments for various pervious foundation conditions. Foundations are normally considered as either shallow or deep because these are by far the most common conditions encountered. However, if the foundation is determined to be of intermediate depth, special construction methods are required that should be supervised by an experienced engineer. Intermediate depth foundations are discussed

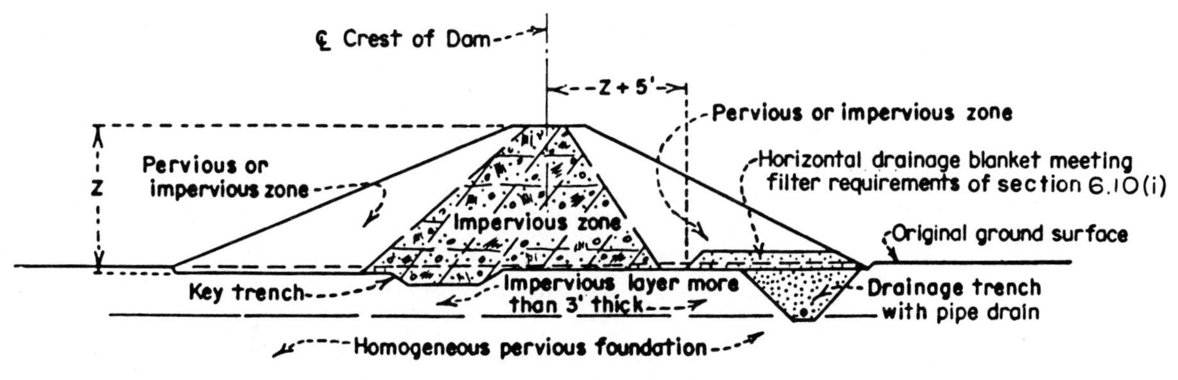

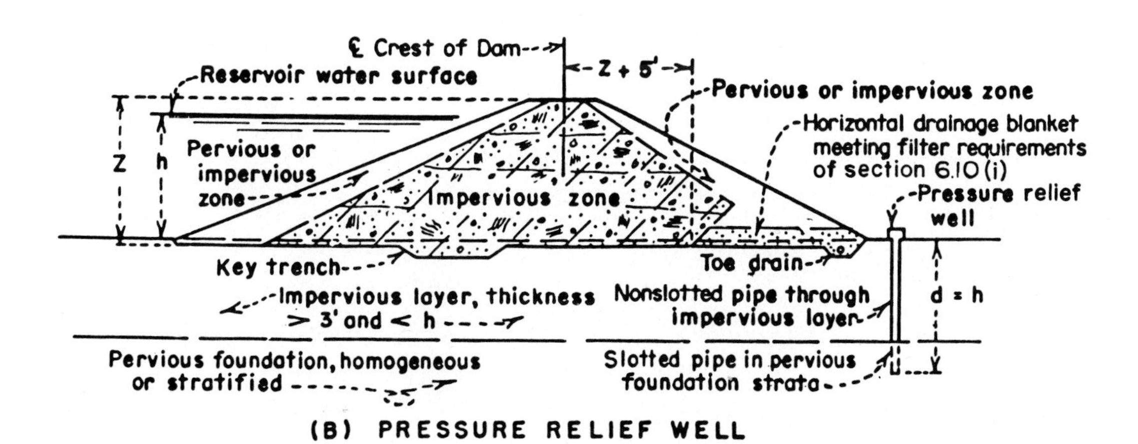

NOTE: Filter criteria given in section 6.10(i) applies between the impervious zone and any downstream zone or a properly designed filter must be provided on both (A) and (B).

Figure 6-30.—Treatment of Case 2: covered previous foundations. With overlying impervious layer of thickness more than 3 feet but less than the reservoir head. 288–D–2488.

in section 6.11(c). The treatments of shallow and deep foundations, both exposed and covered, are discussed in detail in sections 6.11(d) and (e).

6.12. *Methods of Treating Silt and Clay Foundations.*—(a) *General.*—Foundations of fine-grained soils are usually impermeable enough to preclude the necessity of providing design features for underseepage and piping. However, as discussed previously, inclined and horizontal filter-drainage blankets provide good protection against unknown geologic conditions, cracking, dispersive soils, and design and construction defects. Purely homogeneous dams are no longer recommended except for the most unimportant structures. Filter-drainage blankets should meet the criteria in section 6.10(i). The main problem with these foundations is stability. In addition to the obvious danger of bearing failure of foundations of saturated silts and clays, the designs must take into account the effect of foundation saturation of the dam and of appurtenant works by the reservoir.

Methods of foundation treatment are based on the soil type, the location of the water table, and the density of the soil. For saturated foundations of fine-grained soils (including sands containing sufficient fines to make the material impervious), the standard penetration test described in section 5.32(b) provides an approximate measure of the density or relative consistency. This test cannot be relied on, however, in fine-grained soils above the water table, especially very dry soils whose resistance to penetration is high although their unit

Table 6-2.—Treatment of pervious foundations.

Figure	Thickness of overlying impervious layer	Total depth of foundation	Condition of pervious material	Primary device for control of seepage	Additional requirements (other than stripping)
Case 1: Exposed pervious foundations					
6-28(A)	None	Shallow	Homogeneous	Positive cutoff trench	Toe drain Horizontal drainage blanket meeting filter requirements may be required Grouting may be required
6-28(C)	None	Deep	Homogeneous	Upstream impervious blanket	Large core Horizontal drainage blanket meeting filter requirements may be required Key trench Toe drain
Case 2: Covered pervious foundations					
6-28(A)	≤3 ft	Shallow	Homogeneous	Treat as Case 1: exposed pervious foundation (shallow)	
6-28(C)	≤3 ft	Deep	Homogeneous	Treat as Case 1: exposed pervious foundation (deep)	
6-28(A)	>3 ft, <reservoir head	Shallow	Homogeneous	Treat as Case 1: exposed pervious foundation (shallow)	
6-30(A) or (B)	>3 ft, <reservoir head	Deep	Homogeneous	Drainage trench or pressure-relief wells Impervious upstream layer	Key trench Compaction of the upstream layer
	>reservoir	No treatment required as a pervious foundation			
Stratified foundations					
6-28(A)	Not important	Shallow	Stratified	Positive cutoff trench	Horizontal drainage blanket meeting filter requirements Toe drain Grouting may be required
6-29	Not important	Deep	Stratified	Partial cutoff trench	Horizontal drainage blanket meeting filter requirements Toe drain Pressure-relief wells may be required

weight is low. In these soils, the unit weight can be determined by inplace unit weight tests described in section 5.47.

(b) *Saturated Foundations.*—When the foundation of an earthfill dam consists of saturated fine-grained soils or saturated impervious sands, their ability to resist the shear stresses imposed by the weight of the embankment may be determined by their soil group classification and their relative consistency. Soils that have never been subjected to geologic loads greater than the existing overburden are "normally" consolidated. These soils are much weaker than strata that have been consolidated by hundreds or thousands of feet of ice or soil, which have since been removed. Old lake deposits that have experienced cycles of drying and submergence often exhibit the characteristics of preconsolidated soil as a result of the capillary forces associated with the shrinkage phenomenon. Soils that have been preconsolidated are recognized by their large resistance to penetration, which is usually more than 20 blows per foot; they provide satisfactory foundations for small dams. On the other hand, the presence of soft, unconsolidated silts and clays represented by a penetration resistance of less than four blows per foot indicates the need for special sampling and testing techniques and requires the advice of specialists. By identifying the soil and determining its resistance to penetration, the standard penetration test can be used to delimit the saturated foundations that can be designed by the approximate methods used in this text and to provide approximate design values.

For cohesionless soils, the relative density D_d, which equals $(e_{max} - e)/(e_{max} - e_{min})$ (see sec. 5.49(f)), is known to be related to the strength of the material. For saturated cohesive soils, a similar property, the relative consistency, C_r, is also related to strength. C_r is equal to $(LL - w)/(LL - PL) = (e_{LL} - e_w)/(e_{LL} - e_{PL})$. At water contents equal to their liquid limits ($C_r = 0$), the cohesion at the liquid limit, C_{LL}, of all remolded saturated soils is about 0.2 lb/in², and the shear strength can be represented by Coulomb's equation:

$$s_{LL} = 0.2 \text{ lb/in}^2 + \overline{\sigma} \tan \phi_s \quad (4)$$

Tan ϕ_s can be obtained by consolidated-drained (slow) shear tests on saturated soil starting from the liquid-limit condition. Drainage is permitted in these tests and the pore water pressure is zero. Tan ϕ_s is about 0.5 even for fat clays.

At water contents equal to their plastic limits ($C_r = 1.0$), the cohesive strengths of saturated soils vary considerably depending on their types, and the shear strength can be represented by the equation:

$$s_{PL} = C_{PL} + \sigma \tan \phi \quad (5)$$

The value of tan ϕ on an effective stress basis can be obtained from triaxial shear tests on samples compacted at Proctor maximum dry density and optimum water content. This value is usually somewhat smaller than tan ϕ_s. The value of cohesion at the plastic limit, C_{PL}, can be obtained from similar tests made on soil compacted at optimum water content and then saturated. As explained in section 5.18(b), for these samples, the intercept of the ordinate with the tangent to the failure circle making an angle ϕ with the abscissa on the Mohr diagram (fig. 5-13) is designated C_{sat}. The water content corresponding to C_{sat} is usually close to the plastic limit for clayey soils; that is, C_r is near unity. By assuming a linear variation of cohesion with water content between the liquid and plastic limits,

$$C_{PL} = \frac{C_{sat} - 0.2}{C_r} + 0.2 \quad (6)$$

where C_r corresponds to C_{sat}.

Using this assumption, Coulomb's equation for shear strength, equation (10), for a saturated soil at any C_r may be written as follows:

$$s = C_{LL}(1 - C_r) + C_r C_{PL} + \overline{\sigma} \tan \phi \quad (7)$$

The last term ($\overline{\sigma}$ tan ϕ) in equation (7) represents the frictional portion of the shear resistance at any point of the potential surface of sliding in the foundation. For the condition of no drainage of the impervious foundation during construction of the embankment, $\overline{\sigma}$ remains constant. The cohesion portion of the equation is a function of C_r. Because C_r cannot increase without drainage, the shear strength of the foundation remains constant while the shear stresses imposed by the embankment increase, thus decreasing the factor of safety against sliding. The methods of treatment applicable to these conditions are (1) to remove the soils with low shear strength, (2) to provide drainage of the foundation to permit the increase of strength during construction, and (3) to reduce the magnitude of the average shear stress along the potential sliding surface by flattening the slopes of the embankment.

Removing soft foundation soils is sometimes practicable. Relatively thin layers of soft soils overlying firm material may be removed when the cost of excavation and refill is less than the combined cost of special investigations and the flatter embankment slopes required. In the preparation of relatively firm foundations, pockets of material substantially more compressible or lower in strength than the average are usually removed. See appendix E for a discussion of foundation stripping.

In several instances vertical drains have been used to facilitate consolidation so that the strength of the foundation would increase as it was loaded by an embankment. This treatment is applicable primarily to nonhydraulic structures such as highway embankments. Special studies and precautions are required when these drains are used under an earthfill dam, and this device is not recommended for small dams within the scope of this text.

The most practicable solution for foundations of saturated fine-grained soils is flattening the embankment slopes. This requires the critical sliding surface to lengthen, thereby decreasing the average shear stress along its path and increasing the factor of safety against sliding. The selection of design slopes is discussed in section 6.13.

(c) *Relatively Dry Foundations.*—Unsaturated impermeable soils are generally satisfactory for foundations of small dams because the presence of air in the soil voids permits appreciable volume change, increase of normal effective stress, and mobilization of frictional shear resistance without drainage of the pore fluid. That is, for a given void ratio, an impervious soil has greater bearing capacity in the unsaturated condition than in the saturated condition.

In addition, unsaturated soils exhibit the phenomenon of "apparent cohesion," which is the result of less than atmospheric capillary pressures in the water films surrounding the soil particles. The addition of water to these soils first reduces and then destroys the apparent cohesion as saturation is reached. Most soils are sufficiently dense so that reduction of apparent cohesions by saturation causes no serious difficulties in foundations of small dams.

However, an important group of soils have low density and are subject to large settlements when saturated by the reservoir, although these soils have high dry strength in the natural state. If proper measures are not taken to control excessive settlement, failure of the dam may occur (1) by differential settlement that causes rupture of the impervious portion of the embankment and thus allows breaching of the dam by the reservoir, or (2) by foundation settlement resulting in a reduction of freeboard and overtopping of the dam, although the impervious portion of the embankment deforms without rupturing.

These low-density soils are typified by but not restricted to loess, a very loose, wind-deposited soil that covers vast areas of several continents, including North America. True loess has never been saturated and is generally composed of uniform, silt-sized particles bonded together with a small amount of clay. When its water content is low, loess exhibits sufficient cohesive strength to support 100-foot-high earthfills without large settlement. A substantial increase in water content, however, greatly reduces the cohesion and may result in collapse of the loose structure of the soil under the loading imposed by dams only 20 feet high.

The experiences of the Bureau of Reclamation with the construction of dams on loess in the Missouri River Basin are, in part, described in a publication of the American Society of Civil Engineers [36] and in a Bureau monograph [37]. Although the properties of other loessial soils may differ from those found in the Missouri River Basin, a discussion of the Bureau's experience may serve as a guide in other areas.

The typical undisturbed Missouri River Basin loess is a tan to light brown, unstratified, lightweight soil containing many root holes and voids. It consists mostly of silt-sized particles bonded together by a relatively small proportion of clay. The apperance of the loess and the range of gradation are shown on figure 6-31; 75 percent of the samples investigated were silty loess, 20 percent were clayey loess, and the remainder were sandy loess. The density of the loess ranged from a low of 65 lb/ft^3 in unusual cases to a high of 100 lb/ft^3 in areas that had been wetted and consolidated or where the loess had been eroded and redeposited.

With natural water contents of about 10 percent, the supporting capacity of the loess is high regardless of its unit weight. There is little reduction in bearing capacity for water contents up to about 15 percent. However, further increase in moisture is

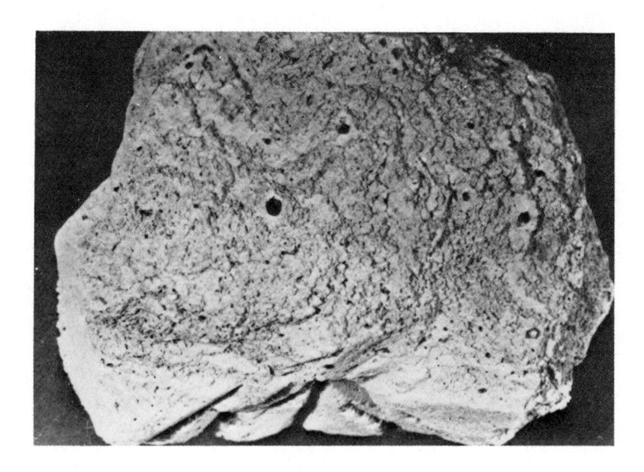

(a) Undisturbed loess.

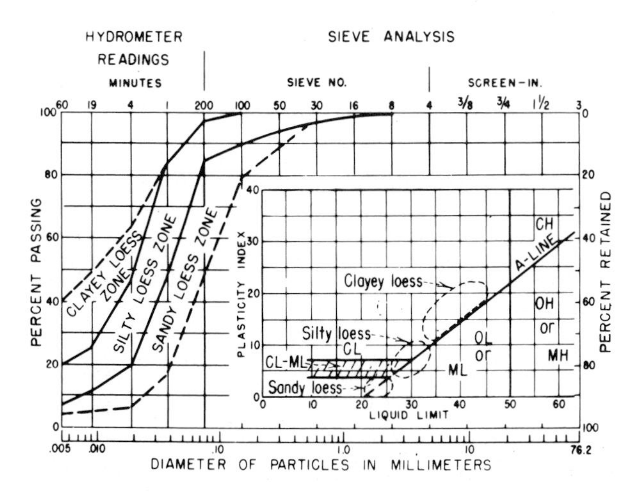

(b) Range of gradation and Atterberg limits. From [36].

Figure 6-31.—Appearance and identification of Missouri River Basin loess. 288-D-2489.

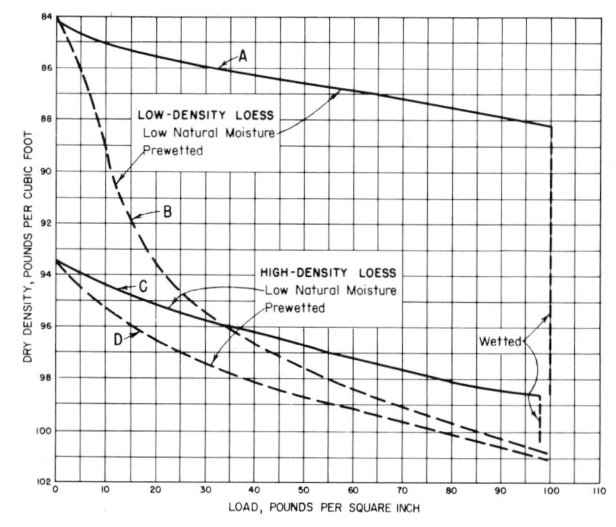

Figure 6-32.—Typical compression curves for Missouri River Basin loess. 288-D-2490.

accompanied by an appreciable reduction in supporting capacity for low-unit weight loess, but has little effect on high-unit weight loess.

Several typical laboratory compression curves for loess test specimens have been plotted on figure 6-32 as load versus dry unit weight. These curves demonstrate the effect of inplace unit weight and of wetting on compression characteristics. The low-unit weight loess that was not prewet (curve A) compressed 5 percent under a load roughly equivalent to a 100-foot-high earthfill dam (100 lb/in^2 on fig. 6-32); it compressed an additional 10.5 percent without an increase in load when saturated. The difference between the compression characteristics of low-density loess at the natural moisture and at the prewet conditions indicates that dangerous settlement would result even for a 20-foot-high dam. Figure 6-32 also demonstrates (curve C) that very little postconstruction foundation settlement will occur for a dam constructed on a high unit weight loess with low natural moisture. Hence, the determination of the inplace unit weight and water content of the loess is of paramount importance in planning its use as a foundation for a dam.

The required treatment of dry, low-unit weight foundations is dictated by the compression characteristics of the soil. These characteristics are best determined by laboratory tests on undisturbed samples at their natural water content to determine whether the postconstruction settlement caused by saturation will be significant (curve A of fig. 6-32) or minor (curve C of fig. 6-32). For small dams, the empirical criteria given in section 6.13(b) can be used in lieu of laboratory tests.

If the foundation of a small dam is not subject to appreciable postconstruction settlement when saturated, little foundation preparation is required. The foundation should be stripped to remove organic material, a key trench (sec. 6.6) should be provided, and a toe drain (sec. 6.10(j)) should be installed to prevent saturation of the foundation at the downstream toe of the dam. Consideration should be given to providing horizontal and inclined filter-drainage blankets, as shown on figure 6-5(C).

If the foundation is subject to appreciable

postconstruction settlement when saturated, measures should be taken to minimize the amount.

If the low-unit weight soil exists in a top stratum, it may be economical to excavate this material and replace it with compacted embankment. If the layer is too thick for economical replacement or if its removal would destroy a natural blanket over a pervious foundation, measures should be taken to ensure that foundation consolidation is achieved during construction.

Curve B of figure 6-32 demonstrates that low-unit weight loess, if prewet, compresses during loading. Hence, postconstruction settlement of low-unit weight loess caused by saturation by the reservoir can be avoided by prewetting the foundation to obtain compression during construction of the embankment. This method cannot be used unless drainage is ensured by an underlying pervious layer or the deposit is so thick that vertical drainage may occur during compression of the upper portion of the deposit.

Because of its structure and root holes, the vertical permeability of a loess deposit is much higher than its horizontal permeability. The Bureau of Reclamation has successfully consolidated foundations of low-unit weight loess during construction by prewetting the foundation, with the result that no difficulty has been experienced with postconstruction settlement upon filling of the reservoir. Sample specifications for the performance of this work are included in appendix G.

6.13. *Designs for Silt and Clay Foundations.*—
(a) *Saturated Foundations.*—The designs of small dams on saturated fine-grained soils given in this section are based on the results of numerous stability analyses using various heights of dam and different sets of slopes for the stabilizing fills for each height. Average values of embankment properties were used and the required shearing strength for a safety factor of 1.5 was determined assuming that no drainage occurred in the foundation during construction.

This construction condition was found to be more severe for stability than either the steady-state seepage condition or the sudden drawdown condition. Furthermore, the type of material used for embankment and stabilizing fills was found to have no appreciable effect on the stability, which was a function of the soil type and the relative consistency of the saturated foundation. The slopes of stabilizing fills were determined by finding the various combinations of cohesion and tan ϕ of the foundation soil needed to provide a 1.5 safety factor for the critical condition using the Swedish slip circle method.

Figure 6-33 shows a typical section design for a small dam on a saturated fine-grained foundation.

Table 6-3 lists the recommended slopes for stabilizing fills for saturated foundations typical of the groups of the Unified Soil Classification System for different degrees of consistency. Blows per foot of the standard penetration test are used to approximate relative consistency: Less than 4 blows corresponds to C_r = 0.50, 4 to 10 blows corresponds to C_r = 0.5 to 0.75, 11 to 20 blows corresponds to C_r = 0.75 to 1.0, and more than 20 blows corresponds to C_r = 1.0. Recommendations are not made for slopes of soils averaging less than four blows per foot within a foundation depth equal to the height of the dam. These very soft foundations require special sampling and testing methods that are beyond the scope of this text.

Example

Required:
Slope of stabilizing fill for a safety factor of approximately 1.5.

Given:
Type of dam = either homogeneous or zoned.
Foundation blow count from field tests = 15.
Saturated foundation material = CL.
Height of dam = 40 feet.

Solution:
From table 6-3 opposite stiff consistency and CL, read 4.5:1 under dam height of 40 feet.

(b) *Relatively Dry Foundations.*—The design of even very small dams on deposits of dry foundations of low density must take into account the possibility of settlement upon saturation by the reservoir. Because the penetration test results on these foundations may be grossly misleading, natural water content and inplace unit weight tests should be made in portions of the deposit above the water table for comparison with laboratory compaction values on the same soils. Section 5.47 describes the procedure for determining inplace unit weight and water content, and section 5.49 describes the laboratory compaction test. The rapid method of compaction control described in test designation USBR 7240 of the Bureau's *Earth Manual* [11] can also be used to determine the percentage of laboratory

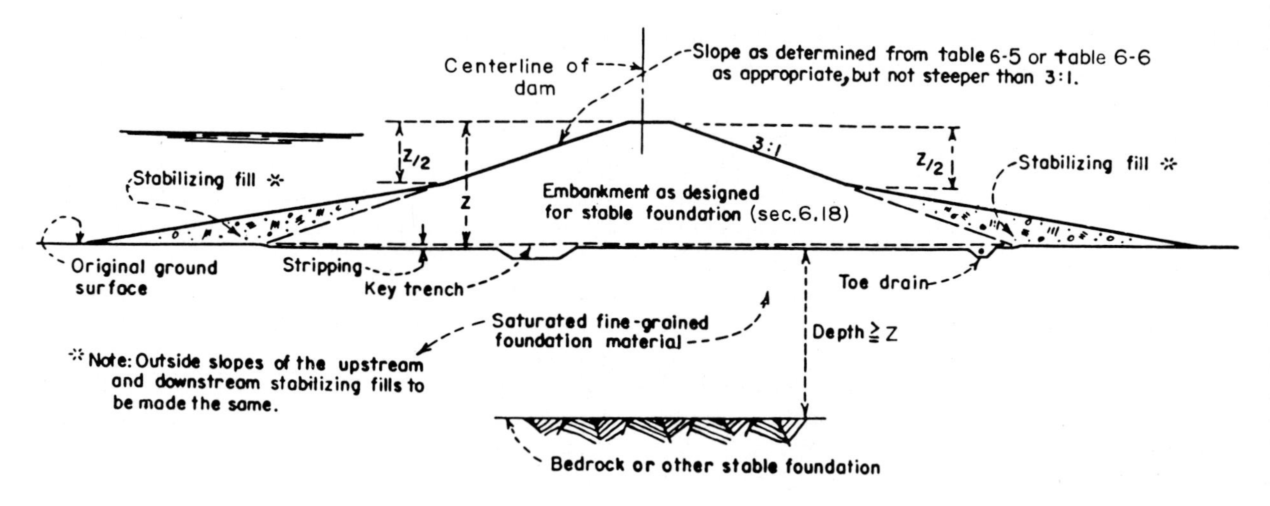

Figure 6-33.—Design of dam on saturated fine-grained foundation. 288–D–2491.

Table 6-3.—Recommended slopes of stabilizing fills for dams on saturated silt and clay foundations.[1]

Consistency	Average number of blows per foot[2] within foundation depth equal to height of dam	Foundation soil group[3]	Slopes of stabilizing fills for various heights of dams: 50 ft	40 ft	30 ft	20 ft	10 ft
Soft	<4	Special soils tests and analyses required					
Medium	4 to 10	SM	4.5:1	4:1	3:1	3:1	3:1
		SC	6:1	5:1	4:1	3:1	3:1
		ML	6:1	5:1	4:1	3:1	3:1
		CL	6.5:1	5:1	4:1	3:1	3:1
		MH	7:1	5.5:1	4.5:1	3.5:1	3:1
		CH	13:1	10:1	7:1	4:1	3:1
Stiff	11 to 20	SM	4:1	3.5:1	3:1	3:1	3:1
		SC	5.5:1	4.5:1	3.5:1	3:1	3:1
		ML	5.5:1	4.5:1	3.5:1	3:1	3:1
		CL	6:1	4.5:1	3.5:1	3:1	3:1
		MH	6.5:1	5:1	4:1	3:1	3:1
		CH	11:1	9:1	6:1	3:1	3:1
Hard	>20	SM	3.5:1	3:1	3:1	3:1	3:1
		SC	5:1	4:1	3:1	3:1	3:1
		ML	5:1	4:1	3.5:1	3:1	3:1
		CL	5:1	4:1	3:1	3:1	3:1
		MH	5.5:1	4:1	3:1	3:1	3:1
		CH	10:1	8:1	5.5:1	3:1	3:1

[1]Stabilizing fills are not needed when embankment slopes required by tables 6-5 and 6-6 are equal to or flatter than the slope listed above.
[2]Standard penetration test (sec. 5.32 (b)).
[3]Unified Soil Classification System (sec. 5.17).

maximum dry density in the natural soil and the approximate difference between optimum water content and inplace water content.

Analysis of the results of 112 tests made by the Bureau of Reclamation on samples of undisturbed foundation soils indicates that density, water content, and applied load influence the susceptibility of a soil to large settlement upon saturation. The following soil groups were represented in the tests: ML, 51 percent; CL, 23 percent; ML-CL 13 percent; SM, 8 percent; and MH, 5 percent.

For loads within the range applicable for small dams, an empirical relationship between D (inplace dry unit weight divided by Proctor maximum dry unit weight) and $w_o - w$ (optimum water content minus inplace water content) is shown on figure 6-34. This relationship differentiates foundation soils requiring treatment from those that do not. There were 70 tests in the former category and 42 in the latter. For foundations of unsaturated soils that fall into the "no treatment required" category on the figure, only the usual foundation stripping and key trench are required. Soils with inplace water content considerably greater than w_o should be checked to determine the degree of saturation. If they are over 95 percent saturated, they should be considered as saturated and designed accordingly.

In the absence of Proctor test facilities and when only the natural density and liquid limit are available, another criterion, shown on figure 6-35, provides an indication of the susceptibility of the soil to collapse on saturation [38]. Figure 6-35 is primarily applicable to loose, fine-grained soils. The theory is based on soil unit weight. If the unit weight is low enough that void spaces are larger than required to hold the liquid-limit moisture content, as shown for case I on figure 6-35, the soil can become wetted to above the liquid-limit consistency and settle from collapse of the soil skeleton. Conversely, if the unit weight is high enough so that the void space is less than required for the liquid-limit moisture, as shown for case III on figure 6-35, the soil will not collapse upon saturation, but will reach a plastic state. Therefore, liquid limits and inplace dry unit weights that plot above the line are indicative of soils susceptible to collapse. Points below the line are indicative of soils that would settle only in a normal manner caused by loading.

The foundation treatment at Medicine Creek Dam is typical of results achieved by preirrigation of a loess foundation. This structure is an earthfill

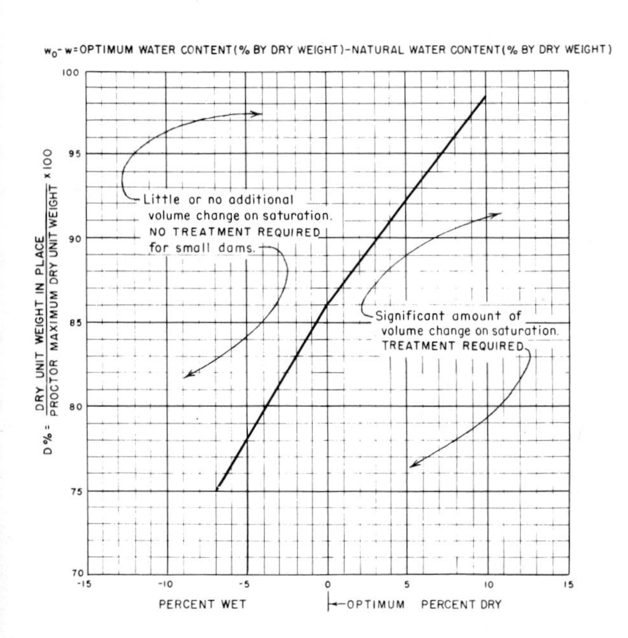

Figure 6-34.—Foundation design criteria for relatively dry fine-grained soils. 288-D-2492.

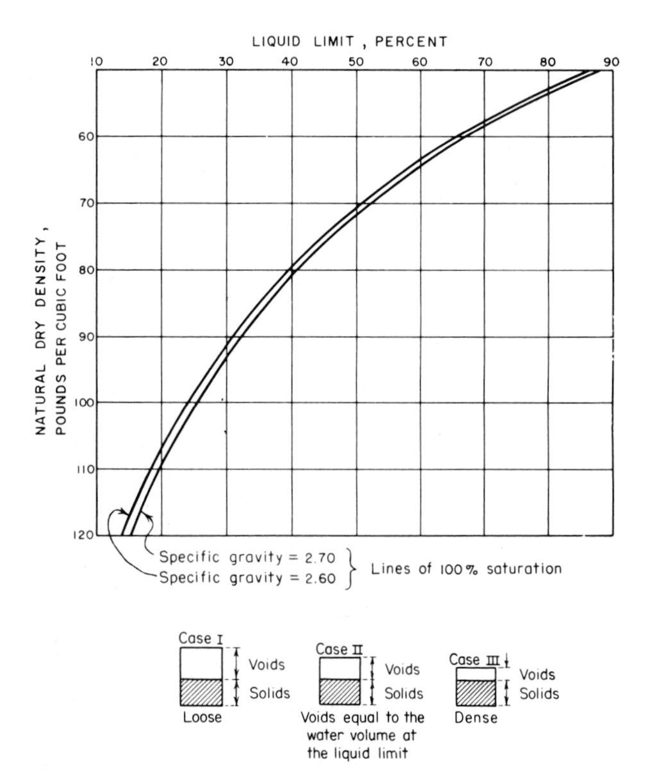

Figure 6-35.—Alternative foundation design criteria for relatively dry fine-grained soils. Adapted from Gibbs [37]. 288-D-2785.

dam located in south-central Nebraska in the center of the Missouri River Basin loess area. As shown on figure 6-36, dry low-unit weight loess occurred on the right abutment of this dam to maximum depths of 60 to 70 feet and an average depth of about 40 feet. Undisturbed samples were secured by sinking a test pit at a representative location to a depth of 50 feet. Table 6-4 summarizes partial results of laboratory tests on these samples. These tests indicated a possibility of dangerous postconstruction settlement upon saturation by the reservoir if the dam were constructed on the natural loess. Therefore, the foundation in this area was thoroughly wetted by ponding and sprinkling before fill construction. Figure 6-37 shows the dikes and ponds full of water; 33,000,000 gallons of water were used over a 2-month period to raise the average water content in the critical area to 28 percent.

Settlement measuring points throughout the ponded areas revealed that no settlement occurred from saturation alone. Baseplate apparatus was installed in the dam to permit measurement of foundation settlement in four locations as the fill was constructed (BP1 to BP4 inclusive, fig. 6-36). The

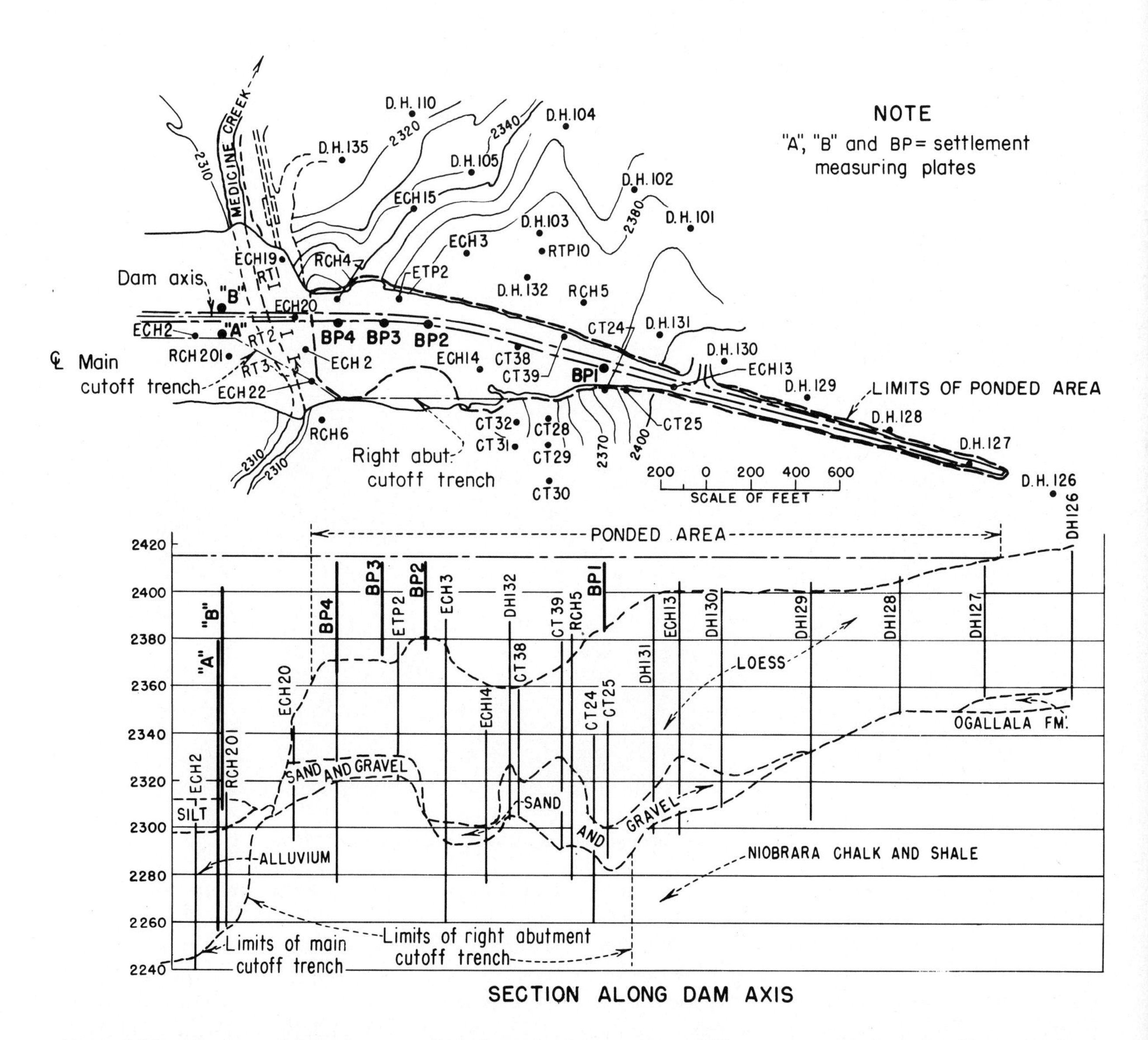

Figure 6-36.—Geology of right abutment of Medicine Creek Dam. An earthfill structure on Medicine Creek in Nebraska. 288–D–2493.

Table 6-4.—Properties of loess in Medicine Creek Dam foundation.

Approximate sample depth, ft	Natural water content, w, %	Average $w_o - w$[1]	Inplace dry unit weight, lb/ft^3	Average D, %[2]	Total load, (fill plus overburden), lb/in^2	Compression at total load, %	
						With natural moisture	After being wetted
5	8.8	7.4	79	75	25	8.4	10.9
17	9.7	6.5	77	74	33	1.3	9.1
19	9.6	6.6	81	77	34.5	1.0	3.9
50	6.6	8.7	92	83	55	1.5	6.5

[1] $w_o - w$ = optimum water content for Proctor maximum dry unit weight minus natural water content.

[2] $\%D = \dfrac{\text{inplace dry unit weight}}{\text{Proctor maximum dry unit weight}} \times 100.$

Figure 6-37.—Ponding on foundation of Medicine Creek Dam. 404–1227B.

foundation settlements recorded by the baseplate installations are shown on figure 6-38. Upon completion of the embankment in the fall of 1949, the apparatus indicated a foundation settlement of from 0.41 to 0.66 foot. By mid-1952, the measured foundation settlement ranged from a maximum of 2 feet at BP1 to 0.8 foot at BP4. There was virtually no further increase in the amount of settlement by mid-1954, when measurements were discontinued. The reservoir filled to elevation 2366.0 (normal water surface) in the spring of 1951, and remained close to that elevation during the period of measurement.

The amount of foundation settlement at Medicine Creek Dam was appreciable, although less than had been anticipated. The foundation consolidation treatment was successful, because, as shown on figure 6-38, a large portion of the settlement took place while the embankment was being constructed, and the subsequent settlement was a slow consolidation over a 2-year period, which allowed the dam embankment to undergo the deformation without distress.

D. EMBANKMENTS

6.14. *Fundamental Considerations.*—Essentially, designing an earthfill dam embankment primarily involves determining the cross section that, when constructed with the available materials, will fulfill its required function with adequate safety at a minimum cost. The designer of an earthfill dam cannot rely on the application of mathematical analyses or formulas to determine the required cross section to the same degree that one can for a concrete dam. Soils occur in infinite combinations of size gradation, composition, and corresponding variations in behavior under different conditions of saturation and loading. In addition, the stress-strain relationships in a soil embankment are very complex.

Considerable progress has been made in investigations and studies directed toward the development of methods that will afford a comprehensive analysis of embankment stability. These methods provide useful design tools, especially for major structures where the cost of detailed explorations and laboratory testing of available construction materials can be justified on the basis of savings achieved through precise design. Even so, present practice in determining the required cross section of an earthfill dam consists largely of designing to the slopes and characteristics of existing successful dams, making analytical and experimental studies for unusual conditions, and controlling closely the selection and placement of embankment materials. While some modifications are necessarily made in specific designs to adapt them to particular conditions, radical innovations are avoided and fundamental changes in design concepts are developed and adopted gradually through practical experience and trial.

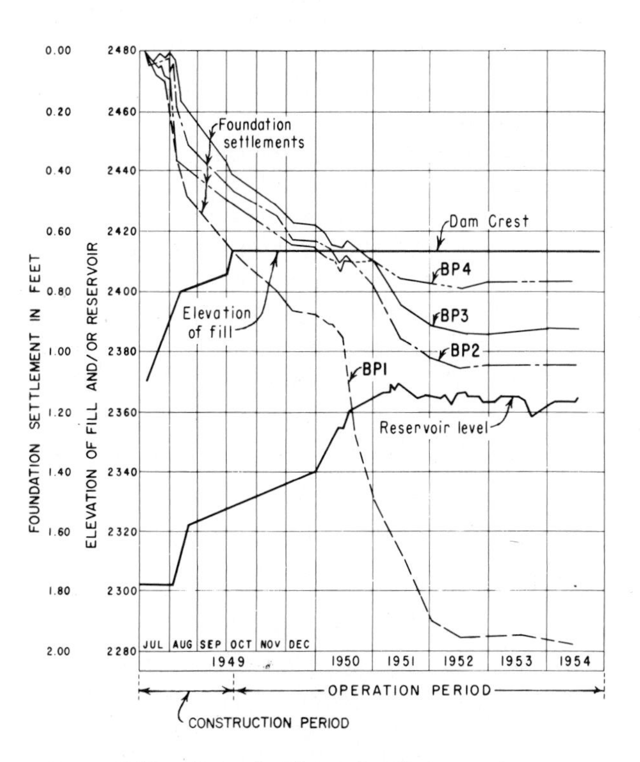

Figure 6-38.—Record of loess foundation settlement at Medicine Creek Dam. 288–D–2494.

Although the above practice may be criticized as being overly cautious and extravagant, no better method has been conclusively demonstrated. Where consideration is given to the possible loss of life, to the possibility of costly property damage, and to the waste of money incidental to the failure of a constructed dam, ample justification is provided for conservative procedures. For small dams, where the cost of explorations and laboratory testing of embankment materials for analytical studies together with the cost of the engineering constitutes an inordinate proportion of the total cost of the structure, the practice of designing on the basis of successful structures and past experience becomes even more appropriate.

The design criteria for earthfill dams are presented in section 6.5. In regard to the embankment, they require that the slopes of the embankment be stable under all conditions of construction and reservoir operation; that excessive stresses not be induced in the foundation; that seepage through the embankment be controlled; that the embankment be safe against overtopping; that the slopes be protected against erosion; and that the embankment be stable under appropriate seismic conditions. This part of the chapter is concerned with the slope stability of the embankment under both static and seismic conditions and with the control of seepage through the embankment. Embankment details concerning the crest, freeboard, slope protection, and surface drainage are discussed in part E of this chapter.

The stability of an embankment is determined by its ability to resist shear stresses, which can cause failure by inducing sliding along a shear surface.

Shear stresses result from externally applied loads, such as reservoir and earthquake loads, and from internal forces caused by the weight of the soil and the embankment slopes. The external and internal forces also produce compressive stresses normal to potential sliding surfaces. These compressive stresses contribute both to the shear strength of the soil and to the development of destabilizing pore water pressures.

Granular, or noncohesive, soils are more stable than cohesive soils because granular materials have a higher frictional resistance and because their greater permeability permits rapid dissipation of pore water pressures resulting from compressive forces. Accordingly, when other conditions permit, somewhat steeper slopes may be adopted for noncohesive soils. Embankments of homogeneous materials of relatively low permeability have slopes generally flatter than those used for zoned embankments, which have free-draining outer zones supporting inner zones of relatively impervious materials.

In brief, the design of an earthfill dam cross section is controlled by the physical properties of the materials available for construction, by the character of the foundation, by the construction methods specified, and by the degree of construction control anticipated.

6.15. *Pore Water Pressure.*—In 1936, Terzaghi [39] demonstrated that in impervious soils subjected to load, a total stress normal to any plane is composed of an effective stress and a fluid pressure. The concepts of plane surfaces and stresses at a point in soils are not identical with those of an ideal homogeneous isotropic material. The "plane" in soils is a rather wavy surface, touching the soil particles only at their contacts with one another, and the "point" of stress is a small region containing enough of the particles to obtain an average stress. With these qualifications, the total normal compressive stress, σ, along a plane in an earth structure can be computed:

$$\sigma = \overline{\sigma} + u \tag{8}$$

where u is pore water pressure, and $\overline{\sigma}$ is the effective normal compressive stress. From considerations of equilibrium [40], the formula for shear stress, τ, along the plane is:

$$\tau = \frac{\sigma_1 - \sigma_3}{2} \sin 2\theta \tag{9}$$

where:

σ_1 = total major principal stress,
σ_3 = total minor principal stress, and
θ = angle between the plane considered and the plane on which σ_1 acts.

It is apparent from equation (9) that the shear stress is the same whether σ_1 and σ_3 or their effective components, $\overline{\sigma_1}$ and $\overline{\sigma_3}$, are used.

The shear strength along a plane can be obtained from Coulomb's equation:

$$s = c' + (\sigma - u) \tan \phi \tag{10}$$

Equation (10) shows that the frictional portion of the resistance along a plane is reduced by the pore water pressure. This equation is discussed and the terms are defined in section 5.18(b).

Pore water pressures in compacted cohesive soils caused by compressive stresses occur in the sealed triaxial shear test in the laboratory and in the impervious zone of an embankment during construction. For the laboratory conditions, the relation between volume change and fluid pressure in a loaded soil mass consisting of solid particles, water, and air, can be derived by using Boyle's law for compressibility of air and Henry's law for solubility of air and water both at constant temperature. For a soil mass buried in an impervious fill where drainage is extremely slow because of the long path of percolation and the very small coefficient of permeability of the material, it is both conservative and reasonable, on the basis of field observations, to assume no drainage to estimate the magnitude of pore water pressure for design and control purposes [41]. The concept is that when the moist soil mass is loaded without permitting air or water to escape, part of the load causes the soil grains to deform elastically or to undergo nonelastic rearrangement, but without significant change in their solid volume. This part of the load is carried on the soil skeleton as effective stress. The remainder of the load is carried by stress in the air and water contained in the voids and is known as pore water pressure.

Analysis shows that the magnitude of pore water pressures from compressive forces depends on the compressibility of the compacted soil and on the amount of air it contains. For given conditions of compressibility and loading, the closer the compacted soil is to saturation, the higher the pore water pressure will be. This leads to the practice of controlling the moisture content of materials to increase the amount of air in the compacted soil. Bureau practice has been to reduce the moisture content below optimum for compaction at Proctor maximum unit weight in the construction of high earthfill dams. However, this procedure is neither necessary nor desirable for the construction of embankments less than 50 feet high. For such heights, compaction of cohesive soils at optimum moisture content and approximately Proctor maximum dry unit weight ensures enough air, even in the most compressible soils, to preclude the development of significant pore water pressures.

Placing the material at optimum moisture content instead of drier than optimum also increases the plasticity of the material and allows it to conform more readily to the shape of the foundation and abutments during postconstruction settlement. It also helps reduce the probability of tension cracks in the embankment.

For small confining loads, placing material drier than optimum is undesirable because it increases the possibility of:

- Low unit weight for the same compactive effort, as shown by the shape of the compaction curve (fig. 5-74)
- Greater permeability in the embankment core
- Excessive softening and settlement after saturation by the reservoir, resulting in possible cracking of the fill

On the other hand, the moisture content should not be appreciably greater than the optimum obtained at Proctor maximum dry unit weight because difficulties have been experienced with unstable fills when very wet soils are used, even in small dams.

The foregoing considerations result in the recommended practice of compacting cohesive soils in the cores of small dams close to their optimum moisture content at Proctor maximum dry unit weight.

6.16. *Seepage Through Embankments.*—The core, or water barrier portion, of an earthfill dam provides the resistance to seepage that contains the reservoir. Although soils vary greatly in permeability, as pointed out in section 5.18(c), even the tightest clays are porous and cannot prevent water from seeping through them.

The progress of percolation of reservoir water through the core depends on the constancy of the reservoir level, the magnitudes of permeability of the core material in the horizontal and vertical directions (anisotropy), the amount of remaining pore water pressures caused by compressive forces during construction, and time. Figure 6-39 shows the penetration of water into a core shortly after the first filling of the reservoir and the penetration when the steady-state seepage condition has finally been reached. The upper surface of seepage is called the phreatic (zero pressure) surface; in a cross section it is referred to as the phreatic line. Although the soil may be saturated by capillarity above this line, giving rise to a line of saturation, seepage is limited to the portion below the phreatic line.

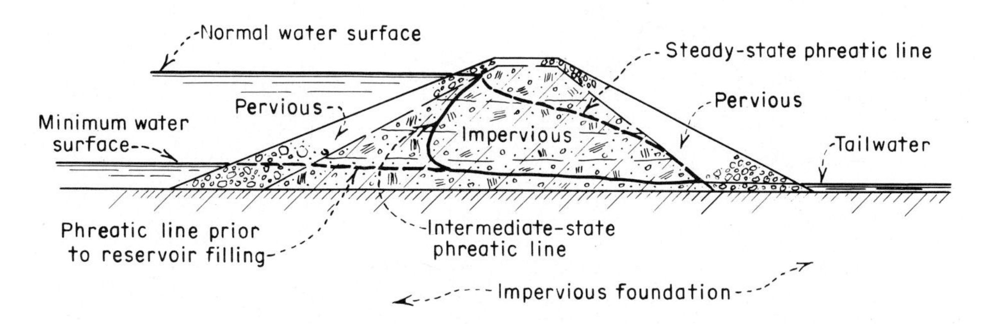

Figure 6-39.—Position of phreatic line in a zoned embankment. 288-D-2495.

The position of the phreatic line depends only on the geometry of the section and anisotropy of the soils. For soils with vastly different permeabilities but with the same ratio of horizontal to vertical permeability, the phreatic lines eventually will reach identical position. It will take much longer for the steady-state condition to be reached in clay than in sand for the same cross section, and the amount of water emerging at the downstream slope will, of course, be much greater for the more pervious material. The pore water pressures below the phreatic line reduce the shear strength of the soil mass in accordance with Coulomb's law, equation (10). The steady-state condition that involves the maximum saturation of the embankment is the most critical postconstruction condition for the stability of the downstream slope.

The most critical operating condition so far as the stability of the upstream slope is concerned is a rapid drawdown after a long period of high reservoir level. Figure 6-40 shows the effect of rapid drawdown on the pore water pressures measured in Alcova Dam, Wyoming. The reservoir water surface was lowered 120 feet in 40 days, an extremely rapid drawdown for a dam of this height. Figure 6-40(A) shows the phreatic line and equal-pressure lines under full reservoir conditions; the position of the phreatic line indicates that virtually steady-state conditions were present before drawdown. Figure 6-40(B) shows the pressures under drawdown conditions.

Figure 6-40 demonstrates that appreciable pore water pressures remain in an embankment after drawdown. If a dam is subject to rapid drawdown after long-term storage at high reservoir levels, special provisions for drainage should be made in the design. The upstream slope of an embankment with an appreciable upstream pervious zone usually is not critical for the rapid drawdown condition. Rapid drawdown may require a flatter slope of a homogeneous embankment than would otherwise be needed for stability.

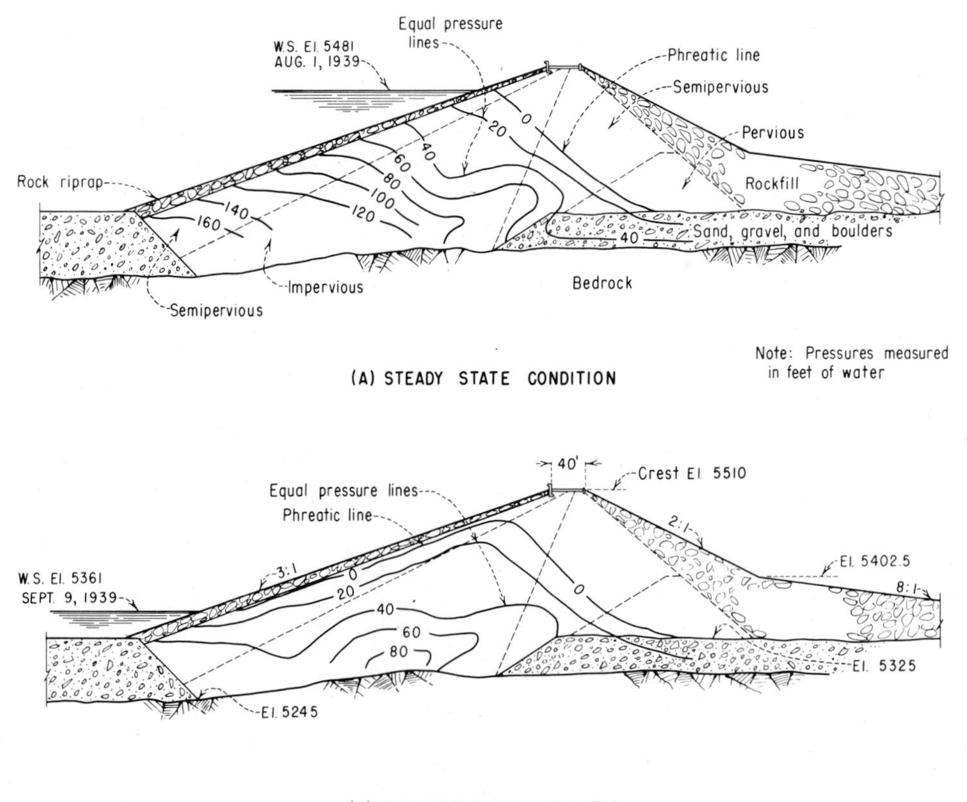

Figure 6-40.—Effect of rapid drawdown on pore pressures. Alcova Dam, an earthfill structure on the North Platte River in Wyoming. 288–D–2496.

The use of the flow net in determining the magnitude and distribution of seepage pressures in pervious foundations has been described previously (sec. 6.9(c)). The flow net can also be used to visualize the flow pattern of percolating water through embankments to estimate the magnitude and distribution of pressures from percolating water, both in the steady state and in the drawdown condition. Analytical methods of stability analyses used in the design of major structures require that such pore water pressures be determined quantitatively. Such a determination is not required for the design procedure given in this text.

6.17. *Stability Analyses.* —Various methods have been proposed for computing the stability of earthfill dams [6]. In general, these methods are based on the shear strength of the soil and certain assumptions with respect to the character of an embankment failure. The Swedish, or slip-circle, method, which supposes the surface of rupture to be a cylindrical surface, is a comparatively simple method of analyzing embankment stability. Although other more strictly mathematical solutions have been developed, the slip-circle method of stability analysis is generally adequate for small dams. In this method, the factor of safety against sliding is defined as the ratio of the average shear strength, as determined from equation (10), to the average shear stress determined by statics on a potential sliding surface. If there are weak lines or segments, such as weak foundation layers, failure surfaces involving these segments should be checked.

The force exerted by any segment within the slip circle is equal to the weight of the segment and acts vertically downward through its center of gravity. The components of this weight acting on a portion of the circle are the force normal to the arc and the force tangent to the arc, as determined by completing the force triangle with lines in the radial and tangential directions. Pore water pressures acting on the arc result in an uplift force, which reduces the normal component of the weight of the segment. Graphical means have been developed by May [42] to facilitate the solution.

The safety factor against sliding for an assumed circle is computed by the equation:

$$\text{Safety factor} = \frac{c'L + \tan \phi' (N - U)}{T} \quad (11)$$

where:

N = summation of normal forces along the arc,
U = summation of uplift forces caused by pore water pressure along the arc,
T = algebraic summation of tangential forces along the arc,
L = length of arc of slip circle,
c' = effective cohesion intercept, and
ϕ' = effective angle of internal friction.

Various centers and radii are used, and computations are repeated until the arc that gives the minimum safety factor is established.

To compute the safety factor by means of equation (11), it is necessary to establish the cohesion, c', and the angle of internal friction, ϕ', of the soil and the magnitude of pore water pressures for construction, steady-state, and drawdown conditions. Furthermore, the strength properties of the foundation must be determined where the overburden above bedrock is silt or clay, because experience has shown that the critical circle extends into the foundation in such cases. It is therefore apparent that this method of analysis is more suited to the design of major structures, where the cost of foundation exploration and laboratory tests of foundation and embankment materials to determine their average strength properties is justified because of the savings that may be achieved by the use of more precise slopes. The recommended designs for small earthfill dams given in this text are based on the Swedish slip-circle method, using average values of soil properties and experience for static conditions usually encountered in seismically inactive regions. These designs will result in adequate safety factors provided proper construction control is obtained. Construction control is discussed in appendix E of this manual. For an in-depth discussion on static stability analyses refer to USBR Design Standards No. 13, chapter 4.

With the availability of high-speed digital computers, it is now possible to use more mathematically complex solution procedures for slope stability analyses [43]. These procedures are not restricted to cylindrical slip surfaces, but can be applied to practically any kinematically admissible slip-surface geometry. One such method commonly used is the method of slices proposed by Spencer [44]. In this method, the slide mass is divided into a number of slices. The magnitude and orientation of forces acting on the interslice boundaries are considered, and the safety factor and interslice force inclination are obtained by satisfying the three equations of planar static equilibrium of each slice.

This procedure has been written into a computer program [45] for static and dynamic slope-stability analyses. This computer program is commonly used for slope-stability calculations.

6.18. *Embankment Design.*—(a) *Use of Materials from Structural Excavation.*—In the discussion of design criteria (sec. 6.5), it was pointed out that for minimum cost, the dam must be designed to make maximum use of the most economical materials available, including the materials excavated for the dam foundation, spillway, outlet works, canals, powerhouse, roadways, and other appurtenant structures. When the yardage from these sources constitutes an appreciable portion of the total embankment volume, it may strongly influence the design of the dam. Although these materials are often less desirable than soil from available borrow areas, economy requires that they be used to the maximum practicable extent. Available borrow areas and structural excavations must both be considered to arrive at a suitable design.

The portion of the cutoff trench excavation above the ground-water table may provide limited amounts of material for the impervious core of the dam. Appreciable quantities of sand and gravel are usually obtained in the dewatered portion of the trench from the strata intercepted. When sand and gravel occur in thick, clean beds, this material can be used in the outer zones of the dam. However, pockets or lenses of silt and clay and highly organic material may also be excavated with the cutoff trench. These materials contaminate the clean soils and result in wet mixtures of variable permeability and poor workability. Such mixtures should usually be wasted.

Excavation for the spillway provides both overburden soils and formation bedrock. In planning the use of these materials, the designer must recognize that moisture control, processing, and meeting special size requirements will add to the project cost. For this reason, material from spillway excavations is ordinarily used primarily in the main structural zones of dam embankments where special control of moisture and processing are not as critical.

Tunnel excavations can provide rockfill material for use in the pervious zones of the dam or can provide rock fines that may serve as a transition between the impervious core material and pervious zones.

The feasibility of using materials from structural excavations is influenced by the sequence of construction operations. The construction sequence is, in turn, influenced by the follwing items:

- Topography of the damsite
- Diversion requirements
- Hydrology of the watershed
- Seasonal climate changes
- Magnitude of required excavations

To use material from the spillway or cutoff trench in the embankments without having to stockpile and later rehandle large quantities of earth and rock, an adequate placing area must be available. The placing area is usually restricted early in the job; hence, the designer must decide whether to specify that spillway excavation be delayed until space is available for it, or to require extensive stockpiling, or to permit large quantities of material to be wasted. The amount of embankment space that can be provided during the early stages of construction depends in part on the diversion requirements and in part on the diversion plan that the contractor selects. Usually, the contractor is allowed considerable flexibility in the method of diversion; this adds to the designer's uncertainty in planning the use of materials from structutural excavations.

Zoned dams provide an opportunity to use structural excavation materials. This type of dam should be used whenever possible. The zoning of the embankment should be based on the most economical use of materials that can be devised; however, the zoning must be consistent with the requirements for stability discussed in section 6.17. For example, the use of rockfill sections can allow continual construction throughout the winter, thus effecting an early completion date. An important use of materials from structural excavation has been in portions of the embankment where the permeability and shear strength are not critical and where weight and bulk are the major requirements. The stabilizing fills required for dams on saturated fine-grained foundations, discussed in section 6.13 (fig. 6-33), are an illustration of this usage.

Areas within the dam into which such excavated material is placed are called random zones. Typical locations for these random zones are shown on figure 6-41.

Because estimates of the percentage of structural excavations usable within the embankment are subject to significant error, provision should be made to use variable zone boundaries to accommodate any excess or deficiency. In some cases, special laboratory tests or a test embankment may be required before determining the disposition of questionable material or selecting the dimensions of a random zone.

In formulating a design, the designer must estimate the percentage of structural excavation that will be suitable in the various zones of the embankment and the shrinkage and swell of the material involved. The designer must then integrate these estimated quantities with the required borrow area quantities to determine a final design that is both economical and has a reasonable constuction sequence. Often, several design schemes are required. The use of a materials distribution chart, such as that shown on figure 6-42, has been found helpful for integrating excavation quantities into the embankment section for determining the amounts of borrow material required for each zone

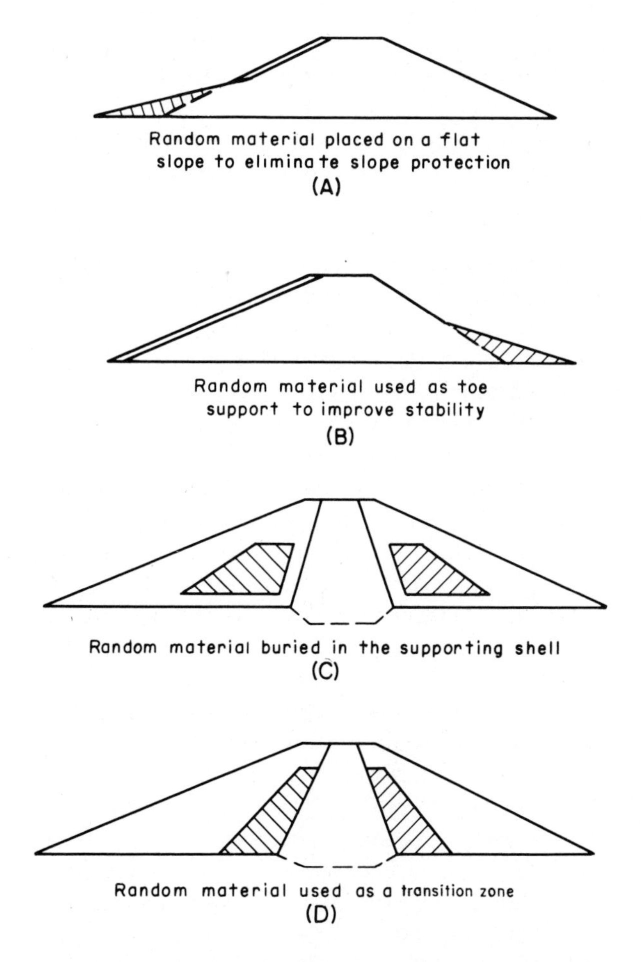

Figure 6-41.—Locations of random zones of fill materials within embankment sections. 288–D–2787.

and for visualizing the construction sequence. The chart shown is for the Bureau of Reclamation's San Justo Dike, the maximum section of which is shown on figure 6-87. In addition to showing the sources of all fill materials, the chart contains the assumptions used for shrinkage, swell, and yield on which specifications quantities are based.

(b) *Embankment Slopes, General.*—The design slopes of an embankment may vary significantly depending on the character of the materials available for construction, foundation conditions, and the height of the structure. The embankment slopes, as determined in this section, are the slopes required for stability of the embankment on a stable foundation. For stability against seepage forces, pervious foundations may require the addition of upstream blankets to reduce the amount of seepage or the addition of downstream inclined and horizontal filter-drainage blankets. Weak foundations may require the addition of stabilizing fills at either or both toes of the dam. The additional embankments needed because of pervious or weak foundations should be provided beyond the slopes determined herein as required for embankment stability. The following procedures should be used with simple, straightforward geologic conditions and trouble-free embankment materials. If more complicated conditions exist, the dam should be analyzed by an experienced embankment dam designer using appropriate analytical techniques.

The upstream slope may vary from 2:1 to as flat as 4:1 for stability; usually it is 2.5:1 or 3:1. Flat upstream slopes are sometimes used to eliminate expensive slope protection. A berm is often provided at an elevation slightly below the maximum drawdown of the reservoir water surface to form a base for the upstream slope protection, which need not be carried below this point. The upstream slope is often steepened above the elevation where water is stored; that is, in the surcharge range.

A storage dam subject to rapid drawdown of the reservoir should have an upstream zone with permeability sufficient to dissipate pore water pressures exerted outwardly in the upstream part of the dam. The rate of reservoir drawdown is important to the stability of the upstream part of the dam. For a method of designing free-draining upstream shells, refer to Cedergren [46]. Where only fine material of low permeability is available, such as that predominating in clays, it is necessary to provide a flat slope if rapid drawdown is a design requirement. Conversely, if free-draining sand and gravel are available to provide a superimposed weight for holding down the fine material of low permeability, a steeper slope may be used. The same result may be secured by using sound and durable rock from required excavations. In the latter case, a layer of sand and gravel or quarry fines must be placed between the superimposed rock and the surface of the impervious embankment to prevent damage and displacement from saturation and wave action.

Flood damage caused by the failure of the upstream face is unlikely. Such a failure can occur only during construction or after a rapid drawdown; in both cases, the reservoir should be virtually empty. The weight of water and seepage forces act as a stabilizing influence on the upstream face when the reservoir is full.

The usual downstream slopes for small earthfill dams are 2:1 where a downstream pervious zone is provided in the embankment, and 2.5:1 where the embankment is impervious. These slopes are stable for soil types commonly used when drainage is provided in the design, so that the downstream slope of the embankment does not become saturated by seepage.

The slopes of an earthfill dam depend on the type of dam (i.e., diaphragm, modified homogeneous, or zoned embankment) and on the nature of the materials for construction. Of special importance is the nature of the soil that will be used for construction of a modified homogeneous dam or of the core of a zoned dam. In the latter case, the relation of the size of the core to the size of the shell is also significant.

In this text, the slopes of the embankment are related to the classification of the soil to be used for construction, especially the impervious soils. The engineering properties of soils in the various classifications are shown in table 5-1. The slopes chosen are necessarily conservative and are recommended only for small earthfill dams within the scope of this text, as discussed in section 6.2.

(c) *Diaphragm Type.*—A diaphragm dam consists of a thin impervious water barrier used in conjuction with a large pervious zone. The diaphragm can be constructed of earth, asphalt, concrete, or metal. If the diaphragm is constructed of impervious earth material, it must have a horizontal thickness at least great enough to accommodate construction equipment. Because it must hold back the full reservoir pressure, it must be constructed carefully. To prevent piping or erosion, the diaphragm must be protected by graded filters meeting criteria listed in section 6.10(i). When an earth diaphragm is centrally located, it is also referred to as a thin core. An earth diaphragm constructed for Amarillo Regulating Reservoir is shown on figure 6-58.

Diaphragm-type dams are generally used under the following conditions:

- A limited quantity of impervious material is available
- Wet climatic conditions
- Short construction seasons

A diaphragm should be used only when the design and construction of the dam are performed under the supervision of an experienced earth dam designer. If this type of dam is selected, it is recommended that a diaphragm of manufactured material be placed on the upstream slope of an otherwise pervious embankment in lieu of a soil blanket. If the pervious material is rock, the dam is classified as a rockfill dam, the design of which is discussed in chapter 7.

The pervious material used in the construction of a diaphragm dam must be such that it can be compacted to form a stable embankment that will be subject to only small amounts of postconstruction settlement. Poorly graded sands (SP) cannot be satisfactorily compacted; well-graded sand-gravel mixtures (SW-GW) or well-graded gravels (GW) make satisfactory embankments. Well-graded sand-gravel mixtures that contain more than 5 percent of material finer than the No. 200 sieve should be tested to determine whether they will form free-draining embankments after compaction. Zones downstream of the diaphragm should be designed in accordance with the filter criteria listed in section 6.10(i).

In all respects, except for the use of pervious materials other than rock in construction of the embankment, the diaphragm earthfill dam design as recommended herein for small dams is identical with the design of rockfill dams, which is discussed in chapter 7. That discussion should be referred to for the design of foundations and upstream facings for a diaphragm earthfill dam.

(d) *Homogeneous Type.*—The homogeneous-type dam is recommended only where the lack of

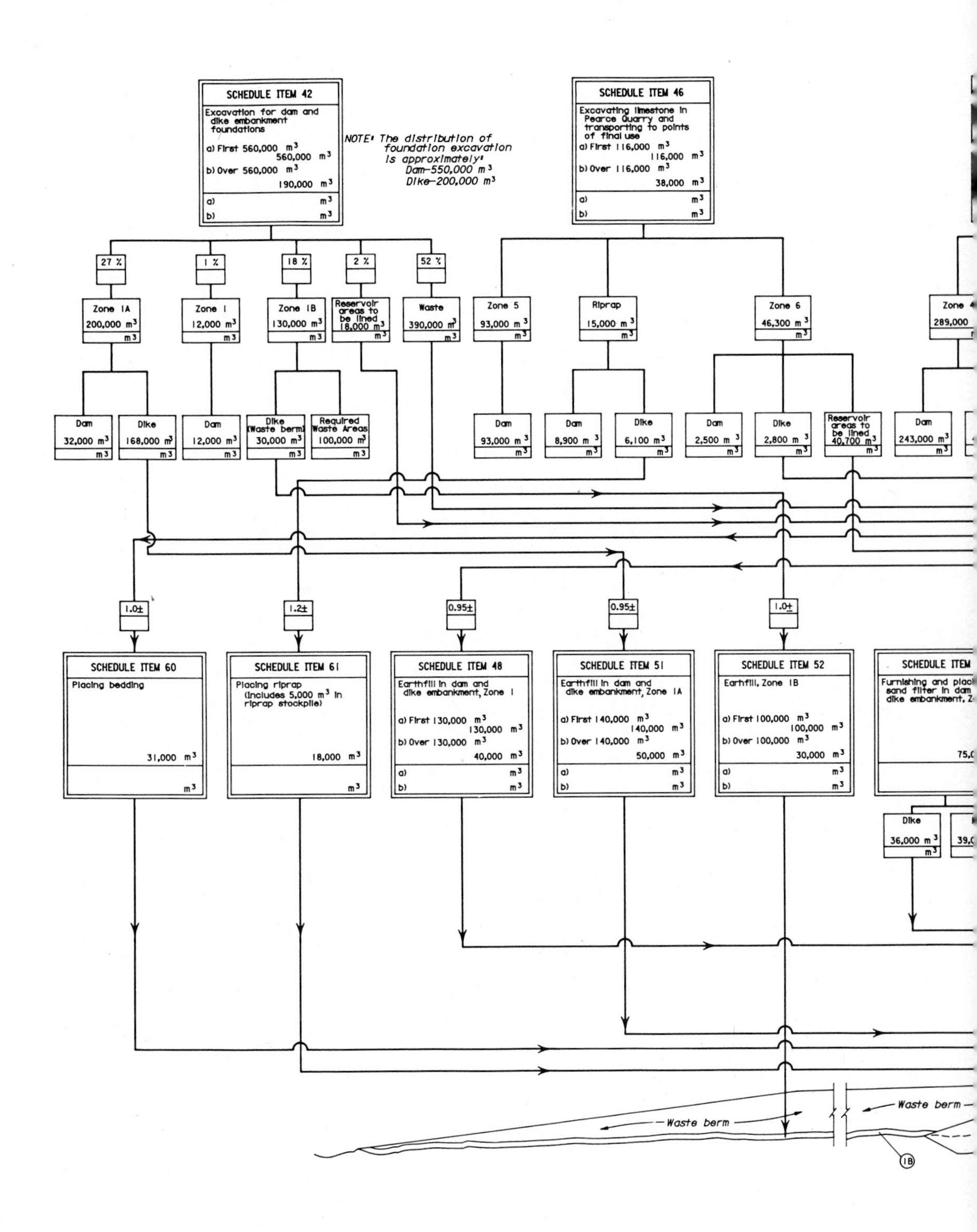

SCHEDULE ITEM 42
Excavation for dam and dike embankment foundations
a) First 560,000 m3
560,000 m3
b) Over 560,000 m3
190,000 m3
NOTE: The distribution of foundation excavation is approximately:
Dam–550,000 m3
Dike–200,000 m3
SCHEDULE ITEM 46
Excavating limestone in Pearce Quarry and transporting to points of final use
a) First 116,000 m3
116,000 m3
b) Over 116,000 m3
38,000 m3
27 %
1 %
18 %
2 %
52 %
Zone 1A 200,000 m3
Zone 1 12,000 m3
Zone 1B 130,000 m3
Reservoir areas to be lined 18,000 m3
Waste 390,000 m3
Zone 5 93,000 m3
Riprap 15,000 m3
Zone 6 46,300 m3
Zone 4 289,000
Dam 32,000 m3
Dike 168,000 m3
Dam 12,000 m3
Dike (Waste berm) 30,000 m3
Required Waste Areas 100,000 m3
Dam 93,000 m3
Dam 8,900 m3
Dike 6,100 m3
Dam 2,500 m3
Dike 2,800 m3
Reservoir areas to be lined 40,700 m3
Dam 243,000 m3
1.0±
1.2±
0.95±
0.95±
1.0±
SCHEDULE ITEM 60
Placing bedding
31,000 m3
SCHEDULE ITEM 61
Placing riprap (Includes 5,000 m3 in riprap stockpile)
18,000 m3
SCHEDULE ITEM 48
Earthfill in dam and dike embankment, Zone 1
a) First 130,000 m3
130,000 m3
b) Over 130,000 m3
40,000 m3
SCHEDULE ITEM 51
Earthfill in dam and dike embankment, Zone 1A
a) First 140,000 m3
140,000 m3
b) Over 140,000 m3
50,000 m3
SCHEDULE ITEM 52
Earthfill, Zone 1B
a) First 100,000 m3
100,000 m3
b) Over 100,000 m3
30,000 m3
SCHEDULE ITEM
Furnishing and placi sand filter in dam dike embankment, Z
75,
Dike 36,000 m3
39,
Waste berm
Waste berm
1B

free-draining materials make the construction of a zoned embankment uneconomical, with the further qualification that for storage dams the homogeneous dam must be modified to include internal drainage facilities. The recommended drainage facilities for modified homogeneous dams are described in section 6.3 and are shown on figure 6-5. If a rockfill toe is provided, a filter must be constructed between the embankment proper and the rockfill toe, as shown on figure 6-5(A). This filter and the horizontal and inclined drainage blanket shown on figure 6-5(B) and 6-5(C) should be designed to meet the filter requirements described in section 6.10(i).

To perform its function of lowering the phreatic line and stabilizing the downstream portion of the dam, the horizontal drainage blanket shown on figure 6-5(B) should extend from the downstream slope of the dam to well within the body of the embankment. However, it should not extend upstream so far as to reduce the length of the path of percolation through the embankment or through the foundation to a dangerous extent. A minimum-length filter blanket is also desirable because filters are expensive to construct. For small dams, it is recommended that the horizontal drainage blanket start at the downstream toe of the embankment and extend upstream to within a distance equal to the height of the dam plus 5 feet from the centerline of the dam. This will afford an ample blanket, yet keep the length of the path of percolation within desirable limits. The distance of height of dam plus 5 feet is selected on the basis that this will place the upstream limit of the horizontal drainage blanket at the downstream edge of minimum core B, that required for dams on deep pervious foundations without positive cutoff trenches, as shown on figure 6-43.

The horizontal drainage blanket should be carried across the valley floor and up the abutments to an elevation corresponding to the highest level at which water will be stored in the reservoir for an appreciable time. It should be a uniformly thick blanket whose upstream position at a given point is downstream from the centerline of the dam a distance equal to the height of the dam at that point plus 5 feet.

Even in the construction of a homogeneous embankment, there is likely to be some variation in the nature of the borrow material. It is important that the coarse and more pervious material be placed at the outer slopes to approach, as much as possible, the advantages of zoned embankment. It is also important to avoid segregation of the larger particles when the fill is dumped. Segregation leads to the formation of layers of much greater permeability than the other embankment; these layers tend to form drainage channels for the percolating water and to increase the possibility of piping.

Because of the possibility of oversights during construction and of cracking, dispersive soil, etc., as discussed previously, consideration should be given to providing an inclined filter-drain to intercept any seepage along defects in the embankment.

The recommended slopes for small homogeneous earthfill dams are shown in table 6-5 for detention and storage dams on stable foundations with and without rapid drawdown as a design condition. Where more than one soil classification is shown for a set of slopes, the table indicates that the dam can be constructed to the slopes shown by using any of the soils or combinations thereof.

(e) *Zoned Embankments.*—(1) *General.*—The zoned embankment dam consists of a central impervious core flanked by zones of material that are considerably more pervious. An excellent example of a zoned dam from the 1950 era is Carter Lake Dam No. 3 (fig. 6-63). An excellent example from a more recent era is Ute Dam Dike (fig. 6-86). This type of embankment should always be constructed where there is a variety of soils readily available because its inherent advantages lead to savings in the costs of construction. Three major advantages in using zoned embankments are listed below.

- Steeper slopes may be used with consequent reduction in total volume of embankment materials
- A wide variety of materials may be used
- Maximum use can be made of material excavated from the foundation, spillway, outlet works, and other appurtenant structures.

(2) *Zoning.*—All zoning schemes are based on the estimated quantities of required excavation and of borrow area materials available. The zoning scheme may divide the dam into two or more zones, depending on the range of variation in the character and gradation of the materials available for construction. In general, the permeability of each zone should increase toward the outer slopes.

Relatively free-draining materials and, therefore, those with a high degree of inherent stability are

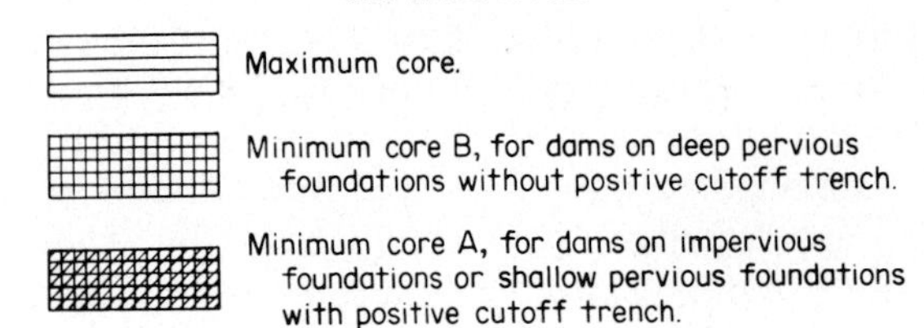

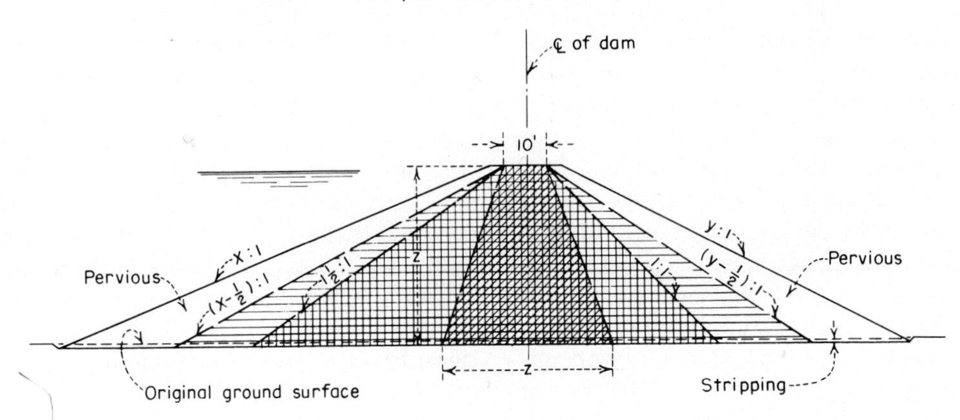

Figure 6-43.—Size range of impervious cores used in zoned embankments. 288–D–2497.

Table 6-5.—Recommended slopes for small homogeneous earthfill dams on stable foundations.

Case	Type	Purpose	Subject to rapid drawdown[1]	Soil classification[2]	Upstream slope	Downstream slope
A	Homogeneous or modified-homogeneous	Detention or storage	No	GW,GP,SW,SP	Pervious, unsuitable	
				GC,GM,SC,SM	2.5:1	2:1
				CL,ML	3:1	2.5:1
				CH,MH	3.5:1	2.5:1
B	Modified-homogeneous	Storage	Yes	GW,GP,SW,SP	Pervious, unsuitable	
				GC,GM,SC,SM	3:1	2:1
				CL,ML	3.5:1	2.5:1
				CH,MH	4:1	2.5:1

[1]Drawdown rates of 6 inches or more per day after prolonged storage at high reservoir levels.
[2]OL and OH soils are not recommended for major portions of homogeneous earthfill dams. Pt soils are unsuitable.

used to enclose and support the less stable impervious core. Pervious materials are placed in the downstream sections to avoid building up pressure from percolating water and to permit lowering the phreatic line so as to keep it well within the embankment. Pervious materials are placed in upstream sections to permit dissipation of pressure on rapid drawdown.

Miscellaneous, or random, zones (fig. 6-41) are often included in the downstream sections of the embankment to use excavated materials having uncertain permeability. Excavated materials unsuitable for use in any zone and excess excavation may be wasted on the upstream or downstream toes. Section 6.18(a) discusses the use of excavated material more fully.

(3) *Transitions.*—It is important that the gradation of adjacent zones be considered so that materials from one zone are not "piped" into the voids of adjoining zones, either by steady-state or by drawdown seepage forces. Transitions prevent piping and also provide the additional advantage that should the embankment crack, partial sealing of the cracks takes place with subsequent reduction in seepage losses.

A transition of sand-gravel or rock fines must be provided between an impervious zone and an adjacent rockfill. Although these transitions need only be a few feet wide, they are usually constructed from 8 to 12 feet wide to accommodate construction equipment.

The transition zone should be designed in accordance with the filter criteria listed in section 6.10(i) or an inclined blanket meeting the criteria provided. Transition zones are not always required between impervious and sand-gravel zones or between sand-gravel zones and rockfill, but the filter criteria (sec. 6.10(i)) should be met between these zones.

(4) *Impervious Cores for Zoned Embankments.*—Figure 6-43 shows the suggested size of the minimum core for the following two conditions:

- Impervious or pervious foundations of shallow depth penetrated by a positive cutoff trench. This core is hereinafter referred to as minimum core A.
- Exposed pervious foundations and covered pervious foundations (<3 ft of cover) not penetrated by a positive cutoff trench regardless of the depth of pervious material. This core is hereinafter referred to as minimum core B.

The maximum size impervious core that allows the dam to function as a zoned embankment is also shown on figure 6-43.

If the core is smaller than minimum core A, the dam is considered to be of the diaphragm type; if the core is larger than the maximum size shown, the pervious zones are largely ineffective in stabilizing the core, and the embankment may be considered as the homogeneous type so far as stability is concerned.

The size of minimum core A shown on figure 6-43 was selected for both practical and theoretical reasons. The width of 10 feet was taken as the minimum that will permit economical placement and compaction of impervious embankment material by construction equipment such as trucks, dozers, and tamping rollers. The criterion that the thickness of the core at any elevation be at least as great as the height of embankment above that elevation was adopted so that the average hydraulic gradient though the core would be less than unity. Appreciably steeper gradients may result in high seepage forces and the necessity for construction of high-quality filter zones, which for small dams may not be economical nor practicable from a construction control standpoint. It should be noted, however, that even for wide cores, the downstream zones should meet the filter criteria in section 6.10(i). Furthermore, if the core were thinner, there would be more danger that it could be ruptured by differential settlement of the foundation.

Minimum core B for dams on pervious foundations (fig. 6-43) is based on consideration of seepage pressures in the foundation. The minimum core applies to dams constructed on exposed deep pervious foundations (Case 1) or on covered deep pervious foundations (Case 2) when the cover is 3 feet or less (see sec. 6.11(a)). It does not apply if the pervious foundations are covered by an impervious layer more than 3 feet thick.

If a positive cutoff trench is not provided in the design, it must be anticipated that regardless of what other type of device is used to control seepage, the loss of head through the foundation will be relatively gradual and proportional to the length of the seepage path. The minimum length of path suggested for use with deep pervious foundations to reduce the seepage pressure sufficiently is that provided by an impervious zone whose thickness at the contact of the dam with the foundation is at least 2½ times the height of the dam. Such an impervious zone avoids the possibility of seepage passing under the core of the dam without an appreciable loss of head because of the ineffectiveness of sheet piling, partial cutoff trench, etc., or because no such device is provided. Minimum core B, shown on figure 6-43 for a dam on a pervious foundation, meets these requirements and should be used for all Case 1 (exposed pervious foundations) and for Case 2 (covered pervious foundations) having 3 feet or less of cover for which positive cutoff trenches are not provided.

If the covered pervious foundation has an impervious layer thickness greater than 3 feet yet less than the reservoir head, the size of the core selected should depend on the designer's judgment of the effectiveness of the natural upstream blanket. In general, minimum core A (fig. 6-43) should provide a sufficient thickness of core material for use with a natural impervious blanket of this depth.

If the thickness of the impervious cover is greater than the reservoir head, the foundation may be considered deep and the embankment should be designed to use stabilizing fills as described in section 6.13(a) and as shown on figure 6-33 for saturated fine-grained foundations. Minimum core A should provide sufficient core thickness for this type foundation condition.

With minimum core A centrally located, as shown on figure 6-43, the stability of the zoned embankment is not greatly affected by the nature of the soil in the core. The outside slopes are governed largely by the stability of the shell material. Rock, well-graded gravels (GW), and poorly graded gravels (GP) provide suitable material for the shell. Well-graded sand (SW) and poorly graded sand (SP) are suitable if they are gravelly. For any of these shell materials, assuming adequate foundation strengths, upstream and downstream slopes of 2:1 are stable for dams not more than 50 feet higher than the lowest point in the streambed, even if subject to rapid drawdown.

(5) *Embankment Slopes.*—Table 6-6 shows the recommended upstream and downstream slopes for small zoned earthfill dams with minimum core A and with maximum core. The assumption is made that the foundation is stable; if the foundation is of the saturated fine-grained type, stabilizing fills, as described in section 6.13, should be added. Slopes of small zoned earthfill dams with cores of intermediate size (including minimum core B for dams on pervious foundations) fall between those given in the table for minimum core A and for the maximum size core.

Where only one slope is shown for more than one soil classification, it indicates that the embankment can be constructed using any of the soils or any combination thereof.

The following example illustrates the procedure:

Example

Required:

Upstream and downstream slopes for a zoned earthfill storage dam, 50 feet high, on a stable foundation subject to rapid drawdown.

Given:

Foundation = shallow, exposed, and pervious.
Shell material = SW and SP, both gravelly.
Core material = CL.

Solution:

Because the foundation is shallow and a positive cutoff trench can be constructed, minimum core A should be used. From table 6-6, select upstream and downstream slopes of 2:1.

Table 6-6.—Recommended slopes for small zoned earthfill dams on stable foundations.

Type	Purpose	Subject to rapid drawdown[2]	Shell material classification	Core material classification[3]	Upstream slope	Downstream slope
Zoned with minimum core A[1]	Any	Not critical[4]	Rockfill, GW, GP, SW (gravelly), or SP (gravelly)	GC, GM, SC, SM, CL, ML, CH, or MH	2:1	2:1
Zoned with maximum core[1]	Detention or storage	No	Rockfill, GW, GP, SW (gravelly), or SP (gravelly)	GC, GM	2:1	2:1
				SC, SM	2.25:1	2.25:1
				CL, ML	2.5:1	2.5:1
				CH, MH	3:1	3:1
Zoned with maximum core[1]	Storage	Yes	Rockfill, GW, GP, SW (gravelly), or SP (gravelly)	GC, GM	2.5:1	2:1
				SC, SM	2.5:1	2.25:1
				CL, ML	3:1	2.5:1
				CH, MH	3.5:1	3:1

[1]Minimum and maximum size cores are as shown on figure 6-43.
[2]Rapid drawdown is 6 inches or more per day after prolonged storage at high reservoir levels.
[3]OL and OH soils are not recommended for major portions of the cores of earthfill dams. Pt soils are unsuitable.
[4]Rapid drawdown will not affect the upstream slope of a zoned embankment that has a large upstream pervious shell.

6.19. *Seismic Design.*—The design and construction practices for small earth dams presented herein are considered adequate in areas of low seismicity, and the safety factors used should preclude major damage for all but the most catastrophic earthquakes.

Although all damsites are subject to earthquake activity, the probability of an earthquake is greater in some regions than in others. This probability is generally determined by the number of previous earthquakes in that region and their intensity. In some cases, maps have been prepared that delineate certain areas having greater earthquake potential. One such seismic risk map is shown on figure 6-44. This map, adapted from Algermissen [47], uses the information collected and abstracted for approximately 28,000 earthquakes in the conterminous United States. If the designer is uncertain about the prospects of an earthquake in any area, a competent geologist or seismologist should be consulted.

After determining that the region is subject to earthquakes, the damsite should be inspected by an experienced engineering geologist to determine whether faults or detrimental geologic formations could affect the location of the dam, reservoir, or appurtenant structures. If active faults, unstable alluvial foundations, or the possibility of massive landslides into the reservoir exist, the damsite should be relocated. In general, the designer should assume that a dam within a seismic zone will be shaken by an earthquake.

If foundations consisting of low relative density sands and silts (sec. 6.9) or uniform, fine-grained, cohesionless materials are encountered, serious damage may result to the structure during an earthquake, and the assistance of an experienced dam designer is required. If an active fault exists at the proposed damsite, the designs proposed herein are inadequate.

Additional considerations concerning seismic design for earth dams are contained in [6, 48, 49, 50, 51, 53]. USBR Design Standards No. 13, chapter 13, gives the Bureau criteria for seismic design.

E. EMBANKMENT DETAILS

6.20. *Crest Design.*—(a) *General.*—In designing the crest of an earthfill dam, the following items should be considered:

- Width
- Drainage
- Camber
- Surfacing
- Safety requirements
- Zoning

In addition, suitable parking areas should be provided at the abutments of the dam for the convenience of visitors and others, especially for a storage dam whose lake will be used for recreational purposes. A turnaround should be provided where vehicular traffic is permitted on a dam crest that dead ends at the opposite abutment.

(b) *Width.*—The crest width of an earthfill dam depends on considerations such as (1) nature of embankment materials and minimum allowable percolation distance through the embankment at normal reservoir water level, (2) height and importance of structure, (3) possible roadway requirements, and (4) practicability of construction. The minimum crest width should provide a safe seepage gradient through the embankment at the level of the full reservoir. Because of practical difficulties in determining this factor, the crest width is, as a rule, determined empirically and largely by precedent. The following formula is suggested for the determination of crest width for small earthfill dams:

$$w = \frac{z}{5} + 10 \qquad (12)$$

where:

w = width of crest, in feet, and
z = height of dam, in feet, above the streambed.

For ease of construction with power equipment, the minimum width should be at least 12 feet. For many dams, the minimum crest width is determined by the requirements for the roadway over the dam.

(c) *Drainage.*—Surface drainage of the crest should be provided by a crown of at least 3 inches, or by sloping the crest to drain toward the upstream slope. The latter method is preferred unless the downstream slope is protected against erosion.

(d) *Camber.*—Camber is ordinarily provided along the crest of earthfill dams to ensure that the freeboard will not be diminished by foundation settlement or embankment consolidation. Selection of the amount of camber is necessarily somewhat arbitrary. It is based on the amount of foundation settlement and embankment consolidation expected for the dam, with the objective of providing

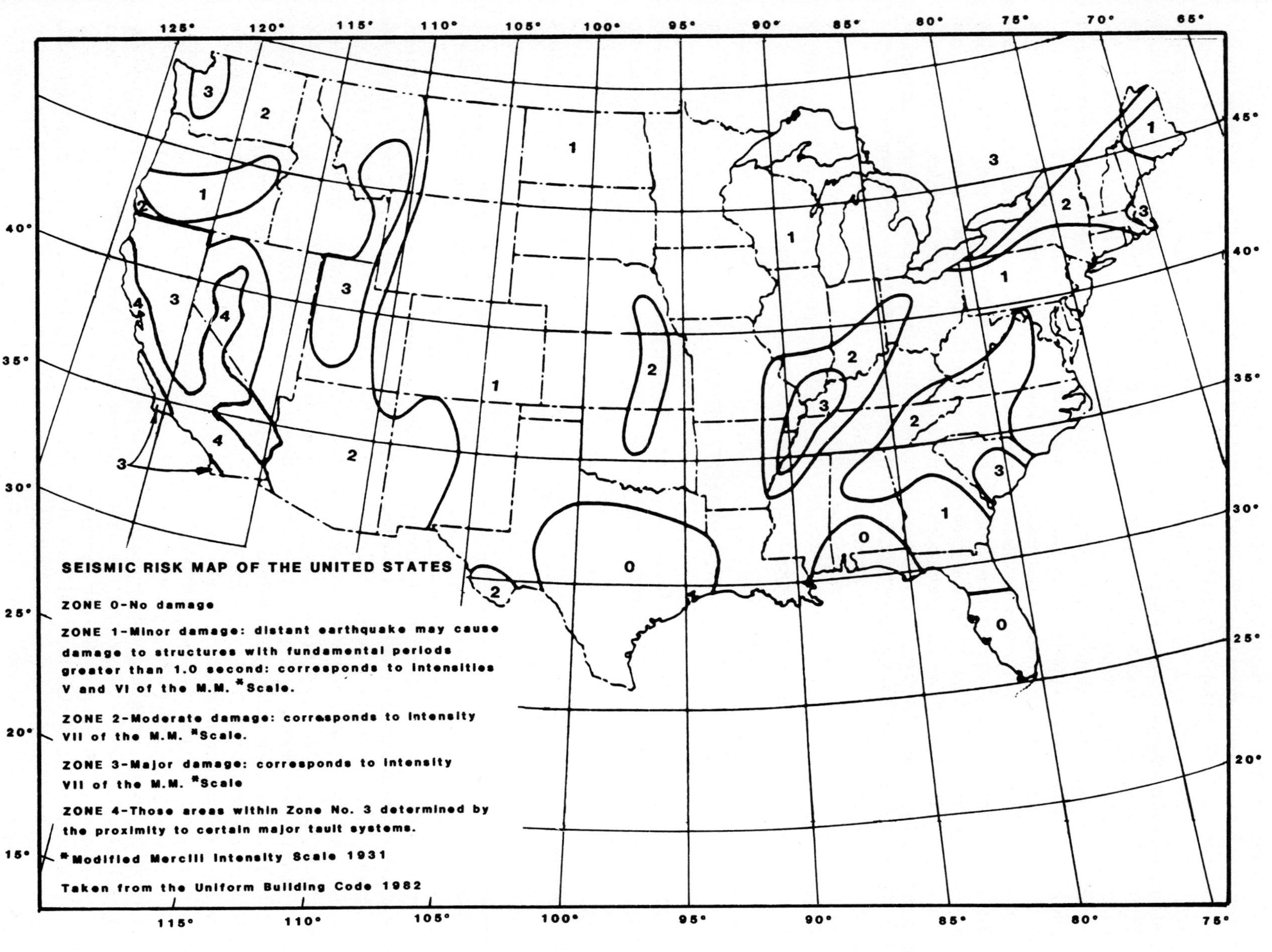

Figure 6-44.—Seismic risk map of the conterminous United States. 103-D-1830.

enough extra height so that some residual camber will remain after settlement and consolidation. This residual camber also improves the appearance of the crest.

Impervious embankment materials placed at densities roughly corresponding to the Proctor laboratory maximum consolidate appreciably when subject to overlying fill loads. It is expected that the major portion of this consolidation will take place during construction before the embankment is completed; therefore, the expected foundation settlement is the more important factor. For dams on relatively noncompressible foundations, cambers of about 1 percent of the height are commonly provided. Several feet of camber may be required for dams constructed on foundations expected to settle. A method of determining foundation settlement is given in [54] and in USBR Design Standards No. 13, chapter 9. Straight-line equations should be used to vary the amount of camber and to make it roughly proportional to the height of the embankment. These equations are easy to use and usually correspond well with the camber lines as constructed in the field.

Little additional embankment material is usually required to provide camber in the crest of an embankment because the embankment height is increased by pitching the slopes near the crest of the dam as shown on figure 6-45. The modifications to the section of the embankment caused by the addition of camber are not taken into account in calculating embankment stability.

(e) *Surfacing.*—Some type of surfacing should be placed on top of the crest for protection against damage by wave splash and spray, rainfall, wind, frost, and traffic when the crest is used as a roadway. The usual treatment consists of placing a layer of selected fine rock or gravelly material at least 4 inches thick. If the crest constitutes a section of highway, the width of roadway and type of surfacing should conform to those of the highway.

(f) *Safety Requirements.*—When the crest of a dam is used as a highway, cable- or beam-type guardrails are usually constructed along both shoulders of the crest. If a highway crossing is not anticipated, the crest can be lined with guard posts at 25-foot intervals or, on very minor structures, by boulders placed at intervals along the crest. If little or no traffic will use the crest, treatment may not be necessary.

(g) *Zoning.*—Incorrect zoning of materials at the crest leads to poor construction control, lost time, and possibly local failure of the crest.

For both homogeneous and zoned dams, the manner in which the slope protection and bedding will intersect the crest must be considered. The thickness of the slope protection may have to be reduced by steepening the slopes near the crest to allow construction of the impervious or pervious zones or to facilitate the installation of guard posts. Care must be taken that the remaining slope protection will adequately resist the wave action. In zoned dams, it is common practice to limit the height of the core material to a few feet below the crest because impervious zones extending to the top of the dam are subject to damage by frost action, which causes loosening of the soil, and to the formation of shrinkage cracks when the soil drys. Either of these occurrences can cause flow paths where erosion and possible failure can occur. In homogeneous dams where frost action or shrinkage cracks may be problems, crest surfacing should always be provided. The top of the impervious core should also be maintained above the maximum water surface to prevent percolation through the embankment or possible capillary siphoning over the top of the core material when the reservoir is full. The need for filters or zoning that will prevent erosion of material out of cracks in impervious zones should also be considered.

The crest pitching provided for camber should not be overly steep to facilitate construction.

(h) *Typical Crest Details.*—Figure 6-84 and 6-85 show the crest detail for Wasco Dam: 6 inches of camber were provided and a minimum top width of 14 feet was maintained for the impervious zone to ensure adequate room for compaction by tamping rollers. The core material was placed 3.5 feet higher than the maximum water surface. Note also that the top of the core material is sloped toward the reservoir to facilitate drainage.

Additional crest details for various Bureau dams are shown on figure 6-45.

6.21. *Freeboard.*—Freeboard is the vertical distance between the crest of the embankment (without camber) and the reservoir water surface. The more specific term "normal freeboard" is defined as the difference in elevation between the crest of the dam and the normal reservoir water level as fixed by design requirements. The term

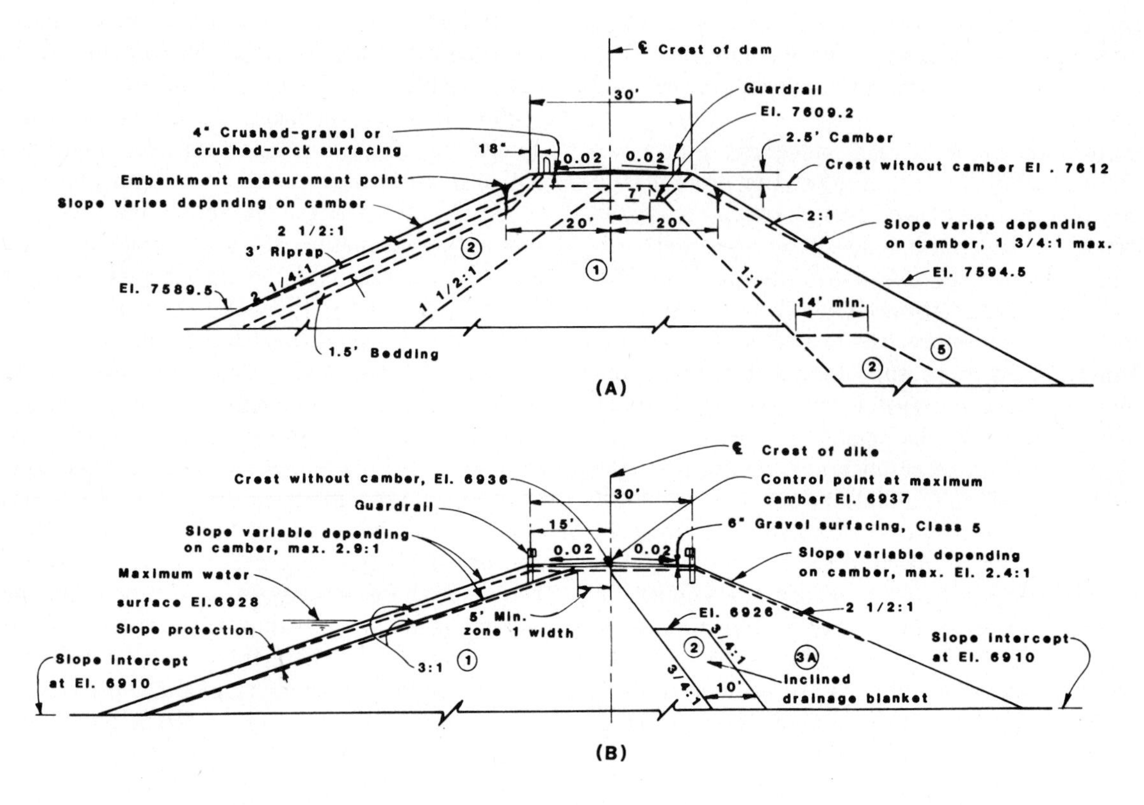

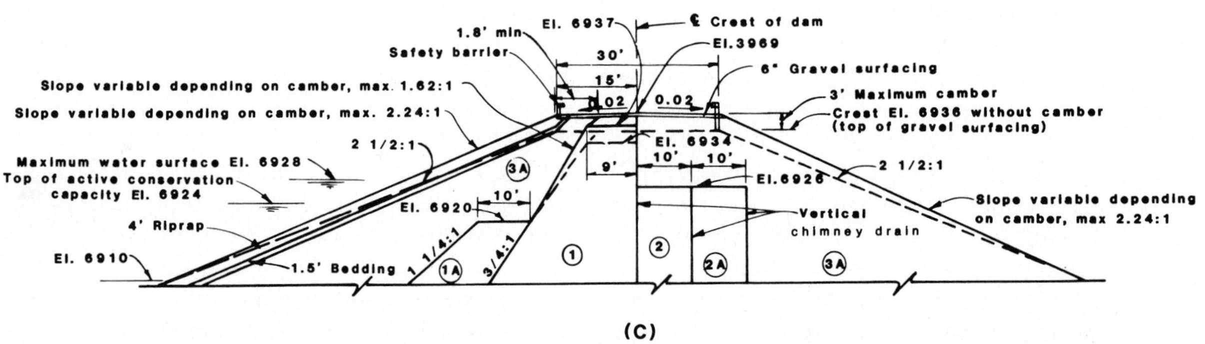

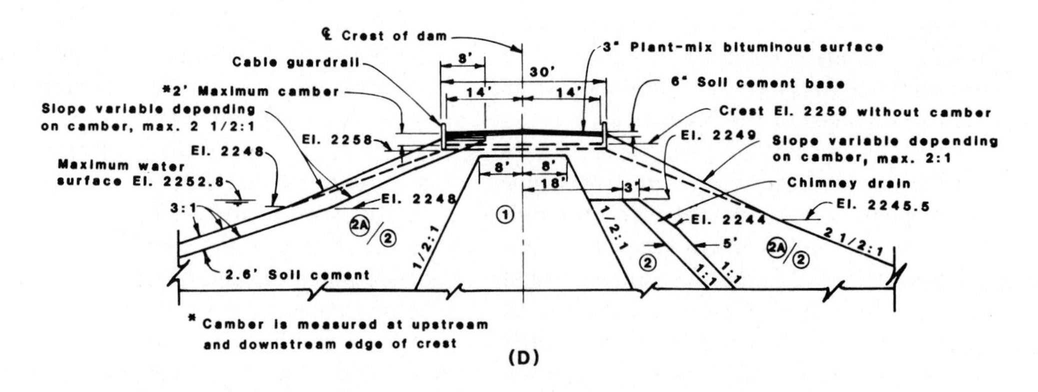

Figure 6-45.—Examples of crest details at maximum camber. 103–D–1831.

"minimum freeboard" is defined as the difference in elevation between the crest of the dam and the maximum reservoir water surface that would result should the inflow design flood occur and the outlet works and spillway function as planned. The difference between normal and minimum freeboard represents the surcharge head (sec. (9.3). If the spillway is uncontrolled, there is always a surcharge head; if the spillway is gated, it is possible for the normal and minimum freeboards to be identical, in which case the surcharge head is zero.

A distinction is made between normal and minimum freeboards because of the different requirements for freeboard if surcharge head is involved. The normal freeboard must meet the requirements for longtime storage. It must be sufficient to prevent seepage through a core that has been loosened by frost action or that has cracked from drying out; otherwise, zoning must be provided to control this condition. This is of particular importance for a dam whose core is a CL or CH material and is located in areas with either a very cold or a very hot dry climate. The normal freeboard must also be sufficient to prevent overtopping of the embankment by abnormal and severe wave action of rare occurrence that may result from unusual sustained winds of high velocity from a critical direction.

Minimum freeboard is provided to prevent overtopping of the embankment by wave action that may coincide with the occurrence of the inflow design flood. Minimum freeboard also provides a safety factor against many contingencies, such as settlement of the dam more than the amount anticipated in selecting the camber, occurrence of an inflow flood somewhat larger than the inflow design flood, or malfunction of spillway controls or outlet works with an increase in maximum water surface above that expected. In some instances, especially where the maximum probable inflow is used as a basis for design, the minimum freeboard may be established on the assumption that the dam should not be overtopped as a result of a malfunction of the controlled spillway or outlet works that would result from human or mechanical failure to open gates or valves. In such instances, allowances for wave action or other contingencies usually are not made.

The rational determination of freeboard would require determining the height and action of waves. The height of waves generated by winds in a reservoir depends on the wind velocity, the duration of the wind, the fetch[3], the depth of water, and the width of the reservoir. The height of the waves as they approach the upstream face of the dam may be altered by the increasing depth of the water, or by the decreasing width of the reservoir. Upon contact with the face of the dam, the effect of waves is influenced by the angle of the wave train with the dam, the slope of the upstream face, and the texture of the slope surface. The sloping face of an earthfill dam reduces the impact with which waves hit the dam. The rough surface of dumped riprap reduces wave runup to approximately 1.5 times the height of the wave; whereas, the runup for smooth surfaces such as concrete is considerably greater. Because there are no specific data on wave height and wave runup, the determination of freeboard requires judgment and consideration of local factors.

A summary of empirical formulas proposed for determining wave heights is given in an American Society of Civil Engineers report [55], from which table 6-7 was extracted.

All conditions affecting exposure of the dam to the wind must be considered in selecting the maximum wind velocity. It is believed that no locality is safe from an occurrence of winds of up to 100 mi/h at least once during a period of many years, although a particular site may be topographically sheltered so that the reservoir is protected from sustained winds of high velocity. Under these conditions, wind velocities of 75 or even 50 mi/h may be used.

For the design of small dams with riprapped slopes, it is recommended that the freeboard be sufficient to prevent overtopping of the dam from wave runup equal to 1.5 times the height of the wave as interpolated from table 6-7, measured vertically from the still water level. Normal freeboard should be based on a wind velocity of 100 mi/h, and minimum freeboard on a velocity of 50 mi/h. Based on these assumptions and on other considerations of the purpose of freeboard, as previously discussed, table 6-8 lists the least amount recommended for both normal and minimum freeboard on riprapped earthfill dams; the design of the dam should satisfy the most critical requirement.

An increase in the freeboard shown in table 6-8

[3]The fetch is the distance over which the wind can act on a body of water. It is generally defined as the normal distance from the windward shore to the structure being designed. However, the "effective" fetch may have a slightly curved path, as when the wind sweeps down a winding river valley between land ridges.

Table 6-7.—Wave height versus fetch and wind velocity. From [55].

Fetch, mi	Wind velocity, mi/h	Wave height, ft
1	50	2.7
1	75	3.0
2.5	50	3.2
2.5	75	3.6
2.5	100	3.9
5	50	3.7
5	75	4.3
5	100	4.8
10	50	4.5
10	75	5.4
10	100	6.1

Table 6-8.—Fetch versus recommended normal and minimum freeboard.

Fetch, mi	Normal freeboard, ft	Minimum freeboard, ft
<1	4	3
1	5	4
2.5	6	5
5	8	6
10	10	7

for dams where the fetch is 2.5 miles and less may be required if the dam is located in a very cold or a very hot dry climate, particularly if CL and CH soils are used for construction of the cores. It is also recommended that the amount of freeboard shown in table 6-8 be increased by 50 percent if a smooth pavement is to be provided on the upstream slope. The above methods for determining freeboard requirements are adequate for small dams. USBR Design Standards No. 13, chapter 6, and Bureau of Reclamation ACER Technical Memorandum No. 2 have a more in-depth discussion of freeboard and determinations of freeboard requirements.

6.22. *Upstream Slope Protection.*

(a) *General.*—The upstream slopes of earthfill dams must be protected against destructive wave action. In some instances, provision must be made against burrowing animals. The usual types of surface protection for usptream slopes are rock riprap, either dry-dumped or hand-placed, and concrete pavement. Other types of protection that have been used are steel facing, bituminous pavement, precast concrete blocks, soil-cement pavement, and (on small and relatively unimportant structures) wood and sacked concrete. The upstream slope protection should extend from the crest of the dam to a safe distance below minimum water level (usually several feet). In some cases, it is advantageous to terminate the slope protection on a supporting berm, but this is generally not required.

(b) *Selecting the Type of Protection.*—Experience has shown that in most cases, dumped riprap furnishes the best upstream slope protection at the lowest ultimate cost. Approximately 100 dams, located in various sections of the Untied States with a wide variety of climatic conditions and wave severity, were examined by the Corps of Engineers. The results of this survey were used as a basis for establishing the most practical and economical means for slope protection [56]. The dams were from 5 to 50 years old and were constructed by various agencies. This survey found that:

1. Dumped riprap failed in 5 percent of the cases it was used; failures were due to improper size of stones.
2. Hand-placed riprap failed in 30 percent of the cases it was used; failures were due to the usual method of single-course construction.
3. Concrete pavement failed in 36 percent of the cases it was used; failures were generally due to inherent deficiencies with this type of construction.

This survey substantiated the premise that dumped riprap is by far the most preferable type of upstream slope protection. The excellent service rendered by dumped riprap is exemplified by Cold Springs Dam, constructed by the Bureau of Reclamation. Figure 6-46 shows the condition of the riprap on the upstream slope of this dam after 50 years of service. The only maintenance required during that period has been the replacement of some riprap that was dislodged near the center of the dam by a severe storm in 1931. Although some beaching action has occurred subsequently, it has not been severe enough to require further maintenance.

The superiority of dumped rock riprap for upstream slope protection and its low cost of maintenance compared with other types of slope

Figure 6-46.—Riprap on upstream slope of an earthfill dam. Dam is in excellent condition after 50 years of service. The structure is Cold Springs Dam, which forms an offstream reservoir on the Umatilla Project in Oregon. IO–2194.

protection have been demonstrated so convincingly that it has been considered economical to transport rock considerable distances for major dams. For example, the Bureau of Reclamation has imported rock from sources that required a rail haul of over 200 miles and a truck haul of 24 miles from the railhead to the dam, and the Corps of Engineers has transported rock a distance of 170 miles.

When the nearest source of suitable rock is far from the site, especially when only small quantities are involved, it may be economical to use hand-placed riprap despite its higher unit cost for labor and material because a thinner layer of rock may be used. Hand-placed riprap is satisfactory where not exposed to heavy ice conditions. However, the rock must be of better quality than the minimum suitable for dumped riprap, and placement must be such that the hand-placed riprap approaches good dry rubble in quality and appearance. It should be recognized that hand-placed riprap is not as flexible as dumped riprap because it does not adjust as well to foundation or local settlements. Consequently, hand-placed riprap should not be used where considerable settlement is expected.

Concrete paving deserves serious consideration for upstream slope protection where riprap is too expensive (usually because of high transportation costs). The success of concrete pavement as a slope protection medium depends on the field conditions, on the behavior of the embankment, and on the ability of the paving to resist cracking and deterioration. Concrete pavement has proved satisfactory in some cases under moderate wave action. An example is at McKay Dam, constructed by the Bureau of Reclamation near Pendleton, Oregon This pavement, although exposed to severe weather conditions, was in excellent condition after more than 40 years of service (see fig. 6-47).

Where severe wave action is anticipated, concrete pavement appears practicable only when the settlement within the embankment after construction will be insignificant. In comparing the cost of concrete pavement with riprap, the cost of all additional foundation measures necessary to minimize settlement and the additional freeboard required because of greater wave runup on the smooth surface should be considered.

Other types of upstream slope protection, such as precast concrete blocks, asphaltic concrete, steel plates, and soil-cement, should also be considered. Asphaltic concrete and soil-cement often provide economical alternatives for slope protection. Wood and sacked concrete should be used only on very minor structures and then only when the cost of a more permanent type of slope protection is prohibitive.

In this chapter, the following types of slope protection will be discussed:

- Dumped rock riprap
- Hand-placed rock riprap
- Concrete pavement
- Soil-cement

Section 7.11 discusses asphaltic-concrete slope protection.

(c) *Dumped Rock Riprap.*—Dumped rock riprap consists of stones or rock fragments dumped in place on the upstream slope of an embankment to protect it from wave action. The riprap is placed on a properly graded filter, which may be a specially placed blanket or the upstream zone of a zoned embankment. Figure 6-48 shows dumped rock riprap being placed on Meeks Cabin Dam, constructed by the Bureau of Reclamation. The riprap is feldspathic sandstone having a specific gravity of 2.58.

The efficacy of dumped rock riprap depends on the following characteristics:

- Quality of the rock
- Weight or size of the individual pieces
- Thickness of the riprap
- Shape of the stones or rock fragments
- Slopes of the embankment on which the riprap is placed
- Stability and effectiveness of the filter on which the riprap is placed

Rock for riprap should be hard, dense, and durable, and able to resist long exposure to weathering. Most of the igneous and metamorphic rocks, many of the limestones, and some of the sandstones make excellent riprap. Limestones and sandstones that have shale seams are undesirable. The suitability of rock for riprap from a quality standpoint is determined by visual inspection, by laboratory tests to determine the resistance to weathering and to abrasion, and by petrographic examination to determine the structure of the rock as it affects durability. The laboratory tests are described in chapter 5.

Figure 6-47.—Paved upstream slope of an earthfill dam. Dam is in excellent condition after 40 years of service. The structure is McKay Dam on a tributary of the Umatilla River in Oregon. 288–D–2878.

The individual rocks must be heavy enough to resist displacement by wave action, which is not necessarily a function of the height of the dam. It is a misconception to think that large rocks are needed only on higher structures and that small rocks afford ample slope protection for low fills, without considering factors such as wind velocity, wind direction, and fetch. This can be demonstrated by comparing figure 6-49 with figure 6-46. Cold Springs Dam (fig. 6-46) is a 90-foot-high dam whose upstream slope is protected by a 24-inch layer of basalt rock whose larger fragments probably do not weigh more than about 100 pounds. The wave action on this reservoir is not severe, and the riprap has given satisfactory service for 60 years with relatively little maintenance required. Figure 6-49 shows riprap containing relatively large fragments that have been dislodged from the upstream slope of a low dike section of another dam subject to heavier wave action.

The weight or size of the individual rocks required to resist displacement by wave action may be determined theoretically by the methods presented in the American Society of Civil Engineers report referred to in the discussion of freeboard requirements [55]. This method is based on the premise that the force a wave exerts on riprap rocks on the face of a dam cannot be greater than that of a current flowing at the velocity of the water particles of the wave. These theoretical methods are consistent with the experience and analysis of results obtained on a large number of earthfill dams by the Bureau of Reclamation.

The thickness of the riprap should be sufficient to accommodate the weight and size of rock necessary to resist wave action. The Bureau of Reclamation has found a 3-foot thickness of dumped riprap to be generally most economical and satisfactory for major dams. Lesser thicknesses are used on low dams or on dike sections where wave action will be less severe than on principal structures.

Figure 6-48.—Placing riprap on an upstream slope. Meeks Cabin Dam, Wyoming. P415–432–720.

Lesser thicknesses have also been specified for the upper slopes of dams whose reservoirs are largely allocated to flood control. This is because of the infrequent and short periods of time that the upper slopes are subject to wave action. Greater thicknesses have been specified in cases where rock having a low specific gravity (less than 2.50) was used. Table 6-9 shows the recommended thickness and gradation of dumped rock riprap for small dams for fetch equal to or less than 2.5 miles and greater than 2.5 miles, based on theoretical considerations and the experience and practice of the Bureau of Reclamation.

The shape of the individual rocks or rock fragments influences the ability of the riprap to resist displacement by wave action. Angular fragments of quarried rock tend to interlock and resist displacement better than boulders and rounded cobbles. The values given in table 6-9 are for angular quarried rock. If boulders or rounded cobbles are to be used, as shown on figure 4-1, a thicker layer containing larger sizes may be required, or the slope of the embankment may need to be made flatter than required for stability so that the boulders and cobbles stay in place. This is especially true if cobbles of relatively uniform diameter are to be used.

Table 6-9 is for riprap thickness and gradation on 3:1 slopes. For 2:1 slopes, a thickness of 36 inches should be used with the gradation corresponding to a 36-inch thickness in the table.

A layer, or blanket, of graded gravel should be provided underneath the riprap when the compacted material of the underlying earthfill is graded so that waves may wash out fines through the voids

Figure 6-49.—Displacement of riprap on a low dike by wave action. 288-D-2936.

in the riprap, resulting in undermining of the riprap. A blanket is usually not required if the outer zone of the zoned embankment is gravel. Blankets of crushed rock or natural gravel graded from 3/16 to 3½ inches with a thickness equal to one-half the thickness of the riprap (but not less than 12 inches) have proved satisfactory in practice. The blanket gradation may be determined more exactly by the filter criteria given in section 6.10(i). An example of a finished riprap slope is shown on figure 6-50. The structure is Blue Mesa Dam in Colorado.

The above procedures are generally adequate for design of small dams. USBR Design Standards No. 13, chapter 7, gives the current Bureau design criteria for dumped riprap slope protection.

(d) *Hand-Placed Rock Riprap.*—A good example of hand-placed rock riprap is shown on figure 6-51. This upstream slope protection was in an excellent state of preservation after 36 years of service. Hand-placed riprap consists of stones carefully laid by hand in a more or less definite pattern with a minimum amount of voids and with the top surface relatively smooth. Rounded or irregular rocks lay up less satisfactorily and rapidly than rock that is roughly square. The flat, stratified rocks should be placed with their large axes parallel to the slope. Joints should be offset as much as possible, and openings to the underlying fill should be filled with spalls or small rock fragments. However, there should be enough openings in the surface of the riprap to allow the water pressure to dissipate without lifting the rocks.

Rock for hand-placed riprap must be of excellent quality. The thickness of hand-placed rock riprap should be one-half of the thickness required for dumped rock riprap, but not less than 12 inches. A filter blanket should be provided underneath the riprap if the underlying zone of the earthfill dam is not gravel.

(e) *Concrete Paving.*—If a complete history were gathered concerning the numerous instances where concrete paving was used for the protection of the upstream slopes of small dams, the number of failures would be tremendous. Concrete paving is used on both earthfill and rockfill dams, although its performance on rockfill dams (ch. 7) has been much better. Unfortunately, the fact that some structures protected with concrete paving have withstood the test of time continues to lead engineers to use this type of construction, often without sufficient reference to other, unsatisfactory performance records. A properly designed and constructed concrete paving is never cheap. The uncertainty and complexity of the forces that may act on a concrete paving make conservative treatment desirable whenever this type of slope protection is considered. The recommendations that follow should provide the necessary degree of conservatism. But the number of situations studied is so limited that there is no assurance that adequate consideration has been given to every type of hazard that may be encountered.

Concrete paving slope protection should extend from the crest of the dam to several feet below the minimum water surface. It should terminate on a berm and against a concrete curb or header, which should extend at least 18 inches below the undersurface of the paving.

For dams nearly 50 feet high, a paving thickness of 8 inches is recommended; for lower dams the minimum thickness should be 6 inches. Although concrete paving has been constructed in blocks, the generally favored method, which has given the best service, is to make the paving monolithic to the greatest extent possible, and every measure should be taken to prevent access of water and consequent development of hydrostatic pressures under the concrete. The good service given by the concrete pavement on the upstream slope of McKay Dam

Table 6-9.—Thickness and gradation limits of riprap on 3:1 slopes. For angular quarried rock.

Reservoir fetch, mi	Nominal thickness inches	Weight of rock (in pounds) at various percentages (by weight)[1]			
		Maximum size	40 to 50%	50 to 60 %	[2]0 to 10%
≤2.5	30	2,500	>1,250	75 to 1,250	<75
>2.5	36	4,500	>2,250	100 to 2,250	<100

[1]Sand and rock dust shall be less than 5 percent, by weight, of the total riprap material.
[2]The percentage of this size material shall not exceed an amount that will fill the voids between the larger rocks.

(fig. 6-47) is due to the monolithic type of construction, durability of the concrete, little settlement of the dam or foundation, and pervious nature of the underlying fill, which prevents development of hydrostatic uplift pressures even though a minor amount of cracking has occurred.

In contrast with the success of concrete paving at McKay Dam is the experience of the Bureau of Reclamation with the concrete paving at Belle Fourche Dam. There, monolithic construction was not used. The paving consists of 8-inch-thick blocks, 6 feet 6 inches by 5 feet, placed directly upon the impervious underlying embankment. The condition of the paving after 40 years of service is shown on figure 6-52. Considerable maintenance of the paving has been required through the years; a number of the blocks have been displaced and broken up by wave action and uplift forces under the slabs. Compared with the general service record of riprap or with the concrete pavement on McKay Dam (fig. 6-47), this slope protection design cannot be considered successful.

If monolithic construction is not possible, expansion joints should be kept to a minimum and construction joints should be spaced as far apart as possible. The slab should be reinforced with bars in both directions, placed at middepth of the slab, and made continuous through the construction joints. An area of steel in each direction equal to 0.5 percent of the area of the concrete is considered good practice. Joints should be sealed with plastic fillers, and subsequent open cracks in the concrete should be grouted or sealed promptly.

(f) *Soil-Cement.*—In recent years, soil-cement as a facing material for earthfill dams has been found economical where suitable riprap is not available near the site. A reasonably firm foundation is preferred so that deformation after placement of soil-cement is not significant; however, no unusual design features need be incorporated into the embankment. Normal embankment construction procedures are used, with perhaps special care being taken to ensure a minimum of embankment consolidation and foundation settlement after construction. Soil-cement slope protection used on Cheney Dam in Kansas is shown on figure 6-53.

The soil-cement is generally placed and compacted in stairstep horizontal layers, as shown on figure 6-54. This promotes maximum construction efficiency and operational effectiveness. With typical embankment slopes of 2:1 and 4:1, a horizontal layer 8 feet wide will provide minimum protective thicknesses of about 2 and 3½ feet respectively, measured normal to the slope. Beginning at the lowest layer of soil-cement, each succeeding layer is stepped back a distance equal to the product of the compacted layer thickness in feet times the embankment slope. For example, if the compacted thickness is 6 inches and the slope is 2:1, the step back is = 0.5(2) = 1 foot. The usual compacted layer thickness is 6 inches. Soil-cement layers of this dimension can be effectively placed and compacted with standard highway equipment.

A plating method that forms a single soil-cement layer parallel to the slope is sometimes used in less critical areas for slope protection.

If the soil-cement facing does not begin at natural ground level, the lower portion of the embankment should be on a flatter slope than the portion protected by the soil-cement; or a berm may be provided at the lowest elevation of the facing. It is essential that the soil-cement extend below the minimum water level and above the maximum water level. The top of the facing should have a freeboard allowance of at least 1.2 times the anticipated maximum wave height, or 5 feet, whichever is greater. The edges of the completed soil-cement layers should not be trimmed because the rounded starstep effect helps retard wave runup (fig. 6-53).

Soil-cement can be made with a wide variety of

Figure 6-50.—Completed riprap slope protection on upstream face of Blue Mesa Dam, Colorado. P662A-427-10496NA.

soils. The principal criterion for determining soil type is gradation. Coarse sandy or gravelly soils containing about 10 to 25 percent material passing the No. 200 sieve are ideal (American Society for Testing and Materials Standard Sieve Series). These soils can be adequately stabilized with from 3 to 5 sacks of cement per cubic yard of compacted soil-cement. Standard compaction and placement control for soil-cement is used; it is described by Holtz and Walker [57]. If the amount of material smaller than the No. 200 sieve exceeds 35 percent, some effort to find a coarse material may be justified from a processing cost standpoint. Soils containing 50 percent or more material passing the No. 200 sieve are not recommended for use in their natural state.

Any type of portland cement meeting the requirements of the latest ASTM (American Society for Testing and Materials), AASHTO (American Association of State Highway and Transportation Officials), or Federal specifications may be used. Type 1, or normal portland cement, is most commonly used because the special properties of other types of portland cement are not usually required for soil-cement construction [55]. Standard laboratory tests are necessary to verify the acceptability of the soil and to determine proper cement content, optimum moisture content, and maximum dry unit weight of the soil-cement.

After the soil has been classified by sieve analyses and other tests, the required cement content may be estimated. Moisture unit weight curves are determined for test mixtures. The estimated cement content and at least four moisture contents are used to determine the optimum moisture content and

Figure 6.51.—Hand-placed rock riprap on Indian Creek Dike. An offstream dike for Strawberry Reservoir, part of a transmountain diversion project in Utah. 288–D–2935.

Figure 6.52.—Concrete paving blocks on the upstream slope of Belle Fourche Dam. Note the deteriorated condition of this paving after 40 years of service despite considerable maintenance. This dam is an earthfill structure on a tributary of the Belle Fourche River in South Dakota. 288–D–2937.

maximum dry unit weight of the mixture accurately.

A number of test cylinders are prepared, using the estimated cement content and cement contents 2 percentage points above and below the estimated content. The results of wet-dry, freeze-thaw, weight-loss criteria will determine the cement content required. This cement content is then increased by 2 percentage points for erosion resistance. If it is necessary to use a soil containing more than 50 percent fines, the cement content should be increased by 4 percentage points for erosion resistance. For most soils, a total required cement content of 10 to 12 percent by compacted volume of soil-cement is considered typical.

Figure 6-53.—Soil-cement paving on the upstream slope of Cheney Dam, Kansas. The soil-cement is in excellent condition after numerous storms. P835–526–1006NA.

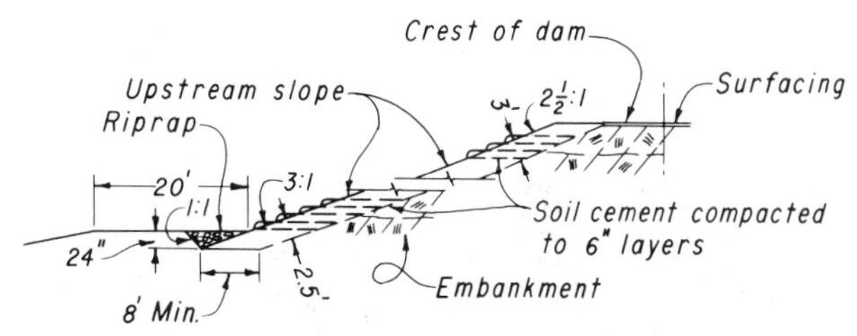

Figure 6-54.—Typical section of soil-cement slope protection. Cheney Dam, Kansas. 288–D–2795.

Compressive strength tests for soil-cement are considered supplementary to the standard soil-cement tests. Soil-cement mixtures with a compressive strength of about 450 lb/in^2 or more at 7 days will generally pass the wet-dry and freeze-thaw tests. Using cement contents of about 10 percent, 7-day compressive strengths of 500 to 1,000 lb/in^2 are common with a wide range of soils. Figure 6-55 shows the placement of soil-cement slope protection at Starvation Dam in Utah.

USBR Design Standards No. 13, chapter 17, should be referred to for current criteria and information on soil-cement design and construction.

6.23. *Downstream Slope Protection.*—If the downstream zone of an embankment consists of rock or cobble fill, no special surface treatment of the slope is necessary. Downstream slopes of homogeneous dams or dams with outer sand and gravel zones should be protected against erosion caused by wind and rainfall runoff by a layer of rock, cobbles, or sod. Because of the uncertainty of obtaining adequate protection by vegetative cover at many damsites, especially in arid regions, protection by cobbles or rock is preferred and should be used where the cost is not prohibitive. Layers 24 inches thick are easier to place, but a 12-inch-thick layer usually affords sufficient protection.

If grasses are planted, only those suitable for the locality should be selected. Figure 6-56 shows the native grasses that have protected the downstream slope of the Bureau's Belle Fourche Dam from erosion for 50 years. Two drainage berms, one of which is shown in the photograph, are located on the downstream slope of this 115-foot-high dam. Usually, fertilizer and uniform sprinkling of the seeded areas is necessary to promote the germination and to foster the growth of grasses. Appendix G contains sample specifications for placing topsoil, planting seed, and watering the seeded area until completion of construction.

6.24. *Surface Drainage.*—The desirability of providing facilities to handle surface drainage on the abutments and valley floor is often overlooked in the design of earthfill dams. The result is that, although the upstream and downstream slopes and the crest of the dam are protected against erosion, unsightly gullying occurs at the contact of the embankment with earth abutments from which vegetation has been removed during the construction operations. This gullying occurs especially when the abutments are steep.

Gullying most often develops along the contact of the downstream slope with the abutments. However, it can usually be controlled by constructing a gutter along the contact. The gutter may be formed from cobbles or rock used in the downstream surfacing; if the downstream slope is seeded, a concrete, asphalt, or dry-rock paved gutter should be provided. The likelihood of gullying of the abutments and gentle slopes of the valley floor caused by runoff from the downstream slope of the dam also should be considered; contour ditches or open drains may be needed to control erosion. Figure 6-57 shows typical sections of a contour ditch and an open drain.

Figure 6-55.—Placement of soil-cement slope protection. Starvation Dam, Utah. P66-418-3549.

Figure 6-56.—Downstream slope of Belle Fourche Dam protected by grass. 288–D–2938.

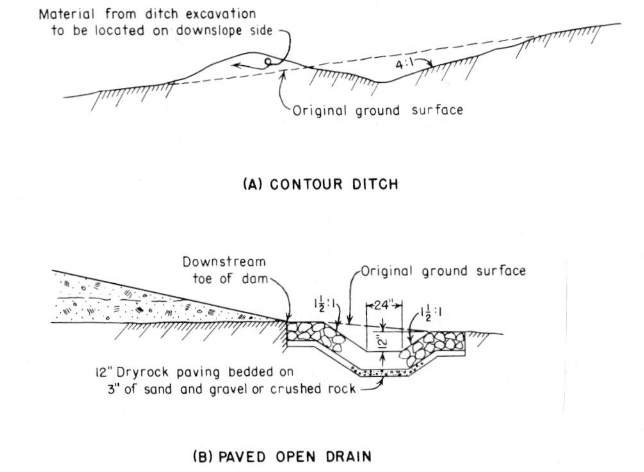

Figure 6-57.—Typical sections of a contour ditch and an open drain. 288–D–2498.

Attention should also be given to the construction of outfall drains or channels to conduct the toe drain discharge away from the downstream toe of the embankment so that an unsightly boggy area will not be created. The need for surface drainage facilities and the most appropriate type for a particular site can usually best be determined by field examination before or during construction.

6.25. *Flared Slopes at Abutments.*—If necessary, the upstream and downstream slopes of the embankment may be flared at the abutments to provide flatter slopes for stability or to control seepage through a longer contact of the impervious zone of the dam with the abutment. If the abutment is pervious and if a positive cutoff cannot be attained economically, it may be possible to obtain the effect of an upstream blanket by flaring the embankment. The design of the transition from normal to flared slopes is governed largely by the topography of the site, the length of contact desired, and the desirability of making a gradual transition without abrupt changes both for ease of construction and for appearance.

F. DESIGN EXAMPLES OF SMALL EARTHFILL DAMS

6.26. *General.*—The designs of 29 Bureau of Reclamation earthfill dams are discussed briefly in the next section. With only a few exceptions, these dams are less than 50 feet higher than the original streambed, or are dikes of that size constructed in conjunction with larger dams. The few exceptions were included to illustrate designs for unusual conditions that were not encountered in the construction of any of the smaller dams. All exceptions chosen, however, are less than 100 feet higher than the original streambed.

These designs include small earthfill dams constructed by the Bureau of Reclamation since 1930. Of these 29 dams, 2 were constructed before 1940, 5 in the 1940's, 14 in the 1950's, 5 in the 1960's, and 3 in the 1980's. Many minor dikes constructed in conjunction with storage dams or canal systems were omitted because of their similarity to other designs that are shown.

The purpose of these examples is to illustrate the changes in designs over the years and the variety of designs that were conceived to meet widely varying conditions in foundations and in availability of construction materials. With few exceptions, the completed structures have given satisfactory service.

Stubblefield Dam has experienced dessication of the upper 15 feet of the embankment. Repair is underway (1986) and will consist of a trench lined with filter fabric and backfilled with pit-run gravel through the upper part of the embankment. The reservoir has remained in service even though restricted to a lower than normal water surface. Lovewell Dam has experienced some riprap damage, which has since been repaired. Several other dams and dikes have been modified to increase their spillway capacity because of revised hydrology or because of spillway damage: Big Sandy Dike, Dickinson Dam, Fruitgrowers Dam, and Tiber Dike. This amount of repair and modification to this number of dams over the time span involved is considered minor. Even though design and maintenance problems have been minor, the designs are not considered unduly conservative. It is believed that a designer of small earthfill dams can gather valuable ideas from a study of these examples.

6.27. Maximum Sections.—Figures 6-58 through 6-88 show the maximum sections of small earthfill dams constructed by the Bureau of Reclamation. A brief explanation of each of the designs follows:

(a) *Amarillo Regulating Reservoir.*—This design (fig. 6-58) illustrates a small dam embankment together with an earth lining over the entire reservoir floor to prevent excessive seepage through the floor. The earth lining continues up the upstream slope of the embankment and is covered by riprap and gravel to protect it from erosion. A toe drain is provided for drainage. The topsoil protecting the downstream slope came from stripping the structure area.

(b) *Cawker City Dike.*—Several different design concepts are illustrated in this example (fig. 6-59). Soil-cement was used for upstream slope protection because of the scarcity of good quality rock for riprap. The soil-cement was satisfactorily compacted into lifts thicker than the 6 inches normally considered standard. The downstream slope was formed by topsoil that was subsequently seeded for slope protection. Because of the extreme depth of alluvial fill, a positive cutoff was uneconomical to achieve. Consequently, a sand drain system was installed at the downstream toe. As shown, a toe drain was also incorporated into the design.

(c) *Big Sandy Dike.*—This dike (fig. 6-60) was constructed in conjunction with Big Sandy Dam (not shown), a 72-foot-high dam of conventional design with a 3:1 upstream slope protected by a 3-foot-thick layer of rock riprap. The design of the upstream slope of the dike represents a departure from usual design and was adopted because of the scarcity and expense of rock for riprap. Note that in the surcharge range, the upstream slope of the dike is 8:1, which is the beaching slope of the embankment material. Freeboard above the maximum water surface is provided by a 3:1 slope, which is planted to make it erosion resistant to wave splash and spray to which it will be subjected only rarely. This design is suitable for upstream slope protection of a detention dam, provided the maximum water surface will not be attained more than several times during the expected life of the dam.

(d) *Carpinteria Reservoir Dike.*—Carpinteria Reservoir is a small equalizing reservoir constructed on a gently sloping sidehill by excavating on the uphill side and constructing a dike (fig. 6-61) on the downhill side. The concrete lining is provided to prevent seepage, which would be serious because of the location of the reservoir with respect to improved property. The concrete lining covers all the side slopes and the bottom of the reservoir. Figure 6-62 shows the reservoir lining being constructed. Because this reservoir is subject to rapid drawdown, a gravel drain is placed under the side lining to prevent uplift. A pipe drainage system is also provided under the reservoir floor lining.

The embankment was constructed of material from the excavation. This soil contained considerable rock fragments larger than 5 inches in diameter, and separation was required by the specifications to obtain an impervious zone that could be compacted satisfactorily. The dumped earth material zone provided for waste disposal of excess excavation. Oversize rock fragments from the

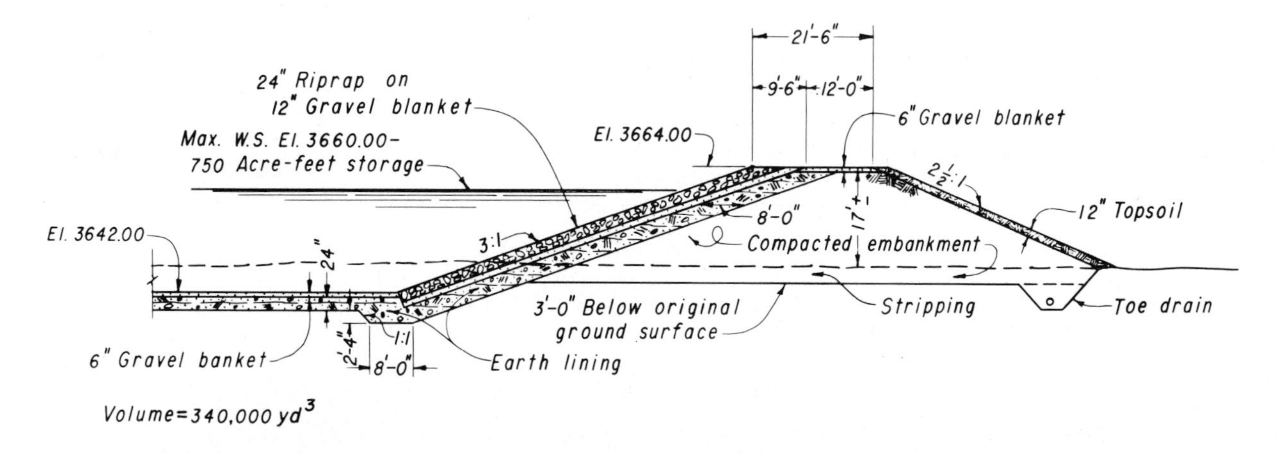

Figure 6-58.—Amarillo Regulating Reservoir. Located offstream on the Canadian River Aqueduct, Texas (completed 1965). From 62–D–322.

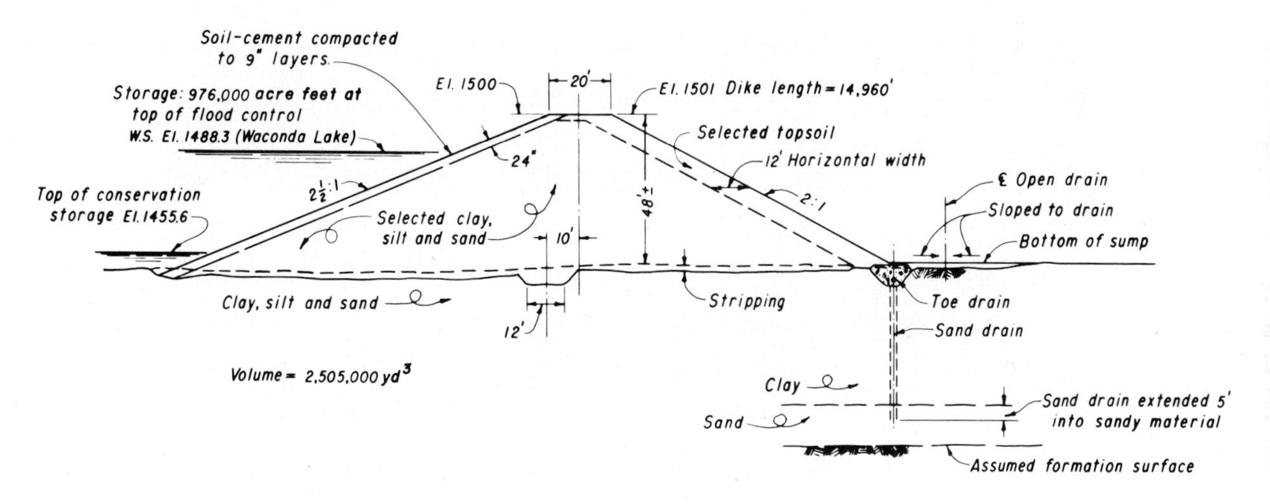

Figure 6-59.—Cawker City Dike. Protecting Cawker City, Kansas, from the waters of Wacondo Lake (constructed 1967). From 495–D–245.

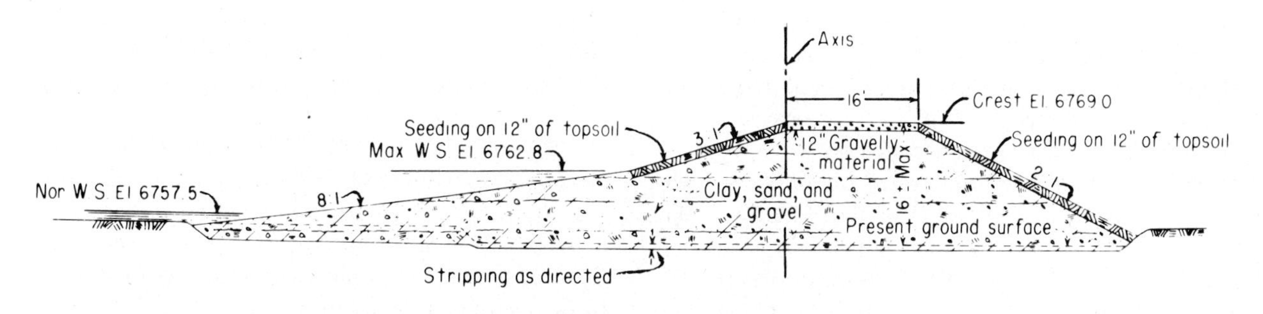

Figure 6-60.—Typical section, Big Sandy Dam. Located on Big Sandy Creek, Wyoming (constructed 1950-52). 288–D–2940.

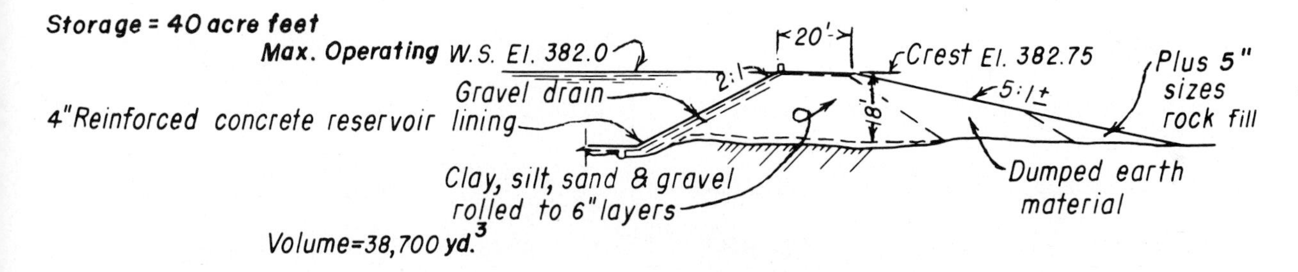

Figure 6-61.—Carpinteria Reservoir Dike. Terminal reservoir of a distribution system located near Carpinteria, California (constructed 1952-53). From 103–D–585.

Figure 6-62.—Construction of concrete lining at Carpinteria Reservoir. SB–3262–R2.

screening operation were used to construct the downstream rockfill toe.

(e) *Carter Lake Dam No. 3.*— This dam (fig. 6-63) illustrates the design of a zoned embankment consisting of an earth impervious core and rock shells. At this site, there was a limited amount of material for an impervious core, no sand-gravel, but a large amount of rock that could be quarried. Quarrying operations were controlled so as to produce the desired amount and gradation of rock fragments. The rockfill consists of rock with a maximum size of 1 yd^3 and sufficient smaller rocks to fill the voids. The zone of quarry fines, which acts as a filter between the rockfill and the impervious core, consists of rock fines not more than 20 percent of which pass a ¼-inch screen with no pieces larger than 8 inches. The cutoff wall shown on this section is no longer used because it is considered unessential for structure of this size.

(f) *Crane Prairie Dam.*—The design of this small dam (fig. 6-64) is conventional. Except for the bottom width of the cutoff trench, the design conforms to the recommendations given in this text.

(g) *Crescent Lake Dam.*—This is a typical modern, small-zoned earthfill dam (fig. 6-65). The large pervious shells allow the use of steep slopes on the embankment. Note the key trench and the modification to the zone lines near the crest of the dam to facilitate construction.

(h) *Dickinson Dam.*—This dam (fig. 6-66) is the

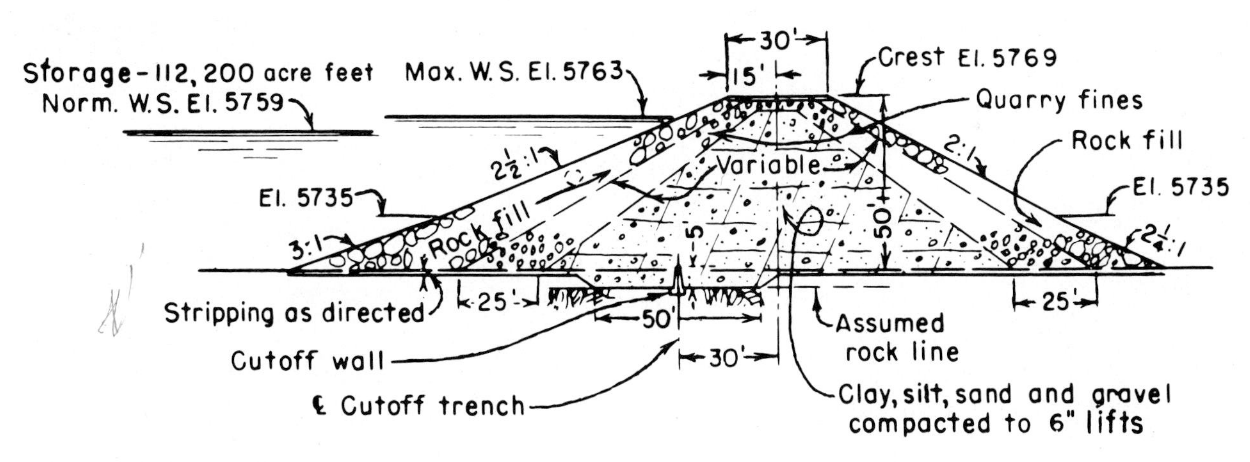

Figure 6-63.—Carter Lake Dam No. 3. Located on Dry Creek (a tributary of the Big Thompson River), Colorado (constructed 1950-52). 288–D–2939.

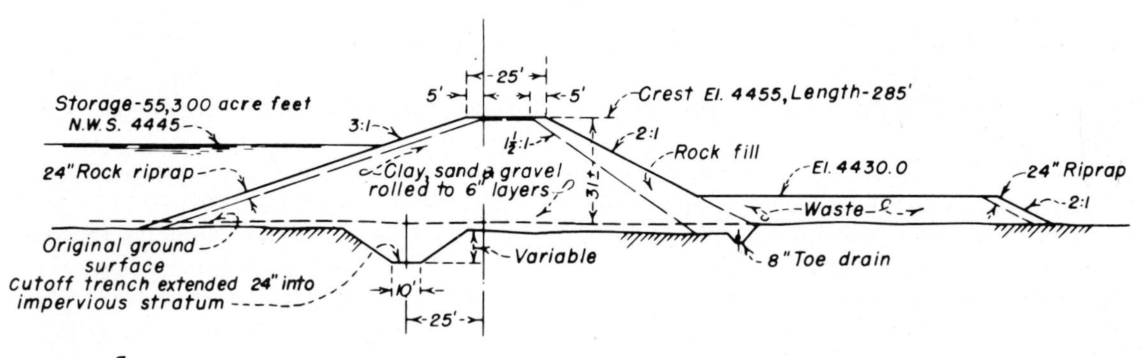

Figure 6-64.—Crane Prairie Dam. Located on the Deschutes River, Oregon (constructed 1939-40). From 103–D–581.

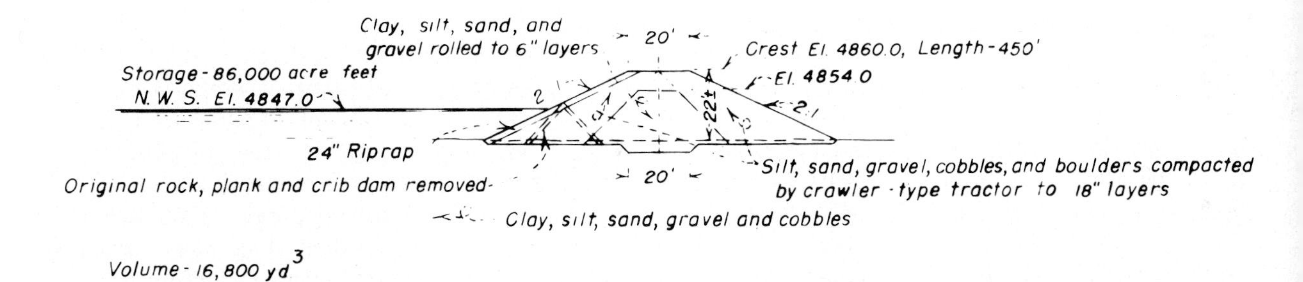

Figure 6-65.—Crescent Lake Dam. Located on Crescent Creek, Oregon (constructed 1954-56). From 103–D–586.

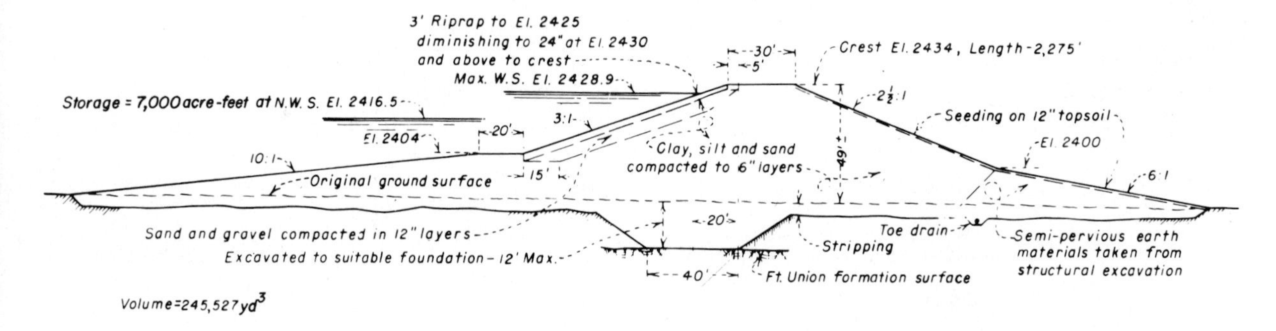

Figure 6-66.—Dickinson Dam. Located on the Heart River, North Dakota (constructed 1948-50). From 103–D–584.

modified homogeneous type. The flat slopes at the toes of the dam form stabilizing fills, which were provided because of the unconsolidated and uncemented foundation material. Note the decrease in the thickness of riprap near the crest of the dam. This was done to decrease the amount of costly rock, and in view of the infrequent exposure to wave action because of the large surcharge head.

(i) *Dry Falls Dam.*—This design (fig. 6-67) illustrates a zoned embankment constructed on a soft foundation. This dam is unusual in that rock was used to construct the stabilizing fills formed by flattening the slopes of the dam. Usually, rock is too expensive to be used for this purpose, but in this case it was excavated for a canal, which heads at the dam. The stability afforded to the section by the heavy rock zones permits steep slopes for the upper part of the dam. Note the filter zone provided between the core and the rockfills and the modifications made to the zoning lines near the crest of the dam to facilitate construction and preserve a sufficiently long path of percolation through impervious material. The 42-foot-wide crest was required because this dam is used for a major highway crossing.

(j) *Fruitgrowers Dam.*—This is another example of a small earthfill dam (fig. 6-68) whose design conforms to modern practices except for the narrow bottom width of the cutoff trench. The construction reports note that the bottom width, in general, was made 12 to 14 feet to accommodate construction equipment. The cutoff trench was extended to shale. The spillway was replaced in 1986 because of damage to the existing spillway and revised hydrology. A downstream drainage berm was also added to increase both the static and dynamic stability.

(k) *Howard Prairie Dam.*—Although this dam (fig. 6-69) is higher than those within the scope of this text, it is included herein as an example of a zoned embankment with a relatively thin impervious core and with heavy rockfill supporting zones. The overburden penetrated by the cutoff trench consisted of topsoil and sand-gravel. Note the transition zones between the impervious core and the rockfill zones, and the modifications made to the zone lines near the crest of the dam to facilitate construction.

(l) *Lion Lake Dikes.*—This is illustrative of a very small embankment (fig. 6-70) constructed to impound a water-supply reservoir. The trench shown is a relatively deep key extending into glacial deposits of considerable depth.

(m) *Lovewell Dam.*—Although this dam (fig. 6-71) is somewhat higher than those within the scope of this text, it is included herein to illustrate the use of stabilizing fills on an extremely soft clay foundation. Note also how a minimum amount of riprap is used in this design. The 20:1 slope of the upstream stabilizing fill does not require protection. Only a minor amount of erosion is expected on the upstream 2.5:1 slope of the stabilizing fill because the extremely short reservoir fetch below elevation 1575.0 will produce little wave action. Minor erosion of this extensive stabilizing fill will not be of consequence.

(n) *Eklutna Dam.*—This dam (fig. 6-72), located in an area of high seismic risk, embodies a large downstream rockfill zone for stability. In addition, special care was taken to ensure that the cutoff trench was excavated to firm clayey soil.

(o) *Lower Two Medicine Dam.*—This dam (fig. 6-73) replaces a previous dam which was overtopped in 1964. A large concrete overflow section now adequately handles flood flows. The embankment is of standard design except for the riprap and bedding

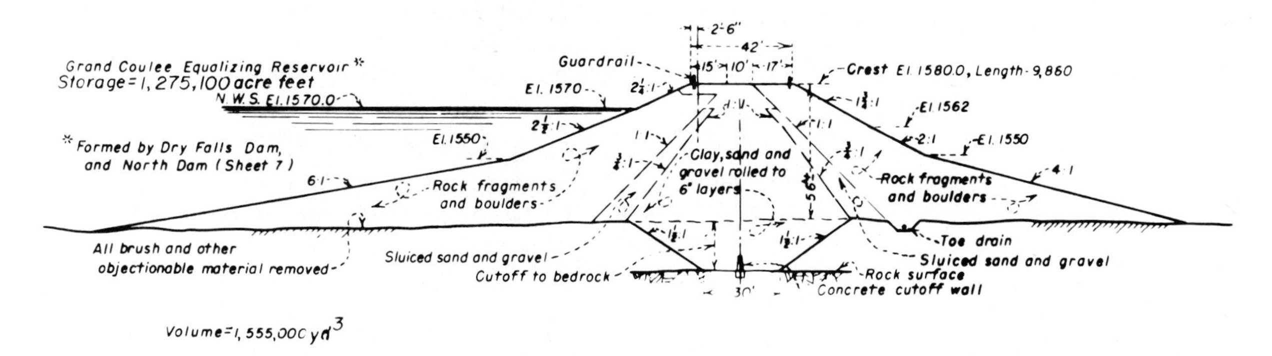

Figure 6-67.—Dry Falls Dam. Located near Coulee City, Washington. It forms the south barrier of Grand Coulee Equalizing Reservoir (constructed 1946-49). From 103–D–583.

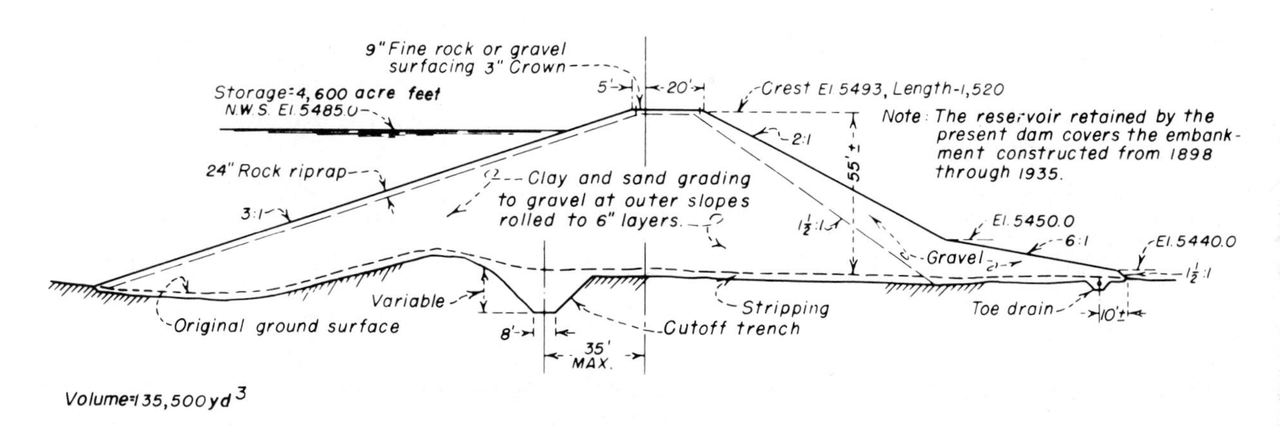

Figure 6-68.—Fruitgrowers Dam. Located on Alfalfa Run Wash in Colorado. Its main water supply is derived from Currant and Surface creeks (constructed 1938-39). From 103–D–581.

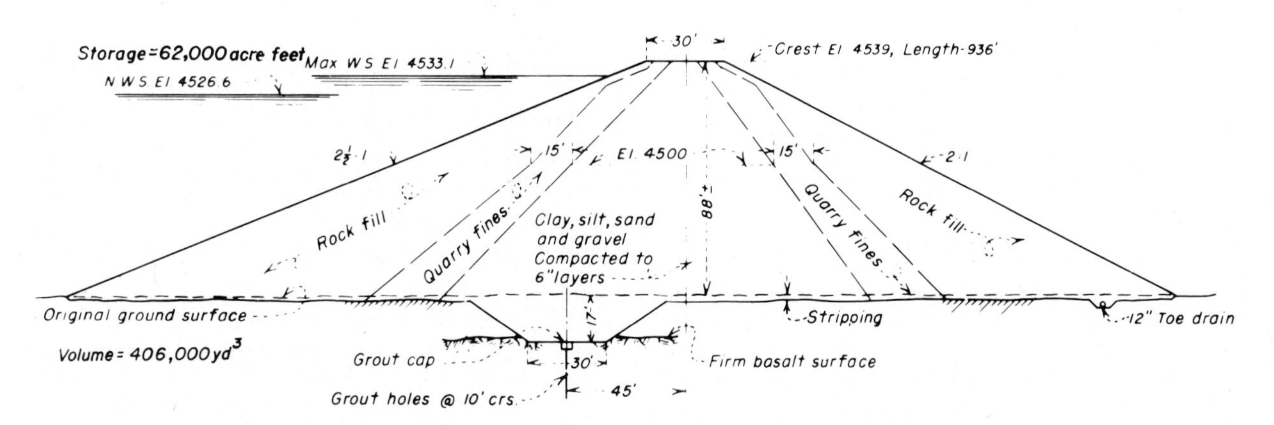

Figure 6-69.—Howard Prairie Dam. Located on Beaver Creek (a tributary of Jenny Creek), Oregon (constructed 1957-59). From 103–D–587.

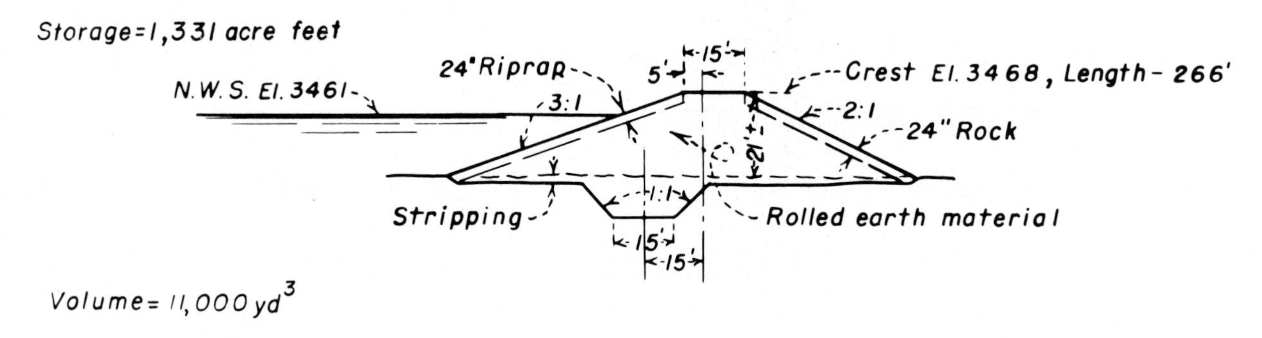

Figure 6-70.—Lion Lake Dikes. Constructed for a water-supply reservoir for Hungry Horse Dam Government Camp, Montana (constructed 1947). From 103–D–583.

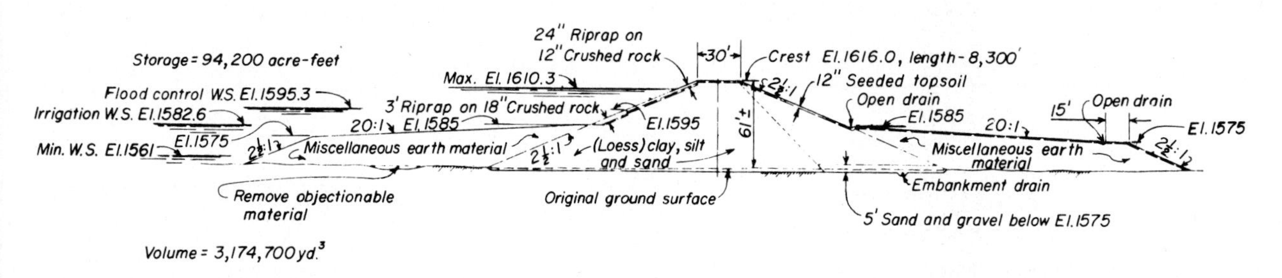

Figure 6-71.—Lovewell Dam. Located on the Republican River (offstream from White Rock Creek), Kansas (constructed 1954-57). From 103–D–586.

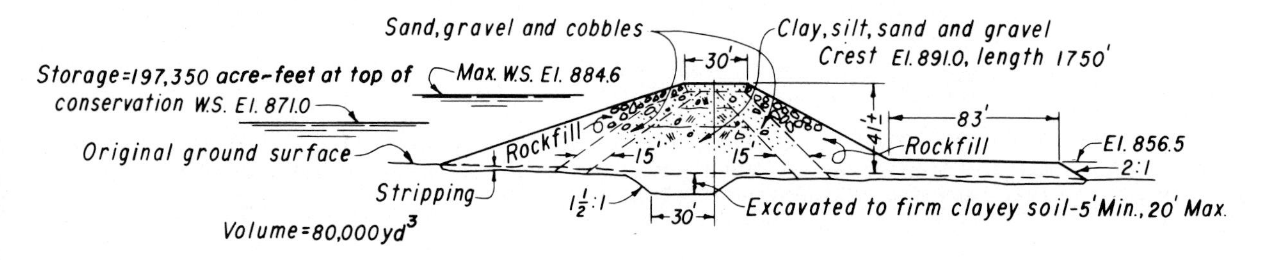

Figure 6-72.—Eklutna Dam, Alaska. Built to replace a former dam damaged by the 1964 Alaskan earthquake (completed 1965). From 783–D–639.

at the downstream toe for protection against erosion by anticipated high tailwater. The downstream drainage was provided in accordance with section 6.10(i). The key trench shown was excavated through weathered, low-density alluvium down to firm material.

(p) *Olympus Dam.*—This design (fig. 6-74) is an example of an earthfill dam with multiple zones. Note the upstream slope protection; the riprap is used only on the upper portion of the slope where heavy wave action is expected. The lower portion of the slope is protected by rock and cobble fill because the water level will rarely be lowered into this range.

(q) *Picacho North Dam.*—This is a detention dam (fig. 6-75) that has no permanent storage pool. It is constructed on a stratified pervious foundation. The impervious zone of the dam was extended to the upstream toe and was made continuous with waste placed upstream from the dam to increase the path of percolation through the foundation. To facilitate the use of available materials from stratified deposits, the design of the embankment was based on the impervious core varying between the slope limits shown.

(r) *Picacho South Dam.*—This dam (fig. 6-76) is also a detention dam with no permanent storage pool. At this site, the foundation was relatively im-

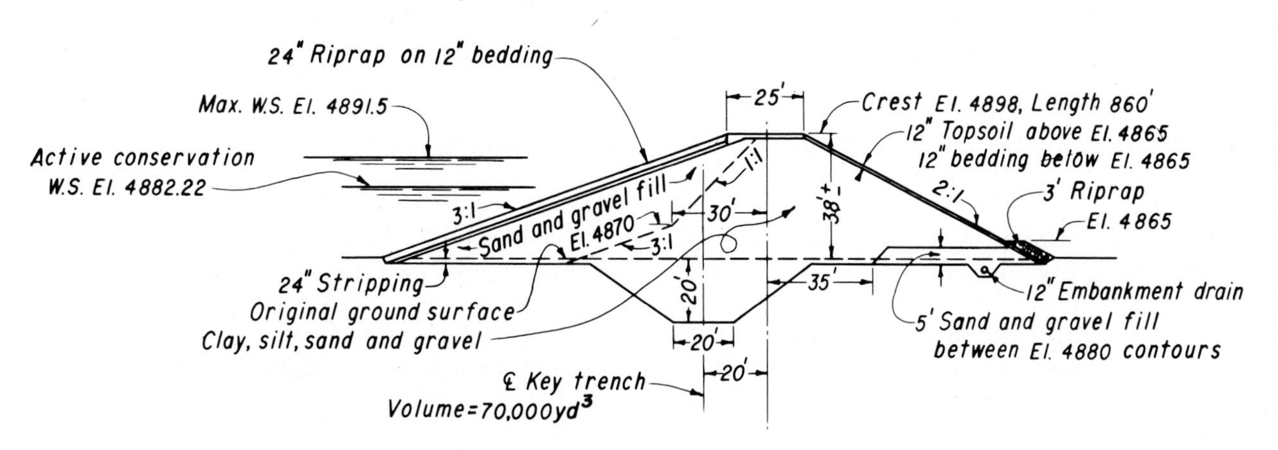

Figure 6-73.—Lower Two Medicine Dam, Montana. This structure replaces a dam that was overtopped in an unprecedented flood (completed 1967). From 2–D–24.

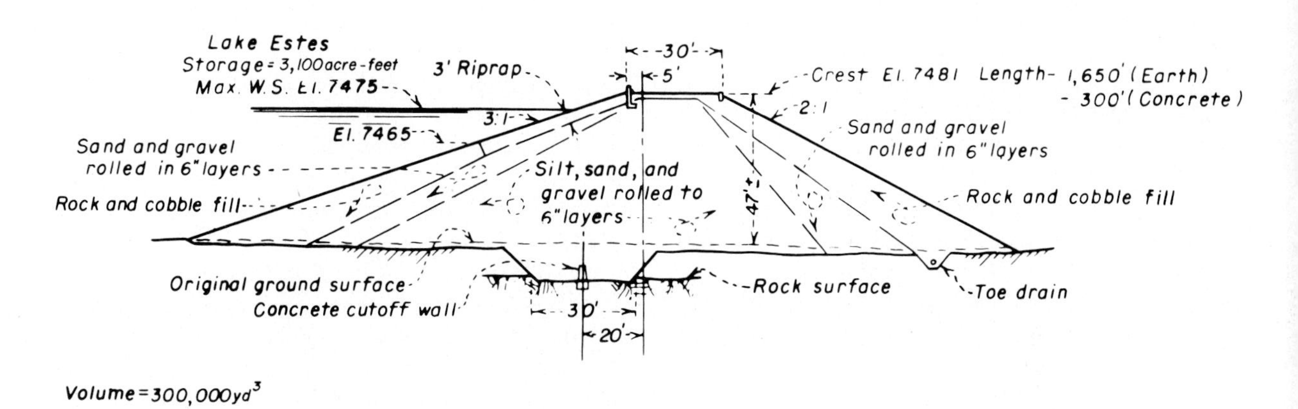

Figure 6-74.—Olympus Dam. Located on the Big Thompson River, Colorado (constructed 1947-49). From 103–D–583.

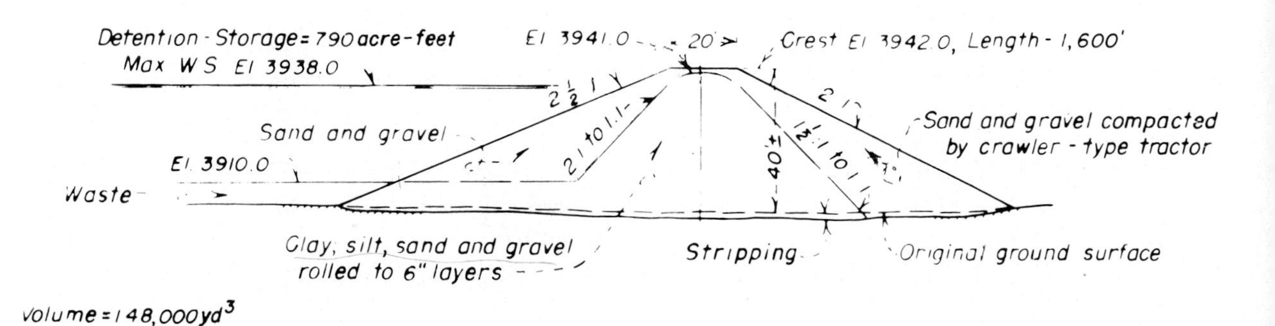

Figure 6-75.—Picacho North Dam. A detention dam located on the North Branch of Picacho Arroyo, New Mexico (constructed 1953-54). From 103–D–586.

pervious; only sufficient pervious material for slope protection of the embankment could be found in the vicinity. A 10-foot-wide sand-gravel-cobble zone was specified on both the upstream and downstream slopes to facilitate compaction. Riprap was not considered necessary because the outlet capacity is sufficient to evacuate the reservoir in a few days.

(s) *Pishkun Dikes.*—This is an interesting design (fig. 6-77) because it illustrates how a 43-foot-high dam was raised 6 feet, 10 years after completion of the initial construction. This embankment is essentially homogeneous; a small downstream pervious zone was provided in the original design to contain the more pervious materials found in the borrow pit. Note the sparing use of costly riprap; it is provided only in the operating range of the reservoir where wave action will be most severe.

(t) *Lubbock Regulating Reservoir.*—Soil-cement provides the slope protection for this small regulating reservoir (fig. 6-78) located on the Canadian River Aqueduct near Lubbock, Texas. Soil-cement on an earth lining is also provided to prevent excessive seepage through the reservoir floor. Topsoil to protect the downstream slope came from stripping of the reservoir area.

(u) *Shadow Mountain Dam.*—This dam (fig. 6-79) has a pervious glacial foundation. The design provides a partial cutoff trench and a flat upstream slope, which functions as a blanket to reduce seepage, and a drainage blanket in the downstream portion of the dam to control seepage uplift.

(v) *Soda Lake Dike.*—In all respects, this dam (fig. 6-80) is well-designed by the standards given in this text. The filter zones between the impervious core and the outer rockfill zones were made 12 feet wide, and the zone lines were modified near the crest of the dam to facilitate construction.

(w) *Stubblefield Dam.*—This design (fig. 6-81) is typical of a homogeneous dam modified by a horizontal drainage blanket meeting filter requirements. It has a toe drain to lower the phreatic line in the downstream portion of the embankment. The dumped earth shown outside the 2:1 downstream slope was for disposal of waste material. It was thought that disposal of waste material (including organic material) in this manner not only would flatten the downstream slope, but also would develop a vegetative cover that would be adequate for slope protection. The dam has been modified because of dessication (sec. 6.26).

(x) *Tiber Dike.*—Drawing (A) of figure 6-82 shows the maximum section of Tiber Dike, which is conventional in design. A 10-foot-deep key trench is excavated into the glacial till foundation, and the upstream slope is protected by riprap. Drawing (B) shows modifications made to the dike where the original ground is above elevation 2995.0, which is above the top of the irrigation storage at elevation 2992.3. Because the slope will be subjected to wave action only during a flood, it was decided that adequate protection would be provided by a 3-foot-thick layer of compacted sand, gravel, and cobbles (maximum size 10 inches) if the slope were flattened to 6:1. This modfication was economical because of the high cost of riprap. It illustrates design flexibility in achieving the most economical structure. Tiber Dike was raised in 1980-81 because of revised hydrology.

(y) *Sheep Creek Barrier Dam.*—This dam (fig. 6-83) was constructed to form a barrier to floodwaters heavily laden with sediment. The sediment will be deposited in the reservoir area, thus clearing up the stream and helping to reduce the rate of erosion upstream by reducing the hydraulic gradient. Because the reservoir pool is designed to fill with sediment, no upstream slope protection was provided, and only a minimum key trench was constructed.

(z) *Wasco Dam.*—This dam (figs. 6-84 and 6-85) is used as an example throughout this text. It is not unusual in design, and it may be considered typical of small zoned earthfill dams constructed on pervious shallow foundations that can economically be cut off by open-trench methods. The cobble and rockfill zones use oversize rock removed from impervious soil and rock fragments from excavations for appurtenant structures. A toe drain was not used in the design because the foundation overburden is definitely pervious.

(aa) *Ute Dam Dike.*—This dike (fig. 6-86) is an extension of Ute Dam, which is located on the Canadian River in eastern New Mexico. The dike was designed and constructed in the early 1980's, in connection with a modification that raised the dam and revised the spillway. The dike is an example of a zoned section with an inclined filter protecting the impervious zone. This type of filter protection is typical of current design procedure. The section also exhibits the concept of using flat beaching slopes instead of slope protection for wave protection. On steeper slopes of the dam and transitions

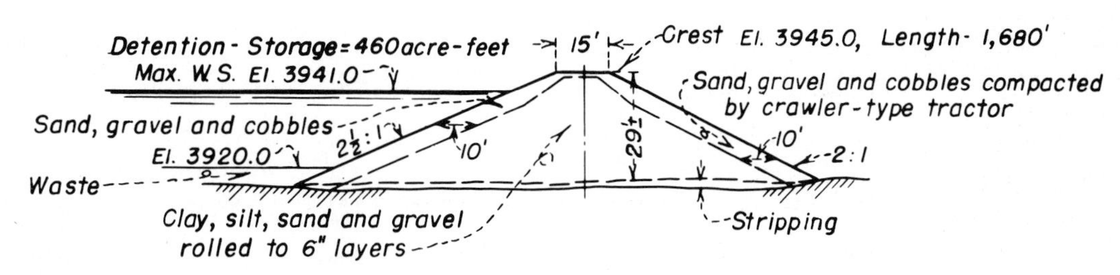

Figure 6-76.—Picacho South Dam. A detention dam located on the South Branch of Picacho Arroyo, New Mexico (constructed 1953-54). From 103–D–586.

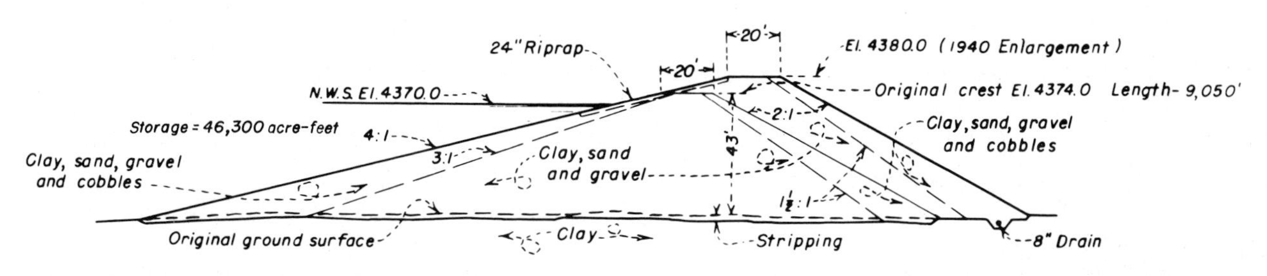

Figure 6-77.—Pishkun Dikes. Located offstream from the Sun River, Montana (constructed 1930-31). From 103–D–580.

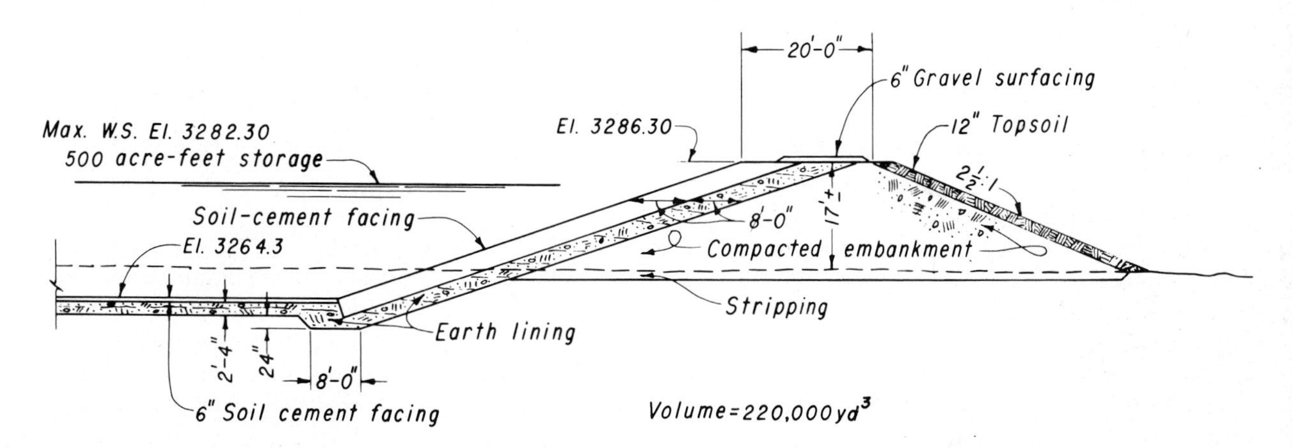

Figure 6-78.—Lubbock Regulating Reservoir. Located offstream near Lubbock, Texas (completed 1966). From 662–D–409.

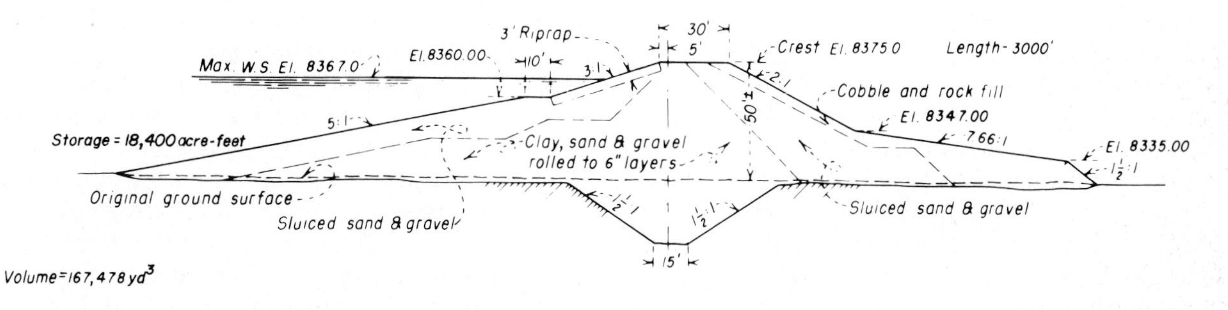

Figure 6-79.—Shadow Mountain Dam. Located on the Colorado River, Colorado (constructed 1943-46). From 103–D–582.

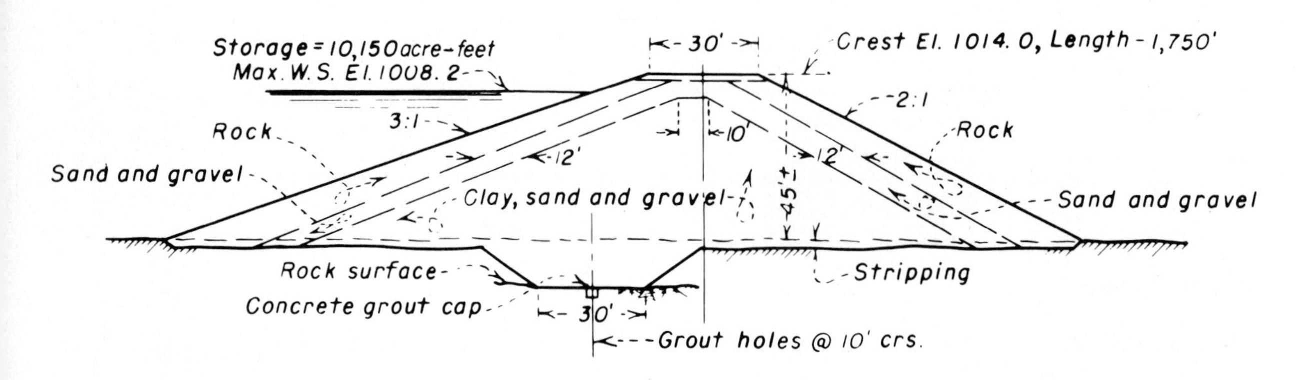

Figure 6-80.—Soda Lake Dike. Located offstream from the Columbia River, Washington (constructed 1950-52). From 103-D-584.

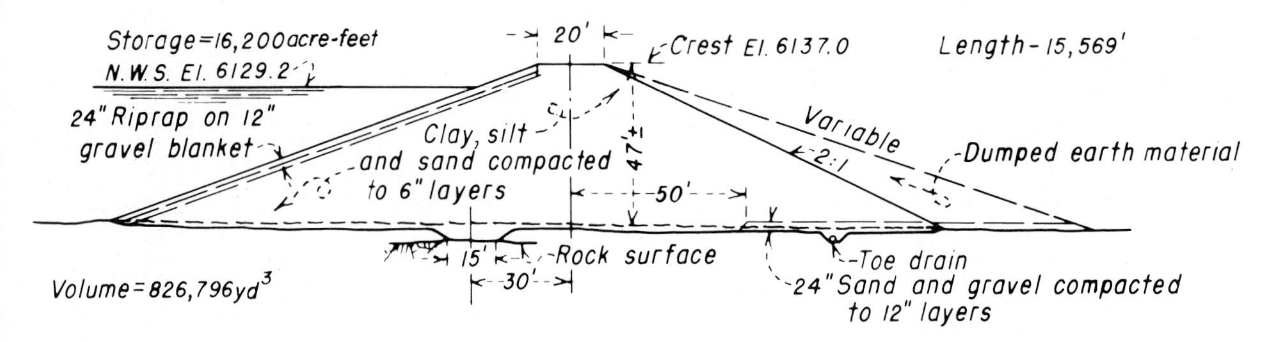

Figure 6-81.—Stubblefield Dam. Located offstream from the Vermejo River, New Mexico (constructed 1953-54). From 103-D-585.

between the dike and the dam, soil-cement was used to protect the embankment. The alluvium was relatively shallow, and an earth cutoff protected by a downstream filter and extending through the alluvium was used as the major seepage control feature of the dam foundation.

(bb) *San Justo Dike.*—This dike (fig. 6-87) is part of an offstream reservoir project located near Hollister, California, between the Calaveras and San Andreas faults. Design and construction were accomplished during the mid-1980's. The dike will almost certainly be shaken one or more times in its lifetime by a large magnitude earthquake. The section illustrates a recent typical embankment dam design for an active seismic region. Note the thick filters and drains in the inclined and horizontal drainage layers downstream of the impervious zone. Also illustrated is the use of stability berms necessary to obtain adequate static stability because weak clay zones are present in the foundation. The upstream berm is provided by waste material from required excavation. Although somewhat higher (70 to 75 ft) than the standard for a small dam, San Justo Dike is a good example of current design practice.

(cc) *Calamus Dam.*—This dam (fig. 6-88) is located in the sandhills of Nebraska. It was designed and constructed during the early to mid-1980's. It is not a small dam (about 95 ft high), but is included because it illustrates so many seepage control features. It is founded on moderately thick alluvial and eolian deposits of silts and sands that overlay the Ogallala Formation. The embankment and foundation materials are very erodible and subject to piping. A total positive cutoff was impossible; therefore, the design concentrated on reducing and controlling seepage. An upstream impervious blanket and slurry wall were used to reduce seepage. An inclined (chimney drain) and horizontal drainage blanket, toe drain, and relief wells were used downstream to collect and control the seepage that will occur. The slurry wall penetrates to the Ogallala Formation on the right side of the river, but only to a depth of 45 feet on the left side of the river. The Ogallala Formation is a thick, pervious formation that is near the surface across much of the midwestern United States and is an important source of water in that area. Its existence precluded a positive impervious cutoff.

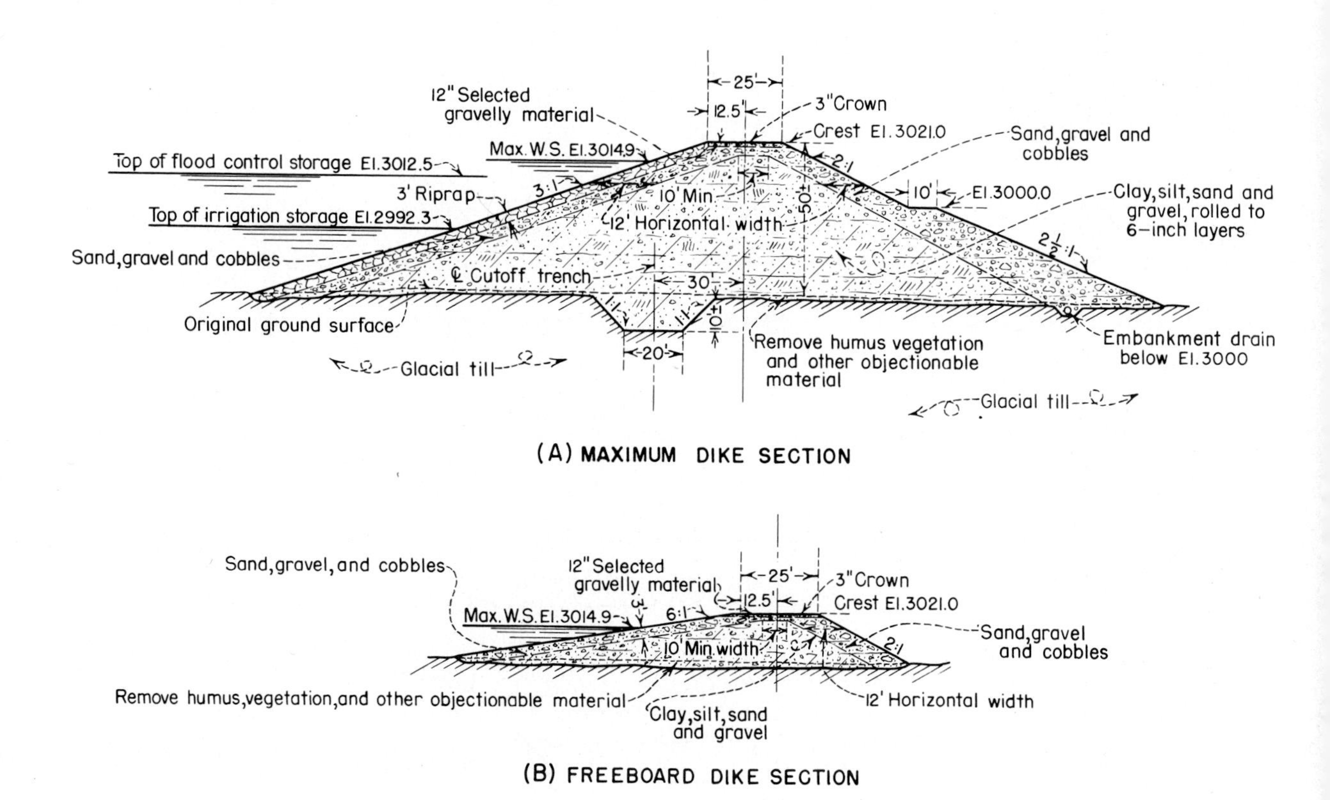

Figure 6-82.—Sections of Tiber Dike. Located on the Marias River, Montana (constructed 1953-56). 288–D–2501.

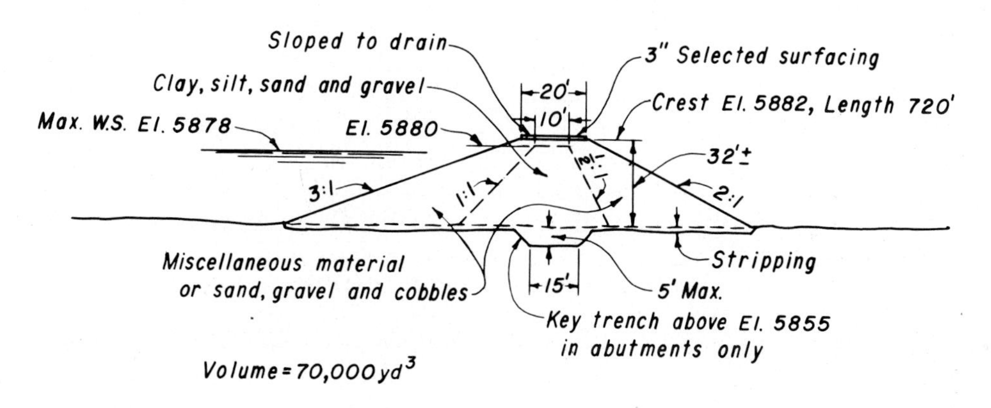

Figure 6-83—Sheep Creek Barrier Dam. A sediment control dam in southern Utah (constructed in 1956). From 788–D–12.

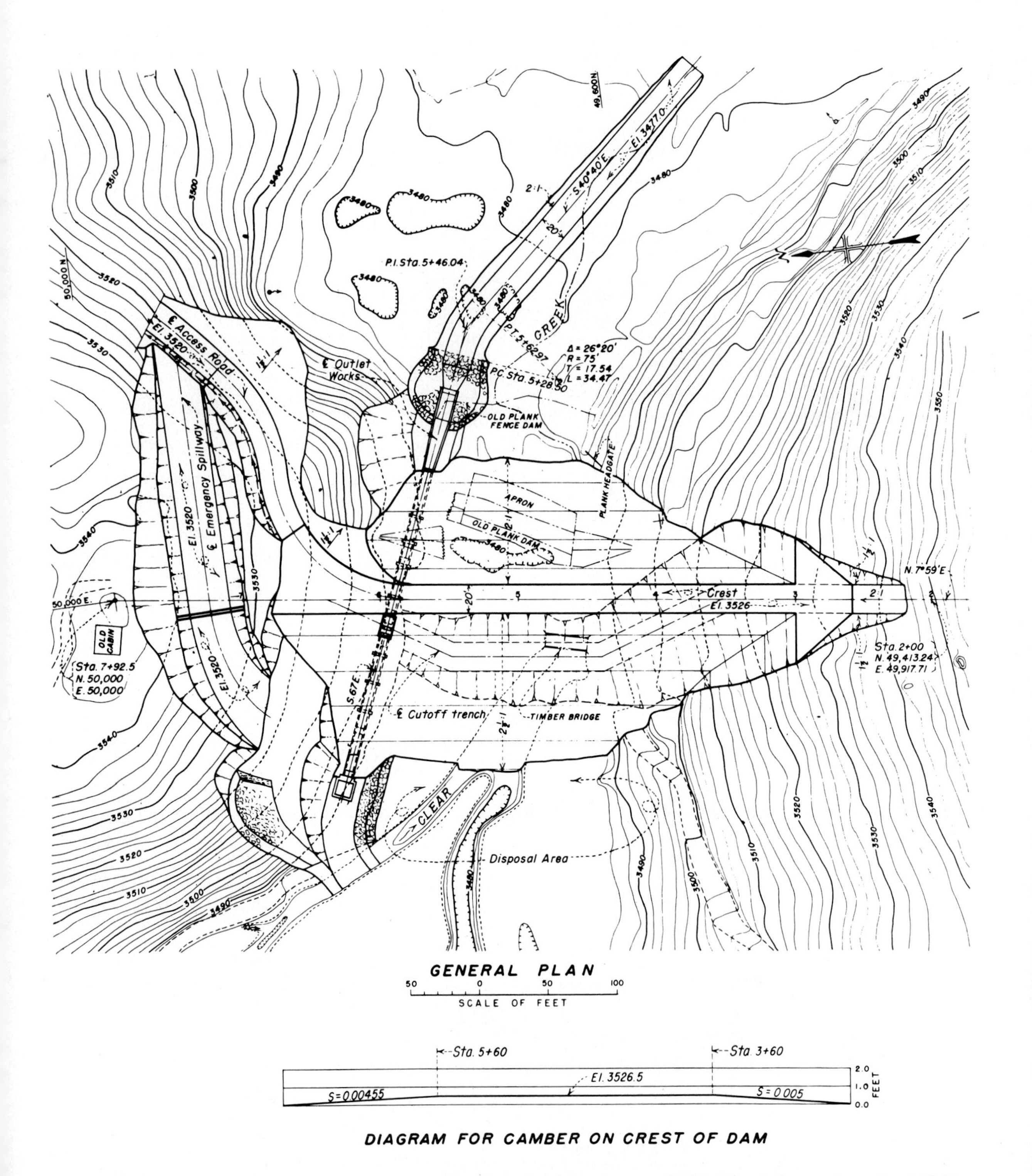

Figure 6-84.—General plan for Wasco Dam. Located on Clear Creek (a tributary of White River), Oregon (completed 1958). From 350–D–4.

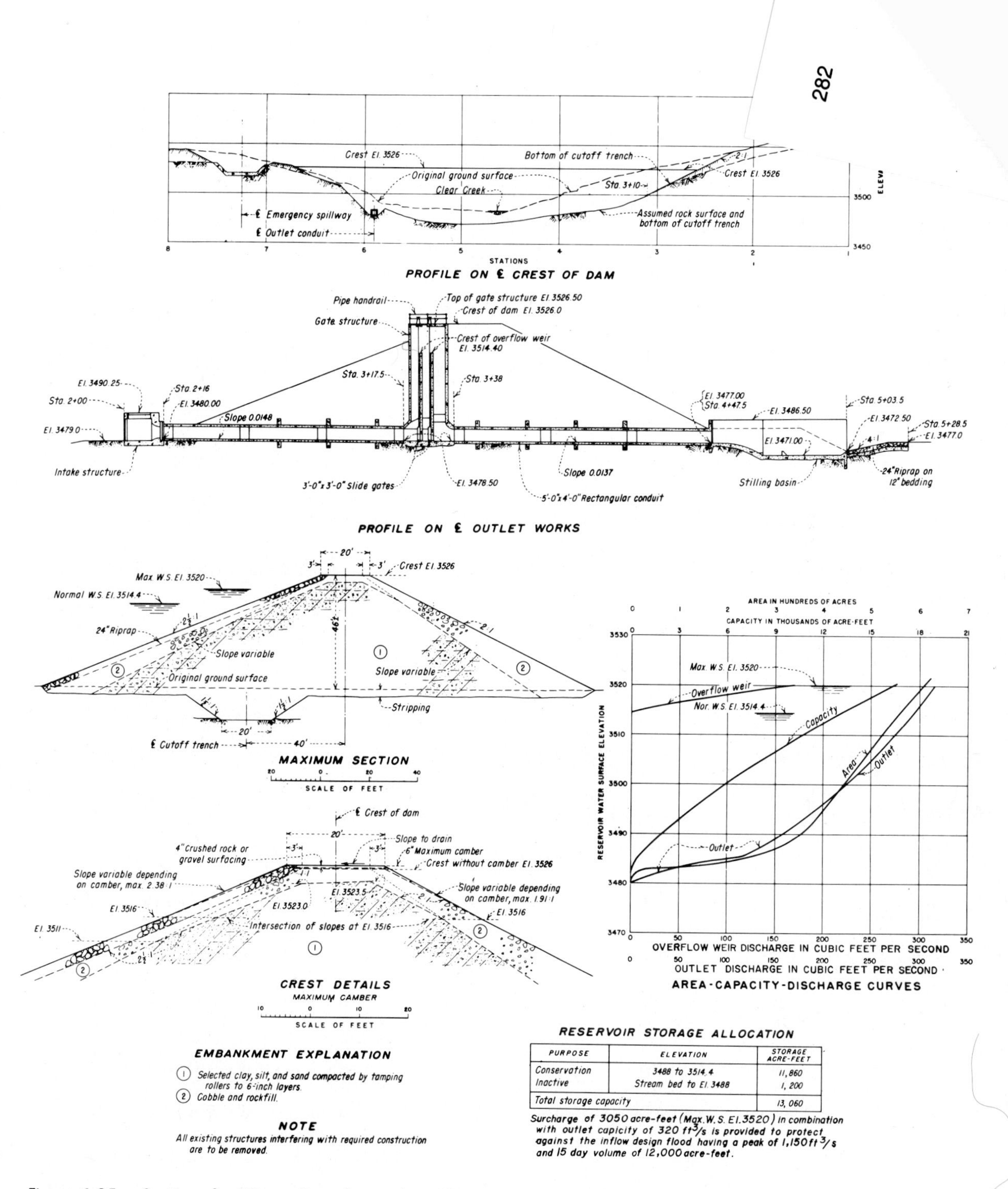

EMBANKMENT EXPLANATION

1. Selected clay, silt, and sand compacted by tamping rollers to 6-inch layers.
2. Cobble and rockfill.

NOTE

All existing structures interfering with required construction are to be removed.

RESERVOIR STORAGE ALLOCATION

PURPOSE	ELEVATION	STORAGE ACRE-FEET
Conservation	3488 to 3514.4	11,860
Inactive	Stream bed to El. 3488	1,200
Total storage capacity		13,060

Surcharge of 3050 acre-feet (Max. W.S. El. 3520) in combination with outlet capicity of 320 ft³/s is provided to protect against the inflow design flood having a peak of 1,150 ft³/s and 15 day volume of 12,000 acre-feet.

Figure 6-85.—Sections for Wasco Dam. Located on Clear Creek (a tributary of White River), Oregon (completed 1958). From 350-D-4.

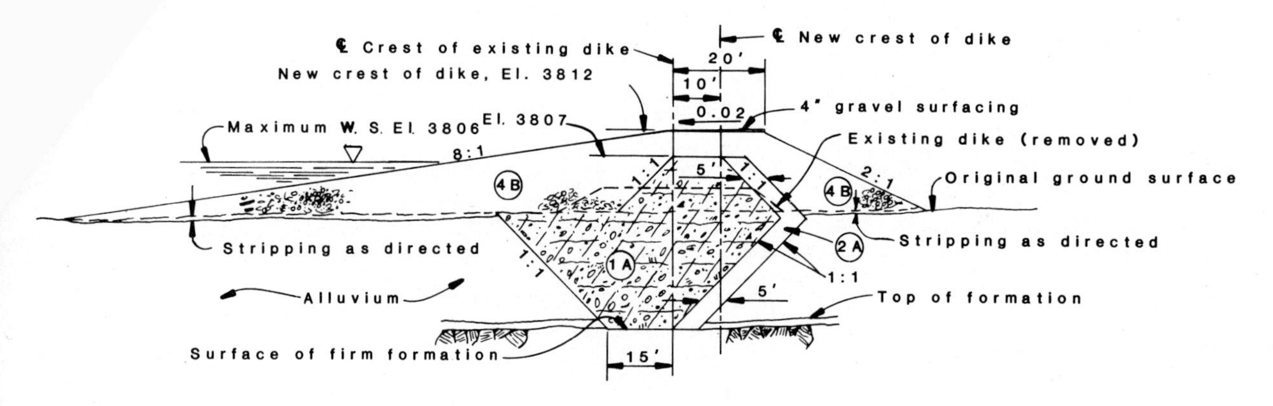

(1A) Impervious material of low plasticity clay and silty sand compacted to 6-inch lifts by tamping rollor, SC, CL, SM.

(2A) Pervious material of well graded to poorly graded sand, compacted by vibratory compactor in 12-inch lifts, SP, SW.

(4B) Pervious sandstone, cobbles, and gravel compacted by vibratory compactor in 18-inch lifts.

Figure 6-86.—Dike section of Ute Dam, New Mexico. This structure on the Canadian River was constructed (1982-83) in conjunction with raising the dam to provide additional storage and flood capacity. 103–D–1832.

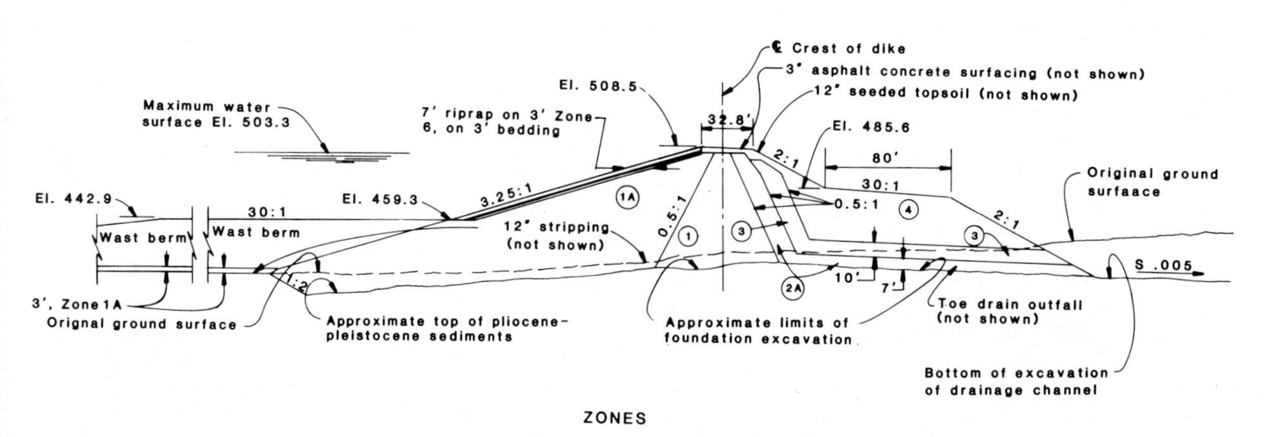

ZONES

(1) Selected CL, SC, SM, and ML materials compacted by tamping rollers to 6-inch lifts.

(1A) Selected CL, SC, SM, and ML materials compacted by pneumatic tired rollers to 12-inch lifts.

(1B) Slected CH, CL, SC, SM, and ML materials compacted by pneumatic tired rollers from 12-inch loose lift.

(2A) Processed SP naterials compacted by vibratory rollers from 12-inch loose lifts.

(3) Processed GP materials compacted by vibratory rollers from 24-inch loose lifts.

(4) Decomposed granite material compacter by pneumatic tired roller from 12-inch loose lifts.

(6) Rock fragments.

Figure 6-87.—San Justo Dike. Constructed (1985) in conjunction with San Justo Dam to form an off-stream reservoir near Hollister, California. From 921–D–1071.

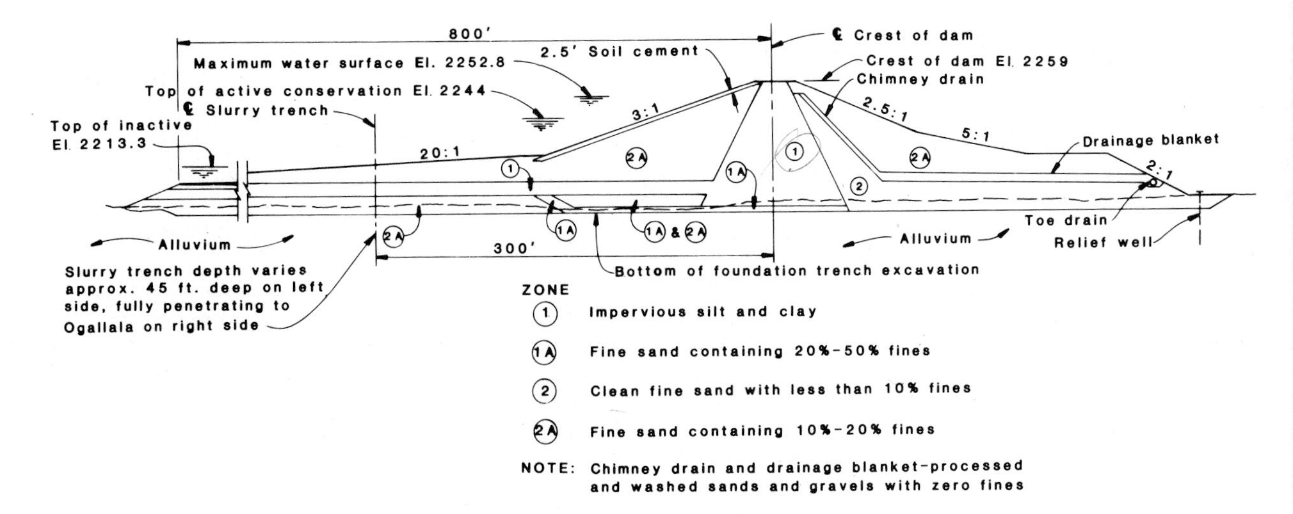

Figure 6-88.—Calamus Dam. Constructed (1985) on the North Loup River, Nebraska. From 628–D–253.

G. BIBLIOGRAPHY

6.28. *Bibliography.*

[1] Schuyler, J. D., *Reservoirs for Irrigation*, John Wiley and Sons, Inc., New York, NY, 1905.

[2] Justin, J. D. *Earth Dams Projects*, John Wiley and Sons, Inc., New York, NY, 1932.

[3] Bassel, Burr, *Earth Dams,* Engineering News Publishing Co., New York, NY, 1907.

[4] Justin, J. D., Julian Hinds, and W. P. Creager, *Engineering for Dams*, John Wiley and Sons, Inc., vol. III, p. 675, New York, NY, 1945.

[5] "Symposium on Cement and Clay Grouting of Foundations," Task Committees on Cement and Clay Grouting, ASCE *Proceedings*, vol. 84, *Journal of the Soil Mechanics and Foundations Division,* No. SM1, papers No. 1544 to 1552, February 1958.

[6] Sherard, J. L., R. J. Woodward, S. F. Gizienski, and W. A. Clevenger, *Earth and Earth-Rock Dams*, John Wiley and Sons, Inc., New York, NY, 1963.

[7] "Pressure Grouting," Bureau of Reclamation, Technical Memorandum No. 646, June 1957.

[8] "Grouts and Drilling Muds in Engineering Practice," Symposium organized by the British National Society of the International Society of Soil Mechanics and Foundation Engineering, Butterworths, London, 1963.

[9] "Policy Statements for Grouting," ACER Technical Memorandum No. 5, Assistant Commissioner-Engineering and Research Center, Bureau of Reclamation, 1984.

[10] Gibbs, H. J., and W. G. Holtz, "Research on Determining the Density of Sands by Spoon Penetration Testing," *Proceedings* of the Fourth International Conference on Soil Mechanics and Foundation Engineering, vol. I, p. 38 (adapted from fig. 7), London, 1957.

[11] *Earth Manual*, vol. 2, "Test Designations," Bureau of Reclamation, Denver, CO, 1987.

[12] *Ground Water Manual,* rev. reprint, Bureau of Reclamation, 480 pp., U.S. Government Printing Office, Washington, D.C., 1981.

[13] Terzaghi, Karl, and R. B. Peck, *Soil Mechanics in Engineering Practice,* p. 230, John Wiley and Sons, Inc., New York, NY, 1948.

[14] Rice, O. L., and H. G. Arthur, "The Most Recent Methods Developed to Avoid Piping or Blowouts in Dams," Third Congress on Large Dams, vol. II, Question No. 10, R. 49, Stockholm, Sweden, 1948.

[15] Casagrande, Arthur, "Seepage Through Dams," *Journal New England Water Works Association*, p. 131, June 1937.

[16] Taylor, D. W., *Fundamentals of Soil Mechanics,* p. 156, John Wiley and Sons, Inc., New York, NY, 1948.

[17] Creager, W. P., J. D. Justin, and Julian Hinds, *Engineering for Dams,* John Wiley and Sons, Inc., vols. I and III, New York, NY, 1945.

[18] Cedergren, H. R., *Seepage, Drainage, and Flow Nets,* p. 110, John Wiley and Sons, Inc., New York, NY, 1967.

[19] Justin, J. D., Julian Hinds, and W. P. Creager, *Engineering for Dams,* John Wiley and Sons, Inc., vol. III, p. 695, New York, NY, 1945.

[20] Lane, K. S., and P. E. Wohlt, "Performance of Sheet Piling and Blankets for Sealing Missouri River Reservoirs," *Proceedings* Seventh Congress on Large Dams, pp. 255-279, 1961.

[21] "Report on Steel Sheet Piling Studies," Soil Mechanics and Materials Division, Canadian Department of Agriculture, Saskatoon, SK, 1951.

[22] "Mixed-In-Place Piles," Special Report No. 109, Intrusion-Prepakt, Inc., Cleveland, OH, 1968.

[23] Jones, Jack C., "Deep Cut-Offs in Pervious Alluvium, Combining Slurry Trenches and Grouting," Ninth Congress on Large Dams, vol. I, p. 509, 1967.

[24] *Mud Technology Handbook*, Baroid Division, National Lead Co., Houston, TX, 1965.

[25] "Bibliography on Chemical Grouting," Third Progress Report - Committee on Grouting, ASCE *Proceedings*, vol. 92, *Journal of the Soil Mechanics and Foundations Division*, No. SM6, p. 39, November 1966.

[26] Bennett, P. T., "The Effect of Blankets on Seepage Through Pervious Foundations," *Transactions* ASCE, vol. III, p. 215, 1946.

[27] Terzaghi, Karl, and R. B. Peck, *Soil Mechanics in Engineering Practice*, p. 164, John Wiley and Sons, Inc., New York, NY, 1967.

[28] Cedergren, H. R., "Geological Considerations in the Design of Reservoir Seepage Control Systems," Symposium Reservoir Leakage and Ground Water Control, Ass. Eng. Geol. Nat. Meeting, Seattle, WA, 1968.

[29] Bertram, G. E., "An Experimental Investigation of Protective Filters," Graduate School of Engineering, Harvard University, Soil Mechanics Series No. 7, January 1940.

[30] "Soil Mechanics Fact Finding Survey; Seepage Studies; Progress Report," Technical Memorandum No. 175-1, U.S. Army Corps of Engineers, Waterways Experiment Station, Vicksburg, MS, March 1, 1941.

[31] "The Use of Laboratory Tests to Develop Design Criteria for Protective Filters," Earth Laboratory Report No. EM-425, Bureau of Reclamation, June 20, 1955.

[32] Middlebrooks, T. A., and W. H. Jervis, "Relief Wells for Dams and Levees," *Transactions* ASCE, vol. 112, p. 1321, 1947.

[33] Turnbull, W. J., and C. I. Mansur, "Relief Well Systems for Dams and Levees," *Transactions* ASCE, vol. 119, p. 842, 1954.

[34] Mansur, C. I., and R. I. Kaufman, "Control of Underseepage, Mississippi River Levees, St. Louis District," ASCE *Proceedings*, vol. 82, *Journal of the Soil Mechanics and Foundations Division*, No. SM1, paper No. 864, January 1956.

[35] Turnbull, W. J., and C. I. Mansur, "Underseepage and Its Control - A Symposium," *Transactions*, ASCE, vol. 126, pt. I, pp. 1,428-1,568, 1961.

[36] Clevenger, W. A., "Experiences With Loess as a Foundation Material," ASCE *Proceedings*, vol. 82, *Journal of the Soil Mechanics and Foundations Division*, No. SM3, paper No. 1025, July 1956.

[37] Gibbs, J. J., and W. Y. Holland, "Engineering and Petrographic Properties of Loessial Soils," Engineering Monograph No. 28, Bureau of Reclamation, November 1969.

[38] "Properties Which Divide Loose and Dense Uncemented Soils," Earth Laboratory Report No. EM-608, Bureau of Reclamation, January 6, 1961.

[39] Terzaghi, Karl, "Simple Tests Determine Hydrostatic Uplift," *Engineering News-Record*, p. 872, June 18, 1936.

[40] Timoshenko, S., and J. N. Goodier, "Theory of Elasticity," p. 14, McGraw-Hill, New York, NY, 1951.

[41] Hilf, J. W., "Estimating Construction Pore Pressures in Rolled Earth Dams," *Proceedings* of the Second Conference on Soil Mechanics and Foundations Engineering, vol. III, p. 234, Rotterdam, June 1948.

[42] May, D. R., "Application of the Planimeter to the Swedish Method of Analyzing the Stability of Earth Slopes," *Transactions*, Second Congress on Large Dams, pt. I of app. A, vol. IV, p. 540, Washington, D.C., 1936.

[43] Wright, S. G., "A Study of Slope Stability and Undrained Shear Strength of Clay Shales," Ph.D. dissertation, University of California, Berkeley, 1969.

[44] Spencer, E., "A Method of Analysis of the Stability of Embankments Assuming Parallel Interslice Forces," *Geotechnique*, pp. 11-26, 1967.

[45] Chugh, A. K., "User Information Manual for Slope Stability Analysis Program 'SSTAB2'—A Modified Version of 'SSTAB1' by S. G. Wright," Bureau of Reclamation, Engineering and Research Center, Denver, CO, 1981.

[46] Cedergren, H. R., *Seepage, Drainage, and Flow Nets*, John Wiley and Sons, Inc., p. 148, New York, NY, 1967.

[47] Algermissen, S. T., "Seismic Risk Studies in the United States," *Proceedings* of the Fourth World Conference on Earthquake Engineering, Chilean Association for Seismology and Earthquake Engineering, Santiago, Chile, 1969; also reprinted by U.S. Department of Commerce, ESSA, Coast and Geodetic Survey, 20 pp., 1969.

[48] Woodward, Clyde, Sherard and Associates, "A Study of the Influence of the Earthquake Hazard on the Design of Embankment Dams," report prepared for the state of California Department of Water Resources, July 1966.

[49] "Vibration Effects of Earthquakes on Soils and Foundations," STP 450, American Society for Testing and Materials, 1969.

[50] Newmark, N. M., "Effects of Earthquakes on Dams and Embankments," *Geotechnique*, vol. XV, No. 2, June 1965.

[51] Seed, H. B., "A Method for Earthquake Resistant Design of Earth Dams," *Journal of the Soil Mechanics and Foundation Division*, ASCE, January 1966.

[52] "Efficacy of Partial Cutoffs for Controlling Underseepage Beneath Levees," Technical Memorandum No. 3-267, U.S. Army Corps of Engineers, Waterways Experiment Station, Vicksburg, MS, January 1969.

[53] Wiegel, R. L. (coordinating editor), *Earthquake Engineering*, Prentice-Hall, Englewood Cliffs, NJ, 1970.

[54] Gibbs, H. J., Estimating Foundation Settlement by One-Dimensional Consolidation Tests," Engineering Monograph No. 13, Bureau of Reclamation, 1953.

[55] "Review of Slope Protection Methods," Subcommittee on Slope Protection, Soil Mechanics and Foundation Division, *Proceedings* ASCE, vol. 74, June 1948.

[56] "Slope Protection for Earth Dams," Preliminary Report, U.S. Army Corps of Engineers, Waterways Experiment Station, Vicksburg, MS, March 1949.

[57] Holtz, W. G., and F. C. Walker, "Soil-Cement as Slope Protection for Earth Dams," *Proceedings* of ASCE, *Journal of Soil Mechanics and Foundation Division*, vol. 88, SM6, pp. 107-134, December 1962.

Billig, K., "Thixotropic Clay Suspensions and Their Use in Civil Engineering," *Civil Engineering and Public Works Review*, p. 1,573, December 1961.

D'Appalonia, David J., "Soil-Bentonite Slurry Trench Cutoffs," *Proceedings* of the ASCE, *Journal of the Geo-*

technical Engineering Division, vol. 106, No. GT4, pp. 399-417, April 1980.

Dunnicliff, John, and Don U. Peere, *Judgment in Geotechnical Engineering - The Professional Legacy of Ralph B. Peck,* John Wiley and Sons, Inc., New York, NY, 1984.

Gardner, W. I., "Dams and Reservoirs in Pleistocene-Eolian Deposit Terrane of Nebraska and Kansas," Symposium Reservoir Leakage and Ground Water Control, Ass. Eng. Geol. Nat. Meeting, Seattle, WA, 1968.

Gadsby, J. W., and F. A. Bares, "Arrow Project Cofferdam," *Canadian Geotechnical Journal,* vol. 5, No. 3, August 1968.

Gerwick, Ben C., "Slurry-Trench Techniques for Diaphragm Walls in Deep Foundation Construction," *Civil Engineering,* pp. 70-72, December 1967.

Gibbs, H. J., and C. T. Coffey, "Application of Pore Pressure Measurements to Shear Strength of Cohesive Soils," Earth Laboratory Report No. EM-761, Bureau of Reclamation, June 1969.

Golze, Alfred R., *Handbook of Dam Engineering*, Van Nostrand Reinhold Co., New York, NY, 1977.

Haug, Moir Dee, "Optimization of Slurry Trench Design," (thesis) University of California, Berkeley, 1980.

Hirschfeld, Ronald C., and Steve H. Poulos, Embankment-Dam Engineering, John Wiley and Sons, Inc., New York, NY, 1973.

Kapp, Martin S., "Slurry-Trench Construction for Basement Wall of World Trade Center," *Civil Engineering,* pp. 36-40, April 1969.

Kulhawy, Fred H., editor, "Recent Developments in Geotechnical Engineering for Hydro Projects," *Proceedings of the Geotechnical Engineering Division at the ASCE International Convention,* New York, NY, May 11, 12, 1981.

Lowe, John, *Embankment Dams, Handbook of Applied Hydraulics,* 3d ed., C. V. Davis and K. E. Sorensen, editors, sec. 18, McGraw-Hill Book Co., New York, NY, 1969.

Millet, Richard A., and Jean Yves-Perez, "Current USA Practice: Slurry Wall Specifications," *Proceedings* of the ASCE, *Journal of the Geotechnical Division,* vol. 107, No. GT8, pp. 1,041-1,055, August 1981.

Morgenstern, N., and I. Amir-Tahmasseb, "The Stability of a Slurry Trench in Cohesionless Soils," *Geotechnique,* vol. 15, pp. 387-395, 1965.

Sherard, James L., "Statistical Survey of the Diaphragm Wall Applications," Specialty Session No. 14, Seventh International Conference on Soil Mechanics and Foundation Engineering, Mexico, 1969.

Xanthahos, Petros P., *Slurry Walls,* McGraw-Hill Book Co., New York, NY, 1979.

"Construction of Slurry Trench Cutoff," U.S. Army Engineer District, Savannah, Corps of Engineers, Savannah, GA, 1968.

"Digging a 95-Foot Deep Slurry Trench," *Western Construction,* pp. 66-70, November 1966.

Drilling Mud Data Book, Baroid Division, National Lead Co., Houston, TX, 1965.

Drilling Mud Reference Manual, Baroid Division, National Lead Co., Houston, TX, 1965.

"Earthquake Activity in Western United States," Dams Branch Report No. DD-8, Bureau of Reclamation, Denver, CO, April 1968.

"Soil-Cement Slope Protection for Earth Dams," Portland Cement Assn., Chicago, IL, (undated).

"Symposium on Earth and Rockfill Dams," vols. I and III, Indian National Society of Soil Mechanics and Foundation Engineering, 1968.

"Wanapum Hydroelectric Development Final Report," Public Utility District of Grant County, vols. I and II, Ephrata, WA, 1969.

Chapter 7

Rockfill Dams

A. GENERAL

7.1. Origin and Usage.—Rockfill dams are generally conceded to have had their origin over 100 years ago during the California Gold Rush. From the late 1800's to the mid-1930's, many rockfill dams were constructed. The design and construction of a number of these dams are described by Galloway [1][1].

Interest in constructing rockfill dams diminished after the mid-1930's because of the increased costs of obtaining and placing large amounts of rockfill material; although a number of large rockfill dams were constructed in the 1950's [2]. Rockfill dam construction has increased markedly since 1960. This is attributed to the use of more remote sites, more economical quarrying and placing operations, the use of excavated material in random zones, better design details, more general knowledge concerning rockfills, and the recent advent of pumped-storage projects in mountainous terrain. Recent progress in rockfill dams is discussed by Cooke [3]. The excellent performance of an increasing number of rockfill dams is another beneficial factor recommending their use.

Rockfill dams can prove economical when any of the following conditions exist:

- Large quantities of rock are readily available or will be excavated in connection with the project, such as from a spillway or tunnel.
- Earthfill materials are difficult to obtain or require extensive processing before use.
- Short construction seasons prevail.
- Excessively wet climatic conditions limit the placement of large quantities of earthfill material.
- The dam is to be raised at a later date.

Other factors that favor the use of a rockfill dam are the ability to place rockfill throughout the winter and the possibility of grouting the foundation while simultaneously placing the embankment. In addition, uplift pressures and erosion caused by seepage through rockfill material do not generally constitute significant design problems.

Increasing interest is being shown in using "flowthrough" rockfill sections in conjunction with diversion dams to handle sudden floodflows when the cost of diversion is high [4, 5, 6, 7]. This type of structure requires that a grid of welded reinforcing rods be placed across the downstream face of the dam, below a given elevation, and anchored to the rockfill so that large flows through the embankment do not displace the rock. The rods are usually ½ to ¾ inch in diameter and are spaced so that rectangles 1 foot vertically by 3 to 4 feet horizontally are blocked out on the downstream face of the embankment. This grid is then welded to reinforcing rods that are anchored 10 to 15 feet in the rockfill. The use of "flowthrough" rockfill dams presents the designer with unique problems concerning the extent of downstream reinforcing and the ability of the section to resist overtopping. Therefore, this type of structure should be designed only by an experienced design engineer.

7.2. Definition and Types of Rockfill Dams.—Rockfill dams have been defined as follows [8, 9]: "A dam that relies on rock, either dumped in lifts or compacted in layers, as a major structural element." An impervious membrane is used as the water barrier and can be placed either within the embankment (internal membrane) or on the upstream slope (external membrane). Various materials have been used for this membrane including earth materials, concrete, steel, asphaltic concrete, and wood.

Rockfill dams may be classified into three groups, depending on the location of the membrane: (1) central core, (2) sloping core, and (3) upstream membrane, or "decked." Each membrane location has its advantages and disadvantages, which vary

[1]Numbers in brackets refer to entries in the bibliography (sec. 7.14).

according to the type of membrane, materials available at the site, and foundation conditions. Central and sloping cores, which are internal membranes, are generally constructed of impervious earth materials. Economic analyses should be made to determine the type of material to use in constructing the membrane, whether it be internal or external. If an internal membrane is selected, a central vertical core is recommended. This type of core provides maximum contact pressure with the foundation and requires less strict construction control than a sloping core.

If an external membrane is used, it should be constructed of concrete, asphaltic concrete, or steel.

Advantages of the internal membrane include (1) less total area exposed to water, (2) shorter grout curtain lengths, and (3) protection from the effects of weathering and external damage. The prime disadvantages of an internal membrane are the inability to place rockfill material without the simultaneous placement of impervious core material and filters, the inaccessibility of the membrane for damage inspection, the difficulty in correcting damage should it occur, and the dependence on a smaller section of the dam for stability against sliding. The difference in the abilities of central (internal) and upstream (external) membranes to distribute stabilizing reactions against sliding is shown on figure 7-1.

Upstream membranes have the following advantages:

- Readily available for inspection and repair.
- Can be constructed after completion of the rockfill section.
- Foundation grouting can be performed simultaneously with rockfill placement.
- A larger portion of the dam is available for stability against sliding.
- Can be used as slope protection.
- It is relatively easy to raise the dam at a later date.
- In wet climates, the absence of impervious soil fill simplifies and speeds construction.

If an upstream membrane is used, the reservoir should be capable of being drawn down to an elevation that will permit inspection and repair; television cameras or audio devices may be used for leak detection, and minor repairs may be made by divers.

If an earth-core rockfill dam is used, it requires the use of adequate filters both upstream and downstream; the filters should satisfy the requirements

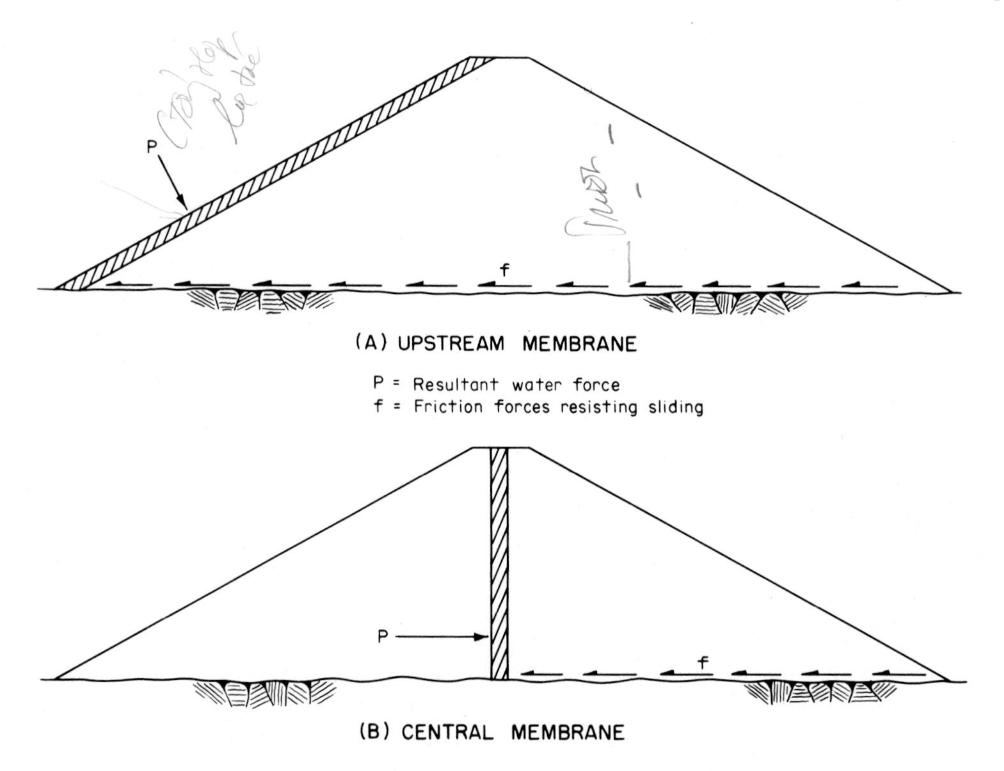

Figure 7-1.—Resistance to sliding for embankments. 288–D–2796.

listed in section 6.10(i). If adequate earth material for either the core or the filter is not available at the site and separations of impervious material or manufactured filters are required, an earth-core rockfill dam may be uneconomical because filter processing costs can be extreme. Construction control costs of the earth-core rockfill dam will also be increased significantly if several filter layers are required to prevent piping.

B. FOUNDATION DESIGN

7.3. Foundation Requirements and Treatment.—The foundation requirements for a rockfill dam are less stringent than those for a concrete gravity dam, but more stringent than those for an earthfill dam.

Bedrock foundations that are hard and erosion resistant are the most desirable for rockfill dams. Foundations consisting of river gravels or rock fragments are acceptable, but the foundation should be inspected by competent engineers and a positive cutoff to bedrock should be used. The foundation should be selected and treated from the viewpoint of providing minimum settlement to the rockfill embankment. All materials in cracks, faults, or deep pits that may eventually erode into the rockfill, either from the foundation or the abutment, should be covered with filters (sec. 6.10(i)) or removed and backfilled with concrete. For an earth-core rockfill dam, all joints and cracks beneath the core and the filters should be cleaned and filled with concrete [10].

The usual method of treating the foundations to prevent underseepage is cement grouting beneath the cutoff; in addition, potential pervious zones upstream from the impervious membrane can be blanketed with impervious material.

The alignment of the dam should be selected so that either minimum embankment volume or minimum membrane exposure is attained, depending on which criterion is economically more important.

Foundation treatment must be sufficient to satisfy the following criteria:

- Minimum leakage
- Prevention of piping
- Limited settlement
- Sufficient friction development between abutments and foundation to ensure sliding stability

7.4. Membrane Cutoffs.—Of critical importance in the functioning of a rockfill dam are the prevention of seepage beneath the dam and the effecting of a watertight seal between the membrane and the foundation. To prevent seepage beneath the dam, foundations are usually grouted. The need for grouting and the extent required should be based on careful study of the site geology, on a visual examination of the drill cores from the rock foundation, and on drill-hole water-loss values. If no such data are available, it should be assumed that grouting will be required, except where the reservoir is completely drawn down each year and grouting requirements can be based on seepage observations during the first few years of operation.

Cutoff walls excavated to various depths into bedrock are generally used to prevent leakage in the upper few feet of the foundation, to facilitate grouting operations, to provide a watertight seal with the membrane, and to support the downward thrust of the membrane. Figures 7-2, 7-3, and 7-4 illustrate typical cutoff wall details. Drainage galleries are sometimes used in conjunction with cutoff walls to facilitate later grouting and to determine seepage locations and quantities, but they are not recommended for small dams.

Recently [11], designers have used the doweled cutoff slab shown on figure 7-5 in conjunction with concrete facings to provide the foundation-membrane seal. Doweled cutoff slabs have the advantage of not requiring extensive excavations in rock, thereby allowing grouting operations to begin earlier, speeding completion time, and reducing design costs. Doweled cutoff slabs can be used where the bedrock is sound and few underseepage problems are expected. When uncertainty concerning the permeability of upper portions of the foundation contact exist, such as for soft rock, a cutoff wall into bedrock can provide increased protection and allow an examination of questionable material.

A minimum width and depth of 3 feet is recommended for cutoff walls in sound rock; deeper walls should be used in unsound, broken, or closely jointed rock. The width of the doweled slab should be determined by foundation, construction, or grouting requirements. In addition to preventing underseepage, both the cutoff wall and the doweled cutoff slab must be designed to provide adequate

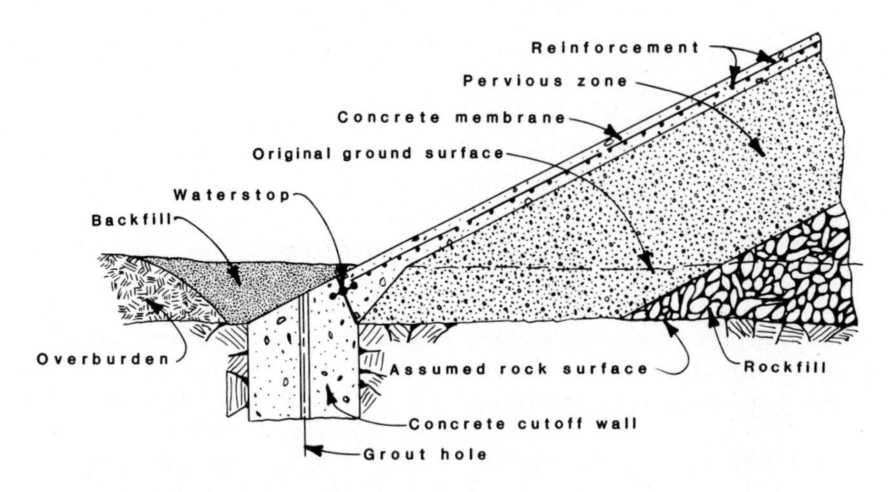

Figure 7-2.—Detail of concrete membrane at cutoff wall. 103–D–1878.

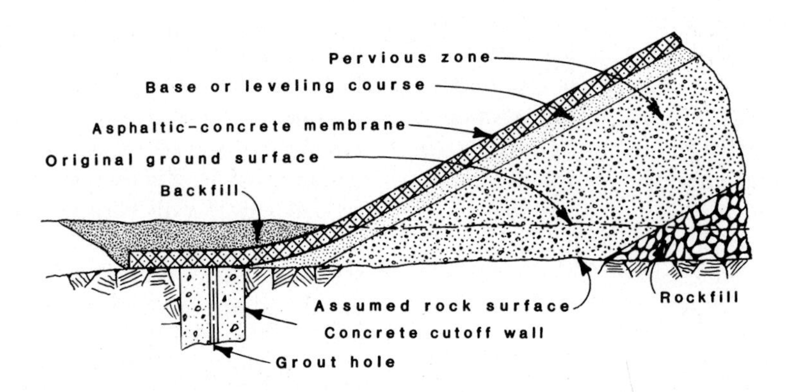

Figure 7-3.—Detail of asphaltic-concrete membrane at cutoff wall. 103–D–1879.

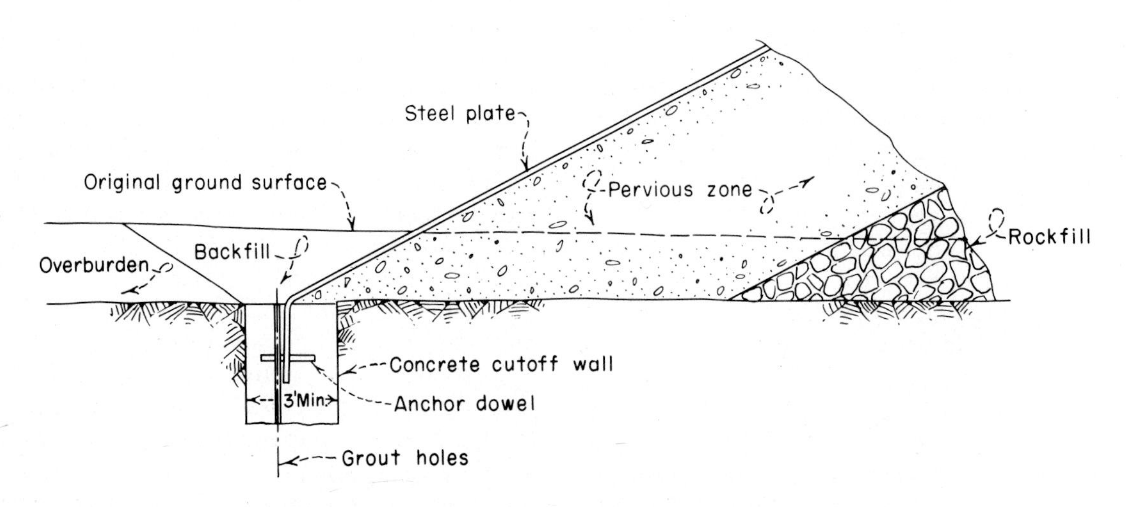

Figure 7-4.—Detail of steel-plate membrane at cutoff wall. 288–D–2503.

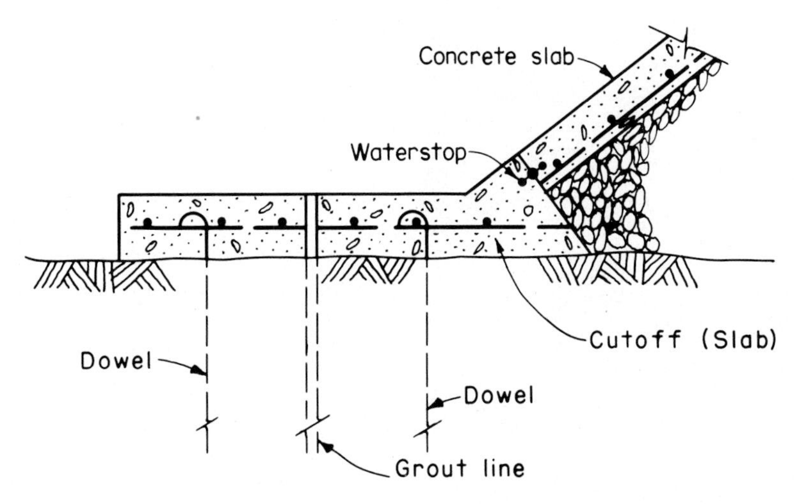

Figure 7-5.—Doweled cutoff slab used with upstream concrete membrane. 288-D-2797.

support for the thrust of the membrane and, in the case of steel membranes, any tension imparted to the cutoff caused by embankment settlement.

The cutoff should extend along the entire upstream contact between the membrane and the foundation.

C. EMBANKMENT DESIGN

7.5. ***Selection of Rock Materials.***—A great variety of rock types have been used in the construction of rockfill dams. The types of rock have ranged from hard, durable, granite and quartzite to weaker materials, such as graywacke sandstone and slaty shale. In earlier years, it was thought that only the highest quality rockfill material should be used; however, with the advent of thinner lifts and more efficient compaction techniques, rock having less desirable characteristics has become feasible for use within embankment sections. The use of rock from excavations for spillways, outlet works, tunnels, and other appurtenant structures has reduced the construction costs of rockfill dams without impairing the usefulness or stability of embankments. If small amounts of the less desirable rock types are available, they can be used in random zones within the embankment; the use of material in random zones is discussed in section 6.18(a).

Preferably, rock material should be hard, durable, able to withstand disintegration from weathering, and able to resist excessive breakdown from quarrying, loading, hauling, and placing operations. (Figure 7-6 shows the granite rockfill on the downstream face of Montgomery Dam.) The rock should also be free of unstable minerals that would weather mechanically or chemically, causing the rock to disintegrate. Igneous, metamorphic, and sedimentary rocks have all been used successfully in embankment sections, and only general advice can be given concerning rock types because each damsite presents a unique problem in the use of the nearby rock materials. As an aid to the designer, part E of chapter 5 gives the classification and engineering properties of rocks.

Results from laboratory tests that measure the abrasion resistance, freeze-thaw characteristics, and the percent of water absorption can be used to evaluate the suitability of the rockfill. Results from petrographic analyses can be used to distinguish minerals known to weather easily, and unconfined or triaxial compression tests can determine the strength properties of the rock. One of the best methods of determining the resistance of a rock to weathering is simply to examine its inplace condition; however, this does not always indicate how the material will perform within the fill. Materials available at the site should be examined by constructing test embankments if economically possible, especially when the material properties are questionable. Test fills can determine the following items:

- Whether or not marginal materials can be used
- How selected embankment materials will perform during compaction

Figure 7-6.—Granite rockfill on downstream face of Montgomery Dam, Colorado. CH-520-150.

- The correct type of compaction equipment for each material
- The required number of compaction passes for each material
- The correct lift thickness for each material
- The necessity for changing the embankment section to accommodate new materials or different material properties

As an example, Crisp [12] reports that significant changes were proposed in the design of Carters Dam from results obtained by testing embankment sections of quartzite, phyllite, and argillite.

The effect of quarry blasting methods on the gradation of the rock should also be examined, as well as the required extent of quarrying.

Also of great importance to the design engineer selecting the type of rock is the degree to which small-scale triaxial compression tests provide strength parameters applicable to the actual rockfill.

Very limited data are available on this subject; however, Leps [13] has summarized available data and Marachi et al. [14] have examined this problem by testing 36-, 12-, and 2.8-inch-diameter specimens in drained triaxial compression tests using parallel grain-size curves and identical grain slopes (modeling) to examine the effects of grain size on the strength and deformation characteristics of rockfill material. They also investigated the effect of particle crushing.

Three types of material were tested as follows:

1. Argillite from Pyramid Dam. – A fine-grained sedimentary rock, quarry blasted, angular, with relatively weak particles (G_s = 2.67)
2. Crushed basalt. – Quarry blasted and crushed to the correct size, angular, and quite sound (G_s = 2.87).
3. Amphibolite from Oroville Dam. – A metavolcanic rock, rounded to subrounded particles with some subangular fine-sand particles, river-dredged material, hard (G_s = 2.86 to 2.94).

The gradation curves for the actual rockfill material and for the modeled material are shown on figure 7-7.

Although [14] was primarily concerned with the use of rockfill material in high dams, the following general conclusions apply to rockfill dams of all sizes:

- Rockfill materials can be successfully modeled so that the strength and deformation characteristics of the actual material can be obtained from small-scale tests.
- At any given confining pressure, as the particle size of the specimen increases, the angle of internal friction decreases a small but significant amount.
- Rockfill materials composed of well-graded and well-rounded particles are superior to uniformly graded angular rockfill materials, especially for high dams.
- For any given particle size, as the confining pressure of the sample increases, the angle of internal friction decreases.

Figure 7-8 illustrates the variation of the angle of internal friction with both particle size and confining pressure. Although most of the confining pressures shown are greater than those attained in small dams, the general reduction in friction angle shown on figure 7-8 should be of great interest to designers.

The details of testing and further conclusions regarding the strength and deformation properties of rockfill materials and the crushing characteristics of rock subjected to high confining pressures can be found in [14].

7.6. Embankment Sections.—Embankment slopes used for rockfill dams have evolved from very steep slopes, usually 0.5:1 to 0.75:1 (horizontal to vertical) on early rockfill dams, to the flatter slopes of 1.3:1 to 1.7:1 used today. Earlier rockfill dams used upstream membranes exclusively and were constructed with steep upstream and downstream slopes to minimize the volume of rockfill. Because these slopes were considerably steeper than the natural slope of dumped rock, they were stabilized by thick zones of crane-placed, dry rubble masonry,

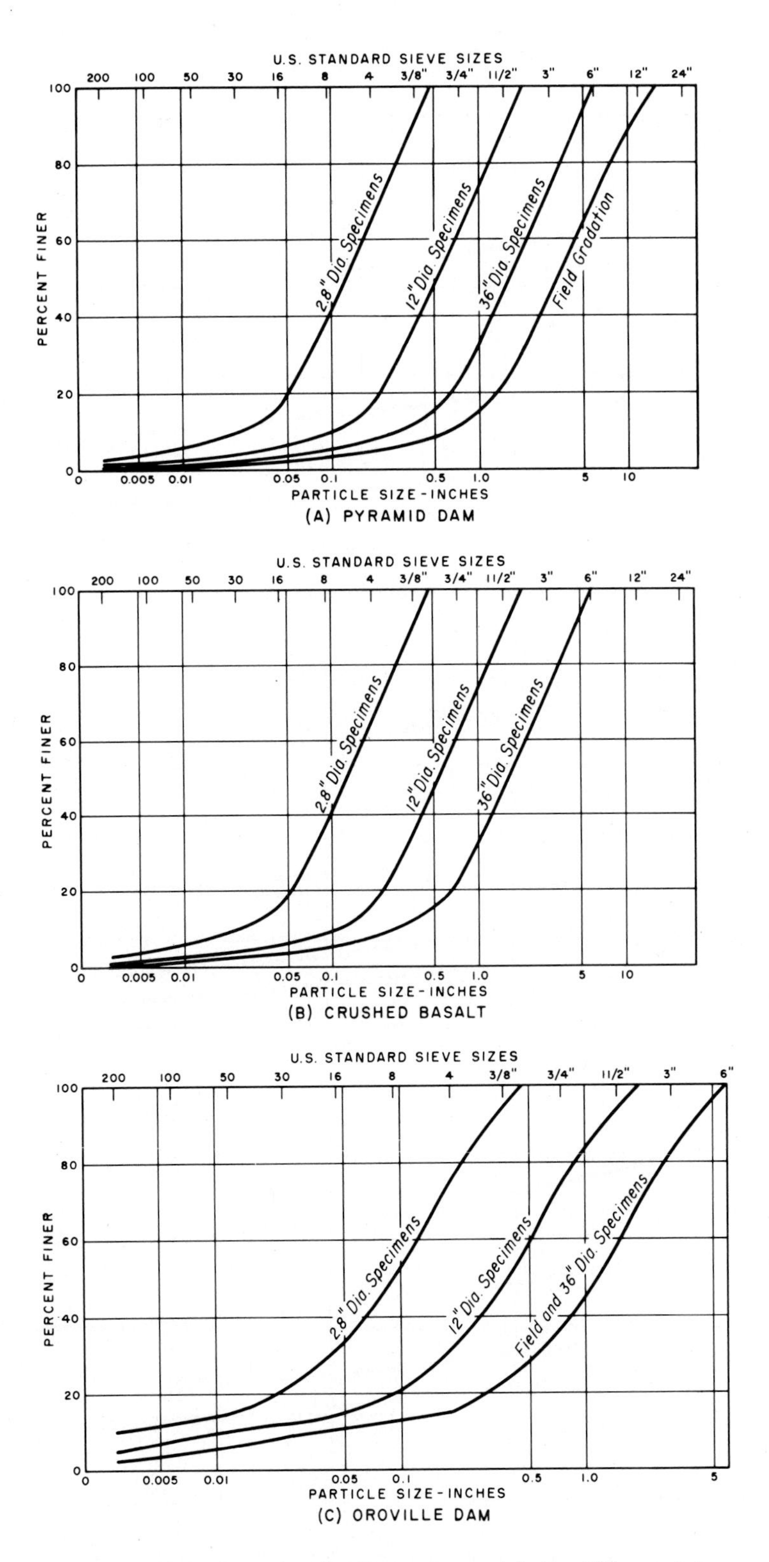

Figure 7-7.—Grain size distribution for modeled rockfill materials. Adapted from [14]. 288–D–2798.

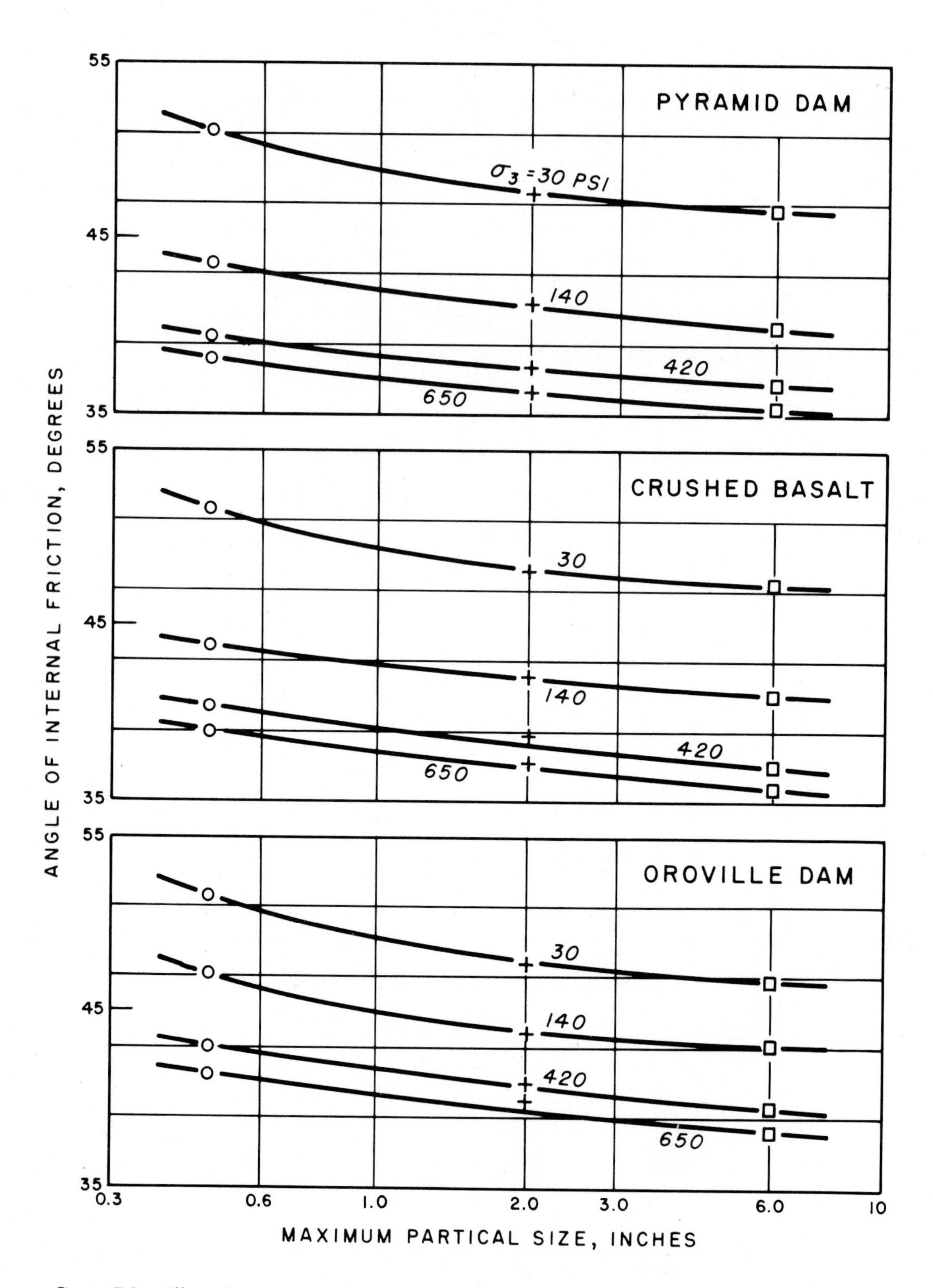

Figure 7-8.—Effect of maximum particle size on the angle of internal friction. Adapted from [14]. 288–D–2799.

which provided the bedding for the upstream slope protection. The rockfill portions of these dams were constructed by dumping the rockfill in thick lifts, which ranged from 30 to 165 feet. Later designs eliminated the rubble masonry on the downstream slope by flattening it to the angle of repose of the rock, but the very steep upstream slope was retained. Because most of the upstream zones were constructed by crane placement of large rocks, the cost of the dams continually increased. Gradually, designers found that it was more economical to use slopes approximating the angle of repose of the rock material and to eliminate crane placement in favor of compacted rockfills.

The upstream and downstream slopes of a dam should be based on the type of impervious membrane and its location. Rockfill dams having central or sloping cores have slopes ranging from 2:1 to 4:1 upstream and downstream—usually tending toward 2:1 or slightly steeper when all conditions are favorable. However, dams with upstream membranes usually have upstream slopes of from 1.3:1 to 1.7:1 and downstream slopes approximating the natural slope of the rock.

Most asphaltic-concrete-faced dams have been constructed with upstream slopes of 1.6:1 to 1.7:1 to facilitate construction of the membrane; whereas, most steel- and concrete-faced rockfill dams have slopes of 1.3:1 to 1.4:1. A review of available literature indicates that very few failures have occurred for these slopes. Therefore, small rockfill dams with good foundations could have 1.3:1 to 1.4:1 upstream slopes for concrete and steel membranes, and a 1.7:1 upstream slope for asphaltic-concrete facings. Downstream slopes of 1.3:1 to 1.4:1 may be used in all cases.

The upstream and downstream slopes for central or sloping earth-core rockfill dams depends on the size and soil properties of the earth core, the width of filter zones required, type of foundation material, drawdown requirements, construction sequence, etc., with each site presenting its own unique problems. Generally, the upstream and downstream slopes of a typical earth-core rockfill dam are 2:1 or slightly steeper where all conditions are favorable, but may be as flat as 4:1 (or flatter) for unfavorable conditions. A typical embankment section for a central earth-core rockfill dam is shown on figure 7-9.

A typical section for a decked (upstream membrane) rockfill dam is shown on figure 7-10. The interior section of the decked rockfill dam can be divided into three major zones, as shown on figure 7-10. These zones can be described as follows:

- Zone C: The larger downstream zone of the dam, consisting of the best quality, larger, compacted rock; this zone provides high stability to the section.
- Zone B: Rock of lesser quality than zone C, such as that excavated from the spillway; used to minimize total dam costs.
- Zone A: Well-graded, smaller rock and gravel; used to provide bedding for the upstream membrane and to retard extreme water losses should the membrane crack.

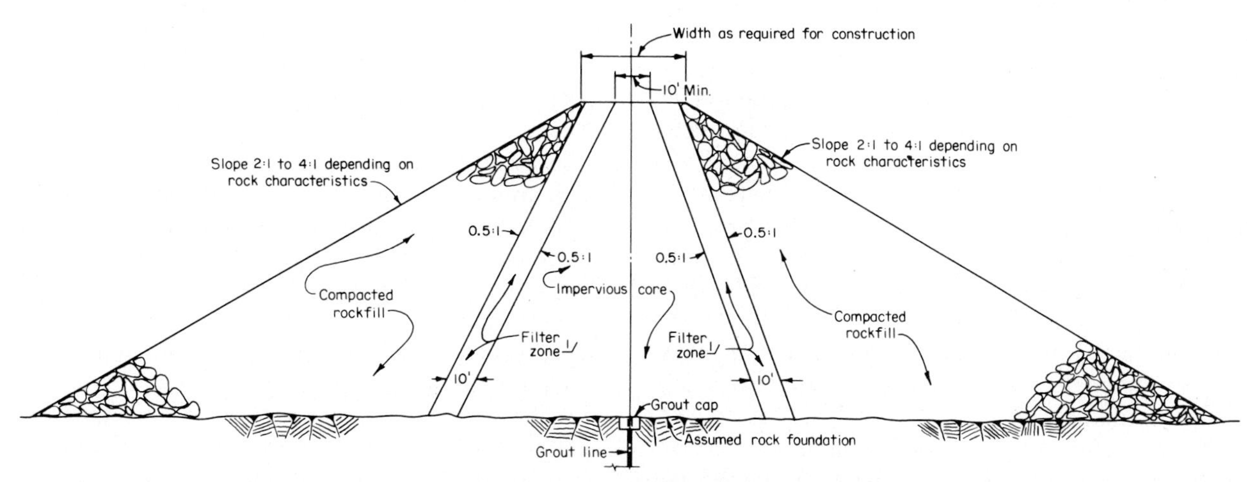

Figure 7-9.—Typical maximum section of an earth-core rockfill dam using a central core. 288-D-2800.

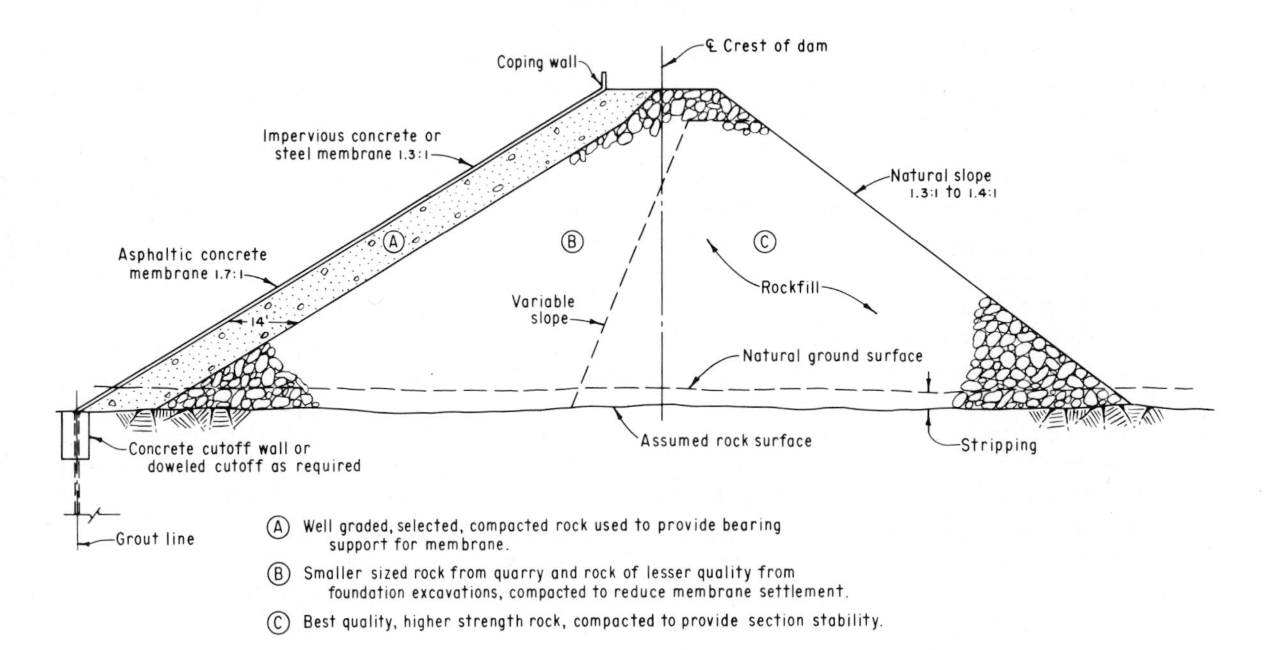

Figure 7-10.—Typical maximum section of a decked rockfill dam. 288–D–2801.

In addition to these major zones, a well-graded sand and gravel base course for the membrane is sometimes necessary. A thin base course also serves as a leveling course and provides a good working surface. Placement conditions for these three zones and the base course are discussed in section 7.7.

Gradation requirements are difficult to specify because they depend on the type of rock available and the quarrying methods used. As with many aspects of dam design, only general rules apply, but filter requirements given in section 6.10(i) must be satisfied. For decked rockfill dams, zone C of the embankment should use the largest and best quality rock available. Large slabby rocks should not be placed in this fill because they tend to bridge, causing large voids that may result in excessive settlement should the rocks break. If possible, rock in zone C should be well-graded from approximately 1 ft^3 to 1 yd^3, and the finer fraction of the gradation should not be sufficient to fill the voids in the compacted material. Optimally, zone B should be well-graded from a maximum size of about 10 ft^3 and should have a high permeability after compaction. Zone A should be well-graded from approximately 3 inches down to 5 to 15 percent passing the No. 100 sieve. If a base course is not necessary (as described later), the gradation of zone A depends on the type of facing used and its method of construction. If a base course is not used, zone A material should provide a smooth uniform bearing surface for the facing, yet be graded to retard large water loss should the facing crack.

A base course may not always be necessary, depending on the need for a leveling course and on the gradation of zone A and its ability to withstand raveling during placement of the deck and to withstand erosion. In any event, the zone immediately beneath the face slab should provide a good working surface for equipment and workmen during placement of the facing element, and it should resist erosion during surface runoff. The base course material should be well-graded, with a maximum size of 1½ inches, 5 to 15 percent passing the No. 100 sieve, and 5 percent or less passing the No. 200 sieve.

In general, material in zones B and C should grade from fine rock upstream to coarse rock downstream, with the largest and strongest material placed in the lower downstream portions of zone C. Selection of the rock for each zone should be made at the quarry.

For central earth-core rockfill dams, the larger and stronger rock should be placed in the outer rockfill zones. This rock should grade from fine rock next to the filter to coarse rock near the downstream slope.

The axis of the dam may be either curved (convex upstream) or straight. A curved axis allows the dam to be compressed as filling occurs; whereas, a straight axis has the benefit of easy construction layout and less total dam cost. For small dams with good foundation and abutment conditions, a straight axis is recommended. For the upstream-membrane rockfill dams, it is also recommended that the layout be such that a minimum area of membrane face be exposed. This expedites face construction, reduces face and cutoff costs, and reduces the cost of any necessary repairs.

Random zones constructed of rock with questionable strength or permeability characteristics may also be used within the rockfill embankment if the stability of the section is not affected. The overriding purpose in the layout of any rockfill section is to make maximum economic use of the material available at the site. Test embankments can be used to determine whether or not materials will be adequate; these are discussed in section 7.5.

Crest width should be determined by the type of membrane used and by its use after construction. The crest should, however, be wide enough to accommodate construction of the upstream membrane; a minimum width of 15 to 20 feet is recommended. Crest camber should be determined by the amount of foundation and embankment settlement anticipated. Because this is difficult to determine, a camber of 1 percent of the embankment height is recommended. A straight-line equation may be used to distribute the cambered material on the crest. Additional considerations concerning crest details are given in section 6.20.

Freeboard requirements depend on maximum wind velocity, fetch, reservoir operating conditions, spillway capacity, and whether coping walls are used. If a coping wall like that shown on figure 7-10 is used to provide wave runup and oversplash protection, the freeboard requirements of the embankment may be less than required for a riprapped earthfill dam (sec. 6.21). If a coping wall is not used, the freeboard should be adequate to prevent wave runup from flowing over the crest (sec. 6.21). Good results have been obtained with coping walls [11], and their use is recommended.

7.7. Placement of Rockfill Materials.—Limiting settlement is critical in the construction of rockfill dams because excessive settlement may rupture the upstream membrane or cause joint separation with subsequent water loss. Early rockfill dams were constructed by dumping the rock in high lifts; it was assumed that dropping rock from heights imparted compaction energy to the fill, decreased the void space and, thus, reduced embankment settlement. Nevertheless, many of these high lift embankments have since settled considerably with concurrent leakage problems. Experience has shown that rock material placed in thin layers and compacted by vibratory rollers forms a more stable mass in which settlement is minimal. For decked rockfill dams, the embankment should preferably be completed before construction of the upstream membrane begins. This reduces the probability of serious membrane cracking by allowing initial settlement to occur.

Settlement of rockfill material has also been correlated with the application of water; Sowers et al. [15] have shown that rockfill material placed dry and subsequently wetted may settle appreciably. Sluicing has long been advocated as a method that ensures that point-to-point bearing occurs between the larger rocks and that finer materials are washed into the voids. However, when rockfill material is placed in thin lifts and compacted by vibratory rollers, there appears to be no definite proof that sluicing operations significantly reduce the total settlement, especially for the smaller rockfill dams considered here.

The quantity of sluicing water used has varied extensively, but usually ranges from two to four times the volume of rock; dirty rock requires more water to wash the fines away. For exceptionally dirty rock, segregations may cause a water-saturated layer of fines to form below the surface of the rock as it is dumped over the edge of the lift and sluiced. The layer will be relatively impermeable and will hinder or prevent wetting of all parts of the rock in the lift below the layer of fines. This may be corrected by using thicker lifts, which allows increased sluicing time, or possibly by wetting the rockfill before placement. Care should also be taken that mud does not form at the toe of the lift as a result of sluicing; if mud problems do arise, periodic removal should be mandatory. Sluicing is usually done with nozzles having diameters from 2½ to 4 inches (a typical sluicing operation is shown on figure 7-11). Enough sluicing equipment should be available to handle maximum rock placing rates; otherwise, the quantity of rockfill placed may be limited. The sluicing equipment should be mobile. Currently, placing rockfill in thin lifts and compacting it with a vibratory roller is the preferred construction method.

Figure 7-11.—Typical rockfill sluicing operation. Montgomery Dam, Colorado (Black and Veatch Engineers photograph). 288-D-2879.

Figure 7-10 shows a typical decked rockfill dam section consisting of three zones of material. The zone C material should be sound, durable rock of high quality dumped in 2- to 4-foot lifts and compacted by a vibratory roller. Zone B material may be rock of lesser quality than that in zone C, such as spillway excavation or tunnel spoil, and should be dumped in 2- to 3-foot lifts and compacted by a vibratory roller. Zone A material provides the bearing surface for the upstream membrane and may be either a processed material or selected material from foundation or borrow pit excavations. Zone A material should be compacted to 12-inch lifts by either crawler-type tractors or vibratory rollers; the material should be thoroughly wetted before compaction. The face of the zone A material should be compacted by drawing a smooth-drum vibratory roller up and down the face. Generally, the vibrator is turned off for the first two passes to prevent displacement. If a base course is installed under the deck, it should also be compacted by drawing a smooth-drum vibratory roller up and down its face in the same manner described for the face of zone A. Suggested gradations for zones A, B, C, and base course material are discussed in section 7.6.

The size of the vibratory roller for each rockfill zone should be based on the properties of the rock in that zone and should, preferably, be established by constructing test embankments. Vibratory rollers weighing from 3 to 10 tons have been the most widely used for rockfill compaction.

In a number of concrete- and asphalt-faced rockfill dams [11, 16, 17, 18], the zone A material has been eliminated and only a thin leveling course has been applied to the face of zone B. In such cases, compaction of the leveling course is performed by drawing a smooth-drum vibratory roller up its face. Figure 7-12 shows the maximum section of Upper

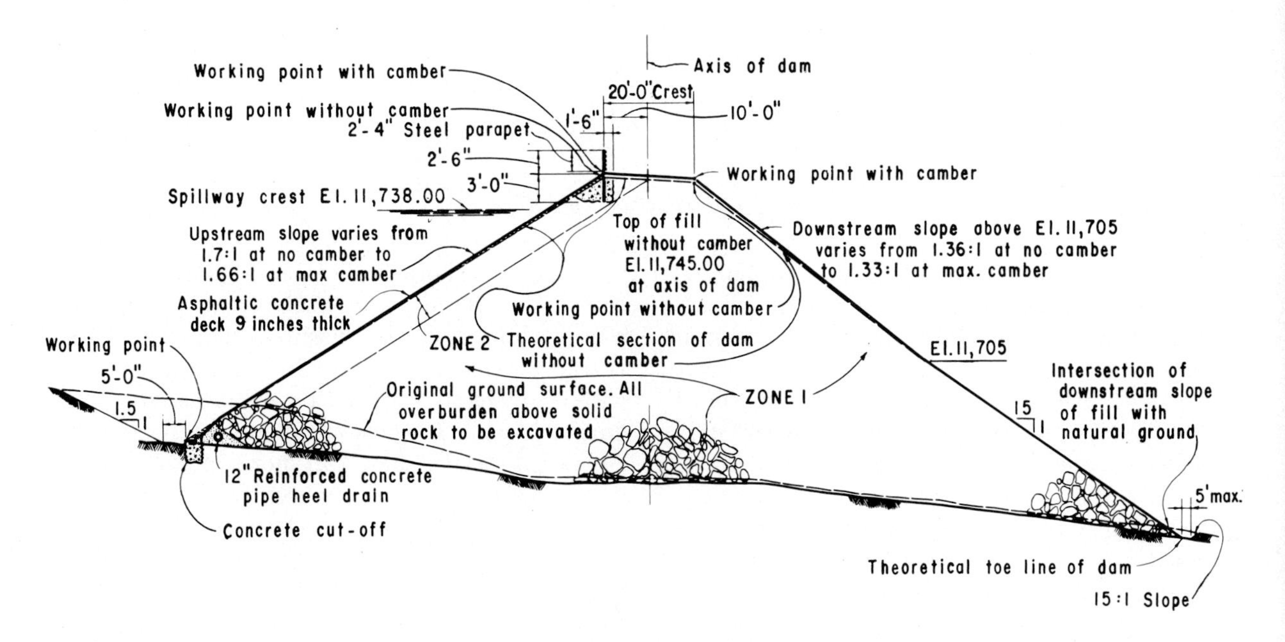

Figure 7-12.—Maximum section of Upper Blue River Dam, Colorado. (Black and Veatch Engineers drawing). 288–D–2880.

Blue River Dam, in which zone A (zone 2 on the fig.) has been eliminated and zone B (zone 1 on the fig.) has been replaced by zone C. When zone A is eliminated, the final upstream surface of zone B may also be finished by pulling the vibratory roller up its face. The advice of an experienced dam designer should be obtained before zone A is eliminated.

For central earth-core rockfill dams, such as that shown on figure 7-9, the upstream and downstream rockfills should be compacted in 2- to 4-foot lifts by vibratory compactors to provide the most stable section possible. The fill should be thoroughly wetted to facilitate compaction. Sluicing operations used with this type dam require that great care be taken to ensure that filters are not clogged or impervious material washed away. The filter material should be compacted to 12-inch lifts either by crawler-type equipment or vibratory rollers. The width of the filter zones should be sufficient to accommodate placing and compacting equipment.

7.8. ***Seismic Design.***—For areas of low seismic activity, the designs recommended herein should be adequate. The determination of potential earthquake activity within a given region can be made from a seismic risk map like that on figure 6-44 or by consultation with a seismologist or engineering geologist. If the damsite lies within a zone of high seismic activity, an experienced dam designer should be consulted.

It is the general opinion of many dam designers that large downstream zones of quarried rock compacted in thin lifts provide maximum stability against seismic shaking and maximum resistance to the flow of large quantities of water through the section should cracking occur. Thus, it is recommended that where seismic activity is expected, decked rockfill dams containing large downstream zones of compacted rockfill be used. The rockfill should, preferably, be well-graded, angular rock fragments of high strength and durability. To accommodate the larger downstream zones, it is recommended that where questionable earthquake conditions are encountered, the downstream slope of the decked rockfill be flattened to 1.7:1 in all cases. The upstream slope of the embankment should also be flattened if additional conservative design measures are warranted.

The foundation of the dam should, preferably, be firm rock; however, free-draining foundations (cobbles, boulders, rock fragments, etc.) may be used if their unit weight is similar to that of the rockfill material and they are approved by a competent dam designer. Trench-type foundation cutoffs are also recommended. In addition, it may be desirable to provide a thicker zone A (fig. 7-10) beneath the membrane, to require better quality rock for zone B, and to reduce the lift thickness to a maximum of 3 feet within zone C. Still another precaution would be using a thicker membrane on the upstream slope and, in the case of a concrete membrane, placing reinforcing in each face.

It should be noted that there are no exact rules for design within earthquake regions, and an authority in this field should be consulted when serious seismic conditions exist.

D. MEMBRANE DESIGN

7.9. Impervious Central Core.—A typical earth-core rockfill section using a central impervious earth core is shown on figure 7-9. Internal membranes of concrete, asphalt, and steel are not recommended because of the inability to inspect or repair them. The rockfill zones of the central core dam are discussed in sections 7.5, 7.6 and 7.7. The upstream rockfill material should be of sufficient size and quality to satisfy the riprap requirements discussed in section 6.22(c); however, riprap bedding requirements need not be met.

Earth-core rockfill dams are economical where site conditions suggest the use of rockfill, but preclude the use of a decked rockfill structure. This can be the case where the upstream abutments show highly weathered rock to great depths and thus present questionable cutoff conditions for an upstream membrane, or where the higher elevations of the abutments are covered with deep layers of overburden and preclude the economical installation of a positive trench-type cutoff for the decked rockfill.

The impervious material used in the core should be similar to the material used for earthfill cores, as discussed in chapter 6. The material should be placed at or near optimum moisture content in about 9-inch lifts and should be compacted to 95 to 100 percent standard laboratory unit weight[2] by a tamping roller. The plasticity index of the material should be sufficient to allow the core to deform without cracking. Specifications for this type of placement are given in appendix G.

Filter zones should be adequate to prevent piping of impervious material during steady-state or rapid drawdown conditions, and it is recommended that the filter criteria in section 6.10(i) be met. Multiple filters may be required if gradation differences between the core and rockfill materials are large. Figure 7-13 shows the placement of fine and coarse filter material for the 55-foot-high New Exchequer Saddle Dike in California.

[2]Standard laboratory compaction as defined by the Bureau of Reclamation.

The foundation and abutments against which the core rests should be carefully treated to prevent piping. Joints, cracks, fissures, and shear zones should be cleaned out to firm material and filled with concrete or grouted. Vertical faces, overhangs, and large rock protrusions should be flattened to slopes not steeper than 0.5:1, horizontal to vertical, by excavation or concrete placement [10]. A trench-type concrete cutoff wall may be necessary with central impervious earth cores when foundation grouting is required and the upper zone of rock is closely fractured, weathered, soft, etc.

The freeboard requirements are the same as those for earthfill dams discussed in section 6.21.

7.10. Reinforced Concrete.—More rockfill dams have been faced with conventionally placed reinforced concrete than with any other type of impervious membrane. In most cases, these facings have performed well for correctly compacted rockfill embankments; leakage has been within acceptable limits, and repairs have been minor. Slab thickness and reinforcing requirements have usually been determined by experience or precedent to satisfy the following criteria:

- Low permeability
- Sufficient strength to bridge subsided areas of the face
- High resistance to weathering
- Sufficient flexibility to tolerate small embankment settlement

Compacted rockfill dams have considerably reduced embankment settlement, and the use of a well-compacted facing layer, which acts as a continuous, firm bedding surface for the concrete face, has reduced the bridging requirements of the face.

For a small dam on a stable foundation, a reinforced concrete slab with a minimum thickness of 8 inches is recommended. The concrete should be dense, durable, weather resistant, and have low permeability (concrete mix designs are discussed in app. F). If foundation settlement could occur, or if other factors such as earthquake conditions exist, it would be wise to increase the membrane thickness. The amount of steel reinforcing should meet

Figure 7-13.—Placement of fine and coarse filter material. For the 55-foot-high New Exchequer Saddle Dike, California. (Tudor Engineering Co. photograph). 288–D–2881.

the generally accepted requirements, 0.5 percent of the concrete area. The reinforcing should be placed both horizontally and vertically in a single layer in the center of the slab.

Because of the low reservoir head and the small amount of settlement expected, horizontal or vertical expansion joints are normally not required in the reinforced concrete facings for low dams. Vertical joints may be required to compensate for horizontal expansion on low dams of considerable length and are often used to facilitate construction of the face. Polyvinyl chloride or rubber waterstops should be used to ensure impermeability along the joints.

The type of cutoff between the concrete facing and the foundation depends on the quality of rock encountered. For sound rock, the doweled cutoff slab shown on figure 7-5 has demonstrated its adequacy and economy [11]; whereas, in closely jointed, weathered rock, or rock of questionable quality, a cutoff wall should be used. Waterstops should be used between the cutoff and the facing.

Because concrete facings provide little resistance to wave runup, increased freeboard is required to prevent wave runup and oversplash. Coping or parapet walls similar to that shown on figure 7-10 may be used to reduce the height of embankment required for freeboard purposes. These walls should be constructed as integral continuations of the concrete face and reinforced accordingly. Coping walls work well. Cooke [11] reports that in one case, walls 10 feet high have stored water to 8 feet without harmful effects; although this procedure is not recommended for the types of structures considered here. When coping walls are used for runup and oversplash protection, freeboard requirements of the embankment can be less than those for an earthfill dam (sec. 6.21). The design top of the rockfill should be above the maximum water surface. The height of the coping wall can be determined either by precedent or the designer's experience. The spillway should be designed so that its capacity increases rapidly as the reservoir surface begins to encroach on the coping walls.

Concrete has generally been placed by the same slip-forming process used in road construction, but in some cases shotcrete has been used effectively. Figure 7-14 shows the placement of concrete by the use of slip-forms on the upstream slope of New Exchequer Dam in California, and figure 7-15 shows shotcreting at Taum Sauk Dam near St. Louis, Missouri. Placement of the concrete membrane should not begin until the entire embankment has been placed; this allows maximum construction settlement and reduces the possibility of cracking and excess leakage. If concurrent slab placement is necessary to complete the job on time, an experienced dam designer should be consulted. Concrete overruns could occur as a result of the voids in the facing layer and should be accounted for in estimating the quantities.

7.11. *Asphaltic Concrete.*—The second most common facing for rockfill dams is asphaltic concrete. Asphaltic concrete provides more flexibility and can thus tolerate larger settlements than reinforced concrete facings. It offers an economical alternative to concrete and has proved dependable when correctly constructed. The recommended upstream slope for asphaltic-concrete-faced rockfill dams is 1.7:1 or flatter, as shown on figure 7-10. The zone A material should provide a well-graded, free-draining rock layer to eliminate uplift pressures in case of rapid drawdown. Yet it should also provide sufficient resistance to limit water velocities and prevent piping if a crack forms in the membrane. The gradation of the zone A material should be smaller than the zone B material. A base course with a minimum thickness of 6 inches should be provided beneath the asphalt as a leveling course, working surface, and smooth base surface for asphalt placement. The base course should consist of well-graded material from a maximum size of about 1 to 2 inches to 5 to 7 percent passing the No. 200 sieve. The base course should be well compacted by a vibratory roller. Figure 7-16 shows the completed rockfill section at Upper Blue River Dam before asphalt membrane placement.

A penetration coat should be applied to the base course surface before asphalt membrane placement to bind and stabilize it. The weight of the paving machine may still gouge the base course, and hand placement of asphalt in the gouged surfaces may be required.

The recommended asphaltic-concrete membrane thickness is between 4 and 12 inches, depending on the hydraulic head. It should be applied by a standard road paver in one to three approximately equal lifts, depending on the total thickness [19]. Figure 7-17 shows placement of an asphaltic-concrete layer at Montgomery Dam in Colorado. A seal coat is desirable on the finished surface of the membrane. The seal coat waterproofs the facing and provides increased durability. Each layer is placed in strips 10 to 12 feet wide and constructed at right angles to the axis of the dam. Paving is placed on the upslope pass only, and the machine is returned to the bottom and reloaded for each strip. If sufficient asphaltic material is not available for each strip, reloading must be performed on the upstream face; a single paving machine should be capable of placing between 25 and 35 tons of asphaltic concrete per hour. Rolling operations should be performed shortly after placing. Smooth-wheel rollers, either the vibratory or standard tandem type, can be used for lift compaction.

Lifts should be compacted to a minimum of 97 percent of standard laboratory density. Construction control can be effected by taking core samples from the asphalt face at random locations and performing asphalt content, unit weight, stability, and permeability tests.

Effecting tight joints between adjacent strips of the facing is important to the imperviousness of the membrane. Transverse joints in the strips should be kept to a minimum and should be hot joints, if possible. Cold joints, either between parallel strips or transversely on a single strip, should be treated as follows:

1. Apply a tack coat of asphaltic cement, the same type used in the mix.
2. Place the asphaltic concrete, overlapping the joint 3 to 6 inches.
3 Reheat the joint with an infrared heater, avoiding open flames.
4. Compact the joint by rolling, immediately after reheating.

Figure 7-14.—Placement of concrete by the use of slip forms. On the upstream slope of New Exchequer Dam, California. (Tudor Engineering Co. photograph). 288–D–2882.

When one lift is placed on top of another, the parallel joints in the strips of the top lift should be offset 3 or 4 feet from the joints of the bottom strip.

The foundation cutoff used with asphalt facings must promote easy placement of the asphalt lift at the contact with the foundation. A trench-type cutoff wall similar to that shown on figure 7-3 is recommended. The cutoff used at Montgomery Dam is shown on figure 7-18; the 12-inch-diameter drain was used to reduce uplift pressure during drawdown. The cutoff used at Upper Blue River Dam is visible at the left edge of figure 7-16.

The upstream asphaltic membrane should be constructed so that it is:

- Durable
- Flexible
- Impervious
- Does not creep
- Resists weathering

Material found within an economical hauling distance of the dam should be used in the asphaltic concrete if possible. A number of different materials and gradations ranging from silty sand [20] to graded gravel [17] have been used to construct adequate upstream facings. Clay fines should not be permitted in mixes because the clay tends to ball during the drying process and to crush when compacted, thereby leaving dry material exposed to the reservoir water.

The gradation limits of the material used for the asphaltic-concrete facing at Montgomery Dam are shown in table 7-1.

Figure 7-15.—Placement of shotcrete on the upstream face of Taum Sauk Dam, Missouri. (Union Electric Co. photograph). 288-D-2883.

Table 7-1.—Gradations of asphaltic-concrete aggregates. Aggregate *specified* and that *used* for the asphaltic-concrete facing at Montgomery Dam.

Sieve designation square openings (U.S. standard sieves)	Percent passing by weight	
	Specifications	Job mix[1]
1½ inch	100	100
¾ inch	80-95	86.4
½ inch	71-89	76.5
No. 4	55-75	58.7
No. 10	40-60	46.5
No. 40	22-36	30.0
No. 80	14-26	19.2
No. 200	7-15	12.8

[1]Average gradation of material used in construction.

Tests should be performed using various gradations, compressive efforts, percent asphaltic cement, and percent lime to determine the mix that has the maximum unit weight and best satisfies the above criteria. In certain cases, 1 to 3 percent lime has been shown to reduce the underwater expansion of the asphaltic concrete, thereby increasing its life expectancy.

The tests that may be performed to evaluate the materials and the different mixes are:

1. Sieve analysis and specific gravity test
2. Immersion-compression test
3. Unconfined-compression test
4. Sustained-load test
5. Permeability test
6. Wave-action test

Tests 1 through 5 are similar to those described in *ASTM Standards*, part II. Test 6, concerning the effect of wave action, is described in [20, 21, 22]; this test was developed by the Bureau of Reclamation to simulate wave effects on asphaltic-concrete facings and has proved useful in helping to select the correct mix proportions.

Special tests that can be performed are:

1. Slope-flow test
2. Coefficient of expansion test
3. Flexural strength test
4. Effect of reservoir ice test

All of the above tests, both standard and special, were performed by the Bureau of Reclamation to

Figure 7-16.—Completed rockfill embankment at Upper Blue River Dam, Colorado, before membrane placement. (Dept. of Public Utilities, Colorado Springs, Colorado, photograph). 288–D–2884.

determine the proper type of asphaltic cement and the correct percentage to be used at Montgomery Dam [21]. These tests led to a mix design incorporating 8.5 percent asphaltic cement. The specifications for the asphaltic cement used at Montgomery Dam are reprinted below:

"All asphalt for use in the asphaltic concrete shall be uniform in character, shall not foam when heated to 350 °F, and shall conform to the following specifications and requirements;

(a) Penetration (tested per ASTM D 5)
  (1) At 77 °F, 100 grams, 5 seconds....................50-60
  (2) At 32 °F, 200 grams, 60 seconds .... min. 12
(b) Ductility at 77 °F, 5 cm/min.............. min. 140 cm
  (tested per ASTM D 113)
(c) Flash point (Cleveland open cup)...... min. 450 °F
  (tested per ASTM D 92)
(d) Solubility in carbon
  tetrachloride... min. 99.5 %
  (tested per ASTM D 165)
(e) Softening point (ring and
  ball method)....................................min. 125 °F
  (tested per ASTM D 36)
(f) Spot test (per paragraph 3 of AASHTO
  Specifications T 102) .... negative
(g) Results of tests made on residues after thin-film overn heating, per test method No. Calif. 337-A, January 3, 1956, of the Division of Highways, Department of Public Works, State of California, shall conform to the following as compared with like tests made on the identical material before such heating. Such method shall be considered to be a part hereof, provided that in lieu of the pertinent AASHTO Specifications there shall be used

Figure 7-17.—Placing asphaltic concrete on the face of Montgomery Dam, Colorado. CH–520–81.

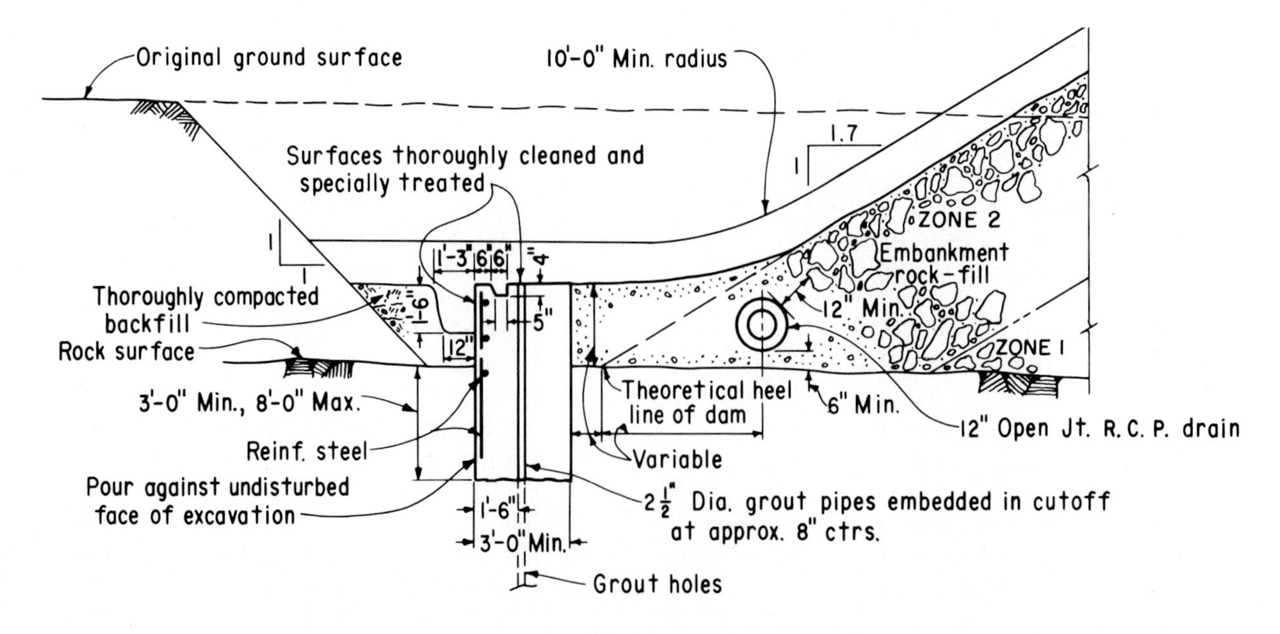

Figure 7-18.—Foundation cutoff used at Montgomery Dam, Colorado. 288–D–2802.

the ASTM Specifications referred to in this item plus ASTM D 6 and E 11. The contractor shall cause the producer of the asphalt to supply the engineer, as required, with data or curves showing the relation between temperature and viscosity representative of the asphalt as furnished for the work."

The results of the tests specified above are shown in table 7-2.

A very low air-void content resulting from proper mix design and compaction is required to obtain durable facings; however, a low air-void ratio cannot be obtained by simply adding more asphalt cement. Air-void ratios of 1 percent are commonly obtained, and the maximum air-void ratio allowed in the construction of an asphalt facing should be 5 percent.

Experience has indicated that densely graded aggregates with ample filler (minus No. 200), correctly proportioned with a 50 to 60 penetration, paving-grade asphalt cement produces a very workable, relatively easily compacted hot mix at about 300 °F. The thicker films of asphalt cement obtained with a rich mix of slightly harder 50 to 60 asphalt cement, as compared with an 85 to 100 or 100 to 150 penetration asphalt cement, can be expected to increase watertightness, stability, and durability. The completed asphaltic-concrete facing at Upper Blue River Dam is shown on figure 7-19.

Parapet walls should be used with asphaltic-concrete facings in lieu of increasing the height of the dam to retard wave runup and oversplash. Galvanized corrugated metal has been used for a number of small dams [17,21] and appears to be performing well; figure 7-19 shows the parapet wall at Upper Blue River Dam. When parapet walls are used to protect against wave runup and oversplash, the freeboard heights of the embankment may be reduced from those heights required for earthfill dams (sec. 6.21); however, the embankment crest must be above maximum water surface. Wall heights can be determined by precedent or design experience.

For further information on asphalt facings, the reader should consult the references at the end of this chapter. Specifications for materials used to manufacture asphaltic concrete are subject to change, and the literature should be consulted.

Table 7-2.—Results of tests on asphaltic concrete. Montgomery Dam and Cawker City Dike.

Test	Percent of result before heating	
	Montgomery Dam	Cawker City Protective Dike[1]
Penetration, at 77 °F, retained, minimum	65	55
Penetration, at 32 °F, retained, minimum	70	45
Ductility, at 77 °F, retained, minimum	80	30
Increase in softening point, minimum	10	15
Loss in weight, maximum	0.3	0.3

[1]The percentages for Cawker City Dike were added for comparison with those used for Montgomery Dam.

7.12. *Steel.*—Steel facings have been used on relatively few dams throughout the world, but their satisfactory performance on these few dams illustrates clearly that they should be given serious economic consideration by dam designers. Few design criteria besides precedent are applicable, and the available literature should be consulted for a complete review of the practices used [18, 23, 24, 25].

Figure 7-20 shows the upstream face of the Bureau of Reclamation's El Vado Dam where the steel plate is in excellent condition after 45 years of service.

Steel-faced dams can be rapidly constructed and should be capable of tolerating greater embankment movements than either concrete or asphalt-faced dams. The most prominent disadvantage to steel facings is the possibility of corrosion reducing their economic life, although this can be effectively controlled by cathodic protection on both faces of the plate. Experience with the few existing steel-faced dams strongly indicates that corrosion failure of the plate is remote, and that for practical purposes, the facing can be assumed to be permanent if proper maintenance is provided.

Steel-faced dams have generally been constructed with upstream slopes from 1.3:1 to 1.7:1. For rockfill dams, the upstream and downstream slopes need not be flatter than the natural slope of the material, which is generally from 1.3:1 to 1.4:1. The steeper slopes lead to reduced costs, but slightly increased face construction difficulties.

The portion of the embankment on which the steel plate bears (zone A on fig. 7-10) should, in general, be constructed of well-graded, pervious gravel to provide a uniform bearing surface for the steel facing. Anchor rods should extend from the facing plates into the embankment to prevent uplift

Figure 7-19.—Completed asphaltic-concrete facing at Upper Blue River Dam, Colorado. (Dept. of Public Utilities, Colorado Springs, Colorado, photograph). 288–D–2885.

or loosening of the face as a result of embankment settlement or wave action. Two methods of anchoring the faceplate to the embankment have been used. The first method requires that the steel plate be constructed on a scaffolding grid that is raised a few feet off the face of the dam; bedding material is then placed between the facing and the embankment either after the plate construction is completed or concurrently with its construction up the face. The second method requires that anchor bar holes be dug in the completed faceplate bedding material, and the anchor bars grouted in with concrete. The first method provides more adequate plate anchoring, but the second method is less costly.

The steel plates should have a thickness of 1/4 to 3/8 inch, depending on the assumed magnitude of the movements of the dam. All joints and seams should have a continuous fillet weld, and nuts used on alignment or anchor bolts should be welded to the plate on all sides to prevent leakage. Plate sizes have varied considerably; large plates are more difficult to handle and appear to provide little advantage over smaller plates.

The foundation cutoff used should be the trench-type cutoff wall shown on figure 7-4. It should be designed to withstand the tension caused by settlement and stresses imposed by any differential face movement adjacent to the cutoff. Coping walls should be used to retard oversplash. Freeboard requirements are similar to those for a concrete-faced rockfill dam (sec. 7.10).

Expansion joints are usually V-shaped metal strips placed perpendicular to the axis of the dam and extending from the crest to the cutoff; the V-strips may have their raised portion placed on either the front or back of the steel face. Design details used for El Vado Dam in New Mexico, Rio Lagartijo Dike in Venezuela, and Sirinumu Dam in New Guinea are shown on figures 7-21, 7-22, and 7-23, respectively.

7.13. *Timber Planking.*—Timber planking has

Figure 7-20.—Steel facing on the upstream slope of El Vado Dam, New Mexico. The facing is in excellent condition after 45 years of service. 288–D–2886.

been used as a temporary type of membrane, but is not recommended for general use, even though it is often the most inexpensive type of membrane to construct. The principal objections to this type of construction are the danger of loss by fire at low water and the relatively short life of timber construction when alternately exposed to wetting and drying.

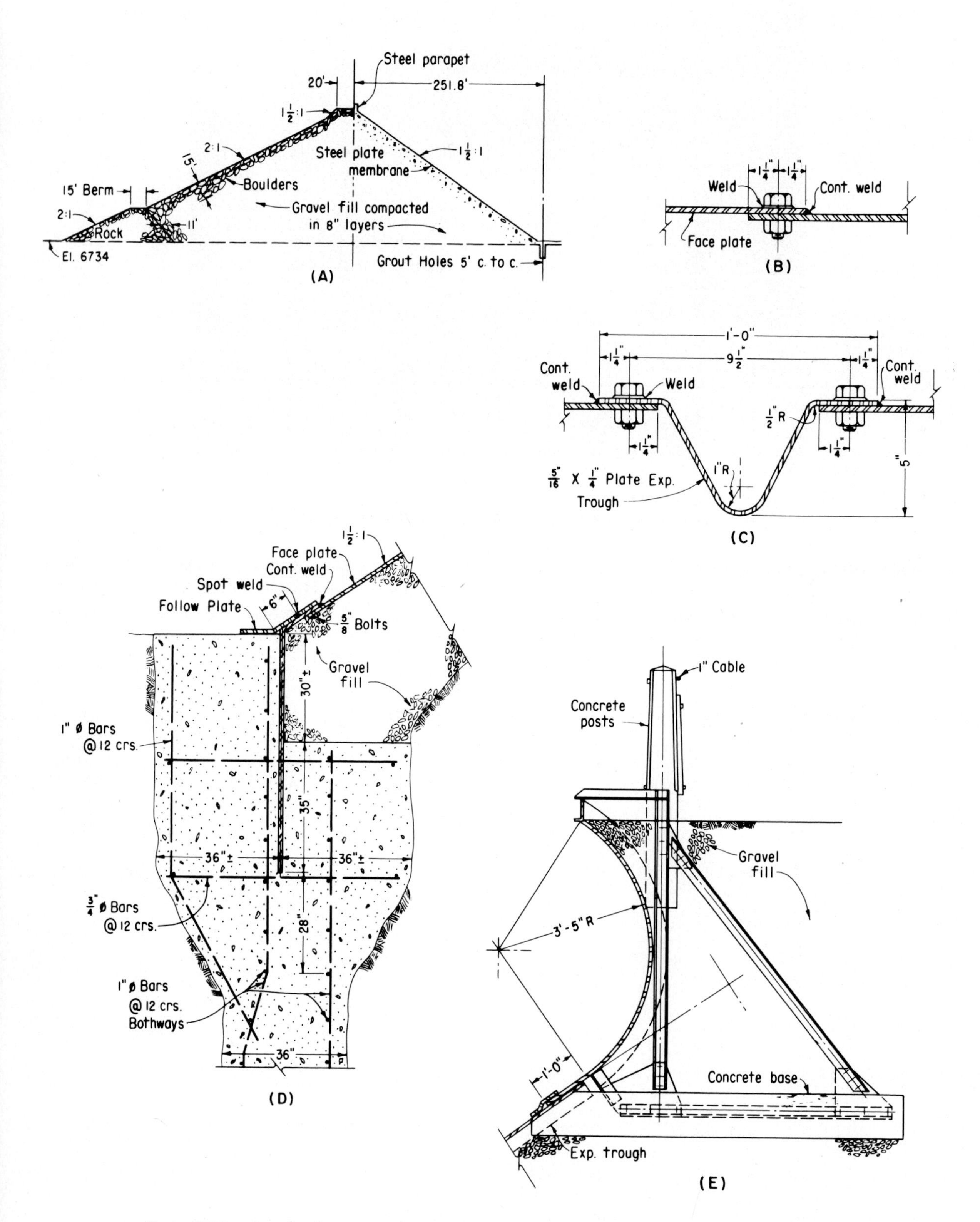

Figure 7-21.—Details of steel membrane used at El Vado Dam, New Mexico. 288-D-2703.

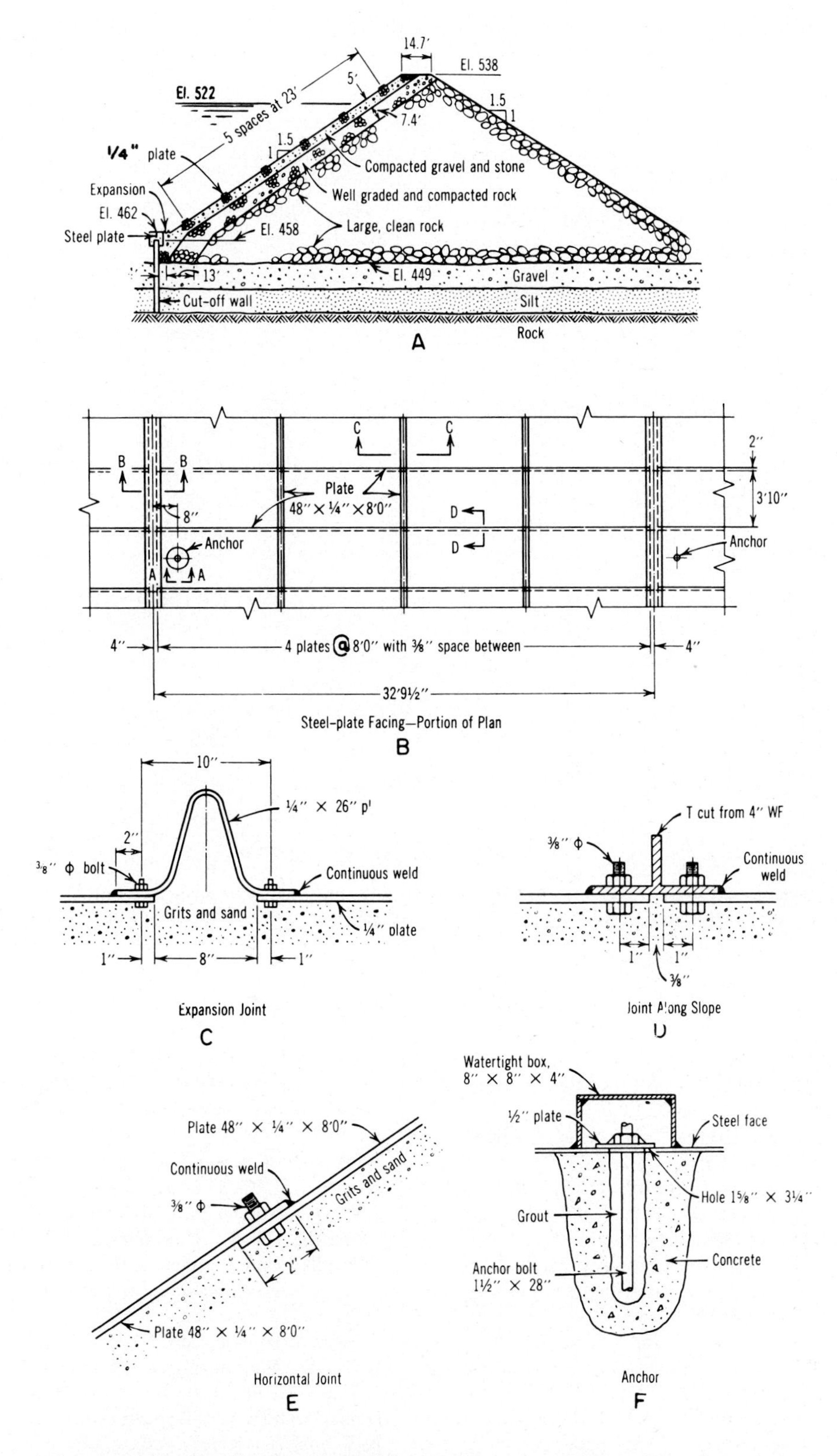

Figure 7-22.—Details of steel membrane used at Rio Lagartijo Dike, Venezuela. Adapted from [24]. 288-D-2804.

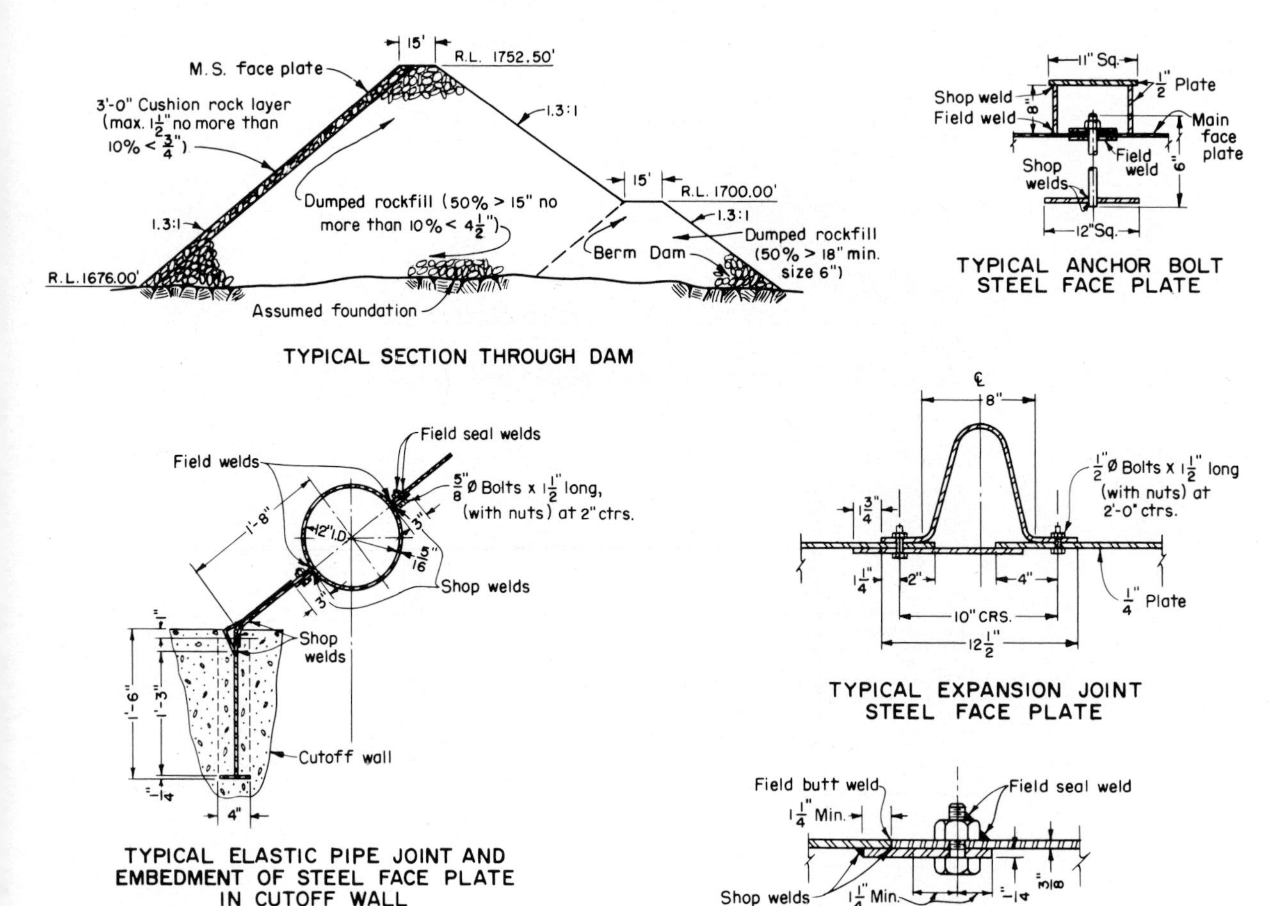

Figure 7-23.—Details of steel membrane used at Sirinumu Dam, New Guinea. Adapted from [25]. 288–D–2805.

E. BIBLIOGRAPHY

7.14. *Bibliography.*

[1] Galloway, J.D., "The Design of Rockfill Dams," *Transactions*, ASCE, No. 104, pt. 2, p. 1, 1939.

[2] "Symposium on Rockfill Dams," *Transactions*, ASCE, vol. 125, pt. 2, 1960.

[3] Cooke, Barry J., "Progress in Rockfill Dams," *Journal of Geotechnical Engineers*, ASCE, vol. 110, No. 10, pp. 1,383-1,414, October 1984.

[4] Fenton, J. D., "Hydraulic and Stability Analysis of Rockfill Dams," Department of Civil Engineering, University of Melbourne, July 1968.

[5] Marsal, R. J., "Large Scale Testing of Rockfill Materials," *Journal of the Soil Mechanics and Foundations Division*, ASCE, vol. 93, No. SM2, March 1967.

[6] Porkin, A. K., D. H. Trollope, and J. D. Lawson, "Rockfill Structures Subject to Water Flow," paper No. 4973, *Journal of the Soil Mechanics and Foundations Division*, ASCE, November 1966.

[7] Shand, N., and P. J. N. Pells, "Experience in the Design and Construction of Reinforced Rockfill Dams," Tenth International Congress on Large Dams, Montreal, pp. 270-317, 1970.

[8] Pinkerton, I. L., and R. J. Paton, "Design and Construction of Geehi Dam," *Journal of the Inst. of Civil Engineers*, Autstralia, March 1968.

[9] Mitchell, W. R., J. Fidler, and M. D. Fitzpatrick, "Rowallan and Parangana Rockfill Dams," *Journal of the Inst. of Civil Engineers*, Australia, October-November 1968.

[10] Bureau of Reclamation, *Design Standard No. 13*, Chapter 3, "Foundation Surface Treatment."

[11] Steele, I. C., and J. B. Cooke, "Concrete-Face Rock-Fill Dams," Handbook of Applied Hydraulics, C. V. Davis and K. E. Sorensen editors, 3rd ed., McGraw-Hill, New York, NY, 1969.

[12] Crisp, R. L., "Design, Construction, and Instrumenta-

tion of Carters Rockfill Dam," Paper presented at USCOLD-CNC/ICOLD meeting, Vancouver, B.C., October 1966.

[13] Leps, T. M., "Review of Shearing Strength of Rockfill," *Journal of the Soil Mechanics and Foundations Division*, ASCE, Vol. 96, No. SM4, pp. 1,159-1,170, 1970.

[14] Marachi, N. Dean, Clarence Chan, and H. Bolton Seed, *Journal of the Soil Mechanics and Foundation Division*, ASCE, January 1972.

[15] Sowers, G. F., R. C. Williams, and J. S. Wallace, "Compressibility of Broken Rock and the Settlement of Rockfills," *Proceedings,* Sixth Int. Conf. Soil Mechanics and Foundations, vol. 2, Montreal, 1965.

[16] Scheidenhelm, F. W., J. B. Snethlage, and A. N. Vanderlip, "Montgomery Dam—Rock Fill with Asphaltic Concrete Deck," *Transactions,* ASCE, vol. 125, pt. 2, 1960.

[17] Proudfit, D. P., "Asphaltic Concrete Facing for a Rock-Fill Dam," *Civil Engineering,* March 1968.

[18] Sherard, J. L., R. J. Woodard, S. F. Gizienski, and W. A. Clevenger, "Earth and Earth-Rock Dams," John Wiley and Sons, Inc., New York, NY, 1963.

[19] Bunn, R. A. , "Asphaltic Concrete Membranes in Embankment Dams," *Water Power and Dam Construction,* January 1983.

[20] "Mix Design Investigations of Asphaltic Concrete for Dam Facing—Glen Elder Dam," Bureau of Reclamation, Chemical Engineering Laboratory Report No. ChE-42, February 18, 1965.

[21] "Laboratory Investigation of Asphaltic Concrete, Montogomery Dam, Colorado, " *Proceedings*, Association of Asphalt Paving Technologists, 1958.

[22] "Mix Design Investigation of Asphaltic Concrete for Facing Downs Protective Dike," Bureau of Reclamation, Chemical Engineering Laboratory Report No. ChE-66, December 29, 1966.

[23] Hovey, O. E., "Steel Dams," American Institute of Steel Construction, p. 79, New York, NY, 1935.

[24] Sherard, J. L., "A Steel Faced Rockfill Dam," *Civil Engineering*, vol. 29, No. 10, pp. 698-701, October 1959.

[25] Fraser, J. B., "A Steel-Faced Rockfill Dam for Papua," *Civil Engineering Transactions,* Institution of Engineers, vol. CE4, No. 1, pp. 35-48, Australia, March 1962.

Asbeck, Baron W. F. van, "Bitumen in Hydraulic Engineering," vol. 11, Elsevier, London, 1964.

Bertram, G. E., "Rockfill Compaction by Vibratory Rollers," *Proceedings*, 2d Pan-American Conference on Soil Mechanics, Brazil, 1963.

Davis, R. E., "Tests on Models of Sariyar Rockfill Dam," Report to International Engineering Co., Berkeley, CA, July 1949.

Ellsperman, L. M., and F. C. Walker, "Factors Affecting the Use of Asphaltic Diaphragms in Earth and Rockfill Dams in the Western United States," Seventh International Congress on Large Dams, Rome, Italy, 1961.

Elsden, O., H. G. Keefe, and A. W. Bishop, "Embankment Dams," *Hydroelectric Engineering Practice*, 2d ed., ch. IX, vol. 1, Glasgow, 1964.

Fumagelli, Emanuele, "Tests on Cohesionless Materials for Rockfill Dams," *Journal of the Soil Mechanics and Foundations Division*, ASCE, vol. 95, No. SM1, pp. 313-330, January 1969.

Giudici, Sergio, "Rockfill Structures Subject to Water Flow," Discussion of Proceedings, paper No. 4973, *Journal of the Soil Mechanics and Foundations Division,* ASCE, vol. 93, No. SM3, pp. 329-337, September 1967.

Kjoernsli, B., and I. Torblaa, "Asphalt on Earth and Rockfill Dams," Publication No. 48, Norwegian Geotechnical Institute, Oslo, 1966.

Mann, J.N., "Aspects of Rockfill Selection, Placement and Sluicing in the Construction of Moondarra Dam," *Journal of the Inst. of Engineers*, Australia, April-May 1963.

Oliver, H., "Through and Overflow Rockfill Dams—New Design Techniques," *Proceedings,* Inst. Civil Engineers, paper No. 7012, 1967.

Robeson, F. A., and R. L. Crisp, "Rockfill Design—Carters Dam," *Proceedings, Journal of the Construction Division,* ASCE, vol. 92, No. CO3, September 1966.

Reid, H. I., "Steel Plates with Welded Joints Seal Rockfill Dam," *Engineering News-Record,* vol. 108, p. 761.

Rowe, P. W., "The Stress-Dilatancy Relation for Static Equilibrium of an Assembly of Particles in Contact," *Proceedings*, Royal Society, series A, vol. 269, No. 1339, October 9, 1962.

Terzaghi, K., and R. B. Peck, "Soil Mechanics in Engineering Practice," 2d ed., art. 62, John Wiley and Sons, Inc., New York, NY, 1967.

Seger, C. P., "Steel Used Extensively in Building El Vado Dam," *Engineering News-Record*, vol. 115, p. 211.

Wesley, L. D., "Settlement of Embankment Materials in Earth and Rockfill Dams,"*New Zealand Engineering*, pp. 179-187, May 15, 1967.

Wilkins, J. K., "Rockfill Structures Subject to Water Flow," Discussion of Proceedings, paper No. 4973, *Journal of the Soil Mechanics and Foundations Division,* ASCE, vol. 93, No. SM 3, p. 177, May 1967.

Wilkins, J. K., "Decked Rockfill Dams," *Journal Inst. of Engineers*, Australia, April 1968.

"Abrasive Rock, Asphalt Facing for Water Supply Dam," *Engineering News-Record,* p. 44, November 15, 1956.

"Asphalt on Earth- and Rock-Fill Dams," Norwegian Geotechnical Institute, Publication No. 48, Oslo, 1962.

"Asphalt Deck is Dams Watertight Layer," *Engineering News-Record,* p. 36, December 5, 1957.

"Question 27 - Sealing of Earth and Rockfill Dams with Bitumen or Other Materials," Seventh International Congress on Large Dams, vol. IV, Rome, Italy, 1961.

"Question 31 - High Rockfill Dams," Eighth International Congress on Large Dams, vol. III, 1964.

Chapter 8

Concrete Gravity Dams

A. INTRODUCTION

8.1. ***Origin and Development.***—A concrete gravity dam is proportioned so that its own weight provides the major resistance to the forces exerted upon it. If the foundation is adequate and the dam is properly designed and constructed, the concrete dam will be a permanent structure that requires little maintenance.

Gravity dams of uncemented masonry were built several thousand years B.C. Evidence found in archeological sites indicate dam base widths as much as four times the height. With the passing of centuries, various types of mortar have been used to bind the masonry, thereby increasing stability and watertightness and permitting steeper slopes to be used. Concrete and cement mortar were used in the construction of cyclopean masonry dams, the forerunners of the modern mass concrete gravity dams.

As an alternative to the conventional method of placing block upon block of mass concrete, RCC (roller-compacted concrete) is fast becoming an accepted method of constructing concrete gravity dams. An RCC dam is constructed in much the same way as an embankment dam. Zero slump concrete is placed, spread, and compacted with vibratory rollers in 1- to 2-foot-thick lifts that are continuous between abutments. Because the RCC construction method is quicker and requires less labor, it is more cost efficient than conventionally placed mass concrete. Some of the concerns associated with the RCC construction method are bond strength and permeability along lift surfaces, cooling requirements, and incorporating transverse contraction joints. Because experience with RCC is still limited, improvements and changes are anticipated. Upper Stillwater Dam, currently (1986) under construction, is the Bureau of Reclamation's first RCC dam.

8.2. ***Scope of Discussion.***—In general, the discussion in this chapter applies to concrete gravity dams of any height. However, for dams much higher than 50 feet, the reader is referred to another Bureau of Reclamation publication [1][1] for additional details and considerations. This publication [1] is also beneficial to the designer of smaller dams and should be referenced in conjunction with the discussion contained herein.

This chapter discusses concrete properties, the forces that act on concrete gravity dams, foundation considerations, requirements for stability, and stress and stability analyses. Additional considerations for concrete structures on pervious (soil-like) foundations are presented, and current practices regarding miscellaneous details of design are briefly described. A brief discussion of current Bureau of Reclamation computer methods is also included.

B. CONCRETE PROPERTIES

8.3. ***Strength.***—A gravity dam should be constructed of concrete that will meet the design criteria for strength, durability, permeability, and other required properties. Properties of concrete vary with age, the type of cement, aggregates, and other ingredients, and their proportions in the mix. Because different concretes gain strength at different rates, laboratory tests must be made on specimens of sufficient age to permit evaluation of ultimate strengths.

Normally, the concrete mix for gravity dams is designed for only compressive strength. However, compression is not the critical stress. Generally, a 10:1 compressive strength to stress ratio results

[1]Numbers in brackets refer to entries in the bibliography (sec. 8.26).

when designing the dam to meet the concrete shear and tensile strength limits. Therefore, tensile and shear strength are the most important concrete strength design parameters, and laboratory tests should be made to determine these values, especially across lift surfaces.

8.4. *Elastic Properties.*—Elastic properties are useful for analyzing deformations related to differential block movement, three-dimensional analyses, and other aspects concerned with deformations. The modulus of elasticity, although not directly proportional to concrete strength, does increase with increasing concrete strength. As with the strength properties, the modulus of elasticity is influenced by mix proportions, cement, aggregate, admixtures, and age. The deformation that occurs immediately with the application of a load, such as during an earthquake, depends on the dynamic modulus of elasticity. The increase in deformation caused by a constant load over a period of time is the result of creep or plastic flow in the concrete. The effects of creep are generally accounted for by determining a sustained modulus of elasticity of the concrete for use in the analyses of static loadings.

The static modulus of elasticity and Poisson's ratio should be determined for the different ages of concrete when test cylinders, made before or during construction, are loaded to failure within a few minutes according to standard ASTM loading rates. The sustained modulus of elasticity under constant load should be determined from these cylinders after specific incremental loading periods for up to 1 and 2 years. The cylinders tested should be the same size and cured in the same manner as those used for compressive strength tests. The values of static modulus of elasticity, Poisson's ratio, and sustained modulus of elasticity used in the analyses should be the average of all test cylinder values.

8.5 *Thermal Properties.*—During construction, heat from cement hydration should be uniformly dissipated or controlled to avoid undesirable cracking. Uniform dissipation is accomplished by circulating cool water through tubing optimally spread atop each lift during conventional construction of vertical blocks. In addition, the heat generated can be reduced by replacing a portion of the cement with pozzolan, which generates only about 50 percent of the heat generated by the same quantity of cement.

Operational temperature changes from ambient air and the reservoir may produce steep nonlinear thermal gradients and associated stresses because of the slower response in the interior of the dam. The thermal properties necessary for the evaluation of temperature changes are the coefficient of thermal expansion, thermal conductivity, specific heat, and diffusivity. The coefficient of thermal expansion is the length change per unit length for a 1°F temperature change. Thermal conductivity is the rate of heat conduction through a unit thickness over a unit area of the material subjected to a unit temperature difference between faces. The specific heat is defined as the amount of heat required to raise the temperature of a unit mass of the material 1°F. Diffusivity of concrete is an index of the ease with which concrete undergoes temperature change. The diffusivity is calculated from the values of specific heat, thermal conductivity, and density.

8.6. *Average Properties.*—(a) *Basic Considerations.*—Concrete properties may be estimated from published data for preliminary studies until laboratory test data are available.

(b) *Criteria.*—The following average values may be used for preliminary designs until site-specific test data are available. Static values represent estimated values from laboratory tests for specimens loaded to failure within a few minutes according to standard ASTM loading rates.

- Compressive strength (static): 3,000 to 5,000 lb/in^2
- Tensile strength (static): 5 to 6 percent of the compressive strength
- Tensile strength (dynamic): 10 percent of the static compressive strength
- Shear strength (static):
  Cohesion: 10 percent of the static compressive strength
  Coefficient of internal friction: 1.0
- Poisson's ratio: 0.2
- Static modulus of elasticity: 5.0×10^6 lb/in^2
- Dynamic modulus of elasticity: 6.0×10^6 lb/in^2
- Sustained modulus of elasticity: 3.0×10^6 lb/in^2
- Coefficient of thermal expansion: 5.0×10^{-6} ft/ft/°F
- Unit weight: 150 lb/ft^3
- Diffusivity: 0.05 ft^2/hr

C. FORCES ACTING ON THE DAM

8.7. *General.*—Essential to the design of gravity dams is knowledge of the forces expected to affect the stresses and stability of the structure. The forces that must be considered are those due to (1) external water pressure, (2) temperature, (3) internal water pressure; i.e., pore pressure or uplift in the dam and foundation, (4) weight of the structure, (5) ice pressure, (6) silt pressure, (7) earthquake, and (8) forces from gates or other appurtenant structures.

Figure 8-1 (A) shows the reservoir and tailwater reactions on a nonoverflow section. Symbols and definitions for this loading are:

ψ = angle between face of the dam and the vertical,

T = horizontal distance between the upstream and downstream faces of a section,

I = moment of inertia of the base of a horizontal section 1 foot wide about its center of gravity, equal to $T^3/12$,

W_c = weight of concrete,

w = unit weight of water, 62.4 lb/ft^3

h or h' = vertical distance from reservoir water or tailwater, respectively, to base of section,

P or P' = reservoir water or tailwater pressure, respectively, at base of section, equal to wh or wh',

W_o = dead load weight above base of section under consideration including the weight of the concrete, W_c, plus such appurtenances as gates and bridges,

W_W or W_W' = vertical component of reservoir water or tailwater load, respectively, on face above base of section,

M_o = moment of W_o about center of gravity of base of section,

M_W or M_W' = moment of W_W or W_W' about center of gravity of base of section,

V or V' = horizontal component of reservoir water or tailwater load, respectively, on face above base section, equal to $wh^2/2$ for V and $w(h')^2/2$ for V' for normal conditions,

M_P or M_P' = moment of V or V' about center of gravity of base of section, equal to $wh^3/6$ for M_P and $w(h')^3/6$ for M_P',

ΣW = resultant vertical force above base of section,

ΣV = resultant horizontal force above base of section,

ΣM = resultant moment from forces above base of section about center of gravity of base of section,

e = distance from center of gravity of base of section to point where resultant of ΣW and ΣV intersects base of section, equal to $\Sigma M/\Sigma W$, and

U = total uplift force on horizontal section without drains or drains inoperable, equal to $T(P+P')/2$.

The summation of horizontal and vertical components imply a horizontal foundation or potential failure plane. Loads should be resolved into components normal and parallel to the foundation or to potential failure planes having significant slope in computing sliding stability.

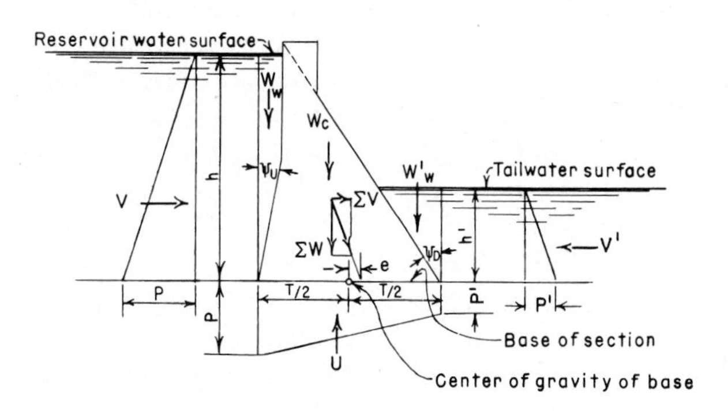

(A) VERTICAL CROSS SECTION

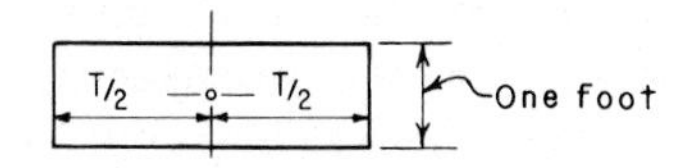

(B) HORIZONTAL CROSS SECTION

FORCES ACTING ON A CONCRETE GRAVITY DAM

Figure 8-1.—Forces acting on a concrete gravity dam. 288-D-2505.

8.8. *External Water Pressure.*—(a) *Basic Considerations.*—Reservoir and tailwater loads are obtained from reservoir operation studies and tailwater curves. These studies are based on operating and hydrologic data such as reservoir capacity, storage allocation, streamflow records, flood hydrographs, and reservoir releases. Reservoir operation curves derived from these studies reflect a normal high water surface, seasonal drawdowns, and the usual low water surface. See figure 8-2 for the following water surface designations.

(1) Maximum water surface.—The highest acceptable water surface elevation considering all factors affecting the safety of the structure. Normally, it is the maximum design reservoir elevation anticipated and usually occurs in conjunction with routing of the IDF (inflow design flood) through the reservoir. Maximum water surface usually corresponds to the dam crest elevation without including the parapet.

(2) Top of exclusive flood control capacity.—The reservoir water surface elevation at the top of the reservoir capacity allocated to exclusive use of regulating flood inflows to reduce damage downstream.

(3) Maximum controllable water surface elevation.—The highest reservoir water surface elevation at which gravity flows from the reservoir can be completely shut off. Generally, this is the top of the spillway gates or the crest of an ungated spillway.

(4) Top of joint-use capacity.—The reservoir water surface elevation at the top of the reservoir capacity allocated to joint uses of flood control and conservation purposes.

(5) Top of active conservation capacity.—The reservoir water surface elevation at the top of the capacity allocated to storage of water for conservation purposes only.

(6) Top of inactive capacity.—The reservoir water surface elevation below which the reservoir will not be evacuated under normal conditions.

(7) Top of dead capacity.—The lowest elevation in the reservoir from which water can be drawn by gravity.

(8) Streambed at the dam axis.—The elevation of the lowest point in the streambed at the axis of the dam before construction. This elevation normally defines the zero for area-capacity tables.

The normal design reservoir elevation is the top of joint-use capacity, if joint-use capacity is included. If not, it is the top of active conservation capacity.

On overflow dams without control features, the total horizontal water pressure on the upstream face is closely represented by the trapezoid (abcd) on figure 8-3, in which the unit pressures at the top and bottom are wh_1 and wh, respectively, with w being the unit weight of water. The total horizontal force, P, passes through the center of gravity of the trapezoid. The vertical pressure component of water flowing over the top of the spillway is not used in the analysis because most of the total head has changed to velocity head. The sheet of water flowing down the downstream face generally does not exert enough pressure on the dam to warrant consideration. Where tailwater or backwater stands against the downstream face, it should be treated in the same manner as the tailwater on figure 8-1(A). However, during major overflows of water, the tailwater pressures are involved in the energy dissipating process and may contribute only minor stabilizing forces on the dam.

(b) *Criteria.*—Reservoir elevations for the loading combinations analyzed should be selected from reservoir operation studies. The minimum tailwater level associated with each reservoir level should be used. Tailwater surface elevations should be obtained from tailwater curves associated with operating studies. For computation of the reservoir and tailwater loads, water pressure is considered to vary directly with depth and to act equally in all directions.

8.9. *Temperature.*—(a) *Basic Considerations.*—Volumetric increases caused by temperature rise transfer load across transverse contraction joints if the joints are grouted. The horizontal thrusts produced by volumetric changes associated with temperature increases result in a transfer of load across grouted contraction joints that increases the twisting effects and the loading of the abutments as discussed in [1]. Similarly, ungrouted contraction joints transfer horizontal thrusts at areas that come into contact when the concrete temperature exceeds the temperature necessary to close the contraction joint.

Temperature effects can also induce cracking in

TYPE OF DAM		REGION	STATE
OPERATED BY	RESERVOIR		
CREST LENGTH FT; CREST WIDTH FT	DAM		
VOLUME OF DAM CU YD	PROJECT		
CONSTRUCTION PERIOD	DIVISION		
STREAM	UNIT		
RES AREA ACRES AT EL	STATUS OF DAM		
ORIGINATED BY: *(Initials)* *(Code)* *(Date)*	APPROVED BY: *(Initials)* *(Code)* *(Date)*		

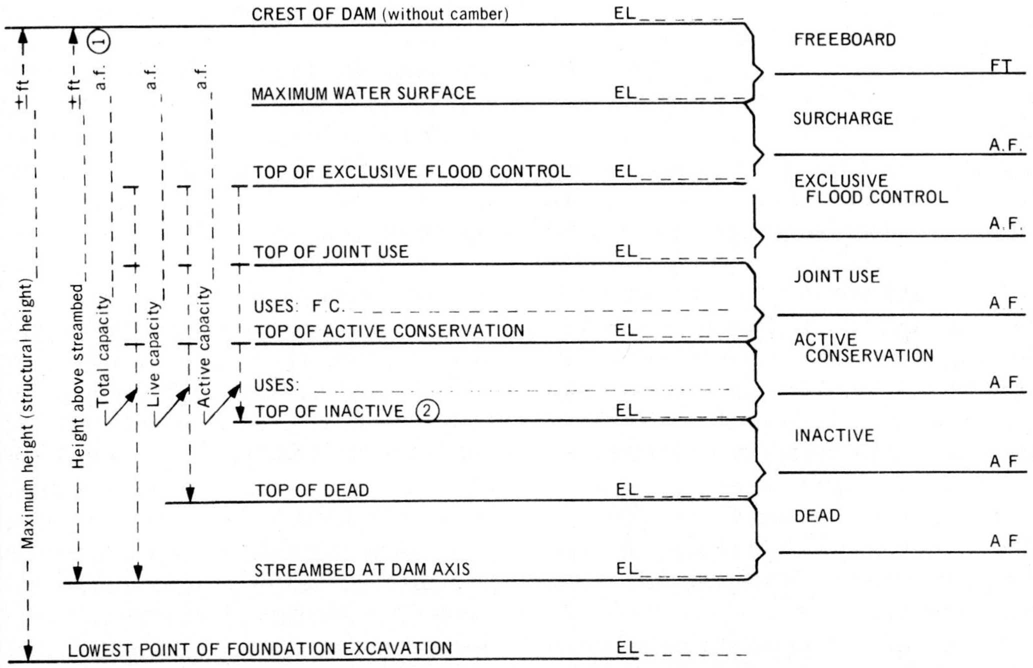

① Includes____________ a.f. allowance for_____ year sediment deposition between streambed and El_________. of which_________ a.f. is above El________.

② Established by______________________________

REFERENCES AND COMMENTS:

Figure 8-2.—Water surface designations. 103–D–1823.

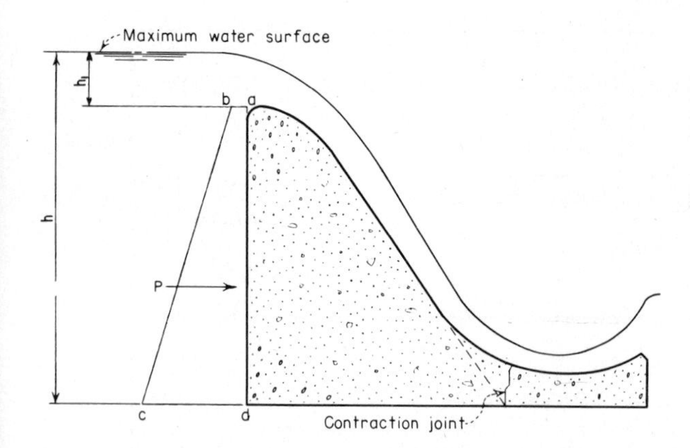

Figure 8-3.—Water pressures acting on an overflow concrete dam. 288-D-2506.

mass concrete structures. Tensile stresses that exceed the concrete tensile strength may be generated because of a restraint against temperature-induced volumetric changes. Temperature cracking can be prevented or greatly reduced by controlling the placement temperatures, the placement schedule, and the cooling of the mass concrete placed. The first two measures are usually sufficient to control cracking in small dams because the concrete dimensions are often thin enough to allow rapid dissipation of heat. For more details, see [2]. In addition, "Concrete Dam Design Standards," currently (1986) being prepared, will address the temperature considerations associated with mass concrete structures.

When the designer is making studies to determine concrete temperature loads, varying weather conditions should be considered. Similarly, a widely fluctuating reservoir water surface will affect the concrete temperatures. In determining temperature loads, the following conditions and temperatures should be used:

- Usual weather conditions.—The combination of three items that accounts for temperatures that are halfway between the mean monthly air temperatures and the minimum/maximum recorded air temperatures at the site [2]. The three items are (1) the daily air temperatures, (2) a 1-week cycle representative of the cold/hot periods associated with barometric pressure changes, and (3) the mean monthly air temperatures.
- Usual concrete temperatures.—The usual concrete temperatures between the upstream and downstream faces are the average of the usual air temperatures and reservoir water temperatures associated with the design reservoir operation. Additional refinement is obtained by considering the effects of solar radiation [2].

(b) *Criteria.*—The effects of temperature change should always be investigated when joints are to be grouted and if the operating temperatures are above the closure temperature when joints are not to be grouted. The possibility of temperature-induced cracking should also be investigated.

8.10. *Internal Water Pressures.*—(a) *Basic Considerations.*—Water pressures caused by reservoir water and tailwater occur within the dam and foundation in pores, cracks, joints, and seams. The distribution of internal water pressures along a horizontal section through the dam or its foundation is assumed to vary linearly from full reservoir pressure at the upstream face to zero or tailwater pressure at the downstream face in the absence of drains or a more detailed analysis.

The internal water pressure, also called uplift, acts to reduce the compressive stresses normal to a horizontal section through the dam. Including a line of vertical formed drains within the dam and parallel to the upstream face serves to reduce the uplift force. The uplift reduction is dependent on the size, location, and spacing of the drains.

The generally accepted current practice assumes pore pressures act over 100 percent of the area of any section through the concrete. Current Bureau of Reclamation practice locates the line of drains at a distance from the upstream face equal to 5 percent of the maximum reservoir depth at the dam or at the same distance from the upstream face as the drains formed within contraction joints. Current Bureau practice assumes that a line of 5-inch-diameter formed drains spaced 10 feet apart reduces the average pore pressure at the line of drains to tailwater pressure plus one-third the differential between tailwater and headwater pressures. These values are based on the assumption that the lowest elevation in the drainage gallery is at or below tailwater level or that pumping of the drains will be a part of the operating criteria. If the gallery is above tailwater elevation, the pressure at the line of drains should be determined as though the tailwater level is equal to the gallery elevation. In no case should these pressures exceed those computed for the dam without drains. Internal pressures are assumed to be unaffected by earthquake accelerations because of the transitory nature of such accelerations.

Forces from water pressures also occur within the foundation. Uplift forces in the foundation decrease the normal forces occurring on potential sliding planes. Water forces occurring on high angle joints increase driving forces on foundation blocks. Both of these reduce foundation sliding stability.

The uplift forces within the foundation and along the foundation-dam contact can be reduced by a line of drain holes drilled into the foundation from the floor of the foundation gallery. The internal pressure distribution through the foundation depends on depth, location, and orientation of the drains, rock permeability characteristics, jointing, faulting, and any other geologic features that may modify the flow. The line of drains should be located a distance downstream from the upstream dam face that will ensure that direct connection from the reservoir will not occur.

Determination of such pressure distributions can be made from flow nets computed by several methods, including two- and three-dimensional physical models, two- and three-dimensional finite element models, electric analogs, and graphical techniques. For preliminary designs, the pressure at the line of drains can be estimated using the same approximation mentioned for formed drains within the dam. Basically, the pressure at the line of drains equals tailwater pressure plus one-third the differential between headwater and tailwater pressures. This uplift assumption is generally conservative when the drain holes are drilled to a depth equal to 40 to 50 percent of the dam height and when the geologic conditions are uniform. Foundation drainage curtains generally consist of 3-inch-diameter holes drilled on 10-foot centers.

Uplift pressures under a concrete dam on a pervious (soil-like) foundation are related to seepage through permeable materials. Water percolating through pore spaces in these materials is retarded by frictional resistance, somewhat the same as water flowing through a pipe. The intensity of the uplift can be controlled by construction of properly placed aprons, cutoffs, drains, and other devices.

Water pressures in the foundation can also initiate piping of weak zones within the foundation. Therefore, exit gradients should be low enough to ensure that piping does not occur.

(b) *Criteria.*—For preliminary design purposes, uplift pressure distribution within a gravity dam, within its foundation, and at their contact are assumed to have an intensity at the line of drains equal to the tailwater pressure plus one-third the differential between headwater and tailwater pressures. The pressure gradient is then extended linearly to headwater and tailwater levels. If there is no tailwater, a similar pressure diagram is determined using zero instead of the tailwater pressure. In all cases, pore pressures are assumed to act over 100 percent of the area.

For the final design, determination of the internal pressures within the dam should be based on the location and spacing of drains. Pressures in the foundation rock or at its contact with the dam should be determined based on geologic structures in the rock and on the location, depth, and spacing of drains. Flow nets computed by electric analog analysis, finite element analysis, or other comparable means should be used for the final determination of water pressure distribution.

8.11. *Dead Load.*—(a) *Basic Considerations.*—The weight of the structure includes the weight of the concrete plus appurtenances such as gates and bridges. The total weight acts vertically through the center of gravity of the cross section, without transfer of shear between adjacent blocks.

(b) *Criteria.*—Total dead load is the weight of the concrete gravity structure plus the weight of appurtenances.

8.12. *Ice.*—(a) *Basic Considerations.*—Ice pressures can produce a significant load against the face of a dam in locations where winter temperatures are cold enough to cause relatively thick ice cover. Ice pressure is created by thermal expansion of the ice and by wind drag. Pressures caused by thermal expansion of the ice depend on the temperature rise of the ice, thickness of the ice sheet, the coefficient of thermal expansion, the elastic modulus, and the strength of the ice. Wind drag depends on the size and shape of the exposed area, the roughness of the surface, and the direction and velocity of the wind. Ice pressure is generally considered to be a transitory loading. Many dams are subjected to little, if any, ice pressure. The designer should decide, after consideration of the above factors, whether an allowance for ice pressure is appropriate.

(b) *Criteria.*—The method of Monfore and Taylor [3] may be used to analyze anticipated ice pressures if the necessary basic data are available.

When basic data are not available to compute pressures, an acceptable estimate of the ice load to be expected on the face of a structure may be taken as 10,000 lb/lin ft of contact between the ice and the dam for an assumed ice depth of 2 feet or more.

8.13. *Silt Pressure.*—(a) *Basic Considerations.*—During both normal flows and floodflows, silt eventually finds its way to the reservoir and is deposited in the still water adjacent to the dam. Methods for determining the amount of silt and its deposition in a reservoir are discussed in appendix A. If allowed to accumulate against the upstream face of the dam, the saturated silt will exert loads greater than the hydrostatic pressure of water alone.

Sluiceways are often provided in gravity dams to reduce the accumulation of silt near the upstream face of the dam. In diversion dams, the main function of the sluiceway is to keep the headworks and canal free from silt, thus reducing somewhat the silt load on the dam.

(b) *Criteria.*—In the absence of reliable test data, assume the saturated silt pressure is analogous and equivalent to that of a fluid having an 85-lb/ft^3 horizontal component and a 120-lb/ft^3 vertical component.

8.14. *Earthquake.*—(a) *Basic Considerations.*—Most earthquakes are the result of crustal movements of the earth along faults. Geologic examinations of the area should be made to locate all faults and to determine how recent the activity has occurred. Records of seismologic activity in the area should also be studied to determine the magnitude and location of all recorded earthquakes that may have affected the site.

When establishing earthquake events to be applied to structures, three levels of earthquake loading and response conditions should be considered: the OBE (operating basis earthquake), the DBE (design basis earthquake), and the MCE (maximum credible earthquake).

The structural response condition expectations associated with each of these earthquakes are:

- OBE.—Structures, systems, and components necessary to the function of a project should be *designed* to remain operable under the vibratory ground motion of the OBE.
- DBE.—Under loading from the design basis event, the project should be *designed* to sustain the earthquake with reparable damage; however, those structures, systems, and components important to safety should remain operable. The degree of damage acceptable would be based on an economic analysis or the estimated repair cost versus the initial cost to control the damage.
- MCE.—The structures of a project vital to retention or release of the reservoir would be *designed* for the loading from the MCE and would be required to function without permitting either a sudden uncontrolled release of the reservoir or a compromise in the controlled evacuation of the reservoir.

To determine the total forces caused by an earthquake, it is necessary to establish the earthquake magnitude and the distance from the site to the causative fault. Small or distant events usually produce little site and structural response. The curve shown on figure 8-4 suggests the need for analyses based on Richter magnitude and distance from causative fault. Bureau studies indicate that the fundamental period of vibration of a 50-foot-high section with a 10-foot-wide roadway varies from 0.086 to 0.05 second for downstream slopes of 0.5:1.0 to 0.8:1.0, respectively. Dams less than 50 feet high have proportionately smaller fundamental periods. The second period of vibration is less than 0.02 second for all cases. For low dams, resonance is not likely to occur during earthquakes. Therefore, uniform accelerations from base to crest may be assumed; they are equal to the estimated site accelerations determined from figure 8-5. Assume the vertical acceleration is 50 percent of the horizontal acceleration. These accelerations can be used to compute inertia loads for pseudostatic analyses.

In pseudostatic analyses, both vertical and horizontal earthquake loads should be applied in the direction that produces the least stable structure. For the full reservoir condition, this will be a foundation movement in the upstream direction and a foundation movement downward. The upstream movement increases the downstream force of the water and silt loads and produces a downstream inertial force from the mass concrete in the dam. The downward movement decreases the effective weight of the water above a sloping face and of the concrete in the dam. Both increasing the horizontal loads in a downstream direction and decreasing the effective weights tend to decrease the stability of the structure. The internal friction of silt may provide considerable damping as has been suggested in the literature [4]. However, until more exact data are determined, it is assumed that the dynamic effect of saturated silt is equivalent to that of water only.

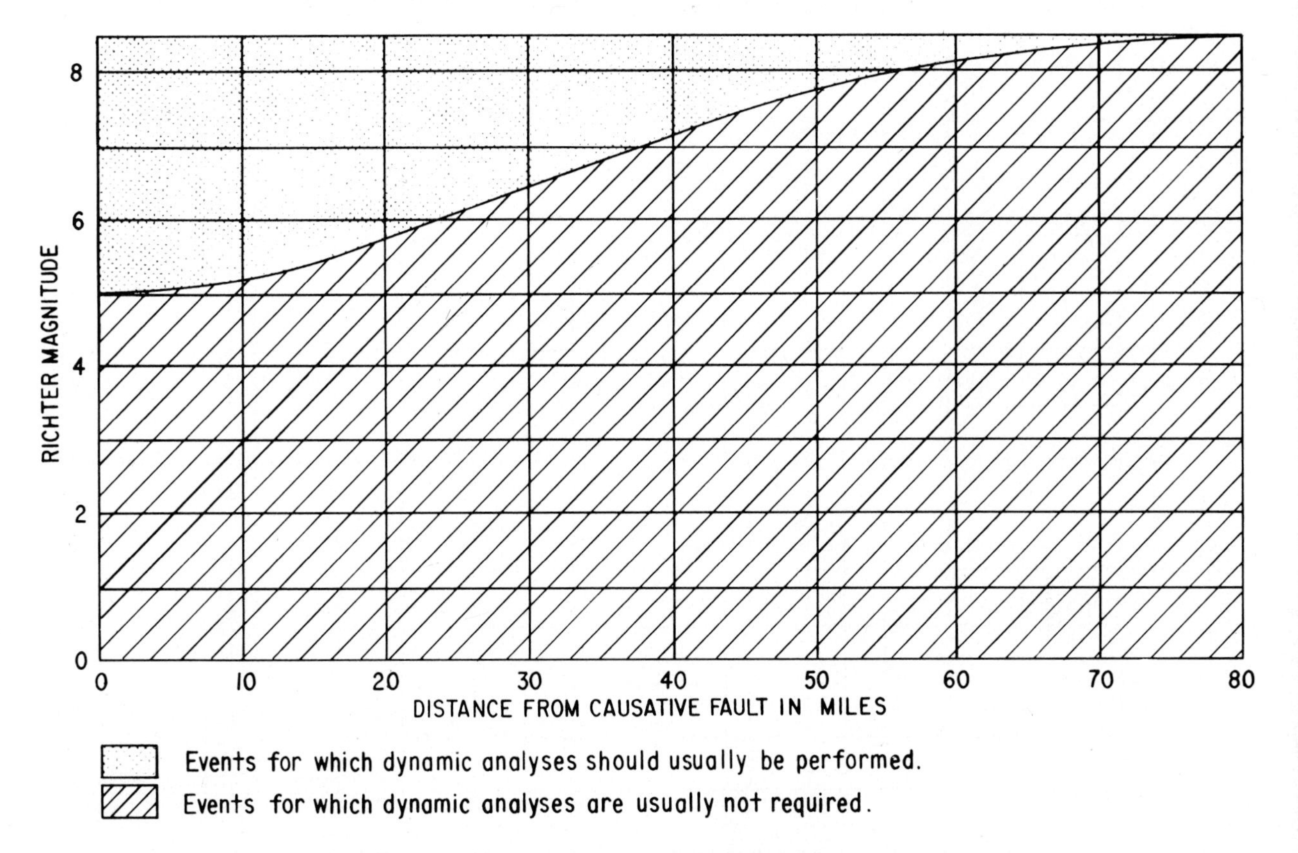

Figure 8-4.—Need for earthquake analyses based on Richter magnitude and distance from causative fault. 103–D–1824.

Special conditions that warrant more detailed dynamic analyses are:

- Active faults directly beneath small dams
- Unusual geometry on small dams, such as large openings for waterways, bridge piers, etc.
- Large masses near the top of small dams, such as gates, bridges, etc.
- Dams higher than about 50 feet

More sophisticated methods of dynamic analysis are described in "Concrete Dams Design Standards," which is currently (1986) being prepared by the Bureau.

The hydrodynamic pressures exerted on the dam face during earthquakes should be included in the analyses. For large gravity dams, the Bureau currently uses the method employed by [4] to incorporate the effects of hydrodynamic and foundation interaction.

In 1952, Zanger [5] presented formulas for computing the hydrodynamic pressures exerted on vertical and sloping faces by horizontal earthquake effects. These formulas, derived by electric analogy and based on the assumption that water is incompressible, are applicable to very stiff small concrete gravity dams. For low dams, the error involved in computing the earthquake force on the water because of this simplifying assumption is probably less than 1 percent.

The effect of horizontal inertia on the concrete should be applied at the center of gravity of the mass, regardless of the shape of the cross section. For dams with vertical or sloping upstream faces, the increase in water pressure, P_e, in pounds per square foot at any elevation due to horizontal earthquake, is given by the following equation:

$$P_e = C\lambda wh \tag{1}$$

where:

C = a dimensionless coefficient giving the distribution and magnitude of pressures,

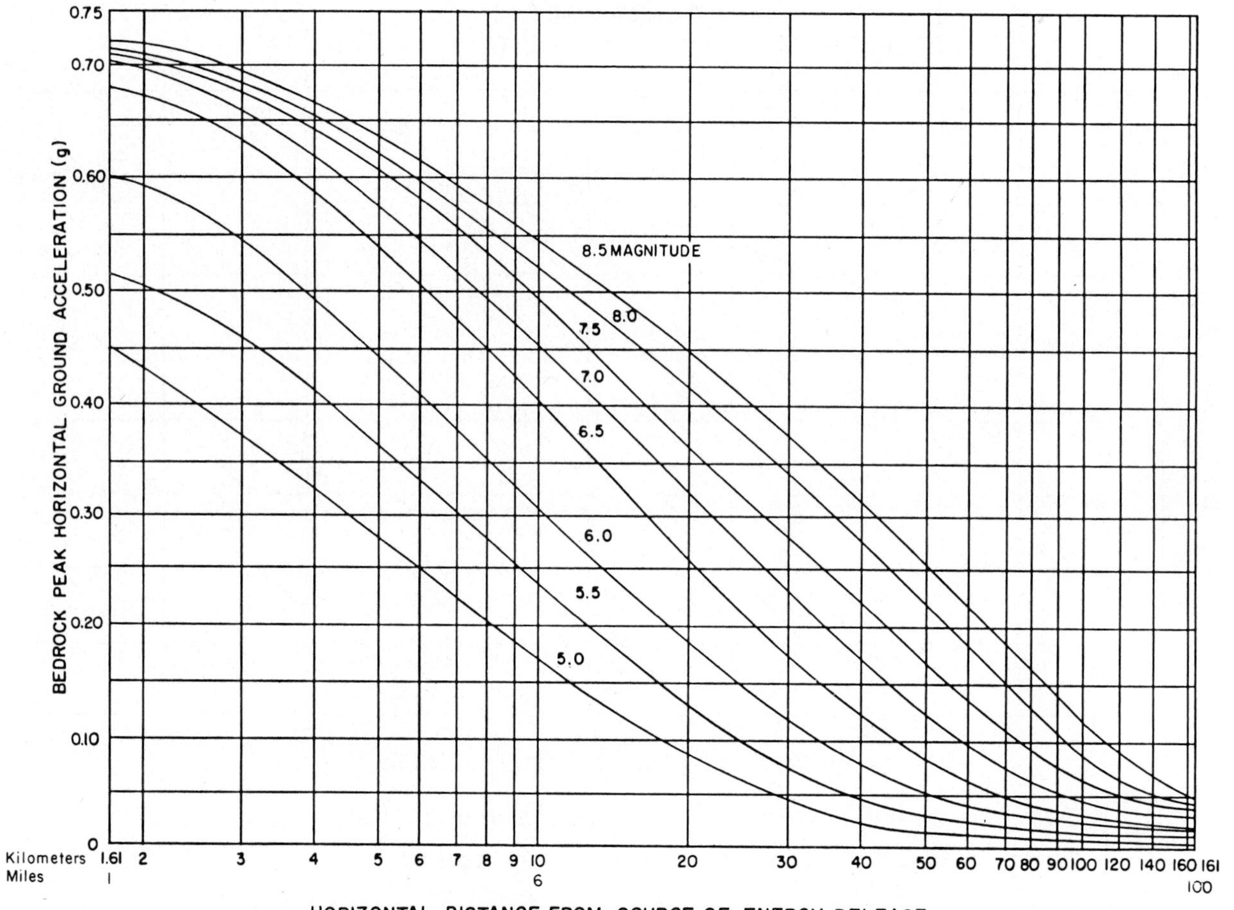

Figure 8-5.—Site estimate of peak ground acceleration. 103–D–1825.

$$C = \frac{C_m}{2}\left[\frac{y}{h}\left(2-\frac{y}{h}\right) + \left(\frac{y}{h}\left(2-\frac{y}{h}\right)\right)^{1/2}\right] \quad (2)$$

λ = earthquake intensity = earthquake acceleration divided by acceleration due to gravity,

w = unit weight of water, in pounds per cubic foot,

h = total depth of reservoir at section being studied, in feet,

y = vertical distance from the reservoir surface to the elevation in question, in feet, and

C_m = maximum value of C for a given constant slope.

Values of C for various degrees of slope and relations of y and h may be obtained from figure 8-6.

The total horizontal force, V_e, above any elevation y distance below the reservoir surface that is due to P_e and the total overturning moment, M_e, above that elevation due to P_e, are:

$$V_e = 0.726\ P_e y \quad (3)$$

and

$$M_e = 0.299\ P_e y^2 \quad (4)$$

For dams with a combination vertical and sloping face, the procedure to be used is governed by the relation of the height of the vertical portion to the total height of the dam as follows:

- If the height of the vertical position of the upstream face of the dam is equal to or greater than one-half of the total height of the dam, analyze as if vertical throughout.

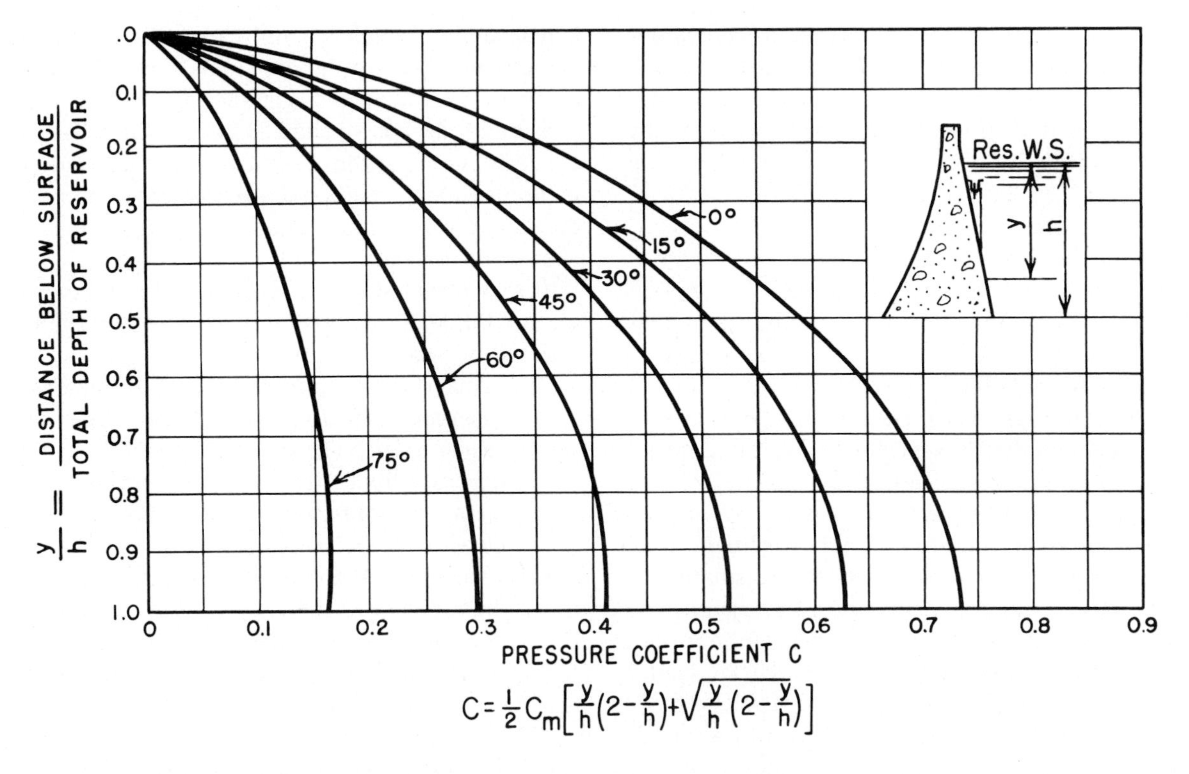

Figure 8-6.—Coefficients for pressure distribution for constant sloping faces. 288-D-2509.

- If the height of the vertical portion of the upstream face of the dam is less than one-half of the total height of the dam, use the pressures on a sloping line connecting the point of intersection of the upstream face of the dam and reservoir surface with the point of intersection of the upstream face of the dam and the foundation.

On sloping faces of dams, the weight of the water above the slope should be modified by the appropriate acceleration factor [5]. The weight of the concrete also should be modified by this acceleration factor.

(b) *Criteria.*—The criteria used for establishing earthquakes events pertinent to the design should be as follows:

- OBE.—An earthquake that could be expected to occur once in 25-year intervals during the economic life of the structure. The recurrence interval for this earthquake at the specific project would be established by the appropriate seismotectonic group. It is anticipated that this earthquake would be provided only for sites near highly seismically active areas for which the necessary information for developing recurrence interval relationships would be available.
- DBE.—An earthquake that would be likely to occur once in 200 years during the economic life of the structure. The recurrence interval for this earthquake for the project site would be set by the appropriate responsible group. The magnitude of this event is determined for each applicable area from recurrence interval relationships if an adequate amount of seismic history data exists but, if not, the magnitude is estimated considering the geology and seismology of the area.
- MCE.—This earthquake would produce the most severe vibratory ground motion capable of being produced at the project site under the known tectonic framework. It is a rational and believable event that is in accord with all known geologic and seismologic facts. In determining the MCE, little regard is given to its probability of occurrence.

Methods of determining the above earthquakes representing the OBE, DBE, or MCE events should consider (1) historical records to obtain frequency of occurrence versus magnitude, (2) useful life of the structure, and (3) a statistical approach to determine probable occurrence of earthquakes of different magnitudes during the life of the structure. When future developments produce such methods, suitable safety factors will be included in the criteria.

Reservoir-induced earthquakes should be considered in the analysis of a structure and its foundation when the reservoir area has parameters conducive to such an event. A dam and its associated foundation that could be affected by a reservoir-induced event should be designed for both a DBRIE (design basis reservoir-induced earthquake) and an ERIE (extreme reservoir-induced earthquake). The magnitude and location of these events should be based on tectonic, seismologic, and geologic site conditions and should be influenced by worldwide data on reservoir-induced seismicity. A reservoir-induced earthquake should be assumed to occur only on an active fault in the hydraulic regime of the reservoir. The DBRIE and the ERIE should have the same general level of probability of occurrence as the tectonic DBE and the MCE, respectively.

Criteria for level of damages, reparability, and safety factor for the dam and foundation should be the same for the DBE and DBRIE and for the MCE and the ERIE.

8.15. *Load Combinations.*—(a) *Basic Considerations.*—Gravity dams should be designed for all appropriate load combinations, using the proper safety factor for each. Combinations of transitory loads, each of which has only a remote probability of occurrence at any given time, have less probability of simultaneous occurrence and should not be considered as appropriate load combinations. For example, an expanding ice sheet is not a factor during a maximum flood, and the chances of an earthquake and a maximum flood occurring at the same time are extremely remote.

(b) *Criteria.*—Gravity dams should be designed for the following load combinations using the corresponding safety factors.

(1) Usual load combinations.—Normal design reservoir elevation with appropriate dead loads, uplift, silt, ice, and tailwater. If temperature loads are applicable to the specific sites, use minimum usual temperatures occurring at that time [2].

(2) Unusual load combinations.—Maximum design reservoir elevation with appropriate dead loads, silt, tailwater, uplift, and minimum usual temperatures occurring at that time, if applicable.

(3) Extreme load combinations.—The usual loading plus the effects of the MCE.

(4) Other loads and investigations:
- The usual or unusual load combination with drains inoperative
- Dead load
- Any other load combination that, the designer thinks should be analyzed for a particular dam

D. FOUNDATION CONSIDERATIONS

The following paragraphs address, in general, foundation considerations associated with concrete dams. "Concrete Dam Design Standards" will address, in more detail, such topics as foundation deformation assessment, foundation seepage analysis, foundation sliding stability analysis, and foundation treatment.

8.16. *Deformation Modulus.*—(a) *Basic Considerations.*—The deformation modulus is defined as the ratio of applied stress to elastic strain plus inelastic strain. It should be determined for each foundation material. Foundation deformations caused by loads from the dam affect the stress distributions within the dam. Conversely, response of the dam to external loads and foundation deformations determines the stresses within the foundation. Proper evaluation of the dam-foundation interaction requires as accurate a determination of foundation deformation charactertistics as possible at enough locations to make the evaluations meaningful. Usually, the differential deformations are of concern, not the absolute magnitude of the deformation.

Foundation investigations should provide information related to or giving deformation moduli. The in situ modulus is usually determined by relationships involving laboratory tests on drill core specimens and fracturing characteristics, or by in situ jacking tests [6, 7, 8]. The in situ modulus should be determined for each material or for zones of similar material with different fracturing characteristics composing the foundation, including any fault or shear zone material. Fracturing in the rock mass reduces the in situ modulus to a value smaller than that measured on an intact core. Therefore, field data concerning rock mass fracture characteristics are helpful for approximating the in situ modulus.

Information on the variation of materials and their prevalence at different locations along the foundation is provided by drill hole logs, by tunnels in the foundation, by onsite inspections, and by good interpretive geologic maps, cross sections, and contour maps. Good compositional descriptions of the zone tested for deformation modulus and adequate geologic mapping and logging of the drill cores usually permit extrapolation of test results to untested zones of similar material.

(b) *Criteria.*—The following data relating to foundation deformability should be obtained for the analysis of a gravity dam:

- The effects of joints, shears, and faults obtained by direct (testing) or indirect (reduction factor) methods
- The deformation modulus of each type of material within and around the loaded area of the foundation

8.17. *Shear Strength.*—(a) *Basic Considerations.*—Resistance to shear within the foundation and between the dam and its foundation depends upon the shear strength inherent in the foundation materials and in the bond between the concrete-rock contact. Shear strength properties can be determined from laboratory and in situ tests, field examination, and back calculation of slides. Evaluating shear strength properties of joints, joint infilling, faults, shears, seams, bedding, foliation, and of other adverse geologic structures should be included.

Assuming linearity is usually realistic for the shear resistance of intact rock over the range of normal stresses of interest. A curve of shear resistance versus normal stress is usually more realistic for open, rough discontinuities. However, it may be approximated by a linear relationship over the normal stress range of interest to the problem. Smooth, open discontinuities usually exhibit linear behavior. The shear resistance versus normal stress relationship shown on figure 8-7 is determined from a number of tests at different normal stresses. The individual tests also give the relationship of shear resistance to displacement for a particular normal stress. The displacement used to determine the shear resistance is the maximum displacement that can be allowed on the possible sliding plane without causing unacceptable stress concentrations within the dam or foundation.

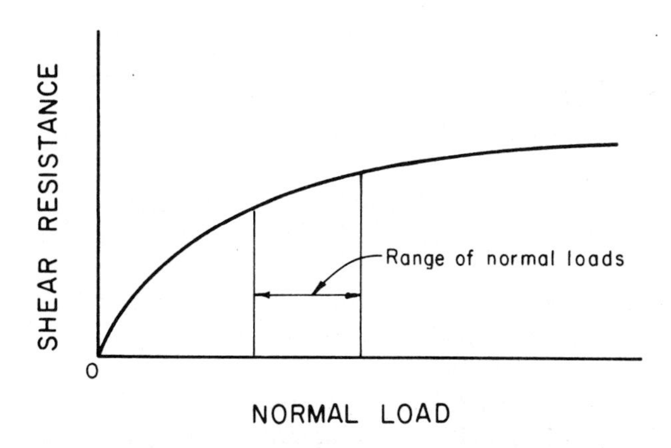

Figure 8-7.—Shear resistance on an existing joint in rock foundation of a gravity dam. 103-D-1826.

Because specimens tested in the laboratory or in situ are small compared with the foundation, the scale effect should be carefully considered in determining the values of shear resistance to be used. Items to consider when assessing large scale behavior should include joint characteristics, fracturing, and variability within similar rock types.

When a foundation is nonhomogeneous, the possible sliding plane may consist of several different materials, some intact and some fractured. Intact rock reaches its maximum break bond resistance with less deformation than is necessary for fractured materials to develop their maximum frictional resistances. Therefore, the shear resistance developed by each fractured material depends upon the displacement of the intact rock part of the potential sliding plane considered in the analysis. An adequate number of tests, as determined by the designer, should be made to obtain a shear resistance versus normal load relationship for each material along the possible sliding planes. The value of shear resistance recorded during tests should include measurements at normal stress levels that correspond to those expected to occur in situ. The total shear resistance against potential sliding along nonhomogeneous foundation planes is the summation of the shear resistance of all the materials along the plane, at compatible shear displacements.

For the shear strength of soil-like foundation materials, many static shear tests have been made and the results published. However, published results should only be used as a guide. For use in design, the shear strength characteristics of the site-specific foundation materials should be determined by testing.

(b) *Criteria.*—Foundation shear strength properties can be determined from laboratory and in situ tests and, in some cases, by field examination and back calculation of slides. The shear strength should be determined for joints, joint infilling, faults, shears, seams, bedding, foliation, and any other geologic feature that may influence stability. Scale effects should be carefully considered when applying shear strength properties obtained from test specimens.

8.18 *Foundation Configuration.*—(a) *Basic Considerations.*—The thickness of a gravity dam at the contact with the foundation and the slope of the concrete-rock contact are factors important to the stability of the structure. Transversely, the foundation contact should be either horizontal or, preferably, sloping upstream. The transverse thickness is usually determined by the dimension necessary for the structure to satisfy stress and stability requirements. Longitudinally, the profile should vary smoothly without abrupt changes to minimize stress concentrations.

(b) *Criteria.*—The foundation contact in the upstream-downstream direction should be either horizontal or sloping upstream. In addition, the foundation contact should vary smoothly, without any abrupt changes, along the profile of the dam.

E. REQUIREMENTS FOR STABILITY

8.19. *Safety Factors.*—(a) *Basic Considerations.*—All loads used in design should be chosen to represent, as nearly as can be determined, the actual loads that will occur on the structure during operation, in accordance with the criteria under "Load Combinations" (sec. 8.15). Methods of determining the load-resisting capacity of the dam should be the most accurate available. All uncertainties regarding loads or load-carrying capacity should be resolved as far as practicable by field or laboratory tests and by thorough exploration and inspection of the foundation. Thus, the safety factor should be as accurate an evaluation as possible of the ability of the structure to resist applied loads.

Although somewhat lower safety factors may be permitted for limited local areas within the foundation, overall safety factors for the dam and its foundation, including the contributions from any remedial treatment, should meet requirements for the load combination analyzed.

For other load combinations where safety factors are not specified, the designer is responsible for selecting safety factors consistent with those for the load combination categories previously discussed (sec. 8.15(b)). Somewhat higher safety factors should be used for foundation studies because of the greater amount of uncertainty involved in assessing foundation load-resisting capability.

Safety factors for gravity dams are based on the use of the gravity method of analysis, and those for foundation sliding stability are based on an assumption of uniform stress distribution on the plane being analyzed.

Like other important structures, dams should be regularly and frequently inspected. Adequate observations and measurements should be made of the structural behavior of the dam and its foundation to ensure that the structure is functioning as designed.

A concrete gravity dam must be designed to resist, with ample safety factor, internal stresses and sliding failure within the dam and foundation. The following subsection discusses recommended allowable stresses and safety factors.

(b) *Criteria.*—(1) *Compressive Stress.*—The maximum allowable compressive stress for concrete in a gravity dam subjected to any of the usual load combinations should not be greater than the specified compressive strength divided by a safety factor of 3.0. Under no circumstances should the allowable compressive stress for the usual load combinations exceed 1,500 lb/in^2.

A safety factor of 2.0 should be used in determining the allowable compressive stress for the unusual load combinations. The maximum allowable compressive stress for the unusual load combinations should never exceed 2,250 lb/in^2.

The maximum allowable compressive stress for the extreme load combinations should be determined in the same way using a safety factor greater than 1.0.

Safety factors of 4.0, 2.7, and 1.3 should be used

in determining allowable compressive stresses in the foundation for usual, unusual, and extreme load combinations, respectively.

(2) *Tensile Stress.*—In order not to exceed the allowable tensile stress, the minimum allowable compressive stress computed without internal water pressure should be determined from the following expression, which takes into account the tensile strength of the concrete at the lift surfaces:

$$\sigma_{z_u} = pwh - \left(\frac{f_t}{s}\right) \tag{5}$$

where:

σ_{z_u} = minimum allowable stress at the face,
p = reduction factor to account for drains,
w = unit weight of water,
h = depth below water surface,
f_t = tensile strength of concrete at lift surfaces, and
s = safety factor.

All parameters must be specified using consistent units.

The value of p should be 1.0 if drains are not present, inoperable, or if cracking occurs at the downstream face, and p should be 0.4 if drains are used. The value 0.4 represents the approximate stress at the upstream face caused by uplift pressures within the dam, assuming drains are spaced 5 percent of the reservoir depth from the upstream face, no tailwater level is included, and drains are fully operable. A more accurate determination of p is required if drains are spaced farther from the face, if tailwater is included, or if the drains are operating at less than 100 percent efficiency. A safety factor of 3.0 should be used for usual, 2.0 for unusual, and 1.0 for extreme load combinations. The allowable value of σ_{z_u} for usual load combinations should never be less than 0. Cracking should be assumed to occur if the stress at the upstream face is less than σ_{z_u}. Cracking is not allowed for the usual and unusual load combinations for new dams; however, cracking is permissible for the extreme load combination if stability is maintained and allowable stresses are not exceeded (see sec. 8.22).

(3) *Sliding Stability.*— the shear-friction safety factor provides a measure of the safety against sliding or shearing on any section. The following expression is the ratio of resisting to driving forces and applies to any section in the structure, in the foundation, or at its contact with the foundation for the computation of the shear-friction safety factor, Q:

$$Q = \frac{CA + (\Sigma N + \Sigma U) \tan \phi}{\Sigma V} \tag{6}$$

where:

C = unit cohesion,
A = area of section considered,
ΣN = summation of normal forces,
ΣU = summation of uplift forces,
$\tan \phi$ = coefficient of internal friction, and
ΣV = summation of shear forces.

All parameters must be specified using consistent units. Uplift is negative according to the sign convention in [1].

The minimum shear-friction safety factor within the dam or at the concrete-rock contact should be 3.0 for usual, 2.0 for unusual, and greater than 1.0 for the extreme load combinations. The safety factor against sliding on any plane of weakness within the foundation should be at least 4.0 for the usual, 2.7 for unusual, and 1.3 for the extreme load combinations [1]. If the computed safety factor is less than required, foundation treatment can be included to increase the safety factor to the required value. For concrete structures on soil-like foundation materials, it is usually not feasible to obtain safety factors equivalent to those prescribed for structures on competent rock. Therefore, safety factors for concrete dams on nonrock foundations are left to the engineering judgment of an experienced designer.

F. STRESS AND STABILITY ANALYSES

The following paragraphs address, in general, considerations relating to sliding stability and internal stresses. The "Concrete Dam Design Standards" will also address these subjects. Additional details are also contained in [1].

8.20. *Sliding Stability.*—(a) *Basic Considera-*

tions.—The horizontal force, ΣV on figure 8-1(A), tends to displace the dam in a horizontal direction. This tendency is resisted by the shear resistance of the concrete or the foundation. As previously discussed in this chapter, the shear strength characteristics of both the concrete and the foundation should be determined by testing.

For sliding within the foundation, the orientation of joints, faults, and shears should be investigated to help identify rock blocks and potential modes of instability. Attention should also be given to joint continuity to help assess the potential for instability.

The rigid block method of analysis, which assumes a uniform stress distribution on the potential sliding plane analyzed, should be sufficient for most cases. However, for cases where rigid block analysis may not be applicable, such as cases involving a variable foundation deformation modulus or special cases involving foundation treatment, finite element modeling may be warranted to more accurately predict stress levels and distributions.

For situations where the recommended safety factors for sliding stability are not satisfied, several remedies are available.

For unsatisfactory stability within the dam, reshaping the dam, increasing the strength of the concrete, and installing posttensioned cables are some possible solutions. Site-specific feasibility and cost effectiveness are factors to consider when selecting the proper alternative.

Unsatisfactory safety factors are more common within the foundation. Various methods of foundation treatment can improve sliding stability. Drainage can reduce uplift forces. Posttensioned cables and rock bolts can increase the normal force acting on a potential sliding plane. Concrete shear keys are also an effective method of foundation treatment. Potential sliding surfaces in the foundation can be intercepted by a key trench excavation. Backfilling the key trench with mass concrete allows the shear strength of the key to be incorporated in the sliding analysis.

Concrete cutoff walls are often provided on structures constructed on soil-like foundations. A properly located and designed cutoff wall engages an additional volume of foundation materials that must be moved before the structure can slide. Sliding stability should also be investigated along any weaker stratum that may exist at depths below the bottom of the cutoff wall.

(b) *Criteria.*—The rigid block method of analysis should be sufficient for most cases. However, the finite element method should be used for cases that are not expected to have a uniform stress distribution along the potential failure surface.

To assess foundation sliding stability, the orientation and continuity of joints, faults, and shears should be investigated to help identify rock blocks and potential modes of instability.

8.21. Internal Stresses—Uncracked Sections.—(a) *Basic Considerations.*—For most gravity dams, internal stresses can be adequately determined for a cross section using the gravity method of analysis. It is applicable to the general case of a gravity section with a vertical upstream face and with a constant downstream slope and to situations where there is a variable slope on either or both faces. The gravity method is substantially correct, except for horizontal planes near the base of the dam where foundation yielding is reflected in stress calculations. Therefore, where necessary in the judgment of an experienced design engineer, finite element modeling should be used to check stresses near the base of a dam. Other methods of analysis, such as the finite element method should also be used to analyze three-dimensional behavior [1]. Grouted or keyed contraction joints, and monolithically constructed RCC dams exhibit three-dimensional behavior, especially along changes in foundation grade or changes in foundation deformation modulus.

The gravity method of analysis uses the following formula to determine the stress distribution along a horizontal plane within the dam:

$$\sigma_z = \frac{\Sigma W}{A} \pm \frac{\Sigma M y}{I} \qquad (7)$$

where:

σ_z = normal stress on a horizontal plane,
ΣW = resultant vertical force from forces above the horizontal plane,
A = area of horizontal plane considered,
ΣM = summation of moments about the center of gravity of the horizontal plane,
y = distance from the neutral axis of the horizontal plane to where σ_z is desired, and
I = moment of inertia of the horizontal plane about its center of gravity.

Uplift from internal water pressures and stresses caused by the moment contribution from uplift along a horizontal plane are usually not included in the computation of σ_z. These stress contributions are considered separately as described in the tensile stress criteria (sec. 8.19(b)(2)).

(b) *Criteria.*—Internal stresses can be computed by the gravity method of analysis to determine the stress distribution along a horizontal plane within the dam. The method may not be applicable near the base where foundation yielding may influence results or for three-dimensional behavior. The effects from uplift are not considered in the computation of stresses, but are considered separately in accordance with the tensile stress criteria (sec. 8.19(b)(2)).

8.22. *Internal Stresses and Sliding Stability – Cracked Sections.*—(a) *Basic Considerations.*—Applied loads tend to produce tension along the upstream face of concrete gravity dams. In general, when allowable concrete tensile strength is exceeded, a crack is assumed to form and propagate horizontally to the point of zero stress, leaving the remaining uncracked section entirely in compression.

Cracking does not occur at all points where excessive tension is indicated, but usually only at the point of maximum tension on each face. However, if cracking at maximum tension location does not sufficiently relieve tension at the other locations, it may be necessary to assume cracking at additional points along the face.

New dams should be designed not to crack for all static loading combinations; however, cracking is permissible for earthquake loading if it can be shown that stress and stability criteria is satisfied during and after the earthquake event. It is also permitted for analyses to indicate that cracking is likely for existing dams, for the condition of maximum water surface with drains inoperative, as long as it can be shown that stress and stability criteria is satisfied.

For various reasons, cracking has occurred in many existing dams. The observed or suspected existence of a crack on either the upstream or downstream face does not necessarily signify instability; however, a crack warrants close examination and, especially, documentation to monitor enlargement or associated deterioration. Investigative methods include core drilling, sonic measurements, and in-place testing. Once the crack location and extent have been identified, stability analyses are essential to evaluate consequences from the various load combinations.

If analyses indicated that unacceptable cracking is likely to occur for new or existing dams, or show that an existing crack has reduced stability to unacceptable levels, modifications should be made to remedy the situation. Some possible modifications are increasing the thickness of the dam, installing post-tensioned cables, installing drains to reduce the uplift from internal water pressures, or increasing the concrete strength.

Cracking should be assumed to occur when analyses indicate the vertical normal stress at the face, computed in accordance with section 8.21, is less than the minimum required stress as computed by equation (5). Once cracking is indicated, a cracked-section analysis is necessary. This involves estimating the potential penetration of a horizontal crack from the upstream face, and then computing the stress distribution and shear-friction safety factor along the uncracked portion.

(b) *Static Method of Analysis.*—Assumptions associated with a static, cracked-section analysis are:

- Stress distribution along a horizontal section, without uplift, varies linearly between upstream and downstream faces.
- Once a crack occurs, uplift pressure equivalent to reservoir pressure above the crack exists throughout the entire crack depth. This is a conservative assumption because if drains exist they are considered inoperable or uneffective after cracking occurs. Uplift is then assumed to vary linearly from crack tip to tailwater pressure at downstream face.
- Crack penetrates to point of zero stress. This assumes no tensile strength at crack tip, which means the entire uncracked length is entirely in compression.

Based on these assumptions, the following equations have been developed to estimate crack length and the resulting stress at the downstream face. The equations apply to the general static case shown on figure 8-8.

$$e' = \frac{\Sigma M}{\Sigma W - \overline{A3} \cdot T} \tag{8}$$

$$T_1 = 3\left(\frac{T}{2} - e'\right) \tag{9}$$

$$\overline{B5} = \frac{2(\Sigma W - \overline{A3} \cdot T)}{T_1} + \overline{A3} \qquad (10)$$

where:

e' = eccentricity of stress diagram after cracking, which is distance from resultant normal force on horizontal section to center of gravity of base at $T/2$;

ΣM = summation of moments from all forces, ΣW and ΣV on figure 8-8(A), but excluding resultant and uplift forces that act on horizontal plane;

ΣW = summation of vertical forces, excluding uplift and resultant force;

$\overline{A3}$ = water pressure at upstream face; equivalent to full reservoir water pressure at elevation in question;

T = thickness of section;

T_1 = thickness of uncracked segment; and

$\overline{B5}$ = stress at downstream face.

These equations can be derived by examining figure 8-8 and by realizing that the weight (ΣW) and the moment (ΣM) are resisted by a combination of the resultant and uplift forces that act on the horizontal plane. On figure 8-8(D), the geometric shape defined by $AB43$ represents the uplift pressure diagram, and triangle $B54$ represents the pressure diagram that defines resultant force. For the purpose of deriving equations (8), (9), and (10), consider only the geometry of the combined pressure diagram. Because the pressure distribution represented by the combined diagram is all directed upward, the diagram can be separated into rectangle $ABB'3$ and triangle $B'54$. Using statics, and separating combined diagram in this manner, the summation of vertical forces produces:

$$\Sigma W - A_{CD} = 0 \qquad (11)$$

where:

$$A_{CD} = \text{area of combined diagram}$$

$$= \overline{A3} \cdot T + (\overline{B5} - \overline{A3}) \left(\frac{T_1}{2}\right) \qquad (12)$$

Solving equation (11) for $\overline{B5}$ results in equation (10). Summation of moments about the center of gravity of the base produces:

$$\Sigma M + (\overline{A3} \cdot T)(0) - (\overline{B5} - \overline{A3}) \left(\frac{T_1}{2}\right)\left(\frac{T}{2} - \frac{T_1}{3}\right) = 0 \qquad (13)$$

From figure 8-8(D), it can be seen that:

$$e' = \frac{T}{2} - \frac{T_1}{3} \qquad (14)$$

Rearranging equation (14) yields equation (9). In equation (13), substitute e' for $(T/2) - (T_1/3)$, and for $\overline{B5}$, substitute expression from equation (10). Solving resulting expression for e' produces equation (8).

(c) *Pseudostatic Method of Analysis.*—To perform a pseudostatic, cracked-section analysis, a similar set of equations to those in subsection (b) can be derived in a similar manner. However, there

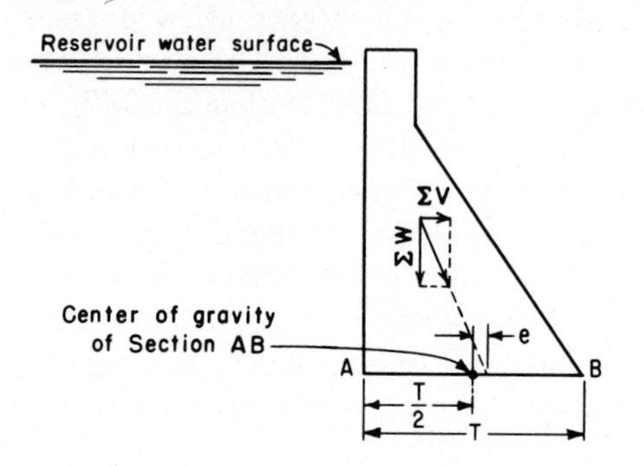

(A) VERTICAL CROSS-SECTION

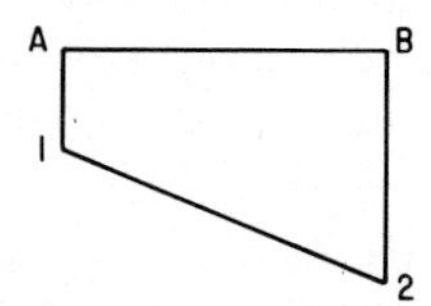

(B) PRESSURE DIAGRAM WITHOUT UPLIFT

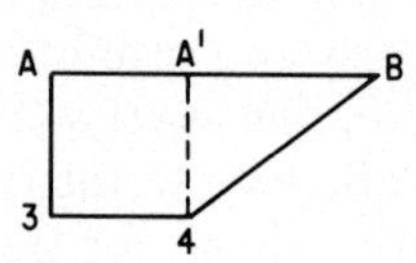

(C) UPLIFT PRESSURE DIAGRAM AFTER CRACKING

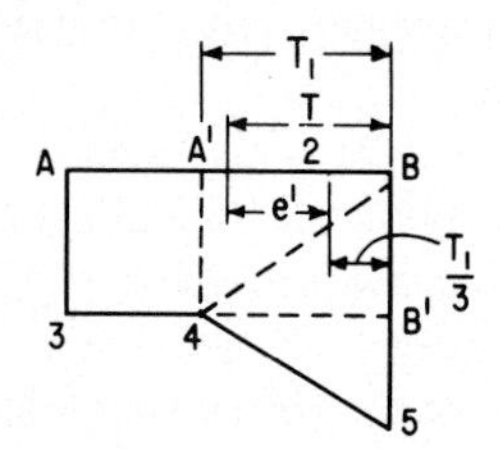

(D) COMBINED PRESSURE DIAGRAM AFTER CRACKING

Figure 8-8.—Static pressure diagrams along the base or any horizontal section of a gravity dam. 103-D-1871.

is one major difference in the assumptions associated with the earthquake, cracked-section analysis. When a crack develops during an earthquake event, uplift pressure within the crack is assumed to be zero. This assumption is based on studies that show the opening of a crack during an earthquake event relieves internal water pressures, and the rapidly cycling nature of opening and closing the crack does not allow reservoir water, and the associated pressure, to penetrate. Based on this assumption and the other assumptions for the static, cracked-section analyses, the following equations have been developed for pseudostatic, earthquake, cracked-section analyses. These equations apply to the general case shown on figure 8-9.

$$e' = \frac{\Sigma M + M_u}{\Sigma W - \overline{A'4}(T_1)} \tag{15}$$

$$\overline{B5} = \frac{2[\Sigma W - (\overline{A'4} \cdot T_1)]}{T_1} + \overline{A'4} \tag{16}$$

where:

e' = eccentricity of stress diagram after cracking, which is distance from resultant normal force on horizontal section to center of gravity of base at $T/2$;

ΣM = summation of moments from all forces including earthquake forces, ΣW and ΣV on figure 8-9(A), but excluding the resultant and uplift force that act on the horizontal plane;

M_u = moment from rectangle $A'BB'4$ portion of combined pressure diagram on figure 8-9(D);

ΣW = summation of vertical forces, excluding uplift and resultant force;

$\overline{A'4}$ = uplift pressure at end of crack, see figure 8-9(C);

T_1 = thickness of uncracked segment; and

$\overline{B5}$ = stress at downstream face.

Using equations (15) and (16) to determine crack depth is an iterative process because the uplift pressure that remains in the uncracked portion depends on the crack depth, and the crack depth depends partially on the remaining uplift. If cracking is indicated at upstream face, the pressure diagram should be revised as on figure 8-9(D). For an initial assumption, a crack depth equal to one-half the thickness can be used. Uplift effects in the uncracked section can then be determined using the uplift pressure diagram shown on figure 8-9(C). This particular uplift diagram represents drained conditions and is discussed in section 8.10. Once the uplift effects are known, the depth of crack may be determined from equations (9) and (15). The computed crack depth is then compared to the estimated crack depth. If a satisfactory degree of accuracy has not been obtained, a new crack depth is estimated and the process repeated until satisfactory accuracy is obtained.

If stability and stress levels are satisfactory for

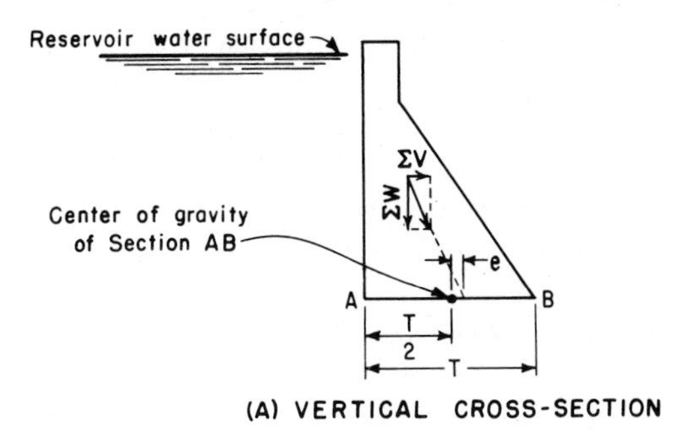

(A) VERTICAL CROSS-SECTION

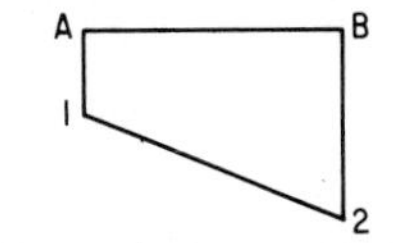

(B) PRESSURE DIAGRAM WITHOUT UPLIFT

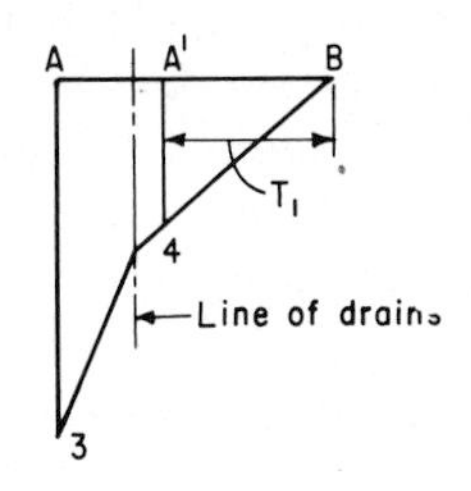

(C) DRAINED UPLIFT PRESSURE DIAGRAM

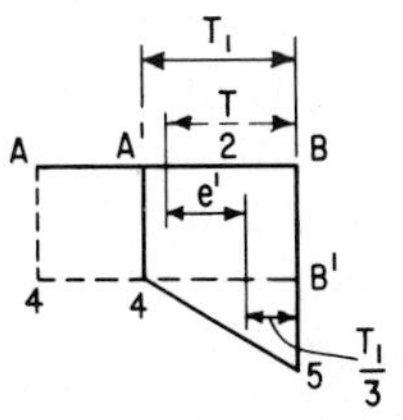

(D) COMBINED PRESSURE DIAGRAM AFTER CRACKING (RECTANGLE A'44A REPRESENTS ZERO PRESSURE)

Figure 8-9.—Pseudostatic pressure diagrams along the base or any horizontal section of a gravity dam. 103-D-1872.

the cracked section during the earthquake event, post-earthquake static conditions should also be checked. Post-earthquake analyses should include full uplift pressure throughout the crack.

(d) *General Iterative Method of Analysis.*—Instead of using the equations in subsections (b) and (c) for static and pseudostatic cracked-section analyses, an iterative method can be used that produces the same results. Using this method, variations of the conditions depicted on figures 8-8 and 8-9 can be readily incorporated. This iterative method also allows the mechanics of cracked-section analysis to be easily discernible, and furnishes a greater appreciation of the factors that influence crack propagation.

To begin this iterative method, crack initiation is still determined as previously explained. Basically, a crack is assumed to form when the vertical normal stress at the upstream face, computed in accordance with section 8.21, is less than the minimum required stress as computed by equation (5).

Once a crack is initiated, a crack depth is estimated and the center of gravity shifts to the center of the uncracked portion. Moments about this center of gravity are computed and summed. Moment contributions from all forces, including uplift, are included in this summation of moments. Stress at the crack tip is then computed using equation (7) and should include uplift in the ΣW and ΣM terms of this equation. The moment of inertia for equation (7) is now based only on the uncracked length.

Based on the computed stress at the crack tip, the estimated crack length is adjusted toward the point of zero stress. The process is then repeated until the crack tip is at the point of zero stress.

(e) *Criteria.*—Cracked-gravity sections require that stress and stability analyses account for the effects from the crack. The analysis process involves determining the crack depth and resulting stress distribution across the uncracked length.

Regardless of the method used to determine the depth of crack, stress and stability criteria need to be checked for the uncracked portion. Equation (6) is used to compute sliding stability, but cohesion is considered only along the uncracked length. Sliding stability and stress levels are considered satisfactory if the criteria established in section 8.19 are satisfied.

G. ADDITIONAL TOPICS

8.23. *Dams on Pervious Foundations.*—The design of dams on pervious (soil-like) foundations involves problems of erosion of the foundation material, settlement, and seepage under the structure. The complexity of these problems varies greatly and depends on the type, stratification, permeability, homogeneity, and other properties of the foundation materials, as well as the size and physical requirements of the structure itself.

The design of concrete gravity storage dams and diversion dams more than 30 feet high on pervious foundations usually requires extensive field and laboratory investigations. Such structures are beyond the scope of this text, which for pervious foundations is limited to gravity dams whose maximum net head (headwater to tailwater) is not appreciably greater than 20 feet.

The control of erosion, seepage, and uplift forces under dams constructed on pervious foundations often requires the use of some or all of the following devices:

- Upstream apron, usually with cutoffs at the upstream end
- Downstream apron, with scour cutoffs at the downstream end, and with or without filters and drains under the apron
- Cutoffs at the upstream or downstream end or at both ends of the overflow section, with or without filters or drains under the section

A concrete apron may be placed upstream of the dam in conjunction with one of the various types of cutoff walls. The function of the apron is to increase the length of the path of percolation to reduce uplift under the main portion of the dam.

Downstream concrete aprons have two functions, they lengthen the path of percolation in the foundations and provide a basin where the energy of the overflowing water can be safely dissipated. Energy dissipation on the concrete helps to prevent dangerous erosion at the toe of the dam. Where it is not feasible to construct a concrete apron long enough to completely avoid erosion, additional protection may be gained by placing riprap downstream from the apron.

Cutoff walls can be constructed under aprons or under the dam itself to prevent or reduce underseepage. Several methods can be used to construct effective cutoff walls; these include concrete walls, steel sheet piling, impervious earth compacted in a trench, and cement-bound curtains.

Cement-bound curtains (sec. 6.10(e)) are composed of overlapping columns consisting of a mixture of cement and the pervious foundation material. The columns are mixed in place and are formed by jet grouting or similar techniques.

A concrete cutoff is probably the best type of cutoff for preventing underseepage and is often used. In addition to acting as a cutoff, it can be designed to contribute substantially to the stability (sliding resistance) of the dam when placed under the dam structure.

Reduction of uplift pressure under the downstream apron or the downstream toe of the dam may be accomplished by pipe drains. Drains are often PVC (polyvinyl chloride) pipe laid in graded material, which acts as a filter. They may be perforated or plain pipe laid with open joints. The drains may be located at the downstream toe of the dam, at selected places under the downstream apron, and immediately upstream from the downstream cutoff.

Weep holes are commonly used for reduction of uplift pressure under aprons and excessive pressure behind walls. It is important that the gradation of the filter materials used in conjunction with the weep holes be carefully selected with respect to the gradation of the foundation materials to prevent piping, see section 6.10(i).

8.24. *Details of Layout and Design.*—

(a) *Nonoverflow Sections.*—The elevation of the top of a nonoverflow dam should be established by assuming a safe freeboard above the maximum high-water surface in the reservoir. The freeboard should be sufficient to allow for the maximum wave height, as given in table 6-7. Although only one-half of the wave height is above the mean water level, the full height is ordinarily used to allow for wave runup on the face of the dam. A minimum freeboard of 3 feet is recommended for most small concrete dams.

The top width is determined by such requirements as climatic conditions, and the need for travel across the dam and for access to the gate-operating mechanism. A top width of less than 4 feet is not recommended.

The width of the base and the slope of the downstream face should be determined by a stability analysis. The customary method is to assume a section with the downstream face sloped approximately 0.70:1.0 (horizontally to vertically) and intersecting a vertical upstream face at the top of the dam. The assumed section is then analyzed and modified as required by the analysis until it meets the stability requirements. If the dam is stable about its base and about any section where there is a break in the continuity of the slope of either the upstream or downstream face, the portion of the dam between any of these sections is stable and does not require analysis.

Abrupt changes of slope on either face of the dam can cause unacceptable stress concentrations and should be avoided whenever possible. The usual intersection near the crest, formed by the vertical and sloping downstream faces, has been replaced with a circular fillet tangent to each face. Nominal size fillets effectively reduce stress concentrations, especially during earthquakes. Similarly, minimizing the mass near the crest helps reduce the inertia effects.

(b) *Overflow Sections.*—In general, the method for determining the stability of overflow dams is the same for nonoverflow dams; however, additional considerations contribute to the configuration of overflow sections. The shape of the crest, the profile of the downstream face, and details of the energy dissipating basin or bucket are discussed in chapter 9. It is customary to provide a longitudinal contraction joint at the downstream toe, as shown on figure 8-3, and then only that portion of the dam upstream of the joint is used in the stability computations.

In cases where the dissipating device extends only a short distance downstream from the toe and is fairly massive, the contraction joint may be omitted. The structure downstream from the toe is then included in the stability analysis and is so reinforced that it and the gravity portion will act as a unit. Under certain conditions, an upstream apron connected by reinforcement to the upstream face of the dam may be the most economical arrangement that will ensure stability.

Overflow dams using control features on the crest introduce an additional problem. The forces acting on these features may produce tension in the upper portion of the dam, which will require adequate reinforcement.

(c) *Contraction Joints.*—If a conventionally placed concrete dam is appreciably longer than 50 feet, it is necessary to divide the structure into blocks by providing transverse contraction joints. The spacing of the joints is determined by the capabilities of the concrete equipment to be used and considerations of volumetric changes and attendant cracking caused by shrinkage and temperature variations. The possibilities of detrimental cracking can be greatly reduced by the selection of the proper type of cement and by careful control of mixing and placing procedures (see app. F). For normal conditions, a 50-foot spacing of contraction joints in constructing concrete dams is usually sufficient. Where foundation conditions are such that undesirable differential settlement or displacement between adjacent blocks can occur, shear keys should be formed in the contraction joints. These may be formed vertically, horizontally, or in a combination of both, depending on the direction of the expected displacement. Leakage through the contraction joints is controlled by imbedding waterstops, usually made of PVC, across the joints.

H. COMPUTER METHODS

8.25. *General.*—The Bureau of Reclamation currently uses several finite element and other computer analysis programs to perform stress analyses on dams and foundations and to perform studies of heat flow through dams and of foundation seepage. Some of the programs now being used and their applications are listed and described below. These programs are mentioned mainly for information purposes.

- ADINA is a finite element program for automatic static and dynamic incremental nonlinear analysis [9].
- SAPIV is a finite element program for static and dynamic response of linear systems [10].
- EADHI is a finite element program for earthquake analysis of gravity dams including hydrodynamic interaction [11].
- EAGD-84 is the improvement to EADHI that also considers damping from the silt accumulated on the reservoir bottom [4].
- HEATFL is a general two-dimensional finite element program for computing the steady-state or time-dependent temperature distribution within the dam cross section [12].
- IRMCT calculates mean range of concrete temperatures in mass concrete with or without solar radiation [13].
- DRAIN2D is a two-dimensional finite element program for solving confined and unconfined seepage problems [14].

I. BIBLIOGRAPHY

8.26. *Bibliography.*

[1] *Design of Gravity Dams*, Bureau of Reclamation, Denver, CO, 1976.

[2] Townsend, C. L., *Control of Cracking in Mass Concrete Structures*, Bureau of Reclamation, Engineering Monograph No. 34, rev. reprint, May 1981.

[3] Monfore, G. E., and F. W. Taylor, "The Problem of an Expanding Ice Sheet," Bureau of Reclamation Technical Memorandum, March 18, 1948.

[4] Chopra, A. K., and G. Fenves, "EAGD-84-A Computer Program for Earthquake Analysis of Concrete Gravity Dams," Report No. UCB-EERC-84/11, College of Engineering, University of California, Berkeley, CA, August 1984.

[5] Zangar, C. N., "Hydrodynamic Pressures on Dams due to Horizontal Earthquake Effects," Bureau of Reclamation, Engineering Monograph No. 11, May 1952.

[6] Bieniawski, Z. T., "Determining Rock Mass Deformability: Experience from Case Histories," *Int. J. Rock Mech. Min. Sci. and Geomech.*, abstract, vol. 15, pp. 237-247, printed in Great Britain, Pergamon Press, 1978.

[7] Heuze, F. E., "Scale Effects in the Determination of Rock Mass Strength and Deformability," *Rock Mechanics* 12, pp. 167-192, 1980.

[8] Coon, R. F., and A. H. Merritt, "Predicting In Situ Modulus of Deformation Using Rock Quality Indexes," Determination of the In Situ Modulus of Deformation of Rock, ASTM STP 477, pp. 154-173, 1970.

[9] Bathe, K. J., "ADINA—A Finite Element Program for Automatic Dynamic Incremental Nonlinear Analysis," Massachusetts Institute of Technology, 1975 (rev. 1978).

[10] Bathe, K. J., E. L. Wilson, and F. E. Peterson, "SAPIV—A Structural Analysis Program for Static and Dynamic Response of Linear Systems," Report No. EERC 73-11, College of Engineering, University of California, Berkeley, CA, 1974.

[11] Chakrabarti, P., and A. K. Chopra, "EADHI—A Computer Program for Earthquake Analysis of Gravity Dams

Including Hydrodynamic Interaction," Report No. EERC 73-7, College of Engineering, University of California, Berkeley, CA 1973.

[12] Wilson, E. L., and R. E. Nickell, "Application of the Finite Element Method to Heat Conduction Analysis," *Nuclear Engineering and Design*, North-Holland Publishing Company, Amsterdam, 1966.

[13] Ingram, D. E., "Program Description—IRMCT," Bureau of Reclamation, Denver, CO, April 1973.

[14] Tracy, F. T., "A Plane and Axisymmetric Finite Element Program for Steady-State and Transient Seepage Problems," U.S. Army Corps of Engineers, Waterways Experiment Station, Vicksburg, MS, May 1973.

Chapter 9

Spillways

A. GENERAL

9.1. *Function.*—Spillways are provided for storage and detention dams to release surplus water or floodwater that cannot be contained in the allotted storage space, and for diversion dams to bypass flows exceeding those turned into the diversion system. Ordinarily, the excess is drawn from the top of the reservoir and conveyed through a constructed waterway back to the river or to some natural drainage channel. Figure 9-1 shows a small spillway in operation.

The importance of a safe spillway cannot be overemphasized; many failures of dams have been caused by improperly designed spillways or by spillways of insufficient capacity. Ample capacity is of paramount importance for earthfill and rockfill dams, which are likely to be destroyed if overtopped; whereas, concrete dams may be able to withstand moderate overtopping. Usually, the increase in cost is not directly proportional to the increase in capacity. The cost of a spillway having ample capacity is often only moderately higher than the cost of a spillway that is too small.

In addition to providing sufficient capacity, the spillway must be hydraulically and structurally adequate and must be located so that spillway discharges do not erode or undermine the downstream toe of the dam. The spillway's bounding surfaces must be erosion resistant to withstand the high scouring velocities created by the drop from the reservoir surface to the tailwater level. Usually, a device is required to dissipate the energy of the water at the bottom of the drop.

The frequency of spillway use should be determined by the runoff characteristics of the drainage basin, which includes the nature of its development. Ordinary riverflows are usually stored in the reservoir, diverted through headworks, or released through outlets; the spillway is not required to function. However, spillway flows do occur during floods or periods of sustained high runoff when the capacities of the other facilities are exceeded. Where large reservoir storage is provided or large outlet or diversion capacity is available, the spillway will be used infrequently. But at diversion dams where storage space is limited and diversions are relatively small compared with normal river flows, the spillway will be used almost constantly.

9.2. *Selection of Inflow Design Flood.*—

(a) *General Considerations.*—Flooding in an unobstructed stream channel is considered a natural event for which no individual or group is responsible. However, when obstructions are placed across the channel, the project sponsors must either ensure that hazards to downstream interests are not appreciably increased or assume responsibility for damages resulting from operation or failure of the structures. The loss of the facility and the loss of project services and revenues occasioned by a failure should also be considered.

If danger to the structures alone were involved, the sponsors of many projects would prefer to rely on the improbability of an extreme flood occurrence rather than to incur the expense necessary to ensure complete safety. However, when the hazards involve downstream interests, including property damage and the loss of human life, a conservative attitude is required in the selection of the IDF (inflow design flood). Consideration of potential damage should not be limited to conditions existing at the time of construction. Probable future development in the downstream flood plain, encroachment by farms and resorts, construction of roads and bridges, and other future developments should be evaluated in estimating damages and hazards to human life that would result from a dam failure.

Dams impounding large reservoirs on principal rivers with high runoff potential should unquestionably be considered to be in the high-hazard category. For such developments, conservative design criteria should be selected because failure could involve the loss of life or damages of disastrous proportions. Conversely, small dams built on isolated streams in rural areas where failure would neither jeopardize human life nor create damages beyond the sponsor's financial capabilities may be considered to be in a low-hazard category. For such developments, design criteria may be established on a much less conservative basis. There have been numerous instances, however, where the failure of a small dam with small storage capacity has resulted in the loss of life and heavy property damage. Most small dams require a reasonable conservatism in design, primarily because a failure must not present a serious hazard to human life.

(b) *Inflow Design Flood Hydrographs.*—Chapter 3 "Flood Hydrology Studies" discusses the determination of flood hydrographs that can be used as inflow design floods. The procedures presented provide for the development of probable maximum floods and of specific-frequency floods.

Determination of the PMF (probable maximum flood) is based on the probability of simultaneous

Figure 9-1.—Small chute spillway in operation. Shadow Mountain Dam on the Colorado River in Colorado. 288–D–2841.

occurrence of the maximum of the several elements or conditions that can contribute to the flood. Such a flood is the largest that reasonably can be expected and is ordinarily accepted as the inflow design flood for dams whose failure would increase the danger to human life.

For a minor structure with significant storage where it is permissible to anticipate failure within the useful life of the project, a flood in the range of a 1 in 50 chance to a 1 in 200 chance of being equalled or exceeded may be used as the IDF. A discussion of these floods and their determination is given in section 3.12. Estimates of floods of these magnitudes may also be required to establish the capacity of a service or principal spillway in those cases where an auxiliary spillway will serve to augment the principal spillway.

9.3. ***Relation of Surcharge Storage to Spillway Capacity.***—Streamflow is normally represented in the form of a hydrograph, which charts the rate of flow (discharge) in relation to time. A typical hydrograph representing a storm runoff is shown on figure 9-2. The flow into a reservoir at any time and the momentary peak can be read from curve A. The area under this curve is the volume of the inflow because it represents the product of rate of flow and time.

Where no storage is impounded by a dam, the spillway must be large enough to pass the peak of the flood. Therefore, the peak rate of inflow is of primary interest, and the total volume of the flood is of lesser importance. However, where a relatively large storage capacity above normal reservoir level can be made available economically by raising the dam, a portion of the flood volume can be retained temporarily in reservoir surcharge space and the spillway capacity may be reduced considerably. If a dam could be made sufficiently high to provide storage space to impound the entire volume of the flood above normal storage level, no spillway other than an emergency type would be required, provided the outlet capacity could evacuate the surcharge storage fast enough to accommodate a recurring flood. In such cases, a meteorologic study may be warranted to determine the interval between floods. In these cases the maximum reservoir level would depend entirely on the volume of the flood and the rate of inflow would be of no concern. From a practical standpoint, however, relatively few sites permit complete storage of an inflow design flood by surcharge storage. Such sites are usually off-channel reservoirs; that is, reservoirs that are supplied by canals and that have small tributary drainage areas.

In many reservoir projects, economic considerations necessitate a design that uses the surcharge storage. Determining the most economical combination of surcharge storage and spillway capacity requires flood routing studies and economic studies of the costs of spillway-dam combinations, subsequently described. However, in making these studies, consideration must be given to the minimum size spillway that must be provided for safety. The IDF hydrographs are determined by the methods given in chapter 3. In many locations it is possible to estimate upper limit or probable maximum floods resulting from several meteorologic combinations, severe rain, rain falling on a snow pack, and snow melt runoff alone. In these cases each type of PMF hydrograph must be developed by the hydrologic engineer to enable the designer to test each against each alternative design. Such a test ensures that the design selected will enable the completed structure to satisfactorily accommodate the most critical flood.

9.4. ***Flood Routing.***—The accumulation of storage in a reservoir depends on the difference between the rates of inflow and outflow. For an interval of time Δt, this relationship can be expressed by the equation:

$$\Delta S = Q_i \Delta t - Q_o \Delta t \qquad (1)$$

where:

ΔS = storage accumulated during Δt,
Q_i = average rate of inflow during Δt, and
Q_o = average rate of outflow during Δt.

The rate of inflow versus time curve is represented by the IDF hydrograph; the rate of outflow is represented by the spillway discharge versus reservoir-elevation curve; and storage is shown by the reservoir storage versus reservoir-elevation curve. For routing studies, the IDF hydrograph is not variable once the inflow design flood has been selected. The reservoir storage capacity also is not variable for a given reservoir site, so far as routing studies are concerned. The spillway discharge curve is variable: it depends not only on the size and type of spillway, but also on the manner of operating the spillway (and the outlets in some instances) to regulate the outflow.

The quantity of water a spillway can discharge depends on the type of control device. For a simple

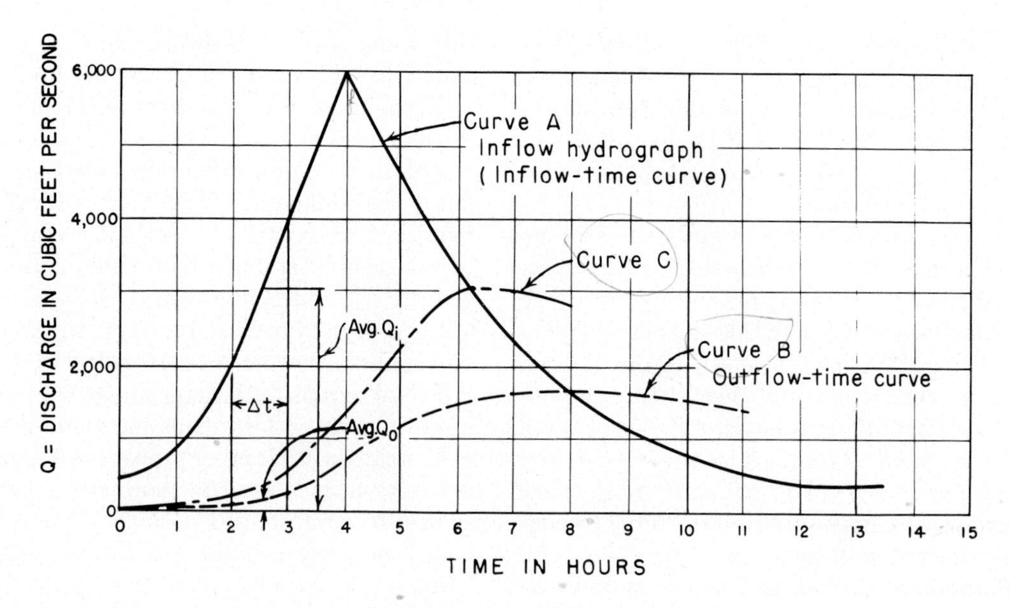

Figure 9-2.—Inflow and outflow hydrographs. 288–D–2399.

overflow crest the flow varies with the head on the crest, and surcharge storage capacity increases with an increase in spillway discharge. For a gated spillway, however, outflow can be varied with respect to reservoir head by operation of the gates. For example, one assumption for an operating gate-controlled spillway might be that the gates will be regulated so that inflow and outflow are equal *until* the gates are wide open; another assumption might be to open the gates at a slower rate so that surcharge storage will accumulate *before* the gates are wide open.

Outflows need not necessarily be limited to discharges through the spillway, but may be supplemented by releases through the outlets. In all such cases the size, type, and method of operation of the spillway and outlets with reference to the storages or to the inflow must be predetermined to establish an outflow-elevation relationship.

If equations could be established for the IDF hydrograph curve, for the spillway discharge curve (as may be modified by operational procedures), and for the reservoir storage curve, a solution of flood routing could be made by mathematical integration. However, simple equations cannot be written for the IDF hydrograph curve or for the reservoir storage curve; therefore, such a solution is not practical. Many techniques of flood routing have been devised, each with its advantages and disadvantages. These techniques vary from a strictly arithmetical integration method to an entirely graphical solution. Computer programs have been developed and are generally available for use in flood routing. For simplicity, the arithmetical trial-and-error tabular method is illustrated in this text.

Table 9-1 is an example of a flood routing for the data given on figures 9-2, 9-3, and 9-4. These data are necessary regardless of the method of flood routing used. They consist of the following:

- Inflow hydrograph (rate of inflow versus time), figure 9-2
- Reservoir capacity (reservoir storage versus reservoir elevation), figure 9-3
- Discharge curve (rate of outflow versus reservoir elevation), figure 9-4

The procedure for computations shown in table 9-1 consists of the following steps:

1. Select a time interval, Δt, for column (2).
2. Obtain column (3) from the inflow hydrograph, figure 9-2.
3. Column (4) represents average inflow for Δt in cubic feet per second.
4. Obtain column (5) by converting column (4) values of second-feet for Δt to acre-feet (1 ft³/s for 12 hours = 1 acre-ft).
5. Assuming the trial reservoir water surface in column (6), determine the corresponding rate of outflow from figure 9-4, and record it in column (7).
6. Average the rate of outflow determined in step 5 above and the rate of outflow for the reservoir

Table 9-1.—Flood routing computations.

(1) Time t, hours	(2) Δt, hours	(3) Inflow at time t, ft³/s	(4) Average rate of inflow, Q_i for Δt, ft³/s	(5) Inflow, acre-feet	(6) Trial reservoir storage-elevation at time t	(7) Outflow at time t, ft³/s	(8) Average rate of outflow, Q, for Δt, ft³/s	(9) Outflow, acre-feet	(10) Incremental storage ΔS, acre-feet	(11) Total storage, acre-feet	(12) Reservoir elevation at end of Δt, feet	(13) Remarks
0		400				0				1,050	300.3	
	1		600	50	~~300.2~~	~~5~~	~~3~~	~~0~~	~~50~~	~~1,100~~	~~300.3~~	~~High~~
1		800			300.3	10	5	0	50	1,100	300.3	OK
	1		1,400	117	~~300.8~~	~~84~~	~~32~~	~~3~~	~~114~~	~~1,214~~	~~301.0~~	~~High~~
2		2,000			301.0	80	45	4	113	1,213	301.0	OK
	1		3,000	250	~~302.3~~	~~300~~	~~190~~	~~16~~	~~234~~	~~1,447~~	~~302.1~~	~~Low~~
3		4,000			302.1	260	170	14	236	1,449	302.1	OK
	1		5,000	417	~~303.9~~	~~710~~	~~485~~	~~40~~	~~377~~	~~1,826~~	~~303.8~~	~~Low~~
4		6,000			303.8	690	475	40	377	1,826	303.8	OK
	1		5,350	446	~~305.6~~	~~1,060~~	~~675~~	~~73~~	~~373~~	~~2,199~~	~~305.3~~	~~High~~
5		4,700			305.3	1,160	925	77	369	2,195	305.3	OK
	1		4,000	333	~~306.3~~	~~1,500~~	~~1,900~~	~~111~~	~~222~~	~~2,417~~	~~306.2~~	~~Low~~
6		3,300			306.2	1,470	1,315	110	223	2,418	306.2	OK
	1		2,850	238	306.6	1,610	1,540	128	110	2,528	306.6	OK
7		2,400										
	1		2,000	167	306.7	1,650	1,630	136	31	2,559	306.7	OK
8		1,600										
	1		1,350	112	306.6	1,610	1,630	136	−24	2,535	306.6	OK
9		1,100										
	2		800	133	306.0	1,400	1,505	251	−118	2,417	306.1	High
11		500			306.1	1,430	1,520	253	−120	2,415	306.1	OK

water surface that existed at the beginning of the period, and enter this average in column (8).

7. Obtain column (9) by converting column (8) values of cubic feet per second for Δt to acre-feet, similar to step 4 above.

8. Column (10) = column (5) − column (9).

9. The initial value in column (11) represents the reservoir storage at the beginning of the inflow design flood. Determine subsequent values for column (11) by adding ΔS values from column (10) to the previous column (11) value.

10. Determine reservoir elevation in column (12) corresponding to storage in column (11) from figure 9-3.

11. Compare reservoir elevation in column (12) with trial reservoir elevation in column (6). If they do not agree within 0.1 foot, make a second trial elevation and repeat procedure until such agreement is reached.

The outflow time curve resulting from the flood routing shown in table 9-1 has been plotted as curve B on figure 9-2. As the area under the inflow hydrograph (curve A) indicates the volume of inflow, so the area under the outflow hydrograph (curve B) indicates the volume of outflow. It follows then that the volume indicated by the area between the two curves is the surcharge storage. The surcharge storage computed in table 9-1 can, therefore, be checked by comparing it with the area measured on the graph.

A rough approximation of the relationship of spillway size to surcharge volume can be obtained without making an actual flood routing by arbitrarily assuming an approximate outflow-time curve and then measuring the area between it and the inflow hydrograph. For example, if the surcharge volume for the problem shown on figure 9-2 is sought where a 3,000-ft³/s spillway would be provided, an assumed outflow curve represented by curve C can be drawn, and the area between this curve and curve A can be measured by planimeter. Curve C reaches its apex of 3,000-ft³/s where it crosses curve A. The volume represented by the area between the two curves indicates the approximate surcharge volume necessary for this capacity spillway.

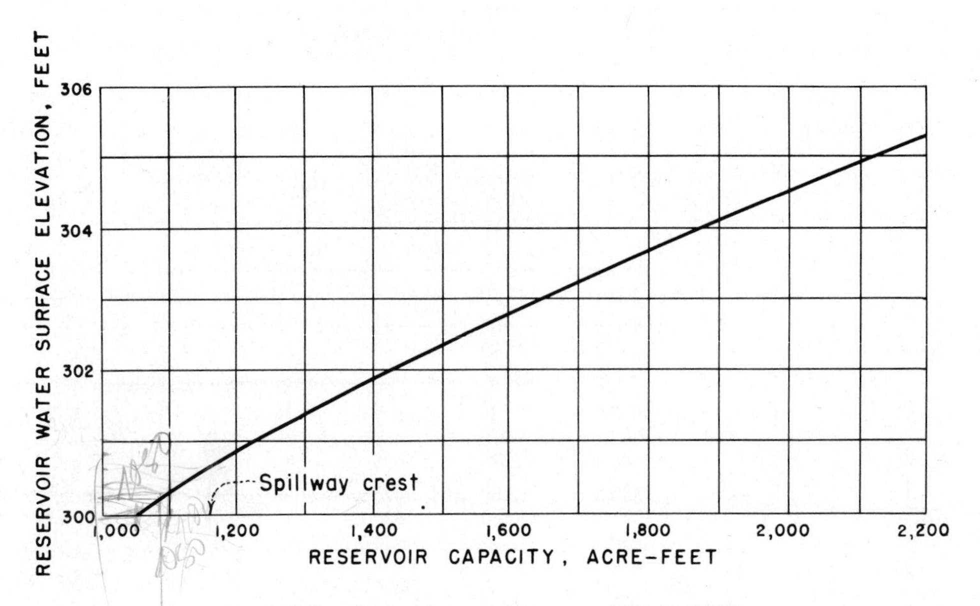

Figure 9-3.—Reservoir capacity curve. 288–D–2400.

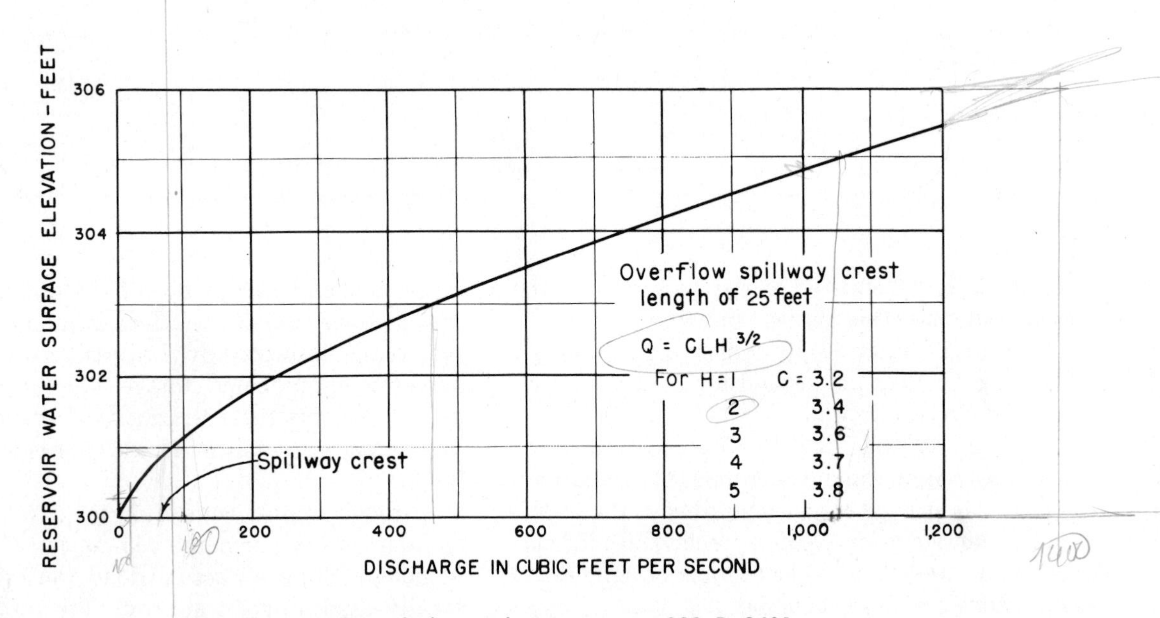

Figuer 9-4.—Spillway discharge-elevation curve. 288–D–2401.

9.5. Selection of Spillway Size and Type.—

(a) *General Considerations.*—In determining the best combination of storage capacity and spillway capacity to accommodate the selected inflow design flood, all pertinent factors of hydrology, hydraulics, design, cost, and damage should be considered. In this connection and when applicable, consideration should be given to such factors as (1) the characteristics of the flood hydrograph, (2) the damages that would result if such a flood occurred without the dam, (3) the damages that would result if such a flood occurred with the dam in place, (4) the damages that would occur if the dam or spillway were breached, (5) the effects of various dam and spillway combinations on the probable damages upstream and downstream of the dam (as indicated by reservoir backwater curves and tailwater curves), (6) the relative costs of increasing the capacity of spillways, and (7) the use of combined outlet facilities to serve more than one function (e.g., control of releases and control or passage of floods.) Service outlet releases may be permitted in passing part of the inflow design flood unless such outlets are considered to be unavailable at the time of flooding.

The outflow characteristics of a spillway depend on the type of device selected to control the discharge. These control facilities may take the form of an overflow weir, an orifice, or a pipe. Such devices may be unregulated, or they may be equipped with gates or valves to regulate the outflow.

After a spillway control device and its dimensions have been selected, the maximum spillway discharge and the maximum reservoir water level should be determined by flood routing. Other components of the spillway can then be proportioned to conform to the required capacity and to the specific site conditions, and a complete layout of the spillway can be established. Cost estimates of the spillway and dam should be made. Estimates of various combinations of spillway capacity and dam height for an assumed spillway type, and of alternative types of spillways, allow the selection of an economical spillway type and the optimum relationship of spillway capacity to height of dam. Figures 9-5 and 9-6 illustrate the results of such a study. The relationships of spillway capacities to maximum reservoir water surfaces obtained from the flood routings are shown on figure 9-5 for two spillways. Figure 9-6 illustrates the comparative costs for different combinations of spillway and dam, and indicates a combination that results in the least total cost.

To make a study such as the one illustrated requires many flood routings, spillway layouts, and spillway and dam estimates. Even then, the study is not necessarily complete because many other spillway arrangements could be considered. However, a comprehensive study to determine alternative optimum combinations and minimum costs may be warranted for large dams, but not for the design of small dams. The designer's judgment is required to select for study only the combinations that show definite advantages, either in cost or adaptability. For example, although an ungated spillway might be slightly more expensive than a gated spillway, it may be more desirable because of its less complicated construction, its automatic and trouble-free operations, its ability to function without an attendant, and its less costly maintenance.

(b) *Combined Service and Auxiliary Spillways.*—Where site conditions are favorable, the possibility of gaining overall economy by using an auxiliary spillway in conjunction with a smaller service-type spillway should be considered. In such cases the service spillway should be designed to pass floods likely to occur frequently, and the auxiliary spillway control set to operate only after such small floods are exceeded. In certain instances the outlet works may be made large enough to serve also as a service spillway. Conditions favorable for the adoption of an auxiliary spillway are the existence of a saddle or depression along the rim of the reservoir that leads into a natural waterway or a gently sloping abutment where an excavated channel can be carried sufficiently beyond the dam to avoid the possibility of damage to the dam or other structures.

Because of its infrequent use, the entire auxiliary spillway need not be designed for the same degree of safety required for other structures. However, the control portion must be designed to forestall failure because its breaching would release large flows from the reservoir. For example, concrete lining may be omitted from an auxiliary spillway channel excavated in competent rock. Where the channel is excavated through less competent material, it might be lined but terminated above the river channel with a cantilevered lip rather than extended to a stilling basin at river level. The design of auxiliary spillways is often based on the premise that some damage to portions of the structure from passage of infrequent flows is permissible. Minor damage by scour to an unlined channel, by erosion and undermining at the downstream end of the channel, and by creation of an erosion pool downstream from the spillway may be acceptable.

An auxiliary spillway can be designed with a fixed crest control, or it can be stoplogged or gated to increase the capacity without additional surcharge head. Fuseplug dikes, which are designed to breach and wash out when overtopped, often are substituted for some or all of the gates. Their advantage over gates is that, if they are properly designed, breaching becomes automatic whenever overtopping occurs. Furthermore, they are cheaper to install and to maintain. Because the chance of their failure from overtopping depends on the occurrence of infrequent floods, their replacement cost is too problematical for evaluation. By dividing the dike into short sections of varying height, so they are not all simultaneously overtopped, smaller floods can be passed with the failure of one or several of

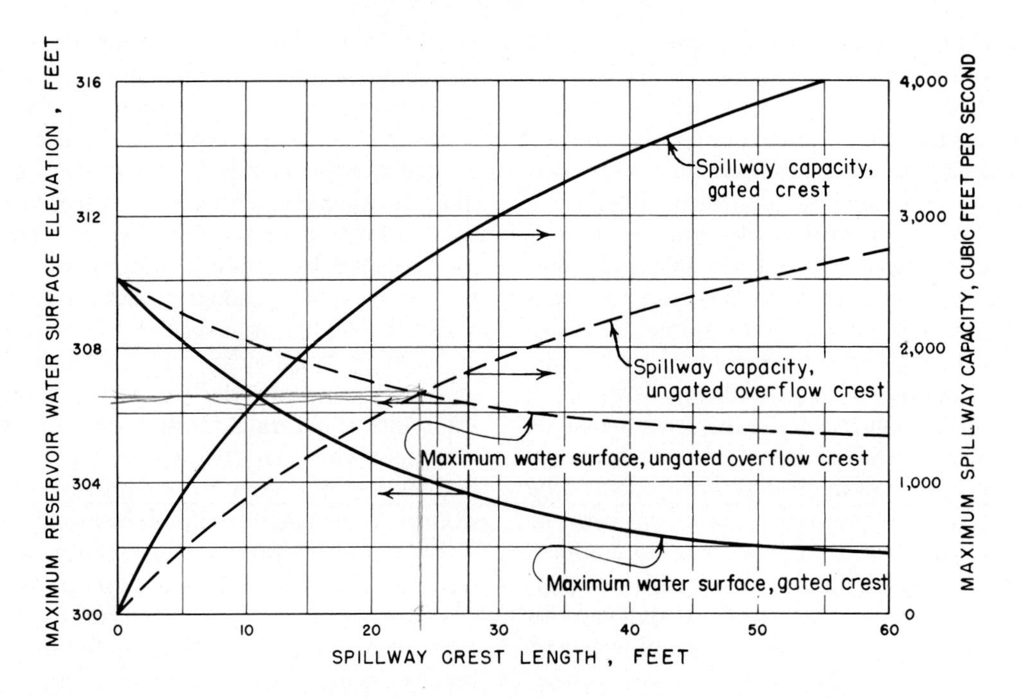

Figure 9-5.—Spillway capacity-surcharge relationship. 288–D–2402.

the sections; total failure will occur only as the probable maximum flood is approached. The breaching of one section at a time will minimize the flood wave and the possibility of a sudden failure of the dike (see [1][1]).

Figure 9-7 shows a general plan and sections of a service and an auxiliary spillway. Figure 9-8 is an aerial photograph showing this service spillway, which consists of a bathtub-shaped side channel crest, a culvert conduit under the dam, a diverging concrete-lined chute, and a hydraulic-jump stilling basin. Figure 9-9 is an aerial photograph showing the wide auxiliary spillway channel with fuseplug control (at the top of the figure) and the service spillway chute. Note the outlet works control house and the outlet works channel, which empties into the spillway stilling basin.

The aforementioned auxiliary spillway channel was excavated in a soft sandstone with only fair erosion-resistant qualities. To minimize erosion should discharge occur, the channel floor was made level so that velocities would be low. Erosion would start at the downstream end and progress slowly upstream. The control structure consists of a concrete-lined section; the cantilever lip and the downstream cutoff are provided to halt erosion upstream. The division walls and the fuseplug sections of varying crest elevations ensure that a failure of the dike will be progressive. The two sections nearest the dam were made the highest so that they will be the last to be overtopped. This was done to keep the flows away from the dam and to make the channel flow distance longer for discharges less than the maximum for which the spillway was designed.

(c) *Emergency Spillways.*—As the name implies, emergency spillways are provided for additional safety should emergencies not contemplated by normal design assumptions arise. Such situations could be the result of an enforced shutdown of the outlet works, a malfunctioning of the spillway gates, or the necessity for bypassing the regular spillway because of damage or failure of some part of that structure. An emergency might arise where flood inflows are handled principally by surcharge storage and a recurring flood develops before a previous flood is evacuated by the small service spillway or the outlet works. Emergency spillways would act as auxiliary spillways if a flood greater than the selected inflow design flood occurred.

Under normal reservoir operation, emergency spillways are never required to function. Therefore, the control crest is placed at or above the designed

[1]Numbers in brackets refer to entries in the bibliography (sec. 9.32).

maximum reservoir water surface. The freeboard requirement for the dam is based on a water surface determined by assuming an arbitrary discharge that might result from a possible emergency. Usually, an encroachment on the freeboard provided for the designed maximum water surface is allowed in considering the design of an emergency spillway.

Emergency spillways are provided primarily to avoid an overtopping of the main dam embankment because of an emergency condition. Therefore, to be effective the emergency spillway must offer resistance to erosion greater than does the dam itself. Emergency spillways are often formed by lowering the crest of a dike section below that of the main embankment, by using saddles or depressions along the reservoir rim, or by excavating channels through ridges or abutments. The outlet channel of an emergency spillway should be far enough from the dam to preclude damage to the main embankment or appurtenances should the spillway operate.

Figure 6-84 shows an emergency spillway at Wasco Dam. This spillway was designed to prevent overtopping of the embankment should the combination outlet works-spillway fail to function properly.

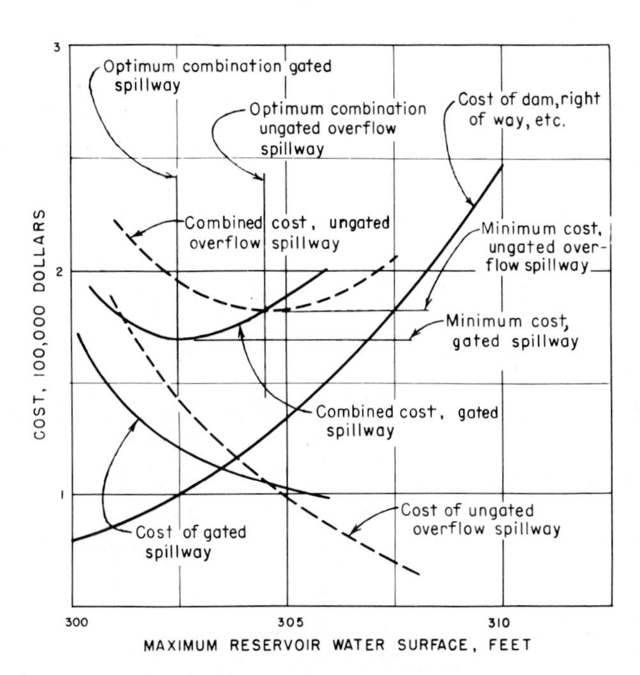

Figure 9-6.—Comparative costs of spillway-dam combinations. 288–D–2403.

B. SERVICE SPILLWAYS

9.6. *Selection of Spillway Layout.*—A composite spillway design should be prepared by considering the various factors that influence the spillway size and type and by correlating alternatively selected components. Many combinations of components can be used in forming a complete spillway layout. After the hydraulic size and outflow characteristics of a spillway are determined by routing of the design flood, the general dimensions of the control can be selected. Then, a specific spillway layout can be developed by considering the topography and foundation conditions and by fitting the control structure and the various components to the prevailing conditions.

Site conditions greatly influence the selection of location, type, and components of a spillway. Consideration must be given to the steepness of the terrain traversed by the spillway control and discharge channel, the class and amount of excavation (and the possibility for its use as embankment material), the possibility of scour of the bounding surfaces (and the need for lining), the permeability and bearing capacity of the foundation, and the stability of the excavated slopes.

The adoption of a particular size or arrangement for one spillway component may influence the selection of other components. For example, a wide control structure with the crest placed normal to the centerline of the spillway would require a long, converging transition to join it to a narrow discharge channel or to a tunnel. A better alternative might be the selection of a narrower gated control structure or a side channel control arrangement. Similarly, a wide stilling basin may not be feasible for use with a cut-and-cover conduit or tunnel because of the long, diverging transition needed.

A spillway may be an integral part of a dam (e.g., an overflow section of a concrete dam) or it may be a separate structure. In some instances, it may be combined as a common discharge structure with the outlet works or integrated into the river diversion plan for economy. Thus, the location, type, and size of other appurtenances may influence the selection of a spillway location or its arrangement. The final

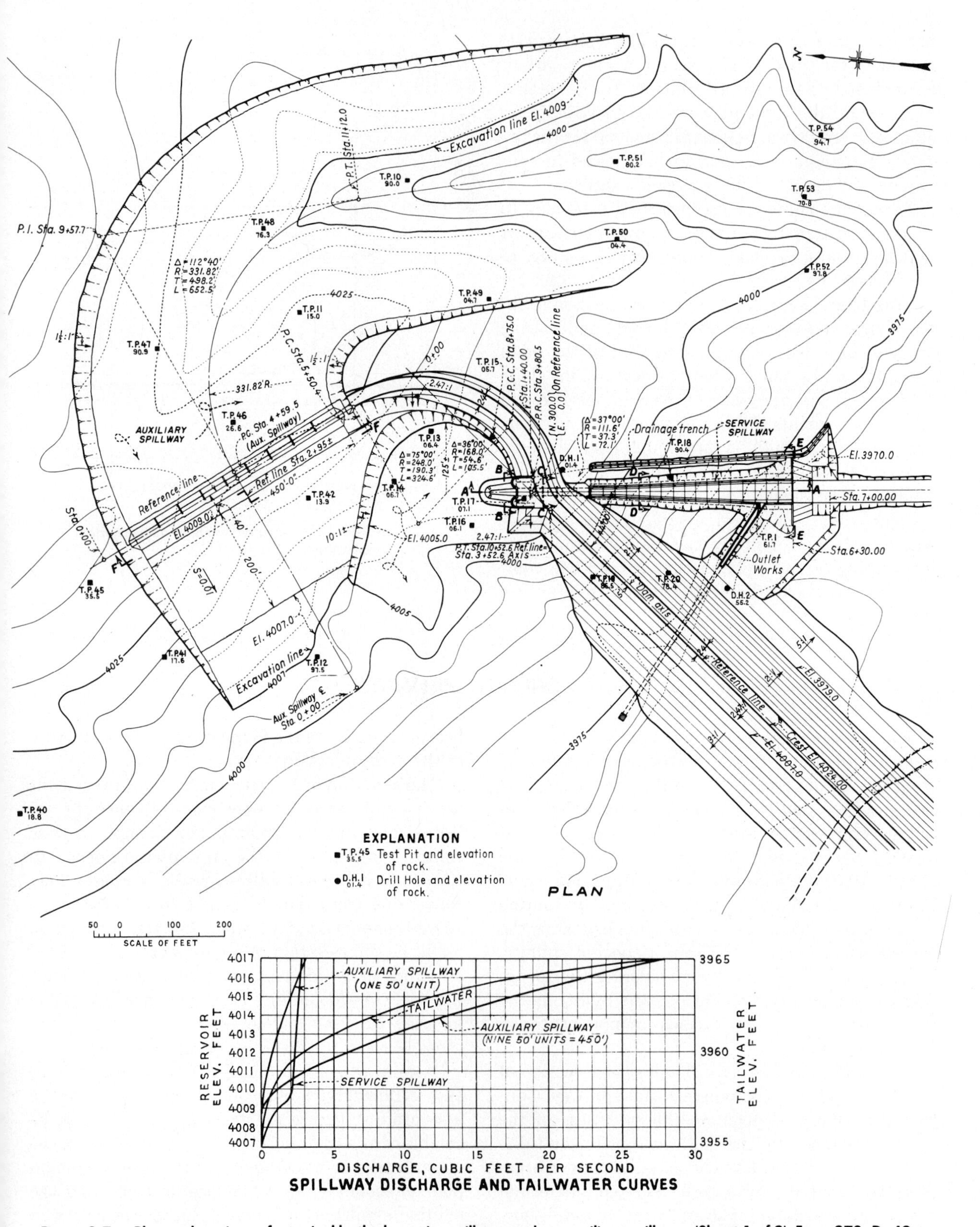

Figure 9-7.—Plan and sections of a typical bathtub service spillway and an auxiliary spillway. (Sheet 1 of 2). From 278-D-49.

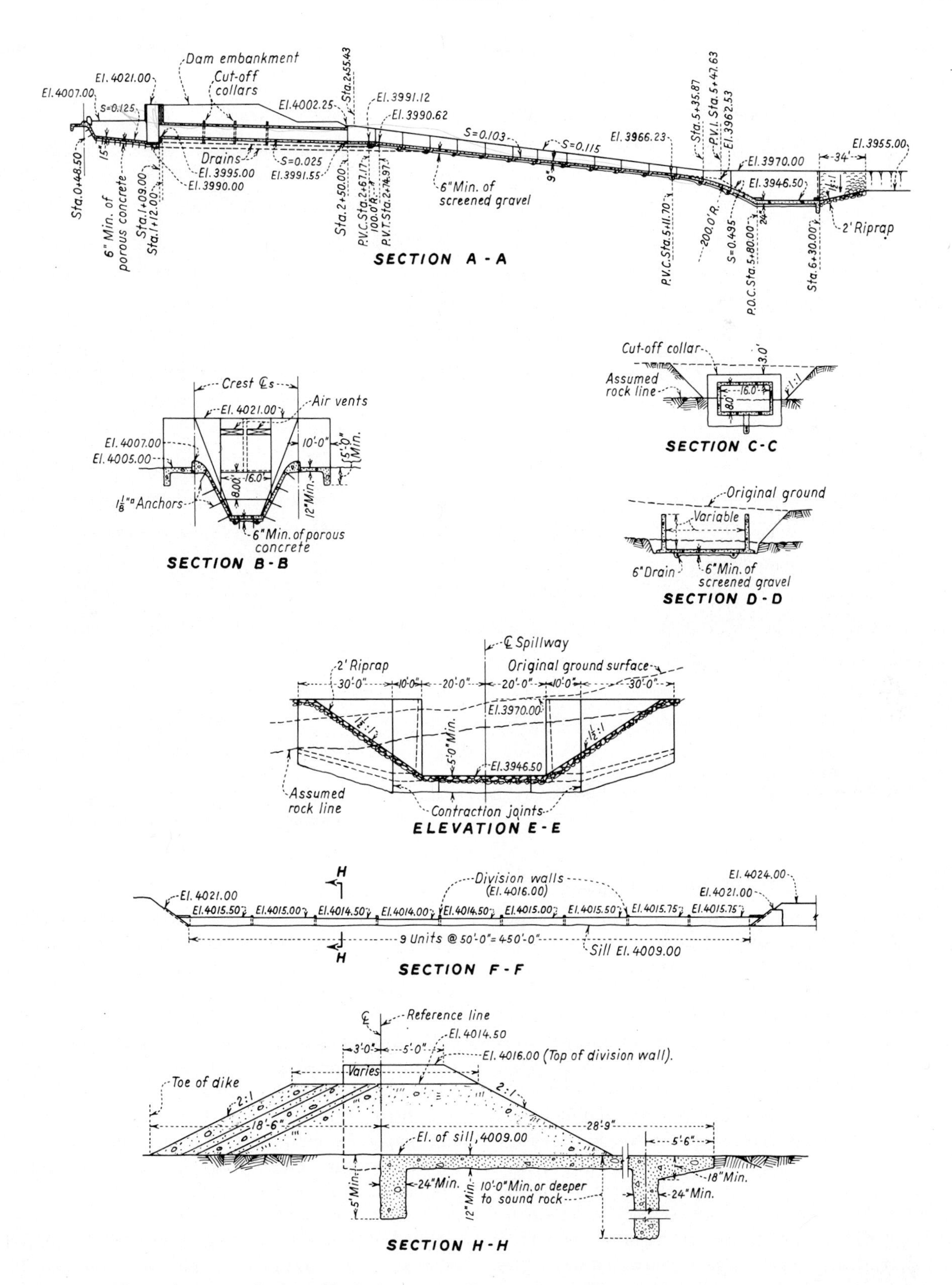

Figure 9-7.—Plan and sections of a typical bathtub service spillway and an auxiliary spillway. (Sheet 2 of 2). From 278–D–49.

Figure 9-8.—Aerial view of service spillway. (Same spillway shown on figs. 9-7 and 9-9). 288-D-2896.

Figure 9-9.—Aerial view of service and auxiliary spillways. (Same spillway shown on figs. 9-7 and 9-8). 288-D-2897.

plan should be governed by overall economy, hydraulic effectiveness, and structural adequacy.

The components of a spillway and common types of spillways are described in the following sections. Hydraulic design criteria and procedures are discussed in parts C through F of this chapter.

9.7. *Spillway Components.*—(a) *Control Structure.*—A major component of a spillway is the control device, which regulates the outflows from the reservoir. A control device limits or prevents outflows below fixed reservoir levels and regulates releases when the reservoir rises above that level. A control structure may consist of a sill, weir, orifice, or pipe. The discharge-head relationship may be fixed, as in the case of a simple overflow crest or unregulated port, or it may be variable, as with a gated crest or a valve- or gate-controlled pipe. The control characteristics of a closed conduit might change with the stage relationship. In a culvert spillway, used in low-head conditions, the entrance acts as a weir when not submerged and as an orifice when submerged. When the amount of submergence increases, the flow comes under the control of the pipe entrance. Finally, with greater submergence, the conduit flows full and the flow is governed by pressure pipe characteristics.

Control structures may take various positions and shapes. In plan, overflow crests can be straight, curved, semicircular, U-shaped, or round. (A semicircular crest for a small spillway is shown on fig. 9-10.) Orifice controls can be placed in a horizontal, inclined, or vertical position. Pipes can be placed vertically, horizontally, or inclined and can be straight, curved, or follow any profile. They can be

Figure 9-10.—Semicircular overflow crest for small chute spillway. Fruitgrowers Dam, Colorado. 288–D–2898.

circular, square, rectangular, horseshoe, or other shape in cross section.

An overflow can be sharp-crested, ogee-shaped, broad-crested, or of varied cross section. Orifices can be sharp-edged, round-edged, or bellmouth-shaped, and can be placed so as to discharge with a fully contracted jet or with a suppressed jet. They may discharge freely or discharge partly or fully submerged. Pipes can discharge freely or, for low-head installations, they can flow full for part or all of their length. Their size can be uniform or variable, with the control placed between the inlet and the downstream end.

(b) *Discharge Channel.*—Flow released through the control structure is usually conveyed to the streambed below the dam in a discharge channel or waterway. Exceptions are where the discharge falls freely from an arch dam crest or where the flow is released directly along the abutment hillside to cascade down the abutment face. The conveyance structure may be the downstream face of a concrete dam, an open channel excavated along the ground surface, a closed cut-and-cover conduit placed through or under a dam, or a tunnel excavated through an abutment. The profile may be variably flat or steep; the cross section may be variably rectangular, trapezoidal, circular, or another shape; and the discharge channel may be wide or narrow, long or short.

Discharge channel dimensions are governed primarily by hydraulic requirements, but the selection of profile, cross-sectional shape, width, length, etc., is influenced by the geologic and topographic characteristics of the site. Open channels excavated in the abutment usually follow the ground surface profile; steep canyon walls may make a tunnel desirable. In plan, open channels may be straight or curved, and their sides may be parallel, convergent, divergent, or a combination of these. A closed conduit may consist of a vertical or an inclined shaft leading to a nearly horizontal tunnel through the abutment or to a cut-and-cover conduit under or through the dam. Occasionally, a combination of a closed conduit and an open channel might be adopted, such as a conduit under an embankment emptying into an open channel leading down the abutment slope. Discharge channels must be cut through or lined with material that is resistant to the scouring action of the accelerating velocities and that is strong enough to withstand the forces from backfill, uplift, waterloads, etc.

(c) *Terminal Structure.*—When spillway flows drop from reservoir pool level to downstream river level, the static head is converted to kinetic energy. This energy manifests itself in the form of high velocities that, if impeded, result in high pressures. Means of returning the flow to the river without serious scour or erosion of the toe of the dam and without damage to adjacent structures must usually be provided.

In some cases the discharge may be delivered at high velocities directly to the stream, where the energy is absorbed along the streambed by impact, turbulence, and friction. Such an arrangement is satisfactory where there is erosion-resistant bedrock at shallow depths in the channel and along the abutments or where the spillway outlet is far enough from the dam and other appurtenances to preclude damage by scour, undermining, or abutment sloughing. A discharge channel may be terminated well above the streambed level, or it may be continued to or below the streambed.

Upturned deflectors, cantilevered extensions, or flip buckets can be provided to project the jet downstream from the end of the structure. Often, erosion in the streambed at the point of contact of the jet can be minimized by fanning the jet into a thin sheet by the use of a flaring deflector.

Where severe scour at the point of jet impingement is anticipated, a plunge basin can be excavated in the river channel and the sides and bottom lined with riprap or concrete. No definite design criteria, except those indicated in section 9.24, have been established for the dimensions of a plunge basin necessary to effectively absorb the impact of the flow or to avoid scouring velocities. For small installations, it may be expedient to excavate a small basin and to permit the flow to erode a natural pool. Protective riprapping or concrete lining may be added later to halt the scour. In such arrangements an adequate cutoff or other protection must be provided at the end of the spillway structure to prevent it from being undermined [2,3].

Where serious erosion to the streambed must be avoided, the high energy of the flow must be dissipated before the discharge is returned to the stream channel. This can be accomplished by the use of an energy dissipating device, such as a hydraulic-jump basin, a roller bucket, a sill-block apron, a basin incorporating impact baffles and walls, or some similar energy absorber or dissipator. A description of these devices and a discussion of their hydraulic design are given in part E of this chapter.

(d) *Entrance and Outlet Channels.*—Entrance channels draw water from the reservoir and convey it to the control structure. Where a spillway draws water directly from the reservoir and delivers it directly to the river, as does an overflow spillway over a concrete dam, entrance and outlet channels are not required. However, spillways placed through abutments or through saddles or ridges, may require channels leading to the spillway control and away from the spillway terminal structure.

Entrance velocities should be limited and channel curvatures and transitions should be made gradual to minimize head loss through the channel (which has the effect of reducing the spillway discharge) and to obtain uniformity of flow over the spillway crest. Effects of an uneven distribution of flow in the entrance channel might persist through the spillway structure to the extent that undesirable erosion could result in the downstream river channel. Nonuniformity of head on the crest may also cause a reduction in the discharge.

The approach velocity and depth below crest level have important influence on the discharge over an overflow crest. As described in section 9.12(a), a greater approach depth with the accompanying reduction in approach velocity will result in a larger discharge coefficient. Thus, for a given head over the crest, a deeper approach will permit a shorter crest length for a given discharge. Within the limits required to secure satisfactory flow conditions and nonscouring velocities, the determination of the relationship of entrance channel depth to channel width is a matter of economics.

Outlet channels convey the spillway flow from the terminal structure to the river channel below the dam. In some instances only a pilot channel is provided, on the assumption that scouring action will enlarge the channel during major spills. Where the channel is in a relatively nonerodible material, it should be excavated to a size large enough to pass the anticipated flow without forming a control that will affect the tailwater stage in the stilling device.

The outlet channel dimensions and its need for protection by lining or riprap depend on the influences of scour on the downstream riverbed and the resultant effects on the tailwater. Although stilling devices are provided, it may be impossible to reduce resultant velocities below the natural velocity in the original stream, therefore, some scouring of the riverbed is unavoidable. Furthermore, under natural conditions the beds of many streams are scoured during the rising stage of a flood and filled during the falling stage by deposition of material carried by the flow. After creation of a reservoir the spillway will normally discharge clear water and the material scoured by the high velocities will not be replaced by deposition. Consequently, there will be a gradual degradation of the downstream riverbed, which will lower the tailwater stage-discharge relationship. Conversely, scouring where only a pilot channel is provided may build up bars and islands downstream, thereby effecting an aggradation of the downstream river channel that will raise the tailwater elevation with respect to discharges. The dimensions and erosion-protective measures at the outlet channel may be influenced by these considerations.

9.8. *Spillway Types.*—(a) *General.*—Spillways are ordinarily classified according to their most prominent feature, either as it pertains to the control, to the discharge channel, or to some other feature. Spillways are often referred to as "controlled" or "uncontrolled," depending on whether they are gated or ungated. Commonly referred to types are the free overfall (straight drop), ogee (overflow), side channel, labyrinth, open channel (trough or chute), conduit, tunnel, drop inlet (shaft or morning glory), baffled apron drop, culvert, and siphon.

(b) *Free Overfall (Straight Drop) Spillways.*—A free overfall, or straight drop, spillway is one in which the flow drops freely from the crest. This type is suited to a thin arch or to a crest that has a nearly vertical downstream face. Flows may be free discharging, as is the case with a sharp-crested weir control, or they may be supported along a narrow section of the crest. Occasionally, the crest is extended in the form of an overhanging lip to direct small discharges away from the face of the overfall section. In free overfall spillways the underside of the nappe is ventilated sufficiently to prevent a pulsating, fluctuating jet.

Where no artificial protection is provided at the base of the overfall, scour will occur in most streambeds and will form a deep plunge pool. The volume and depth of the hole are related to the range of discharges, the height of the drop, and the depth of tailwater. The erosion-resistant properties of the streambed material, including bedrock, have little influence on the size of the hole, they only effect the time necessary to scour the hole. Probable depths of scour are discussed in section 9.25. Where erosion cannot be tolerated, an artificial pool can be created by constructing an auxiliary dam downstream from the main structure, or by excavating a basin, which is then provided with a concrete apron or bucket.

If tailwater depths are sufficient, a hydraulic jump will form when a free overfall jet falls upon a flat apron. It has been demonstrated that the momentum equation for the hydraulic jump may be applied to the flow conditions at the base of the fall to determine the elements of the jump.

A free overfall spillway that will be effective over a wide range of tailwater depths can be designed for use with low earthfill dams [4]. An artist's conception of such a structure is shown on figure 9-11. It consists principally of a straight wall weir set at the upper end of a rectangular flume section, with its horizontal apron placed at or below streambed level. Floor blocks and an end sill are provided to help establish the jump and to reduce the downstream scour. This type of structure is not adaptable for high drops on unstable foundations because of the large impact forces that must be absorbed by the apron at the point of impingement of the jet. Vibrations incident to the impact caused by high drops might crack or displace the structure, with danger of failure by piping or undermining. Ordinarily, the use of this structure for hydraulic drops from head pool to tailwater of 20 feet or more should not be considered. The hydraulic design of the free overfall spillway is discussed in section 9.26.

(c) *Ogee (Overflow) Spillways.*—The ogee spillway has a control weir that is ogee-shaped (S-shaped) in profile. The upper curve of the ogee spillway ordinarily conforms closely to the profile of the lower nappe of a ventilated sheet falling from a sharp-crested weir. Flow over the crest adheres to the face of the profile by preventing access of air to the underside of the sheet. For discharges at designed head, the flow glides over the crest with no interference from the boundary surface and attains near-maximum discharge efficiency. The profile below the upper curve of the ogee is continued tangent along a slope to support the sheet on the face of the overflow. A reverse curve at the bottom of the slope turns the flow onto the apron of a stilling basin or into the spillway discharge channel.

The upper curve at the crest may be either broader or sharper than the nappe profile. A broader curve will support the sheet, and positive hydrostatic pressure will occur along the contact surface. The supported sheet thus creates a backwater effect and reduces the efficiency of discharge. For a sharper curve, the sheet tends to pull away from the crest and to produce subatmospheric pressure along the contact surface. This negative pressure effect increases the effective head and, thereby, increases the discharge.

An ogee crest and apron may make up an entire spillway, such as the overflow portion of a concrete gravity dam, or the ogee crest may only be the control structure for another type of spillway. Because of its high discharge efficiency, the nappe-shaped profile is used for most spillway control crests. Crest shapes and discharge coefficients are discussed in sections 9.10, 9.11, and 9.12.

(d) *Side Channel Spillways.*—A side channel spillway is one whose control weir is placed alongside and approximately parallel to the upper portion of the spillway discharge channel. Flow over the crest falls into a narrow trough opposite the weir, turns approximately 90°, and then continues into the main discharge channel. The side channel design is concerned only with the hydraulic action in the upstream reach of the discharge channel and is more or less independent of the details selected for the other spillway components. Flows from the side channel can be directed into an open discharge channel or into a closed conduit or inclined tunnel. Flow into the side channel might enter the trough on only one side in the case of a steep hillside location, or on both sides and over the end of the trough if it is located on a knoll or gently sloping

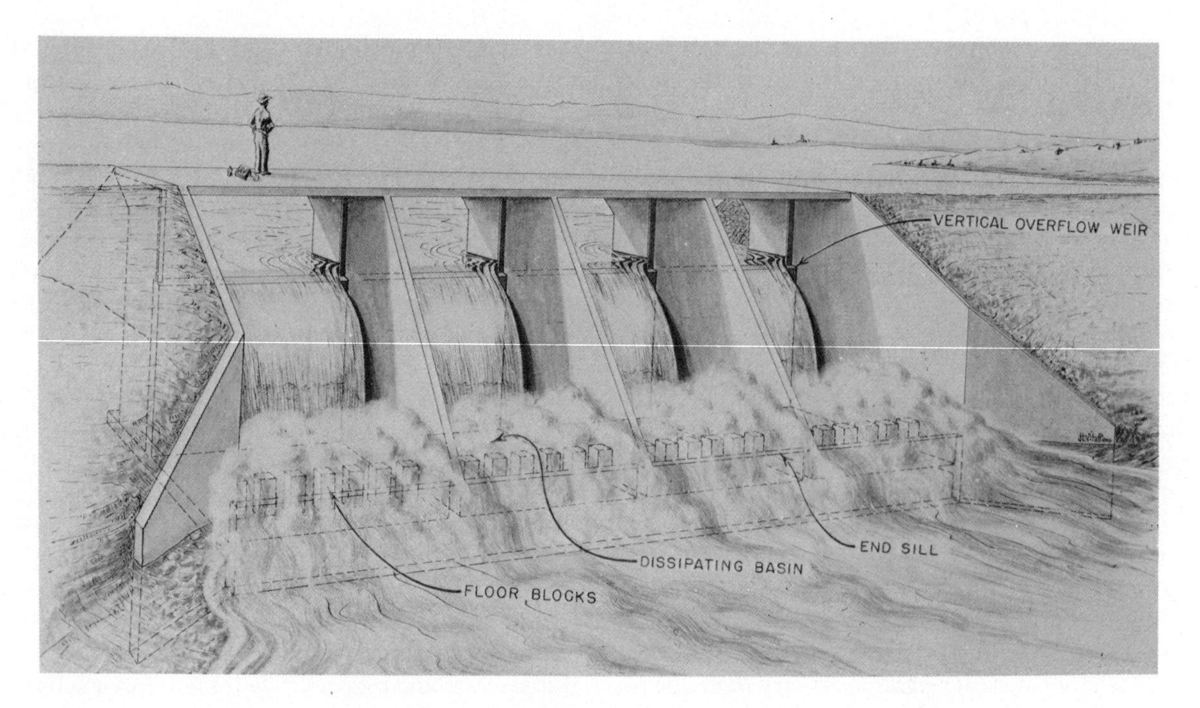

Figure 9-11.—Typical straight drop spillway installation for small heads. 288–D–2899.

abutment. The bathtub-type side channel spillway shown on figures 9-7, 9-8, and 9-9 illustrates the latter case. Figure 9-12 is an artist's conception of a side channel spillway where flow enters only one side of the trough.

Discharge characteristics of a side channel spillway are similar to those of an ordinary overflow spillway and are dependent on the selected profile of the weir crest. However, for maximum discharges the side channel flow may differ from that of the overflow spillway in that the flow in the trough may be restricted and may partly submerge the flow over the crest. In this case the flow characteristics are controlled by a constriction in the channel downstream from the trough. The constriction may be a point of critical flow in the channel, an orifice control, or a conduit or tunnel flowing full.

Although the side channel is neither hydraulically efficient nor inexpensive, it has advantages that make it desirable for certain spillway layouts. Where a long overflow crest is needed to limit the surcharge head and the abutments are steep and precipitous, or where the control must be connected to a narrow discharge channel or tunnel, the side channel spillway is often the best choice.

The hydraulic design of side channel spillways is discussed in section 9.17.

(e) *Labyrinth Spillways.*—The concept behind the labyrinth spillway is to provide added crest length for a given total spillway width, so that less head is required to pass a given discharge. The additional spillway crest length is obtained by a series of trapezoidal or triangular walls within the total spillway width (see fig. 9-13). These walls are thin and cantilevered, vertical on the upstream face and steeply sloping (1:10 or 1:16) on the downstream face. They are supported with a concrete base slab or are tied into an existing good quality foundation. The crest consists of a quarter-circle arc on the upstream edge and a slight chamfer on the downstream edge.

Labyrinth spillways have many advantages and applications. They are suitable for use anywhere an overflow structure is required depending upon the site conditions. A labyrinth design is particularly beneficial when the spillway width is fixed, upstream water surface elevations are restricted, and large discharges must be passed. The increased crest length produced by the labyrinth configuration allows passage of greater discharges under less head. Labyrinths are particularly suitable for use at a reservoir site, either as a service spillway or an auxiliary spillway. Where an inflow design flood has been increased and the capacity of an existing spillway must also be increased, a labyrinth spillway is an excellent alternative to traditional methods of adding another spillway. Labyrinths have also been used as control or diversion structures on canals. Storage capacity can also be increased because the labyrinth crest can be set at a higher elevation than a straight crest while still passing the required discharge. Labyrinth spillways are more economical than gated structures. Cost savings may be realized during initial construction and in future operation and maintenance costs. An example of the labyrinth spillway geometry and a typical application is shown on figure 9-13.

Flow patterns for the labyrinth spillway are very complicated. The primary parameters affecting flow patterns and, thus, spillway performance, are the length magnification, crest length per cycle width, the discharge and head over the spillway, the angle of the spillway side walls with respect to the flow, and the ratio of the spillway cycle width to the spillway height.

Ideally, discharge over the spillway should increase in direct proportion to the increase in crest length. However, this occurs only for small crest length to spillway width ratios and for small head to crest height ratios. Because labyrinth spillways are most advantageous when designed to operate under conditions that exceed these restrictions, analysis of spillway performance is complicated. Basically, spillway performance is determined by the flow patterns in the upstream and downstream channels of each cycle. Therefore, the spillway geometry chosen must allow optimum flow distribution in these areas [5]. Hydraulic model studies for Hyrum Dam auxiliary labyrinth spillway and for Ute Dam labyrinth can be found in [6] and [7], respectively.

(f) *Chute (Open Channel or Trough) Spillways.*—

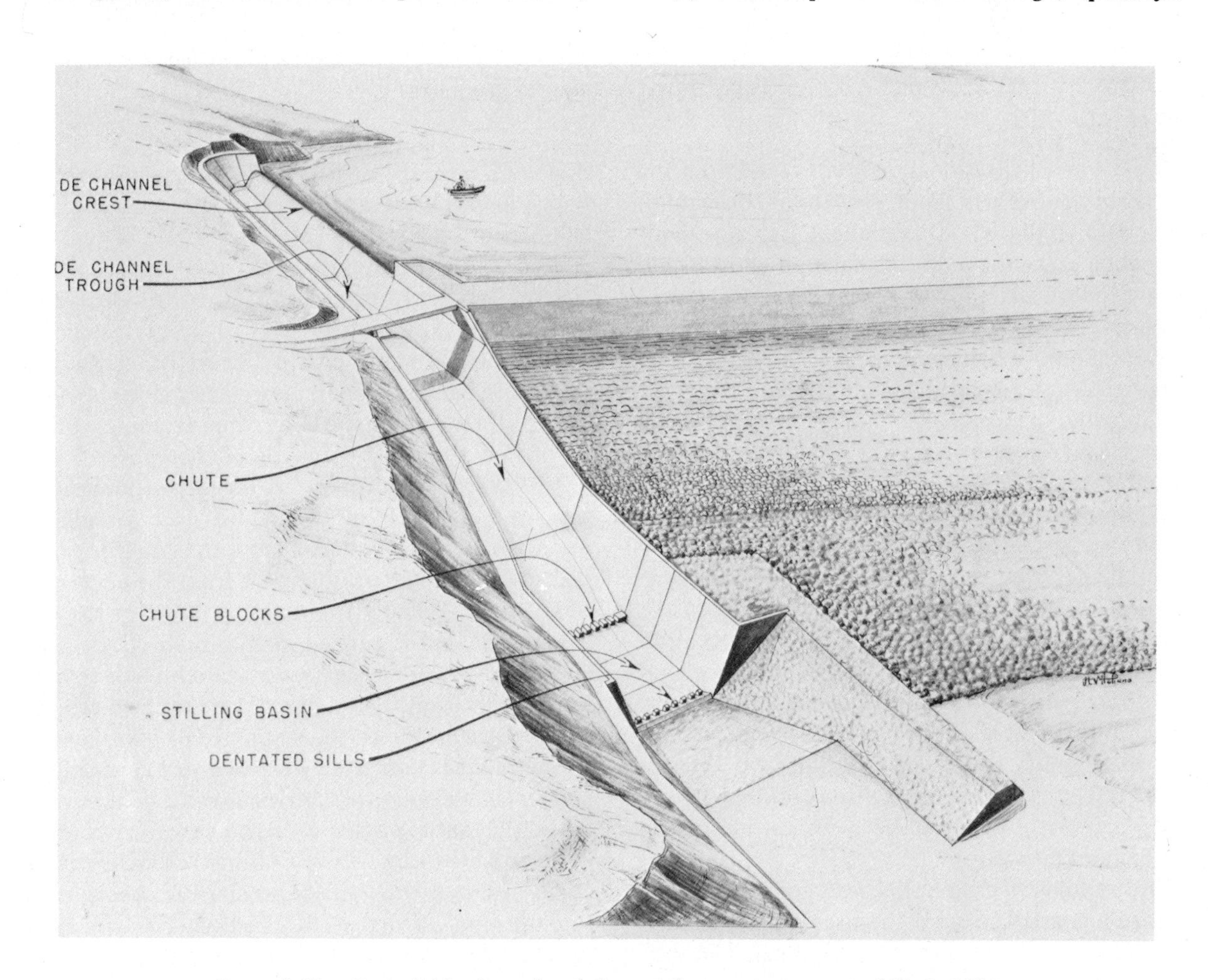

Figure 9-12.—Typical side channel and chute spillway arrangement. 288–D–2900.

Figure 9-13.—Ute Dam 14-cycle labyrinth spillway. Total length of 3,360 feet contained in a width of 840 feet. The spillway height is 30 feet and will pass a design discharge of 590,000 ft^3/s under the design head of 19 feet. P801-D-81045.

A spillway whose discharge is conveyed from the reservoir to the downstream river level through an open channel, placed either along a dam abutment or through a saddle, might be called a chute, open channel, or trough spillway. These designations apply regardless of the control device used to regulate the flow. Thus, a spillway having a chute-type discharge channel, though controlled by an overflow crest, a gated orifice, a side channel crest, or some other control device, may still be called a chute spillway. However, the name is most often applied when the spillway control is placed normal or nearly normal to the axis of an open channel, and where the streamlines of flow both above and below the control crest follow in the direction of the axis.

The chute spillway has been used more often with earthfill dams than with any other type. Factors influencing the selection of chute spillways are the simplicity of their design and construction, their adaptability to almost any foundation condition, and the overall economy often obtained by the use of large amounts of spillway excavation in the dam embankment.

Chute spillways ordinarily consist of an entrance channel, a control structure, a discharge channel, a terminal structure, and an outlet channel. The simplest form of chute spillway has a straight centerline and uniform width, such as that shown on figure 9-14. Often, either the axis of the entrance channel or that of the discharge channel must be curved to fit the alignment to the topography. If possible, the curvature is confined to the entrance channel because of the low approach velocities. When the discharge channel must be curved, its floor is sometimes superelevated to guide the high-velocity flow around the bend, thus avoiding a piling up of flow toward the outside of the chute.

Chute spillway profiles are usually influenced by the site topography and by subsurface foundation conditions. The control structure is generally placed in line with or upstream from the centerline of the dam. Usually the upper portion of the discharge channel is carried at minimum grade until it "daylights" along the downstream hillside to minimize excavation. The steep portion of the discharge channel then follows the slope of the abutment.

Flows upstream from the crest are generally at subcritical velocity, with critical velocity occurring when the water passes over the control. Flows in the chute are ordinarily maintained at supercritical stage, either at constant or accelerating rates, until the terminal structure is reached. For good hydraulic performance, abrupt vertical changes or sharp convex or concave vertical curves in the chute

Figure 9-14.—Chute spillway for Scofield Dam, Utah. 288–D–2901.

profile should be avoided. Similarly, the convergence or divergence in plan should be gradual to avoid cross waves, wave runup on the walls, excessive turbulence, or uneven distribution of flow at the terminal structure.

The hydraulic design of the chute spillway crest is discussed in part C, the determination of hydraulic properties for the discharge channel in part D, and stilling basin designs in part E of this chapter.

(g) *Conduit and Tunnel Spillways.*—Where a closed channel is used to convey the discharge around or under a dam, the spillway is often called a tunnel or conduit spillway, as appropriate. The closed channel may take the form of a vertical or inclined shaft, a horizontal tunnel through earth or rock, or a conduit constructed in open cut and backfilled with earth materials. Most forms of control structures, including overflow crests, drop inlet entrances, and side channel crests, can be used with conduit and tunnel spillways.

With the exception of those with drop inlet entrances, tunnel and conduit spillways are designed to flow partly full throughout their length. With the drop inlet, the tunnel or conduit size is selected so that it flows full for only a short section at the control and thereafter partly full for its remaining length. Ample aeration must be provided in a tunnel or conduit spillway to prevent a make-and-break siphonic action that would occur if some part of the tunnel or conduit sealed temporarily. This sealing could be the result of an exhaustion of air caused by surging of the water jet, or by wave action or backwater. To guarantee free flow in the tunnel, the ratio of the flow area to the total tunnel area is often limited to about 75 percent. Air vents should be provided at critical points along the tunnel or conduit to ensure an adequate air suply, which would preclude unsteady flow through the spillway.

Air slots may be appropriate in some instances to introduce air into the flow for prevention of cavitation where high velocity flow occurs. The Bureau of Reclamation has prepared model studies of air slots for the spillways at Blue Mesa and Glen Canyon dams [8], Hoover Dam [9], and Yellowtail Dam [10]. Additional information on aeration of spillway flows is presented in [11].

Tunnel spillways may present advantages for damsites in narrow canyons with steep abutments or at sites where there is danger to open channels from snow slides or rockslides. Conduit spillways may be appropriate at damsites in wide valleys, where the abutments rise gradually and are far from the stream channel. Use of a conduit will permit the spillway to be located under the dam near the streambed.

(h) *Drop Inlet (Shaft or Morning Glory) Spillways.*—As the name implies, a drop inlet or shaft spillway is one in which the water enters over a horizontal lip, drops through a vertical or sloping shaft, and then flows to the downstream river channel through a horizontal or nearly horizontal conduit or tunnel. The structure is considered to comprise three elements: an overflow control weir, a vertical transition, and a closed discharge channel. Where the inlet is funnel-shaped, this type of structure is often called a "morning glory," or "glory hole," spillway.

Discharge characteristics of the drop inlet spillway may vary with a range of head. The control shifts according to the relative discharge capacities of the weir, the transition, and the conduit or tunnel. For example, as the heads increase on a morning glory spillway, the control shifts from weir flow over the crest to tube flow in the transition and then to full pipe flow in the downstream portion. Full pipe flow design for spillways, except those with extremely low drops, is not recommended. This is discussed in section 9.20(e).

A drop inlet spillway can be used advantageously at damsites in narrow canyons where the abutments rise steeply or where a diversion tunnel or conduit is available for use as the downstream leg. Another advantage of this type of spillway is that near maximum capacity is attained at relatively low heads; this characteristic makes the spillway ideal for use where the maximum spillway outflow is to be limited. This characteristic also may be considered disadvantageous, because there is little increase in capacity beyond the design head should a flood larger than the selected inflow design flood occur. However, this would not be a disadvantage if this type of spillway were used as a service spillway in conjunction with an auxiliary or emergency spillway.

An artist's conception of a drop inlet spillway is shown on figure 9-15. Figure 9-16 shows such a conduit under construction. The hydraulic design is discussed in section 9.26. Additional information on the design and performance of drop inlet spillways is given in [12, 13, 14].

(i) *Baffled Chute Spillways.*—Baffled chutes, or aprons, are used in spillways where water is to be lowered from one level to another, and where a stilling basin is not desirable. The baffle piers partially obstruct the flow, dissipating energy as the water flows down the chute so that the flow velocities entering the downstream channel are relatively low. Advantages of baffled chutes include economy, low terminal velocities of the flows regardless of the height of the drop, spillway operation unaffected by downstream degradation, and effective stilling action without requirements for initial tailwater depth.

The chute is normally constructed at a slope of 2:1 or flatter, extending below the outlet channel floor. Chutes having slopes steeper than 2:1 should be model tested [15, 16, 17] and their structural stability should be checked. The lower end of the chute should be constructed far enough below the channel floor to prevent damage from degradation or from scour.

Design capacities of baffled chutes have varied from less than 10 to over 80 ft^3/s per foot of width. At Conconully Dam, the scale model of the spillway baffled chute was designed to represent prototype

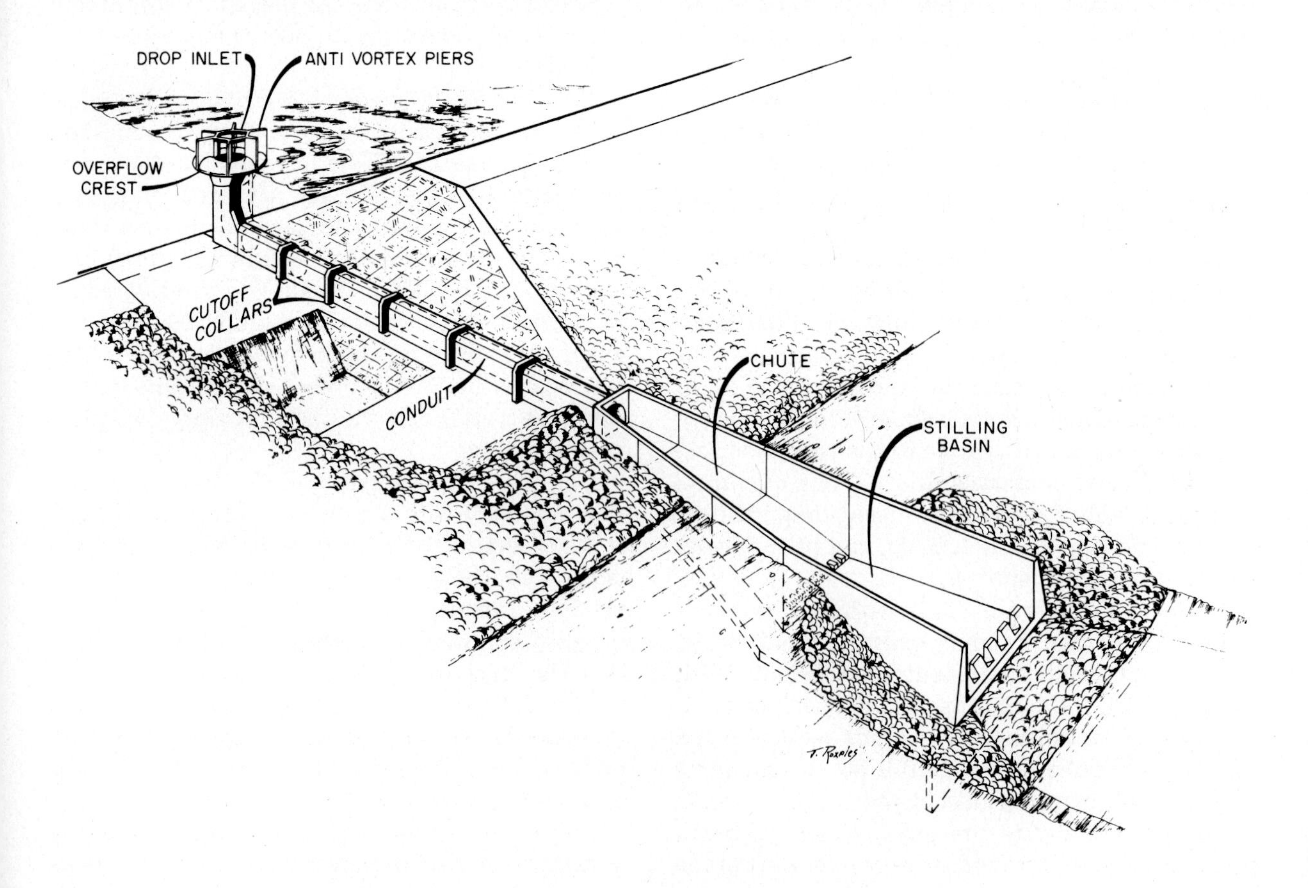

Figure 9-15.—Drop inlet spillway for a small dam. 103–D–1873.

Figure 9-16.—Conduit and stilling basin for drop inlet spillway. Ridgway Dam during construction (1984). Dam is on the Uncompahgre River, Dallas Creek Project, Colorado. P894–427–6200NA.

discharge up to 78 ft^3/s per foot of width and to operate effectively at 150 ft^3/s per foot of width. The completed spillway for Conconully Dam is shown on figure 9-17. The generalized design procedures discussed in this section were obtained from test results on several models of baffled chutes developed by the Bureau of Reclamation [15, 16, 17].

The typical hydraulic design procedure for a baffled chute drop spillway is given in the steps listed below, which relate to figures 9-18, 9-19 and 9-20.

(1) Determine the maximum expected discharge, Q.

(2) Determine unit design discharge $q = Q/W$, where W is the chute width. The chute width may depend on the upstream channel width, the downstream channel width, economy, topography, and frequency of discharge, as well as on maximum discharge.

Figure 9-17.—Baffled chute drop spillway. Conconully Dam, Washington. The flow shown passing over the spillway is about 50 ft³/s. P21-141-178NA.

Model studies have shown that a baffled chute spillway design for a large unit discharge can be based on a discharge about two-thirds of the maximum expected discharge. However, the height of the chute sidewalls must be higher than the value determined in step (10). It is suggested that the height be increased by an amount equivalent to the critical depth of one-third the maximum expected discharge.

(3) The entrance velocity, V, should be as low as practical. Ideal conditions exist when the entrance velocity $V_1 = \sqrt[3]{gq} - 5$ (curve D on fig. 9-20) for discharges up to 69 ft³/s per foot of width. Velocities near or above critical, $V_c = \sqrt[3]{gq}$, (curve C on fig. 9-20), cause the flow to be thrown into the air after striking the first baffle pier. Proper flow conditions must be provided at the entrance to the baffled apron because satisfactory performance of the entire structure may depend on proper entrance flow conditions.

(4) A vertical offset between the approach channel floor and the chute is used to establish a desirable uniform entrance velocity, V_1. This offset varies with the installation. A short-radius curve provides a crest on the sloping chute. The first row of baffle piers should be placed no more than 12 inches in elevation below the crest. Alternate rows should be staggered to provide a baffle pier below each space and a space below each baffle pier. An alternative entrance configuration, the Fujimoto entrance (fig. 9-19), has been used successfully on several structures where the design unit discharge exceeds 100 ft³s. If the Fujimoto entrance is used, hydraulic model studies should be performed to determine the optimum location for the first row of baffle piers.

(5) The baffle pier height, H, should be about $0.8D_c$ or $0.9D_c$, where the critical depth for the rectangular chute $D_c = \sqrt[3]{q^2/g}$ (curve A on fig. 9-20). Baffle pier height is not a critical dimension, but it should not be less than recommended. For unit discharges greater than 60 ft³/s, curve A on figure 9-20 may be extrapolated.

(6) Baffle pier widths and spaces should equal, preferably, about 1.5 H but not less than H. Other baffle pier dimensions are not critical hydraulically. Suggested cross-sectional dimensions are given on figure 9-18.

(7) The spacing between the rows of baffle piers down the chute slope should be H divided by the slope, where the slope is given in decimal form. For example, a 2:1 slope (0.50 in decimal form) makes the row spacing equal to $2H$ parallel to the chute floor.

(8) The baffle piers are usually constructed with the upstream face normal to the chute floor surface; however, piers with vertical faces may be used. Vertical-faced piers tend to produce more splash and less bed scour, but the differences are minor.

(9) At least four rows of baffle piers are usually needed to establish full control of the flow (although spillways with fewer rows have occasionally operated successfully). As many additional rows as required beyond

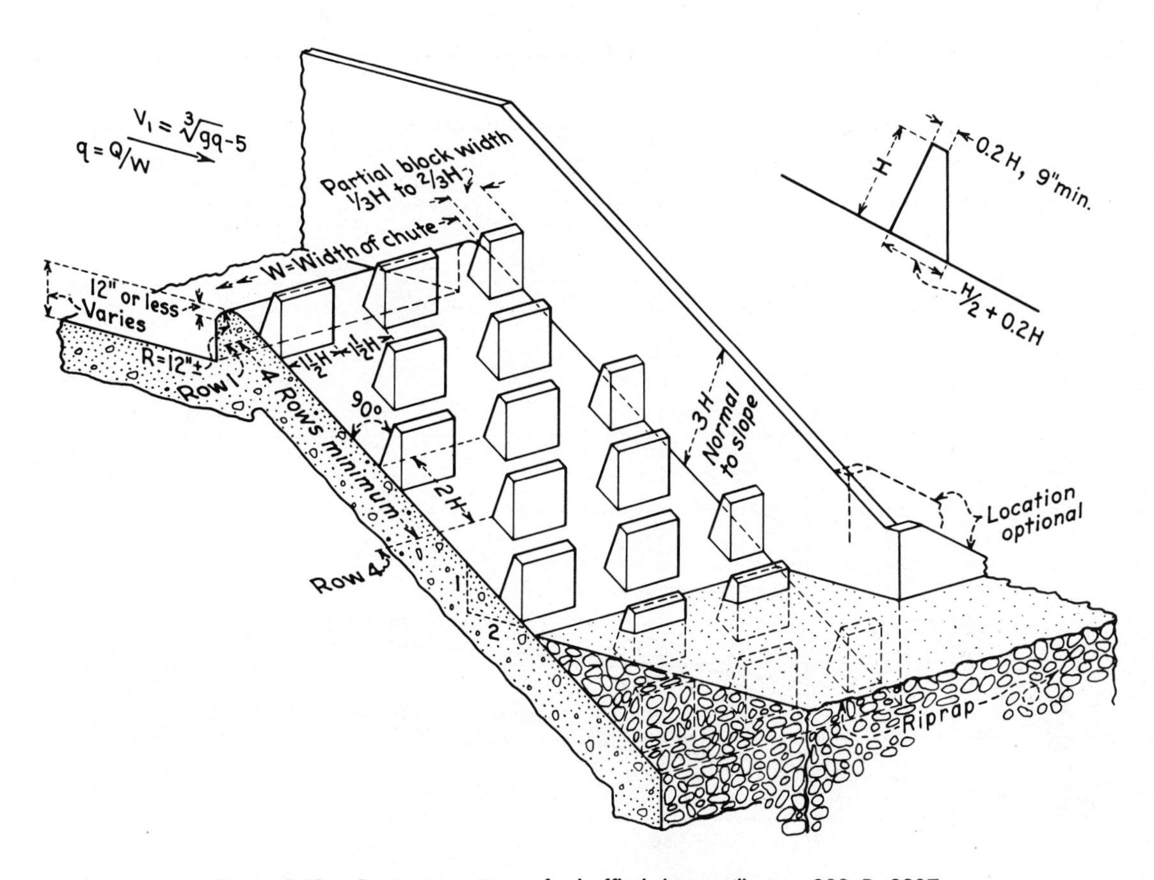

Figure 9-18.—Basic proportions of a baffled chute spillway. 288–D–2807.

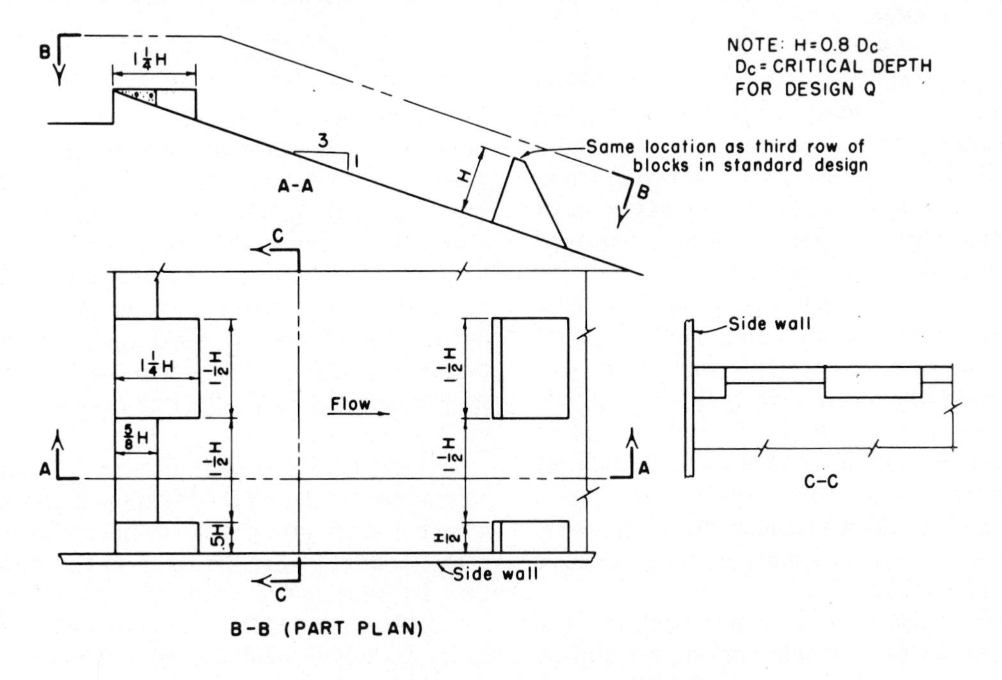

Figure 9-19.—Fujimoto entrance for baffled chutes.

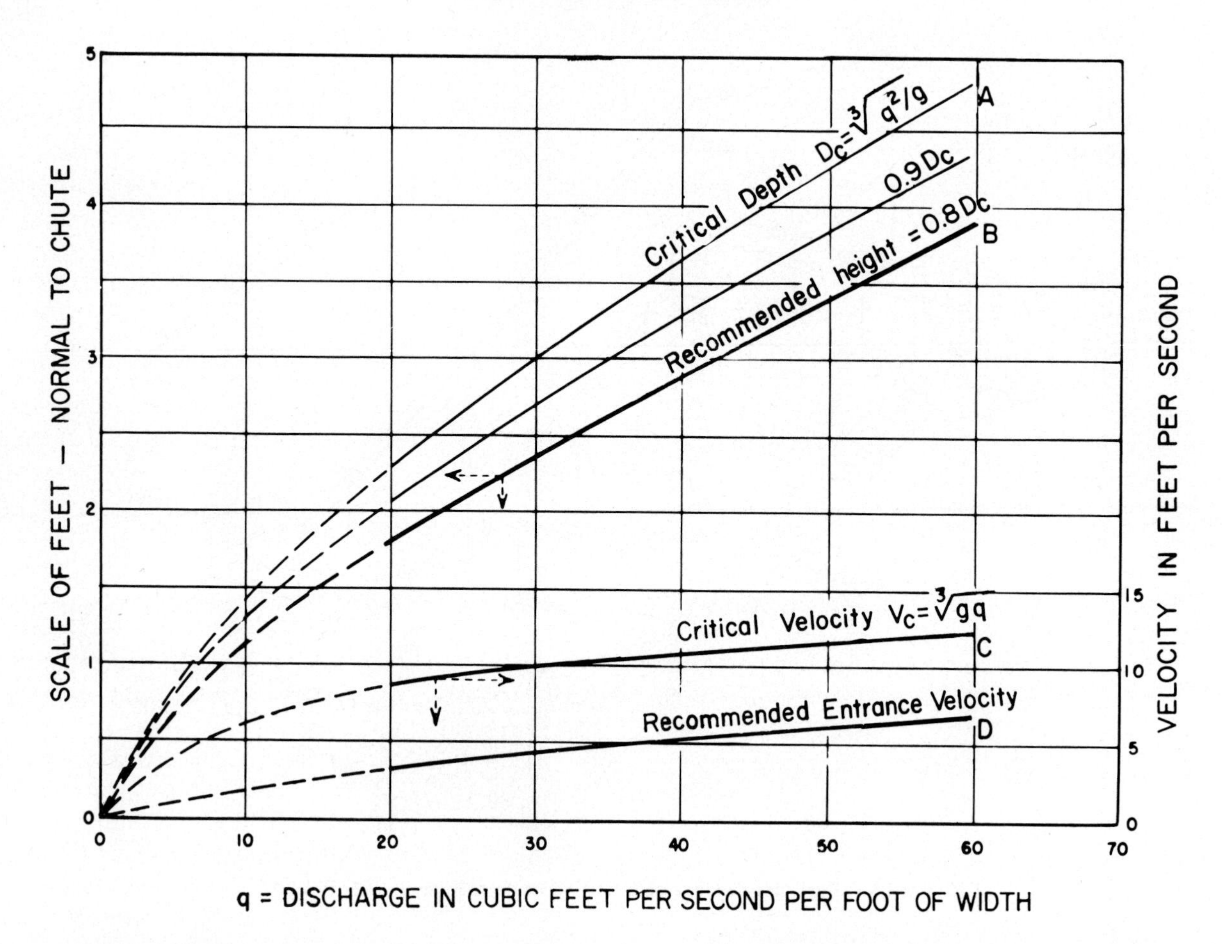

Figure 9-20.—Recommended baffle pier heights and allowable velocities for baffled chute spillways. 288-D-2806.

the fourth maintain the control established upstream. At least one row of baffles should be buried below the outlet channel grade to protect against scour. Additional rows of baffles should be buried as needed to protect against degradation.

(10) The chute training walls should be three times as high as the baffle piers measured normal to the floor. This wall height will contain the main flow and most of the splash. It is not necessary or practical to build the walls high enough to contain all the splash.

(11) Riprap should be placed at the downstream ends of the training walls to prevent erosion of the banks.

(j) *Culvert Spillways.*—A culvert spillway is a special adaptation of the conduit or tunnel spillway. It is distinguished from the drop inlet in that its inlet opening is placed either vertically or inclined upstream or downstream, and its profile grade is uniform or nearly uniform at any slope. The spillway inlet opening may be sharp-edged or rounded, and the approach to the conduit may have flared or tapered sidewalls with a level or sloping floor. If it is desired that the conduit flow partly full for all conditions of discharge, special precautions should be taken to prevent the conduit from flowing full; if full flow is desired, bellmouth or streamlined inlet shapes are provided.

Culvert spillways operating with the inlet unsubmerged act similarly to an open channel spillway. Those operating with the inlet submerged, but with the inlet orifice arranged so that full conduit flow is prevented, act similarly to an orifice-controlled drop inlet spillway or to an orifice-controlled chute spillway. Where priming action is induced and the conduit flows full, the operation will be similar to that of a siphon spillway.

When culvert spillways placed on steep slopes flow full, reduced or negative pressures prevail along the boundaries of the conduit. Large negative pressures may cause cavitation to the surfaces of the conduit or even its collapse. Where cracks or joints occur along the low-pressure regions, there is also the possibility of drawing in the soil surrounding the conduit. Culvert spillways, therefore, should not be used for high-head installations where large negative pressures can develop. Furthermore, the transition flow phenomenon, when the flow changes from partial flow to full stage, is accompanied by severe pulsations and vibrations that increase in magnitude with increased culvert fall. For these reasons, culvert spillways should not be used for hydraulic drops exceeding 25 feet.

For drops less than 25 feet, culvert spillways offer advantages over similar types because of their adaptability for either partial flow or full flow operation and because of their simplicity and economy of construction. They can be placed on a bench excavated along the abutment on a relatively steep sidehill or they can be placed through the main section of the dam to discharge directly into the downstream river channel. As is the case with a drop inlet, a principal disadvantage of the culvert spillway is that it does not provide a safety factor against underestimation of the design flood because its capacity does not substantially increase with increase in head. This disadvantage would not apply if the culvert spillway were used as a service spillway in conjunction with an auxiliary or emergency spillway.

The hydraulic design and details for culvert spillways are discussed in section 9.27.

9.9. Controlled Crests.—(a) *General.*—The simplest form of control for a spillway is the free, or uncontrolled, overflow crest, which automatically releases water whenever the reservoir water surface rises above crest level. The advantages of the uncontrolled crest are the elimination of the need for constant attendance and regulation of the control devices by an operator and the freedom from maintenance and repairs of the devices.

A regulating gate or other form of movable crest control is required if a sufficiently long uncontrolled crest or a sufficiently large surcharge head cannot be obtained for the required spillway capacity. Such devices are also required if the spillway is to release storages below the normal reservoir water surface.

Selection of the type and size of the crest control device may be influenced by such conditions as the discharge characteristics of the device, the climate, frequency and nature of floods, winter storage requirements, flood control storage and outflow provisions, the need for handling ice and debris, and special operating requirements. Whether an operator will be in attendance during flood periods and the availability of electric power, operating mechanisms, operating bridges, etc., are also factors that could influence the type of control device selected.

Many types of crest control have been devised. The type selected for a specific installation should be based on a consideration of the factors noted above as well as economy, adaptability, reliability, and efficiency. Movable crests include such devices as flashboards, stoplogs, and drum gates. Regulating devices include vertical or inclined rectangular lift gates, wheel-mounted gates, roller-mounted gates, and radial gates. Radial gates and wheel-mounted slide gates are most commonly used for large spillways.

For simplicity of design and operation, the simpler control devices are considered appropriate for spillways for small dams. These devices include flashboards, stoplogs, rectangular gates, and radial gates, which should be used whenever possible because they can be easily fabricated and obtained commercially.

(b) *Flashboards and Stoplogs.*—Flashboards and stoplogs can be used as a means of raising the reservoir storage level above a fixed spillway crest level when the spillway is not needed for releasing floods. However, safety of dams considerations often preclude the use of these devices. Flashboards usually consist of individual wooden boards, or structural panels anchored to the crest; stoplogs are wooden boards or structural panels spanning horizontally between slots or grooves recessed into the sides of the supporting piers. To provide adequate spillway capacity, the flashboards or stoplogs must be removed before the floods occur, or they must be designed or arranged so that they can be removed while being overtopped. These devices should be used only where adequate removal is ensured.

Various arrangement of flashboards have been devised. Some must be placed and removed manually, some are designed to fail after being overtopped, and others are arranged to drop out of position either automatically or after being manually triggered when the reservoir exceeds a certain stage. Flashboards provide a simple economical type of movable crest device, and they have the advantage that an unobstructed crest is provided when the flashboards and their supports are removed. However, flashboards have several disadvantages that greatly limit their adaptability. Among these disadvantages are the following: (1) they present a hazard if not removed in time to pass floods, especially where the reservoir area is small and the stream drainage basin is subject to flash floods; (2) they require the attendance of an operator or crew and equipment for their removal, unless they are designed to fail automatically; (3) if they are designed to fail when the water reaches a predetermined stage, their operation is uncertain, and when they fail they release sudden and undesirably large outflows; (4) ordinarily, they cannot be placed back into position while flow is passing over the crest; (5) if the spillway functions frequently, the repeated replacement of flashboards may be costly; and (6) in some cases, they can be used only during low inflow periods.

Stoplogs are usually wooden beams or structural steel panel units stacked one upon the other to the desired height. They form a bulkhead that is supported in slots or in grooves recessed into the supporting piers at each end of the span. The spacing of the supporting piers depends on the material from which the stoplogs are constructed, the head of water acting against the stoplogs, and the handling facilities available for installing and removing them. Stoplogs that are removed individually as the need for increased discharge occurs are the simplest form of a crest gate.

Stoplogs can be an economical substitute for more elaborate gates where relatively close spacing of piers is not objectionable and where removal is required only infrequently. However, stoplogs that must be removed or installed in flowing water may require elaborate handling mechanisms that make them as costly as gates with attached hoists. A stoplogged spillway requires the attendance of an operating crew for removing and installing the stoplogs. Furthermore, the arrangement may present a hazard to the safety of the dam if the reservoir is small and the stream is subject to flash floods, because the stoplogs must be removed in time to pass the flood.

(c) *Rectangular Lift Gates.*—Rectangular lift gates span horizontally in slots or grooves recessed into the supporting piers. Although these gates may be made of wood or concrete, they are often made of cast iron or fabricated structural steel. The supporting slots or grooves are generally placed vertically, and the gates are raised or lowered by an overhead hoist.

For sliding gates the vertical side members of the gate structure bear directly on support members anchored on the downstream side of the pier slot or groove; sealing is effected by the contact pressure. The size of this type of installation is limited by the relatively powerful hoisting equipment required to operate the gate because of the sliding friction that must be overcome.

(d) *Wheel- or Roller-Mounted Gates.*—Where larger gates are needed, wheels or rollers can be mounted along each side of the rectangular lift gates to make a wheel- or roller-mounted gate. Water loads are carried through the wheels into vertical tracks anchored on the downstream side of the pier slot or groove. The use of wheels greatly reduces the amount of friction and thereby permits operation of the gate with a less powerful hoist.

(e) *Radial Gates.*—Radial gates are usually constructed of structural steel. They consist of a cylindrical segment supported by radial arms and trunnion pins. The center of curvature of the cylindrical segment is usually made coaxial with the common centerline of the trunnion pins so that the entire thrust of the waterload passes directly through the trunnion pins; thus, only a small friction moment need be overcome in raising or lowering the gate. Hoisting loads then consist of only part of the gate weight, friction between side seals and pier walls, frictional moment at the pins, and static pressure head on bottom seal protection. The gate may be counterweighted to partially counterbalance its weight, which further reduces the required capacity of the hoist.

The small hoisting effort needed to operate radial gates makes hand operation practical for small installations that might require power if another type of gate is installed. The hoisting forces involved also make the radial gate more adaptable to operation by a relatively simple automatic control apparatus. Where a number of gates are used on a spillway, they may be automatically controlled to open incrementally at increasing reservoir levels. Or only one or two gates might be equipped with automatic controls, while the remaining gates would be operated by hand or power hoists. Small radial gates that may be hand or motor operated are available commercially.

C. HYDRAULICS OF CONTROL STRUCTURES

9.10. *Shape for Uncontrolled Ogee Crest.*—As discussed in section 9.8(c), crest shapes that approximate the profile of the undernappe of a jet flowing over a sharp-crested weir provide the ideal form for obtaining optimum discharges. The shape of such a profile depends upon the head, the inclination of the upstream face of the overflow section, and the height of the overflow section above the floor of the entrance channel (which influences the velocity of approach to the crest). Crest shapes have been studied extensively in the Bureau of Reclamation hydraulics laboratories, and data from which profiles for overflow crests can be obtained have been published [18]. For most conditions the data can be summarized according to the form shown on figure 9-21(A), where the profile is defined as it relates to axes at the apex of the crest. That portion upstream from the origin is defined as either a single curve and a tangent or as a compound circular curve. The portion downstream is defined by the equation:

$$\frac{y}{H_o} = -K\left(\frac{x}{H_o}\right)^n \qquad (2)$$

in which K and n are constants whose values depend on the upstream inclination and on the velocity of approach. Figure 9-21 gives values of these constants for different conditions.

The approximate profile shape for a crest with a vertical upstream face and negligible velocity of approach is shown on figure 9-22. The profile is constructed in the form of a compound circular curve with radii expressed in terms of the design head, H_o. This definition is simpler than that shown on figure 9-21, because it avoids the need for solving an exponential equation; furthermore, it is represented in a form easily used by a layman for constructing forms or templates. For ordinary design conditions for small spillways where the approach height, P, is equal to or greater than one-half the maximum head on the crest, this profile is sufficiently accurate to avoid seriously reduced crest pressures and does not materially alter the hydraulic efficiency of the crest. When the approach height is less than one-half the maximum head on the crest, the profile should be determined from figure 9-21.

9.11. *Discharge Over an Uncontrolled Overflow Ogee Crest.*—(a) *General.*—The discharge over an ogee crest is given by the equation:

$$Q = CLH_e^{3/2} \qquad (3)$$

where:

Q = discharge,
C = variable discharge coefficient,
L = effective length of crest, and
H_e = actual head being considered on the crest, including velocity of approach head, h_a.

The discharge coefficient, C, is influenced by a number of factors, such as (1) the depth of approach, (2) relation of the actual crest shape to the ideal nappe shape, (3) upstream face slope, (4) downstream apron interference, and (5) downstream submergence. The effect of these various factors is discussed in section 9.12.

The total head on the crest, H_e, does not include allowances for approach channel friction losses or other losses caused by the curvature of the upstream channel, entrance loss into the inlet section, and inlet or transition losses. Where the design of the approach channel results in appreciable losses, they must be added to H_e to determine reservoir elevations corresponding to the discharges given by equation (3).

(b) *Pier and Abutment Effects.*—Where crest piers and abutments are shaped to cause side contractions of the overflow, the effective length, L, is less than the net length of the crest. The effect of the end contraction may be taken into account by reducing the net crest length as follows:

$$L = L' - 2(NK_p + K_a)H_e \qquad (4)$$

where:

L = effective length of crest,
L' = net length of crest,
N = number of piers,
K_p = pier contraction coefficient
K_a = abutment contraction coefficient, and
H_e = actual head on crest.

The pier contraction coefficient, K_p, is affected by the shape and location of the pier nose, the thickness of the pier, the design head, and the approach velocity. For conditions of design head, H_o, average pier contraction coefficients may be assumed as follows:

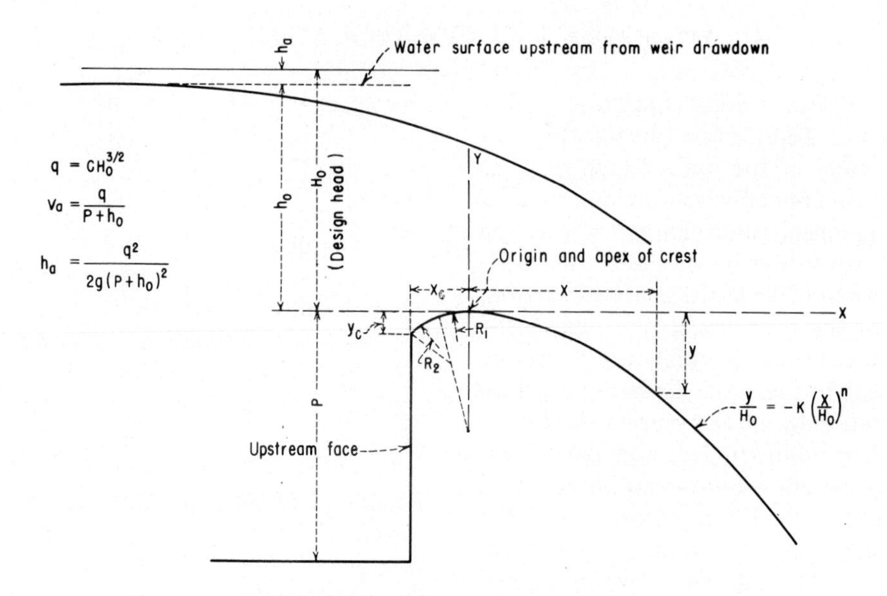

(A) ELEMENTS OF NAPPE-SHAPED CREST PROFILES

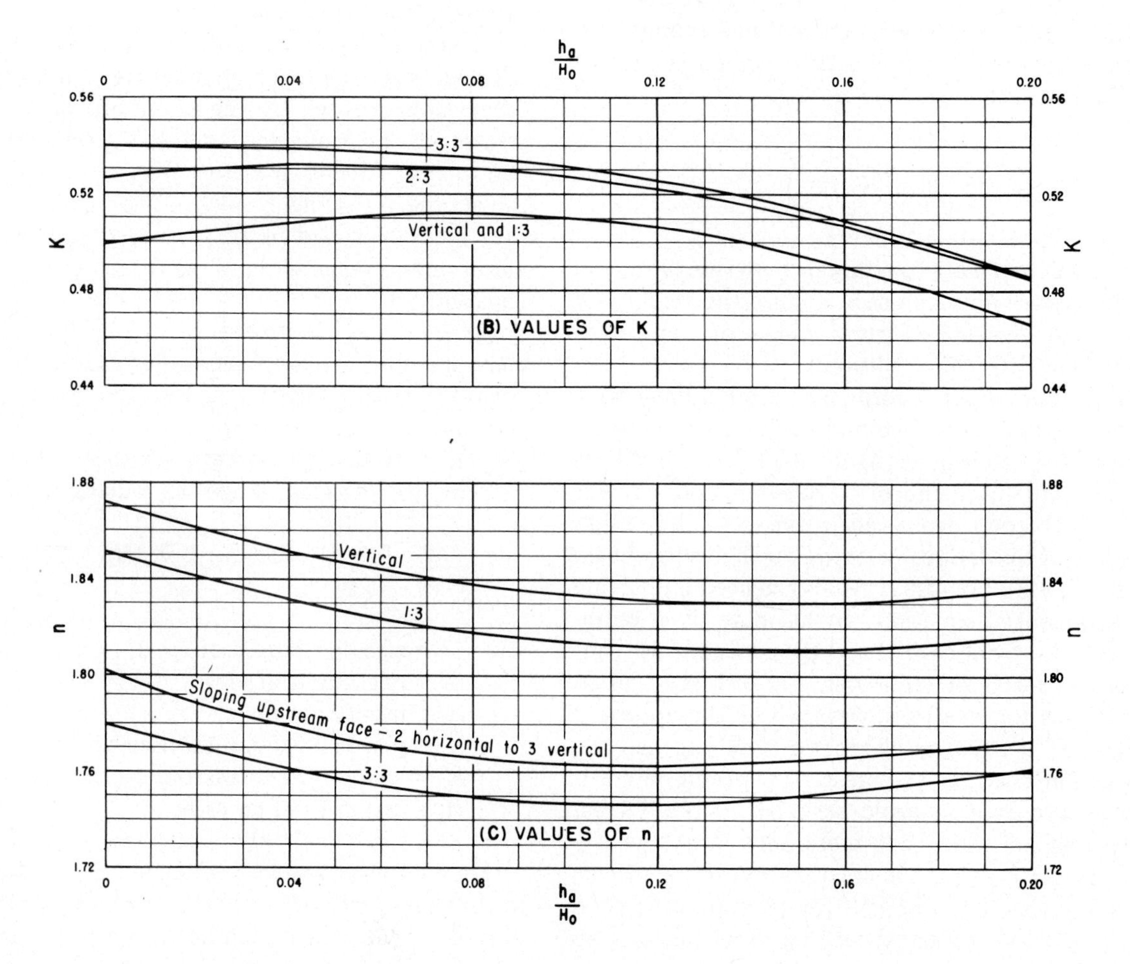

Figure 9-21.—Factors for definition of nappe-shaped crest profiles. 288–D–2406. (Sheet 1 of 2).

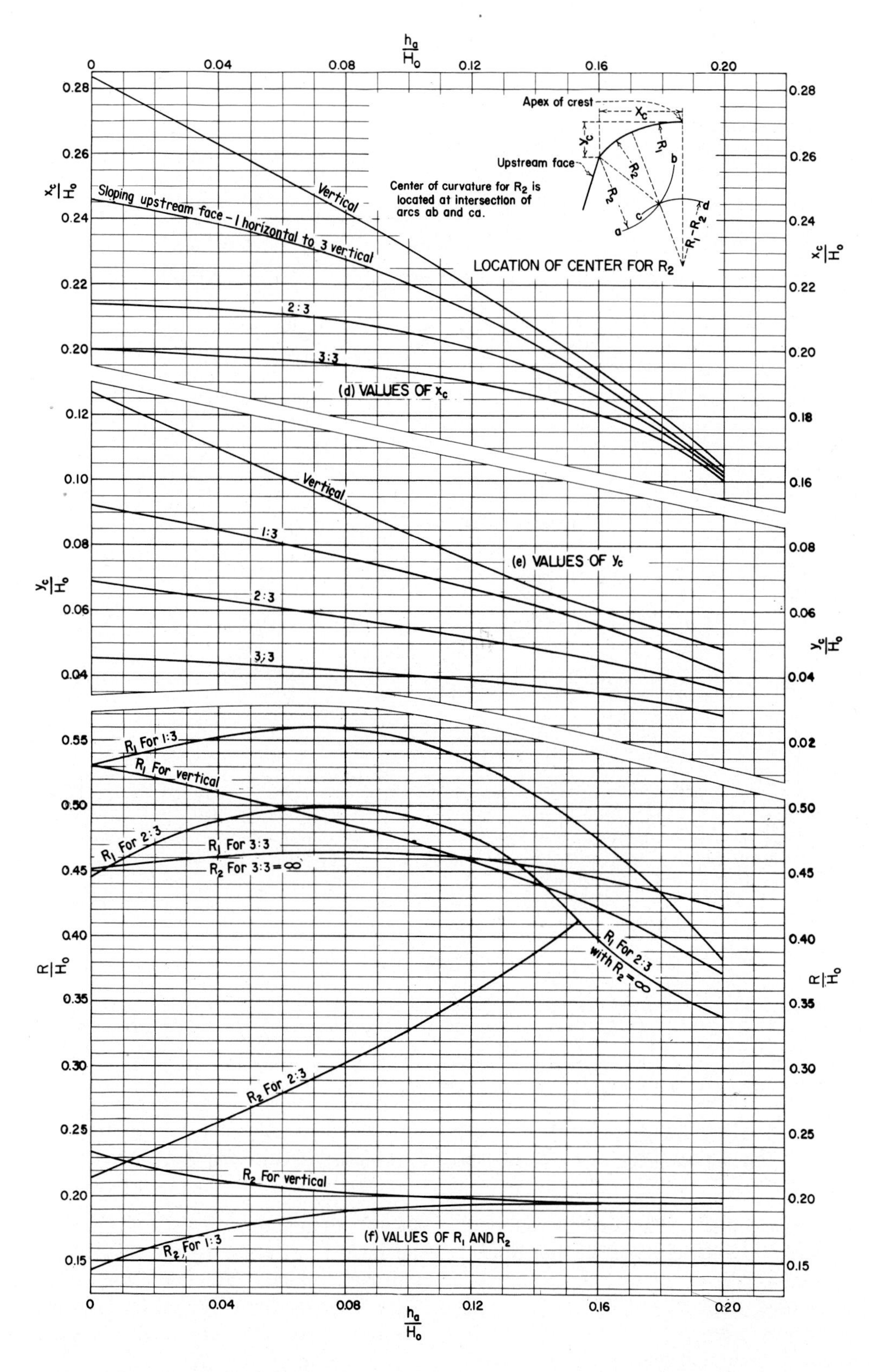

Figure 9-21.—Factors for definition of nappe-shaped crest profiles. 288–D–2407. (Sheet 2 of 2).

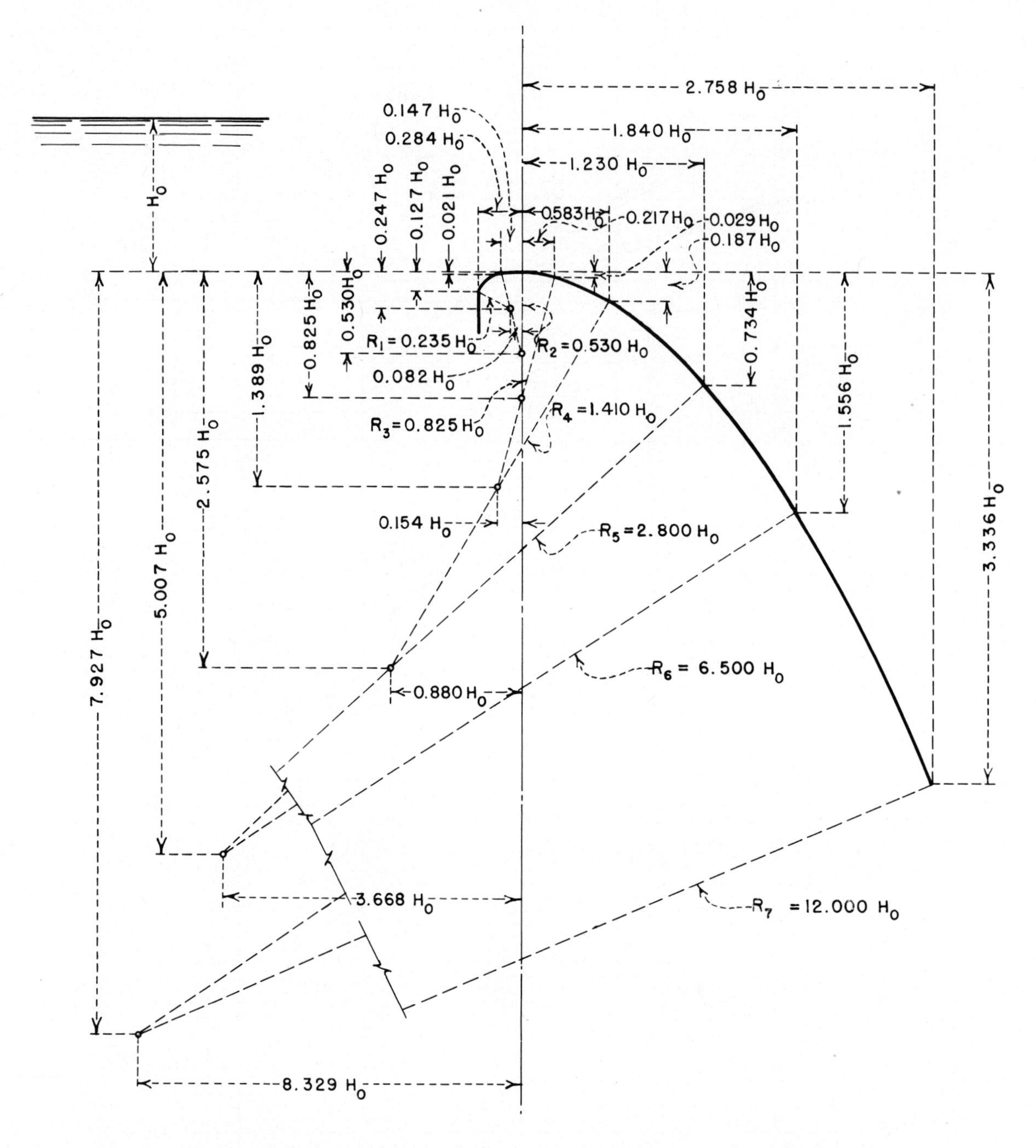

Figure 9-22.—Ogee crest shape defined by compound curves. 288–D–2408.

- For square-nosed piers with corners rounded on a radius equal to about 0.1 of the pier thickness: K_p = 0.02
- For round-nosed piers: K_p = 0.01
- For pointed-nose piers: K_p = 0.0

The abutment contraction coefficient is affected by the shape of the abutment, the angle between the upstream approach wall and the axis of the flow, the head in relation to the design head, and the approach velocity. For conditions of design head, H_o, average coefficients may be assumed as follows:

- For square abutments with headwall at 90° to direction of flow: K_a = 0.20
- For rounded abutments with headwall at 90°

to direction of flow, when $0.5H_o \leq r \leq 0.15H_o$: $K_a = 0.10$

- For rounded abutments where $r > 0.5H_o$ and headwall is placed not more than 45° to direction of flow: $K_a = 0.0$

where r = radius abutment rounding.

9.12. *Discharge Coefficient for Uncontrolled Ogee Crests.*—(a) *Effect of Depth of Approach.*— For a high sharp-crested weir placed in a channel, the velocity of approach is small and the underside of the nappe flowing over the weir attains maximum vertical contraction. As the approach depth is decreased, the velocity of approach increases and the vertical contraction diminishes. For sharp-crested wiers whose heights are not less than about one-fifth the heads producing flow over them, the discharge coefficient remains fairly constant with a value of about 3.3, although the contraction diminishes. For weir heights less than about one-fifth the head, the contraction of the flow becomes increasingly suppressed and the crest coefficient decreases. When the weir height becomes zero, the contraction is entirely suppressed and the overflow weir becomes, in effect, a channel or a broad-crested weir, for which the theoretical discharge coefficient is 3.087. If the sharp-crested weir coefficients are related to the head measured from the point of maximum contraction instead of to the head above the sharp crest, coefficients applicable to ogee crests shaped to profiles of undernappes for various approach velocities can be established. The relationship of the ogee crest coefficient, C_o, to various values of P/H_o is shown on figure 9-23. These coefficients are valid only when the ogee is formed to the ideal nappe shape; that is, when $H_e/H_o = 1$.

(b) *Effect of Heads Different from Design Head.*—When the ogee crest shape is different from the ideal shape or when the crest has been shaped for a head larger or smaller than the one under consideration, the discharge coefficient will differ from that shown on figure 9-23. A wider shape will result in positive pressures along the crest contact surface, thereby reducing the discharge. With a narrower crest shape, negative pressures along the contact surface will occur, resulting in an increased discharge. Figure 9-24 shows the variation of the coefficient as related to values of H_e/H_o, where H_e is the actual head being considered.

An approximate discharge coefficient for an irregularly shaped crest whose profile has not been formed according to the undernappe of the overflow jet can be estimated by finding the ideal shape that most nearly matches it. The design head, H_o, corresponding to the matching shape can then be used as a basis for determining the coefficients [19].

The coefficients for partial heads on the crest, for preparing a discharge-head relationship, can be determined from figure 9-24.

(c) *Effect of Upstream Face Slope.*—For small ratios of the approach depth to the head on the crest, sloping the upstream face of the overflow results in an increase in the discharge coefficient. For large ratios the effect is a decrease in the coefficient. Within the range considered in this text, the discharge coefficient is reduced for large ratios of P/H_o only for relatively flat upstream slopes. Figure 9-25 shows the ratio for the coefficient for an overflow ogee crest with a sloping (inclined) face, C_i, to the coefficient for a crest with a vertical upstream face, C_v, as obtained from figure 9-23 (and as adjusted by figure 9-24 if appropriate), as related to values of P/H_o.

(d) *Effect of Downstream Apron Interference and Downstream Submergence.*—When the water level below an overflow weir is high enough to affect the discharge, the weir is said to be submerged. The vertical distance from the crest of the overflow to the downstream apron and the depth of flow in the downstream channel, as it relates to the head pool level, are factors that alter the discharge coefficient.

Five distinct characteristic flows can occur below an overflow crest, depending on the relative positions of the apron and the downstream water surface: (1) flow can continue at supercritical stage; (2) a partial or incomplete hydraulic jump can occur immediately downstream from the crest; (3) a true hydraulic jump can occur; (4) a drowned jump can occur in which the high-velocity jet will follow the face of the overflow and then continue in an erratic and fluctuating path for a considerable distance under and through the slower water; and (5) no jump may occur—the jet will break away from the face of the overflow and ride along the surface for a short distance and then erratically intermingle with the slow moving water underneath. Figure 9-26 shows the relationship of the floor positions and downstream submergences that produce these distinctive flows.

Where the downstream flow is at supercritical stage or where the hydraulic jump occurs, the decrease in the discharge coefficient is principally caused by the back-pressure effect of the downstream apron and is independent of any submergence effect from the tailwater. Figure 9-27 shows the effect of downstream apron conditions on the discharge coefficient. It should be noted that this curve plots, in a slightly different form, the same data represented by the vertical dashed lines on figure 9-26. As the downstream apron level nears the crest of the overflow, $(h_d + d)/H_e$ approaches 1.0, and the discharge coefficient is about 77 percent of the coefficient for unretarded flow. On the basis of a coefficient of 4.0 for unretarded flow over a high weir, the coefficient when the weir is submerged will be about 3.08, which is virtually the coefficient for a broad-crested weir.

From figure 9-26, it can be seen that when $(h_d + d)/H_e$ exceeds about 1.7, the downstream floor position has little effect on the coefficient, but there is a decrease in the coefficient caused by tailwater submergence. Figure 9-28 shows the ratio of the discharge coefficient where affected by tailwater conditions to the coefficient for free flow conditions. This curve plots, in a slightly different form, the data represented by the horizontal dashed lines on figure 9-26. Where the dashed lines on figure 9-26 are curved, the decrease in the coefficient is the result of a combination of tailwater effects and downstream apron position.

9.13. *Examples of Designs of Uncontrolled Ogee Crests.*—The two examples cited below illustrate the methods of designing uncontrolled ogee crests, including the computation of approach channel losses and velocity head, the determination of the total length of the crest, and the correction of the discharge coefficient for various effects.

(a) *Example 1.*—Design an uncontrolled overflow ogee crest for a chute spillway that will discharge 2,000 ft³/s at a 5-foot head, and prepare a discharge-head curve. The upstream face of the

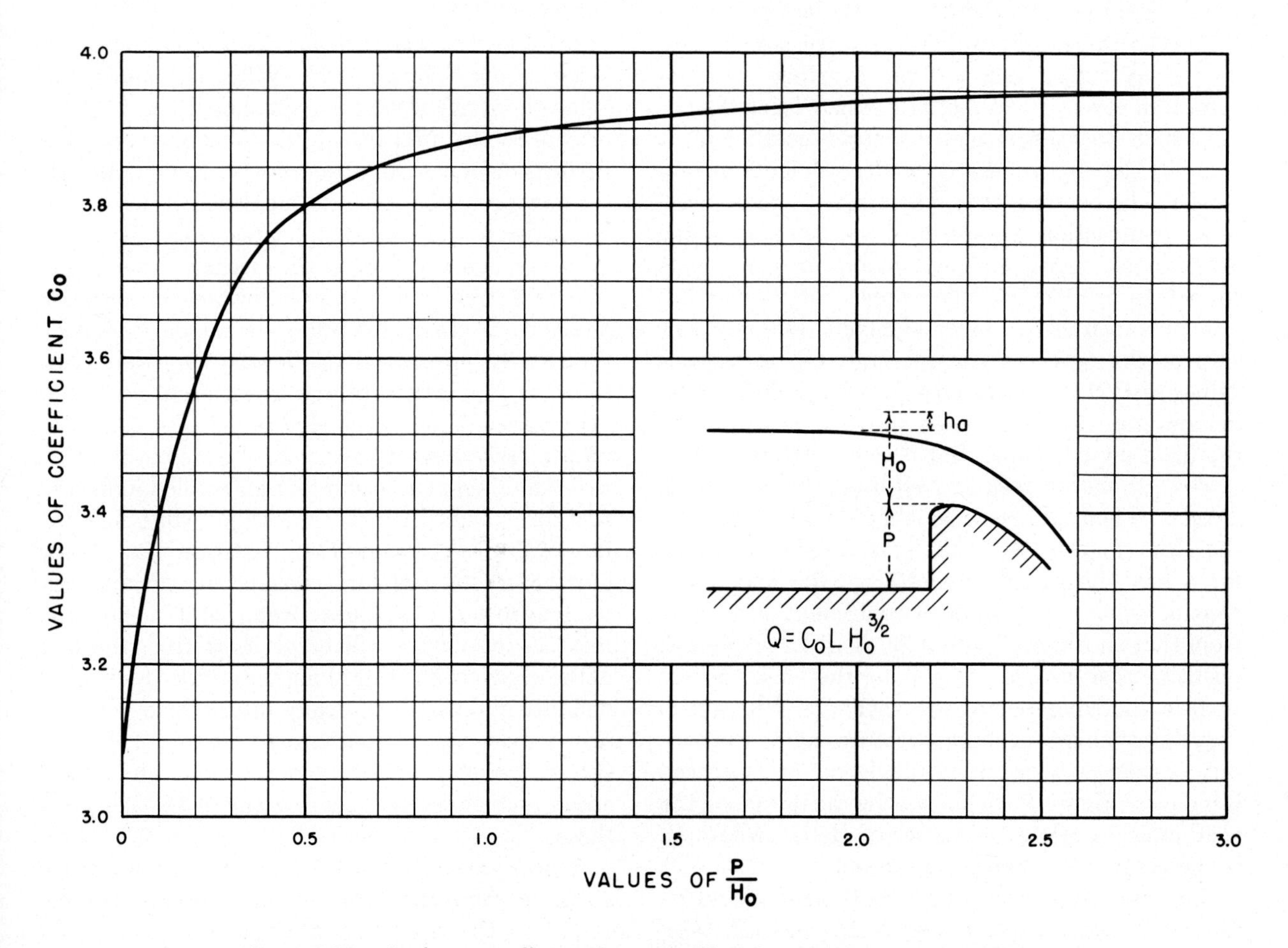

Figure 9-23.—Discharge coefficients for vertical-faced ogee crest. 288-D-2409.

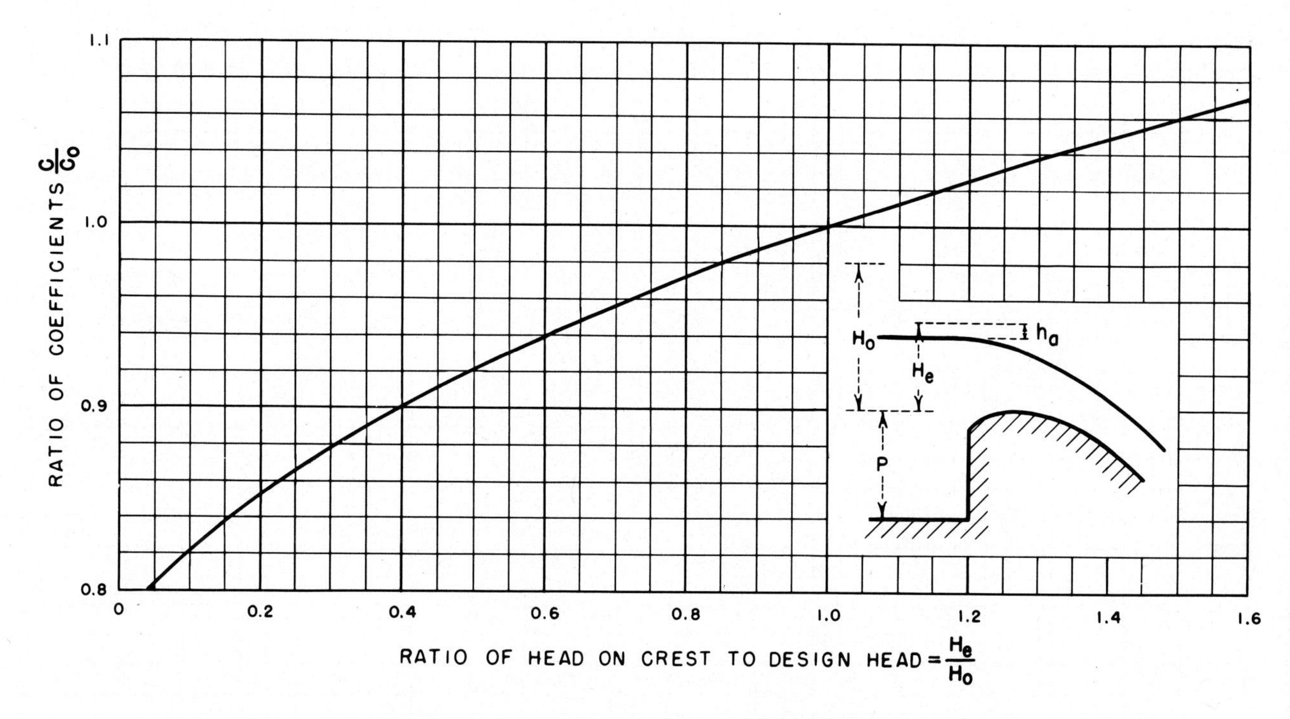

Figure 9-24.—Discharge coefficients for other than the design head. 288-D-2410.

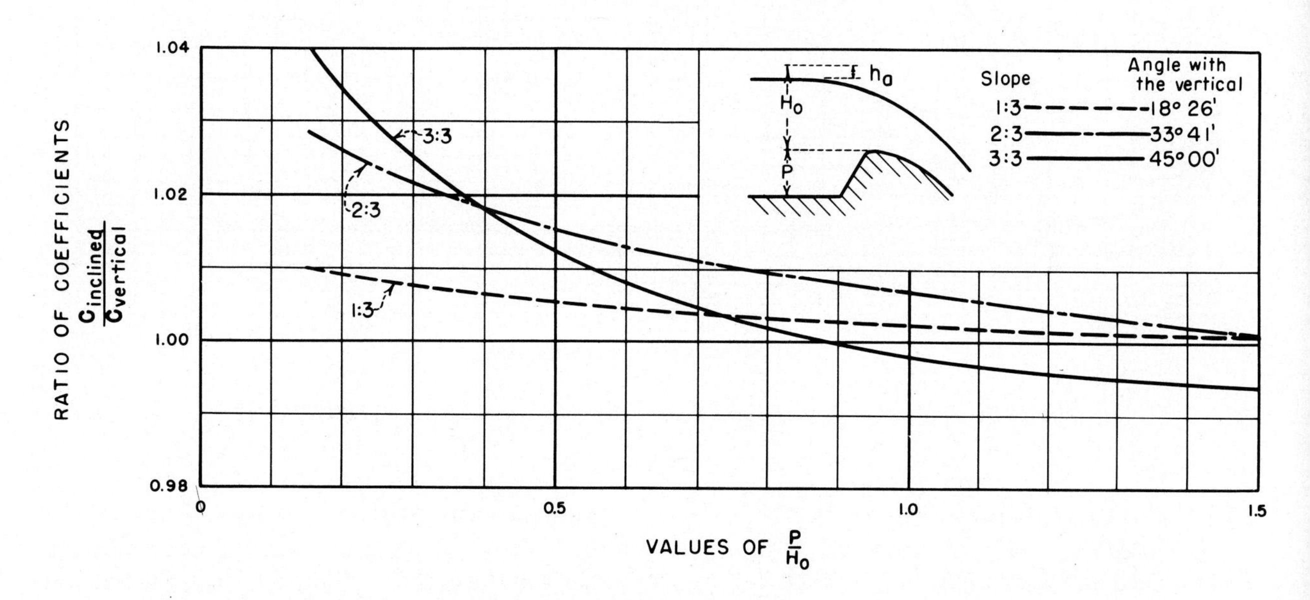

Figure 9-25.—Discharge coefficients for ogee-shaped crest with sloping upstream face. 288-D-2411.

crest is sloped 1:1, and the entrance channel is 100 feet long. A bridge is to span the crest, and 18-inch-wide bridge piers with rounded noses are to be provided. The bridge spans are not to exceed 20 feet. The abutment walls are rounded to a 5-foot radius, and the approach walls are to be placed at 30° with the centerline of the spillway entrance.

To solve the problem, either the approach depth and apron position with respect to the crest must be selected and the appropriate coefficient determined, or an arbitrary coefficient must be selected and the appropriate dimensions determined. The

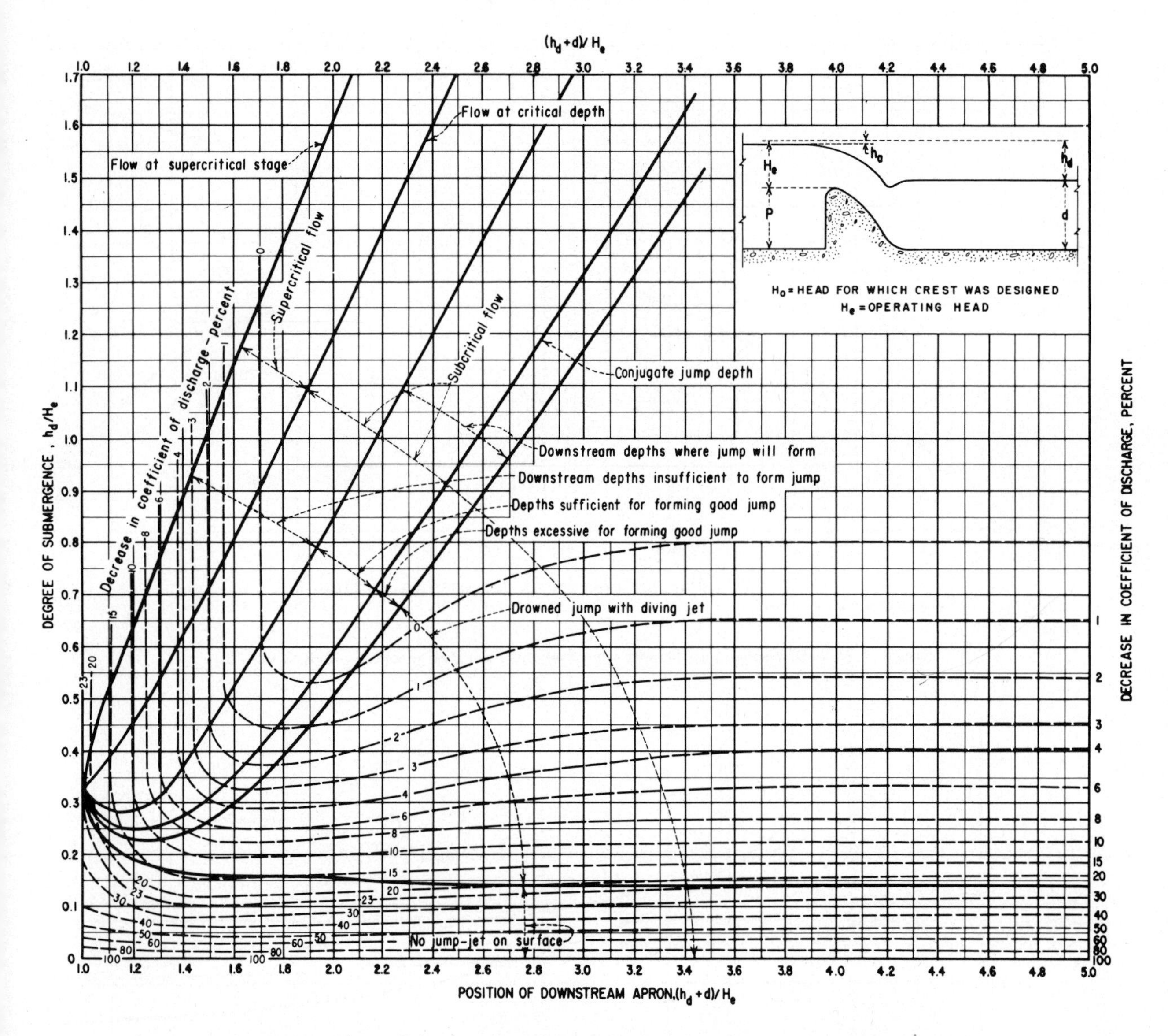

Figure 9-26.—Effects of downstream influences on flow over weir crests. 288–D–2412.

solutions will show both procedures.

(1) *Procedure 1.*—First, assume the position of the approach and downstream apron levels with respect to the crest level, say 2 feet below crest level. Then $H_e + P$ is approximately 7 feet.

To evaluate the approach channel losses, assume a value of C to obtain an approximate approach velocity, say $C = 3.7$. Then the discharge per unit of crest length, q, is equal to $CH_e^{3/2} = 3.7 \times 5^{3/2} = 41$ ft³/s. Therefore, the velocity of approach $v_a = q/(H_e + P) = 41/7 = 5.9$ ft/s, and the approach velocity head, $h_a = v_a^2/2g = 5.9^2/64.4 = 0.5$ feet.

Assuming the friction coefficient in Manning's formula $n = 0.0225$, and assuming the hydraulic radius r = the depth of approach, then the friction slope is equal to:

$$s = \left(\frac{v_a n}{1.486 r^{2/3}}\right)^2 = \left(\frac{5.9 \times 0.0225}{1.486 \times 7^{2/3}}\right)^2 = 0.0006$$

Therefore, the total approach channel friction loss, $h_f = 100\ (0.0006) = 0.06$ feet. Assuming an entrance loss into the approach channel equal to $0.1h_a$, the total loss of head in the approach is approximately $0.06 + (0.1 \times 0.5) = 0.11$ feet.

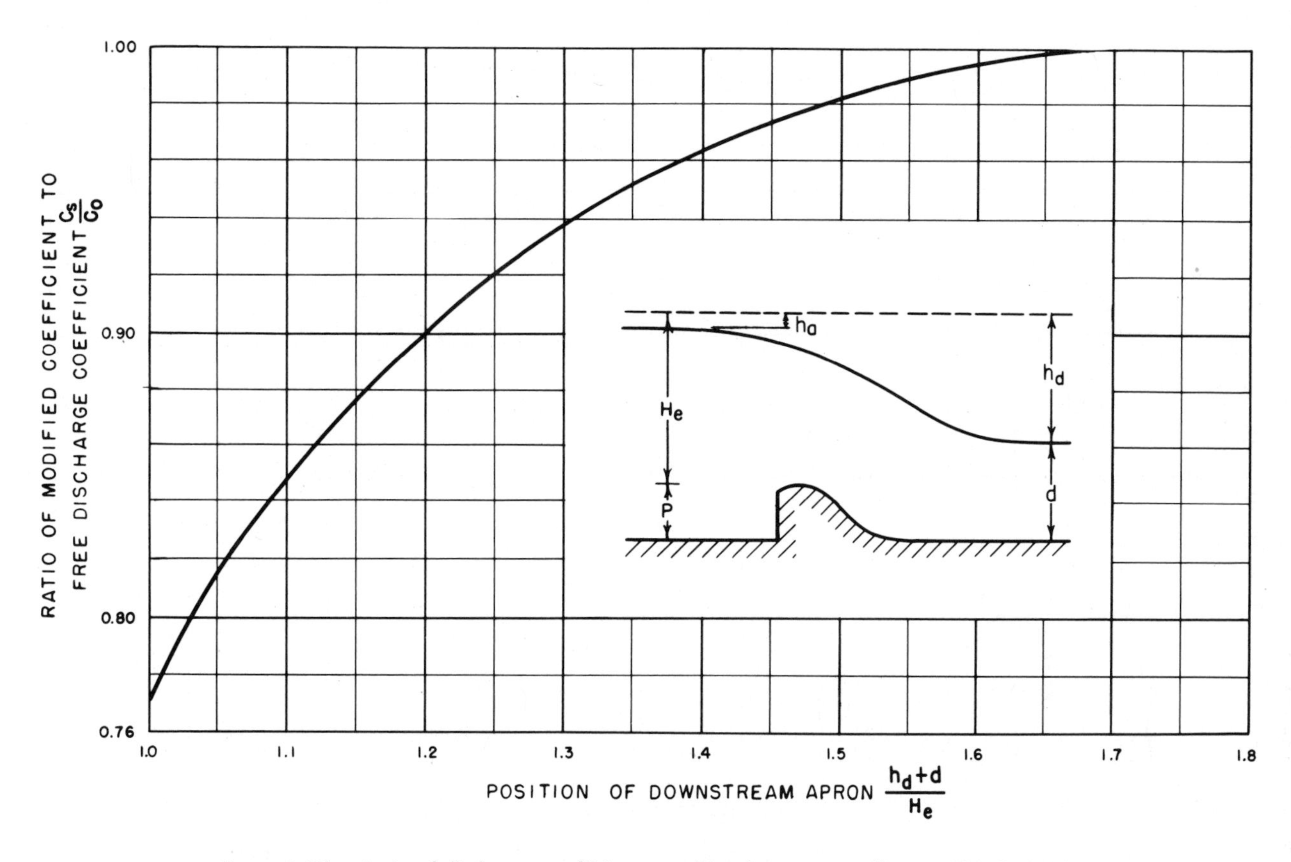

Figure 9-27.—Ratio of discharge coefficients resulting from apron effects. 288–D–2413.

The effective head, $H_o = 5.0 - 0.11 = 4.89$ feet, and $P/H_o = 2/4.89 = 0.41$. From figure 9-23, if $P/H_o = 0.41$, then $C_o = 3.77$.

Figure 9-25 is used to correct the discharge coefficient for the inclined upstream slope. For a 1:1 slope and $P/H_o = 0.41$, $C_i/C_v = 1.018$. Then, $C_4 = 1.018(3.77) = 3.84$.

Next, the relationships $(h_d + d)/H_e$ and h_d/H_e are evaluated to determine the downstream effects. The value of $(h_d + d)/H_e$ is approximately 6.89/4.89 = 1.41. From figure 9-26, for $(h_d + d)/H_e = 1.41$, h_d/H_e at supercritical flow = 0.91. If supercritical flow prevails, h_d should be equal to $0.91H_e = 0.91(4.89) = 4.44$, and d should be 6.89 − 4.44 = 2.45 feet. With the indicated unit discharge of approximately 41 ft³/s, the downstream velocity will be approximately 41/2.45 = 16.7 ft/s, and the velocity head, $h_v = 16.7^2/64.4 = 4.3$ feet. The closeness of h_d and h_v verifies that the flow is supercritical. From figure 9-26, it can be seen that the downstream effect is caused by apron influences only, and that the corrections shown on figure 9-27 will apply. The ratio of the modified C_s to the coefficient C_o for a downstream apron position determined by the $(h_d + d)/H_e$ ratio of 1.41 is 96.6 percent. The coefficient has now been corrected for all influencing effects.

The next step is to determine the required crest length. For the design head $H_o = 4.89$ feet, the required effective crest length is:

$$L = \frac{Q}{CH_o^{3/2}} = \frac{2,000}{3.71(4.89)^{3/2}} = 49.9 \text{ feet}$$

To correct for pier effects, the net length from equation (4) is:

$$L' = L + [2(NK_p + K_a)H_e]$$

If the bridge spans are not to exceed 20 feet, two piers will be required for the approximately 50-foot total span; therefore, $N = 2$. Therefore:

$$L' = 49.9 + [2(2[0.01] + 0)4.89 = 50.1 \text{ feet}$$

The foregoing procedure establishes a discharge coefficient for the design head. For computing a

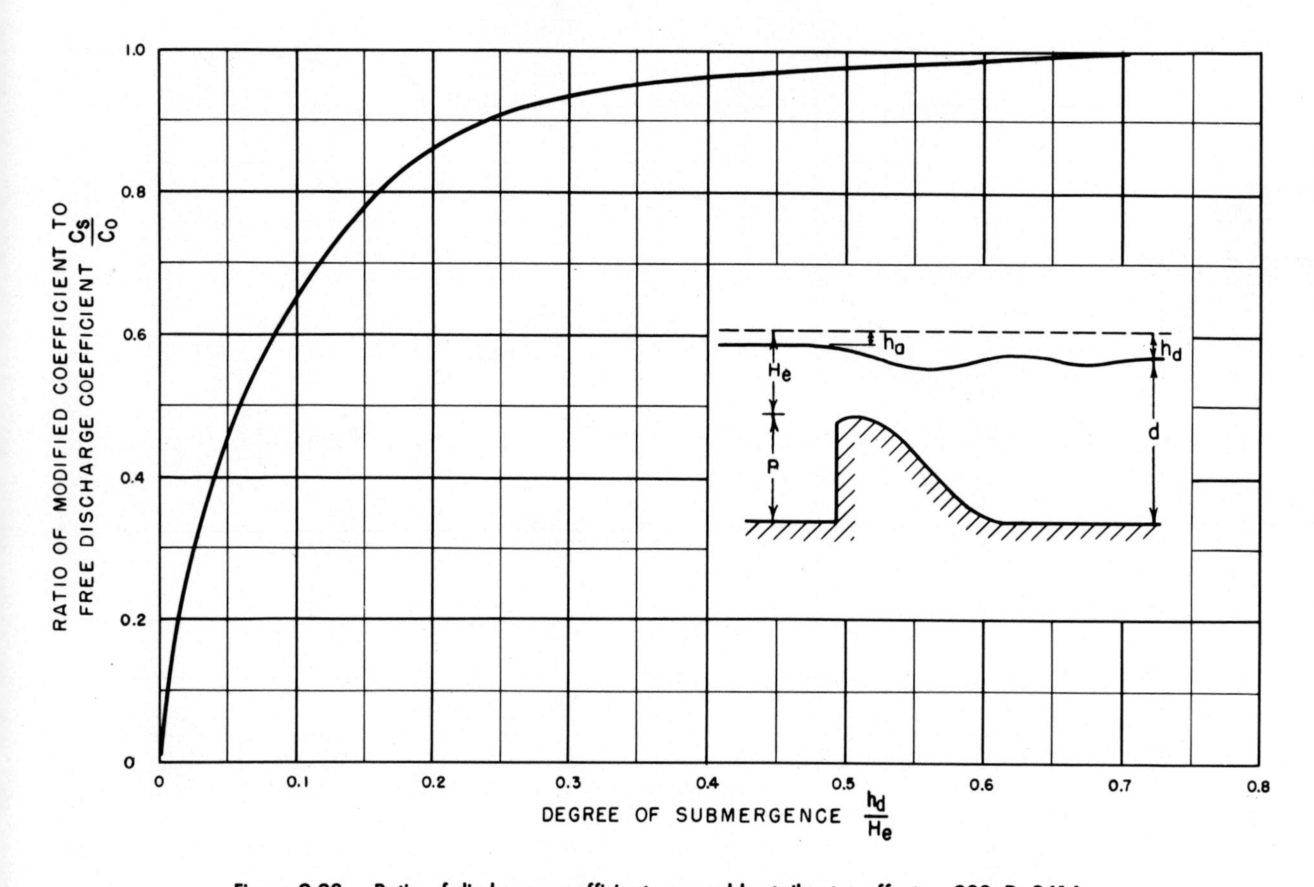

Figure 9-28.—Ratio of discharge coefficients caused by tailwater effects. 288-D-2414.

rating curve, coefficients for lesser heads must be obtained. Because the variations of the different corrections are not consistent, the procedure for correcting the coefficients must be repeated for each lesser head. The variables can be tabulated in a form similar to that used in table 9-2.

(2) *Procedure 2.*—First, assume an overall discharge coefficient, say 3.5. The discharge per unit length, q, is then equal to $3.5H_e^{3/2}$ = 39.2 ft³/s for H_e = 5 feet. Then the required effective length of the crest, L, is equal to Q/q = 2,000/39.2 = 51 feet.

Next, the approach depth is approximated from figure 9-23; for C = 3.5, P/H_o is approximately 0.2. Thus, the approach depth cannot be less than 1 foot. To allow for other factors that may reduce the coefficient, an approach depth of about 2 feet might reasonably be assumed.

With a 2-foot approach depth, the computation for approach losses is the same as in the procedure 1 solution, and the effective head H_o = 4.89 feet. Similarly, C_i = 3.84.

Because the overall coefficient of 3.5 was assumed for the 5-foot gross head, the corresponding coefficient, C_o, for the 4.89-foot effective head can be calculated from the equation $C_o/C_g = H_g^{3/2}/H_e^{3/2}$; where the subscript g refers to gross head. Therefore, $C_o = C_g\,(H_g/H_e)^{3/2} = 3.5(5.0/4.89)^{3/2} = 1.035(3.5) = 3.62$.

Therefore, submergence ratio C_s/C_o = 3.62/3.84 = 0.94, and from figure 9-27, $(h_d + d)/H_e$ = 1.3. Thus, $h_d + d$ = 1.3(4.89) = 6.4 feet. The downstream apron should therefore be placed 1.4 feet below the crest level.

Because it was demonstrated previously that pier and contraction effects are small, they can be neglected in this example, and the net crest length is, therefore, 51 feet. This crest length and downstream apron position can be varied by altering the assumptions of overall coefficient and approach depth.

The discharge rating curve may be developed by a process similar to that used in procedure 1.

(b) *Example 2.*—Design an uncontrolled overflow crest for a diversion dam to pass 2,000 ft³/s

Table 9-2.—Design of an uncontrolled overflow ogee crest. Example 1, procedure 1; given L=50 feet[1], H_o=4.89 feet, and P=2 feet.

$\frac{H_e}{H_o}$	H_e, feet	$\frac{C}{C_o}$ [2]	C_i	h_d+d	$\frac{h_d+d}{H_e}$	$\frac{C_s}{C}$ [4]	C_s	$C_sH_e^{3/2}$	H_e+P	v_a (approx.)	h_a	s	Entrance loss, 0.1 h_a	Total approach losses, feet	Gross head, feet	Total discharge, ($Q = C_sLH_e^{3/2}$), ft³/s
0.1	0.49	0.82	3.15	2.49	5.08	1.00	3.15	1.1	2.49	0.44	0.003	0.00001	0.00	0.00	0.49	55
.2	.98	.85	3.26	2.98	3.04	1.00	3.26	3.2	2.98	1.07	.02	.00006	.00	0.1	.99	160
.4	1.96	.90	3.46	3.96	2.02	1.00	3.46	9.5	3.96	2.40	.09	.0002	.01	.03	1.99	475
.6	2.93	.94	3.61	4.93	1.68	1.00	3.61	18.1	4.93	3.67	.21	.0004	.02	.06	2.99	905
.8	3.91	.97	3.73	5.91	1.51	0.982	3.66	28.3	5.91	4.79	.36	.0005	.04	.09	4.00	1,415
1.0	4.89	1.0	[3]3.84	6.89	1.41	.966	3.71	40.0	6.89	5.80	.52	.0006	.05	.11	5.00	2,000
1.2	5.87	1.03	3.96	7.87	1.34	.95	3.76	53.5	7.87	6.80	.72	.0007	.07	.14	6.01	2,675

[1]The effective crest length and the net crest length for H_o are 49.9 feet and 50.1 feet, respectively. Because of the small magnitude of the pier effects, an average length of 50 feet is taken for the effective crest length for all values of H_e. If the pier effects are significant, separate effective crest lengths should be computed for each H_e value.
[2]From fig. 9-24.
[3]C_i for H_o.
[4]From fig. 9-27.

with a depth of flow upstream from the dam not exceeding 5 feet above the crest. The overflow dam is 8 feet high. The abutment headwall is 90° to the direction of flow, and the edge adjacent to the crest is rounded to a 12-inch radius. For 2,000 ft³/s flow, the tailwater will rise 3.5 feet above the crest.

For an approximate head, H_e, of 5 feet, a crest height of 8 feet, and a crest submergence of 3.5 feet, $(h_d + d)/H_e = 13/5 = 2.6$, and $h_d/H_e = 1.5/5 = 0.3$. Figure 9-26 shows that for these relations the downstream flow phenomena will be that of a drowned jump and that the coefficient will be reduced 6 percent.

Roughly, $P/H_o = 8/5 = 1.6$, and the unretarded coefficient from figure 9-23 is 3.93. Reducing this by 6 percent because of submergence results in an approximate coefficient of 3.7.

The approximate discharge per foot of crest $q = CH_o^{3/2} = 3.7(5)^{3/2} = 41.5$ ft³/s. Therefore, the velocity of approach $v_a = 41.5/13 = 3.2$ ft/s, and the approach velocity head $h_a = 0.16$ feet. $H_o = 5.0 + 0.16 = 5.16$ feet.

The revised value of P/H_o does not appreciably alter the coefficient obtained from figure 9-23. The revised value of $(h_d + d)/H_o = 13.16/5.16 = 2.55$, and the revised value of $h_d/H_o = 1.66/5.16 = 0.32$. The reduction in coefficient caused by submergence effects from figure 9-26 is 5 percent. The revised discharge coefficient, C, is 95 percent of 3.93 = 3.73.

The effective crest length L equals $Q/CH_o^{3/2} = 2{,}000/3.73(5.16)^{3/2} = 45.7$ feet.

The net crest length is determined by using equation (4). Without piers the net crest length $L' = L + 2K_aH_e$. For 90° abutment walls rounded to a radius larger than $0.15H_o$, $K_a = 0.10$. Therefore, the net crest length, $L' = 45.7 + 2[0.10(5.16)] = 46.7$ feet.

9.14. Uncontrolled Ogee Crests Designed for Less than Maximum Head.—Economy in the design of an ogee crest may sometimes be effected by using a design head that is less than the maximum expected head. As discussed previously, use of a smaller design head results in increased discharges for the full range of heads. The increase in capacity makes it possible to achieve economy by reducing either the crest length or the maximum surcharge head.

Tests have shown that the subatmospheric pressures on a nappe-shaped crest do not exceed about one-half the design head when the design head is not less than about 75 percent of the maximum head. For most conditions in the design of spillways, these negative pressures will be small, and they can be tolerated because they will not approach absolute pressures that can induce cavitation. Care must be taken, however, in forming the surface of the crest where these negative pressures will occur, because unevenness caused by abrupt offsets, depressions, or projections will amplify the negative pressures to a magnitude where cavitation conditions can develop.

The negative pressure on the crest may be resolved into a system of forces acting both upward and downstream. These forces should be considered in analyzing the structural stability of the crest structure.

An approximate force diagram of the subatmospheric pressures when the design head used to determine the crest shape is 75 percent of the maximum head is shown on figure 9-29. These data are based on average results of tests made on ideally shaped weirs with negligible approach velocities. Pressures for intermediate head ratios can be assumed to vary linearly, considering that no subatmospheric pressure prevails when $H_o/H_e = 1$.

9.15. *Gate-Controlled Ogee Crests.*—Releases for partial gate openings for gated crests occur as orifice flow. With full head on a gate that is opened a small amount, a free discharging trajectory will follow the path of a jet issuing from an orifice. For a vertical orifice the path of the jet can be expressed by the parabolic equation:

$$-y = \frac{x^2}{4H} \qquad (5)$$

where H is the head on the center of the opening. For an orifice inclined an angle θ from the vertical, the equation is:

$$-y = x \tan \theta + \frac{x^2}{4H \cos^2 \theta} \qquad (6)$$

If subatmospheric pressures are to be avoided along the crest contact, the shape of the ogee downstream from the gate sill must conform to the trajectory profile.

Gates operated with small openings under high heads produce negative pressures along the crest in the region immediately below the gate if the ogee profile drops below the trajectory profile. Tests showed the subatmospheric pressures would be equal to about one-tenth of the design head when the gate is operated at small openings and the ogee is shaped to the ideal nappe profile, equation (2), for maximum head H_o. The force diagram for this condition is shown on figure 9-30.

The adoption of a trajectory profile rather than a nappe profile downstream from the gate sill will result in a wider ogee, and reduced discharge efficiency for full gate opening. Where the discharge efficiency is unimportant and where a wider ogee shape is needed for structural stability, the trajectory profile may be adopted to avoid subatmospheric pressure zones along the crest. Where the ogee is shaped to the ideal nappe profile for maximum head, the subatmospheric pressure area can be minimized by placing the gate sill downstream from the crest of the ogee. This will provide an orifice that is inclined downstream for small gate openings and will result in a steeper trajectory closer to the nappe-shaped profile.

9.16. *Discharge Over Gate-Controlled Ogee Crests.*—The discharge for a gated ogee crest at partial gate openings will be similar to flow through an orifice and may be computed by the equation:

$$Q = CDL \sqrt{2gH} \qquad (7)$$

where:

H = head to the center of the gate opening (including the velocity head of approach),
D = shortest distance from the gate lip to the crest curve, and
L = crest width.

The coefficient, C, is primarily dependent upon the characteristics of the flow lines approaching and leaving the orifice. In turn, these flow lines are dependent on the shape of the crest and the type of gate. Figure 9-31, which shows coefficients of discharge for orifice flows for different θ angles, can be used for leaf gates or radial gates located at the crest or downstream of the crest. The θ angle for a particular opening is that angle formed by the tangent to the gate lip and the tangent to the crest curve at the nearest point of the crest curve for radial gates. This angle is affected by the gate radius and the location of the trunnion pin. For additional information and geometric computations see [20].

9.17. *Side Channel Spillways.*—(a) *General.*—The theory of flow in a side channel spillway [21] is based principally on the law of conservation of linear momentum, assuming that the only forces producing motion in the channel result from the fall in the water surface in the direction of the axis. This premise assumes that the entire energy of the flow over the crest is dissipated through its intermingling with the channel flow and is therefore of

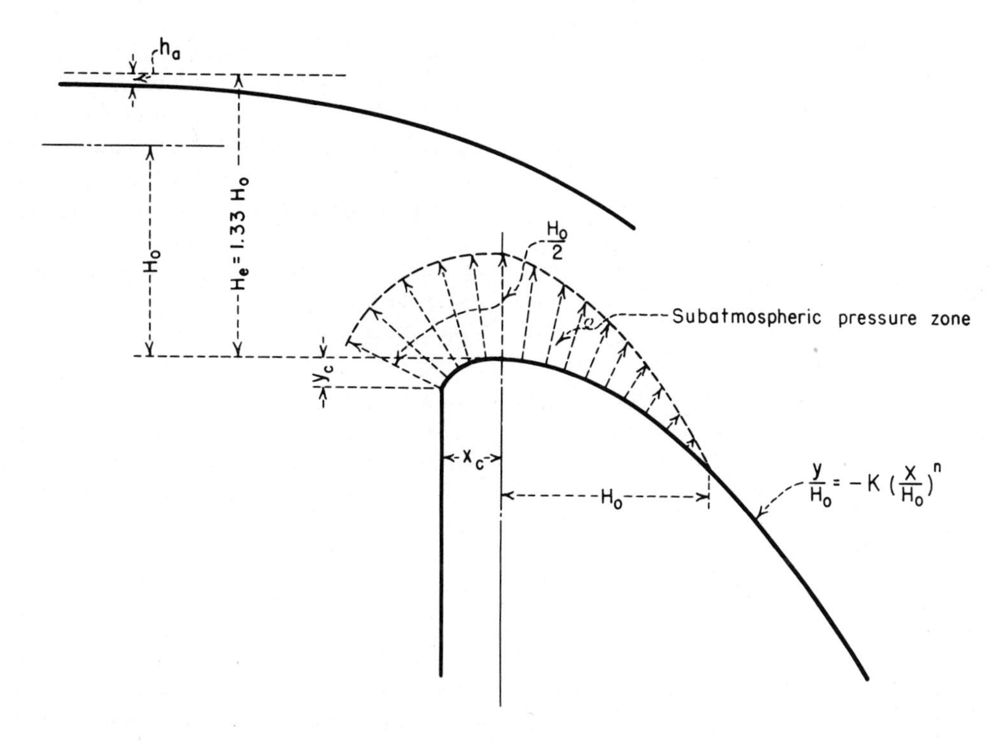

Figure 9-29.—Subatmospheric crest pressures for H_o/H_e = 0.75. 288–D–2415.

no assistance in moving the water along the channel. Axial velocity is produced only after the incoming water particles join the channel stream.

For any short reach of the side channel, the momentum at the beginning of the reach plus any increase in momentum from external forces must equal the momentum at the end of the reach. If a short reach, Δx in length, is considered and the velocity and discharge at the upstream section are v and Q, respectively, then the velocity and discharge at the downstream section will be $v + \Delta v$ and $Q + q(\Delta x)$, where q is the inflow per foot of length of weir crest. Therefore, the momentum[2] at the upstream section will be:

$$M_u = \frac{Qv}{g} \tag{8}$$

And the momentum at the downstream section will be:

$$M_d = \frac{[Q + q(\Delta x)]}{g}(v + \Delta v) \tag{9}$$

[2]The weight of 1 ft³ of water is taken as a unit force to eliminate the necessity of multiplying all forces and momenta by 62.4 to convert them into pounds.

Subtracting equation (8) from equation (9):

$$\Delta M = \frac{Q(\Delta v)}{g} + \frac{q(\Delta x)}{g}(v + \Delta v) \tag{10}$$

Dividing by Δx:

$$\frac{\Delta M}{\Delta x} = \frac{Q(\Delta v)}{g(\Delta x)} + \frac{q}{g}(v + \Delta v) \tag{11}$$

Since the rate of change of momentum with respect to time is v times the rate of change with respect to x, and considering the average velocity = $v+(\Delta v/2)$, equation (11) can be written:

$$\frac{\Delta M}{\Delta t} = \frac{Q(\Delta v)}{g(\Delta x)}\left[v + \frac{1}{2}(\Delta v)\right] + \frac{q}{g}(v + \Delta v)\left[v + \frac{1}{2}(\Delta v)\right] \tag{12}$$

Since $\Delta M/\Delta t$ is the accelerating force, which is equal to the slope of the water surface, $\Delta y/\Delta x$, times the average discharge, equation (12) becomes:

$$\frac{\Delta y}{\Delta x}\left[Q + \frac{1}{2}(\Delta Q)\right] = \frac{Q(\Delta v)}{g(\Delta x)}\left[v + \frac{1}{2}(\Delta v)\right]$$

$$+ \frac{q}{g}(v + \Delta v)\left[v + \frac{1}{2}(\Delta v)\right] \qquad (13)$$

from which the change in water surface elevation is:

$$\Delta y = \frac{Q\left[v + \frac{1}{2}(\Delta v)\right]}{g\left[Q + \frac{1}{2}(\Delta Q)\right]}\left[\Delta v + \frac{q(\Delta x)}{Q}(v + \Delta v)\right] \qquad (14)$$

If Q_1 and v_1 are values at the beginning of the reach, and Q_2 and v_2 are the values at the end of the reach, the equation can be written:

$$\Delta y = \frac{Q_1}{g}\frac{(v_1+v_2)}{(Q_1+Q_2)}\left[(v_2-v_1) + \frac{v_2(Q_2-Q_1)}{Q_1}\right] \qquad (15)$$

Similarly, the derivation can be developed so that:

$$\Delta y = \frac{Q_2}{g}\frac{(v_1+v_2)}{(Q_1+Q_2)}\left[(v_2-v_1) + \frac{v_1(Q_2-Q_1)}{Q_2}\right] \qquad (16)$$

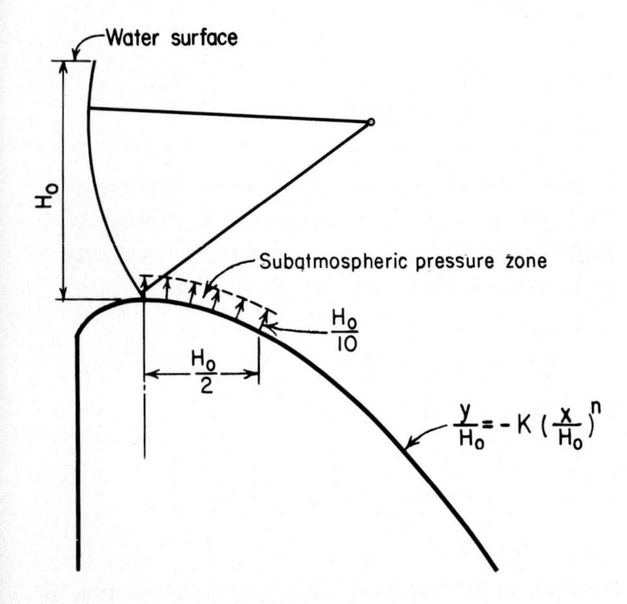

Figure 9-30.—Subatmospheric crest pressures for undershot gate flow. 288-D-2416.

By use of equation (15) or (16), the water surface profile can be determined for any particular side channel by assuming successive short reaches of channel once a starting point is found. The solution of equation (15) or (16) is obtained by a trial-and-error procedure. For a reach of length Δx in a specific location, Q_1 and Q_2 will be known. If the depth at one end of the reach has been established, a trial depth at the other end of the reach can be found that will satisfy the indicated and computed values of Δy.

As in other water surface profile determinations, the depth of flow and the hydraulic characteristics of the flow will be affected by backwater influences from some control point or by critical conditions along the reach of the channel under consideration. The selection of a control for starting the water surface profile computations is treated in the subsequent discussion.

When the bottom of the side channel trough is selected so that its depth below the hydraulic gradient is greater than the minimum specific energy depth, flow will be either at the subcritical or supercritical stage, depending either on the relation of the bottom profile to critical slope or on the influences of a downstream control section. If the slope of the bottom is greater than critical and a control section is not established below the side channel trough, supercritical flow will prevail throughout the length of the channel. For this stage, velocities will be high and water depths will be shallow, resulting in a relatively high fall from the reservoir water level to the water surface in the trough. This flow condition is illustrated by profile B′ on figure 9-32. Conversely, if a control section is established downstream from the side channel trough to increase the upstream depths, the channel can be made to flow at the subcritical stage. Velocities at this stage will be less than critical, and the greater depths will result in a smaller drop from the reservoir water surface to the side channel water surface profile. The condition of flow for subcritical depths is illustrated on figure 9-32 by water surface profile A′.

The effect of the fall distance from the reservoir to the channel water surface for each type of flow is depicted on figure 9-32(B). It can be seen that for the subcritical stage, the incoming flow will not develop high transverse velocities because of the low drop before it meets the channel flow, thus effecting a good diffusion with the water bulk in the trough.

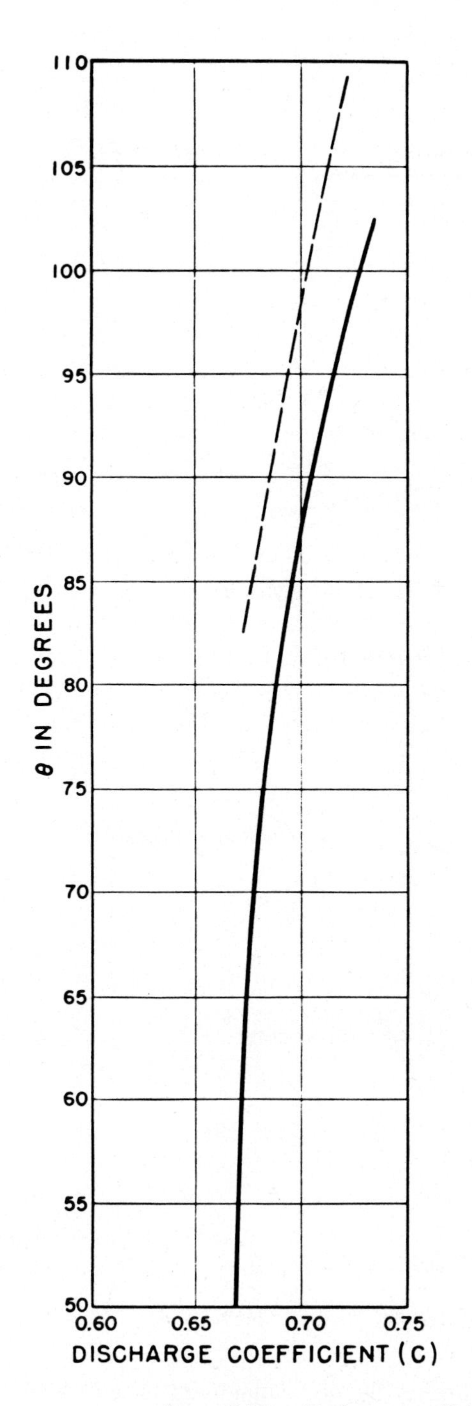

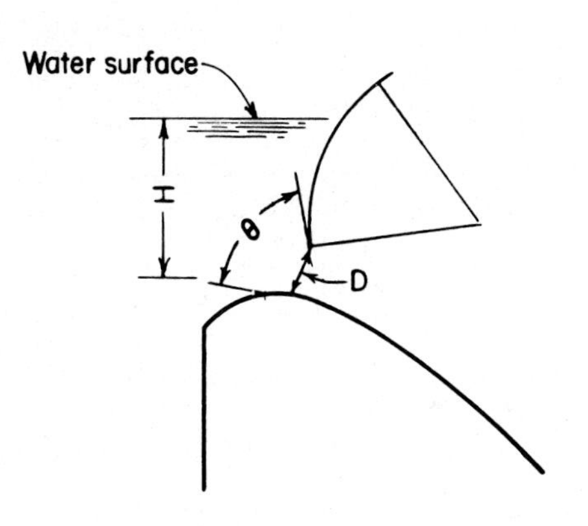

EQUATION FOR DISCHARGE

$Q = CDL\sqrt{2gH}$

D = Net gate opening
L = Crest width
H = Head to center of gate opening
For C, use dashed line when gate seats on crest and solid line when gate seats below crest.

REFERENCE

U.S. Army
Corps Of Engineers
Hydraulic Design Criteria
Design Chart 311-1

Figure 9-31.—Discharge coefficient for flow under gates. 103–D–1875.

Because both the incoming velocities and the channel velocities will be relatively slow, a fairly complete intermingling of the flows will occur, thereby producing a comparatively smooth flow in the side channel. Where the channel flow is at the supercritical stage, the channel velocities will be high, and the intermixing of the high-energy transverse flow with the channel stream will be rough and turbulent. The transverse flows will tend to sweep the channel flow to the far side of the channel, producing violent wave action with attendant vibrations. Therefore, it is evident that flows should be

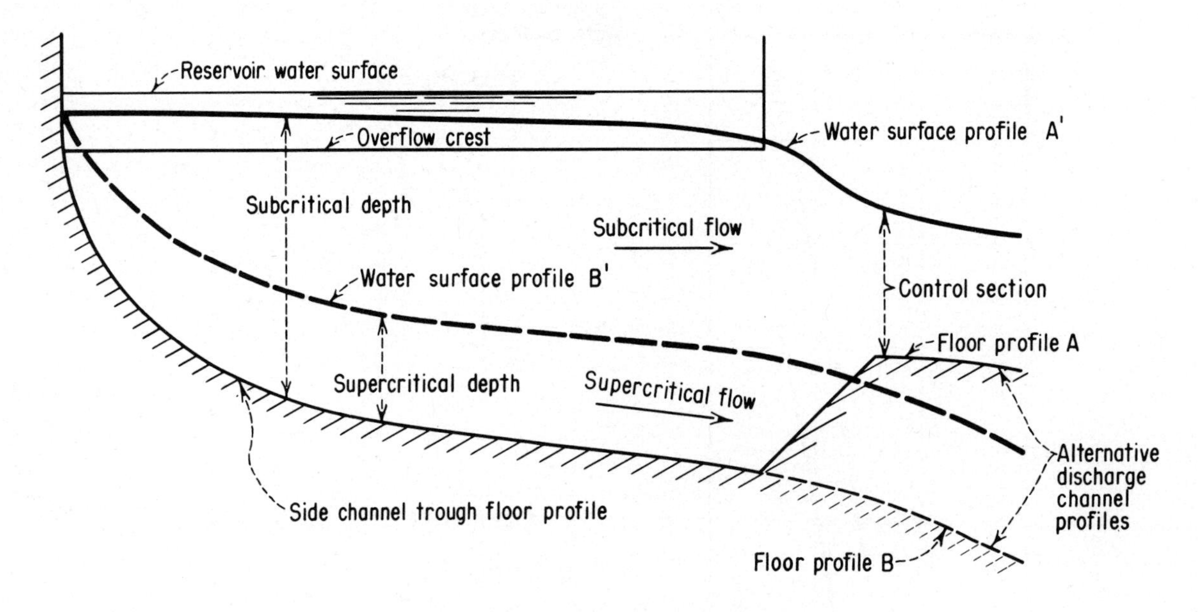

(A) SIDE CHANNEL PROFILE

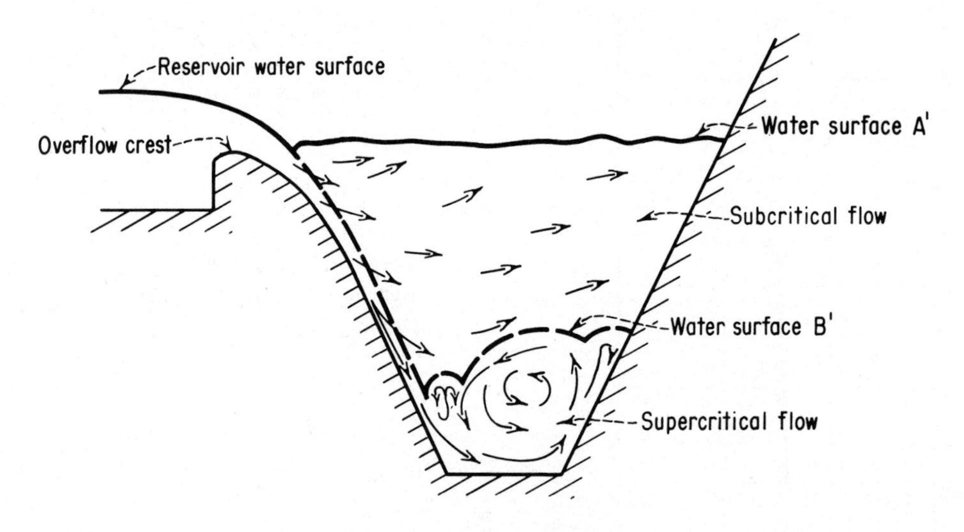

(B) SIDE CHANNEL CROSS SECTION

Figure 9-32.—Side channel flow characteristics. 288-D-2418.

maintained at subcritical stage for good hydraulic performance. This can be achieved by establishing a control section downstream from the side channel trough.

The cross-sectional shape of the side channel trough will be influenced by the overflow crest on the one side and by the bank conditions on the opposite side. Because of turbulence and vibrations inherent in side channel flow, a side channel design is ordinarily not considered except where a competent foundation such as rock exists. The channel sides will, therefore, usually be a concrete lining placed on a slope and anchored directly to the rock. A trapezoidal cross section is the one most often used for a side channel trough. The width of such a channel in relation to the depth should be considered. If the width to depth ratio is large, the depth of flow in the channel will be shallow, similar to that depicted by the cross section *abfg* on figure 9-33. It is evident that for this condition a poor diffusion of the incoming flow with the channel flow will result. A cross section with a minimum width to depth ratio will provide the best hydraulic performance; this indicates that a cross section approaching *adj* (on fig. 9-33) would be the ideal choice both from the standpoint of hydraulics and economy. However, some bottom width is needed to avoid construction difficulties caused by confined working space. Furthermore, the stability of both the structure and the hillside, which might be jeopardized by an extremely deep cut in the abutment, must also be considered. Therefore, the minimum bottom width selected must be commensurate with both the practical and structural aspects of the problem.

A control section downstream from the side channel trough is achieved by constricting the channel sides or elevating the channel bottom to produce a point of critical flow. Flows upstream from the control will be at the subcritical stage and will provide a maximum of depth in the side channel trough. The side channel bottom and control dimensions are then selected so that flow in the trough opposite the crest will be at the greatest depth possible without submerging the flow over the crest. Flow in the discharge channel downstream from the control will be the same as that in an ordinary channel or chute spillway.

(b) *Design Example.*—A design example illustrates the procedures for determining the hydraulic design of a side channel spillway control structure. The problem is to design a side channel spillway 100 feet long (station 0+00 to station 1+00) to discharge a maximum of 2,000 ft³/s. The spillway crest is at elevation 1000.0 feet, and the discharge per foot of length $q = 2{,}000/100 = 20$ ft³/s. Assume the crest coefficient $C = 3.6$, $H_o = (q/C)^{2/3} = 3.1$ feet.

For the side channel trough, assume a trapezoidal section with ½:1 side slopes and a bottom width of 10 feet, whose rise in bottom profile is 1.0 foot in the 100 feet of channel length. (The slope of the channel profile is arbitrary; however, a relatively flat slope will provide greater depths and lower velocities and, consequently, will ensure better intermingling of flows at the upstream end of the channel and avoid the possibility of accelerating or supercritical flows occurring in the channel for smaller discharges.) Furthermore, assume that a control section is placed downstream from the side channel trough with its bottom at the same elevation as the bottom of the side channel floor at the downstream end. Assume that a transition is made from the ½:1 slopes of the trough section to a rectangular section at the control. Arbitrarily assume a datum for the control section bottom at elevation 100.0.

Therefore, the critical depth for flow at the control is $d_c = (q_1^2/g)^{1/3}$.

For this example:

$$q_1 = \frac{2{,}000}{10} = 200 \text{ ft}^3/\text{s per foot of width}$$

$$d_c = \left(\frac{200^2}{32.2}\right)^{1/3} = 10.75 \text{ feet}$$

$$v_c = \frac{q_1}{d_c} = \frac{200}{10.75} = 18.6 \text{ ft/s}$$

$$h_{v_c} = \frac{v_c^2}{2g} = \frac{18.6^2}{64.4} = 5.37 \text{ feet}$$

Assume a transition loss from the end of the side channel trough to the control section (to provide for losses caused by contraction, by diffusion of the flows not affected in the side channel proper, and by friction losses) equal to 0.2 of the difference in velocity heads between the ends of the transition. The flow characteristics at the downstream end of the side channel can be obtained from Bernoulli's equation (app. B). For figure 9-34, Bernoulli's equation may be written as follows:

$$d_{(1+00)} + h_{v_{(1+00)}} = d_c + h_{v_c} + 0.2(h_{v_c} - h_{r_{(1+00)}})$$

This expression must be solved by trial and error. First, assume a value of $d_{(1+00)}$, and solve for $h_{v\,(1+00)}$. If the use of these values does not result in a balanced equation, a new value must be assumed for $d_{(1+00)}$ and the process repeated. A value of 16.34 feet for $d_{(1+00)}$ was found to satisfy the equation as follows:

For $d_{(1+00)} = 16.34$, the area of flow at station 1+00 in the trapezoidal cross section with 10-foot bottom width and ½:1 side slopes = 297 ft².

$$v_{(1+00)} = \frac{2{,}000}{297} = 6.73 \text{ ft/s}$$

$$h_{v(1+00)} = \frac{6.73^2}{64.4} = 0.70 \text{ foot}$$

$$0.2(h_{v_c} - h_{v(1+00)}) = 0.2\ (5.37 - 0.70) = 0.93 \text{ foot}$$

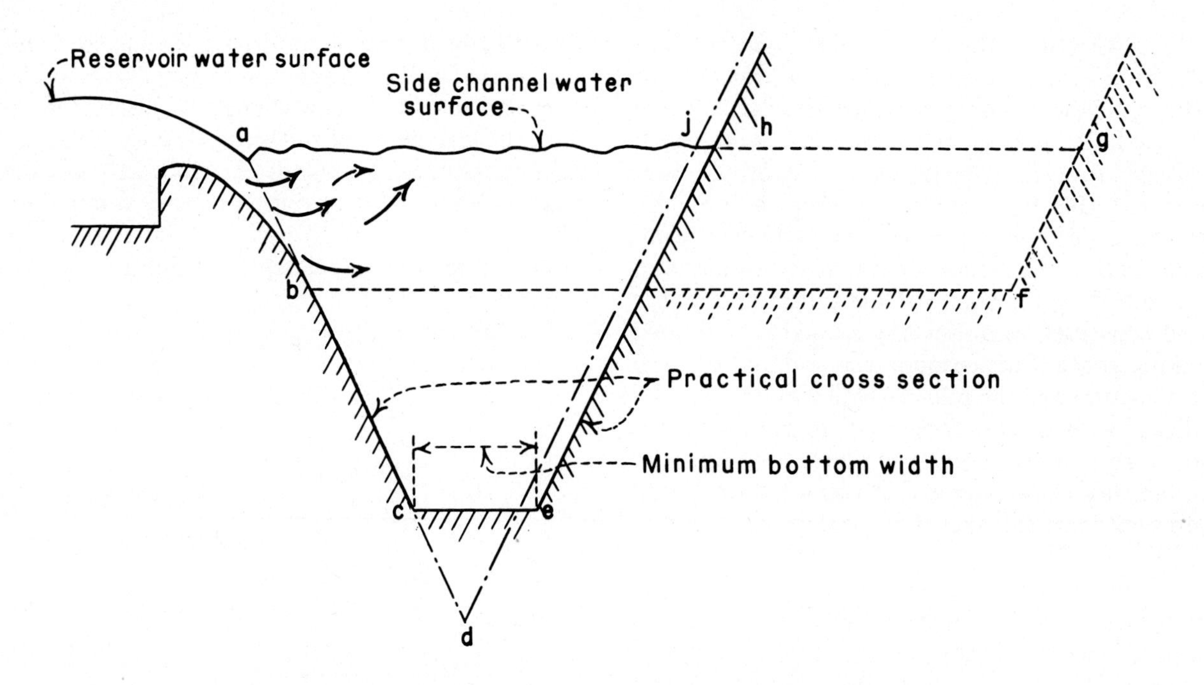

Figure 9-33.—Comparison of side channel cross sections. 288–D–2419.

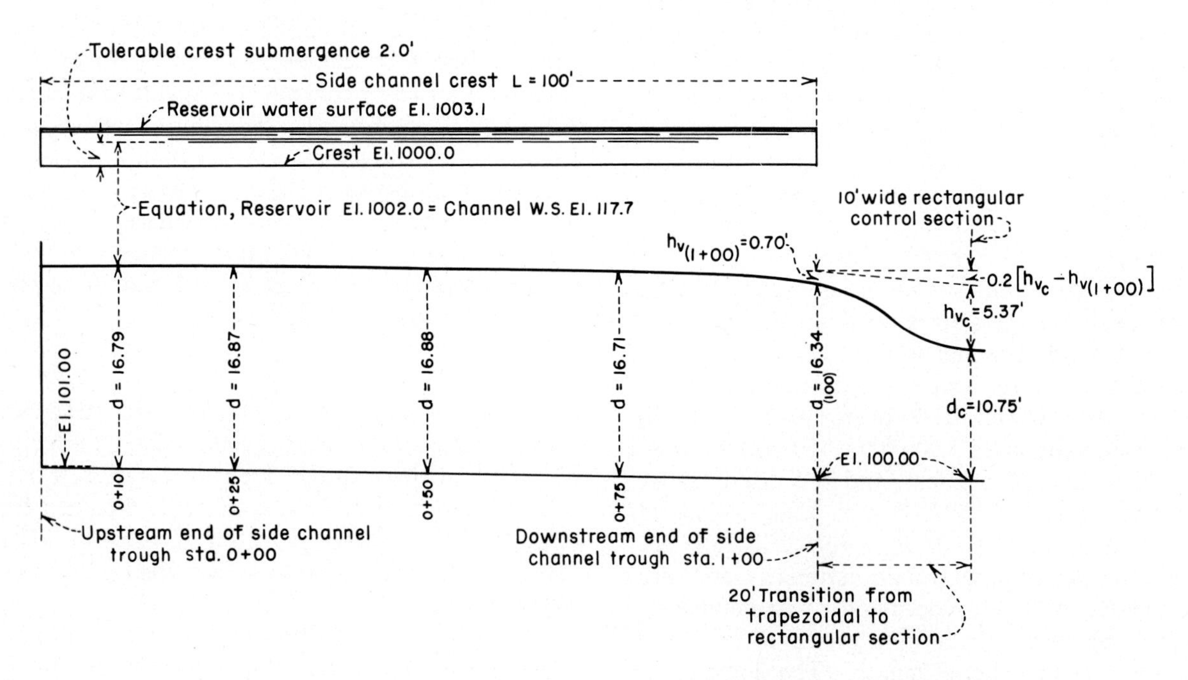

Figure 9-34.—Example of hydraulic design for side channel spillway. 288–D–2420.

Substituting the values in Bernoulli's equation:

$$16.34 + 0.70 = 10.75 + 5.37 + 0.93$$
$$17.04 = 17.05 \text{ (A satisfactory check)}$$

With the hydraulic properties of the side channel at station 1+00 determined, the water surface profile along the side channel trough can be determined from equation (15). The trial-and-error computations are shown in table 9-3. The resulting water surface profile is shown on figure 9-34.

Next, the channel profile is fitted to the crest datum by relating the water surface profile to the

Table 9-3.—Side channel spillway computations. Using eq(15) for design example in section 9.17(b): given Q = 2,000 ft³/s, bottom width = 10 feet, side slopes = ½:1, and bottom slope = 1 foot in 100 feet.

(1) Station	(2) Δx	(3) Elevation bottom	(4) Trial Δy	(5) Water surface elevation	(6) d	(7) A	(8) Q	(9) v	(10) Q_1+Q_2	(11) $\frac{Q_1}{g(Q_1+Q_2)}$	(12) v_1+v_2	(13) v_2-v_1	(14) Q_2-Q_1	(15) $\frac{Q_2-Q_1}{Q_1}$	(16) $\frac{v_2(Q_2-Q_1)}{Q_1}$	(17) (13)+(16)	(18) Δy = (11) ×(12)×(17)	(19) Remarks
1+00	-	100.0	-	116.34	16.34	297	2,000	6.73	-	-	-	-	-	-	-	-	-	-
0+75	25	100.25	1.00	117.34	17.09	317	1,500	4.73	3,500	0.01332	11.46	2.00	500	0.333	2.24	4.24	0.64	Too low
			.62	116.96	16.71	307	-	4.89	-	-	11.62	1.84	-	-	-	4.08	.63	OK
0+50	25	100.50	.50	117.46	16.96	313	1,000	3.19	2,500	.01244	8.08	1.70	500	.50	2.44	4.14	.42	Too low
			.42	117.38	16.88	311	-	3.22	-	-	8.11	1.67	-	-	-	4.11	.41	OK
0+25	25	100.75	.30	117.68	16.93	313	500	1.60	1,500	.01036	4.82	1.62	500	1.00	3.22	4.84	.24	Too low
			.24	117.62	16.87	311	-	1.61	-	-	4.83	1.61	-	-	-	4.83	.24	OK
0+00	15	100.90	.10	117.72	16.82	310	200	.64	700	.00888	2.25	.97	300	1.50	2.41	3.38	.07	Too low
			.07	117.69	16.79	309	-	.65	-	-	2.26	.96	-	-	-	3.37	.07	OK

reservoir water level. To obtain the assumed crest coefficient value of 3.6, excessive submergence of the overflow must be avoided. If it is assumed that a maximum of two-thirds submergence at the upstream end of the channel can be tolerated, the maximum water surface level in the channel will be ⅔H_o above the crest, or elevation 1002.0. Then at station 0+10, the channel datum water surface level elevation 117.7 will become elevation 1002.0, placing the channel floor level for station 0+00 at approximately elevation 985.3, and for station 1+00 at approximately elevation 984.3.

The design of the side channel control structure would be completed by designing the uncontrolled ogee crest by the methods shown in section 9.13, to obtain the crest coefficient value of 3.6 that was assumed.

Variations in the design can be made by assuming different bottom widths, different channel slopes, and varying control sections. A proper and economical design can usually be achieved after comparing several alternatives.

D. HYDRAULICS OF FREE-FLOW DISCHARGE CHANNELS

9.18. *General.*—Discharge generally passes through the critical stage in the spillway control structure and enters the discharge channel as supercritical or shooting flow. To avoid a hydraulic jump below the control, the flow must remain at the supercritical stage throughout the length of the channel. The flow in the channel may be uniform or it may be accelerated or decelerated, depending on the slopes and dimensions of the channel and on the total drop. Where it is desired to minimize the grade to reduce excavation at the upstream end of a channel, the flow might be uniform or decelerating, followed by accelerating flow in the steep drop leading to the downstream river level. Flow at any point along the channel will depend upon the specific energy, $d+h_v$, available at that point. This energy will equal the total drop from the reservoir water level to the floor of the channel at the point under consideration, less the head losses accumulated to that point. The velocities and depths of flow along the channel can be fixed by selecting the grade and the cross-sectional dimensions of the channel.

The velocities and depths of free surface flow in a channel, whether it be an open channel, a conduit, or a tunnel, conform to the principle of the conservation of energy as expressed by Bernoulli's theorem, which states "the absolute energy of flow at any cross section is equal to the absolute energy at a downstream section plus intervening losses of energy." As applied to figure 9-35 this relationship can be expressed as follows:

$$\Delta Z + d_1 + h_{v_2} = d_2 + h_{v_2} + \Delta h_L \qquad (17)$$

When the channel grades are not too steep, for practical purposes the normal depth, d_n, can be considered equal to the vertical depth d. The term Δh_L includes all losses that occur in the reach of channel, such as friction, turbulence, impact, and transition losses. Because changes in most channels are made gradually, all losses except those from friction

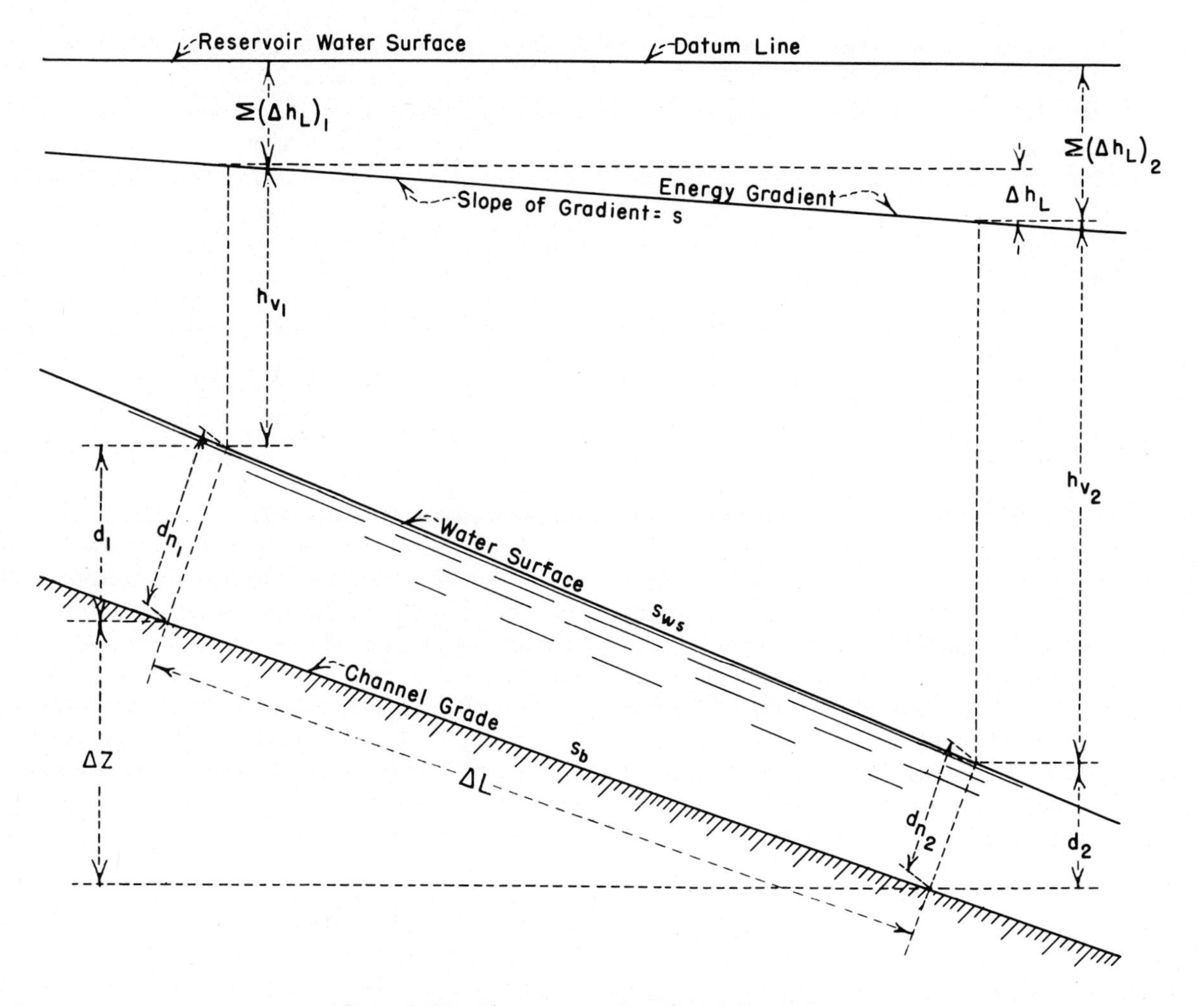

Figure 9-35.—Flow in open channels. 288-D-2421.

can ordinarily be neglected. The friction loss can then be expressed as:

$$\Delta h_L = s\Delta L \qquad (18)$$

where s is the average friction slope expressed by either the Chezy or the Manning formula. For the reach ΔL, the head loss can be expressed as:

$$\Delta h_L = \left(\frac{s_1 + s_2}{2}\right) \Delta L$$

From the Manning formula (eq. (30), app. B), $s = (vn/1.486r^{2/3})^2$.

The roughness coefficient, n, will depend on the nature of the channel surface. For conservative design the frictional loss should be maximized when evaluating depths of flow and minimized when evaluating the energy content of the flow. For determining depths of flow in a concrete-lined channel, an n of about 0.014 should be assumed. For determining specific energies of flow needed to design the dissipating device, an n of about 0.008 should be assumed.

Where only rough approximations of depths and velocities of flow in a discharge channel are desired, the total head loss $\Sigma\Delta h_L$ to any point along the channel might be expressed in terms of the velocity head. Thus, at any section the relationship can be stated: reservoir water surface elevation minus floor grade elevation $= d + h_v + Kh_v$. For spillways with small drops, K can be assumed as approximately 0.2 for determining depths of flow and 0.1 or less for evaluating the energy of flow. Rough approximations of losses can also be obtained from figure B-5.

9.19. *Open Channels.*—(a) *Profile.*—The profile of an open channel is usually selected to conform to topographic and geologic site conditions. It is generally defined as straight reaches connected by vertical curves. Sharp convex and concave vertical curves would develop unsatisfactory flows in the channel and should be avoided. Convex curves should be flat enough to maintain positive pressures and thus preclude the tendency for the flow to separate from the floor. Concave curves should have a sufficiently long radius of curvature to minimize the dynamic forces on the floor brought about by the centrifugal force from a change in the direction of flow.

To avoid the tendency for the water to spring away from the floor and, thereby, reduce the surface contact pressure, the floor shape for convex curvature should be made slightly flatter than the trajectory of a free-discharging jet issuing under a head equal to the specific energy of flow as it enters the curve. The curvature should approximate a shape defined by the equation:

$$-y = x \tan\theta + \frac{x^2}{K[4(d + h_v)\cos^2\theta]} \qquad (19)$$

where θ is the slope angle of the floor upstream from the curve. Except for the factor K, the equation is that of a free-discharging trajectory issuing from an inclined orifice. To ensure positive pressure along the entire contact surface of the curve, K should be equal to or greater than 1.5.

For the concave curvature, the pressure exerted upon the floor surface by the centrifugal force of the flow varies directly with the energy of the flow and inversely with the radius of curvature. An approximate relationship of these criteria can be expressed in the equations:

$$R = \frac{2qv}{p} \text{ and } R = \frac{2dv^2}{p} \qquad (20)$$

where:

R = the minimum radius of curvature, in feet,

q = the discharge, in cubic feet per second per foot of width,

v = the velocity, in feet per second,

d = the depth of flow, in feet, and

p = the normal dynamic pressure exerted on the floor, in pounds per square foot.

An assumed value of p = 1,000 will normally produce an acceptable radius; however, in no case should the radius be less than $10d$. For the reverse curve at the lower end of the ogee crest, radii of not less than $5d$ have been found acceptable.

(b) *Convergence and Divergence.*—The best hydraulic performance in a discharge channel is obtained when the confining sidewalls are parallel and the distribution of flow across the channel is maintained uniform. However, economy may dictate a channel section narrower or wider than either the crest or the terminal structure, thereby requiring converging or diverging transitions to fit the various components together. Sidewall convergence must be made gradual to avoid cross waves, wave runup on the walls, and uneven distribution of flow across the channel. Similarly, the rate of divergence of the sidewalls must be limited or else the flow will not spread to occupy the entire width of the channel uniformly. This will result in undesirable flow conditions at the terminal structure.

The inertial and gravitational forces of streamlined kinetic flow in a channel can be expressed by the Froude number parameter, $v/(gd)^{1/2}$. Variations from streamlined flow caused by outside interferences that cause an expansion or a contraction of the flow can also be related to this parameter. Experiments have shown that an angular variation of the flow boundaries not exceeding that produced by the equation,

$$\tan\alpha = \frac{1}{3F} \qquad (21)$$

will provide an acceptable transition for either a contracting or an expanding channel. In this equation, $F = v/(gd)^{1/2}$, and α is the angular variation of the sidewall with respect to the channel centerline; v and d are the velocity and depth at the start of the transition. Figure 9-36 is a nomograph from which the tangent of the flare angle or the flare angle in degrees may be obtained for known values of depth and velocity of flow.

(c) *Channel Freeboard.*—In a channel conducting flow at the supercritical stage, the surface roughness, wave action, air bulking, splash, and spray are related to the velocity and energy content of the flow. Expressed in terms of v and d, the energy per foot of width $qh_v = v^3d/2g$. Therefore the relationship of velocity and depth to the flow energy also can be expressed in terms of v and $d^{1/3}$. An empirical expression based on this relationship that gives a reasonable indication of desirable freeboard values is:

$$\text{Freeboard (in feet)} = 2.0 + 0.025v\sqrt[3]{d} \qquad (22)$$

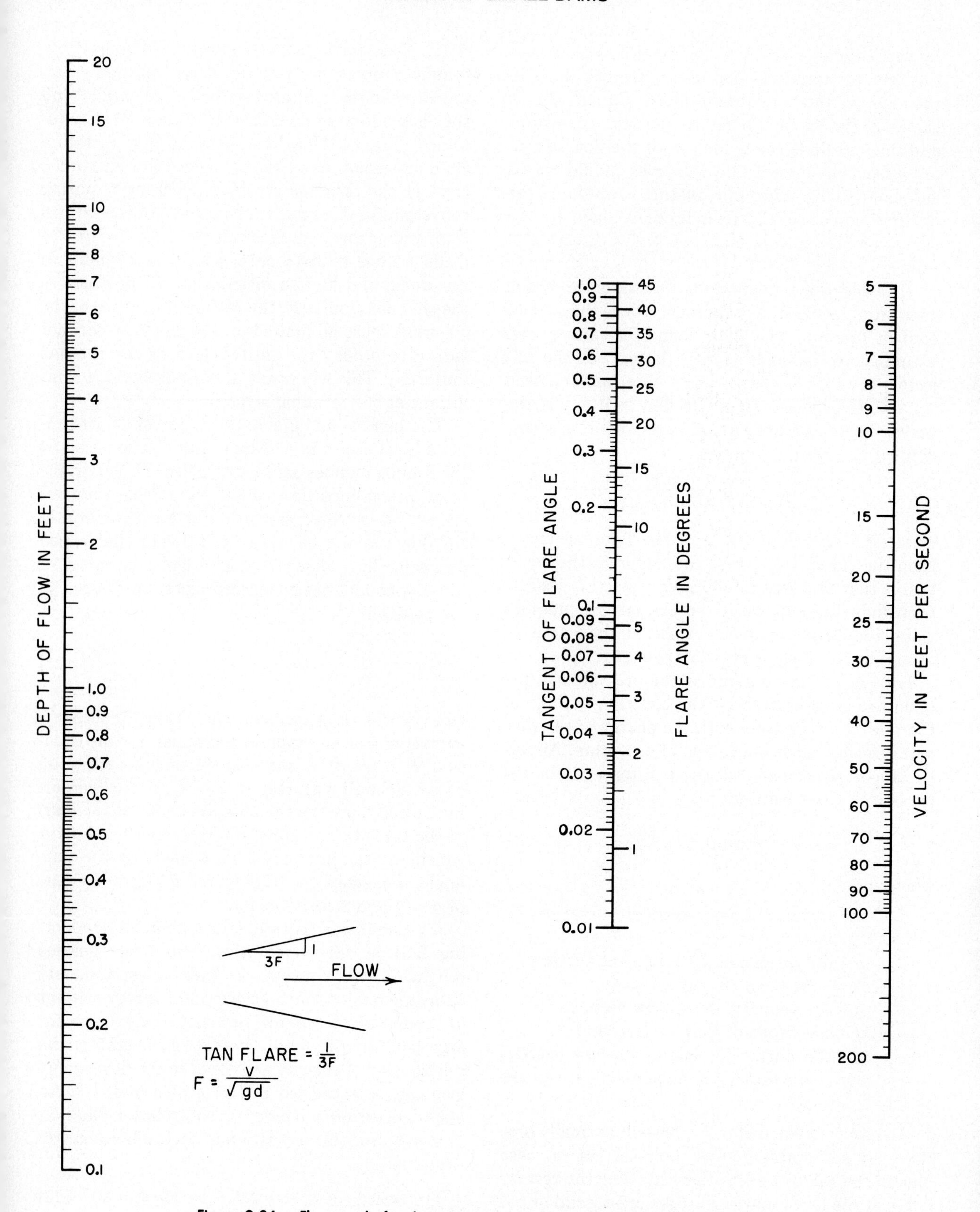

Figure 9-36.—Flare angle for divergent or convergent channels. 288–D–2422.

E. HYDRAULICS OF TERMINAL STRUCTURES

9.20. *Deflector Buckets.*—Where the spillway discharge may be safely delivered directly to the river without providing a dissipating or stilling device, the jet is often projected beyond the structure by a deflector bucket or lip. Flow from these deflectors leaves the structure as a free-discharging upturned jet and falls into the stream channel some distance from the end of the spillway. The path the jet assumes depends on the energy of flow available at the lip and the angle at which the jet leaves the bucket.

With the origin of the coordinates taken at the end of the lip, the path of the trajectory is given by the equation:

$$y = x \tan \theta - \frac{x^2}{K[4(d + h_v) \cos^2 \theta]} \qquad (23)$$

where:

θ = angle of the edge of the lip with the horizontal, and

K = a factor, equal to 1, for the theoretical jet.

To compensate for loss of energy and the velocity reduction caused by air resistance, internal turbulences, and disintegration of the jet, $K = 0.9$ should be assumed.

The horizontal range of the jet at the level of the lip is obtained by making $y = 0$ in equation (23). Then, $x=4K(d+h_v)\tan \theta \cos^2 \theta =2K(d+h_v)\sin 2\theta$. The maximum value of x will be $2K(d + h_v)$ when $\theta = 45°$. However, the angle of the lip is influenced by the bucket radius and the height of the lip above the bucket invert; ordinarily the exit angle should not be more than 30°.

The bucket radius should be made long enough to maintain concentric flow as the water moves around the curve. The rate of curvature must be limited, similar to that of a vertical curve in a discharge channel (sec. 9.19), so that the floor pressures will not alter the streamline distribution of the flow. The minimum radius of curvature, R, can be determined from equation (20), except that values of $p \leq$ 1,000 lb/ft^2 will produce values of the radius that have proved satisfactory in practice. However, the radius should not be less than $5d$, five times the depth of water. Structurally, the cantilever bucket must be strong enough to withstand this normal dynamic force in addition to the other applied forces.

9.21. *Hydraulic-Jump Basins.*—(a) *General.*—Where the energy of flow in a spillway must be dissipated before the discharge is returned to the downstream river channel, the hydraulic-jump stilling basin is an effective device for reducing the exit velocity to a tranquil state. The jump that will occur in such a stilling basin has distinctive characteristics and assumes a definite form, depending on the relation between the energy of flow that must be dissipated and the depth of the flow.

A comprehensive series of tests have been performed by the Bureau of Reclamation [15] to determine the properties of the hydraulic jump. The jump form and the flow characteristics can be related to the kinetic flow factor, v^2/gd, of the discharge entering the basin; to the critical depth of flow, d_c ; or to the Froude number parameter, $v/(gd)^{1/2}$. Forms of the hydraulic-jump phenomena for various ranges of the Froude number are illustrated on figure 9-37.

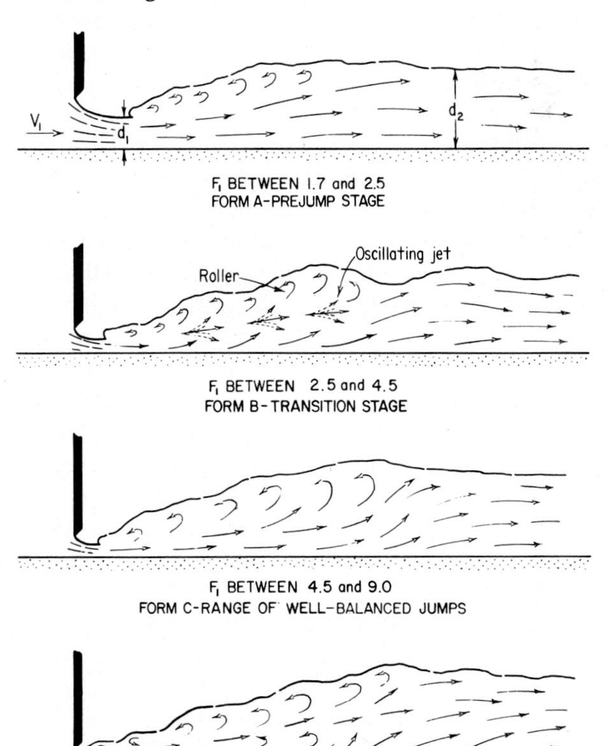

Figure 9-37.—Characteristic forms of hydraulic jump related to the Froude number. 288-D-2423.

When the Froude number of the incoming flow is 1.0, the flow is at critical depth and a hydraulic jump cannot form. For Froude numbers from 1.0 to about 1.7, the incoming flow is only slightly below critical depth, and the change from this low stage to the high stage flow is gradual and manifests itself only by a slightly ruffled water surface. As the Froude number approaches 1.7, a series of small rollers begins to develop on the surface. These become more intense with increasingly higher values of the number. Other than the surface roller phenomena, relatively smooth flows prevail throughout the Froude number range up to about 2.5. Stilling action for the range of Froude numbers from 1.7 to 2.5 is shown as form A on figure 9-37. Forms B, C, and D on figure 9-37 show characteristic forms at hydraulic jumps related to higher Froude numbers.

For Froude numbers between 2.5 and 4.5, an oscillating form of jump occurs. The entering jet intermittently flows near the bottom and then along the surface of the downstream channel. This oscillating flow causes objectionable surface waves that carry far beyond the end of the basin. The action represented through this range of flows is designated as form B on figure 9-37.

For Froude numbers between 4.5 and 9, a stable and well-balanced jump occurs. Turbulence is confined to the main body of the jump, and the water surface downstream is comparatively smooth. As the Froude number increases above 9, the turbulence within the jump and the surface roller becomes increasingly active, resulting in a rough water surface with strong surface waves downstream from the jump. Stilling action for Froude numbers between 4.5 and 9 is designed as form C on figure 9-37, and that above 9 is designated as form D.

Figure 9-38 plots relationships of conjugate depths and velocities for the hydraulic jump in a rectangular channel. The ranges for the various forms of jump described above are also indicated on the figure.

(b) *Basin Design in Relation to Froude Numbers.*—Stilling basin designs suitable to provide stilling action for the various forms of jump are described in the following paragraphs.

(1) *Basins for Froude Numbers Less Than 1.7.*—For a Froude number of 1.7, the conjugate depth, d_2, is about twice the incoming depth, or about 40 percent greater than the critical depth. The exit velocity, v_2, is about one-half the incoming velocity, or 30 percent less than the critical velocity. No special stilling basin is needed to still flows where the Froude number of the incoming flow is less than 1.7, except that the channel lengths beyond the point where the depth starts to change should be not less than about $4d_2$. No baffles or other dissipating devices are needed. These basins, designated type I, are not shown here (see [15]).

(2) *Basins for Froude Numbers Between 1.7 and 2.5.*—Flow phenomena for these basins will be in the form designated as the prejump stage, as shown on figure 9-37. Because such flows are not attended by active turbulence, baffles or sills are not required. The basin should be long enough to contain the flow prism while it is undergoing retardation. Conjugate depths and basin lengths shown on figure B-15 will provide acceptable basins. These basins, designated type I, are not shown here (see [15]).

(3) *Basins for Froude Numbers Between 2.5 and 4.5.*—Flows for these basins are considered to be in the transition flow stage because a true hydraulic jump does not fully develop. Stilling basins that accommodate these flows are the least effective in providing satisfactory dissipation because the attendant wave action ordinarily cannot be controlled by the usual basin devices. Waves generated by the flow phenomena will persist beyond the end of the basin and must often be dampened by means apart from the basin.

Where a stilling device must be provided to dissipate flows for this range of Froude number, the basin shown on figure 9-39(A), which is designated a type IV basin, has proved relatively effective for dissipating the bulk of the energy of flow. However, the wave action propagated by the oscillating flow cannot be entirely dampened. Auxiliary wave dampeners or wave suppressors must sometimes be used to provide smooth surface flow downstream.

Because of the tendency of the jump to sweep out and as an aid in suppressing wave action, the water depths in the basin should be about 10 percent greater than the computed conjugate depth.

Often, the need to design this type of basin can be avoided by selecting stilling basin dimensions that will provide flow conditions that fall outside the range of transition flow. For example, with an 800-ft^3/s capacity spillway where the specific energy at the upstream end of the basin is about 15 feet and the velocity into the basin is about 30 ft/s, the Froude number will be 3.2 for a basin width of 10 feet. The Froude number can be raised to 4.6 by widening the basin to 20 feet. The selection of basin

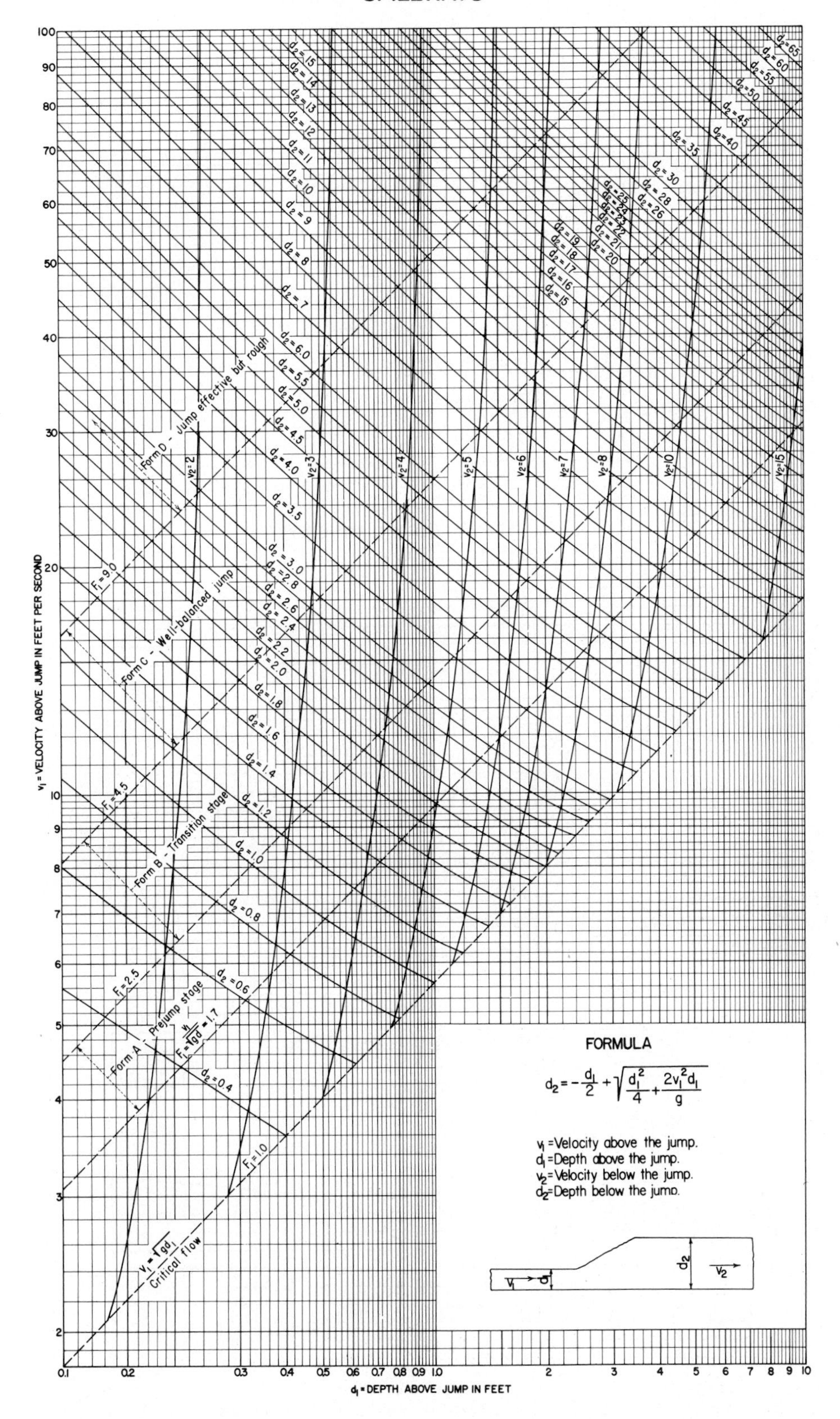

Figure 9-38.—Relations between variables in hydraulic jump for rectangular channel. 288–D–2424.

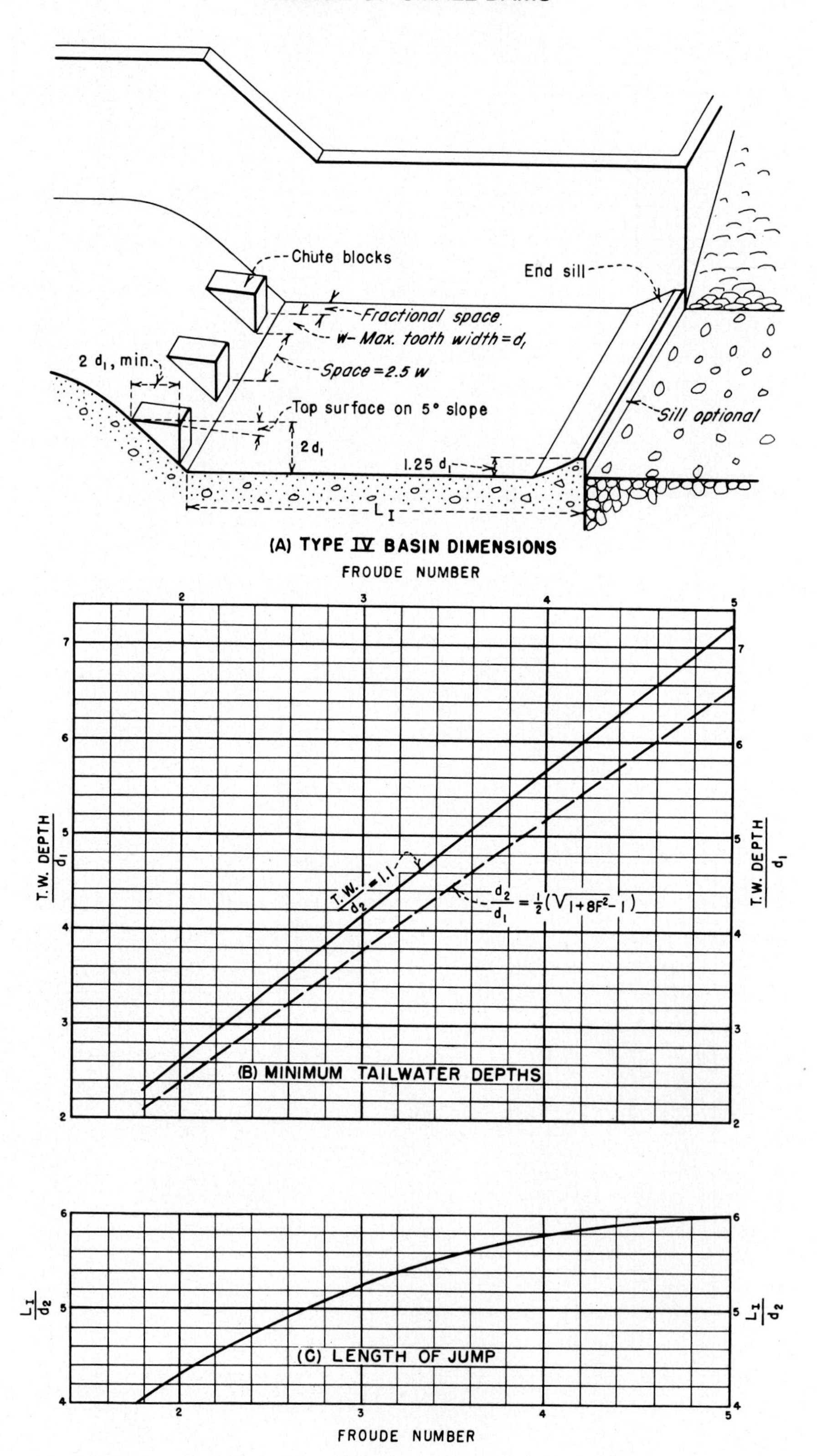

Figure 9-39.—Stilling basin characteristics for Froude numbers between 2.5 and 4.5. 288–D–2425.

width then becomes a matter of economics as well as hydraulic performance.

(4) *Alternative Low Froude Number Stilling Basins.*—Type IV basins are fairly effective at low Froude number flows for small canals and for structures with small unit discharges. However, recent model tests have developed designs quite different from the type IV basin design, even though the type IV basin design was included in the initial tests.

Palmetto Bend Dam stilling basin [22] is an example of a low Froude number structure, modeled in the Bureau of Reclamation Hydraulics Laboratory, whose recommended design is quite different from type IV design. The type IV design has large deflector blocks, similar to but larger than chute blocks, and an optional solid end sill; the Palmetto Bend design has no chute blocks, but has large baffle piers and a dentated end sill.

The foregoing generalized designs have not been suitable for some Bureau applications, and the increased use of low Froude number stilling basins has created a need for additional data on this type of design. A study was initiated to develop generalized criteria for the design of low Froude number hydraulic-jump stilling basins. The criteria and guidelines from previous studies were combined with the results of this study to formulate the design guidelines recommended for low Froude number stilling basins [23]. However, it should be noted that a hydraulic-jump stilling basin is not an efficient energy dissipator at low Froude numbers; that is, the efficiency of a hydraulic-jump basin is less than 50 percent in this Froude number range. Alternative energy dissipators, such as the baffled apron chute or spillway, should be considered for these conditions.

The recommended design has chute blocks, baffle piers, and a dentated end sill. All design data are presented on figure 9-40. The length is rather short, approximately three times d_2 (the conjugate depth after the jump). The size and spacing of the chute blocks and baffle piers are a function of d_1 (incoming depth) and the Froude number. The dentated end sill is proportioned according to d_2 and the Froude number. The end sill is placed at or near the downstream end of the stilling basin. Erosion tests were not included in the development of this basin. Observations of flow patterns near the invert downstream from the basin indicated that no erosion problem should exist. However, if hydraulic model tests are performed to confirm a design based on these criteria, erosion tests should be included. Tests should be made over a full range of discharges to determine whether abrasive materials will move upstream into the basin and to determine the erosion potential downstream from the basin. If the inflow velocity is greater than 50 ft/s, hydraulic model studies should be performed.

(5) *Basins for Froude Numbers Higher Than 4.5.*—For these basins, a true hydraulic jump will form. The elements of the jump will vary according to the Foude number, as shown on figure B-15. The installation of accessory devices such as blocks, baffles, and sills along the floor of the basin produce a stabilizing effect on the jump, which permits shortening the basin and provides a safety factor against sweepout caused by inadequate tailwater depth.

The basin shown on figure 9-41, which is designated a type III basin, can be adopted where incoming velocities do not exceed 60 ft/s. The type III basin uses chute blocks, impact baffle blocks, and an end sill to shorten the jump length and to dissipate the high-velocity flow within the shortened basin length. This basin relies on dissipation of energy by the impact blocks and on the turbulence of the jump phenomena for its effectiveness. Because of the large impact forces to which the baffles are subjected by the impingement of high incoming velocities and because of the possibility of cavitation along the surfaces of the blocks and floor, the use of this basin must be limited to heads where the velocity does not exceed 60 ft/s.

Cognizance must be taken of the added loads placed on the structure floor by the dynamic force brought against the upstream face of the baffle blocks. This dynamic force will approximate that of a jet impinging upon a plane normal to the direction of flow. The force, in pounds, may be expressed by the formula:

$$\text{Force} = 2wA(d_1+h_{v_1}) \tag{24}$$

where:

w = unit weight of water, in pounds per cubic foot,
A = area of the upstream face of the block, in square feet, and
$(d_1+h_{v_1})$ = the specific energy of the flow entering the basin, in feet.

Negative pressure on the back face of the blocks

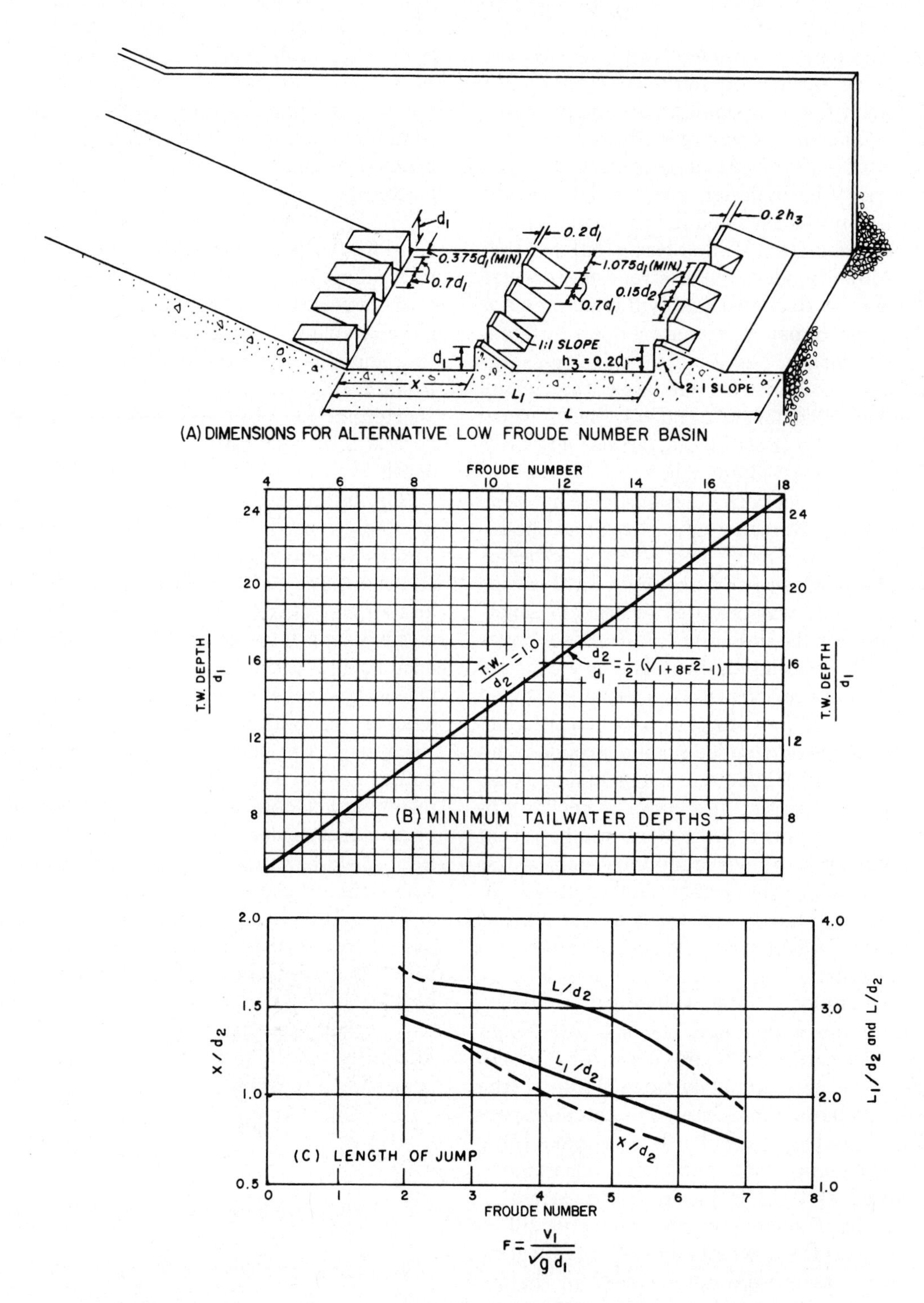

Figure 9-40.—Characteristics for alternative low Froude number stilling basins. 103–D–1876.

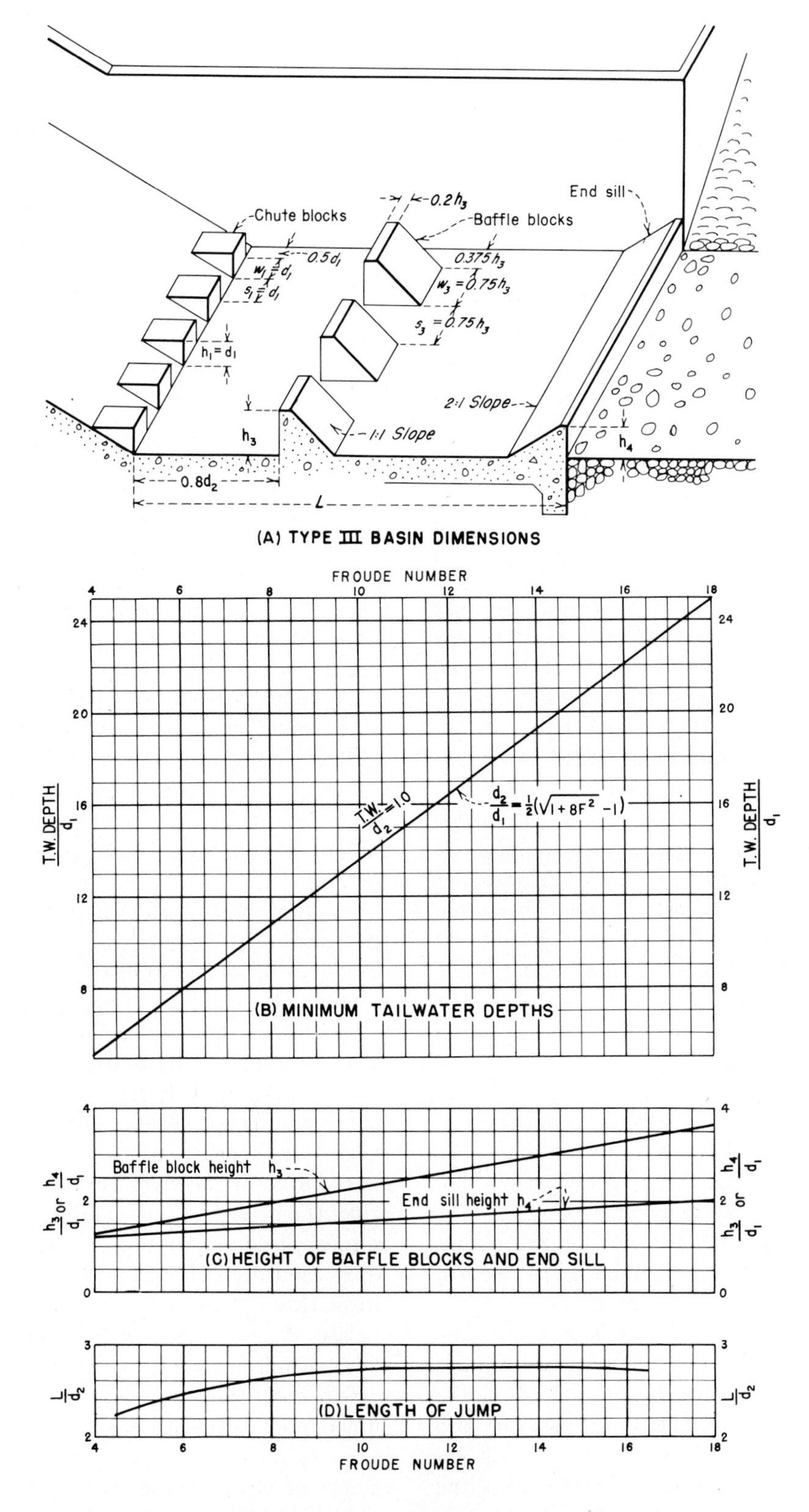

Figure 9-41.—Stilling basin characteristics for Froude numbers above 4.5 where incoming velocity, $V_1 \leq$ 60 ft/s. 288–D–2426.

will further increase the total load. However, because the baffle blocks are placed a distance equal to $0.8d_2$ beyond the start of the jump, there will be some cushioning effect by the time the incoming jet reaches the blocks, and the force will be less than that indicated by the above equation. If the full force computed by equation (24) is used, the negative pressure force may be neglected.

Where incoming velocities exceed 60 ft/s, or where impact baffle blocks are not used, the type II basin (fig. 9-42) may be adopted. Because the dissipation is accomplished primarily by hydraulic-jump action, the basin length will be greater than that indicated for the type III basin. However, the chute blocks and dentated end sill will still effectively reduce the length. Because of the reduced margin of safety against sweepout, the water depth in the basin should be about 5 percent greater than the computed conjugate depth.

(c) *Rectangular Versus Trapezoidal Stilling Basin.*—The use of a trapezoidal stilling basin instead of a rectangular basin may often be proposed where economy favors sloped side lining over vertical wall construction. Model tests have shown, however, that the hydraulic-jump action in a trapezoidal basin is much less complete and less stable than it is in the rectangular basin. In a trapezoidal basin, the water in the triangular areas along the sides of the basin adjacent to the jump does not oppose the incoming high-velocity jet. The jump, which tends to occur vertically, cannot spread sufficiently to occupy the side areas. Consequently, the jump will form only in the central portion of the basin, while areas along the outside will be occupied by upstream-moving flows that ravel off the jump or come from the lower end of the basin. The eddy or horizontal roller action resulting from this phenomenon tends to interfere and interrupt the jump action to the extent that there is incomplete dissipation of the energy and severe scouring can occur beyond the basin. For good hydraulic performance, the sidewalls of a stilling basin should be vertical or as close to vertical as practicable.

(d) *Basin Depths Versus Hydraulic Heads.*—The nomograph on figure 9-43 can help determine approximate basin depths for various basin widths and for various differences between reservoir and tailwater levels. Plots are shown for the condition of no loss of head to the upstream end of the stilling basin, and for 10, 20, and 30 percent loss as scales A, B, C, and D, respectively. The required conjugate depths, d_2, will depend on the specific energy available at the entrance of the basin, as determined by the procedure discussed in section 9.18. Where the specific energy is known, the head loss in the channel upstream can be related to the velocity head, the percentage loss can be determined, and the approximate conjugate depth can be read for the nomograph. Where head losses have not been computed, a quick approximation of the head losses can be obtained from figure B-5. Where only a rough determination of basin depths is needed, the choice of the loss to be applied for various spillway designs may be generalized as follows:

(1) For a design of an overflow spillway where the basin is directly downstream from the crest, or where the chute is not longer than the hydraulic head, consider no loss of head.
(2) For a design of a channel spillway where the channel length is between one and five times the hydraulic head, consider 10 percent loss of head.
(3) For a design of a spillway where the channel length exceeds five times the hydraulic head, consider 20 percent loss of head.

The nomograph on figure 9-43 gives values of the conjugate depth of the hydraulic jump. Tailwater depths for the various types of basin described should be increased as noted earlier in this section.

(e) *Tailwater Considerations.*—Determination of the tailwater rating curve, which gives the stage-discharge relationship of the natural stream below the dam, is discussed in appendix B, part B. Tailwater rating curves for the regime of river below a dam are fixed by the natural conditions along the stream and ordinarily cannot be altered by the spillway design or by the release characteristics. As discussed in section 9.7(d), the retrogression or aggradation of the river below the dam, which will affect the ultimate stage-discharge conditions, must be recognized in selecting the tailwater rating curve to be used for stilling basin design. Usually, river flows that approach the maximum design discharges do not occur, and an estimate of the tailwater rating curve must either be extrapolated from known conditions or computed on a basis of assumed or empirical criteria. Thus, the tailwater rating curve is, at best, only approximate, and safety factors must be included in the design to compensate for variations in tailwater.

For a jump-type stilling basin, downstream water

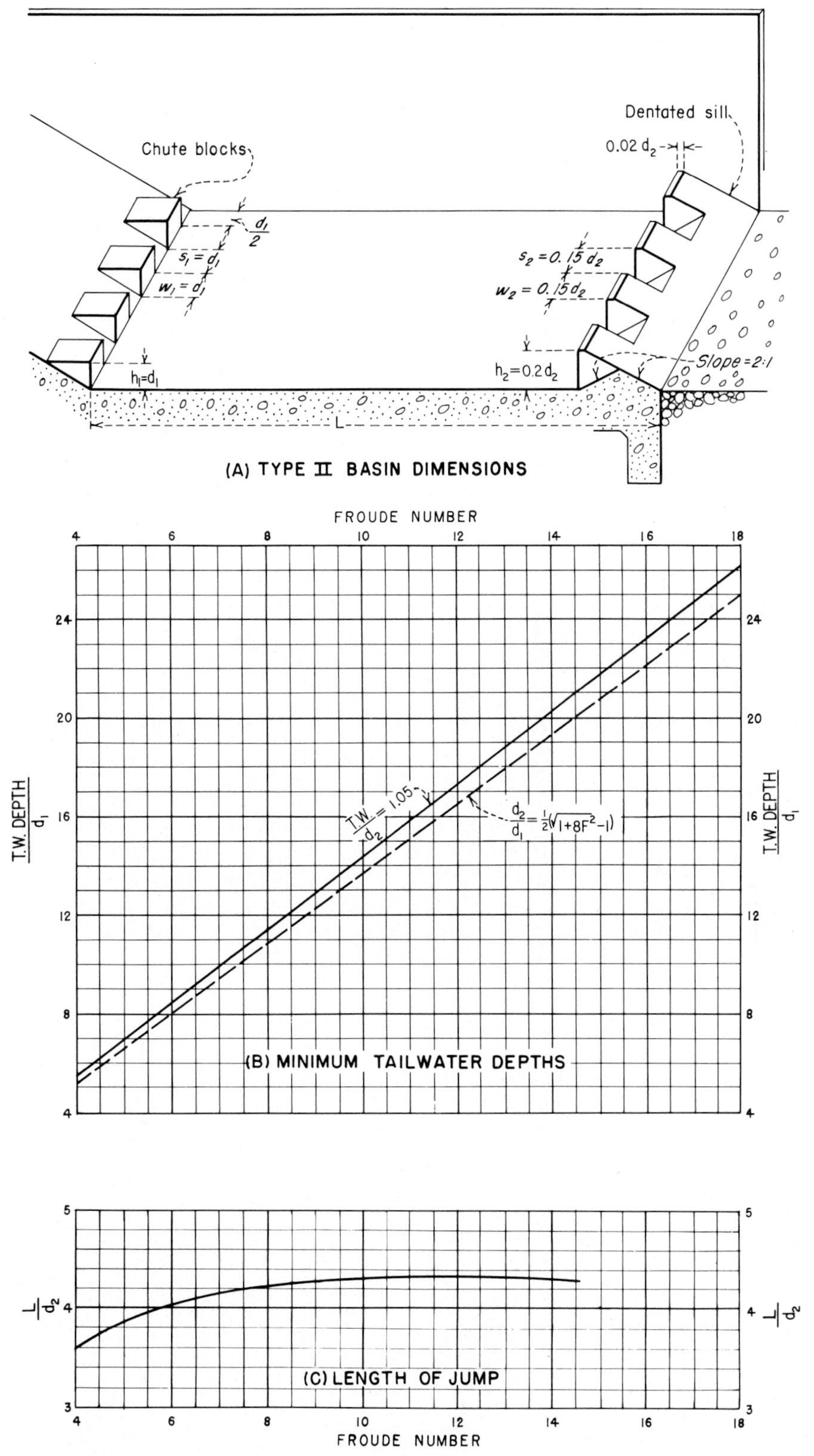

Figure 9-42.—Stilling basin characteristics for Froude numbers above 4.5. 288–D–2427.

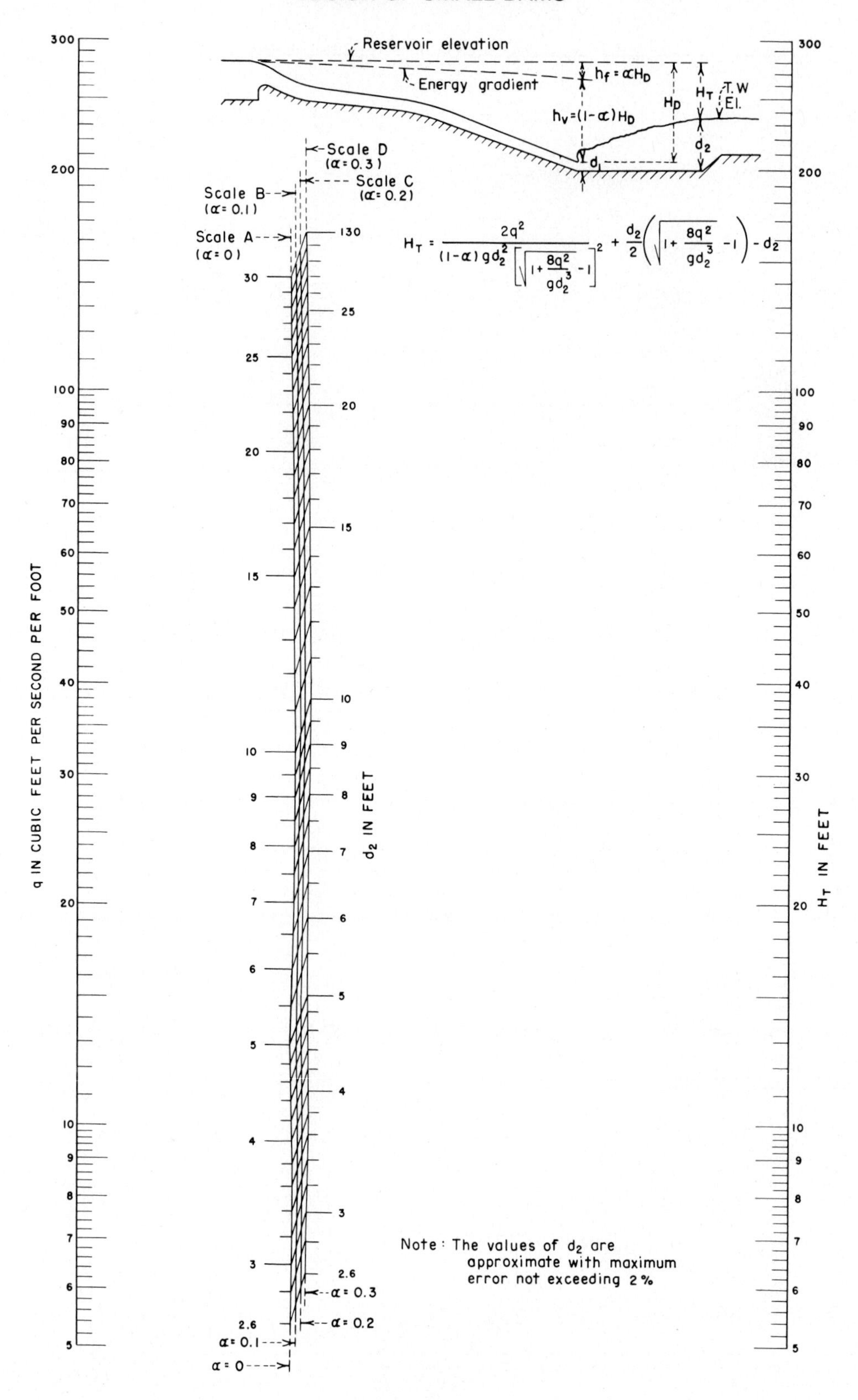

Figure 9-43.—Stilling basin depths versus hydraulic heads for various channel losses. 288-D-2428.

levels for various discharges must conform to the tailwater rating curve. The basin floor level must therefore be selected to provide jump depths that most nearly agree with the tailwater depths. For a given basin design, the tailwater depth for each discharge seldom corresponds to the conjugate depth needed to form a perfect jump. Thus, the relative shapes and relationships of the tailwater curve to the depth curve will determine the required minimum depth to the basin floor. This is shown on figure 9-44(A) where the tailwater rating curve is shown as curve 1, and a conjugate depth versus discharge curve for a basin of certain width is represented by curve 3. Because the basin must be deep enough to provide for full conjugate depth (or some greater depth to provide a safety factor) at the maximum spillway design discharge, the curves will intersect at point D. For lesser discharges the tailwater depth will be greater than the required conjugate depth, thus providing an excess of tailwater, which is conducive to the formation of a "drowned jump." (With the drowned jump condition, instead of achieving good jump-type dissipation by the intermingling of the upstream and downstream flows, the incoming jet plunges to the bottom and carries along the entire length of the basin floor at high velocity.) If the basin floor is higher than indicated by the position of curve 3 on figure 9-44, the depth curve and tailwater rating curve will intersect to the left of point D. This indicates an excess of tailwater for smaller discharges and a deficiency of tailwater for higher discharges.

As an alternative to the selected basin represented by curve 3, a wider basin might be considered for which conjugate depth curve 2 will apply. This design will provide a shallower basin, in which the ideal jump depths will more nearly match the tailwater depths for all discharges. The choice of basin widths, of course, involves consideration of economics, as well as of hydraulic performance.

Where a tailwater rating curve shaped similar to that represented by curve 4 on figure 9-44(B) is encountered, the level of the stilling basin floor must be determined for some discharge other than the maximum design capacity. If the tailwater curve intersects the required water surface elevation at the maximum design capacity, as in figure 9-44(A), there would be insufficient tailwater depth for most smaller discharges. In this case the basin floor elevation is selected so that there will be sufficient tailwater depth for all discharges. For a basin of

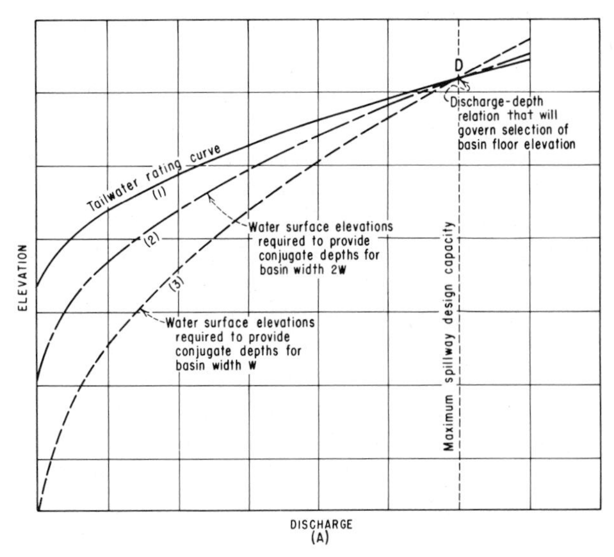

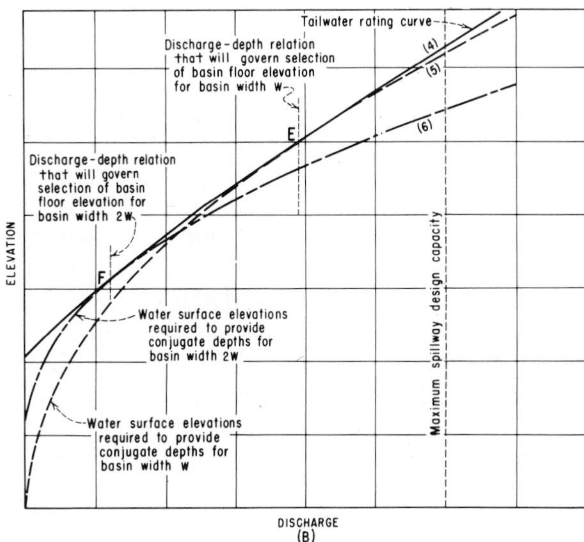

Figure 9-44.—Relationships of conjugate depth curves to tailwater rating curves. 288-D-2429.

width W, the floor level should be selected so that the two curves would coincide at the discharge represented by point E on the figure 9-44(B). For all other discharges the tailwater depth will be greater than that needed to form a satisfactory jump. Similarly, if a basin width of $2W$ were considered, the basin floor level would be selected so that curve 6 would intersect the tailwater curve at point F. Here also, the selection of basin widths should be based on economics as well as on hydraulic performance.

Where exact conjugate depth conditions for forming the jump cannot be attained, the relative desirability of having insufficient tailwater as compared with having excessive tailwater should be considered. With insufficient tailwater the back pressure will be deficient and sweepout of the basin will occur. With an excess of tailwater the jump will be formed, and energy dissipation within the basin will be complete until the drowned-jump phenomenon becomes critical. Chute blocks, baffles, and end sills will also assist in energy dissipation, even with a drowned jump.

(f) *Stilling Basin Freeboard.*—Freeboard is ordinarily provided so that the stilling basin walls will not be overtopped by surges, splash and spray, and wave action set up by the turbulence of the jump. The surface roughness of the flow is related to the energy dissipated in the jump and to the depth of flow in the basin. The following empirical expression provides values that have proved satisfactory for most basins:

$$\text{Freeboard in feet} = 0.1(v_1 + d_2) \tag{25}$$

9.22. *Submerged Bucket Dissipators.*—When the tailwater depth is too great for the formation of a hydraulic jump, the high energy can be dissipated by the use of a submerged bucket deflector. The hydraulic behavior in this type of dissipator is manifested primarily by the formation of two rollers: one occurs on the surface, moves counterclockwise, and is contained within the region above the curved bucket; the other is a ground roller, moves clockwise, and is situated downstream from the bucket. The movements of these rollers, along with the intermingling of the incoming flows, effectively dissipate the high energy of the water and prevent excessive scouring downstream from the bucket.

Two types of roller buckets have been developed and model tested [15]. Their shape and dimensions are shown on figure 9-45. The general nature of the dissipating action for each type is represented on figure 9-46. The hydraulic actions of the two buckets have the same characteristics, but distinctive features of their flows differ to the extent that each has certain limitations. The high-velocity flow leaving the deflector lip of the solid bucket is directed upward (fig. 9-46(A)). This creates a high boil on the water surface and a violent ground roller moving clockwise downstream from the bucket. This ground roller continuously pulls loose material back towards the lip of the bucket and keeps some of the intermingling material in a constant state of agitation. The typical scour pattern that results from this action is shown on figure 9-47. The high-velocity jet leaves the lip of a slotted bucket at a flatter angle, and only a part of the high-velocity flow finds its way to the surface (fig. 9-46(B)). Thus, a less violent surface boil occurs, and there is a better dissipation of flow in the region above the ground roller. This results in less concentration of high-energy flow throughout the bucket and a smoother downstream flow.

Use of a solid bucket dissipator may be objectionable because of the abrasion on the concrete surfaces caused by material that is swept back along the lip of the deflector by the ground roller. In addition, the more turbulent surface roughness induced by the severe surface boil carries farther down the river, causing objectionable eddy currents that contribute to riverbank sloughing. Although the slotted bucket provides better energy dissipation with less severe surface and streambed disturbances, it is more sensitive to sweepout at lower tailwaters and is conducive to a diving and scouring action at excessive tailwaters. This is not the case with the solid bucket. Thus, the tailwater range that provides good performance with the slotted bucket is much narrower than that of the solid bucket. A

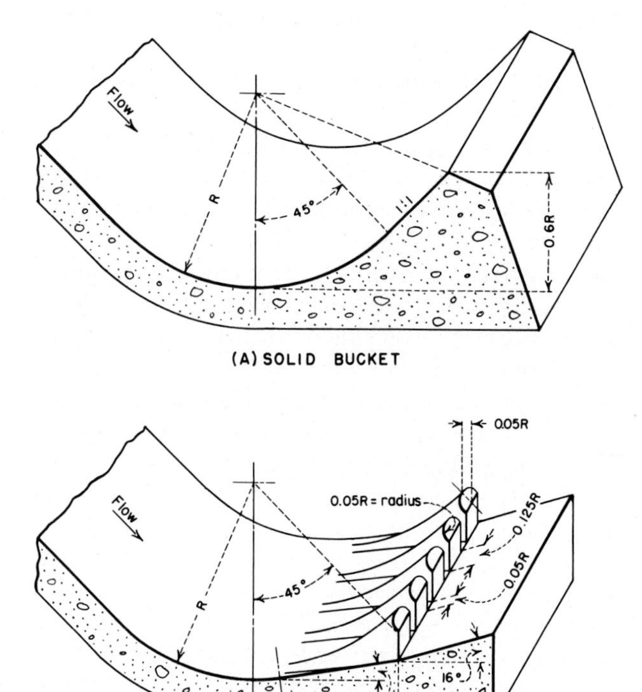

Figure 9-45.—Submerged buckets. 288-D-2430.

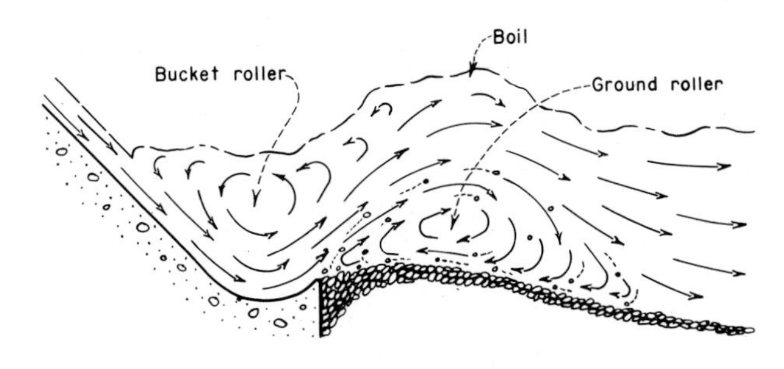

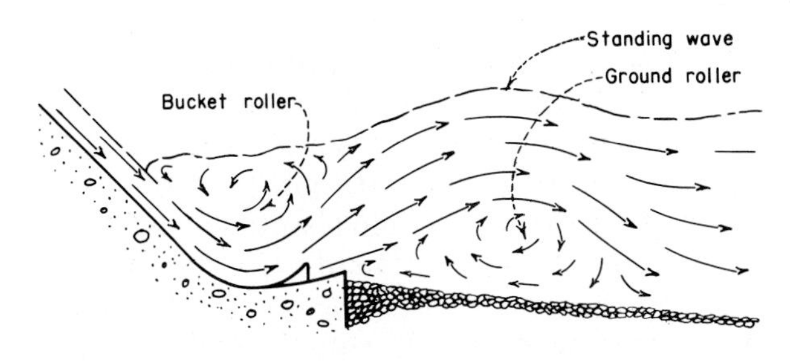

Figure 9-46.—Hydraulic action of solid and slotted buckets. 288-D-2431.

Figure 9-47.—Scour patterns downstream from a solid bucket dissipator for an ogee overflow crest. 288-D-2904.

solid bucket dissipator should not be used where the tailwater limitations of the slotted bucket can be met. Therefore, only the design of the slotted bucket will be discussed.

Flow characteristics of the slotted bucket are shown on figure 9-48. For deficient tailwater depths the incoming jet will sweep the surface roller out

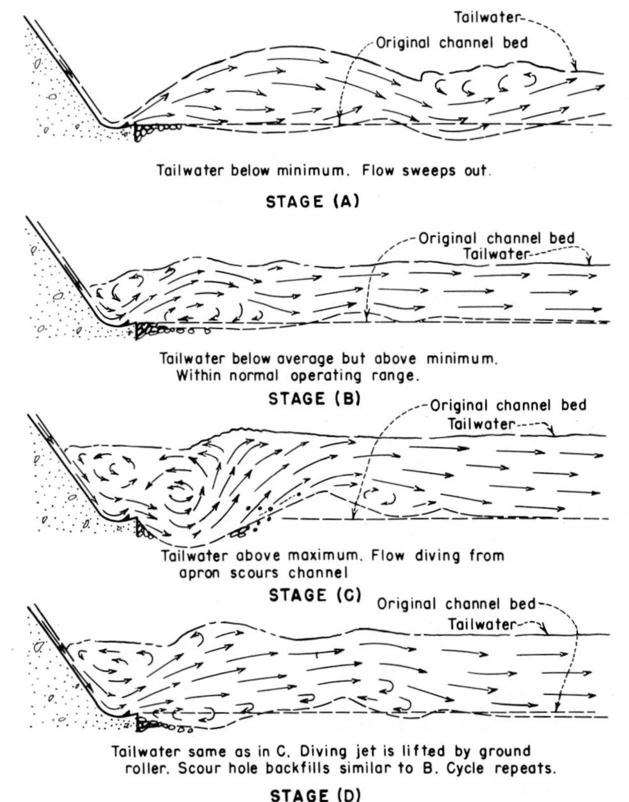

Figure 9-48.—Flow characteristics of a slotted bucket. 288-D-2432.

of the bucket and will produce a high-velocity flow downstream, both along the water surface and along the riverbed. This action is depicted as stage (A) on figure 9-48. As the tailwater depth is increased, there will be a depth at which instability of flow will occur, where sweepout and submergence will alternately prevail. To obtain continuous operation at the submerged stage, the minimum tailwater depth must be above this unstable state. Flow action within the acceptable operating stage is depicted as stage (B) on figure 9-48.

When the tailwater becomes excessively deep, the phenomenon called "diving flow" will occur. At this stage the jet issuing from the lip of the bucket will no longer rise and continue along the surface, but will intermittently become depressed and dive to the riverbed.

The position of the downstream roller will change with the change in position of the jet. It will occur at the surface when the jet dives and will form along the river bottom as a ground roller when the jet rides the surface. Scour will occur in the streambed at the point of impingement when the jet dives, but will be filled in by the ground roller when the jet rides. The characteristic flow pattern for the diving stage is depicted in (C) and (D) of figure 9-48. Maximum tailwater depths must be limited to forestall the diving flow phenomenon.

The design of the slotted bucket involves determination of the radius of curvature of the bucket and the allowable range of tailwater depths. These criteria, as determined from experimental results, are plotted on figure 9-49 in relation to the Froude number. The Froude numbers are for flow at the point where the incoming jet enters the bucket. Symbols and criteria are defined on figure 9-50.

9.23. *Examples of Designs of a Stilling Basin and an Alternative Submerged Bucket Dissipator.*— The designs of a stilling basin and of a submerged bucket dissipator are best explained by examples. Consider that it is required to make comparative designs of a stilling basin and of a submerged bucket dissipator for an overflow dam whose maximum discharge is 2,000 ft³/s and whose controlling dimensions and tailwater conditions are shown on figure 9-51.

For a first trial design, assume a crest length of 20 feet. The criteria for different discharges are then as follows:

Total discharge, Q, in cubic feet per second	2,000	1,000	500
Unit discharge, q, in cubic feet per second per foot	100	50	25
Assumed coefficient of discharge, C	3.9	3.7	3.5
Head, in feet on crest, $H_e = (q/C)^{2/3}$	8.7	5.7	3.7
Reservoir water level, elevation	1008.7	1005.7	1003.7
Tailwater level, elevation	985.0	981.0	978.0
Reservoir water level minus tailwater level, in feet	23.7	24.7	25.7
Velocity head at tailwater level, h_{v_t}, in feet (assuming no loss of specific energy)	23.7	24.7	25.7
Velocity of flow, in feet per second at tailwater level, $v_t = \sqrt{2gh_{v_t}}$	39.1	39.9	40.7
Depth of flow, in feet, at tailwater level, $d_t = q/v_t$	2.56	1.25	0.61
Froude number at tailwater level, $F_t = v_t/\sqrt{gd_t}$	4.3	6.3	9.2
Specific energy at tailwater level, $d_t + h_{v_t}$	26.3	25.9	26.3

Table 9-4 shows computations for a hydraulic-jump basin design. Conjugate depths and the required apron elevation for the various discharges are calculated to determine the critical condition. The lowest apron elevation is for the 2,000-ft³/s discharge. The Froude number of 6.2 and the incoming velocity not exceeding 60 ft/s determine that the type III stilling basin shown on figure 9-41 should be used for this design. The basin length will be 42 feet and the apron elevation will be 968.3.

For the submerged slotted bucket design, the minimum bucket radius for the maximum discharge is determined by use of figure 9-49. For a Froude number at tailwater level $F_t = 4.3$, the minimum radius is $0.42(d_t + h_{v_t}) = (0.42)(26.3) = 11.0$ feet. In this instance the riverbed slopes up, and the use of figure 9-49 results in the following values for the maximum and minimum tailwater for $F_t = 4.3$ and $R/(d_t + h_{v_t}) = 0.42$:

$$T_{max} = 7.5d_t = (7.5)(2.56) = 19.2 \text{ feet}$$
$$T_{min} = 6.5d_t = (6.5)(2.56) = 16.6 \text{ feet}$$

An average tailwater depth of 18 feet will place the bucket invert at elevation 985.0 − 18.0 = 967.0. It is now necessary to check the radius and tailwater conditions for less than maximum flows to determine whether the design is satisfactory throughout the range of discharge.

For a unit discharge of 50 ft³/s and for $F_t = 6.3$, the minimum radius is $0.26(d_t + h_{vt}) = 0.26(25.9) = 6.8$ feet. Therefore, the minimum radius of 11.0 feet determined for the maximum discharge will govern. The maximum and minimum tailwater values for $F_t = 6.3$ and $R/(d_t + h_{v_t}) = 11/25.9 = 0.42$ are:

$$T_{max} = 20.0d_t = 20.0(1.25) = 25.0 \text{ feet}$$
$$T_{min} = 10.1d_t = 10.1(1.25) = 12.6 \text{ feet}$$

The bucket invert level at elevation 967.0 as determined for the maximum discharge will provide a tailwater depth of 981.0 − 967.0 = 14 feet, which is within the safe limit for producing satisfactory roller action.

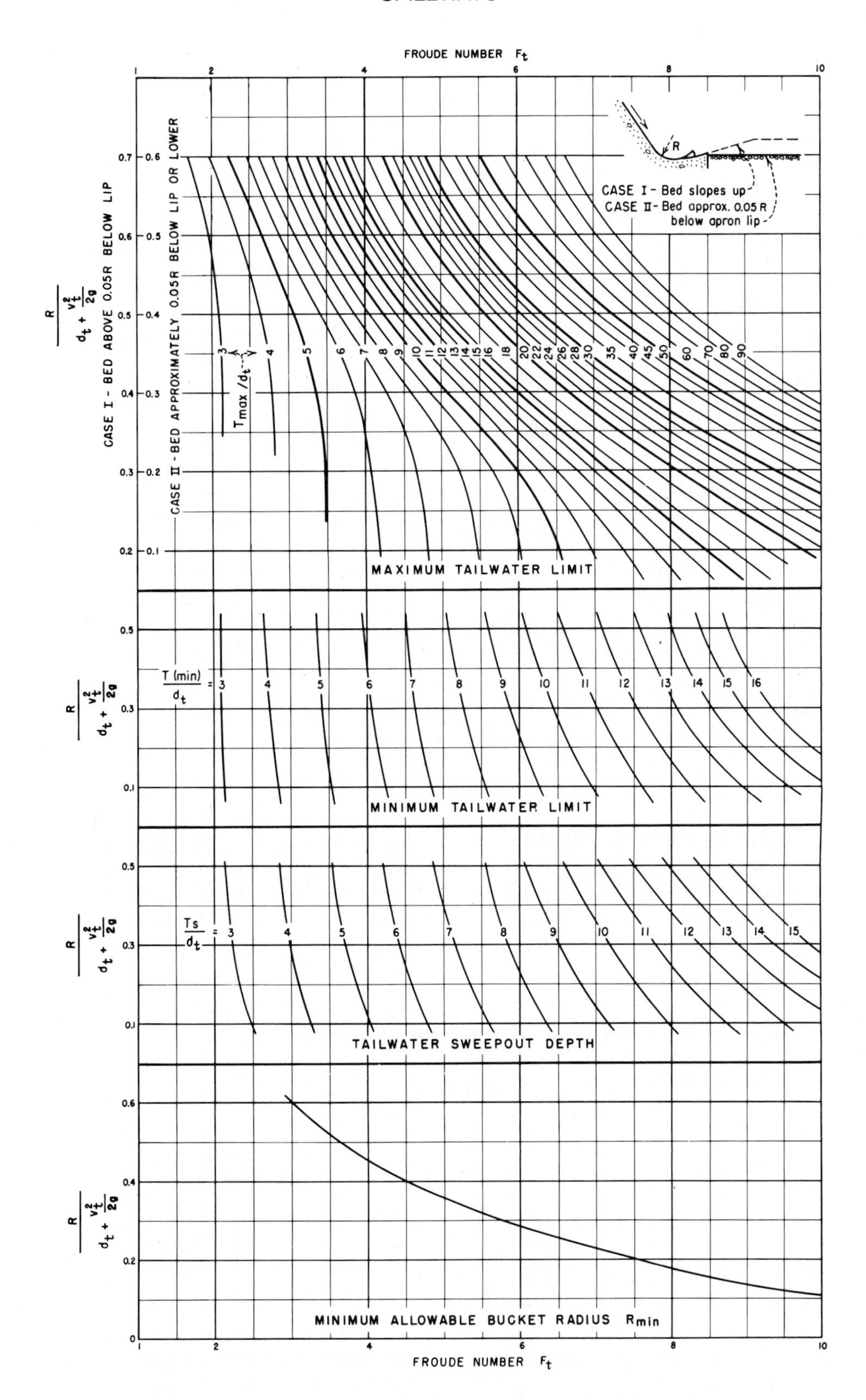

Figure 9-49.—Limiting criteria for slotted bucket design. 288–D–2433.

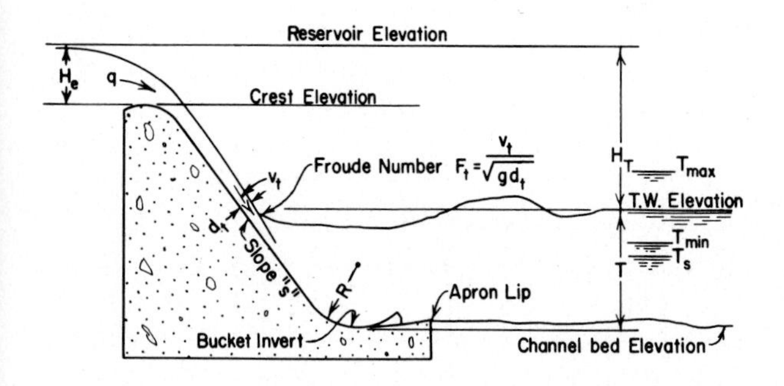

Figure 9-50.—Definition of symbols for submerged buckets. 288-D-2434.

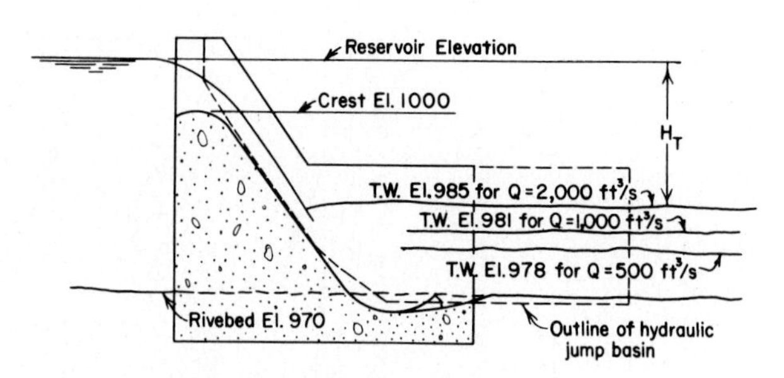

Figure 9-51.—Example of design of stilling device for overflow spillway. 288-D-2435.

Table 9-4.—Computations for hydraulic-jump basin design. For design example in section 9.23.

Discharge, Q, ft³/s	Discharge per foot, q, ft³/s	Reservoir level minus tailwater, feet	Conjugate depth, d_2, feet[1]	Tailwater elevation, feet	Required apron elevation, feet	Specific energy, H_E, at upstream end of basin,[2] feet	Upstream depth of flow at basin floor level,[3] d_1, feet	Upstream velocity at basin floor level,[3] v_1 ft/s	Froude number,[4] F_1
2,000	100	23.7	16.7	985.0	968.3	40.4	2.01	49.8	6.2
1,000	50	24.7	11.8	981.0	969.2	36.5	1.05	47.6	8.1
500	25	25.7	8.6	978.0	969.4	34.3	0.54	46.3	11.1

[1]From figure 9-43, assuming no loss in specific energy.
[2]H_E = Reservoir water surface minus apron elevation, assuming no loss in specific energy.
[3]$H_E = d_1 + (v_1^2/2g)$.
[4]$F_1 = v_1/\sqrt{gd}$.

The same procedure should be followed to verify that satisfactory roller action will result for a unit discharge of 25 ft³/s. In this case the minimum radius of 11.0 feet determined for the maximum discharge was found to govern. T_{max} and T_{min} were found to be 50 feet and 10.4 feet, respectively, compared with the 11 feet of tailwater depth provided by the invert elevation placed at 967.0 feet. It may now be considered that the design based on maximum discharges will be satisfactory for all lower discharges.

If a wider range of safe tailwater depths is desired, the radius of curvature of the bucket can be increased. Thus, for a bucket radius of 12 feet, for the maximum discharge, $T_{min} = 6.5d_t = 16.6$, and $T_{max} = 8.5\, d_t = 22.5$ feet. An average tailwater depth of 20 feet, placing the bucket invert at elevation 965.0, will provide more leeway for tailwater variations.

9.24. *Plunge Basins.*—When a free jet falls vertically into a pool in a riverbed, a plunge pool will be scoured to a depth that is related to the discharge, the height of the fall, the depth of tailwater, and the bed material [2]. The riverbed will be scoured as a result of the abrading action of the churning water and sediment in the pool. Ultimately, the scour will reach a limiting depth as the energy of the jet is no longer able to remove bed material from the scour hole. A simple empirical approximation of the ultimate scour depth is:

$$D = 1.32H^{0.225}q^{0.54} \tag{26}$$

where:

D = the ultimate scour depth below tailwater level, in feet,
H = the elevation drop from reservoir to tailwater, in feet, and
q = the unit discharge, in cubic feet per second per foot.

When a jet is issued from a structure in a more horizontal direction, a trapezoidal plunge pool may be used. Such a basin should be used only where the jet discharges into the air and then plunges downward into the basin. Tests have shown that if the angle of impingement is less than about 25° above the horizontal, the jet will ride and skip across the surface at high velocity. This will cause waves and eddies in the basin sufficient to erode the side slopes, and there will be high exit velocities.

No fixed criteria have yet been established for plunge basins that will provide satisfactory dissipation for all heads, discharges, and incoming jet conditions. However, criteria established for several small outlet works plunge basins that have operated reasonably satisfactorily are presented only as a preliminary guide for approximate basin geometry (the general arrangement of this basin is shown on fig. 9-52): The basin depths were about one-fifth of the difference in elevation between maximum reservoir water surfaces and maximum tailwater levels. The minimum bottom widths were the width of the incoming jet or the width required to limit the average velocity at the end of the basin to about 3 ft/s, whichever was greater.

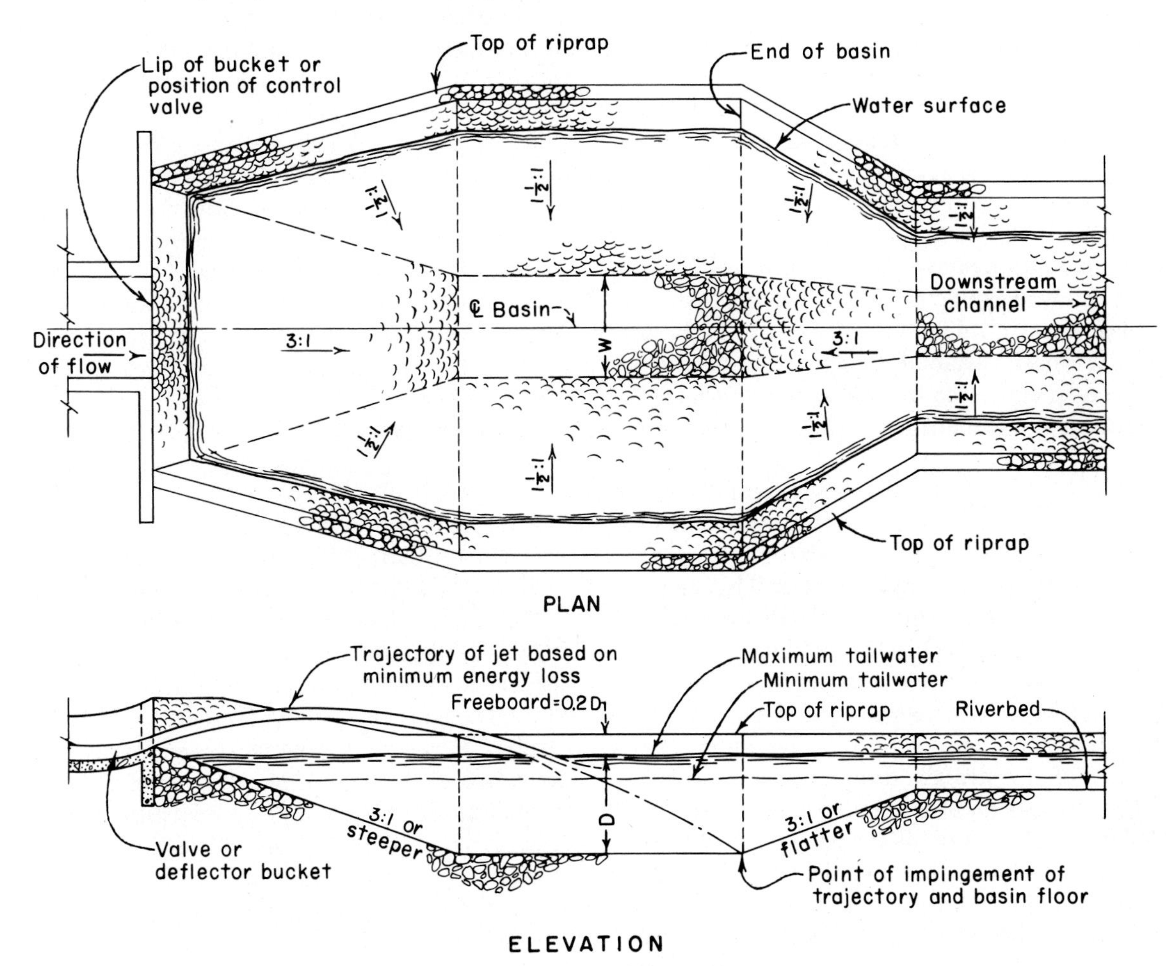

Figure 9-52.—Plunge basin energy dissipator. 288–D–2534.

F. HYDRAULICS OF SPILLWAYS

9.25. *Free Overfall (Straight Drop) Spillways.*—(a) *General.*—The hydraulic problems of the free overfall spillway are concerned with the characteristics of the control and with the dissipation of flow in the downstream basin. Flow over the control ordinarily is free discharging; air is admitted to the underside of the nappe to avoid depression of the jet by reduced underneath pressure. The flow in the downstream basin may be dissipated by the hydraulic jump, by impact and turbulence induced in a basin with impact blocks, or by a slotted grating dissipator installed immediately downstream from the control.

The control may be either sharp-crested to provide a fully contracted vertical jet, broad-crested to effect a fully suppressed jet, or shaped to increase the crest efficiency. Discharge coefficients will approximate those indicated in section 9.12. The sides of the control usually are arranged to allow full-side contraction to provide side space for the access of air to the underside of the nappe. This contraction is effected by providing square abutment headwalls or by installing square-cornered vertical offsets along the piers or walls opposite the crest. The effective length of the crest is then determined according to equation (4) where both K_p and K_a are approximately 0.20.

The dimensions of the stilling basin for the free overfall spillway can be related to two independent variables: the drop distance, Y, and the unit discharge, q. These variables, which are dimensional terms, can be expressed in a dimensionless ratio by expressing q in lineal form by means of the equation for critical depth, $d_c = \sqrt[3]{q^2/g}$; dividing by Y: $d_c/Y = \sqrt[3]{q^2/gY^3}$. From this expression it can be seen that q^2/gY^3 is a dimensionless ratio that can be used as an independent variable to which the individual dimensions may be related. This ratio is called the "drop number" and is designated $\overline{D}$. It can be shown that $\overline{D}$ is the product of $F_1{}^2$ and $(D_1/Y)^3$, where the Froude number $F_1 = v_1/\sqrt{d_1 g}$ at the point where the nappe meets the basin floor.

(b) *Hydraulic-Jump Basins.*—The jump characteristics of the straight drop basin are basically the same as those for other jump basins, except that the position of the start of the jump cannot be determined as readily. On figure 9-53, the point of the start of the jump (point X) will vary with the vertical drop distance and is influenced by the upper nappe pool depth, d_f. The basin design downstream from point X will be patterned after the designs discussed in section 9.21, once distance L_d is determined. Values of the depth d_1, and of the Froude number, F_1, at the start of the jump in relation to the drop number, $\overline{D}$, are shown on figure 9-53. These relations may be used for determining the basin dimensions.

Where tailwater depths are greater than the conjugate depth d_2, the jump will move back on the free-falling nappe, raising the depth d_f of the undernappe pool. With greater depths of the undernappe pool, the nappe will not plunge immediately to the floor of the basin, but will be deflected upward along the top of the underpool so that it will meet the floor to the right of point X. The distance to the start of the jump, L_d, will become progressively longer as the tailwater depth is increased. Average values of L_d in relation to h_d/H_e, as determined from tests, are plotted on figure 9-53. For a basin with excessive depth, the type III basin discussed in section 9.21 is most adaptable. The impact block type basin, discussed below, also can be adopted for low drop spillways with excessive tailwater depths.

(c) *Impact Block Type Basins.*—An impact block basin that has been developed [4] for low heads dissipates energy reasonably well for a wide range of tailwater depths. The high energy is principally dissipated by turbulence induced by the impingement of the incoming flow on the impact blocks. The required tailwater depths, therefore, become more or less independent of the drop height. The linear proportions are as follows:

Minimum basin length $L_B = L_p + 2.55d_c$
Minimum length to upstream face of baffle block $= L_p + 0.8d_c$
Minimum tailwater depth $d_{tw} = 2.15d_c$
Optimum baffle block height $= 0.8d_c$
Width and spacing of baffle blocks $= \pm 0.4d_c$
Optimum height of end sill $= 0.4d_c$

(d) *Slotted-Grating Dissipators.*—An effective dissipator for small drops is shown on figure 9-54. This device has been tested for values of the Froude number, F_1, as determined at basin apron level, in the range of 2.5 to 4.5. For this arrangement the overfalling sheet is separated into a number of long, thin segments that fall nearly vertically into the basin below, where the energy is dissipated by turbulence. To be effective, the length of the grating, L_G, must be such that the entire incoming flow falls through the slots before reaching the downstream end. The length is therefore a function of the total discharge, the velocity of the incoming flow, and the area of the grating slots. Experimental tests indicate that the following relation gives an effective design:

$$L_G = \frac{Q}{0.245wN\sqrt{2gH_e}} \tag{27}$$

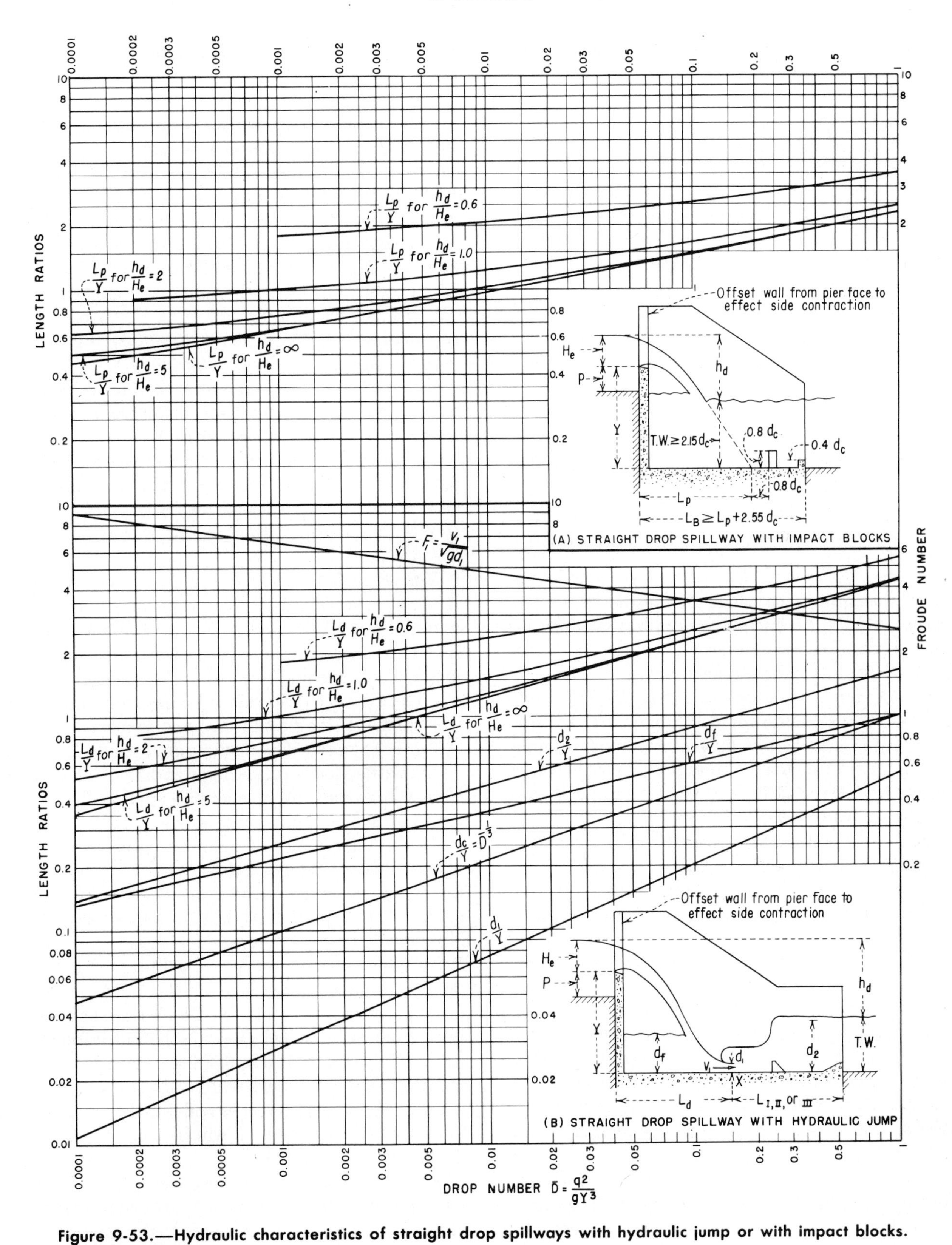

Figure 9-53.—Hydraulic characteristics of straight drop spillways with hydraulic jump or with impact blocks. 288-D-2437.

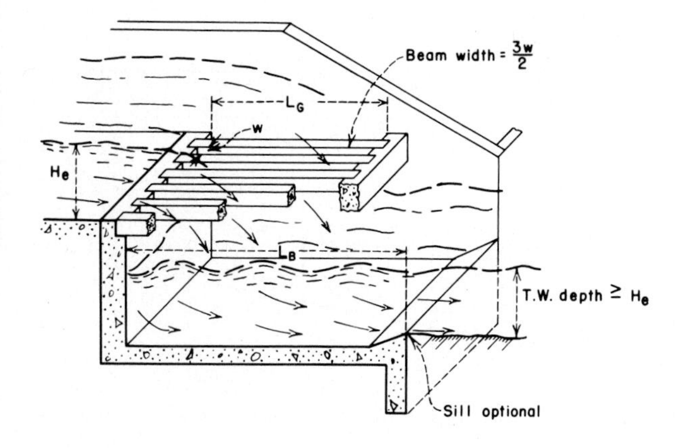

Figure 9-54.—Slotted-grating dissipator. 288-D-2438.

where:

L_G = the length of the grating, in feet,
w = the width of the slot, in feet,
N = the number of slots, and
H_e = the depth of flow upstream from the drop.

The length of the basin, L_B, should be approximately $1.2L_G$. An end sill similar to that for basin type I, discussed in section 9.21, may be provided to improve the hydraulic action.

(e) *Example of Design of a Free Overfall Spillway.*—The procedure for designing a free overfall spillway is best shown by means of an example. Consider that such a spillway must be designed to discharge 500 ft³/s. The drop from the spillway crest to the tailwater level for a flow of 500 ft³/s is 12 feet. The tailwater elevation is 108.0. The approach channel is 20 feet long, and the approach floor is level with the spillway crest, which is at elevation 120.0. Each type of energy dissipator is to be investigated.

The procedure for designing a hydraulic-jump basin is as follows: First, assume the effective length of the spillway crest is 15 feet and that C is approximately 3.0. The unit discharge q = 500/15 = 33.3 ft³/s and $H_e = (q/C)^{2/3} = (33.3/3.0)^{2/3} = 5.0$ feet. The reservoir water surface elevation, therefore, is 120.0 + 5.0 = 125.0. Therefore, the drop from reservoir level to tailwater level will be approximately 17 feet.

Assume that an offset of 0.5 foot is provided along each side of the weir to effect side contractions for aerating the underside of the sheet, and that the offset is square-cornered. Then the net crest length, which will also be the stilling basin width, is $L' = L+2K_aH_e+2(0.5) = 15+2(0.2)(5)+1.0 = 18.0$ feet.

The nomograph on figure 9-43 is used to determine the approximate apron level of the jump basin, assuming the effective width of the basin is 15 feet and (for the first trial) that there will be no loss of energy between the reservoir and the point where the jet strikes the basin floor. From scale A, the conjugate depth d_2 = 8.8 feet for q = 33.3 ft³/s and H_T = 17 feet. This places the apron floor at elevation 99.2. The drop distance $Y = 120-99.2 = 70.8$ feet, and drop number $\overline{D} = q^2/gY^3 = 33.3^2/32.2(20.8)^3 = 0.0038$. From the figure 9-53, for $\overline{D} = 0.0038$, $d_2/Y = 0.375$, and d_2 = 7.8 feet. The apron level then must be adjusted to an elevation that is d_2 below the tailwater elevation 108.0, or elevation 100.2.

For the second trial, the adjusted value of Y is 19.8, and $\overline{D} = 33.3^2/32.2\ (19.8)^3 = 0.0044$. From figure 9-53, for $\overline{D} = 0.0044$ and $h_d/H_e = 17/5 = 3.4$, $L_d/Y = 1.02$, and L_d = 20.2 feet, d_1 = 1.1 feet, and $F_1 = 5.3$.

With $F_1 = 5.3$, $d_1 = 1.1$, and $d_2 = 7.8$, the type III basin arrangement, shown on figure 9-41, can be used. From figure 9-41, $L/d^2 = 2.37$, and $L = 18.5$ feet. The length of the basin measured from the vertical crest is equal to $L_d+L = 20.2+18.5 = 38.7$ feet. The distance of the baffle blocks from the vertical crest for this basin will be 20.2 feet + $0.8d_2$ = 20.2 + 0.8(7.8) = 26.4 feet, approximately.

The baffle blocks will be approximately $1.5d_1$, or 1.6 feet, high and will be about 14 inches wide and spaced at about 28-inch centers.

For the impact block basin, the procedure is as follows: The critical depth $d_c = \sqrt[3]{33.3^3/32.2} = 3.3$ feet. Then from figure 9-53, for $\overline{D} = 0.0044$ and $h_d/H_e = 3.4$, $L_p/Y = 0.85$, and L_p = 17.0 feet. The minimum length of the basin $L_B = L_P + 2.55d_c = 17.0 + 2.55(3.3) = 25.4$ feet, say 26 feet. The minimum tailwater depth of $2.15d_c$ = 7.1 feet, which places the basin floor at elevation 100.9. The distance from the vertical crest to the baffle blocks will be $L + 0.8d_c = 17.0 + 0.8(3.3) = 19.6$ feet, say 20 feet. The baffle blocks will be about $0.8d_c$ = 3.0 feet high and about 18 inches wide, spaced at about 3-foot centers. The end sill will be $0.4d_c$ = 1.5 feet high.

It can be seen from the above result that an impact block basin can be almost 13 feet shorter than a hydraulic-jump basin, and that the impact block basin will be 0.7 foot shallower. The baffle blocks for the hydraulic-jump basin will be smaller and spaced closer together than those for the impact block basin.

This example shows that the impact block basin is considerably smaller than the hydraulic-jump basin. However, the impact block basin should be limited to uses where the drop distance does not exceed 20 feet. Furthermore, as previously explained, the foundation for an impact block basin must be of better quality because of the concentrated forces involved. The hydraulic-jump basin, therefore, has a much wider application.

The slotted-grating dissipator is not suitable in this case because the Froude number of 5.3 is greater than 4.5, which is the tested limit for a practical slotted-grating design.

9.26. Drop Inlet (Shaft or Morning Glory) Spillways.—(a) *General Characteristics.*—Typical floor conditions and discharge characteristics of a drop inlet spillway are shown on figure 9-55. The discharge curve shows that crest control (condition 1) will prevail for heads between the ordinates of *a* and *g*; orifice or tube control (condition 2) will govern for heads between the ordinates of *g* and *h*; and the spillway conduit will flow full for heads above the ordinate of *h* (condition 3).

The flow characteristics of a drop inlet spillway vary according to the proportional sizes of the different elements. Changing the diameter of the crest will change the curve *ab* on figure 9-55 so that the ordinate of *g* on curve *cd* will be either higher or lower. For a larger diameter crest, greater outflows can be discharged over the weir at low heads, the transition will fill up, and tube control will occur with a lesser head on the crest. Similarly, by altering the size of the throat of the tube, the position of curve *cd* will change, indicating the heads above which tube control will prevail. If the transition is made of such size that curve *cd* is moved to coincide with or lie to the right of point *j*, the control will shift directly from the crest to the downstream end of the conduit. The details of the hydraulic flow characteristics are discussed in the following subsections.

(b) *Crest Discharge.*—For small heads, flow over the drop inlet spillway is governed by the characteristics of crest discharge. The vertical transition beyond the crest will flow partly full and the flow will cling to the sides of the shaft. As the discharge over the crest increases, the overflowing annular nappe will become thicker and, eventually, the nappe flow will converge into a solid vertical jet. The point where the annular nappe joins the solid jet is called the crotch. After the solid jet forms, a "boil" will occupy the region above the crotch; both the crotch and the top of the boil become progressively higher with large discharges. For high heads the crotch and boil may almost flood out, showing only a slight depression and eddy at the surface.

Until the nappe converges to form a solid jet, free-discharging weir flow prevails. After the crotch and boil form, submergence begins to affect the weir flow and, ultimately, the crest will drown out. Flow is then governed either by the contracted jet formed by the overflow entrance, or by the shape and size of the vertical transition if it does not conform to the jet shape. Vortex action must be minimized to maintain converging flow into the drop inlet. Guide piers are often installed along the crest for this purpose [13, 14].

If the crest profile and transition conform to the shape of the lower nappe of a jet flowing over a sharp-crested circular weir, the discharge for flow over the crest and through the transition can be expressed as $Q = CLH^{3/2}$ (see eq. (3)); where H is the head measured either to the apex of the undernappe of the overflow, to the spring point of the circular sharp-crested weir, or to some other established point on the overflow. Similarly, the choice of the length, L, is related to some specific point of measurement such as the length of the circle at the apex, along the periphery at the upstream face of the crest, or along some other chosen reference line. C will change with different definitions of L and H. If L is taken at the outside periphery of the overflow crest (the origin of the coordinates on figure 9-56) and if the head is measured to the apex of the overflow shape, equation (3) can be written:

$$Q = C_o(2\pi R_s)H_o^{3/2} \tag{28}$$

It is apparent that the discharge coefficient for a circular crest differs from that for a straight crest because of the effects of submergence and back pressure incident to the joining of the converging flows. Thus, C_o must be related to both H_o and R_s, and can be expressed in terms of H_o/R_s. The relationship of C_o, as determined from model tests [24], to H_o/R_s for three conditions of approach depth is plotted on figure 9-57. These coefficients are valid only if the crest profile and transition shape conform to that of the jet flowing over a

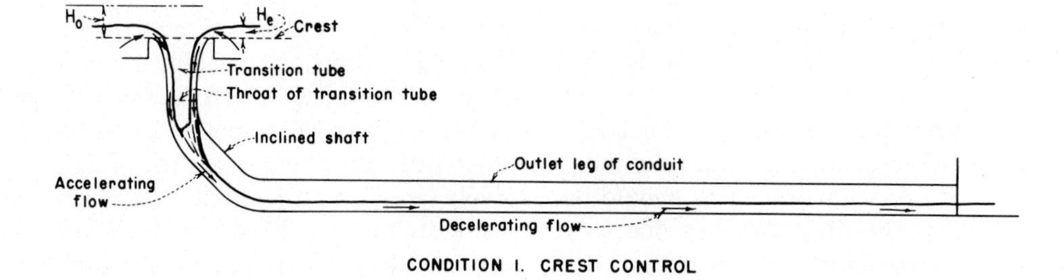

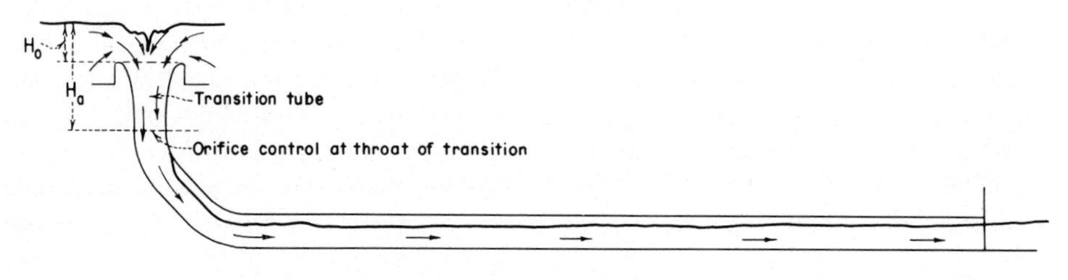

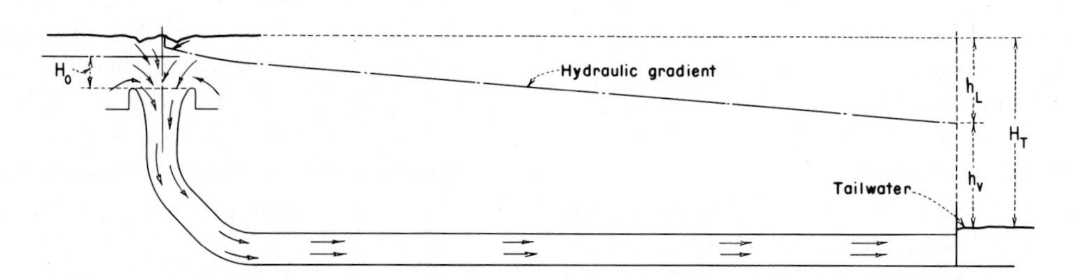

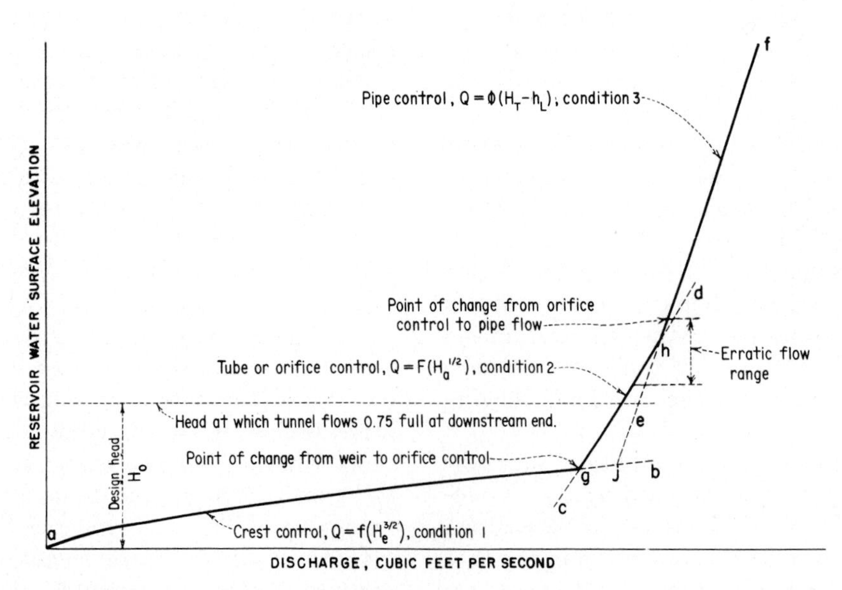

Figure 9-55.—Nature of flow and discharge characteristics of a morning glory spillway. 288–D–2439.

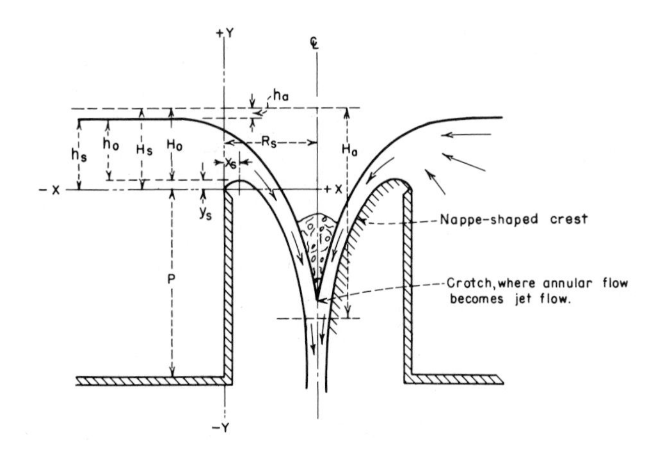

Figure 9-56.—Elements of nappe-shaped profile for circular weir. 288–D–2440.

sharp-crested circular weir at H_o head and if aeration is provided so that subatmospheric pressures do not exist along the lower nappe surface contact.

When the crest outline and transition shape conform to the profile of the nappe shape for an H_o head over the crest, free flow prevails for H_o/R_s up to approximately 0.45, and weir control governs. As H_o/R_s increases above 0.45, the weir partly submerges, and flow showing characteristics of a submerged weir is the controlling condition. When the H_o/R_s ratio approaches 1.0, the water surface above the weir is completely submerged. For this and higher stages of H_o/R_s, the flow phenomenon is that of orifice flow. The weir formula, $Q = CLH^{3/2}$, is used as the measure of flow through the drop inlet entrance regardless of the submergence, by using a coefficient that reflects the flow conditions through the various H_o/R_s ranges. Thus, from figure 9-57 it can be seen that the weir coefficient only changes slightly from that normally indicated for $H_o/R_s <$ 0.45, but reduces rapidly for the higher H_o/R_s values.

It should be noted that for most conditions of flow over a circular weir, the discharge coefficient increases with a reduction in the approach depth; whereas, the opposite is true for a straight weir. For both weirs, a shallower approach lessens the upward vertical velocity component and, consequently, suppresses the contraction of the nappe. However, for the circular weir, the submergence effect is reduced because of a depressed upper nappe surface, giving the jet a quicker downward impetus, which lowers the position of the crotch and increases the discharge.

Discharge coefficients for partial heads of H_e on the crest can be determined from figure 9-58 to prepare a discharge-head relationship. The designer must be cautious in applying the above criteria because subatmospheric pressure or submergence effects may alter the flow conditions differently for various profile shapes. This criteria, therefore, should not be applied for flow conditions where $H_e/R_s > 0.4$.

(c) *Crest Profiles.*—Values of coordinates that define the shape of the lower surface of a nappe flowing over an aerated sharp-crested circular weir for various conditions of P/R_s and H_s/R_s are shown in tables 9-5, 9-6, and 9-7. These data are based on experimental tests [24] conducted by the Bureau of Reclamation. The relationships of H_s to H_o are shown on figure 9-59. Typical upper and lower nappe profiles for various values of H_s/R_s are plotted on figure 9-60 in terms of X/H_s and Y/H_s for the condition of $P/R_s = 2.0$.

Figure 9-61 shows typical lower nappe profiles, plotted for various values of H_s for a given value of R_s. In contrast to the straight weir where the nappe springs farther from the crest as the head increases, it can be seen from figure 9-61 that the lower nappe profile for the circular crest springs farther only in the region of the high point of the trace, and then only for H_s/R_s values up to about 0.5.

The profiles become increasingly suppressed for larger H_s/R_s values. Below the high point of the profile, the traces cross and the shapes for the higher heads fall inside those for the lower heads. Thus, if the crest profile is designed for heads where H_s/R_s exceeds about 0.25 to 0.3, it appears that subatmospheric pressure will occur along some portion for the profile when heads are less than the designed maximum. If subatmospheric pressures are to be avoided along the crest profile, the crest shape selected should give support to the overflow nappe for the smaller H_s/R_s ratios. Figure 9-62 shows the approximate increase in radius required to minimize subatmospheric pressures on the crest. The crest shape for the enlarged crest radius is then based on $H'_s/R'_s = 0.3$.

(d) *Transition Design.*—The diameter of a jet issuing from a horizontal orifice can be determined for any point below the water surface if it is assumed that the continuity equation, $Q = av$, is valid and if friction and other losses are neglected.

For a circular jet the area is equal to πR^2. The discharge is equal to $av = \pi R^2 \sqrt{2gH_a}$. Solving for R,

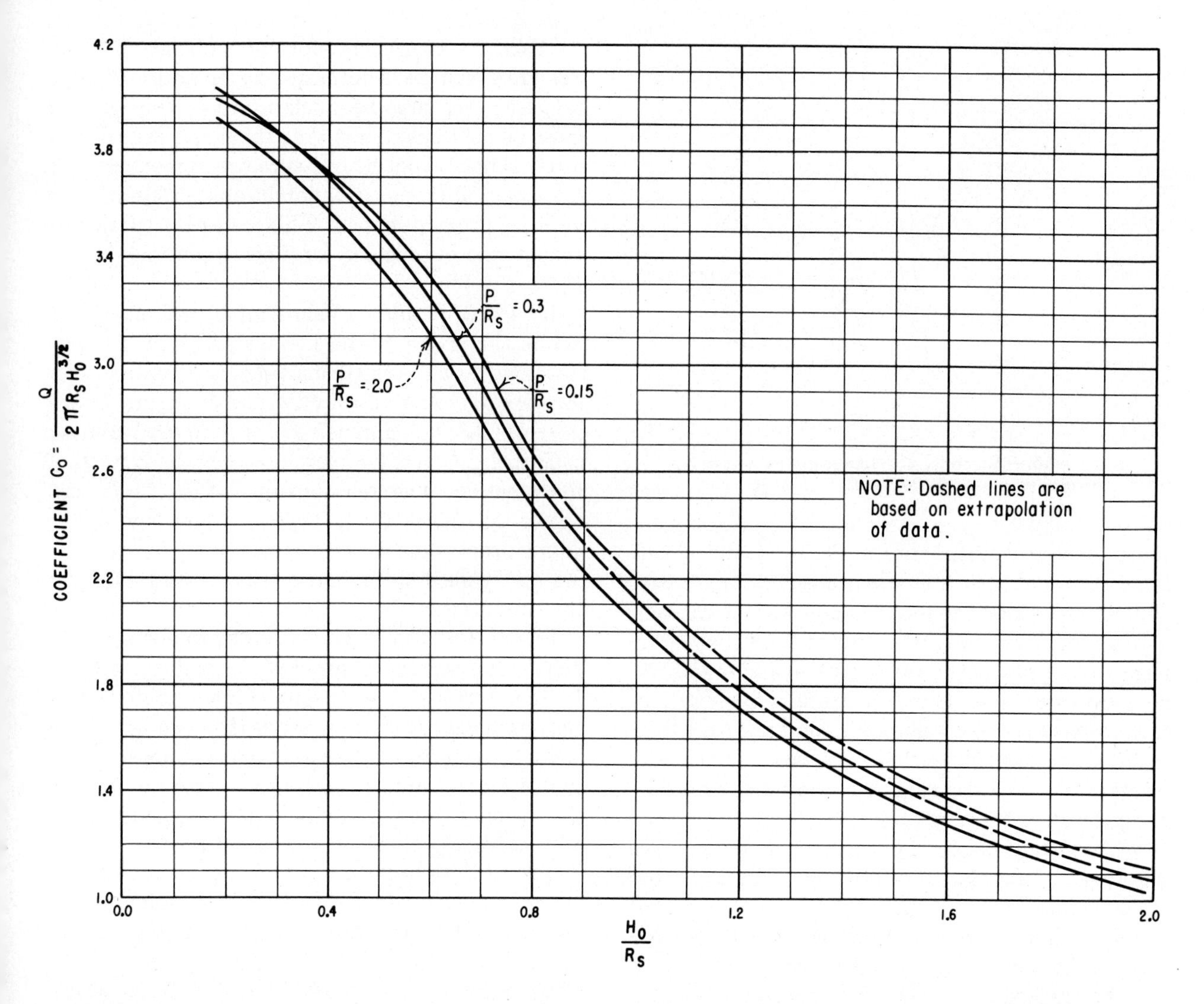

Figure 9-57.—Relationship of circular crest coefficient C_o to H_o/R_s for different approach depths (aerated nappe). 288–D–2441.

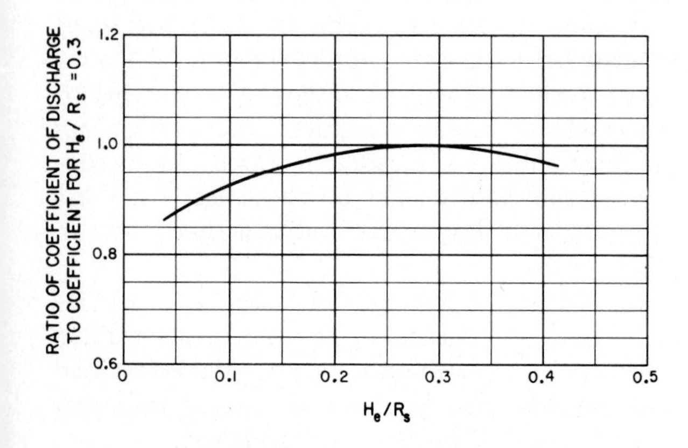

Figure 9-58.—Circular crest discharge coefficient for other than design head. 288–D–2442.

$R = Q_a^{1/2}/5H_a^{1/4}$; where H_a is equal to the distance between the water surface and the elevation under consideration. The diameter of the jet thus decreases with the distance of the free vertical fall for normal design applications.

If an assumed total loss (including jet contraction losses, friction losses, velocity losses from direction changes, etc.) is taken as 0.1 H_a, the equation for determining the approximate required shaft radius may be written:

$$R = 0.204 \frac{Q_a^{1/2}}{H_a^{1/4}} \tag{29}$$

Because this equation is for the shape of the jet,

Table 9-5.—Coordinates of lower nappe surface for different values of H_s/R_s when P/R_s = 2.0.

[Negligible approach velocity and aerated nappe]

H_s/R_s	0.00	0.10*	0.20	0.25	0.30	0.35	0.40	0.45	0.50	0.60	0.80	1.00	1.20	1.50	2.00
X/H_s	Y/H_s for portion of profile above weir crest														
0.000	0.0000	0.0000	0.0000	0.0000	0.0000	0.0000	0.0000	0.0000	0.0000	0.0000	0.0000	0.0000	0.0000	0.0000	0.0000
.010	.0150	.0145	.0133	.0130	.0128	.0125	.0122	.0119	.0116	.0112	.0104	.0095	.0086	.0077	.0070
.020	.0280	.0265	.0250	.0243	.0236	.0231	.0225	.0220	.0213	.0202	.0180	.0159	.0140	.0115	.0090
.030	.0395	.0365	.0350	.0337	.0327	.0317	.0308	.0299	.0289	.0270	.0231	.0198	.0168	.0126	.0085
.040	.0490	.0460	.0435	.0417	.0403	.0389	.0377	.0363	.0351	.0324	.0268	.0220	.0176	.0117	.0050
.050	.0575	.0535	.0506	.0487	.0471	.0454	.0436	.0420	.0402	.0368	.0292	.0226	.0168	.0092	
.060	.0650	.0605	.0570	.0550	.0531	.0510	.0489	.0470	.0448	.0404	.0305	.0220	.0147	.0053	
.070	.0710	.0665	.0627	.0605	.0584	.0560	.0537	.0514	.0487	.0432	.0308	.0201	.0114	.0001	
.080	.0765	.0710	.0677	.0655	.0630	.0603	.0578	.0550	.0521	.0455	.0301	.0172	.0070		
.090	.0820	.0765	.0722	.0696	.0670	.0640	.0613	.0581	.0549	.0471	.0287	.0135	.0018		
.100	.0860	.0810	.0762	.0734	.0705	.0672	.0642	.0606	.0570	.0482	.0264	.0089			
.120	.0940	.0880	.0826	.0790	.0758	.0720	.0683	.0640	.0596	.0483	.0195				
.140	.1000	.0935	.0872	.0829	.0792	.0750	.0 05	.0654	.0599	.0460	.0101				
.160	.1045	.0980	.0905	.0855	.0812	.0765	.0710	.0651	.0585	.0418					
.180	.1080	.1010	.0927	.0872	.0820	.0766	.0705	.0637	.0559	.0361					
.200	.1105	.1025	.0938	.0877	.0819	.0756	.0688	.0611	.0521	.0292					
.250	.1120	.1035	.0926	.0850	.0773	.0683	.0596	.0495	.0380	.0068					
.300	.1105	.1000	.0850	.0764	.0668	.0559	.0446	.0327	.0174						
.350	.1060	.0930	.0750	.0650	.0540	.0410	.0280	.0125							
.400	.0970	.0830	.0620	.0500	.0365	.0220	.0060								
.450	.0845	.0700	.0450	.0310	.0170	.000									
.500	.0700	.0520	.0250	.0100											
.550	.0520	.0320	.0020												
.600	.0320	.0080													
.650	.0090														
Y/H_s	X/H_s for portion of profile below weir crest														
0.000	0.668	0.615	0.554	0.520	0.487	0.450	0.413	0.376	0.334	0.262	0.158	0.116	0.093	0.070	0.048
−.020	.705	.652	.592	.560	.526	.488	.452	.414	.369	.293	.185	.145	.120	.096	.074
−.040	.742	.688	.627	.596	.563	.524	.487	.448	.400	.320	.212	.165	.140	.115	.088
−.060	.777	.720	.660	.630	.596	.557	.519	.478	.428	.342	.232	.182	.155	.129	.100
−.080	.808	.752	.692	.662	.628	.589	.549	.506	.454	.363	.250	.197	.169	.140	.110
−.100	.838	.784	.722	.692	.657	.618	.577	.532	.478	.381	.266	.210	.180	.150	.118
−.150	.913	.857	.793	.762	.725	.686	.641	.589	.531	.423	.299	.238	.204	.170	.132
−.200	.978	.925	.860	.826	.790	.745	.698	.640	.575	.459	.326	.260	.224	.184	.144
−.250	1.040	.985	.919	.883	.847	.801	.750	.683	.613	.490	.348	.280	.239	.196	.153
−.300	1.100	1.043	.976	.941	.900	.852	.797	.722	.648	.518	.368	.296	.251	.206	.160
−.400	1.207	1.150	1.079	1.041	1.000	.944	.880	.791	.706	.562	.400	.322	.271	.220	.168
−.500	1.308	1.246	1.172	1.131	1.087	1.027	.951	.849	.753	.598	.427	.342	.287	.232	.173
−.600	1.397	1.335	1.260	1.215	1.167	1.102	1.012	.898	.793	.627	.449	.359	.300	.240	.179
−.800	1.563	1.500	1.422	1.369	1.312	1.231	1.112	.974	.854	.673	.482	.384	.320	.253	.184
−1.000	1.713	1.646	1.564	1.508	1.440	1.337	1.189	1.030	.899	.710	.508	.402	.332	.260	.188
−1.200	1.846	1.780	1.691	1.635	1.553	1.422	1.248	1.074	.933	.739	.528	.417	.340	.266	
−1.400	1.970	1.903	1.808	1.748	1.653	1.492	1.293	1.108	.963	.760	.542	.423	.344		
−1.600	2.085	2.020	1.918	1.855	1.742	1.548	1.330	1.133	.988	.780	.553	.430			
−1.800	2.196	2.130	2.024	1.957	1.821	1.591	1.358	1.158	1.008	.797	.563	.433			
−2.000	2.302	2.234	2.126	2.053	1.891	1.630	1.381	1.180	1.025	.810	.572				
−2.500	2.557	2.475	2.354	2.266	2.027	1.701	1.430	1.221	1.059	.838	.588				
−3.000	2.778	2.700	2.559	2.428	2.119	1.748	1.468	1.252	1.086	.853					
−3.500	--------	2.916	2.749	2.541	2.171	1.777	1.489	1.267	1.102						
−4.000	--------	3.114	2.914	2.620	2.201	1.796	1.500	1.280							
−4.500	--------	3.306	3.053	2.682	2.220	1.806	1.509								
−5.000	--------	3.488	3.178	2.734	2.227	1.811									
−5.500	--------	3.653	3.294	2.779	2.229										
−6.000	--------	3.820	3.405	2.812	2.232										
H_s/R_s	0.00	0.10	0.20	0.25	0.30	0.35	0.40	0.45	0.50	0.60	0.80	1.00	1.20	1.50	2.00

*The tabulation for H_s/R_s = 0.10 was obtained by interpolation between H_s/R_s = 0 and 0.20.

Table 9-6.—Coordinates of lower nappe surface for different values of H_s/R_s when $P/R_s = 0.30$.

H_s/R_s	0.20	0.25	0.30	0.35	0.40	0.45	0.50	0.60	0.80
X/H_s	Y/H_s for portion of profile above weir crest								
0.000	0.0000	0.0000	0.0000	0.0000	0.0000	0.0000	0.0000	0.0000	0.0000
.010	.0130	.0130	.0130	.0125	.0120	.0120	.0115	.0110	.0100
.020	.0245	.0242	.0240	.0235	.0225	.0210	.0195	.0180	.0170
.030	.0340	.0335	.0330	.0320	.0300	.0290	.0270	.0240	.0210
.040	.0415	.0411	.0390	.0380	.0365	.0350	.0320	.0285	.0240
.050	.0495	.0470	.0455	.0440	.0420	.0395	.0370	.0325	.0245
.060	.0560	.0530	.0505	.0490	.0460	.0440	.0405	.0350	.0250
.070	.0610	.0575	.0550	.0530	.0500	.0470	.0440	.0370	.0245
.080	.0660	.0620	.0590	.0565	.0530	.0500	.0460	.0385	.0235
.090	.0705	.0660	.0625	.0595	.0550	.0520	.0480	.0390	.0215
.100	.0740	.0690	.0660	.0620	.0575	.0540	.0500	.0395	.0190
.120	.0800	.0750	.0705	.0650	.0600	.0560	.0510	.0380	.0120
.140	.0840	.0790	.0735	.0670	.0615	.0560	.0515	.0355	.0020
.160	.0870	.0810	.0750	.0675	.0610	.0550	.0500	.0310	
.180	.0885	.0820	.0755	.0675	.0600	.0535	.0475	.0250	
.200	.0885	.0820	.0745	.0660	.0575	.0505	.0435	.0180	
.250	.0855	.0765	.0685	.0590	.0480	.0390	.0270		
.300	.0780	.0670	.0580	.0460	.0340	.0220	.0050		
.350	.0660	.0540	.0425	.0295	.0150				
.400	.0495	.0370	.0240	.0100					
.450	.0300	.0170	.0025						
.500	.0090	−.0060							
.550									
Y/H_s	X/H_s for portion of profile below weir crest								
−0.000	0.519	0.488	0.455	0.422	0.384	0.349	0.310	0.238	0.144
−.020	.560	.528	.495	.462	.423	.387	.345	.272	.174
−.040	.598	.566	.532	.498	.458	.420	.376	.300	.198
−.060	.632	.601	.567	.532	.491	.451	.406	.324	.220
−.080	.664	.634	.600	.564	.522	.480	.432	.348	.238
−.100	.693	.664	.631	.594	.552	.508	.456	.368	.254
−.150	.760	.734	.701	.661	.618	.569	.510	.412	.290
−.200	.831	.799	.763	.723	.677	.622	.558	.451	.317
−.250	.893	.860	.826	.781	.729	.667	.599	.483	.341
−.300	.953	.918	.880	.832	.779	.708	.634	.510	.362
−.400	1.060	1.024	.981	.932	.867	.780	.692	.556	.396
−.500	1.156	1.119	1.072	1.020	.938	.841	.745	.595	.424
−.600	1.242	1.203	1.153	1.098	1.000	.891	.780	.627	.446
−.800	1.403	1.359	1.301	1.227	1.101	.970	.845	.672	.478
−1.000	1.549	1.498	1.430	1.333	1.180	1.028	.892	.707	.504
−1.200	1.680	1.622	1.543	1.419	1.240	1.070	.930	.733	.524
−1.400	1.800	1.739	1.647	1.489	1.287	1.106	.959	.757	.540
−1.600	1.912	1.849	1.740	1.546	1.323	1.131	.983	.778	.551
−1.800	2.018	1.951	1.821	1.590	1.353	1.155	1.005	.797	.560
−2.000	2.120	2.049	1.892	1.627	1.380	1.175	1.022	.810	.569
−2.500	2.351	2.261	2.027	1.697	1.428	1.218	1.059	.837	
−3.000	2.557	2.423	2.113	1.747	1.464	1.247	1.081	.852	
−3.500	2.748	2.536	2.167	1.778	1.489	1.263	1.099		
−4.000	2.911	2.617	2.200	1.796	1.499	1.274			
−4.500	3.052	2.677	2.217	1.805	1.507				
−5.000	3.173	2.731	2.223	1.810					
−5.500	3.290	2.773	2.228						
−6.000	3.400	2.808							
H_s/R_s	0.20	0.25	0.30	0.35	0.40	0.45	0.50	0.60	0.80

Table 9-7.—Coordinates of lower nappe surface for different values of H_s/R_s when P/R_s = 0.15.

H_s/R_s	0.20	0.25	0.30	0.35	0.40	0.45	0.50	0.60	0.80
X/H_s	Y/H_s for portion of profile above weir crest								
0.000	0.0000	0.0000	0.0000	0.0000	0.0000	0.0000	0.0000	0.0000	0.0000
.010	.0120	.0120	.0115	.0115	.0110	.0110	.0105	.0100	.0090
.020	.0210	.0200	.0195	.0190	.0185	.0180	.0170	.0160	.0140
.030	.0285	.0270	.0265	.0260	.0250	.0235	.0225	.0200	.0165
.040	.0345	.0335	.0325	.0310	.0300	.0285	.0265	.0230	.0170
.050	.0405	.0385	.0375	.0360	.0345	.0320	.0300	.0250	.0170
.060	.0450	.0430	.0420	.0400	.0380	.0355	.0330	.0265	.0165
.070	.0495	.0470	.0455	.0430	.0410	.0380	.0350	.0270	.0150
.080	.0525	.0500	.0485	.0460	.0435	.0400	.0365	.0270	.0130
.090	.0560	.0530	.0510	.0480	.0455	.0420	.0370	.0265	.0100
.100	.0590	.0560	.0535	.0500	.0465	.0425	.0375	.0255	.0065
.120	.0630	.0600	.0570	.0520	.0480	.0435	.0365	.0220	
.140	.0660	.0620	.0585	.0525	.0475	.0425	.0345	.0175	
.160	.0670	.0635	.0590	.0520	.0460	.0400	.0305	.0110	
.180	.0675	.0635	.0580	.0500	.0435	.0365	.0260	.0040	
.200	.0670	.0625	.0560	.0465	.0395	.0320	.0200		
.250	.0615	.0560	.0470	.0360	.0265	.0160	.0015		
.300	.0520	.0440	.0330	.0210	.0100				
.350	.0380	.0285	.0165	.0030					
.400	.0210	.0090							
.450	.0015								
.500									
.550									
Y/H_s	X/H_s for portion of profile below weir crest								
−0.000	0.454	0.422	0.392	0.358	0.325	0.288	0.253	0.189	0.116
−.020	.499	.467	.437	.404	.369	.330	.292	.228	.149
−.040	.540	.509	.478	.444	.407	.368	.328	.259	.174
−.060	.579	.547	.516	.482	.443	.402	.358	.286	.195
−.080	.615	.583	.550	.516	.476	.434	.386	.310	.213
−.100	.650	.616	.584	.547	.506	.462	.412	.331	.228
−.150	.726	.691	.660	.620	.577	.526	.468	.376	.263
−.200	.795	.760	.729	.685	.639	.580	.516	.413	.293
−.250	.862	.827	.790	.743	.692	.627	.557	.445	.319
−.300	.922	.883	.843	.797	.741	.671	.594	.474	.342
−.400	1.029	.988	.947	.893	.828	.749	.656	.523	.381
−.500	1.128	1.086	1.040	.980	.902	.816	.710	.567	.413
−.600	1.220	1.177	1.129	1.061	.967	.869	.753	.601	.439
−.800	1.380	1.337	1.285	1.202	1.080	.953	.827	.655	.473
−1.000	1.525	1.481	1.420	1.317	1.164	1.014	.878	.696	.498
−1.200	1.659	1.610	1.537	1.411	1.228	1.059	.917	.725	.517
−1.400	1.780	1.731	1.639	1.480	1.276	1.096	.949	.750	.531
−1.600	1.897	1.843	1.729	1.533	1.316	1.123	.973	.770	.544
−1.800	2.003	1.947	1.809	1.580	1.347	1.147	.997	.787	.553
−2.000	2.104	2.042	1.879	1.619	1.372	1.167	1.013	.801	.560
−2.500	2.340	2.251	2.017	1.690	1.423	1.210	1.049	.827	
−3.000	2.550	2.414	2.105	1.738	1.457	1.240	1.073	.840	
−3.500	2.740	2.530	2.153	1.768	1.475	1.252	1.088		
−4.000	2.904	2.609	2.180	1.780	1.487	1.263			
−4.500	3.048	2.671	2.198	1.790	1.491				
−5.000	3.169	2.727	2.207	1.793					
−5.500	3.286	2.769	2.210						
−6.000	3.396	2.800							
H_s/R_s	0.20	0.25	0.30	0.35	0.40	0.45	0.50	0.60	0.80

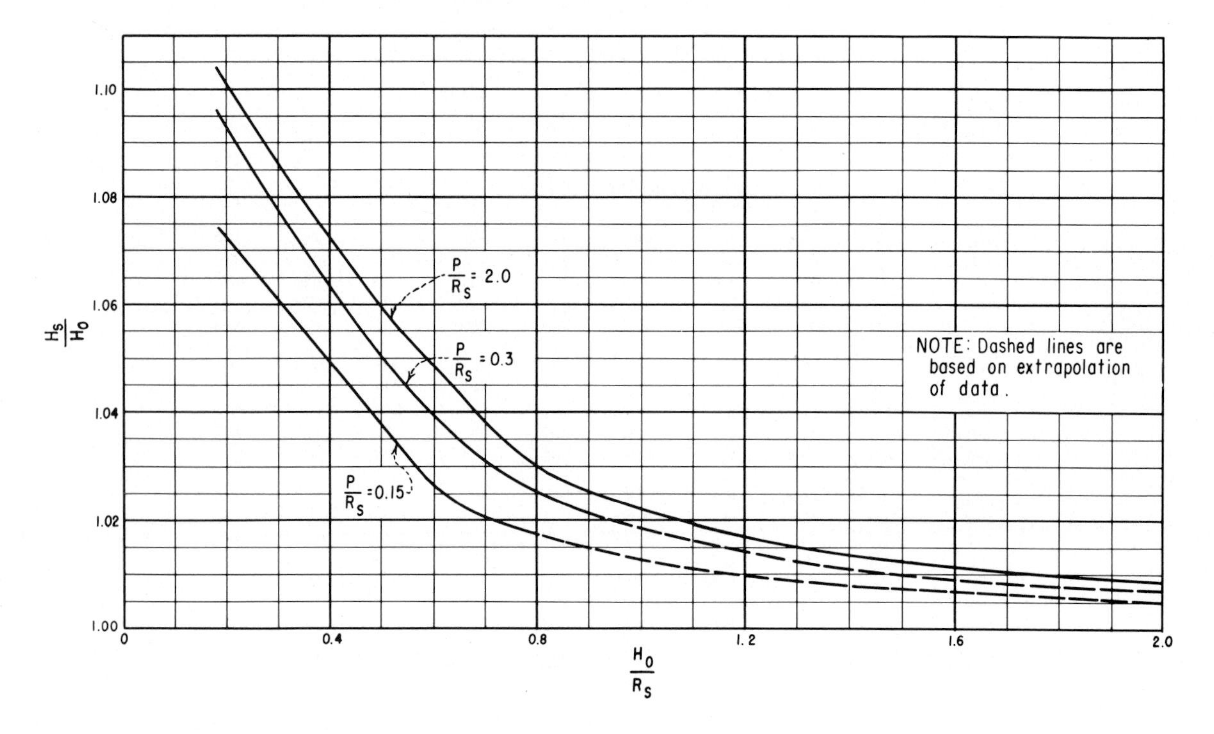

Figure 9-59.—Relationship of H_s/H_o to H_o/R_s for circular sharp-crested weirs. 288–D–2443.

its use for determining the shape of the shaft will result in the minimum size that will accommodate the flow without restrictions and without developing pressures along the side of the shaft.

A typical shaft profile obtained by equation (29) is shown by the lines designated *abc* on figure 9-63. If the shaft profile, *abc*, is enlarged above selected points *b*, as shown by the dashed lines *db*, the flow at section A-A will be under pressure; below section A-A the free jet profile should follow lines *bc*.

Aeration is required at the control either through the introduction of air into a sudden enlargement of the shaft or the installation of a deflector to ensure free flow below the control section A-A. Elbows and passageway sizes and slopes must be such that free flow is maintained below the point of control. Failure to provide adquate aeration at the point of control could introduce cavitation and make-and-break siphonic action that could cause severe vibration. For a profile (e.g., *abe*) established for a specific head, the control must remain at section A-A for any higher head so that above the section pressure flow will prevail. The flow below section A-A must be kept free flow. If the profile *dbe* is adopted, once a head is reached to make the shaft flow full at point *b*, section A-A will be the point of control, and pressure flow above the control will prevail for that and all greater heads.

For submerged crest flow, the corresponding nappe shape, as determined from section 9.26(c), for design head H_o will be such that along its lower levels it will closely follow the profile determined from equation (29) if H_e approximates H_o. It must be remembered that on the basis of the losses assumed in equation (29), profile *abc* will be the minimum shaft size that will accommodate the required flow and that no part of the crest shape should be permitted to project inside this profile. As noted in section 9.14, small subatmospheric crest pressures can be tolerated if proper precautions are taken to obtain a smooth surface and if the negative pressure forces are recognized in the structural design. The choice of the minimum crest and transition shapes rather than wider shapes, then becomes a matter of economics, structural arrangement, and layout adaptability.

Where the transition profile corresponds to the continuation of the crest shape as determined by tables 9-5, 9-6, and 9-7, the discharge can be computed from equation (28) using a coefficient from figure 9-57. Where the transition profile differs

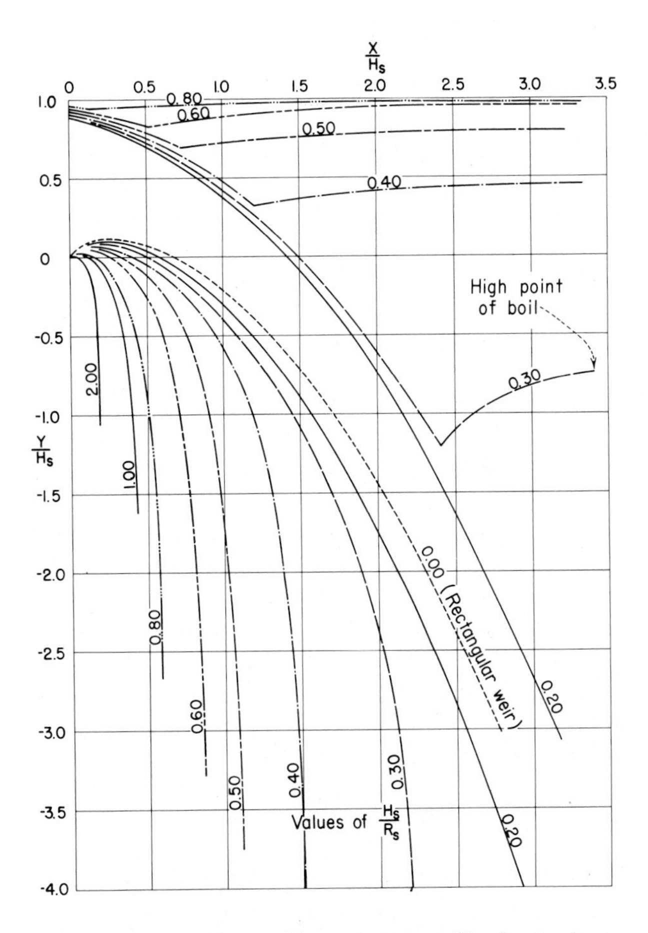

Figure 9-60.—Upper and lower nappe profiles for circular weir (aerated nappe and negligible approach velocity). 288–D–2444.

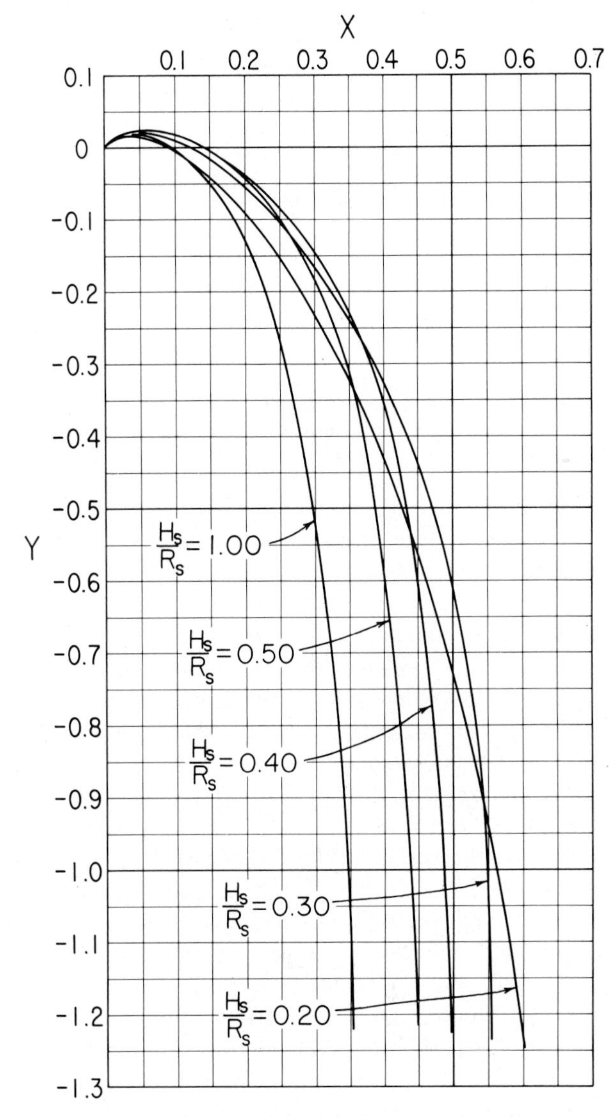

Figure 9-61.—Comparison of lower nappe shapes for circular weir for different heads. 288–D–2445.

from the crest shape profile so that a constricted control section is established, the discharge must be determined from equation (29). On figure 9-55, the discharge-head relationship curve *ag* can then be computed from the coefficients determined from figure 9-58, while the discharge-head relationship curve *gh* will be based on equation (29).

(e) *Conduit Design.*—If, for a designated discharge, the conduit of a drop inlet spillway were to flow full below the transition without being under pressure, the required size of the shaft and outlet leg would vary according to the available net head along its length. So long as the slope of the hydraulic gradient that is dictated by the hydraulic losses is flatter than the slope of the conduit, the flow will accelerate and the required size of conduit will decrease. When the conduit slope is flatter than the slope of the hydraulic gradient, the flow will decelerate and the required size of conduit will increase. All points along the conduit will act simultaneously to control the rate of flow. For heads greater than that used to size it, the conduit will flow under pressure with the control at the downstream end; for heads less than that used to size it, the conduit will flow partly full for its entire length, and the control will remain in the transition upstream. On figure 9-55, the head at which the conduit just flows full is represented by point *h*. At heads above point *h*, the conduit flows full under pressure; at heads less than *h* the conduit flows partly full with controlling conditions dictated by the transition design.

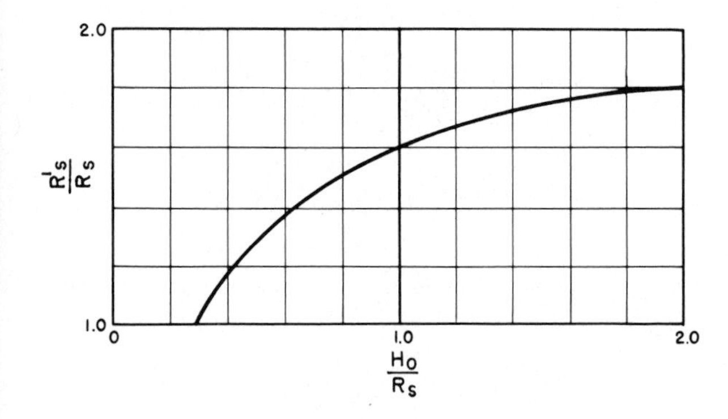

Figure 9-62.—Increased circular crest radius needed to minimize subatmospheric pressure along crest. 288-D-2446.

Because it is impractical to build a conduit with a varying diameter, it's size is ordinarily constant beyond the inlet transition. Thus, the conduit from the control point in the transition to the downstream end will have an excess of area. If atmospheric pressure can be maintained along the portion of the conduit flowing partly full, it will continue to flow at that stage even though the downstream end fills. Progressively greater discharges will not alter the partly full flow in the upper lengths of the conduit, but full-flow conditions under pressure will occupy increasing lengths of the downstream end of the conduit. At the discharge represented by point *h* on figure 9-55, the full flow condition has moved back to the transition control section and the conduit will flow full for its entire length.

If the conduit flows at such a stage that the downstream end flows full, both the inlet and outlet will be sealed. To forestall siphon action by the withdrawal of air from the conduit would require an adequate venting system. Unless venting is effected over the entire length of conduit, it may prove inadequate to prevent subatmospheric pressures along some portion of the length because of the possibility of sealing at any point by surging, wave action, or eddy turbulences. Thus, if no venting is provided or if the venting is inadequate, a make-and-break siphon action will attend the flow in the range of discharges approaching full-flow conditions. This action is accompanied by erratic discharges, by thumping and vibration, and by surges at the entrance and outlet of the spillway.

To avoid siphonic flow conditions, the size of the downstream conduit for ordinary designs (especially for those handling higher heads) should be chosen so that it will never flow full beyond the inlet transition. To allow for air bulking, surging, etc., the conduit size should ordinarily be selected so that it will not flow more than 75 percent full (in area) at the downstream end at maximum discharge. Under this limitation, air will be able to pass up the conduit from the downstream portal and thus prevent the formation of subatmospheric pressure along the conduit length. Care must be taken, however, in selecting the vertical and horizontal curvatures of the conduit profile and alignment to prevent sealing along some portion by surging or wave action.

(f) *Design Example.*—The following example problem illustrates the procedure for designing a morning glory drop inlet spillway: Design an ungated drop inlet spillway that will operate under a maximum surcharge head of 10 feet, but will limit the outflow to 2,000 ft³/s. Determine alternative overflow crest shapes and discharge head relationships, considering that (1) the overflow crest radius must be minimized because the intake is formed as a tower away from the abutment, and subatmospheric pressures along the crest can be tolerated; and (2) the crest radius may be any size because it is located on a knoll at the abutment, and subatmospheric pressures along the crest should be minimized. In both cases the conduit must not flow more than 75 percent full at the downstream end. The controlling dimensions are shown on figure 9-64.

(1) *Case 1.*—The radius of the overflow crest must be minimized, and subatmospheric pressures may be tolerated:

Assume $P/R_s \geq 2$ (see fig. 9-57). R_s is determined by a trial-and-error procedure of assuming values of R_s and computing the discharge.

Assume R_s = 7.0 feet; then $H_o/R_s = 10/7 = 1.43$. For $H_o/R_s = 1.43$ and $P/R_s \geq 2$, from figure 9-57, $C_o = 1.44$. Then; $Q = C_o(2\pi R_s)H_o^{3/2} = 1.44(2\pi)(7.0)10^{3/2} = 2{,}010$ ft³/s, which is approximately the required discharge. From figure 9-59, for $H_o/R_s = 1.43$ and $P/R_s \geq 2$, $H_s/H_o = 1.014$, $H_s = 1.014\ H_o$, and $H_s = 1.014(10) = 10.14$ feet. Then, $H_s/R_s = 10.14/7.0 = 1.45$.

Using table 9-5, points on the profile of the crest shape that conforms to the lower nappe surface for $H_s/R_s = 1.45$ are computed by interpolation. These points are then plotted as shown on figure 9-65.

The next step is to determine the transition shape required to pass 2,000 ft³/s with an H_o of 10 feet above the crest (water surface elevation 110.0).

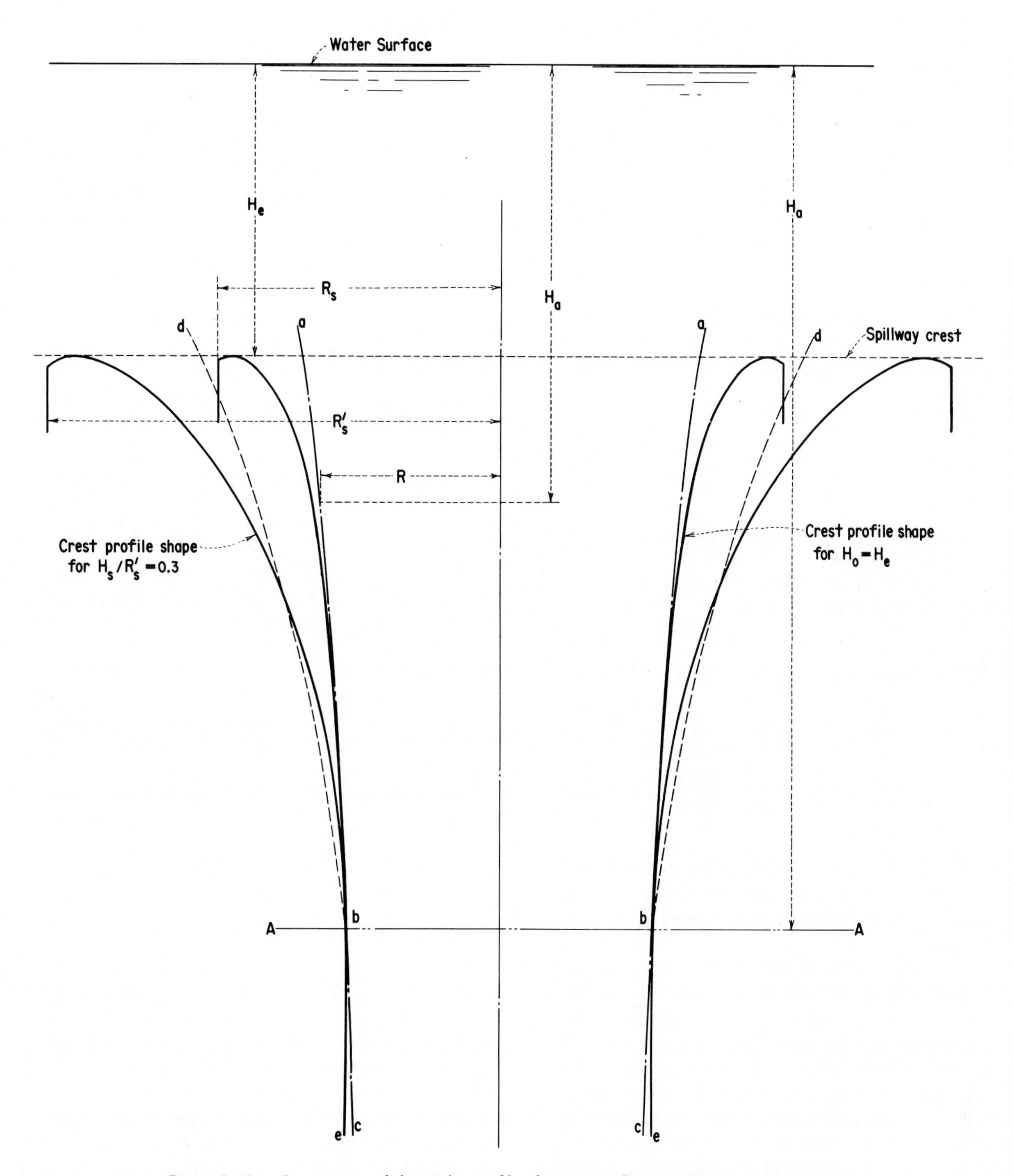

Figure 9-63.—Comparison of drop inlet profiles for various flow conditions. 288–D–2447.

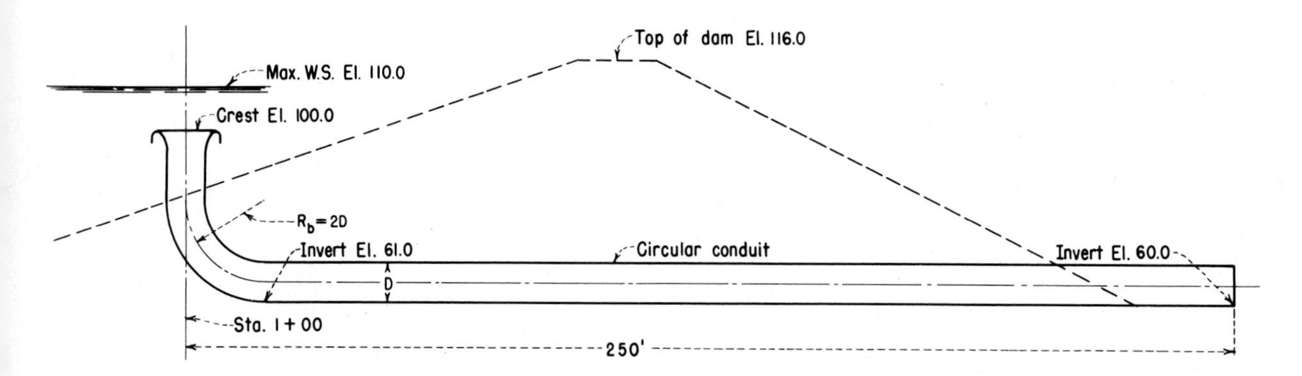

Figure 9-64.—Drop inlet spillway profile. For design example in section 9.26(f). 228–D–2448.

This shape is determined by the use of equation (29):

$$R = 0.204\frac{Q_a^{1/2}}{H_a^{1/4}} = 0.204\frac{(2{,}000)^{1/2}}{H_a^{1/4}} = \frac{9.12}{H_a}$$

Points on the transition are computed as shown in the following table and are plotted on the same graph on which points for the crest shape have already been plotted (fig. 9-65).

Elevation of section	H_a	$H_a^{1/4}$	$R=\frac{9.12}{H_a^{1/4}}$
100	10	1.78	5.13
98	12	1.86	4.90
96	14	1.93	4.72
94	16	2.00	4.56
92	18	2.06	4.43
88	22	2.17	4.20

A smooth curve should be drawn through the controlling points on the crest and transition shapes to determine the final shape of the crest and transition.

The final step is to determine the minimum uniform conduit diameter that will pass the flow from the transition section to the conduit portal without the conduit flowing more than 75 percent full. The procedure is as follows: (1) Select a trial conduit and throat diameter and find the corresponding throat location, (2) compute the length from transition throat to outlet portal, (3) approximate the friction losses in the conduit by assuming the conduit flows three-fourths full for its entire length, and (4) check the elevation of the invert at the outlet portal required to pass the design discharge through the selected size conduit. After an approximate conduit size has been determined in this manner, it should be checked by computing the water surface profile through the conduit by open channel flow computations.

For this problem assume a conduit diameter of 9.0 feet. From figure 9-65, a radius of 4.5 feet is found to be at 6.9 feet below the crest; therefore, the elevation of the 9.0-foot-diameter throat is 93.1. The tunnel length may be scaled or calculated by approximate methods. In this example the approximate tunnel length is 270 feet.

Assuming that the conduit flows 75 percent full, area = $0.75\pi(4.5^2)$ = 47.7 ft², velocity = 2,000/47.7 = 41.9 ft/s, and h_v = $41.9^2/64.4$ = 27.3 feet.

From table B-3, for 75 percent full flow, d/D = 0.702, and the hydraulic radius r = 0.2964(9.0) = 2.67.

Using a value of n = 0.014 to maximize the losses, by Manning's equation (equation (30), app. B):

$$s = \left(\frac{vn}{1.486r^{2/3}}\right)^2 = \left[\frac{(41.9)\ (.014)}{(1.486)\ (2.67)^{2/3}}\right]^2 = 0.04$$

and h_f = 0.04(270) = 10.8 feet.

The invert elevation at the downstream portal of the conduit will then be equal to (1) the elevation of the throat, plus (2) the velocity head at the throat, minus (3) the velocity head in the conduit flowing 75 percent full, minus (4) the friction losses in the conduit, minus (5) the depth of flow at the downstream portal. The required portal invert elevation for this trial conduit diameter is approximately 93.1 + (1/1.1)(110.0 − 93.1) − 27.3 − 10.8 − 0.702(9.0) = 64.1.

Although this elevation is somewhat higher than the established portal invert elevation, 60.0, actual losses through the conduit will be larger than those

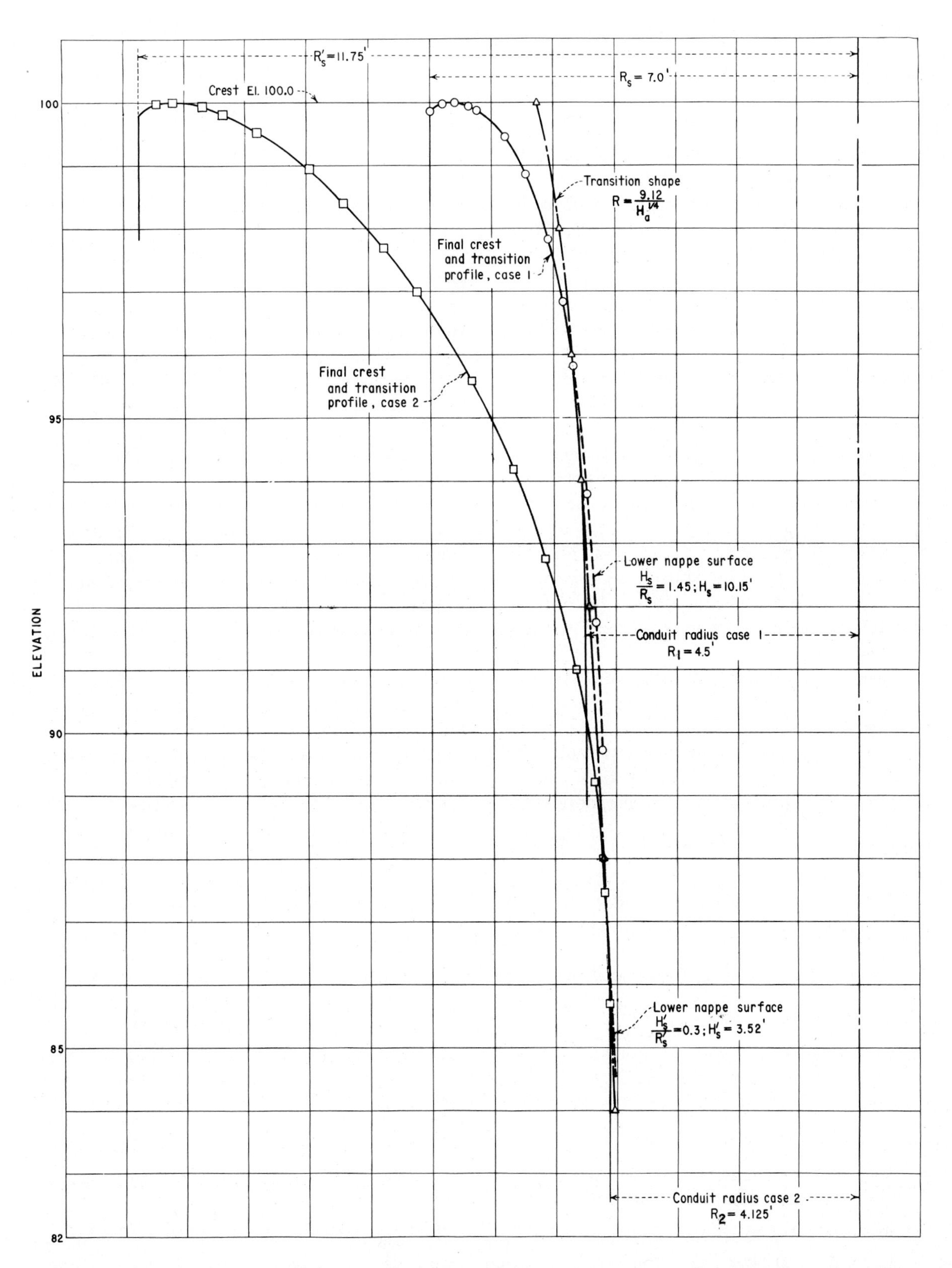

Figure 9-65.—Drop inlet crest, transition, and conduit plottings. For design example in section 9.26(f). 288-D-2515.

estimated because the conduit will flow 75 percent full throughout its length.

Therefore, the 9.0-foot-diameter conduit appears to be, for all practical purposes, the minimum uniform diameter conduit that will meet the requirements of the problem. Computations of the water surface profile through the 9.0-foot-diameter conduit, shown in table 9-8, are then performed to verify the approximate solution given above. These computations are based on Bernoulli's theorem (eq. (32), app. B).

Discharge-head computations for this design are shown in table 9-9. For the lower range of heads, the coefficient relationships of various H_e/R_s values are obtained from figure 9-58, assuming a coefficient of 3.75 for $H_e/R_s = 0.3$. For the higher ranges of head, the discharges can be obtained from equation (29) using a throat radius of 4.50 at elevation 93.1. Smooth curves are then plotted for both head range computations. The intersection of the curves is replaced by an approximate transition curve to more nearly represent actual conditions. The discharge curve is plotted on figure 9-66. The computations show that the conduit will be only 76 percent full at the downstream end; therefore, the design is satisfactory.

(2) *Case 2.*—The radius of the overflow crest may be any size, and subatmospheric pressures along crest must be minimized:

First, determine the minimum crest radius for the given: H_o = 10 feet, and Q = 2,000 ft³/s for case 1. Assume $P/R_s = 0.15$ and, as in case 1, determine R_s by trial and error.

Assuming R_s = 7.0 feet, $H_o/R_s = 10/7 = 1.43$. For $H_o/R_s = 1.43$ and $P/R_s = 0.15$ from figure 9-57, $C_o = 1.55$. Then, $Q = C_o(2\pi R_s)H_o^{3/2} = 1.55(2\pi)7.0(10)^{3/2} = 2{,}155$ ft³/s. Since a 2,000-ft³/s discharge is required, the assumed value of R_s is too large.

Assuming R_s = 6.7 feet, $H_o/R_s = 10/6.7 = 1.49$. From figure 9-57, $C_o = 1.49$ and Q = 1,985 ft³/s, which is approximately the required discharge.

Using $H_o/R_s = 1.49$, enter figure 9-62 and find the approximate increased crest radius required to minimize subatmospheric pressures. For $H_o/R_s = 1.49$, $R_s'/R_s = 1.74$ and $R_s' = 1.74(6.7) = 11.7$ feet; use 11.75 feet. Points on the profile of the crest shape that conform to the lower nappe surface for $H_s'/R_s' = 0.30$ and $R_s' = 11.75$ are computed using values from table 9-7 and are plotted as shown on figure 9-65.

Computations for the required transition shape to pass 2,000 ft³/s with a head of 10 feet on the crest are identical to those given in case 1. Figure 9-65 shows the plotted points and the crest and transition curves.

From an inspection of the transition and crest shape plots for case 2, it can be seen that the conduit diameter for case 1 is too large for case 2. If the 9.0-foot-diameter conduit used in case 1 were used in case 2, a smooth transition connecting the crest and conduit would be considerably outside the transition shape determined by equation (29). This means that for a head of 10 feet on the crest, the discharge would not longer be limited to 2,000 ft³/s by the transition, but would increase because of the larger size transition. This discharge would require a larger uniform diameter conduit to pass the discharge and not flow more than 75 percent full. A still larger uniform diameter conduit with a still larger maximum discharge would finally be required for a satisfactory hydraulic design. However, a smaller uniform diameter conduit would flow more

Table 9-8.—Water surface profile computations for case 1. Conduit diameter = 9.0 feet; Q = 2000 ft³/s, n = 0.014.

Station	ΔL	Trial d/D	d	a	v	h_v	r	$r^{2/3}$	s	$\frac{s_1+s_2}{2}$	Δh_L	$\Sigma\Delta h_L$	$d_2+h_{v_2}+\Sigma\Delta h_L$	Invert elevation	Datum gradient	Remarks
1+00	-	1.00	-	63.6	31.4	15.3	2.25	1.72	0.030	-	-	-	-	93.1	108.4	-
1+19	39	0.56	5.04	36.66	54.6	46.2	2.41	1.80	.081	0.056	2.2	2.2	53.4	61.0	114.4	Too high
		.59	5.37	39.06	51.2	40.7	2.48	1.83	.069	.049	1.9	1.9	47.9	-	108.9	OK
2+30	111	.63	5.67	42.2	47.4	34.8	2.54	1.86	.057	.063	7.0	8.9	49.4	60.5	109.9	Too high
		.64	5.76	42.99	46.5	33.6	2.58	1.88	.054	.062	6.8	8.7	48.0	-	108.5	OK
3+50	120	.72	6.48	49.04	40.8	25.8	2.69	1.93	.039	.047	5.6	14.3	45.7	60.0	105.7	Too low
		.70	6.30	47.56	42.0	27.5	2.67	1.92	.042	.048	5.8	14.5	48.3	-	108.3	OK

Table 9-9.—Computations for discharge curve for case 1, R_s=7.0 feet.

Head on crest, feet	Crest control			Throat control	
	$\frac{H_e}{R_s}$	^1C	$Q = C(2\pi R_s)H_e^{3/2}$	H_a	$Q_a = \left(\frac{R}{0.204}\right)^2 H_a^{1/2}$
1	0.14	3.56	157	–	–
2	.29	3.75	467	–	–
3	.43	3.58	820	–	–
4	–	–	–	10.9	1,600
6	–	–	–	12.9	1,750
8	–	–	–	14.9	1,880
10	–	–	–	16.9	2,000

[1] Coefficient of 3.75 assumed for H_e/R_s=0.3 (from fig. 9.57). Coefficients for H_e/R_s values other than 0.3 based on ratios shown on figure 9-58.

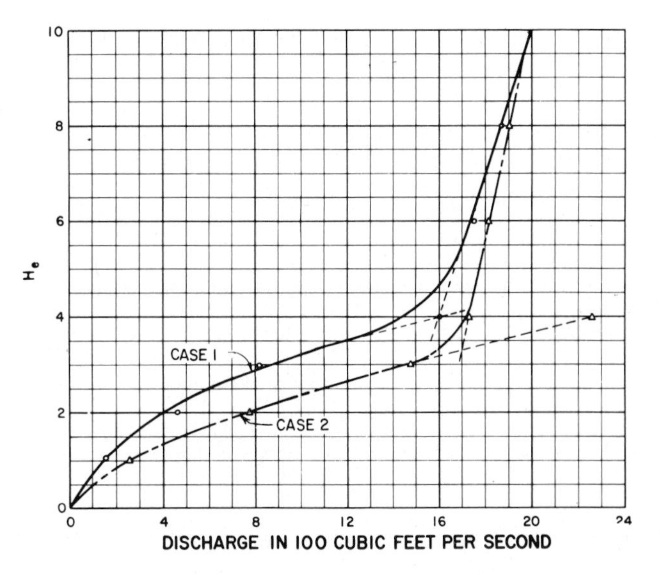

Figure 9-66.—Drop inlet spillway discharge curves. For design example in section 9.26(f). 288–D–2516.

than 75 percent full at the downstream end.

The simplest solution to this problem is to vary the diameter of the conduit. An upstream diameter should be chosen based on the crest profile and transition where they converge. This procedure establishes the throat size necessary to limit the maximum discharge to 2,000 ft³/s. At some suitable location downstream from the throat, the conduit should be enlarged to prevent it from flowing more than 75 percent full. The location of this enlargement should be determined by economic or construction considerations to meet hydraulic requirements.

For this problem, an 8.25-foot-diameter conduit with its throat at elevation 86.0 is selected. It will be assumed that the most economical design is obtained by extending this conduit to the point where it flows 75 percent full. At this point the conduit is enlarged to the diameter needed to make it flow 75 percent full at the downstream portal. To determine the point at which the tunnel must be enlarged, water surface profiles are run downstream by the step method, as shown in table 9-10. A bend radius of 16.5 feet ($2D$) is used. The table shows that the conduit must increase in size starting at the P.T. (point of tangency) of the vertical bend, station 1+16.5. The size of the downstream conduit may be approximated by assuming a given size conduit flowing 75 percent full at the downstream portal and using the distance from the point of enlargement to the portal as one reach in the water surface profile computations. Although this method results in losses slightly larger than would be obtained by using shorter reaches, it is accurate enough to determine conduit size if the length of the conduit downstream from the expansion is not excessively long. Use of shorter steps and an assumed minimum value of n would be required to determine the depth and velocity at the downstream portal for use in designing an energy dissipator. The transition from the smaller to the larger diameter conduit should be proportioned as explained in section 9.19(b).

Discharge-head relationships for this case are computed similarly to those for case 1. The throat radius in this instance is 4.13 feet at elevation 86.0. Computations are shown in table 9-11, and the discharge curve is plotted on figure 9-66.

9.27. *Culvert Spillways.*—(a) *General.*—As described in section 9.8(j), a culvert spillway ordinarily consists of a simple culvert conduit placed through a dam or along an abutment, generally on a uniform grade, with its entrance placed vertically or inclined. The culvert cross section can be round if it is constructed of fabricated or precast pipe, or it may be square, rectangular, or of some other shape if cast in place. The culvert can freely discharge, or it can empty into an open channel so that the outflowing jet is supported along the channel floor.

The factors that combine to determine the nature of flow in a culvert spillway include such variables as the slope, size, shape, length, and roughness of the conduit barrel, and the inlet and outlet geometry. The combined effect of these factors determines the location of the control which,

Table 9-10.—Water surface profile computations for case 2. Varying diameter conduit, Q = 2,000 ft³/s, n = 0.014.

Station	ΔL	Trial d/D	d	a	v	h_v	r	$r^{2/3}$	s	$\frac{s_1+s_2}{2}$	Δh_L	$\Sigma\Delta h_L$	$d_2+h_{v_2}+\Sigma\Delta h_L$	Invert elevation	Datum gradient	Remarks
1+00	-	1.000	-	53.5	37.4	21.7	2.06	1.62	0.047	-	-	-	-	86.0	107.7	-
1+16.5	30	0.650	5.36	36.9	54.4	45.9	2.38	1.78	.082	0.065	1.9	1.9	53.2	61.0	114.2	Too high
		.690	5.69	39.3	50.8	40.1	2.43	1.81	.070	.058	1.8	1.8	47.6	-	107.6	OK
Try 9.0-foot-diameter conduit flowing 75 percent full at the portal																
3+50	234	.690	6.21	46.8	42.7	28.3	2.65	1.92	.044	.057	13.3	15.1	49.6	60.0	109.6	Too high
Try 9.25-foot-diameter conduit flowing 75 percent full at the portal																
3+50	234	.690	6.82	49.5	40.4	25.4	2.73	1.95	.038	.054	12.6	14.4	46.6	60.0	106.6	OK

Table 9-11.—Computations for discharge curve for case 2, R_s' = 11.75 feet.

Head on crest, feet	Crest control			Throat control	
	$\frac{H_e}{R_s'}$	^1C	$Q = C(2\pi R_s')H_e^{3/2}$	H_a	$Q_a = \left(\frac{R}{0.204}\right)^2 H_a^{1/2}$
1	0.09	3.55	260	-	-
2	.17	3.74	780	-	-
3	.26	3.85	1,480	17	1,680
4	.34	3.82	2,260	18	1,730
6	-	-	-	20	1,830
8	-	-	-	22	1,920
10	-	-	-	24	2,000

[1]Coefficient of 3.86 assumed for H_e/R_s = 0.3 (from fig. 9-57). Coefficients for H_e/R_s values other than 0.3 based on ratios shown on figure 9-58.

in turn, determines the discharge characteristics of the conduit. The location of the control dictates whether the conduit flows partly full or full, and thereby, establishes the head-discharge relationship.

The grade of the conduit might be mild or steep; that is, its slope may be flatter or steeper than one which for a given discharge will just support flow at the critical stage. For both the mild and steep slope conduit, the control may be either at the inlet or at the outlet, depending on the entrance geometry and head relationship and on the flow conditions at the outlet. The various conditions that may govern a particular flow are shown on figure 9-67.

If the inlet is not submerged, the control for a conduit on a mild slope flowing partly full will be at the outlet. If the outlet discharges freely, the flow at that point will pass through critical depth. This condition is shown as condition 1 on figure 9-67. If the tailwater is high enough to maintain a depth greater than critical, the tailwater level will control the flow in the upstream barrel. If the tailwater submerges the outlet, the conduit might flow full for its entire length and thus submerge the inlet. This flow condition is depicted as condition 6 on figure 9-67. Until the conduit flows full, the flow ordinarily will be at subcritical stage, and the discharge relationships will be determined according to Bernoulli's equation. Computations will start at the outlet where the reservoir level submerges the inlet and where $H/D>1.2$. The control at critical depth may be placed at the inlet if the culvert is relatively short so that a jump does not form within the barrel. This condition is shown as condition 4 on figure 9-67.

When the conduit is on a steep slope and the entrance is not submerged, the flow will be controlled by critical depth at the inlet, as indicated by condition 3 on figure 9-67. The water surface will drop rapidly to critical depth at the entrance, and open channel flow at supercritical velocities will exist throughout the conduit barrel. Discharge for a given reservoir level will be governed by channel or weir flow, assuming critical depth occurs at the culvert entrance.

After the inlet has been submerged or where H exceeds about $1.2D$, it is still possible to have open channel flow at supercritical stage in the conduit barrel, as depicted for condition 5, if the control remains at the entrance. In this case, flow at the inlet is analogous to orifice or sluice flow. This flow condition is contingent on the formation of a contraction at the top of the entrance so that an airspace is maintained along the top of the barrel to

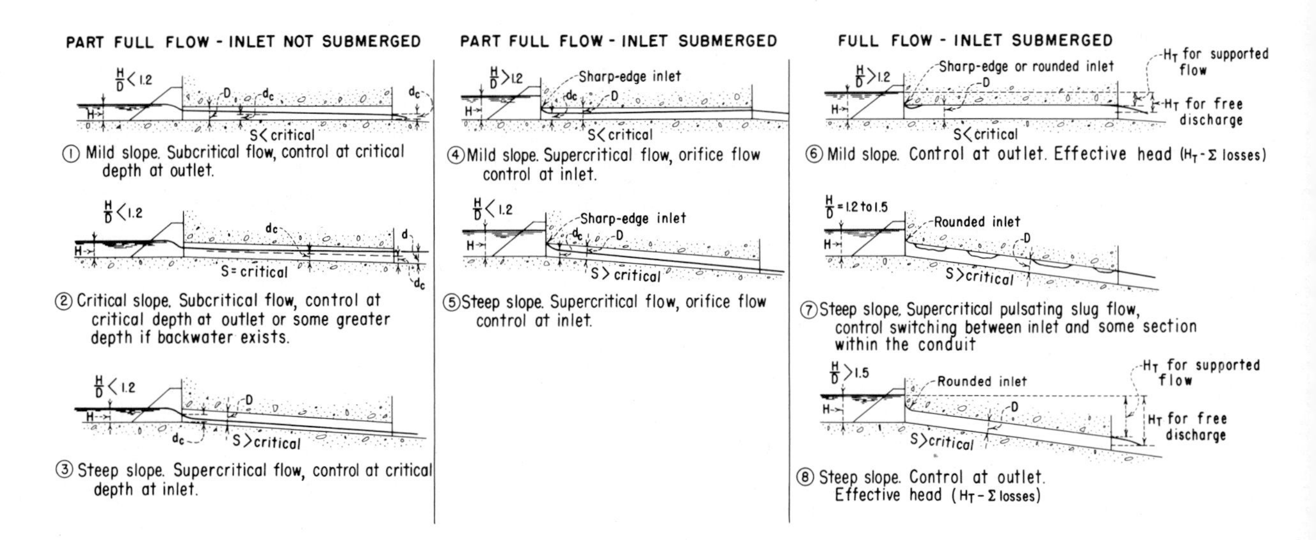

Figure 9-67.—Typical flow conditions for culvert spillways on mild and steep slopes. 288–D–2517.

permit partly full flow throughout the conduit length.

As the head at the entrance and the resulting discharge increase, channel friction or local disturbances may force the barrel to flow full near the outlet, sealing the conduit at the downstream end. The high-velocity flow in the culvert will carry away some of the air trapped at the top of the barrel, reducing the pressure in the conduit to less than atmospheric. Furthermore, if the entrance is shaped to eliminate the inlet contraction, the barrel will start to flow full near the inlet, after which the full-flow zone will extend rapidly down the conduit toward the outlet. The effect of the full-flow condition will be a draft-tube action (similar to siphonic action) that will increase the discharge. The increased discharge will cause a deeper drawdown just upstream from the inlet. A vortex will form, and the air that will be introduced into the culvert will break the draft-tube action. The reduction in discharge will result in the return to orifice control at the inlet. Immediately, the full-flow action will begin again, and the cycle will be repeated. This alternate priming and breaking action will cause a pulsating flow stage having the slug flow phenomenon indicated by condition 7 on figure 9-67. When the reservoir stage condition is such that $H/D>1.5$, the entrance drawdown may be insufficient to interface with the full-flow action, and a steady state of full pipe flow indicated by condition 8 will prevail.

If it is intended that the spillway conduit not flow full, the geometry of the inlet becomes an important consideration. The inlet must be shaped to obtain a maximum discharge efficiency and yet maintain a top contraction that will provide a freely aerated surface in the conduit barrel for all reservoir stages. The sharp-edged square inlet produces the desired contraction without materially reducing the discharge capacity. The inlet contraction can also be formed (but at reduced hydraulic capacity) by a projecting inlet, by a mitered inlet with a downstream sloping face, by an inlet orifice ring that is smaller than the remainder of the conduit, or by a curtain wall closing off the top of the conduit entrance.

If the conduit is permitted to flow full at the higher reservoir stages, the control will be at the outlet and the geometry of the inlet will have much less significance. For this case the inlet must be shaped to minimize the jet contraction to avoid separation of the incoming flow from the conduit barrel because full pipe flow is desired for all conditions except when the inlet is not submerged. The more streamlined shape will reduce entrance losses for the full pipe flow condition. The suppression of the contraction is achieved by rounding the inlet or by providing a gradually tapering transition to the conduit barrel.

Culvert inlets may have various approach conditions, cross-sectional shapes, and entrance arrangements. For example, an entrance may be rounded, beveled, square or bellmouthed; it may be installed either flush with or protruding through a vertical or sloping headwall. The approach to the inlet may or may not be a well-defined channel. Wing walls or warped transition approaches may be used. In cross section, a culvert entrance may be round, square, rectangular, or arch-shaped. All such variations have a significant effect on the culvert performance because they affect orifice discharge, inlet contractions, and the entrance losses for full pipe flow.

A common arrangement for a circular pipe culvert installation involves a vertical headwall with the pipe end placed flush with the wall. Similarly, box culvert arrangements usually involve a trapezoidal approach channel with vertical or warped approach walls leading to the culvert entrance. The hydraulic designs of these two types of installation are discussed in detail below.

(b) *Circular Conduit with Vertical Headwall.*—Figure 9-68 shows a plot of head-discharge relationships for a circular conduit placed flush with a vertical headwall, for both square-edged and rounded inlets. This plot is based on an average of numerous experimental tests [25, 26, 27] of pipe culvert entrances with the conduit placed on steep slopes. The head-discharge relationships for the square-edged inlet are based on the control remaining at the inlet for all reservoir heads. Where $H/D<1.2$ (approx.), the flow characteristics are those of critical depth flow in a circular pipe, modified only by the effects of the jet contraction. For

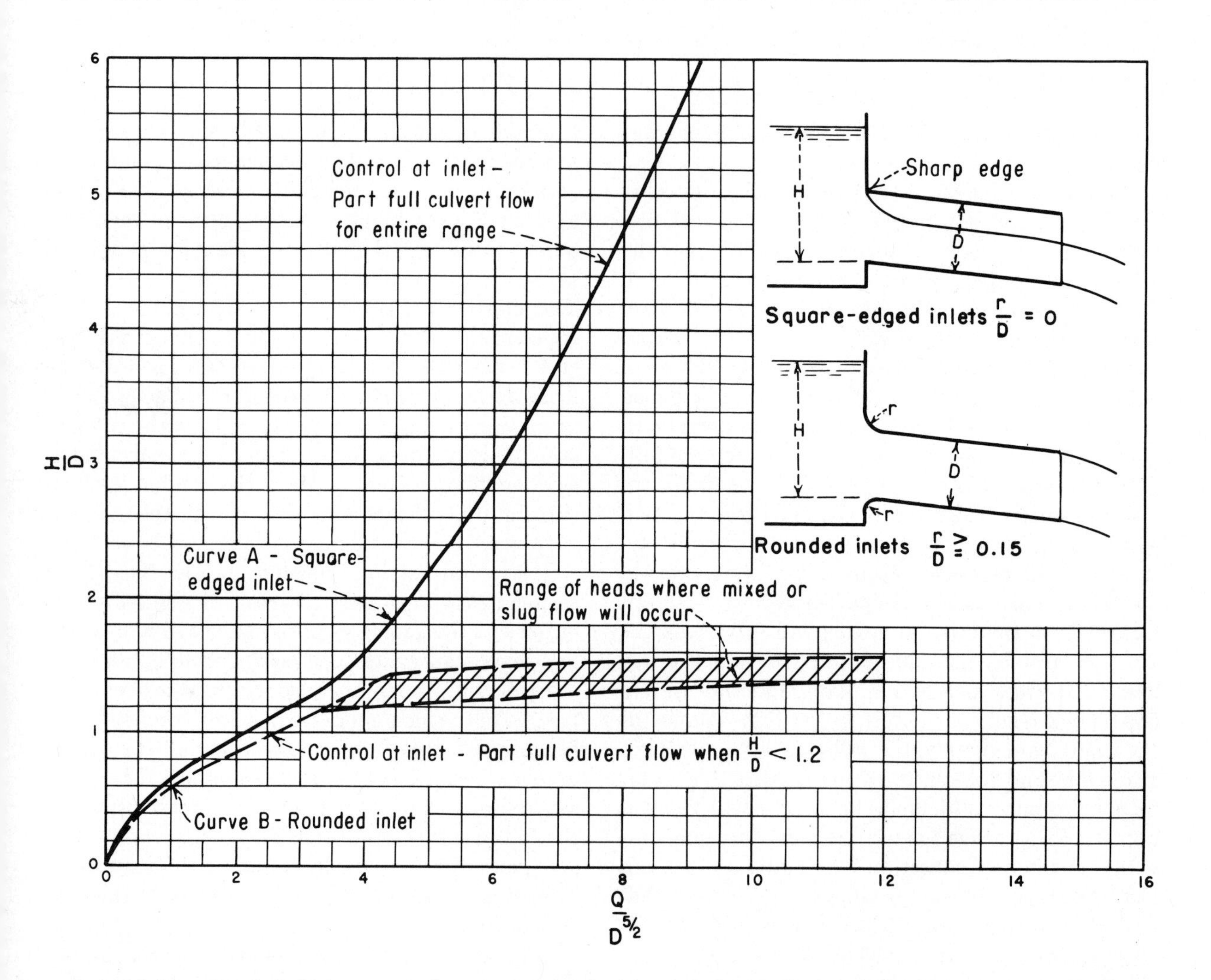

Figure 9-68.—Head-discharge curves for square-edged and rounded inlets for circular culverts on steep slopes. 288-D-2518.

$H/D>1.2$, the flow characteristics are those of orifice or sluice flow. Because the conduit is considered to be flowing partly full at supercritical stage for all H/D ranges indicated, the downstream conditions have no influence on the discharge.

On figure 9-68, the head-discharge relationship for the rounded inlet for values of $H/D<1.2$ (approx.) lie to the right of those for the square-edged inlet. This indicates slightly greater discharges for equal size conduits. The increased discharge capacity through the critical-depth flow range is the result of improved streamlined flow brought about by the suppression of the inlet contractions. For $H/D>1.2$, the pulsating flow characteristics begin, and the discharge-head relationship in this range of flow is uncertain; it cannot be determined until the flow stabilizes at full flow stage. Because full pipe flow is governed by control at the outlet, the head-discharge relationship can be determined by the application of Bernoulli's theorem. Referring to figure 9-69:

$$H_T = H + L\sin\theta - \frac{D}{2} \qquad (30)$$

Similarly,

$$H_T = h_v + h_e + h_f$$

or

$$H_T = \left(1 + K_e + \frac{29.1n^2L}{r^{4/3}}\right)\frac{v^2}{2g} \qquad (31)$$

where:

K_e = entrance loss coefficient, and
n = friction factor in Mannings equation,
$h_f = (29.1\ n^2L/r^{4/3})(v^2/2g)$.

Combining equations (30) and (31), dividing by D, and stating the equation in terms of Q instead of v yields:

$$\frac{H}{D} + \frac{L}{D}\sin\theta - \frac{1}{2} = 0.0252\left(1 + K_e + \frac{29.1n^2L}{r^{4/3}}\right)\left(\frac{Q}{D^{5/2}}\right)^2 \qquad (32)$$

In equation (32), it is assumed that the culvert discharges freely at the outlet and that the pressure line at the outlet is approximately at the center of the pipe. If the outlet discharges into a channel so that the outflowing jet is supported, equation (32) becomes:

$$\frac{H}{D} + \frac{L}{D}\sin\theta - 1.0 = 0.0252\left(1 + K_e + \frac{29.1n^2L}{r^{4/3}}\right)\left(\frac{Q}{D^{5/2}}\right)^2 \qquad (33)$$

Equations (32) and (33) are for full-flow conditions. They are expressed in terms of H/D and $Q/D^{5/2}$ so that by referring to figures 9-67 and 9-68, it can be determined whether or not the full-flow condition exists.

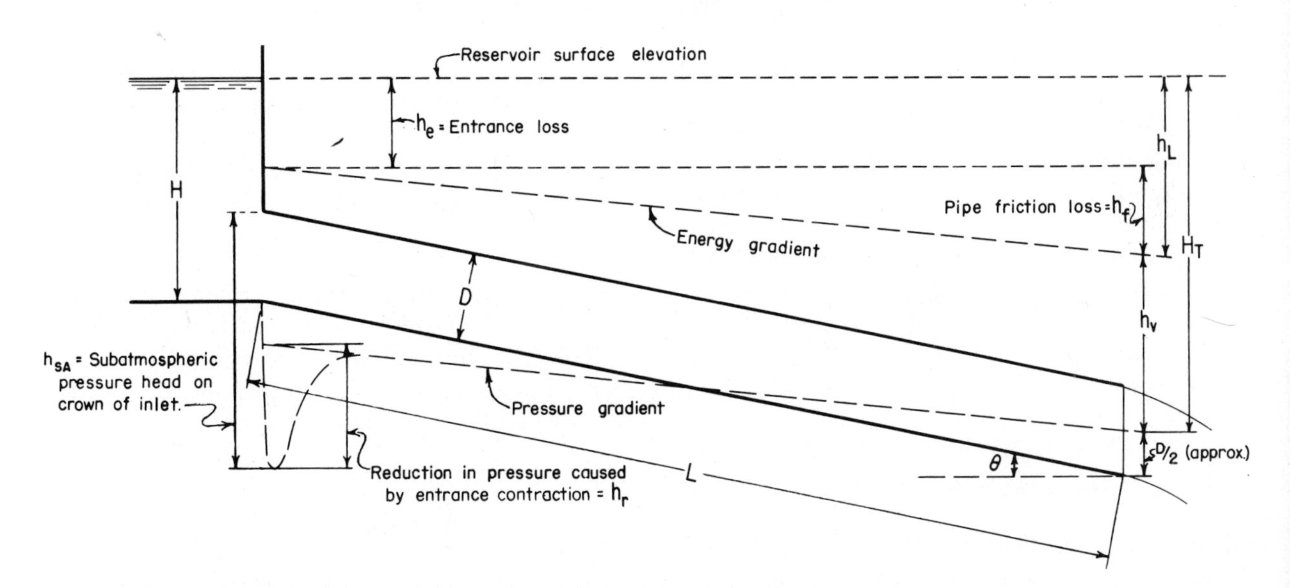

Figure 9-69.—Hydraulic characteristics of full pipe flow for culvert spillways. 288–D–2519.

Appropriate values of n are given in section 10.15(b). Values of K_e for various entrance conditions have been determined by different experimenters, as shown in the listing below:

Entrance condition	*K_e range*	*Average*
For square-edged inlets installed flush with vertical headwalls	0.43 to 0.70	0.50
For rounded inlets installed flush with vertical headwalls, $r/D \geq 0.15$	0.08 to 0.27	.10
For grooved or socket-ended concrete pipe installed flush with vertical headwall	0.10 to 0.33	.15
For projecting concrete pipe with grooved or socket ends	—	.20
For projecting steel or corrugated metal pipes	0.5 to 0.9	.85

Nomographs for determining flow in full-flowing circular pipes with entrance controls have been developed by the Federal Highway Administration. These nomographs, which are included in appendix B, can be used as design aids in determining flow in circular culvert spillways. Figure B-7 is for flow in concrete pipe culverts having entrance control and the following types of entrances: (1) headwall with square-edged entrance, (2) headwall with groove-end pipe, and (3) headwall with groove end of pipe projecting. Figure B-8 is for flow in corrugated metal pipe culverts having entrance control and the following types of entrances: (1) flush headwall, (2) end mitered to conform to slope, and (3) projecting pipe. Figure B-9 is for concrete pipe culverts flowing full, based on n = 0.012 and entrance loss coefficients of 0.1, 0.2, and 0.5. Figure B-10 is for corrugated metal pipe flowing full, based on n = 0.024 and entrance loss coefficients of 0.5 and 0.9.

(c) *Box Culvert with Vertical or Warping Inlet Walls.*—If the inlet is such that the bottom and side contractions will be suppressed, flow through a box culvert on a steep slope can alternately go through the three distinct phases of flow described previously, depending on submergence conditions and on the factors that dictate flow conditions within the conduit.

For conditions when the inlet is not submerged, critical flow will occur in the region of the inlet, in which case for a rectangular section, $d_c = \sqrt[3]{q^2/g}$ or $H = 1.5\sqrt[3]{q^2/g}$. Relating this equation of critical flow to the discharge Q:

$$Q = w\sqrt{g}\left(\frac{H}{1.5}\right)^{3/2} \tag{34}$$

where w is the width at the culvert entrance.

When the conduit entrance is submerged, the flow may be considered analogous to that of a sluice if the entrance has a square edge at the top. For this condition, top contraction of the jet will occur, and flow can be computed according to orifice flow, or $Q = CA\sqrt{2gh}$. The coefficient, C, depends on whether the area, A, is defined as the area of the opening, the area of the contracted jet, or some similar referenced area. Similarly, C will depend on the definition of the head, h: whether it is measured to the top, center, or bottom of the opening. Ordinarily, for a square-edged orifice in a vertical headwall, the area, a, is measured at the plane of the headwall face. If the head, H, is measured from the water surface to the bottom of the opening, the discharge can be computed by the equation:

$$Q = C_d a\sqrt{2gH}, \text{ or } Q = C_d wD\sqrt{2gH} \tag{35}$$

where D is the height of the opening. Values of C_d as determined from experiments [28] are plotted on figure 9-70.

As with circular culverts, full flow in box culverts depends on suppression of the top contraction. Full culvert flow will be governed by control at the outlet, and discharge-head relationships can be computed according to the equation:

$$Q = a\sqrt{2g(H_T - h_L)} \tag{36}$$

where a is the area of the culvert barrel, and H_T and h_L are the heads indicated on figure 9-69.

Reducing the equation and expressing it in terms of the entrance loss coefficient, K_e, and of the friction loss coefficient, Manning's n:

$$Q = a\sqrt{2g}\left[\frac{H + L\sin\theta - \frac{D}{2}}{1 + K_e + \frac{29.1n^2L}{r^{4/3}}}\right]^{1/2} \tag{37}$$

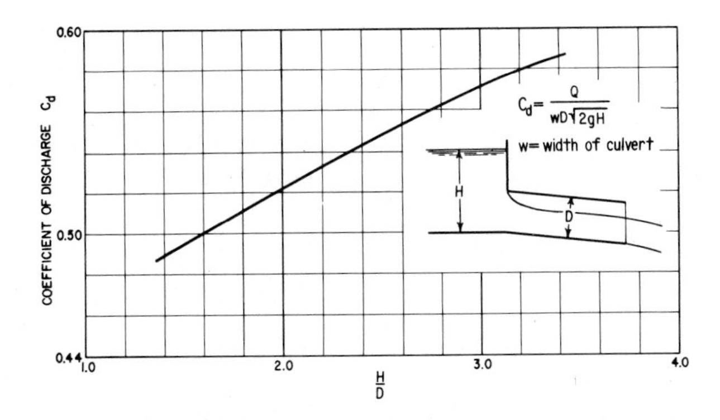

Figure 9-70.—Discharge coefficient for submerged box culvert spillways with square-edged top opening. From [28]. 288-D-2520.

where r is the hydraulic radius of the culvert flowing full. Equation (37) is based on free discharge at the outlet. If the outflowing jet is supported, equation (37) will become:

$$Q = a\sqrt{2g}\left[\frac{H + L\sin\theta - D}{1 + K_e + \frac{29.1n^2L}{r^{4/3}}}\right]^{1/2} \qquad (38)$$

Federal Highway Administration nomographs for solution of flow in box culverts are also included in appendix B. Figure B-11 is for box culverts with entrance control for various positions of the wingwalls. The discharges are based on discharge coefficients that approximate those shown on figure 9-70. Figure B-12 is for concrete box culverts flowing full, based on n = 0.0013 and entrance loss coefficients of 0.1, 0.2, 0.5, and 0.7.

(d) *Conduit Pressures.*—When the grade of a culvert spillway is greater than the friction slope, for full pipe flow the pressure gradient will lie below the center of the pipe, as indicated on figure 9-69. The difference in head between this hydraulic gradient and any point on the pipe vertically above it will be the subatmospheric pressure at the point. Cavitation will occur whenever the subatmospheric pressure approaches 1 Atm (1 atmosphere), so that the residual absolute pressure is near vapor pressure. To avoid cavitation along the pipe surfaces, the minimum absolute pressure must be greater than the vapor pressure. The pressure reduction in the pipe will be greatest at the crown immediately downstream from the entrance. It can be reduced further by any pressure drop caused by an inlet contraction, such as a sharp-edged or constricted opening.

From figure 9-69 it can be seen that:

$$h_v + h_e + h_r = h_{SA} + (H - D) \qquad (39)$$

where:

h_r = reduction of pressure head caused by contraction, and
h_{SA} = resulting subatmospheric pressure head.

The vapor pressure of water varies with temperature. It is equivalent to about 0.2 foot of head at 32 °F and about 1.4 feet of head at 85 °F. To ensure that cavitation is avoided and to allow for other uncertainties, the residual pressure ordinarily should not be significantly less than 10 feet absolute. Based on probable maximum atmospheric pressures at different elevations above sea level, the limiting subatmospheric pressures indicated in table 9-12 are recommended.

Table 9-12.—Allowable subatmospheric pressures for conduits flowing full.

Elevation above sea level	Allowable subatmospheric pressure, h_{SA}, feet of water
0	22
2000	20
4000	18
6000	16
8000	14

The reduction in pressure head caused by jet contraction will depend on the geometry of the inlet. For streamlined entrances very little reduction will be effected, but for sharp-edged projecting inlets, the reduction can be almost equal to the velocity head. For sharp-edged square inlets the reduction in pressure may approach $0.7h_v$. Written in terms of loss coefficients (sec. 10.14), equation (39) becomes:

$$\frac{v^2}{2g}(K_v + K_e + K_r) = h_{SA} + (H - D) \qquad (40)$$

or

$$\frac{v^2}{2g} = h_v = \frac{h_{SA} + (H - D)}{K_v + K_e + K_r} \qquad (41)$$

where K_r is the pressure reduction coefficient.

For a square-edged entrance where $K_e = 0.5$, $K_r = 0.7$, $K_v = 1.0$, $H = 1.5D$, and h_{SA} (for an installation at 6,000 feet above sea level) = 16 feet, equation (41) can be written:

$$h_v = \frac{16 + 0.5D}{1.0 + 0.5 + 0.7} = \frac{16 + 0.5D}{2.2}$$

For a 4-foot-diameter conduit, $h_v = 8.2$ feet, and the volocity in the conduit would have to be limited to about $v = 23$ ft/s. From equation (31), the total drop from the reservoir water surface to the centerline of the downstream end of a 200-foot-long conduit for $D = 4$ and $n = 0.014$ is:

$$H_T = 8.2\left(1.5 + \frac{29.1n^2L}{r^{4/3}}\right)$$

or

$$H_T = 8.2\left(1.5 + \frac{29.1(0.014)^2 200}{1^{4/3}}\right) = 21.7 \text{ feet}$$

(e) *Antivortex Devices.*—Although experiments have shown that for a properly rounded entrance the culvert begins to flow full after $H/D > 1.2$, the full pipe flow condition could not be stabilized until $H/D \geq 1.5$. This condition was caused by the "slug flow action," which resulted from the introduction of air into the conduit by entrance drawdown and by vortices immediately upstream from the inlet. To reduce the range where slug flow action prevails, antivortex devices have been used above conduit entrances. These devices not only stabilize the flow condition at a lower H/D, but they also help to start the priming action sooner. The devices have consisted of grillages, rafts, or fixed solid hoods placed so as to break up the vortices or to prevent their formation where they could feed air into the conduit [29]. To be effective, the hood or grillage must be placed immediately above the entrance and must extend at least two diameters in front of and to each side of the inlet.

(f) *Energy Dissipators.*—A culvert spillway may discharge freely, or it may empty into an open channel chute that conveys the flow to a downstream terminal structure. The flow from a freely discharging conduit may empty directly into the natural stream channel, into a trapezoidal plunge basin (described in sec. 9.24), or into an impact basin (sec. 10.17(b)). Where the discharge from the full-flowing culvert empties into an open chute, the hydraulics beyond the portal will be according to open channel flow, as discussed in section 9.19. Stilling devices such as those described in sections 9.18 through 9.24 can be used to dissipate the energy of flow before returning the discharge to the river channel.

(g) *Design Examples.*—To illustrate the procedures for a culvert spillway design, several typical examples are presented.

(1) *Example 1.*—The size of a culvert spillway required to discharge 100 ft³/s at reservoir elevation 110.0 is to be determined. The normal sill level of the spillway entrance is at elevation 100.0. The culvert is to flow partly full for all heads. If a circular conduit is selected, the design procedure is as follows:

The head-discharge-diameter relationship for a circular conduit with entrance placed flush with a vertical headwall can be obtained from figure 9-68. Curve A is used because the conduit is to flow partly full. By assuming various sizes of conduit, a size can be found that meets the requirements, as follows:

Assume a conduit 3.5 feet in diameter, then $D^{5/2} = 23$ and $Q/D^{5/2} = 4.35$. For $Q/D^{5/2} = 4.35$, $H/D = 1.75$ and $H = 6.1$. Because $H = 10$ feet is allowable, the culvert can be made smaller.

As a second trial, assume a 3-foot-diameter conduit. Then $D^{5/2} = 15.6$ and $Q/D^{5/2} = 6.41$. From curve A, $H/D = 3.2$ and $H = 9.6$, which approximates the 10 feet available.

If a box culvert is selected, the design procedure is as follows:

$$Q = C_d wD\sqrt{2gH} \quad \text{(eq. (35))}$$

$$wD = \frac{Q}{C_d\sqrt{2gH}}$$

Assuming a 2.5-foot-high culvert, $H/D = 10/2.5 = 4.0$, and C_d from figure 9-70 is approximately 0.6. Then,

$$2.5w = \frac{100}{0.6\,(8.02)\sqrt{10}} = 6.6,$$

and $w = 2.6$ feet.

(2) *Example 2.*—Find the discharge through the conduits in the previous example if the entrances are shaped to provide full conduit flow. The conduit length is 200 feet, and the invert grade at the outlet

is elevation 80.0. The conduit discharges freely at the outlet end. The procedure is as follows:

Equation (32) may be written:

$$\left(\frac{Q}{D^{5/2}}\right)^2 = \frac{1}{0.0252}\left[\frac{\frac{H}{D} + \frac{L}{D}\sin\theta - \frac{1}{2}}{1 + K_e + \frac{29.1n^2L}{r^{4/3}}}\right]$$

For a 3-foot circular conduit with $K_e = 0.10$ and $n = 0.014$:

$$\left(\frac{Q}{15.6}\right)^2 = \frac{1}{0.0252}\left[\frac{\frac{10}{3} + \frac{200}{3}\left(\frac{20}{200}\right) - \frac{1}{2}}{1 + 0.10 + \frac{29.1(0.014)^2 200}{(0.75)^{4/3}}}\right]$$

$$= 136, \text{ therefore}$$

$$Q = 182 \text{ ft}^3/\text{s}$$

This flow will provide a velocity of 25.7 ft/s in the conduit.

Equation (40) may be written:

$$h_{SA} = \frac{v^2}{2g}(K_v + K_e + K_r) - (H - D)$$

The subatmospheric pressure in the conduit, based on a pressure reduction coefficient $K_r = 0.1$ and $K_e = 0.1$ for a rounded entrance is equal to:

$$\frac{(25.7)^2}{64.4}(1.0 + 0.1 + 0.1) - (10.0 - 3.0) = 5.3 \text{ feet}$$

This subatmospheric pressure is less than the limit allowed in table 9-12; therefore, the design is satisfactory.

For the box culvert spillway, from equation (37), assuming $K_e = 0.1$ and $n = 0.014$:

$$Q = 2.5(2.6)8.02\left[\frac{10 + 200\left(\frac{20}{200}\right) - 1.25}{1 + 0.1 + \frac{29.1(200)0.014^2}{0.64^{4/3}}}\right]^{1/2}$$

$$= 157 \text{ ft}^3/\text{s}.$$

G. STRUCTURAL DESIGN DETAILS

9.28. *General.*—The structural design of a spillway and the selection of specific structural details are generally performed after the spillway type has been selected, its components have been arranged, and the hydraulic design has been completed.

Usually, the foundation material of a spillway is not able to adequately resist the destructive action of high-velocity flows; therefore, a nonerodible lining must ordinarily be provided along the spillway waterway. Such a lining prevents erosion, reduces friction losses by providing smooth bounding surfaces for the channel (this also permits smaller hydraulic sections), and provides a relatively watertight conveyance channel for directing flow past the dam. Economy and durability most often favor concrete as the appropriate lining material for water conveyance structures.

A spillway may be constructed on almost any foundation capable of sustaining applied loads without undue deformation. Although it is not usually advisable, a spillway may be placed on the face of or through an earthfill dam, provided design details are carefully selected to accommodate settlement and to prevent leakage from the structure. The type of walls, linings, and associated structures of a spillway and its design details should depend on the nature of the foundation. For example, the design details for a spillway founded entirely on rock should differ from one constructed on softer material. Structural details should differ according to foundation bearing capacities, settlement or heave characteristics, and permeability and seepage features. Concrete walls, linings, and associated structures must be designed to withstand normal hydrostatic and earth loadings, movements caused by temperature changes, and unequal or large foundation movements. The design must also provide for handling leakage from the channel or underseepage from the foundation, which might cause saturation of the underlying materials and large uplift forces on the structure.

Subsequent sections discuss the structural designs and miscellaneous details of open channel spillways, including crest structures, walls, and channel linings. The structural designs of spillway conduits and tunnels are similar to those for outlet conduits and tunnels, which are discussed in chapter 10.

9.29. *Crest Structures and Walls.*—Spillway

control structures and overflow crests against which reservoir heads act are essentially overflow dams, and spillway abutment structures or flanking dikes are similar to concrete nonoverflow dams or earthfill embankments. The design of earthfill dams is discussed in chapter 6, and the design of overflow and nonoverflow concrete dams is discussed in chapter 8.

The nature or type of confining side walls selected for open channel spillways should depend on the material upon which they are founded and on the loading to which they will be subjected. For spillway channels excavated in rock or firm material, where sloping the wall faces is permissible, a lining placed directly against the excavated slopes may provide sufficient stability for forming the channel sidewalls. Otherwise, self-supporting retaining walls of the gravity, cantilever, or counterforted type are required. A monolithic flume-type section whose walls are continuous with the floor and heels is often used.

The design of a gravity or reinforced concrete retaining wall for a spillway is similar to that for a gravity dam in that the stability against sliding and overturning and the magnitude and distribution of the foundation reaction resulting from the weight and applied loads must be determined. Methods of analyzing gravity structures for stability, including allowable sliding factors, and of determining foundation reactions are discussed in chapter 8. Suggested allowable bearing values are presented in appendix C.

Earth loadings can be assumed on the basis of equivalent fluid pressures. Figure C-1 gives criteria for determining soil loadings on vertical and inclined walls using Coloumb's theory of active earth pressure. Additional design criteria for concrete retaining walls are covered in "Design Criteria for Concrete Retaining Walls" [29]. Wall footings must be safeguarded against frost heave, and wall panels must be articulated to accommodate foundation yielding or unequal settlement. To avoid differential settlement in soft or yielding foundations, wall footing dimensions should be selected to minimize foundation load concentrations and to provide nearly uniform bearing reactions across the base areas.

Inlet channel and chute walls may be subjected to various combinations of loading. When flow is occurring through the spillway, hydrostatic loads on the channel side of the wall tend to offset the backfill loads. If, however, the fill has shrunk away from the walls, they may be subjected to full channel-side waterload before deflecting enough to gain support from the backfill. This condition is more likely to exist where the top of the wall inclines toward the backfill. On the other hand, when the reservoir is drawn down below the spillway level and there is no flow through the structure, the walls are subjected to full backfill loads without any support from waterloads. The structural design of wall members must consider all these loading possibilities. When the backfill is not expected to be tight against the wall to help support it against water pressures, an increase in the allowable stresses may be considered.

When permeable backfill is placed behind stilling basin walls or when the back of the wall is partly exposed to tailwater, the water pressure resulting from tailwater must be added to the backfill loading. For higher spillway discharges, the water level inside the basin will be depressed by the profile of the jump, and an unbalanced hydrostatic load acting to overturn the walls will occur. Unbalanced water loads may also result from wave action. The design loading assumptions must recognize this condition of unbalanced pressures and the increased uplift forces when sliding and overturning analyses are considered.

9.30. *Open Channel Linings.*—Floor slabs for articulated floor and wall systems are provided primarily to form a reasonably watertight protective surfacing over the channel to prevent erosion or damage to the foundation. During spillway flows, the floor may be subjected to hydrostatic forces from the weight of the water in the channel, to boundary drag forces caused by frictional resistance along the surface, to dynamic forces caused by flow impingement, to uplift forces caused by the reduction of pressure along the boundary surface, and to uplift pressure caused by leakage through joints or cracks. When there are no spillway flows, the floor is subjected to the action of the elements, including expansion and contraction caused by temperature variations, alternate freezing and thawing, and weathering and chemical deterioration; to the effects of settlement and buckling; and to uplift pressures brought about by underseepage or high ground-water conditions. Because evaluating the various forces that might occur and making the lining heavy enough to resist them is not always possible, the thickness of the lining is most often selected empirically, and underdrains, anchors, cutoffs, etc., are provided to stabilize the floor.

When a spillway channel is excavated in rock, the concrete slab is cast directly on the excavated surface. Anchor bars grouted into holes drilled into the rock may be provided to tie the slab to the foundation. Slabs tied to the foundation should be provided with control or contraction joints to control cracking caused by expansion and contraction. Typical details for articulated slabs on rock are shown on figure 9-71. The anchorage increases the effective weight of the slab by the weight of foundation rock to which the anchors can be tied. Depth and spacing of anchors should depend on the nature of the bedrock and the design loading. Anchors should be large enough to support the weight of the foundation to which they are attached without exceeding the yield stress of the steel. A gridwork of perforated underdrains laid on a lean concrete pad in gravel-filled trenches should be provided to prevent a buildup of uplift under the slab. Rubber or polyvinyl chloride waterstops are generally provided at the joints.

Monolithic floor and wall systems for narrow structures serve the same purpose and are subjected to the same loads discussed for articulated structures. However, design details and procedures vary because of the type of structure. The thickness of a monolithic slab is generally determined from backfill loads, water and uplift loads, and an elastic foundation analysis. Transverse joints should be located at approximately 25- to 50-foot spacing. Cutoffs and transverse drains are usually placed at these joints (fig. 9-71).

When a spillway channel is excavated through earth, the slab may be cast directly on the excavated surface, or an intervening pervious blanket may be required. The choice depends on the nature of the foundation as related to its permeability, susceptibility to frost heave, and heterogeneity as it may affect differential settlement. Because the slab is not bonded to the foundation, it will expand and contract, and it must be restrained from creeping when it is constructed on a slope. This is best achieved by installing cutoffs (sec. 9.31(a)), which can be held relatively fixed with respect to the slab and to the foundation, or by tying the slab to walls, piles, or similar rigid members of the spillway structure. Because a slab on an earth foundation is relatively free to move, the paving should be reinforced sufficiently to permit its sliding without cracking of the concrete or yielding of the reinforcement. To further assist in holding the slab to the foundation, bulb anchors are sometimes used, as shown on figure 9-71. These anchors, in effect, tie the slab to a cone of earth, the volume of which depends on the anchor depth and spacing and on the angle of internal friction of the soil.

A pervious gravel blanket is often provided between the slab and the foundation when the foundation is sufficiently impervious to prevent leakage from draining away, or where the foundation is subjected to capillarity, which will draw moisture to the underside of the lining. The blanket serves as a free-draining medium and helps insulate the foundation against frost penetration. Therefore, the thickness of the blanket selected should be based on the climate and on the susceptibility of the foundation to frost heaving. A gridwork of perforated underdrains laid in gravel and bedded on a lean concrete pad to prevent the foundation material from being leached into the pipe should be provided as a collection system for the seepage. The network of drainage pipe should empty into one or more trunk drains that carry the seepage flow to outlets through the channel floor or walls.

In stratified foundations, ground water or seepage can cause uplift on layers below the floor lining, and drainage holes are sometimes augered into the underlying material and backfilled with gravels to relieve the underpressure.

When watertightness of the slab against exterior water heads is required, polyvinyl chloride or rubber waterstops should be installed to seal the joints. If watertightness is desired, such seals are provided in floor slabs upstream from the control structure to increase the percolation path under the structure. They are commonly provided at transverse joints along concave curved portions of the downstream channel where the dynamic pressures on the floor cause a high head for introducing water into the joint. Seals may be desirable along longitudinal joints in a stilling basin on a permeable base. Differential heads resulting from the sloping water surface of the jump can cause a circulating flow under the slab if leakage is allowed to enter the joint at the downstream end of the basin and to flow out of the joint at the upstream end.

Joints should generally be spaced from 25 to 50 feet apart in both the floor and walls. Joints should also be provided where angular changes of the floor surface occur and where they are required to avoid reentrant angles in the slab, which often cause

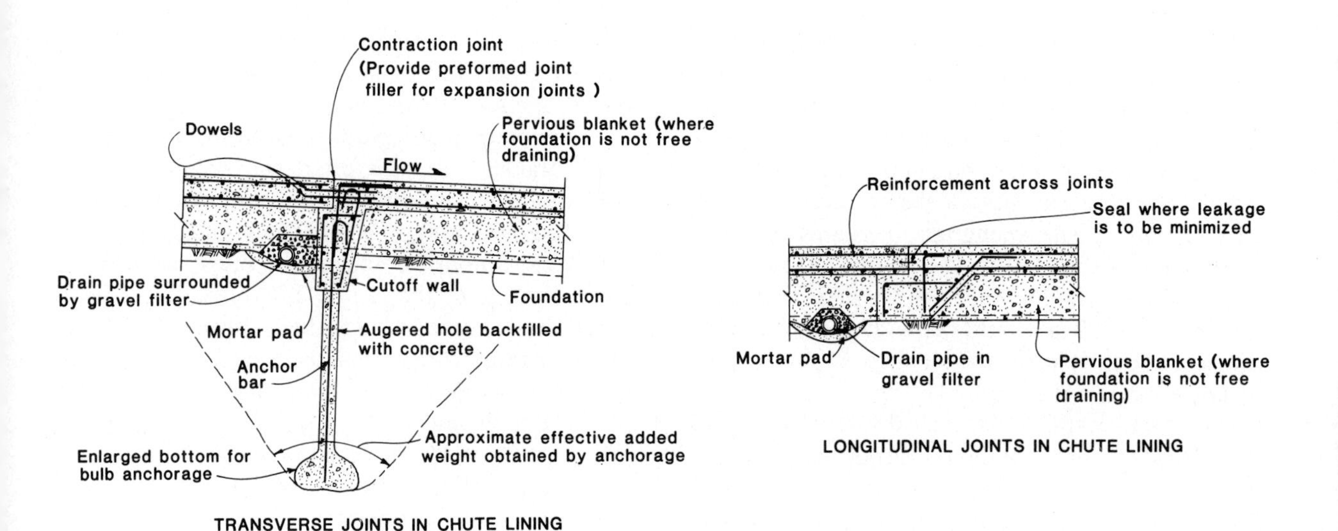

ARTICULATED FLOOR LINING ON EARTH FOUNDATIONS

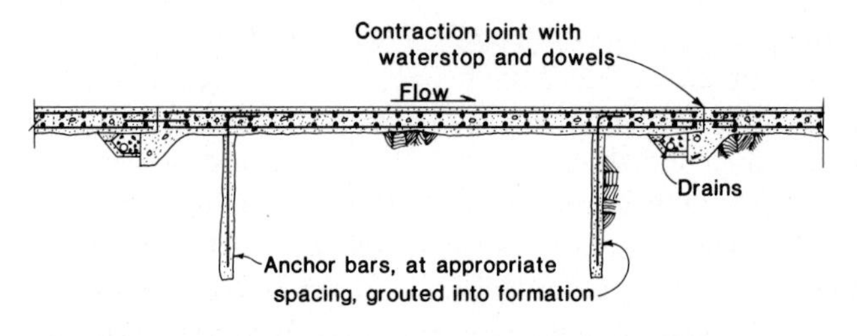

ARTICULATED FLOOR LINING ON FIRM FORMATION

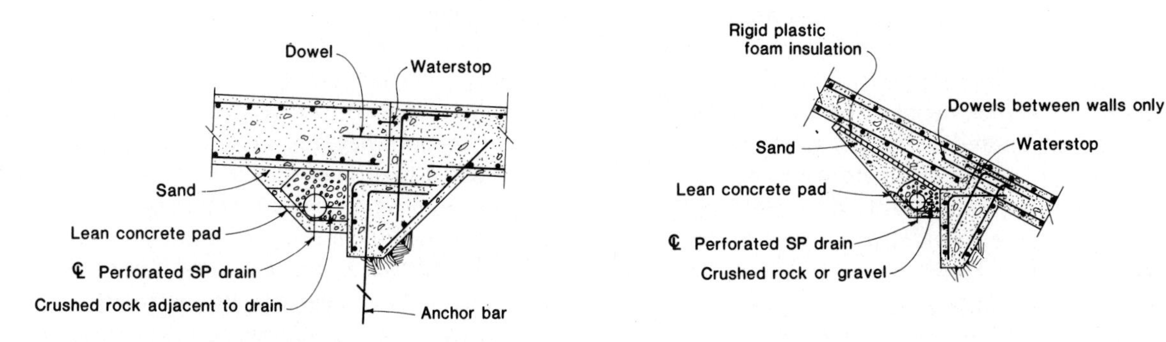

Figure 9-71.—Floor lining details for spillway channels. 103–D–1877.

cracking of the slab. The use of joint fillers in contraction joints should be minimized because deterioration of these fillers will result in an open joint that is difficult to maintain. If joints are provided at the proper spacings, contraction or expansion may not be severe, and filler material in the joint may not be necessary. Floor slabs can be constructed in alternate panels; the initial placement shrinkage of the concrete may then afford sufficient joint opening for subsequent expansion. Keyed joints in thin floors and walls that may be subjected to differential movement are unsatisfactory, because differential deflection across the joint places high stress on the keys or keyways and causes them to spall; an unkeyed joint with slip dowels is preferable.

Normally, the floor of a stilling basin will be subjected to uplift pressures resisting the tailwater loads and waterloads whose magnitudes depend on hydraulic-jump depths. For articulated slabs, the uplift pressure must be resisted by the weight of the slab and the water inside the basin and by anchor bars. Floors cast monolithically with walls experience uplift loads, inside waterloads, and backfill loads and waterloads transferred through the walls. A transverse strip of the floor is usually analyzed with appropriate loadings and elastic foundation procedures. Flotation stability is computed assuming water to the elevation of the outlet channel and no water inside the basin.

9.31. *Miscellaneous Details.*—(a) *Cutoffs.*—One or more cutoffs are generally provided at the upstream end of a spillway for various purposes. They can be used to form a watertight curtain against seepage under the structure, or they can increase the path of percolation under the structure and thus reduce uplift forces. Cutoffs can also be used to intercept permeable strata in the foundation to minimize seepage and prevent a buildup of uplift pressure under the spillway or adjacent areas. When the cutoff trench for the dam extends to the spillway, it is generally joined to the upstream spillway cutoff to provide a continuous barrier across the abutment area. In jointed rock the cutoff acts as a grout cap for a grout curtain, which is often extended across the spillway foundation.

A cutoff is usually provided at the downstream end of a spillway structure as a safeguard against erosion and undermining of the end of the structure. Cutoffs at intermediate points along the length of a spillway are sometimes provided as barriers against water flowing along the contact between the structure and the foundation and to lengthen the path of percolation under the structure. Wherever possible, cutoffs in rock foundations are placed in vertical trenches. In earth foundations where the cutoffs must be formed in a trench with sloping sides, care must be taken to compact the trench backfill properly with impervious material to obtain a reasonably watertight barrier.

(b) *Backfill.*—When a spillway is placed adjacent to a dam so that the impervious zone of the embankment abuts the spillway walls, the wall backfill is actually the impervious zone of the dam and should be compacted accordingly. Backfill elsewhere along the spillway walls should ordinarily be free-draining material to minimize hydrostatic pressures against the walls. Backfill other than that adjacent to the dam may be either compacted or uncompacted. The choice of backfill material and the compaction methods used in placing such material will affect the design loadings on the walls.

(c) *Riprap.*—When the spillway approach channel is excavated in material that will be eroded as a result of high approach velocities, a zone of riprap is often provided immediately upstream from the inlet lining to prevent scour of the channel floor and of the side slopes adjacent ot the spillway concrete. This riprap, which is generally a continuation of that along the upstream face of the dam, should have similar size and gradation and similar bedding. Riprap is normally used in the outlet channel adjacent to the downstream cutoff to prevent excessive erosion and undermining of the downstream end of the structure. To resist scour from high exit velocities, the riprap should be the largest possible and should be bedded on a graded material. The riprap should be graded to prevent the underlying material from washing out, which would cause the riprap to settle or to be displaced.

H. BIBLIOGRAPHY

9.32. *Bibliography.*

[1] Pugh, C. A., *Hydraulic Model Studies of a Fuse Plug Spillway*, Bureau of Reclamation, Hydraulics Laboratory Report, REC-ERC-85-7, 1985.

[2] Mason, Peter J., "Free Jet Scour Below Dams and Flip Buckets," ASCE, *Journal of Hydraulic Engineering*, vol. III, No. 2, February 1985.

[3] Johnson, P. L., *Hydraulic Model Studies of Plunge Basins for Jet Flow,* Bureau of Reclamation, Hydraulics Laboratory Report, REC-ERC-74-9, June 1974.

[4] Donnelly, C. A., and F. W. Blaisdell, "Straight Drop Spillway Stilling Basin," University of Minnesota, Saint Anthony Falls Hydraulics Laboratory, Technical Paper No. 15, Series B, November 1954.

[5] Hinchliff, David L., and Kathleen L. Houston, "Hydraulic Design and Application of Labyrinth Spillways," *Proceedings of the Fourth Annual USCOLD Lecture,* January 24, 1984.

[6] Houston, Kathleen L., *Hydraulic Model Studies of Hyrum Dam Auxiliary Labyrinth Spillway,* Bureau of Reclamation Report GR-82-13, May 1983.

[7] Houston, Kathleen L., *Hydraulic Model Studies of Ute Dam Labyrinth Spillway*, Bureau of Reclamation Report GR-82-07, August 1982.

[8] Pugh, C. A., "Hydraulic Model Studies of Aeration Devices for Blue Mesa and Glen Canyon Tunnel Spillways," Bureau of Reclamation Hydraulics Laboratory Report, 1987.

[9] Houston, Kathleen L., "Hydraulic Model Studies of Hoover Dam Arizona Tunnel Spillway - Aerator Design," Bureau of Reclamation Hydraulics Laboratory Report, 1987.

[10] Borden, R. C., D. Colgate, J. Legas, and C. E. Selander, *Documentation of Operation, Damage, Repair, and Testing of Yellowtail Dam Spillway,* Bureau of Reclamation Report No. REC-ERC-71-23, 1971.

[11] Pinto, N. L. de S., and S. H. Neidert, "Model Prototype Conformity in Aerated Spillway Flow," International Conference on the Hydraulic Modeling of Civil Engineering Structures, BHRA Fluid Engineerings, Coventry, England, September 1982.

[12] Peterka, A. J., "Spillway Tests Confirm Model-Prototype Conformance," Bureau of Reclamation, Research Report No. 16, 1954.

[13] Peterka, A. J., "Morning Glory Shaft Spillways," ASCE, *Transactions,* vol. 121, 1956.

[14] Bradley, J. N., "Morning Glory Shaft Spillway: Prototype Behavior," ASCE, *Transactions,* vol. 121, 1956.

[15] Peterka, A. J., "Hydraulic Design of Spillways and Energy Dissipators," Bureau of Reclamation, 1984.

[16] Rhone, T. J., "Baffled Apron as a Spillway Energy Dissipator," ASCE, *Journal of the Hydraulics Division*, vol. 103, No. HY12, December 1977.

[17] George, R. L., *T or C Baffled Apron Spillway*, Bureau of Reclamation, Hydraulics Laboratory Report, GR-79-02, April 1979.

[18] "Studies of Crests of Overfall Dams," Bureau of Reclamation, Bulletin 3, part VI, Hydraulic Investigations, Boulder Canyon Project, Final Reports, 1948.

[19] Bradley, J. N., "Discharge Coefficients for Irregular Overfall Spillways," Bureau of Reclamation, Engineering Monograph No. 9, March 1952.

[20] "Hydraulic Design Criteria," U. S. Army Corps of Engineers, Waterways Experiment Station, Vicksburg, MS, issued serially since 1952.

[21] Hinds, Julian, "Side Channel Spillways," ASCE, *Transactions*, vol. 89, p. 881, 1926.

[22] Zeigler, E. R., *Hydraulic Model Studies for Palmetto Bend Spillway,* Bureau of Reclamation, Hydraulics Laboratory Report, GR-78-8, November 1978.

[23] George, R. L., *Low Froude Number Stilling Basin Design,* Bureau of Reclamation, Hydraulics Laboratory Report, REC-ERC-78-8, August 1978.

[24] Wagner, W. E., "Morning Glory Shaft Spillways: Determination of Pressure Controlled Profiles," ASCE, *Transactions,* vol. 121, 1956.

[25] Straub, L. G., A. G. Anderson, and C. E. Bowers, "Importance of Inlet Design on Culvert Capacity, Culvert Hydraulics," Highway Research Board of the National Academy of Sciences, National Research Council, Publication 287, Research Report No. 15-B, p. 53, 1953.

[26] Karr, M. H., and L. A. Clayton, "Model Studies of Inlet Designs for Pipe Culverts on Steep Grades," Engineering Experiment Station, Oregon State College, Bulletin No. 35, June 1954.

[27] Schiller, R. E., Jr., "Tests on Circular Pipe Culvert Inlets," Culvert Flow Characteristics, Highway Research Board of the National Academy of Sciences, National Research Council, Publication 413, Bulletin No. 126, p. 11, 1956.

[28] Schoemaker, R. H., Jr., and L. A. Clayton, "Model Studies of Tapered Inlets for Box Culverts," Culvert Hydaulics, Highway Research Board of the National Academy of Sciences, National Research Council, Publication 287, Research Report No. 15-B, p. 1.

[29] Aisenbrey, Jr., A. J., R. B. Campbell, R. W. Kramer, J. Legas, and L. M. Stimson, "Design Criteria for Concrete Retaining Walls—Report of Task Committee on Design Criteria for Retaining Walls," Bureau of Reclamation, Engineering and Research Center, Denver, CO, August 1971.

[30] Blaisdell, F. W., and C. A. Donnelly, "Hydraulics of Closed Conduit Spillways—Part X—The Hood Inlet," Univ. of Minnisota, Saint Anthony Falls Hydraulics Laboratory, Technical Paper No. 20, series B, April 1958.

Beichley, G. L., "Hydraulic Design of Stilling Basin for Pipe or Channel Outlets," Bureau of Reclamation Research Report No. 24, 1976.

Chapter 10

Outlet Works

A. GENERAL

10.1. ***Functions.***—An outlet works regulates or releases water impounded by a dam. It can release incoming flows at a retarded rate, as does a detention dam; it can divert incoming flows into canals or pipelines, as does a diversion dam; or it can release stored waters at rates dictated by downstream needs, by evacuation considerations, or by a combination of multiple-purpose requirements.

Outlet works structures can be classified according to their purpose, their physical and structural arrangement, or their hydraulic operation. An outlet works that empties directly into a river could be designated a "river outlet"; one that discharges into a canal could be designated a "canal outlet"; and one that delivers water into a closed pipe system could be designated a "pressure pipe outlet." An outlet works may be described according to whether it consists of an open-channel or closed-conduit waterway, or whether the closed waterway is a conduit in cut-and-cover or in a tunnel. An outlet works may also be classified according to its hydraulic operation: whether it is gated or ungated or, for a closed conduit, whether it flows under pressure for part or all of its length or only as a free flow waterway. Typical outlet works installations are shown on figures 10-1 through 10-7.

Occasionally, the outlet works may be placed at a level high enough to deliver water to a canal, while a bypass is extended to the river to furnish necessary flows below the dam. Such bypass flows may be required to satisfy prior-right uses downstream or to maintain a live stream for abatement of stream pollution, preservation of aquatic life, or other purposes. Dams constructed to provide reservoirs principally for recreation or for fish and wildlife conservation require a fairly constant reservoir level. For such dams an outlet works may be needed only to release the minimum flows necessary to maintain a live stream below the dam.

In certain cases, the outlet works of a dam may be used in lieu of a service spillway combined with an auxiliary or secondary spillway. In such a case, the usual outlet works installation might be modified to include a bypass overflow so that the structure can serve as both an outlet works and a spillway. Such structures are typified by Wasco Dam and Lion Lake dikes, figures 6-84 and 10-7(B), respectively. In these installations, the overflow weirs in the control shaft automatically bypass surplus inflows whenever the reservoir rises above normal storage level.

An outlet works may act as a flood control regulator to release waters temporarily stored in flood control storage space or to evacuate storage in anticipation of flood inflows. Furthermore, the outlets may be used to empty the reservoir to permit inspection, to allow needed repairs, or to maintain the upstream face of the dam or other structures normally inundated. The outlets may also aid in lowering the reservoir storage when controlling or poisoning scrap fish or other objectionable aquatic life in the reservoir is desired.

10.2. ***Determination of Required Capacities.***—Outlet works are designed to release water at specific rates. These rates are dictated by downstream needs, by flood control regulation, by storage considerations, by power generation needs (where the outlet works is used as the penstock for small powerplants), and by legal requirements. Delivery of irrigation water is usually determined from project or farm needs and is related to the consumptive use and to the special water requirements of the irrigation system. Delivery for domestic use can be similarly established. Releases of flows to satisfy prior rights must generally be included with other needed releases. Minimum downstream flows for pollution abatement, fish preservation, and associated needs are often accommodated through other required releases. A small bypass pipe is often used to provide these minimum releases. This pipe usually origi-

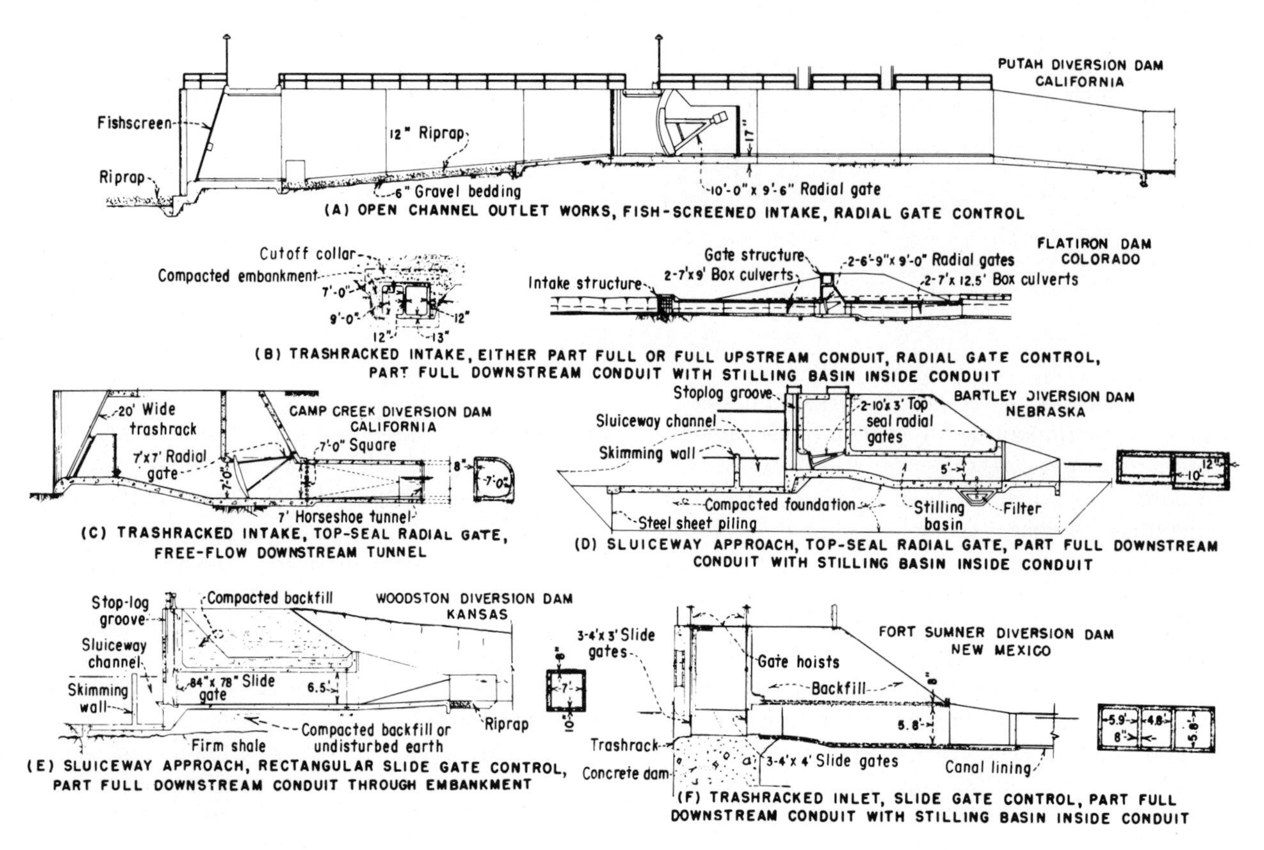

Figure 10-1.—Typical low-head outlet works installations. 288–D–2523.

nates at the gate chamber or in the downstream control structure, depending on the type of outlet works.

Irrigation outlet capacities are determined from reservoir operation studies. They must be based on a consideration of a critical period of low runoff when reservoir storages are low and daily irrigation demands are at their peak. The most critical draft from the reservoir, considering such demands (commensurate with remaining reservoir storage) together with prior rights and other needed releases, generally determines the minimum irrigation outlet capacity. These requirements are stated in terms of discharge at either a given reservoir content or a given water surface elevation. Occasionally, outlet capacity requirements are established for several reservoir contents or alternative water surfaces. For example, outlet requirements may be set forth as 20 ft^3/s capacity at reservoir content 500 acre-feet, and 100 ft^3/s capacity at reservoir content 3,000 acre-feet.

Evacuation of water stored in an allocated flood control storage space of a reservoir can be accomplished through a gated spillway at the higher reservoir levels or through an outlet at the lower levels. Flood control releases generally can be combined with the irrigation releases if the outlet empties into a river instead of into a canal. The capacity of a flood control outlet can be determined by the required time of evacuation of the given storage space, considering the inflow into the reservoir during the evacuation. Combined flood control and irrigation releases ordinarily must not exceed the safe channel capacity of the river downstream from the dam and must allow for all anticipated inflows immediately below the dam. These inflows may be natural runoffs, or the results of releases from storage developments along the river or from developments on tributaries emptying into the river.

If an outlet is to serve as a service spillway in releasing surplus inflows from the reservoir, the discharge required for this purpose may determine the outlet capacity. Similarly, the minimum outlet capacity can be determined by the discharge and the time required to empty the reservoir for inspection, maintenance, repair, or emergency drawdown. Here

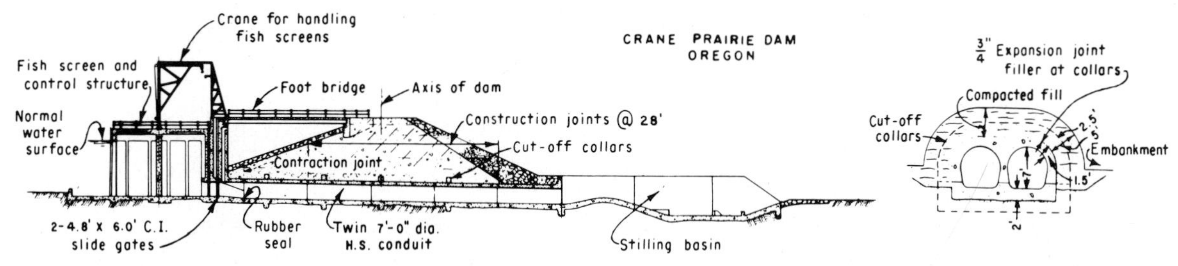

(A) FISH-SCREENED INTAKE, UPSTREAM SLIDE GATE CONTROL, FREE-FLOW CONDUIT, HYDRAULIC JUMP STILLING BASIN

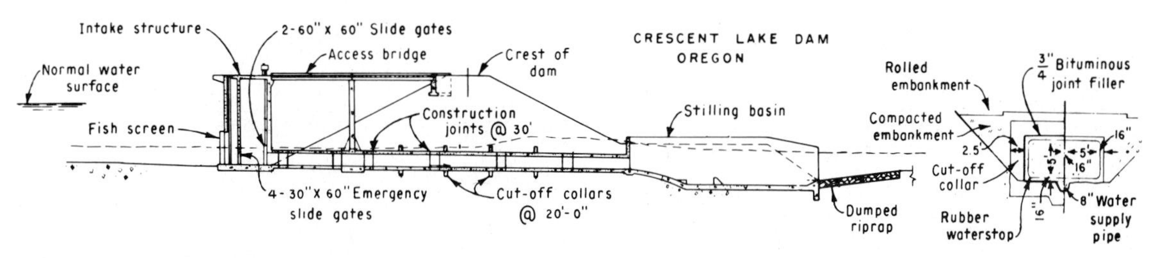

(B) FISH-SCREENED INTAKE, UPSTREAM SLIDE GATE CONTROL, FREE-FLOW CONDUIT, HYDRAULIC JUMP STILLING BASIN

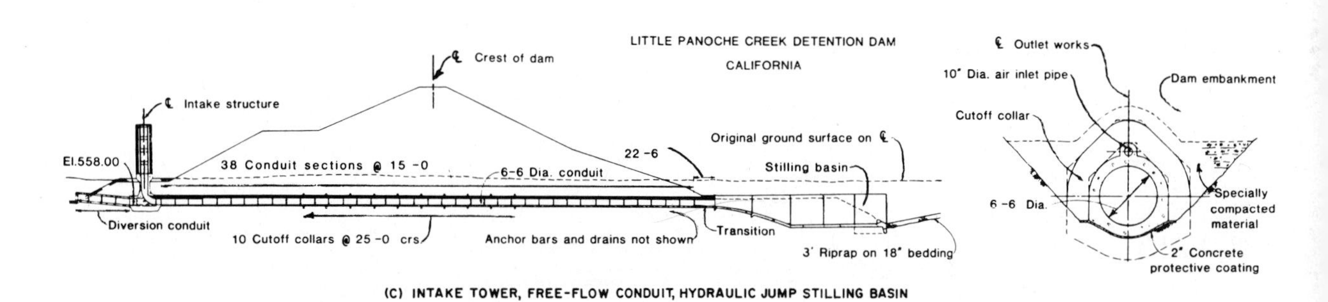

(C) INTAKE TOWER, FREE-FLOW CONDUIT, HYDRAULIC JUMP STILLING BASIN

Figure 10-2.—Typical free-flow conduit outlet works installations. 103–D–1837.

again, the inflow into the reservoir during the emptying period must be considered. The capacity at low reservoir level should be at least equal to the average inflow expected during the maintenance or repair period. It can, of course, be assumed that required repair will be delayed until service demands are light and that repairs will be made during low inflow and during seasons favorable to such construction.

An outlet works cut-and-cover conduit or tunnel is often used to divert the riverflow during the construction period, precluding supplementary installations for that purpose. The outlet structure size dictated by this use, rather than the size dictated by ordinary outlet works requirements, may determine the final outlet works capacity. A diversion bypass pipe may be required to satisfy downstream requirements during placement of second-stage concrete and gates in the outlet works.

10.3. *Outlet Works Position in Relation to Reservoir Storage Levels.*—The establishment of the intake level and the elevations of the outlet controls and the conveyance passageway, as they relate to the reservoir storage levels, are influenced by many factors. Primarily, to attain the required discharge capacity, the outlet must be placed sufficiently below the minimum reservoir operating level to provide the head required for outlet works flows.

Outlet works for small detention dams are generally constructed near riverbed level because permanent storage space, except for silt retention, is ordinarily not provided. (These outlet works may

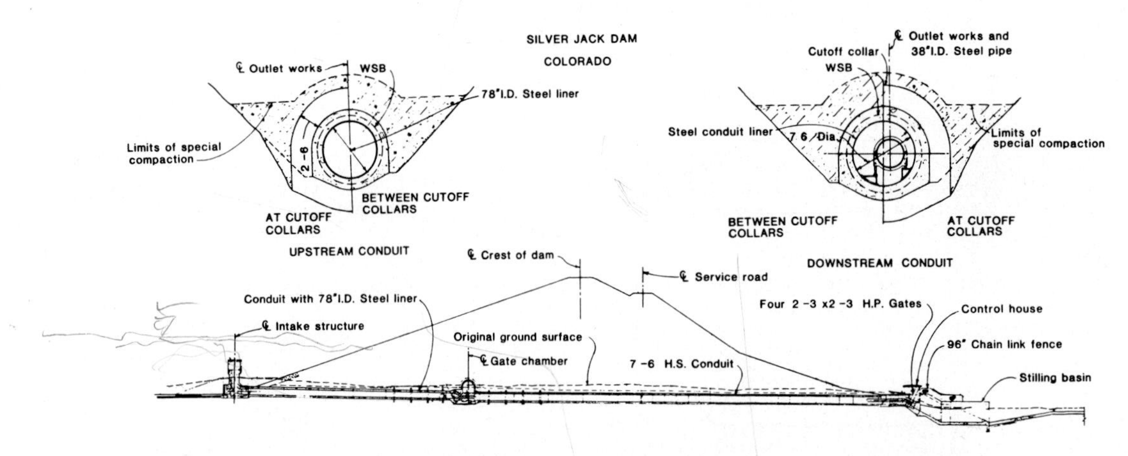

TRASHRACKED DROP INLET INTAKE, STEEL LINED UPSTREAM PRESSURE CONDUIT, HIGH PRESSURE GUARD GATE, PIPE IN DOWNSTREAM TUNNEL, CONDUIT, CONTROL GATES, STILLING BASIN

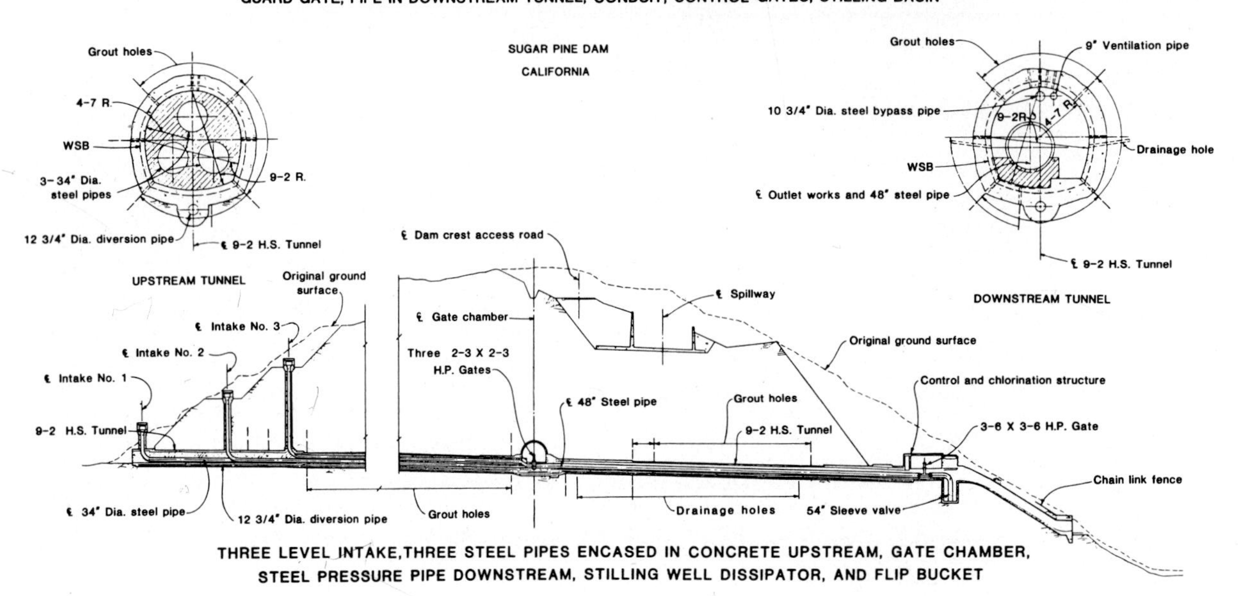

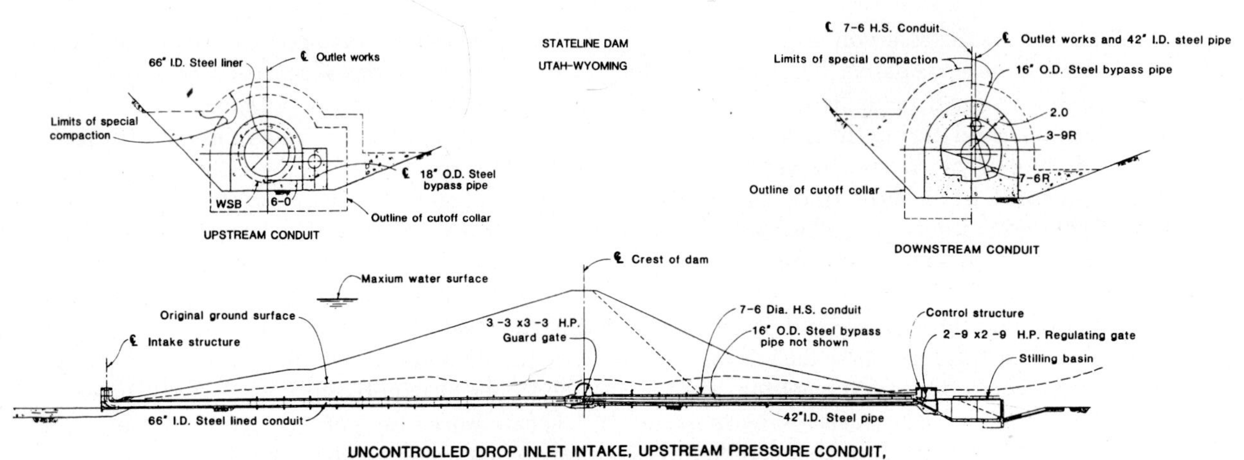

Figure 10-3.—Typical pressure conduit and tunnel outlet works installations. 103–D–1835.

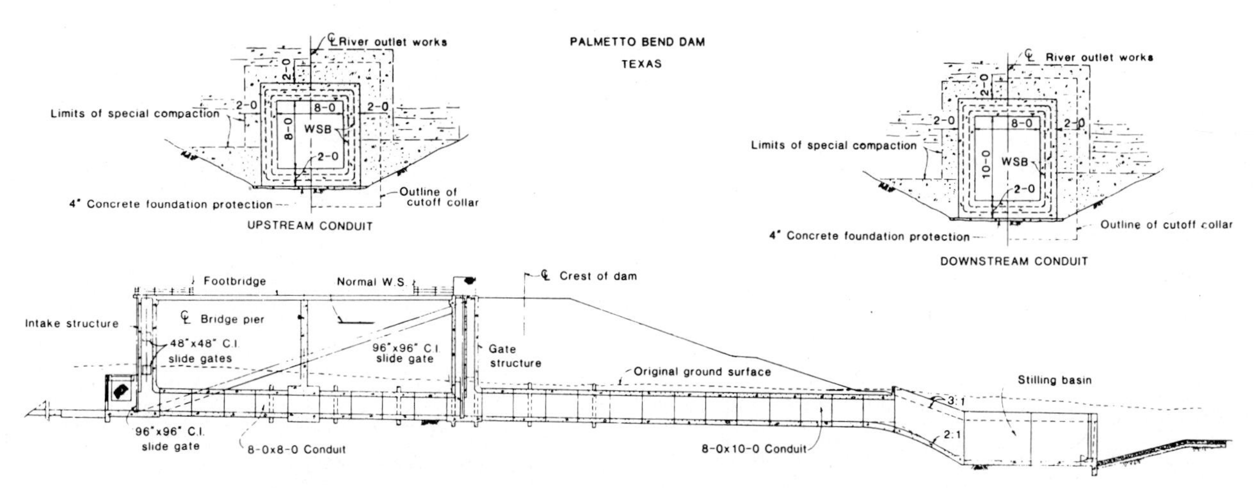

GATED SELECTIVE LEVEL INTAKE, PRESSURE UPSTREAM CONDUIT, SLIDE GATE CONTROL, FREE-FLOW DOWNSTREAM CONDUIT, STILLING BASIN

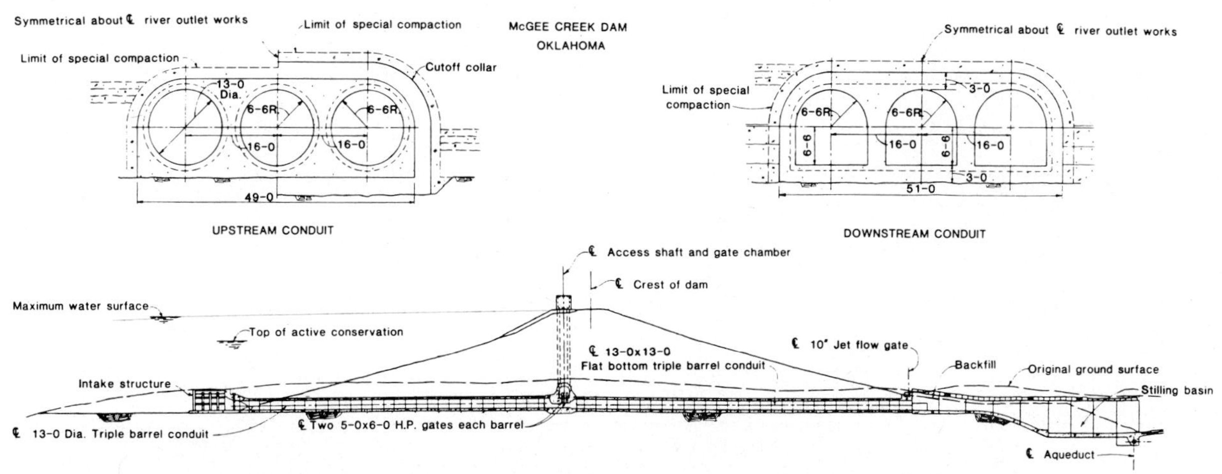

TRASHRACKED BOX INTAKE, UPSTREAM PRESSURE CONDUIT, GATE CONTROL, FREE FLOW DOWNSTREAM CONDUIT,STILLING BASIN

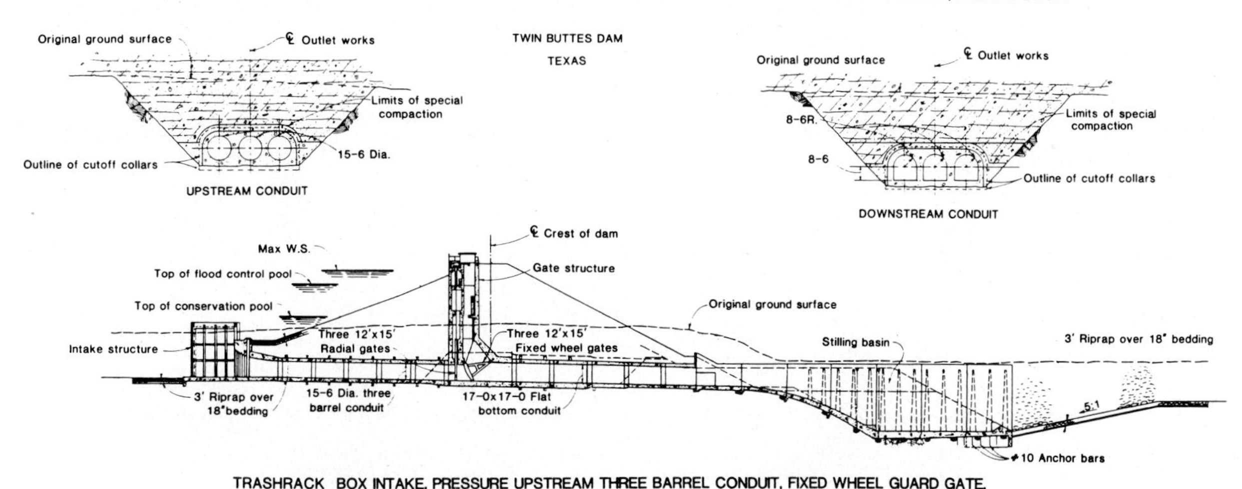

TRASHRACK BOX INTAKE, PRESSURE UPSTREAM THREE BARREL CONDUIT, FIXED WHEEL GUARD GATE, RADIAL REGULATING GATE, FREE FLOW THREE BARREL DOWNSTREAM CONDUIT, STILLING BASIN.

Figure 10-4.—Typical combined pressure and free-flow conduit outlet works installations. 103–D–1833.

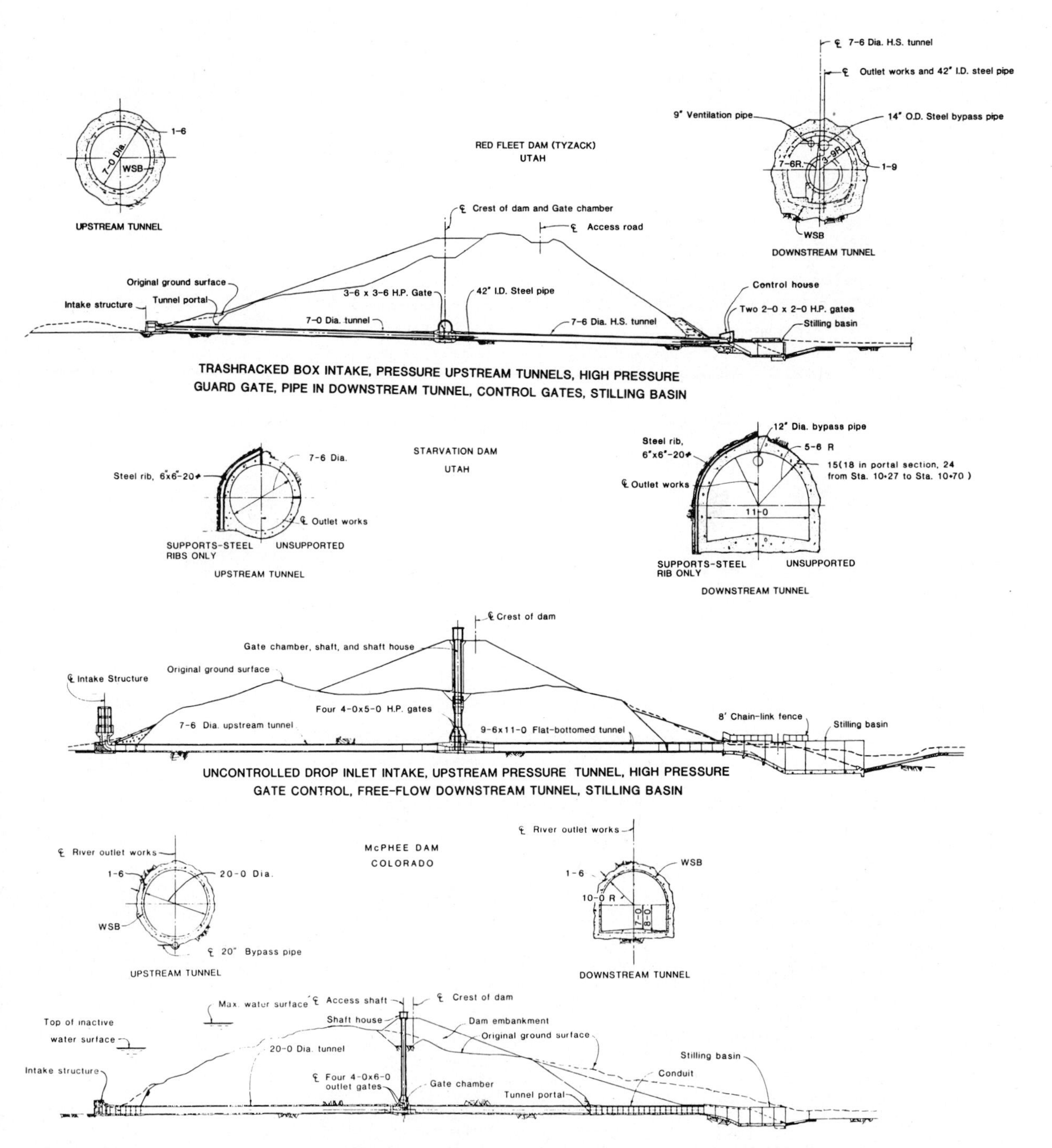

Figure 10-5.—Typical tunnel outlet works installations. 103-D-1834.

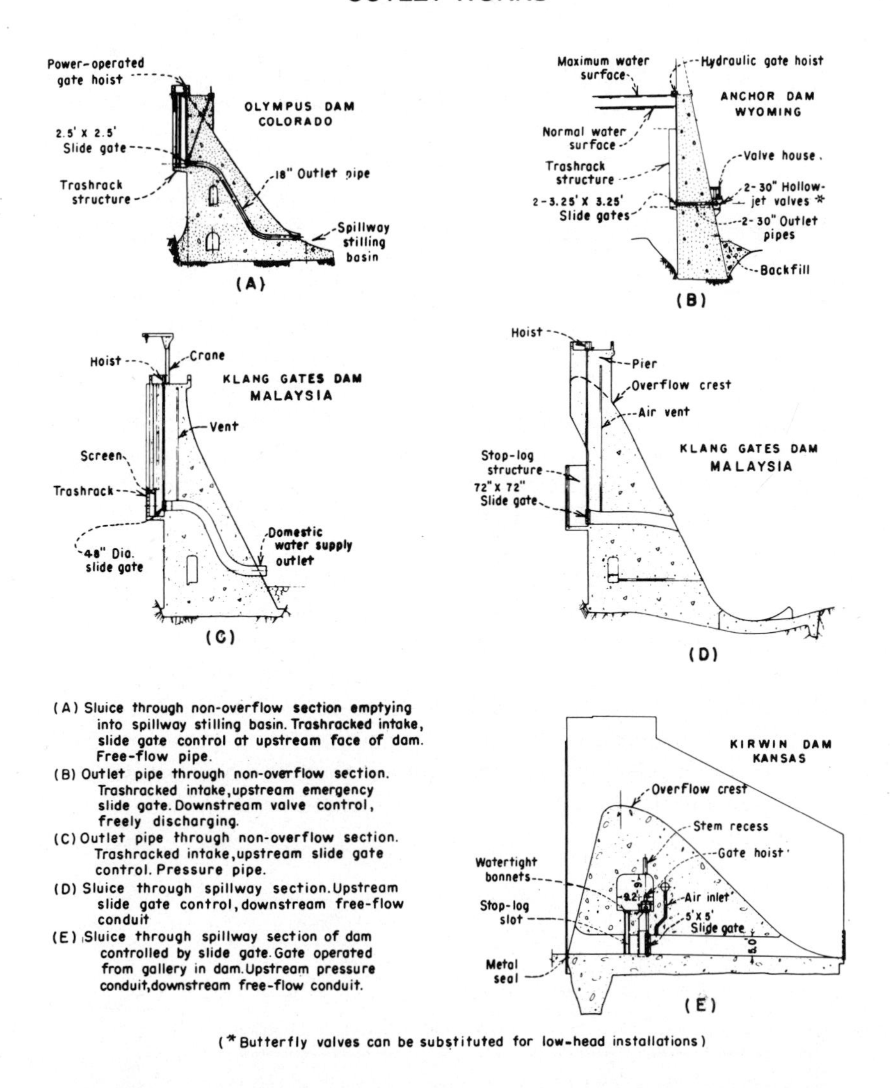

Figure 10-6.—Typical outlet works installations for concrete dams. 288–D–2941.

be ungated to retard the outflow while the reservoir temporarily stores the bulk of the flood runoff, or they may be gated to regulate the releases of the temporarily stored waters.) If the purpose of the dam is only to raise the reservoir and divert incoming flows at low heads, the main outlet works generally should be a headworks or regulating structure at a high level. A sluiceway or small bypass outlet should also be provided to furnish water to the river downstream or to drain the water from behind the dam during off-season periods. Dams that impound water for irrigation, for domestic use, or for other conservation purposes, must have outlet works low enough to draw the reservoir down to the bottom of the allocated storage space; however, the outlet works may be placed above the riverbed, depending on the established minimum reservoir storage level.

It is common practice to make an allowance in a storage reservoir for inactive storage to accommodate sediment deposition, for fish and wildlife conservation, and for recreation. The positioning of the intake sill then becomes an important consideration; it must be high enough to prevent interference from the sediment deposits, but at the same time, low enough to permit either a partial or a complete drawdown below the top of the inactive storage.

As discussed in section 10.14, the size of an outlet conduit for a required discharge varies according to an inverse relationship with the available head for producing the discharge. This relationship may be expressed by the following equation:

$$H_T = K_1 h_v \text{ or } H_T = K_2 \frac{Q^2}{a^2} \quad (1)$$

where:

H_T = total available head for producing flow,
K_1 and K_2 = coefficients,
h_v = velocity head,
Q = required outlet works discharge, and
a = required area of the conduit.

The above relationship for a particular design is shown on figure 10-8(A). This example shows that if the head available for the required outlet works discharge is increased from 1.6 to 4.6 feet, the corresponding conduit diameter can be decreased from 6 to 4.75 feet. This shows that the conduit size can be reduced significantly if the inactive storage level can be increased. The reduction in active storage capacity resulting from a 3-foot increase in the inactive storage level must be compensated for by the addition of an equivalent capacity to the top of the pool. The reservoir capacity curve on figure 10-8(B) shows that for equivalent storages (represented by *de* and *gh*), the 3 feet of head (represented by *cd*) added to obtain a reduced outlet works size would require a much smaller increase (represented by *fg*) in the height of the dam. Thus, economic studies can be used to determine the proper outlet size in relation to the minimum reservoir storage level.

Where an outlet is placed at riverbed level to accommodate the construction diversion plan (ch. 11) or to drain the reservoir, the operating sill may be placed at a higher level to provide a sediment and debris basin and other desired inactive storage space, or the intake may be designed to permit raising the sill as sediment accumulates. During construction, a temporary diversion opening may be formed in the base of the intake to handle diversion flows. Later, this opening may be plugged. For emptying the reservoir, a bypass around the intake may be installed at riverbed level. This bypass may either empty into the lower portion of the conduit or pass under it. Water can be delivered to a canal at a higher level by a pressure riser pipe connecting the conduit to the canal.

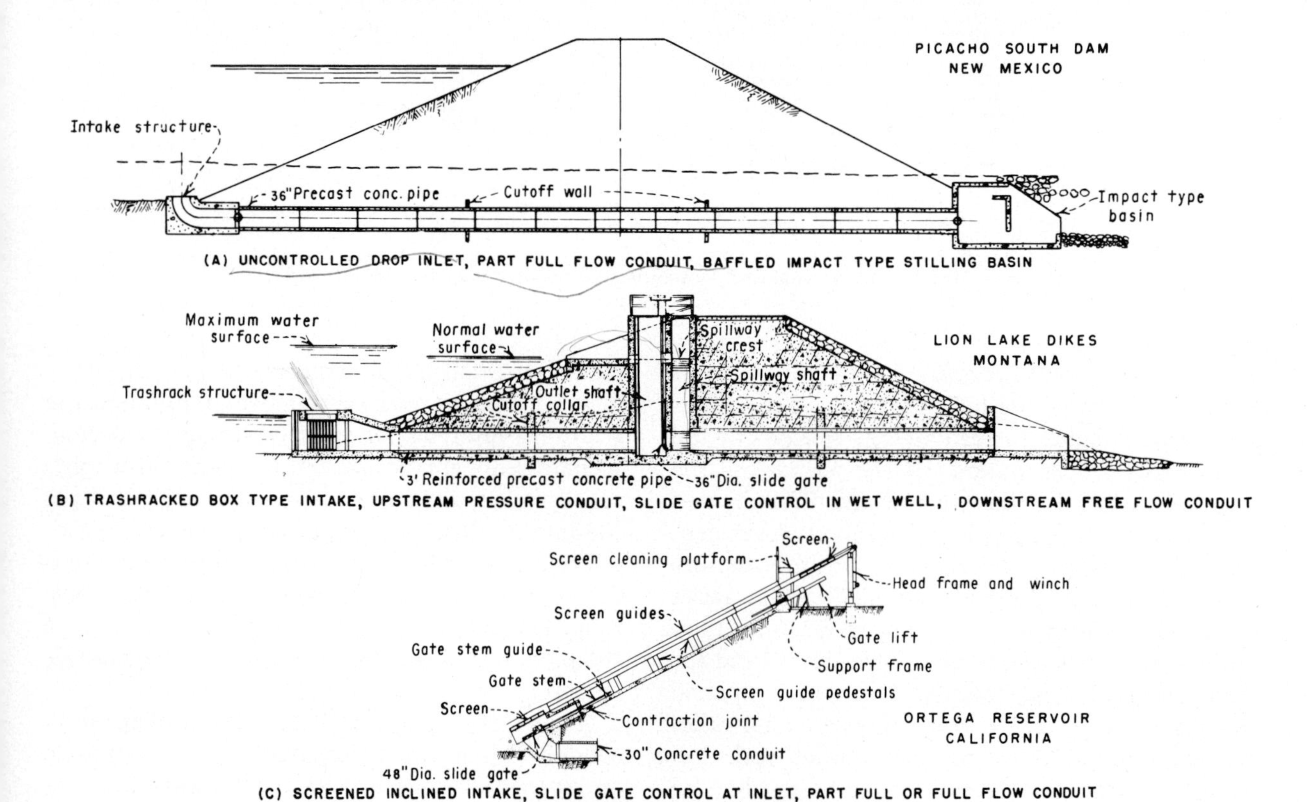

Figure 10-7.—Typical precast pipe outlet works installations. 288–D–2528.

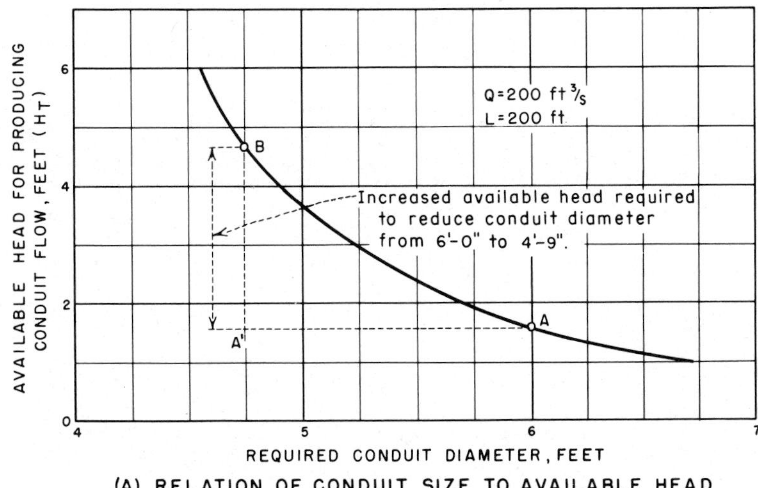

(A) RELATION OF CONDUIT SIZE TO AVAILABLE HEAD

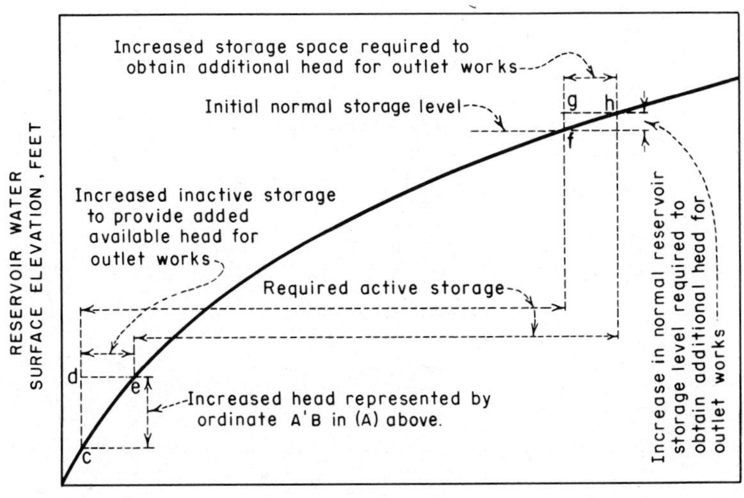

(B) RELATION OF CONDUIT SIZE TO NORMAL STORAGE LEVEl

Figure 10-8.—Relation of minimum design head to conduit size. 288-D-2529.

10.4. ***Conditions That Determine Outlet Works Layout.***—The layout of an outlet works is influenced by many conditions relating to the hydraulic requirements, to the site adaptability, to the interrelation of the outlet works and the construction procedures, and to the other appurtenances of the development. Thus, an outlet works leading to a high-level canal or into a closed pipeline might differ from one emptying into the river. Similarly, a scheme in which the outlet works is used for diversion might vary from one where diversion is effected by other means. In certain instances, the proximity of the spillway may permit combining some of the outlet works and spillway components in a single structure. For example, the spillway and outlet works layout might be arranged so that discharges from both empty into a common stilling basin. An interesting arrangement in which a spillway and outlet works are combined in a single structure is shown on figure 10-9. In this installation, for Heart Butte Dam, the outlet works intake encircles the drop inlet tower of the spillway, and the outlet conduit extends along the top of the spillway conduit and empties into it downstream. Two other arrangements where the outlet works and spillway discharges empty into a common stilling basin, for Rifle Gap and Bottle Hollow dams, are shown on figure 10-9.

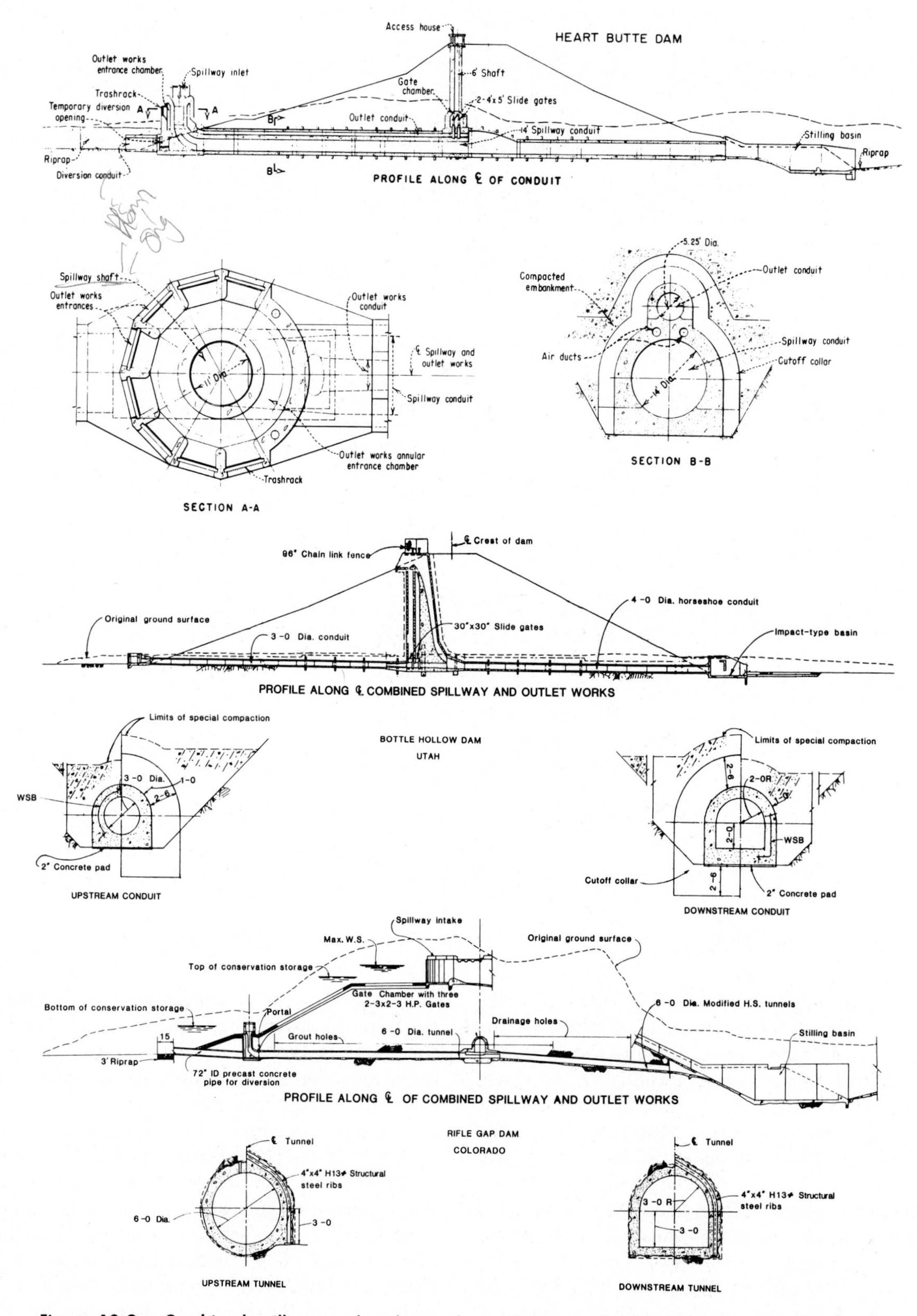

Figure 10-9.—Combined spillway and outlet works, and structures with common stilling devices. 103-D-1836.

The topography and geology of a site may have a great influence on the layout selection. Some sites may be suited only for a cut-and-cover conduit type of outlet works; whereas, at other sites, either a cut-and-cover conduit or a tunnel may be selected. Unfavorable foundation geology, such as deep overburdens or inferior foundation rock, precludes the selection of a tunnel scheme. On the other hand, sites in narrow canyons with steep abutments may make a tunnel outlet the only choice. Because of confined working space and excessive costs where hand-construction methods must be used, building a tunnel smaller than about 6 feet in diameter is not practicable. However, a cut-and-cover conduit can be built to almost any size if it is precast or cast-in-place with the inside bore formed by a prefabricated liner. Thus, the minimum size dictated by construction conditions, more than the size dictated by hydraulic requirements, influences the choice of either the cut-and-cover conduit or the tunnel scheme. The amount of load to be taken by a conduit will also affect this choice.

Some sites favorable for a tunnel outlet may have unfavorable portal conditions that make it difficult to fit the inlet and exit structures to the remainder of the outlet works. In this situation, a central tunnel with cut-and-cover conduits leading to and away from the tunneled portion of the outlet may be feasible. Such an arrangement is shown on figure 10-5 for McPhee Dam.

If water is to be taken from a reservoir for domestic use, or if temperature and heavy-metal control are required, special consideration must be given to the positioning of the intake. To ensure the proper quality of the water, it may be necessary to draw from different levels of the reservoir during different seasons or to restrict the draft to specific levels, depending on the reservoir stage. To prevent silt from being carried into the outlet system, intakes at low points or pockets in the reservoir must be avoided. Similarly, intakes must not be placed at points in the reservoir where stagnant water or algae can accumulate or where prevailing winds will drift debris or undesirable trash to the intake entrance.

10.5. *Arrangement of Outlet Works.*—The outlet works for a low dam, whether it is to divert water into a canal or release it to the river, often consists of an open-channel or cut-and-cover structure at the dam abutment. The structure may consist of a conventional open flume or rectangular channel with a gate similar to that used for ordinary spillway installations, or it may be regulated by a submerged gate placed to close off openings in a curtain or headwall. Where the outlet is to be placed through a low earthfill embankment, a closed structure may be used. This structure may consist of single or multiple units of buried pipe or box culverts placed through or under the embankment. Flow for such an installation could be controlled by gates placed at the inlet or at an intermediate point along the conduit, such as at the crest of the embankment, where a shaft would be provided for gate operation. Downstream from the control structure, the channel would continue to the canal or to the river where, depending on the exit velocities, a stilling device similar to one described in chapter 9 may be used. Figure 10-1 shows typical installations of the arrangements described above.

For higher earthfill dams, where an open-channel outlet structure would not prove feasible, the outlet might be carried through, under, or around the dam as a cut-and-cover conduit or through the abutment as a tunnel. Depending on the position of the control device, the conduit or tunnel may be free flowing, flowing under pressure for a portion of its length, or flowing under pressure for its entire length. Intakes may be arranged to draw water from the bottom of the reservoir, or the inlet sills may be placed at some higher reservoir level. Dissipating devices similar to those described in chapter 9 may be used at the downstream end of the conduit. The outlet works also may discharge into the spillway stilling basin. Depending on the method of control and the flow conditions in the structure, access to the operating gates may be by bridge to an upstream intake tower, by shaft from the crest level of the dam, by walkway within the conduit or tunnel with entrance from the downstream end, or by a separate conduit or tunnel access adit. Arrangements typical of those described above are shown on figures 10-2 through 10-5.

For a concrete dam, the outlet works installation should usually be carried through the dam as a formed conduit or a sluice, or as a pipe embedded in the concrete mass. Intakes and terminal devices may be attached to the upstream and downstream faces of the dam. Often, the outlet is formed through the spillway overflow section using a common stilling basin to dissipate both spillway and outlet works flows. Where an outlet works conduit is installed in the nonoverflow section of the dam or where an outlet must empty into a canal, a separate dissipating device will, of course, be necessary. Instead of one large conduit, several smaller conduits may be used in a concrete dam to provide a less expensive and more feasible arrangement for handling the outlet works releases. The multiple conduits may be placed at a single level or, for added flexibility, at several levels. Such an arrangement would reduce the cost of the control gates because of the lower heads on the upper-level gates. Typical outlet works installations for concrete dams are shown on figure 10-6.

A diversion tunnel used during the construction of a concrete dam can often be converted into a permanent outlet works by providing outlet sluices or conduits through the tunnel plug. Ordinarily, the diversion tunnel for a concrete dam will be in good quality rock and will therefore require little lining protection. Furthermore, the outlet portal of the tunnel will generally be located far enough downstream from the dam so that no dissipating structure will be needed or, at most, only a deflector will be required to direct the flow to the downstream river channel.

10.6. *Location of Outlet Works Controls.*—

(a) *General.*—Where the outlet works is ungated, as is the case for many detention dams, flow in the conduit will be similar to that in a culvert spillway, as described in section 9.27. Where water must be stored and the release regulated at specific rates, control gates or valves must be installed at some point along the conduit.

Gates and valves for outlet works are categorized according to their function in the structure. Regulating gates and valves are used to control and regulate the outlet works flow and are designed to operate in any position from closed to fully open. However, care should be taken in operating large gates at small openings because of potential cavitation problems. Guard gates are designed to effect closure only when the regulating gates fail or when unwatering is desired either to inspect the conduit below the guard gates or to inspect or repair the regulating gates. Generally, slots are provided at the conduit or tunnel entrance, and stoplogs or bulkheads are stored nearby for use in the conduit or tunnel for inspection or during an emergency. For such installations, guard gates may or may not be provided, depending on whether or not the stoplogs can be placed readily in an emergency during normal reservoir operating periods.

The control gate for an outlet works may be placed at the upstream end of the conduit, at an intermediate point along its length, or at the lower end of the structure. Where flow from a control gate is released directly into the open as free discharge, only that portion of the conduit upstream from the gate is under pressure. Where a control gate or valve is placed at the lower end of the structure, full internal pressure should be considered in the design of the conduit tunnel or pipe. However, when a control discharges into a free-flow conduit, the location of the control gate becomes important in the design of the outlet. The effects of locating the control at various positions in a conduit are discussed in the following subsections.

(b) *Control at Upstream End of Conduit.*—For an outlet works with an upstream control discharging into a free-flow conduit, partial full flow will occur throughout the length of the structure. Ordinarily, the operating head and the conduit slope will result in flow at the super-critical stage. The structural design of the conduit and the safety and practical aspects of the layout should then be concerned only with the effects of external loadings and of outside water pressures on the structure. Along the upstream portion of the conduit and extending until sufficient rock cover is available over a tunnel or until an adequate thickness of impervious embankment is obtained over a cut-and-cover conduit, practically full reservoir head will be exerted against the outside of the conduit barrel. The conduit walls must be designed to withstand such pressures, and the design details selected must preserve the watertightness of the conduit. For a cut-and-cover conduit where settlement of the structure (caused by foundation consolidation with increasing embankment load) must be anticipated, special care must be taken in the design to prevent the cracking of the conduit barrel and to seal all formed joints. Cracks and open joints invite excessive leakage or piping of surrounding embankment material into the conduit.

With the controls placed at the upstream end of a conduit, fishscreens, stoplog slots, trashracks, guard gates, and regulating gates or valves may all be combined in a single intake structure. This arrangement simplifies outlet works operation by centralizing all control features at one point. Furthermore, the entire conduit may be readily unwatered for inspection or repair. The intake will consist of a tower rising from the base of the outlet conduit to an operating deck placed above maximum reservoir water level, with the tower located in the reservoir area near the upstream toe of the dam. Access to the structure operating deck will then be possible only by boat, unless an access bridge is provided from the reservoir shore or from the crest of the dam. The intakes at Crane Prairie and Crescent Lake dams (fig. 10-2) and McGee Creek and Palmetto Bend dams (fig. 10-4) illustrate typical tower arrangements. Figure 4-1 is a photograph of the intake tower and access bridge at Crescent Lake Dam.

(c) *Control at Intermediate Point along Conduit.*—Where a control gate is placed at an intermediate point along a conduit and discharges freely into the downstream section or where the flow is conveyed in a separate downstream pipe, the internal pressure upstream from the control is approximately equal to full reservoir head. The structural design and safety aspects of the upstream portion will then be concerned with the effects of both the external loadings and the internal hydrostatic pressure acting on the conduit shell. The watertightness of the conduit in the extreme upstream section will be less important because the external and internal hydrostatic pressures will closely balance, and leakage into or out of the conduit will be minimized. However, the external pressure around the conduit normally diminishes with increasing distance from the reservoir. At downstream portions of the pressure conduit, there may be excess internal pressure, which could cause leakage through joint or cracks into the material surrounding the conduit barrel. Such leaks may flow along the outside of the conduit to the section not under pressure where piping through joints could occur. Where a pressure conduit is carried through an embankment, the development of piping, and the eventual failure of the dam, is a possibility. Where such a conduit is a tunnel, leakage through seams in the rock could saturate the hillside overburden above the tunnel and cause a sloughing or landslide on the abutment.

To minimize the possibilities of failures such as those described above, it is normal practice to limit the length of the pressure portion of a cut-and-cover conduit to that part of the outlet upstream from the crest of the dam or to approximately the upstream third of the dam. Where there is concern regarding the watertightness of a pressure conduit in the upstream portion of a dam, but there are compelling reasons why the control cannot be located near the upstream end of the conduit, that portion upstream from the control may be provided with a steel liner. This method was used at Sugar Loaf Dam (fig. 10-3).

For a tunnel installation, except for the possibilities of leakage discussed previously, the location of the control gate is not as critical as it is for a cut-and-cover outlet. However, the pressure portion of the tunnel ordinarily should not extend downstream beyond a point where the weight of the column of rock above the tunnel or the side resistance to a blowout is less than the internal pressure forces. The exception is where the tunnel lining is reinforced to withstand the internal pressure and a waterproof liner is provided to prevent a buildup of hydrostatic pressures outside the lining.

There may be instances where excessive settlement or movement of a conduit is expected and cracking and opening of joints cannot be avoided. In this situation, to forestall serious leakage that would occur if a free flow or pressure conduit were used, a separate steel pipe can be installed inside the larger conduit to convey the flow. The control gate or valve is normally installed at the downstream end of such a pipe. Guard gates are normally provided in a chamber at the upstream end of the pipe to effect closure in the event of a leak or failure along any part of the pipe. See Silver Jack and Stateline dams on figure 10-3.

Where a control gate discharges into a free flow conduit, an access and operating shaft extending from the conduit to a level above the high water surface in the reservoir is required. For a cut-and-cover conduit under an earthfill dam, the location of the control gates should usually be selected so that the operating shaft is positioned immediately upstream from the crest of the dam. See McGee Creek and Twin Buttes dams on figure 10-4.

The control gates or valves for a conduit or sluice through a concrete dam can be positioned at any point, either upstream to afford free flow in the sluice or at the downstream end to provide pressure pipe flow. Where the sluices are placed in the overflow section of the dam, upstream gates controlling the entrance or valves operated from an interior gallery in the dam are ordinarily used. Where the outlets are placed in the nonoverflow section, either upstream gates or downstream valves are used (fig. 10-6).

B. OUTLET WORKS COMPONENTS

10.7. *General.*—For an open-channel outlet works or for a conduit-type outlet where partial full flow prevails, the control gates or valves should determine the outlet works capacity. Where an outlet works operates as a pressure pipe, the size of the waterway and that of the control device should determine the capacity. The overall size of an outlet works is determined by its hydraulic head and the required discharge. The selection of the size of some of the component parts of the structure, such as the tunnel, is dictated by practical considerations or by interrelated requirements such as diversion, reservoir evacuation, and initial filling. Because the capacity of a closed system outlet is influenced by the hydraulic losses through the components (see part C of this chapter), the sizes of various features can be changed in relation to one another for a given capacity. For example, a streamlined inlet may permit the installation of a smaller gate for a given size conduit, but a larger gate may allow the use of a smaller conduit. Or, for a given discharge, enlargement of the upstream pressure conduit of a closed pipe system may permit reduction in the size of the downstream pressure pipe and, consequently, in the size of the downstream conduit. The determination of the best overall layout to achieve economy in the design may, therefore, require alternative studies involving various trial sizes of the different components of the outlet works.

When the type of waterway has been chosen and the method of control established, the associated structures to complete the layout can be selected. The type of intake structure depends on its location and function and on the various appurtenances, such as fishscreens, trashracks, stoplog arrangements, or operating platforms, that must be furnished. A means for dissipating the energy of flow before returning the discharge to the river should normally be provided. This can be accomplished by a flip bucket, a stilling basin, a baffled apron drop, a stilling well, or a similar dissipation device. Gate chambers, control platforms, or enclosures may be required to provide operating space and protective housing for the control devices. An outlet works may also require an outlet channel to return releases to the river and an entrance channel to lead diversion flows or low-reservoir flows to the intake structure.

(a) *Tunnels.*—Because of its inherent advantages, a tunnel outlet works is preferred where abutment and foundation conditions permit its use and it is more economical than the other types of outlet works. A tunnel is not in direct contact with the dam embankment and, therefore, provides a much safer and more durable layout than can be achieved with a cut-and-cover conduit. Little foundation settlement, differential movement, and structural displacement is experienced with a tunnel that has been bored through competent abutment material, and seepage along the outer surfaces of the tunnel lining or leakage into the material surrounding the tunnel is less serious. Furthermore, it is less likely that failure of some portion of a tunnel would cause failure of the dam than the failure of a cut-and-cover conduit that passes under or through the dam.

Ordinarily, pressure tunnels in competent rock do not require lining reinforced to withstand full internal hydrostatic pressures because the surrounding rock can normally assume such stresses. If the rock cover has sufficient weight and enough side resistance to prevent blowouts, only an unreinforced lining is necessary to provide watertightness in seamy rock and smoother surfaces for better hydraulic flow.

Where pressure tunnels are placed through less competent foundations, such as jointed or yielding rock, the tunnel lining must be designed to withstand external hydrostatic and rock loadings in addition to internal hydrostatic pressures. At the extreme upstream end of an outlet works tunnel, where external hydrostatic pressures may nearly balance the internal pressures, the lining must be reinforced to withstand rock loads only. However, if provision is made for unwatering the tunnel by use of intake gates, bulkheads, or stoplogs, an unbalanced hydrostatic condition will exist. At the downstream portions of the tunnel where outside water pressures diminish, the design of the tunnel lining must consider both external loads from the rock and internal water pressures.

For free flow tunnels in competent rock, a lining may be needed only along the sides and bottom to form a smooth waterway. In less competent material, lining the complete cross section may be necessary to prevent caving. For that portion of a free flow tunnel immediately adjacent to the reservoir or just downstream from a pressure tunnel, the possibility of hydrostatic pressure buildup behind the lining caused by leakage through the walls of the pressure tunnel or by seepage from the reservoir must be considered. Ordinarily, such external water pressure can be reduced by grouting and by providing drain holes through the lining of the free flow tunnel.

A tunnel in which an independent pipe is installed should be lined with concrete, even if the rock is competent enough to stand unsupported. Because such a tunnel houses the pressure pipe and provides access to an upstream gate, the lining is needed to protect the pipe and operating personnel against rockfall. It also minimizes seepage and protects the pipe, lighting installations, and electrical conduits from seepage water. Site-specific conditions, economy of installation, safety of personnel, and maintenance costs should be carefully considered before deciding to leave such a tunnel unlined.

For a pressure tunnel, a circular cross-sectional shape is the most efficient, both hydraulically and structurally. For a free flow tunnel, a horseshoe-shaped, or flat-bottomed, tunnel provides better hydraulic flow, but is not as efficient as the circular shape for carrying external loads. For small tunnels under only moderate heads, the horseshoe-shaped pressure tunnel and either the horseshoe or the flat-bottomed free flow tunnel may be appropriate, depending on the foundation conditions. As discussed in section 10.4, it is not practical to build a tunnel smaller than about 6 feet in diameter. The structural design of tunnels, including reinforcement of linings, is discussed in section 10.20.

(b) *Cut-and-Cover Conduits.*—If a closed conduit is to be provided and foundation conditions are not suitable for a tunnel, or if the required size of the waterway is too small to justify the minimum-sized tunnel, a cut-and-cover conduit should be used. Because this type of conduit passes through or under the dam, conservative and safe designs must be used. Numerous failures of earthfill dams caused by improperly designed or constructed cut-and-cover outlet conduits have demonstrated the need for conservative procedures.

A conduit should be placed on the most competent portion of the dam foundation. Design details must allow for expected settlement, shrinkage, and lateral or longitudinal displacement without interfering with the continuity of the structure, which must provide a safe and leakproof waterway.

When there is bedrock at the site, every attempt should be made to place the entire conduit on such a foundation. If this is not physically or economically feasible, the structure should be located where overburden is shallow so there will be minimal foundation settlement. If a uniform foundation exists and it is determined that settlement will not be excessive, the excavation for the conduit should be to grade and the conduit supported on undisturbed material. However, where the conduit foundation in its natural state is not suitable, the unsuitable material should be excavated until a material competent to support the load is reached. The trench should then be filled with compacted material of the desired stability and impermeability. It may be necessary, where a conduit is placed on other than competent rock, to line the conduit with steel. This is particularly appropriate through the impervious zone of the dam for structural stability and prevention of piping of fine material into the conduit. Unsuitable foundation materials include those permeable enough to permit excessive seepage, those subject to excessive settlement on loading, and those subject to settlement on saturation of the foundation by the reservoir. These materials are described in chapter 6. In all cases, regardless of the nature of the foundation, the contact of the conduit with the foundation must provide a watertight bond, free of void spaces and unconsolidated areas.

Cut-and-cover conduits must be designed to withstand the load of the fill overlying the structure. If high fill loads must be supported, a cut-and-cover conduit may not be economical. Pressure conduits must also be designed to resist an internal hydrostatic pressure loading equal to the full reservoir head where appropriate. Design loadings for conduits are further discussed in section 10.21.

The adaptability of a cut-and-cover conduit and the desirability of using such a conduit as a pressure pipe or as a free flow waterway are discussed in section 10.6. Because in most instances a cut-and-cover conduit must be constructed before the embankment, the conduit will settle as a result of the foundation settlement caused by embankment loading. Therefore, the conduit settlement will be maximum at the point of highest fill and will diminish toward each end. The structural details selected must provide for such settlement, and the conduit profiles must be adjusted to provide for the drop in grade near the center of the dam. Joint treatment and reinforcement requirements are discussed in section 10.21.

10.8. *Controls.*—(a) *Control Devices.*—Selection of the outlet works arrangement should be based on the use of commercially available gates and valves or relatively simple gate designs where possible. The use of special devices that involve expensive design and fabrication costs should be avoided. Cast iron slide gates, which may be used for control and guard gates, are available for both rectangular and circular openings and for design heads up to about 50 feet. However, higher head installations require special gate designs. Simple radial gates are available for ordinary surface installations, and top-seal radial gates can be secured from manufacturers on the basis of simple designs and specifications. For low heads up to about 50 feet, commercial gate and butterfly valves are suitable for control at the downstream end of pressure pipes if they are designed to operate under free discharge conditions with the jet well aerated all around. Gate and butterfly valves are also suitable for use as inline guard valves and can be adapted for inline control valves if air venting and adequate aeration of the discharge jet are provided immediately downstream from the valve.

(b) *Arrangement of Controls.*—Flows through low-head outlet works can be controlled by various devices, as shown on figure 10-1. A surface radial gate may be installed in an open channel, as shown for Putah Diversion Dam. Top-seal radial gates installed at the entrance or within a culvert outlet works are shown for Flatiron Dam and for Camp Creek and Bartley Diversion dams. Slide gates, similar to those shown for Woodston and Fort Sumner Diversion dams, may be used to control flows through either open-channel or culvert outlet works provided with headwall structures.

Upstream gate controls for conduits are generally placed in a tower structure with the gate hoists mounted on the operating deck (fig. 10-2). With this arrangement, the tower must extend above the maximum water surface.

If controls are to be located at some intermediate point along the conduit, high-pressure gates, slide gates, and top-seal radial gates may be used. These controls may be located in a wet-well shaft that extends vertically from the conduit level to the crest of the dam. Typical arrangements of these installations are shown on figure 10-4.

A variation of the slide-gate control can eliminate the need for a wet-well shaft. In this instance, watertight bonnet covers are provided over the gate slots, and the gates are operated either from a dry shaft or from an operating chamber located above the conduit level. Watertight bushings are provided where the gate stems extend through the bonnets.

High-pressure gates or valves are used as controls at intermediate points along tunnels or conduits. These gates are normally accessed through a shaft leading to the crest of the dam. This type of installation is shown on figure 10-4. If the flow is carried by separate pipe in a conduit large enough to afford access along the pipe from the downstream end, a domed chamber may be used rather than a dry-well shaft. Such a chamber is provided at Tyzack (Red Fleet) Dam, as shown on figure 10-5.

If a concrete dam uses a slide-gate control on its upstream face, the gate frame and stem guides may be mounted directly on the concrete face, and the hoist may be placed on a platform cantilevered from the crest of the dam. If the gate is placed at an intermediate point along a conduit formed through the concrete dam, the gate can be operated either in a wet well, with the hoist placed at the crest of the dam, or from a gallery if the watertight bonnet cover is provided over the gate well. Inline gates and valves can also be operated from the gallery or from a chamber formed inside the dam. A control gate or valve placed on the end of the conduit at the downstream face of the dam can be operated from a platform extending from the face of the dam. Typical installations are illustrated on figure 10-6.

(c) *Control and Access Shafts.*—Where a free flow conduit is provided downstream from the control devices, access for operating is usually from a shaft located directly over the controls. If the wet-well arrangement is used, a shaft large enough to accommodate the several wells must be provided. When the type of controls permits dry-well installations, only sufficient space to provide operating room at the bottom of the shaft is needed. A smaller access shaft, either directly above or offset from the chamber and just large enough to permit passage of removable and replaceable gate parts, will then be needed.

The operating or access shaft for a tunnel outlet works can be sunk into the undisturbed hillside and lined with concrete as necessary to keep the shaft walls intact. Where such a shaft is used for access and ventilation only, little wall lining is needed. Where an access shaft is to be used for a wet-well arrangement, adequate lining to make the shaft reasonably watertight is required. If a cut-and-cover conduit scheme is used, the shaft must be constructed through the dam embankment. The structural design must consider the possibility of settlement and of lateral displacement caused by the movement of the embankment. Where a wet-well shaft is used, care must be taken in the design to prevent cracking and the opening of joints, which would permit leakage from the interior of the shaft into the surrounding embankment. The walls of the wet-well shaft must be designed to resist the internal hydrostatic pressure from full reservoir head and the external embankment loading. If a shaft extends through the embankment and projects into the reservoir, external hydrostatic loads and, where applicable, earthquake loads must also be considered. The protruding portion of the shaft is a tower, which is subject to the ice loads discussed in section 10.9.

(d) *Control Houses.*—A housing is sometimes provided around the outlet controls where operating equipment would otherwise be exposed or where adverse weather conditions will prevail during operating periods. A house is sometimes provided to enclose the top of an access shaft, although the controls may be located elsewhere. Such houses are usually made large enough to accommodate auxiliary equipment, such as ventilating fans, heaters, flow-measuring and recording meters, air pumps, small power-generator sets, and equipment needed for maintenance.

10.9. *Intake Structures.*—In addition to forming the entrance to the outlet works, an intake structure may accommodate control devices. It also supports necessary auxiliary appurtenances (such as trashracks, fishscreens, and bypass devices), and it may include temporary diversion openings and provisions for installation of bulkhead or stoplog closure devices.

Intake structures may appear in many forms. The type of intake structure selected should be based on several factors: the functions it must serve, the range in reservoir head under which it must operate, the discharge it must handle, the frequency of reservoir drawdown, the trash conditions in the reservoir (which will determine the need for or the frequency of cleaning of the trashracks), reservoir ice conditions or wave action that could affect the stability, and other similar considerations. Depending on its function, an intake structure may be either submerged or extended in the form of a tower above the maximum reservoir water surface. A tower must be provided if the controls are placed at the intake, or if an operating platform is needed for trash removal, maintaining and cleaning fishscreens, or installing stoplogs. Where the structure serves only as an entrance to the outlet conduit and where trash cleaning is ordinarily not required, a submerged structure may be adopted.

The conduit entrance may be placed vertically, inclined, or horizontally, depending on intake requirements. Where a sill level higher than the conduit level is desired, the intake can be a drop inlet similar to the entrance of a drop inlet spillway. A vertical entrance is usually provided for inlets at the conduit level. In certain instances, an inclined intake structure may be placed along the upstream slope of the dam or along the reservoir bank upstream of the dam. Such an arrangement is typified by the Ortega Reservoir outlet shown on figure 10-7. In most cases, conduit entrances should be rounded or bellmouthed to reduce hydraulic entrance losses.

The necessity for trashracks on an outlet works depends on the size of the sluice or conduit, the type of control device used, the nature of the trash burden in the reservoir, the use of the water, the need for excluding small trash from the outflow, and other factors. These factors determine the type of trashracks and the size of the openings. Where an outlet consists of a small conduit with valve controls, closely spaced trash bars are needed to exclude small trash. Where an outlet involves a large conduit with large slide-gate controls, the racks can be more widely spaced. If there is no danger of clogging or damage from small trash, a trashrack may consist simply of struts and beams placed to exclude only larger trees and similarly sized floating debris. The rack arrangement should also be based on the accessibility for removing accumulated trash. Thus, a submerged rack that seldom will be unwatered must be more substantial than one at or near the surface. Similarly, an outlet with controls at the entrance, where the gates can be jammed by trash protruding through the rack bars, must have a more substantial rack arrangement than one whose controls are not at the entrance.

Trash bars usually consist of thin, flat steel bars that are placed on edge from 3 to 6 inches apart and assembled in a grid pattern. The area of the trashrack required is fixed by a limiting velocity through the rack which, in turn, depends on the nature of the trash to be excluded. Where the trashracks are inaccessible for cleaning, the velocity through the racks ordinarily should not exceed 2 ft/s. A velocity of up to approximately 5 ft/s may be tolerated for racks that are accessible for cleaning.

Trashrack structures may have varied shapes, depending on how they are mounted or arranged on the intake structure. Trashracks for a drop inlet intake are generally formed as a cage atop the entrance. They may be arranged as an open box placed in front of a vertical entrance, or they may be positioned along the front side of a tower structure. Figures 10-1 through 10-7 show various arrangements of trashracks at entrances to outlet works.

At some reservoir sites, it may be desirable or required to screen the inlet entrance to prevent fish from being carried through the outlet works. Two such installations are illustrated on figure 10-2. Because small openings must be used to exclude fish, the screens can easily become clogged with debris. Provisions must therefore be made for periodically removing the fish screens and cleaning them by brooming or water jetting.

Where the control is placed at an intermediate point along a conduit, some means of unwatering the upstream pressure section of the conduit and the intake is desirable to make inspections and needed repairs. Stoplog or bulkhead slots are generally provided for this purpose in the intake or immediately downstream from the intake. In intake towers containing control devices, the stoplog slots are placed upstream from the controls. A circular, flat bulkhead that can drop down over the entrance is generally provided for a drop inlet structure. This type of bulkhead is normally lowered into place from a barge and positioned on a seat embedded in the intake sill concrete by divers. It can, however, be put in place in the dry condition and used for initial filling or refilling of the outlet works pipe.

For an intake structure with an inlet sill above the invert of the conduit, it may be desirable for various reasons to draw the reservoir down below the level of the sill. In such an instance, a bypass may be provided near the base of the structure to connect the reservoir to the conduit downstream. In other instances where flow must be maintained while installing or maintaining the control gates and outlet pipes or while repairing or maintaining the free flow conduit concrete, it may be desirable to carry a separate pipe under or alongside the conduit to bypass it entirely. In either case, the bypass inlet may be placed in the intake structure where it usually can be controlled by a gate or butterfly valve mounted on or in the structure and operated from some higher level.

Where winter reservoir storage is maintained and the surface ices over, the effect of such conditions on the intake structure must be considered. When the reservoir surface freezes around an intake structure, there is danger to the structure not only from the ice pressures acting laterally, but also from the uplift forces if a filling reservoir lifts the ice mass vertically. These effects must be considered when the advantages or disadvantages of a tower are compared with those of a submerged intake.

If a tower is constructed where icing conditions present a hazard, ice may be prevented from forming around the structure by the subsurface release of compressed air. The released air causes the slightly warmer water at lower depths to rise and mix with the cooler surface water, thus preventing freezing. However, if not enough warm water is available, as when the approach channel to the tower is shallow or the reservoir storage is small, the release of air may actually enhance freezing around the structure.

10.10. ***Terminal Structures and Dissipating Devices.***—The discharge from an outlet, whether it be a gate valve, or free flow conduit, will emerge at a high velocity, usually in a nearly horizontal direction. If erosion-resistant bedrock exists at shallow depths, the flow may be discharged directly into the river. Otherwise, it should be directed away from the toe of the dam by a deflector. Where erosion is to be minimized, a plunge basin may be excavated and lined with riprap or concrete. The design of such a basin is discussed in section 9.24.

When more energy dissipation is required for free flow conduits, the terminal structures described for spillways (part E, ch. 9) may be used. The hydraulic-jump basin is most often used for energy dissipation of outlet works discharges. However, flow that emerges from the outlet in the form of a free jet, as is the case for valve-controlled outlets of pressure conduits, must be directed onto the transition floor approaching the basin so it will become uniformly distributed before entering the basin. Otherwise, proper energy dissipation will not be obtained.

Two types of dissipating devices used more commonly with outlet works than with spillways are the impact-type stilling basin and the stilling well. An impact-type stilling basin dissipates energy by impeding the flow with a stationary concrete baffle.

A stilling well dissipates energy through turbulence as flow rises in a water-filled well. The design of both of these devices is discussed in section 10.17.

10.11. *Entrance and Outlet Channels.*—An entrance channel and an outlet channel are often required for a tunnel or cut-and-cover conduit layout. An entrance channel may be required to convey diversion flows to a conduit in an abutment or to deliver water to the outlet works intake during low reservoir stage. And an outlet channel may be required to convey discharges from the end of the outlet works to the river downstream or to a canal.

All entrance and outlet channels should be excavated to stable slopes and to dimensions that will provide nonscouring velocities. Entrance channel velocities are usually made less than those through the trashracks, and the entrance channel is often widened near the intake structure to permit a smooth, uniform flow into all trashrack openings.

The outlet channel dimensions and the need for lining or riprap protection should be based on the nature of the material through which the channel is to be excavated. Occasionally, a control or a measuring station is placed in the outlet channel. In such cases the selection of the grade and cross section of the channel becomes an important consideration. The aggradation or degradation of the main river channel must be considered in selecting the outlet works outlet channel dimensions.

C. HYDRAULIC DESIGN

10.12. *Nature of Flow in Outlet Works.*—The hydraulics of outlet works usually involve either open-channel (free) flow or full conduit (pressure) flow. Analysis of open-channel flow in outlet works, either in an open waterway or in a partly full conduit, is based on the principle of steady nonuniform flow conforming to the law of conservation of energy. Full-pipe flow in closed conduits is based on pressure flow, which involves a study of hydraulic losses to determine the total heads needed to produce the required discharges.

Hydraulic-jump basins, baffle or impact-block dissipators, stilling wells, or other stilling devices are normally used to dissipate the energy of flow at the downstream end of the outlet works. Many of these devices are designed on the basis of the law of conservation of momentum.

10.13. *Open-Channel Flow in Outlet Works.*—Flow in an open-channel outlet works is similar to that in an open-channel spillway, which is discussed in chapter 9. Where unsubmerged radial or slide gates are used, discharges through the control with the gates completely open will be open-crest flow as computed by equation (3) of chapter 9:

$$Q = CLH^{3/2}$$

Discharge coefficients applicable to various crest arrangements are discussed in section 9.12.

When open-channel outlet flow is controlled by partly open surface gates, or where top-seal radial gates or submerged slide gates control the flow, sluice flow will result. Discharges for such flow are given by equation (7) of chapter 9:

$$Q = CDL\sqrt{2gH}$$

Discharge coefficients for sluice control can be determined from figure 9-31 or table 10-1 (sec. 10.15).

Where there is high tailwater caused by canal water surfaces or by downstream influences in the streambed, the control openings may be partly or entirely submerged. For such conditions, the discharge through the control should be in accordance with the submerged orifice or the tube flow as computed by the equation:

$$Q = CA\sqrt{2gH} \tag{2}$$

where:

A = area of the opening,
H = difference between the upstream and downstream water levels, and,
C = discharge coefficient for the submerged orifice or the tube flow.

Coefficients for various conditions of orifice suppression and tube geometry can be evaluated from figure 10-10 or from data in various hydraulic handbooks [1, 2][1] and textbooks.

[1]Numbers in brackets refer to entries in the bibliography (sec. 10.23).

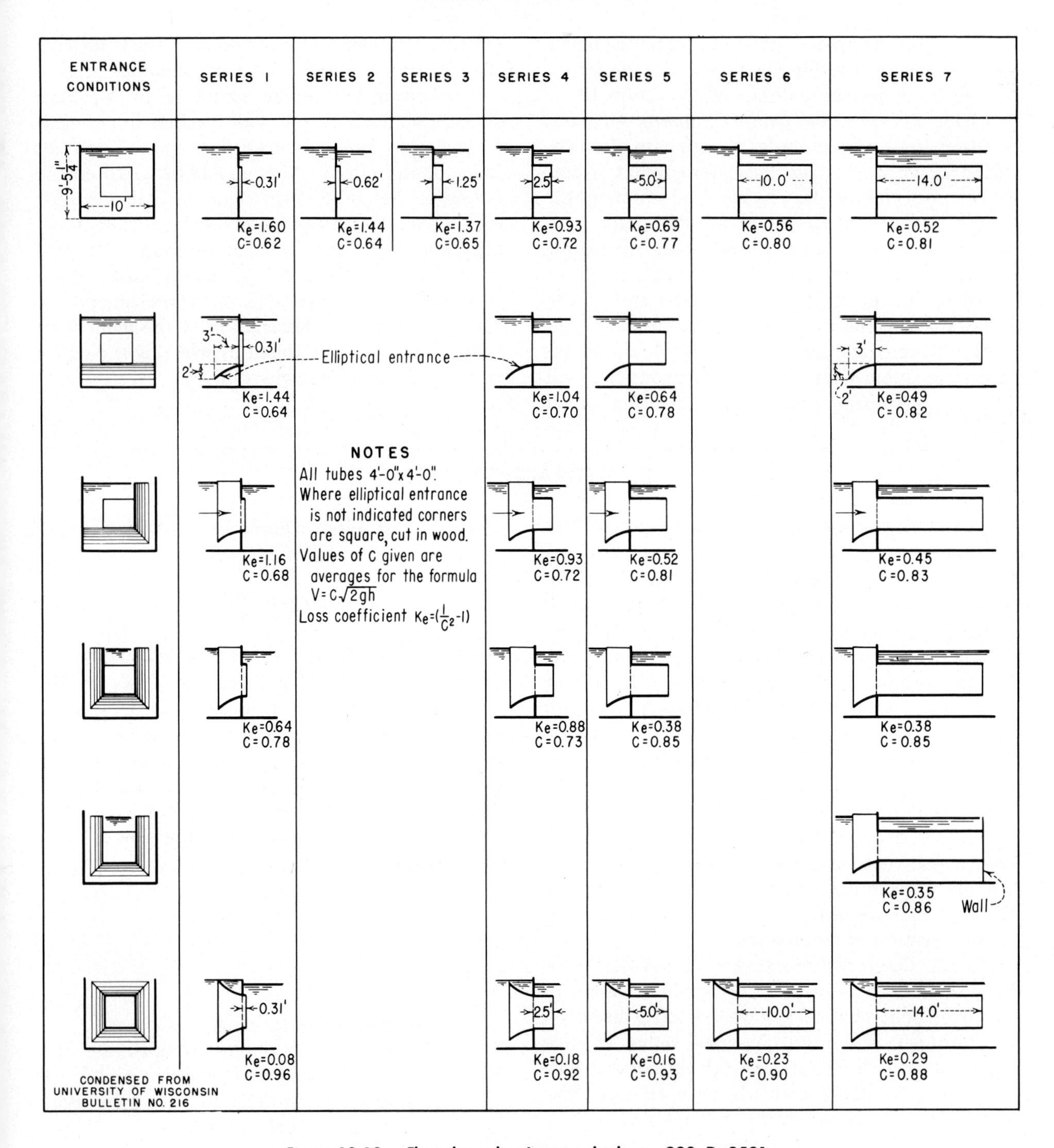

Figure 10-10.—Flow through submerged tubes. 288–D–2531.

Flow in an open channel downstream from the headworks will be at either the subcritical or the supercritical stage, depending on the flow conditions through the control structure. In either case, flow depths and velocities throughout the channel can be determined from Bernoulli's equation (see sec. 9.18).

Flow in an ungated outlet conduit is similar to that in a culvert spillway (discussed in sec. 9.27). Where the inlet geometry and the conduit slope are such that the control remains at the inlet, partly full flow will prevail and flow depths and velocities will be in accordance with the Bernoulli's equation for open-channel flow. When flow from a pressure conduit discharges into a free flow conduit, the flow in the latter most often will be at the supercritical stage with flow depths and velocities comparable with those that would prevail in an open channel. Computation procedures to determine the flow conditions according to Bernoulli's equation are presented in section 9.18.

Outlet conduits flowing partly full should be analyzed using maximum and minimum assumed values of the coefficient of roughness, n, when evaluating the required conduit size and the energy content of the flow (as is done for spillway design (see sec. 9.18)). For computing the energy of flow at the end of the conduit to design the dissipator, an n of about 0.008 should be assumed. To ensure a free surface in the conduit for all stages of flow and to preclude sealing of some portion from splashing or surging, the conduit should be designed to flow not more than 75 percent full at maximum capacity.

Terminal deflectors or energy dissipating devices placed at the downstream end of free flow outlet conduits should be similar to those discussed for spillways in part E of chapter 9. Transitions to divert the flow from the conduit portal to the stilling device and the allowable convex curvature of the floor entering the stilling device should be determined as discussed in section 9.19.

10.14. ***Pressure Flow in Outlet Conduits.***—If a control gate is placed downstream from the conduit entrance, that portion above the control gate will flow under pressure. An ungated conduit can also flow full depending on the inlet geometry. The phenomena and the hydraulic equations for flow through an ungated conduit under pressure are discussed in section 9.27. The hydraulic design of a gated pressure conduit should be similar to that for an ungated pressure conduit discussed in section 9.27.

For flow in a closed pipe system, as shown on figure 10-11, Bernoulli's equation can be written as follows:

$$H_T = h_L + h_{v_2} \tag{3}$$

where:

H_T = total head needed to overcome the various head losses to produce discharge,
h_L = cumulative losses of the system, and
h_{v_2} = velocity head at the valve.

Equation (3) can be expanded to list each loss as follows:

$$H_T = h_t + h_e + h_{b_5} + h_{f_5} + h_{ex_{(5\text{-}4)}} + h_{f_4} + h_{c_{(4\text{-}3)}} + h_{g_3} + h_{ex(3\text{-}1)} + h_{f_1} + h_{b_1} + h_{c_{(1\text{-}2)}} + h_{g_2} + h_{v_2} \tag{4}$$

where:

h_t = trashrack losses,
h_e = entrance losses,
h_b = bend losses,
h_f = friction losses,
h_{ex} = expansion losses,
h_c = contraction losses,
h_g = gate or valve losses, and
h_v = velocity head exit loss at the outlet.

In equation (4), the number subscripts refer to the various components, transitions, and reaches to which head losses apply.

For a free-discharging outlet, H_T is measured from the reservoir water surface to the center of the outlet gate or the outlet opening. If the outflowing jet is supported on a downstream floor, the head is measured to the top of the emerging jet at the point of greatest contraction; if the outlet portal is submerged, the head is measured to the tailwater level.

Where the various losses are related to the individual components, equation (4) may be written:

$$H_T = K_t\left(\frac{v_6^2}{2g}\right) + K_e\left(\frac{v_5^2}{2g}\right) + K_{b_5}\left(\frac{v_5^2}{2g}\right) + \frac{fL_5}{D_5}\left(\frac{v_5^2}{g}\right) + K_{ex}\left(\frac{v_5^2}{2g} - \frac{v_4^2}{2g}\right) + \frac{fL_4}{D_4}\left(\frac{v_4^2}{2g}\right) + K_c\left(\frac{v_3^2}{2g} - \frac{v_4^2}{2g}\right) + K_g\left(\frac{v_3^2}{2g}\right) + K_{ex}\left(\frac{v_3^2}{2g} - \frac{v_1^2}{2g}\right) + \frac{fL_1}{D_1}\left(\frac{v_1^2}{2g}\right) + K_{b_1}\left(\frac{v_1^2}{2g}\right) + K_c\left(\frac{v_2^2}{2g} - \frac{v_1^2}{2g}\right) + K_g\left(\frac{v_2^2}{2g}\right) + K_v\left(\frac{v_2^2}{2g}\right) \tag{5}$$

where:

K_t = trashrack loss coefficient,
K_e = entrance loss coefficient,
K_b = bend loss coefficient,
f = friction factor in the Darcy-Weisbach equation (eq. (9) in sec. 10.15(b)) for pipe flow.

K_{ex} = expansion loss coefficient,
K_c = contraction loss coefficient,
K_g = gate loss coefficient, and
K_v = exit velocity head coefficient at the outlet.

Equation (5) can be simplified by expressing the individual losses in terms of an arbitrarily chosen velocity head. The velocity head chosen is usually that in a significant section of the system. If the various velocity heads for the system shown on figure 10-11 are related to that in the downstream conduit, area (1), the conversion for x area is found as follows:

Since:

$$Q = a_1 v_1 = a_x v_x;\ a_1^2 v_1^2 = a_x^2 v_x^2;$$

$$\text{and } \frac{a_1^2 v_1^2}{2g} = \frac{a_x^2 v_x^2}{2g}$$

then:

$$\frac{v_x^2}{2g} = \left(\frac{a_1}{a_x}\right)^2 \frac{v_1^2}{2g}$$

Equation (5) can then be written:

$$H_T = \frac{v_1^2}{2g}\Bigg[\left(\frac{a_1}{a_6}\right)^2 K_t + \left(\frac{a_1}{a_5}\right)^2 \left(K_e + K_{b_5} + \frac{fL_5}{D_5} + K_{ex}\right) + \left(\frac{a_1}{a_4}\right)^2 \left(\frac{fL_4}{D_4} - K_{ex} - K_c\right) + \left(\frac{a_1}{a_3}\right)^2 (K_c + K_g + K_{ex}) + \left(\frac{fL_1}{D_1} - K_{ex} + K_{b_1} - K_c\right) + \left(\frac{a_1}{a_2}\right)^2 (K_c + K_g + K_v)\Bigg] \quad (6)$$

If the bracketed part of the expression is represented by K_L, the equation can be written:

$$H_T = K_L \frac{v_1^2}{2g} \quad (7)$$

then:

$$Q = a_1 \sqrt{\frac{2gH_T}{K_L}} \quad (8)$$

10.15. *Pressure Flow Losses in Conduits.*— (a) *General.*—Head losses in outlet works conduits are caused primarily by the frictional resistance to flow along the conduit sidewalls. Additional losses result from trashrack interferences, entrance contractions, contractions and expansions at gate installations, bends, gate and valve constrictions, and other interferences in the conduit. As with free flow conduits, greater than average loss coefficients should be assumed for computing required conduit and component sizes, and smaller loss coefficients should be used for computing energies of flow at the outlet. The major contributing losses of a conduit or pipe system are discussed in this section.

(b) *Friction Losses.*—For flow in large pipes, the Darcy-Weisbach formula is most often used to determine the energy losses from frictional resistances of the conduit:

$$h = \frac{fL}{D}\left(\frac{v^2}{2g}\right) \quad (9)$$

where f is the friction loss coefficient, which varies with the conduit surface roughness and with the Reynolds number. The latter is a function of the diameter of the pipe and the velocity, viscosity, and density of the fluid flowing through it. Data and procedures for evaluating the loss coefficient are presented in [3].

Manning's equation has been used in the hydraulic design of many structures by the Bureau of Reclamation. Its use has resulted in satisfactory designs that have been verified by operational performance. However, because Manning's equation does not consider the Reynolds number or the relative roughness, the designer should be aware that its use could result in significant inaccuracies where these parameters predominate. Manning's equation as applied to closed-circuit flow is:

$$h_f = 29.1n^2 \left(\frac{L}{r^{4/3}}\right) \frac{v^2}{2g} \quad (10)$$

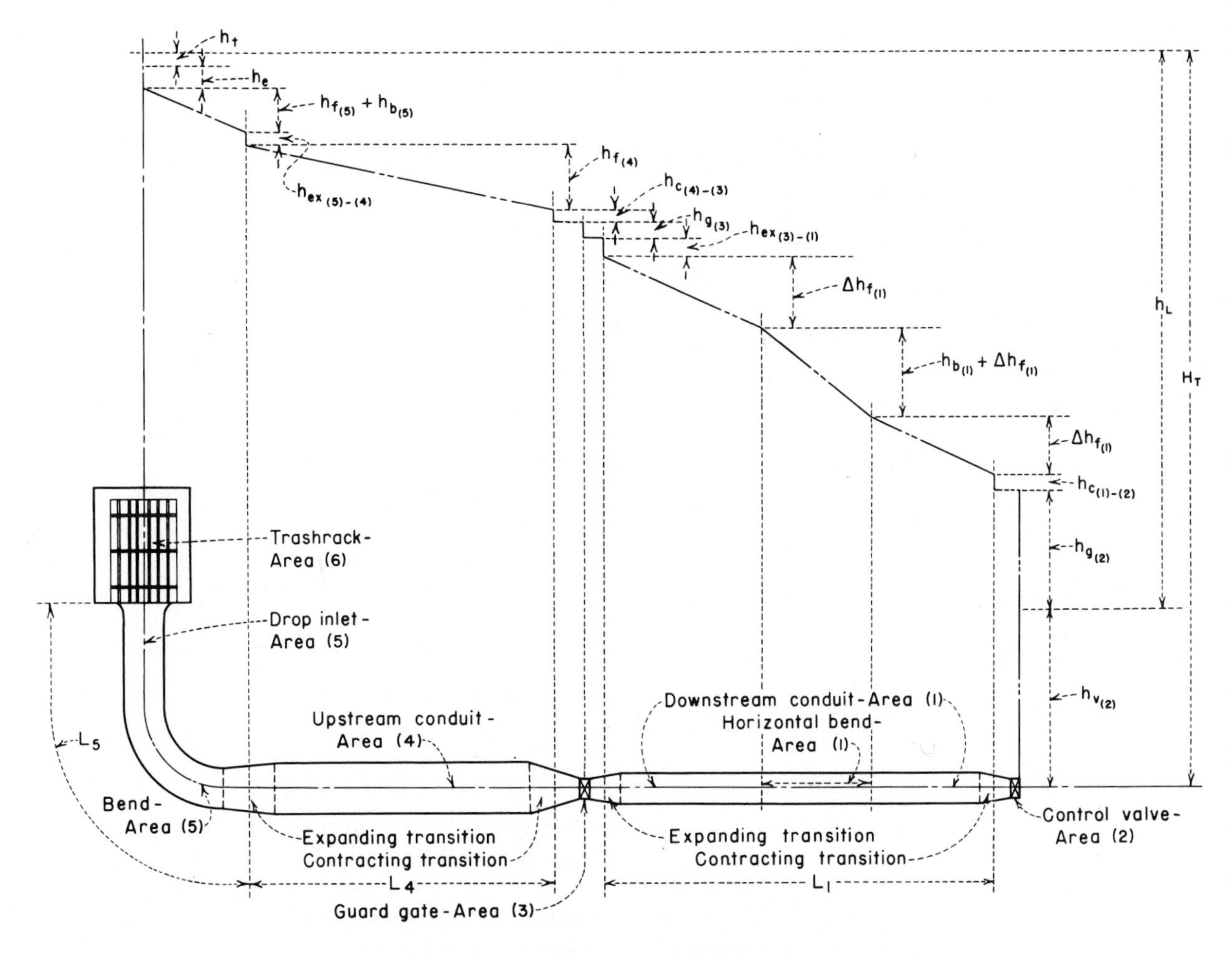

Figure 10-11.—Head losses in conduit flowing under pressure. 288-D-2532.

where:

L = length of section over which losses are being computed, and
r = hydraulic radius.

The maximum and minimum values of n that may be used to determine the conduit size and the energy of flow are as follows:

	Maximum value	*Minimum value*
Concrete pipe or cast-in-place conduit	0.014	0.008
Steel pipe with welded joints	.012	.008
Unlined rock tunnel	.035	.020

(c) *Trashrack Losses.*—Trashrack structures that consist of widely spaced structural members without rack bars cause very little head loss. Therefore, trashrack losses for these structures may be neglected in computing conduit losses. When the trashrack structure consists of racks of bars, the loss depends on the bar thickness, depth, and spacing. An average approximation of the trashrack loss, h_t, can be obtained [2] from the equation $h_t = K_t(v_n^2/2g)$:

$$K_t = 1.45 - 0.45\frac{a_n}{a_g} - \left(\frac{a_n}{a_g}\right)^2 \qquad (11)$$

where:

K_t = trashrack loss coefficient (empirical),
a_n = net area through the rack bars,
a_g = gross area of the racks and supports, and
v_n = velocity through the net trashrack area.

Where maximum loss values are desired, assume that 50 percent of the rack area is clogged. This will result in twice the velocity through the trashrack. For minimum trashrack losses, assume no clogging of the openings when computing the loss coefficient, or neglect the loss entirely.

(d) *Entrance Losses.*—The loss of head at the entrance of a conduit is comparable with the loss in a short tube or in a sluice. If H is the head producing the discharge, C is the discharge coefficient, and a is the area, the discharge, Q, is equal to $Ca\sqrt{2gH}$, and the velocity, v, is equal to $C\sqrt{2gH}$, or

$$H = \frac{1}{C^2}\left(\frac{v^2}{2g}\right) \qquad (12)$$

Since $H = h_v + h_e$ (the velocity head plus the head lost at the entrance), equation (12) may be written:

$$\frac{v^2}{2g} + h_e = \frac{1}{C^2}\left(\frac{v^2}{2g}\right), \text{ or } h_e = \left(\frac{1}{C^2} - 1\right)\frac{v^2}{2g}$$

then:

$$K_e = \left(\frac{1}{C^2} - 1\right) \qquad (13)$$

Discharge coefficients for square sluice entrances are shown on figure 10-10. Discharge coefficients and loss coefficients for typical entrances for conduits, as given in various texts and technical papers, are listed in table 10-1.

(e) *Bend Losses.*—Bend losses in closed conduits (not including the friction loss in the bend) are a function of the bend radius, pipe diameter, and the angle through which the bend turns. Because experimental data on bend losses in large pipes are meager, such losses can be related to those determined for smaller pipe. Figure 10-12 (A) shows the coefficients found by various investigators for 90° bends for various ratios of bend radius to pipe diameter and an adjusted curve assumed to be suitable for large pipes.

Figure 10-12 (B) shows the correction factors to be applied to the values indicated on figure 10-12 (A) for other than 90° bends. The value of the loss coefficient, K_b, for various values of R_b/D can be applied directly for circular conduits; for rectangular conduits, D is taken as the height of the section in the plane of the bend.

Table 10.1.—Discharge and loss coefficients for conduit entrances.

	Discharge coefficient, C			Loss coefficient, A		
	Max.	*Min.*	*Avg.*	*Max.*	*Min.*	*Avg.*
(a) Gate in thin wall – unsuppressed contraction	0.70	0.60	0.63	1.80	1.00	1.50
(b) Gate in thin wall – bottom and sides suppressed	.81	.68	.70	1.20	0.50	1.00
(c) Gate in thin wall – corners rounded	.95	.71	.82	1.00	.10	0.50
(d) Square-cornered entrances	.85	.77	.82	0.70	.40	.50
(e) Slightly rounded entrances	.92	.79	.90	.60	.18	.23
(f) Fully rounded entrances ($r/D \geq 0.15$)	.96	.88	.95	.27	.08	.10
(g) Circular bellmouth entrances	.98	.95	.98	.10	.04	.05
(h) Square bellmouth entrances	.97	.91	.93	.20	.07	.16
(i) Inward projecting entrances	.80	.72	.75	.93	.56	.80

(f) *Transition Losses.*—Head losses in gradual contractions or gradual expansions in a conduit should be considered in relation to the increase or decrease in velocity head. These head losses vary according to the rate of change of the area and the length of the transition. For contractions, the loss of head, h_c, is approximately $K_c\,[(v_2^2/2g) - (v_1^2/2g)]$, where K_c varies from 0.1 for gradual contractions to 0.5 for abrupt contractions. Where the flare angle does not exceed that indicated in section 10.16 (b), the loss coefficient can be assumed as 0.1. For greater flare angles, the loss coefficient can be assumed to vary in a straight-line relationship to a maximum of 0.5 for a right-angle contraction.

For expansions, the loss of head, h_{ex}, is approximately equal to $K_{ex}\,[(v_1^2/2g) - (v_2^2/2g)]$, where the expansion loss coefficient, K_{ex}, is as follows:

Flare angle α	2°	5°	10°	12°	15°	20°	25°	30°	40°	50°	60°
K_{ex} [1]	0.03	0.04	0.08	0.10	0.16	0.31	0.40	0.49	0.60	0.67	0.72
K_{ex} [4]	.02	.12	.16	—	.27	.40	.55	.66	.90	1.00	—

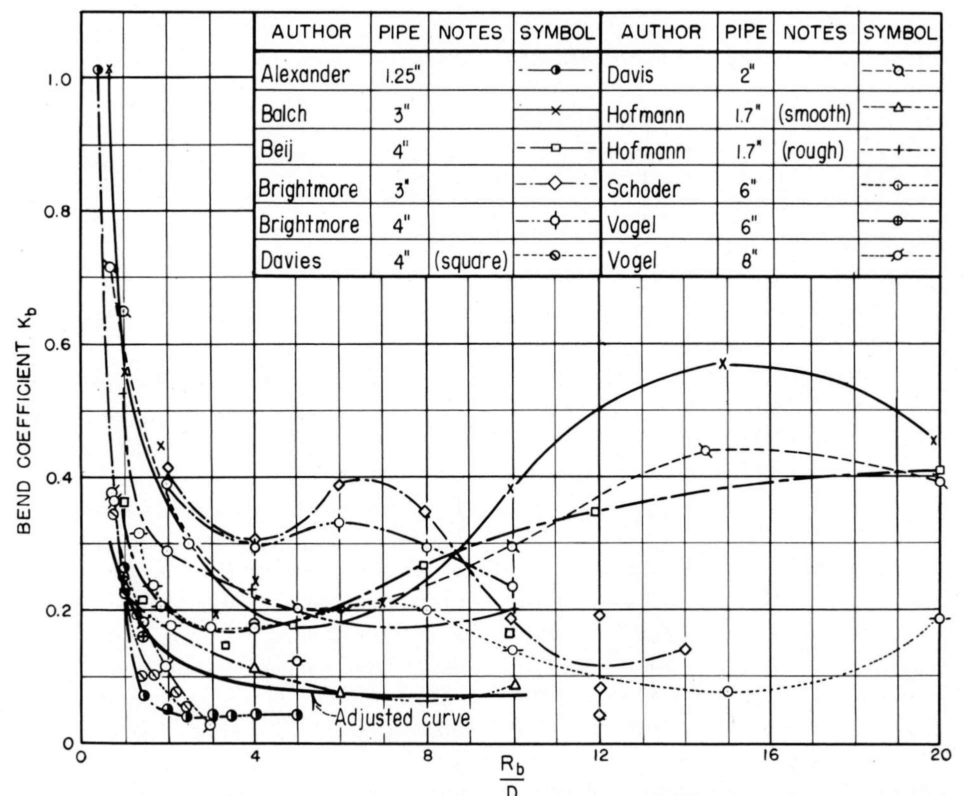

(A) VARIATION OF BEND COEFFICIENT WITH RELATIVE RADIUS FOR 90° BENDS OF CIRCULAR CROSS SECTION, AS MEASURED BY VARIOUS INVESTIGATORS

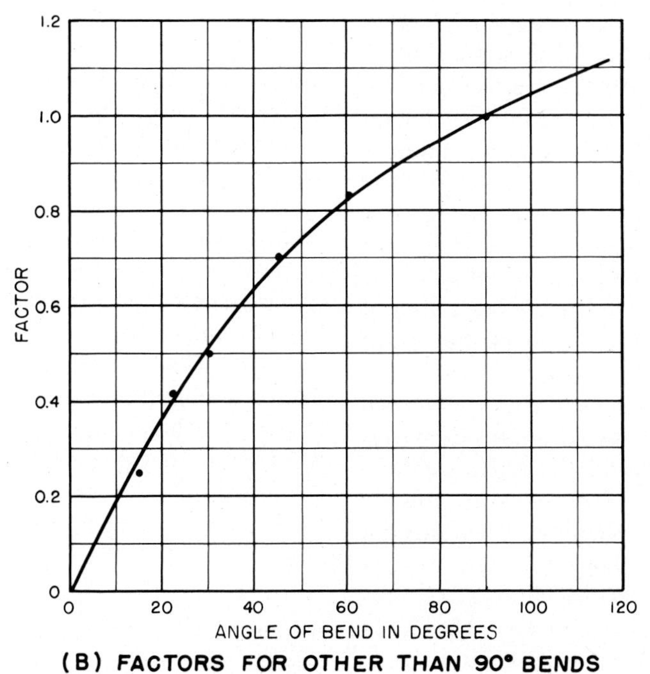

(B) FACTORS FOR OTHER THAN 90° BENDS

Figure 10-12.—Bend loss coefficients. 288–D–2533.

(g) *Gate and Valve Losses.*—No gate loss need be assumed for a gate mounted at the entrance to a conduit so that when wide open it does not interfere with the entrance flow conditions. However, where a gate is mounted at either the upstream or the downstream side of a thin headwall so that the sides and bottom of the jet are suppressed but the top is contracted, the loss coefficients shown as item (b) in table 10-1 apply. Where a gate is mounted in a conduit so that the floor, sides, and roof, both upstream and downstream, are continuous with the gate opening, only the losses caused by the slot must be considered; for this a value of K_g not exceeding 0.1 should be assumed. For partly open gates, the loss coefficient depends on the top contraction; for smaller openings, it approaches the value of 1.0, as shown for item (b) in table 10-1.

For wide-open gate valves, K_g approximates 0.19. As for partly open gates, values of the loss coefficient increase for smaller valve openings. Indicated loss coefficients for partly open gate valves are 1.15 for three-fourths open, 5.6 for one-half open, and 24.0 for one-fourth open. Average values of K_g for butterfly valves in the wide-open position are about 0.15; values vary between 0.1 and 0.5, depending on the thickness of the gate leaf in relation to the gross area. Losses in spherical valves are negligible.

(h) *Exit Losses.*—No recovery of velocity head occurs where the release from a pressure conduit freely discharges or is submerged or supported on a downstream floor. In these instances, the velocity-head loss coefficient, K_v, equals 1.0. When a diverging tube is provided at the end of a conduit, a portion of the velocity head will be recovered if the tube expands gradually and if the end of the tube is submerged. The velocity-head loss coefficient will then be reduced from 1.0 by the degree of velocity-head recovery. If a_1 is the area at the beginning of the diverging tube and a_2 is the area at the end of the tube, then $K_v = (a_1/a_2)^2$.

10.16. *Transition Shapes.*—(a) *Entrances.*—To minimize head losses and to avoid zones where cavitation pressures can develop, the entrance to a pressure conduit should be streamlined to provide smooth, gradual changes in the flow. To obtain the best inlet efficiency, the shape of the entrance should simulate that of a jet discharging into air. As with the nappe-shaped weir, the entrance shape should guide and support the jet with minimum interference until it is contracted to the dimensions of the conduit. If the entrance curve is too sharp or too short, subatmospheric pressure areas that may induce cavitation will develop. A bellmouth entrance that conforms to or slightly encroaches upon the free-jet profile is the best entrance shape. For a circular entrance, this shape can be approximated by an elliptical entrance curve represented by the equation:

$$\frac{x^2}{(0.5D)^2} + \frac{y^2}{(0.15D)^2} = 1 \qquad (14)$$

where x and y are coordinates whose x-x axis is parallel to and $0.65D$ from the conduit centerline, and whose y-y axis is normal to the conduit centerline and $0.5D$ downstream from the entrance face. The factor D is the diameter of the conduit at the end of the entrance transition.

The jet issuing from a square or rectangular opening is not as easily defined as one issuing from a circular opening; the top and bottom curves may differ from the side curves both in length and curvature. Consequently, it is more difficult to determine a transition that will eliminate subatmospheric pressures. An elliptically curved entrance, which tends to minimize the effects of negative pressure, is defined by the equation:

$$\frac{x^2}{D^2} + \frac{y^2}{(0.33D)^2} = 1 \qquad (15)$$

where D is the vertical height of the conduit for defining the top and bottom curves and is the horizontal width of the conduit for defining the side curves. The major and minor axes are positioned similarly to those indicated for the circular bellmouth.

For a rectangular entrance with the bottom placed even with the upstream floor and with curved guide piers at each side of the entrance opening, both the bottom and side contractions will be suppressed and a sharper contraction will occur at the top of the opening. For this condition, the top contraction curve is defined by the equation:

$$\frac{x^2}{D^2} + \frac{y^2}{(0.67D)^2} = 1 \qquad (16)$$

where D is the vertical height of the conduit downstream from the entrance shape.

(b) *Contractions and Expansions.*—To minimize head losses and to avoid cavitation along the conduit surfaces, contraction and expansion transitions to and from gate control sections in a pressure conduit should be gradual. For contractions, the maximum convergent angle should not exceed that indicated by the relationship:

$$\tan \alpha = \frac{1}{U} \qquad (17)$$

where:

α = angle of the conduit wall surfaces with respect to its centerline, and
U = an arbitrary parameter = $v/\sqrt{gD}$.

The values of v and D are the average of the velocities and diameters, respectively, at the beginning and end of the transition.

Expansions should be more gradual than contractions because of the danger of cavitation at sharp changes in the sidewalls. Furthermore, as indicated in section 10.15 (f), loss coefficients for expansion increase rapidly after the flare angle exceeds about 10°. Expansions should be based on the relationship:

$$\tan \alpha = \frac{1}{2U} \qquad (18)$$

For normal installations, the flare angle should not exceed about 10°.

The criteria for establishing maximum contraction and expansion angles for conduits flowing partly full are the same as those for open-channel flow (see sec. 9.19 (b).

(c) *Exit Transitions.*—When a circular conduit flowing partly full empties into a chute, the transition from the circular section to one with a flat bottom can be made in the open channel downstream from the conduit portal. Otherwise, the transition can be made within the conduit so that the bottom is flat at the portal section.

Two types of transition are commonly used. The first type is made by constructing a straight line of intersection between the 45° points on each side of the invert of the upstream circular section to the corners of the flat bottom at the downstream end of the transition. The radius of curvature between the springline and the intersection line increases from the radius of the conduit at the upstream end to a radius of infinity along the vertical wall at the downstream end. The radius of curvature of the bottom of the transition also increases from the radius of the conduit at the upstream end to infinity along the flat bottom of the downstream end. Figure 10-13 shows a typical example of this type of transition, including the conduit transition table. The distance X on figure 10-13 denotes the flare from the upstream end of the transition to the wider section downstream, as in the case of a stilling basin.

The second type of transition is made by gradually decreasing the radius of the circular quadrants in the lower half of the pipe from their initial radius at the upstream end to a radius of zero at the corners of the flat bottom at the downstream end.

In both transitions discussed above, the roof of the conduit remains curved. These transitions must satisfy the expansion criteria established in section 10.16 (b).

For normal installations, the length of the transition can be related to the exit velocity. An empirical rule that will yield a satisfactory transition is:

$$L \text{ (in feet)} = \frac{vD}{5} \qquad (19)$$

where:

v = exit velocity, in feet per second, and
D = conduit diameter, in feet.

Downstream from a free flow conduit, the chute sections, including the transition into a stilling basin, should be governed by open-channel flow criteria. Floor curvatures and maximum flare angles should be determined by equations (19) and (21), respectively, of chapter 9. To reduce the length of the open-channel portion from the conduit portal to the stilling basin, the beginning of the flare and of the convex curve may be located inside the conduit. This transition may be combined with the transition of the bottom shape.

In certain instances, an adverse slope and a hump have been used immediately downstream from the portal to permit more rapid widening of the channel before it enters the basin. No firm criteria have been established for the design of these devices, and details should be determined by model tests. Certain inherent disadvantages to this type of design are (1) care must be taken to avoid a hump of such height that back pressure will cause a hydraulic jump inside the conduit, (2) the floor section

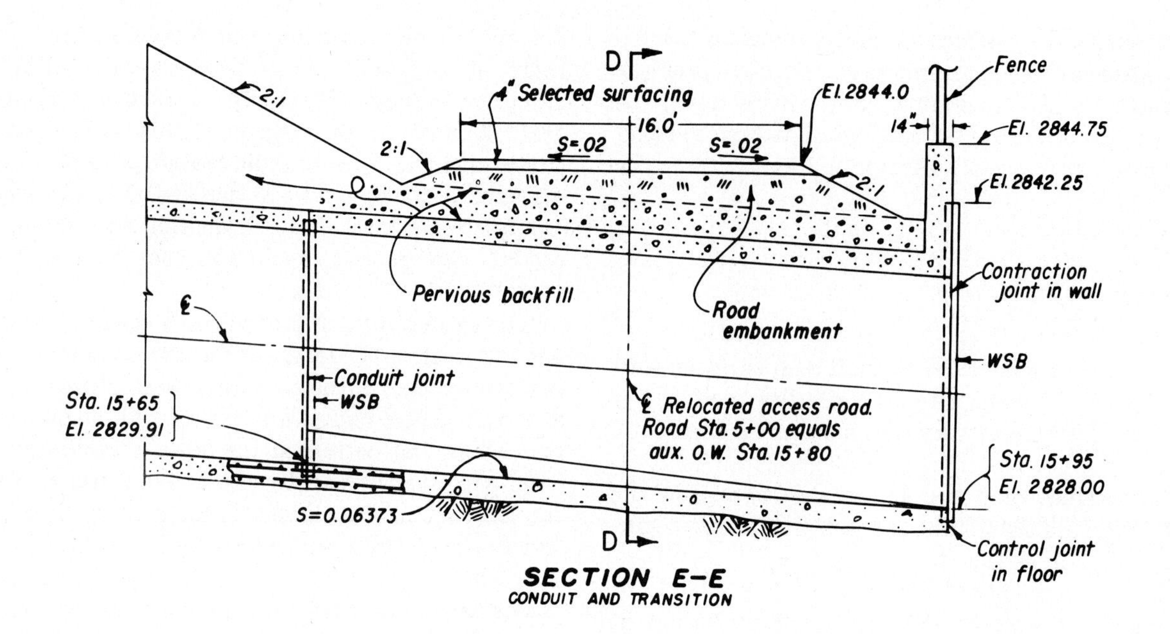

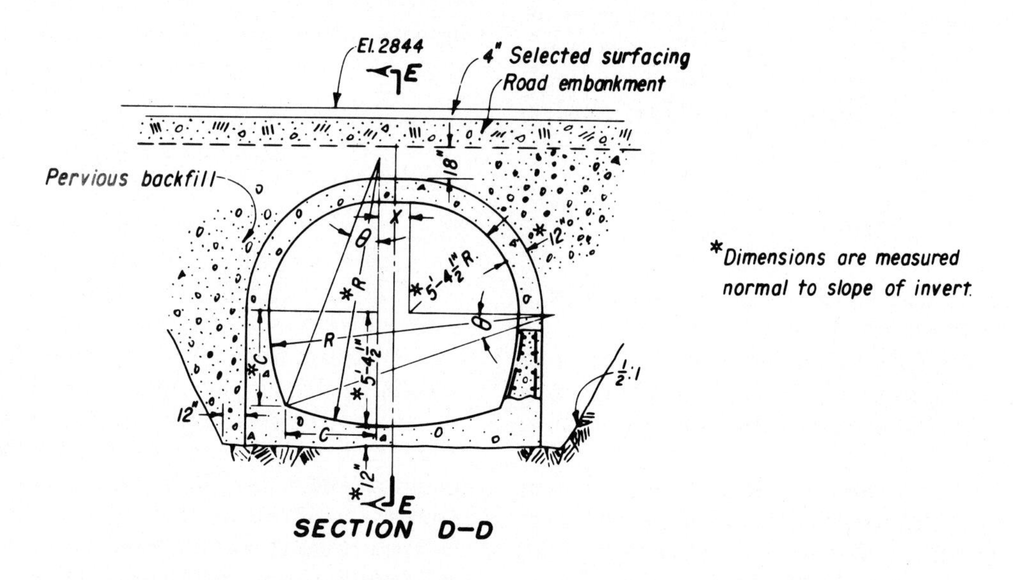

STA.	θ	R	C	X
15+65	45°	5'-4 1/2"	3'-9 5/8"	0
+67	41°31'45"	5'-10 9/16"	3'-10 3/4"	0-2 11/16"
+69	37°59'10"	6'-5 15/16"	4'-0"	0-5 3/8"
+71	34°33'21"	7'-2 3/4"	4'-1 3/16"	0-8 1/16"
+73	31°13'39"	8'-1 1/4"	4'-2 7/16"	0-10 3/4"
+75	27°59'30"	9'-2"	4'-3 5/8"	1'-1 7/16"
+77	24°51'12"	10'-5 3/4"	4'-4 7/8"	1'-4 1/8"
+79	21°47'56"	12'-1 5/8"	4'-6 1/16"	1'-6 3/4"

STA.	θ	R	C	X
15+81	18°49'53"	14'-3 3/8"	4'-7 5/16"	1'-9 7/16"
+83	15°56'38"	17'-1 15/16"	4'-8 9/16"	2'-0 1/8"
+85	13°7'42"	21'-2 11/16"	4'-9 7/8"	2'-2 13/16"
+87	10°23'18"	27'-3 7/8"	4'-11 1/8"	2'-5 1/2"
+89	7°42'48"	37'-6 1/4"	5'-0 7/16"	2'-8 3/16"
+91	5°6'22"	57'-9 3/4"	5'-1 3/4"	2'-10 7/8"
+93	2°33'32"	117'-9 3/16"	5'-3 1/16"	3'-1 9/16"
+95	0°	—	5'-4 1/2"	3'-4 1/4"

CONDUIT TRANSITION TABLE
STATIONS ARE AT INVERT

Figure 10-13.—Typical conduit transition. 288-D-2809.

at the hump must be made structurally adequate to withstand the large dynamic forces from impingement of the flow on the rising floor, (3) during periods of no flow, a pond, which can freeze during the winter, is formed in the conduit unless provision is made to drain the sump, and (4) access into the downstream conduit is difficult unless drainage is provided. Depending on tailwater conditions, pumping may be required to provide drainage.

10.17. *Terminal Structures.*—(a) *General.*—Deflector buckets, hydraulic-jump basins, and plunge pools are commonly used in conjunction with spillways. However, hydraulic-jump basins and plunge pools are also often used for energy dissipation of outlet works discharges. The hydraulic design of these structures is discussed in part E of chapter 9. The stilling devices used more often with outlet works than with spillways are the impact-type stilling basins and stilling wells. The hydraulic designs of these structures are discussed in this section.

To evaluate the energy that must be dissipated by the stilling device, the losses through the outlet system should be minimized, as discussed in sections 10.13 and 10.15(b). The specific energy immediately downstream from gate or valve controls will equal the exit velocity head based on minimum losses through the pressure system, as measured above the outflowing water surface. If specific energies have not been computed, approximate basin depths can be obtained from figure 9-43, as discussed in section 9.21(d).

(b) *Impact-Type Stilling Basin.*—This type of energy dissipator [5] is an effective stilling device that does not depend on the tailwater. The capacity of an impact-type stilling basin is limited by the feasibility of the structural design to an incoming velocity of about 50 ft/s. Such a basin can be used with either an open chute or a closed-conduit structure. The design shown on figure 10-14 has proved effective for discharges up to about 400 ft^3/s; for larger discharges, multiple basins could be placed side by side.

Dissipation is accomplished by the impact of the incoming jet on the vertical hanging baffle and by eddies formed from the changed direction of the jet after it strikes the baffle. The best hydraulic action is obtained when the tailwater height approaches but does not exceed half the height of the baffle. For proper performance, the bottom of the baffle should be placed at the same level as the invert of the upstream channel or pipe.

The general arrangement of the basin and the dimensional requirements, including riprap, are shown on figure 10-14. Figure 10-15 shows an impact-type stilling basin operating at about 80 percent of its designed capacity. This type of basin is subjected to large dynamic forces and turbulence, which must be considered in the structural design. The structure must be made stable enough to resist sliding caused by the impact load on the baffle wall. The entire structure must also resist the severe vibrations inherent with this type of device, and the individual structural members must be strong enough to withstand the large dynamic loads.

Riprap should be provided along the bottom and sides adjacent to the structure to avoid scouring of the outlet channel downstream from the end sill when a shallow tailwater exists. Downstream wingwalls placed at 45° may also be effective in reducing scouring and flow concentrations downstream.

(c) *Stilling Wells.*—Where an outlet is terminated as a submerged pipe, a stilling-well dissipator is sometimes used to dissipate the flow energy. Its size is generally based on the allowable wave action in the downstream channel. This device consists of a vertical water-filled well in which dissipation is achieved by turbulence and diffusion in the water in the well. The incoming flow can be directed horizontally into the well near its bottom, as shown on figure 10-16, or it may be directed vertically downward into the bottom of the well through a pipe, as illustrated on figure 10-17. In both cases, the flow rises upward and emerges from the top of the well.

The well dimensions and performance criteria for the two designs illustrated were established from model tests. General design has been developed for stilling wells using a standard sleeve valve or a multijet sleeve valve, as shown on figure 10-17, [6, 7]. The net area of the well is generally selected by limiting the average rising velocity to between 1 and 3 ft/s. The total depth of the well should be dictated by the energy of the incoming flow and by the effectiveness of the diffuser blocks and fillets incorporated along the sides and in the corners of the well. To prevent cavitation and abrasion damage to the stilling well, a steel liner is normally required on the floor and on the lower walls of the well. Basins with similar criteria can be patterned after those illustrated on the figures. Basins for considerably different conditions should be model tested.

10.18. *Design Examples.*—To illustrate the

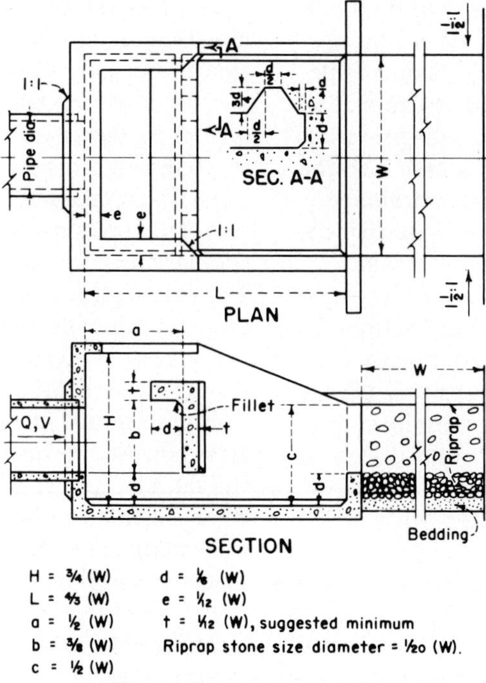

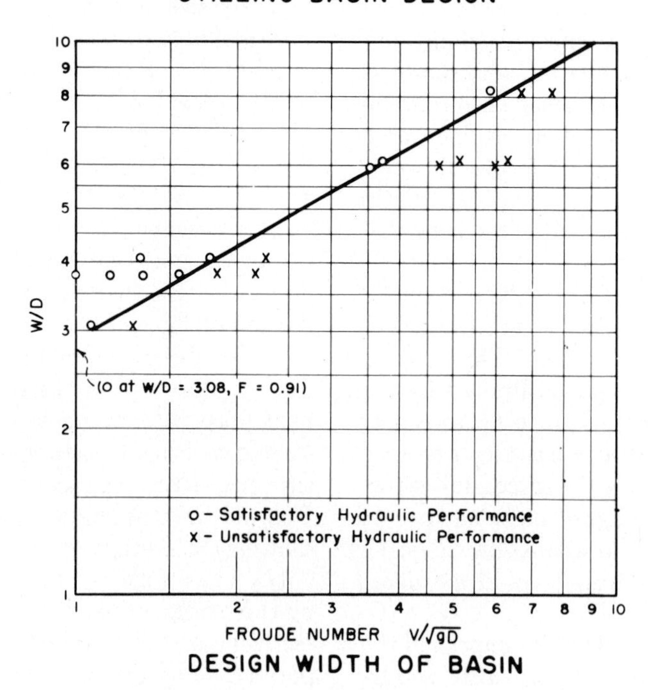

NOTES:

W is the inside width of the basin.

D represents the depth of flow entering the basin and is the square root of the flow area.

V is the velocity of the incoming flow.

Figure 10-14.—Dimensional criteria for impact-type stilling basin. 288-D-2436.

Figure 10-15.—Impact-type stilling basin in operation. 288-D-2905.

procedures for hydraulic design of outlet works, two examples are presented below.

(a) *Example 1.*—The problem is to compute a discharge curve for the river outlet works for McPhee Dam, shown on figure 10-5, and to check the stilling basin for the condition of maximum discharge. The solution is as follows:

First determine the total loss coefficients for both maximum and minimum assumed losses by relating the loss coefficients of each component to the area of the upstream tunnel. These assumptions and computations are shown in table 10-2.

From equation (8), for maximum loss conditions:

$$Q = 314.2\sqrt{\frac{64.4H_T}{56.42}} = 336\sqrt{H_T}$$

A discharge curve for this relationship can be computed if the value of H_T is determined. Because the jet issuing from the gate opening is supported, H_T is measured from the reservoir water surface to the top of the jet. For low flows, weir control at the intake sill is assumed, and $Q = CLH^{3/2}$. A discharge coefficient, C, of 3.0 is often assumed for the crest length, L.

The depth of water just downstream from the rectangular gate openings may be estimated by using the discharge coefficient for the gates which, in this case, is an approximate measure of the top contraction. The approximate depth of water will, therefore, be 0.96 multiplied by the height of the gates (6.0 ft), or 5.8 feet. The values of H_T are found by subtracting the elevation of the top of the jet from the reservoir water surface elevation. At the maximum water surface elevation of 6928.0 feet, H_T = 6,928.0 − (6,671.0 + 5.8) = 251.2 feet. For maximum losses, the corresponding discharge is $Q = 336\sqrt{251.2} = 5{,}325$ ft³/s. This computed discharge for maximum losses corresponds with the 5,000-ft³/s rated capacity of the river outlet works; therefore, the portion of the system that flows under pressure can be considered to meet the hydraulic design requirements. For minimum loss conditions:

$$Q = 314.2\sqrt{\frac{64.4H_T}{53.73}} = 344\sqrt{H_T}$$

$$= 344\sqrt{251.2} = 5{,}450 \text{ ft}^3/\text{s}$$

This discharge should be used to check the stilling basin design.

To analyze the downstream free flow portion of the river outlet works, the hydraulic gradients immediately below the gates for both maximum and minimum losses must be determined.

With maximum losses, the discharge is equal to 5,325 ft³/s at maximum reservoir water surface elevation 6928.0. The total area of the jets downstream from the regulating gates is 2(4) 5.8 = 46.4 ft². The velocity at the contracted section downstream from the gates is, therefore, 5,325/46.4 = 114.8 ft/s, and the velocity head is 204 feet. This provides a gradient at the center of the gates of 6,674 + 204 = 6,878 feet. For the 20-foot-wide free flow downstream tunnel, assuming a transition loss of $0.2\Delta h_v$, the computed depth is 2.82 feet and the velocity head is 204.5 feet. The hydraulic gradient is established at elevation 6877.2 feet.

With minimum losses, the discharge is equal to 5,450 ft³/s at elevation 6928.0 feet. Following the same procedure as above, the initial hydraulic gradient for the free flow tunnel is found to be at elevation 6886.9 feet, with a depth of 2.82 feet.

The next step is to compute the water surface profiles through the downtream free flow tunnel. Here again, the losses should be maximized and minimized to determine the extreme conditions at the downstream portal. Computations can be tabulated as shown in tables 10-3 and 10-4 (for the procedure, see sec. 9.18).

For the stilling basin design d_1 = 1.92 feet and v_1 = 94.6 ft/s, as computed in table 10-3. Therefore, from appendix B, equation (49):

$$d_2 = -\frac{d_1}{2} + \sqrt{\frac{d_1^2}{4} + \frac{2v_1^2 d_1}{g}} = 31.7 \text{ feet}$$

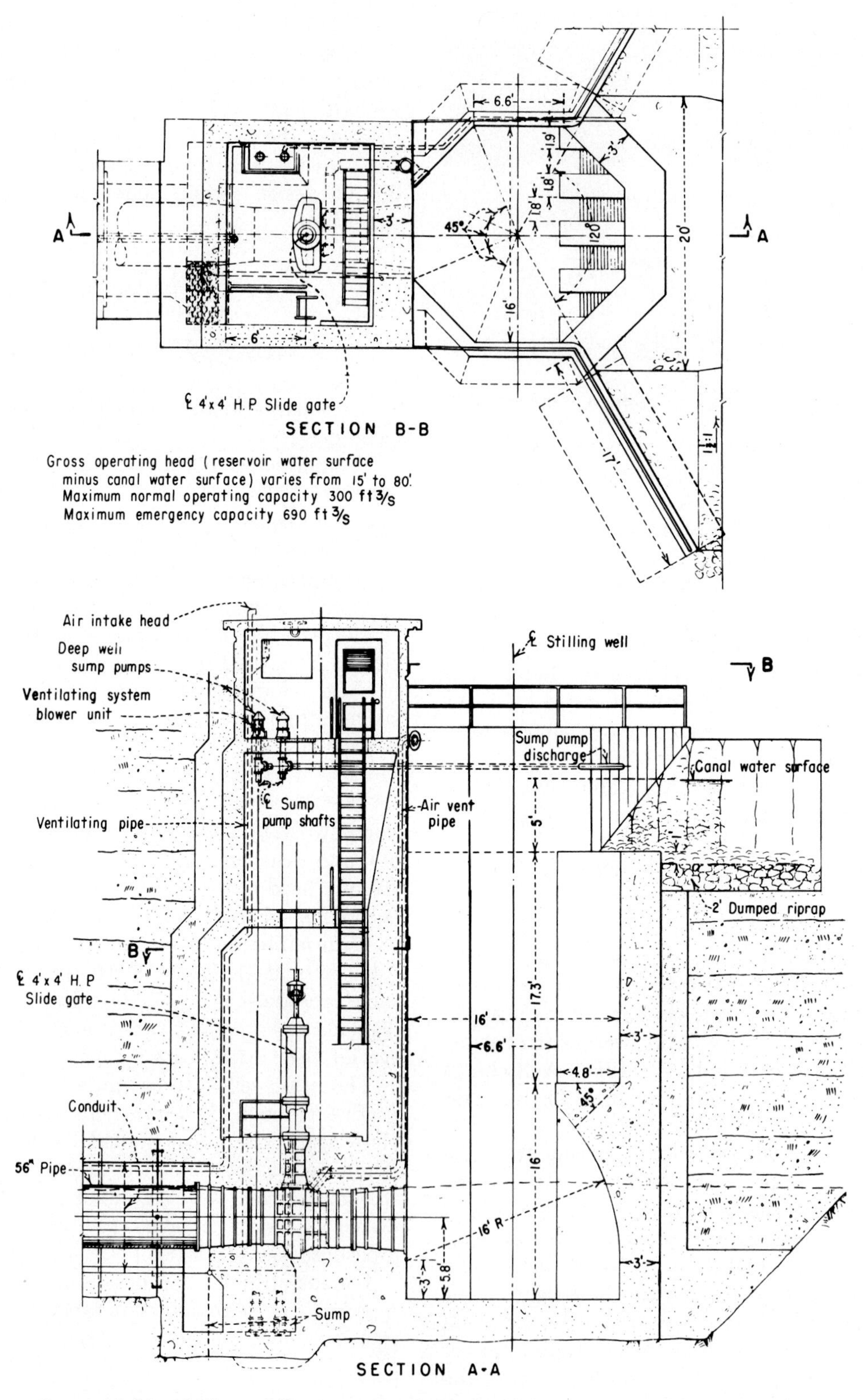

Figure 10-16.—Stilling well energy dissipator installation. Trenton Dam, Nebraska. 288–D–2535.

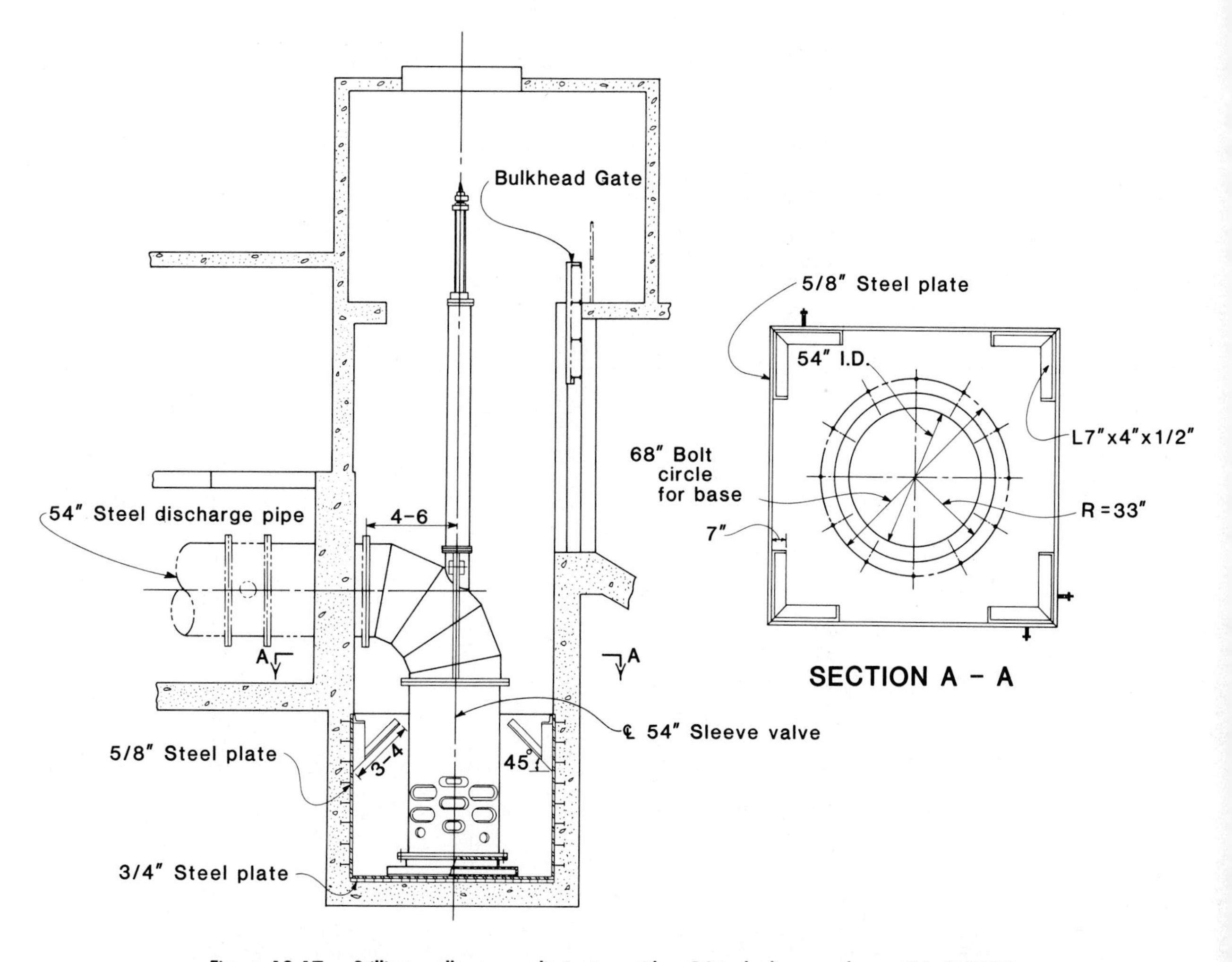

Figure 10-17.—Stilling well energy dissipator with a 54-inch sleeve valve. 103–D–1838.

The required tailwater elevation is 6636.0 + 31.7 = 6667.7, which closely matches the actual tailwater elevation of 6668.0. The length of the basin, for $F_1 = v_1/\sqrt{gd_1} = 12.0$, should be $4.25d_2 = 4.25\ (31.7) = 134.7$ feet, from figure 9-42. The actual basin length is 134 feet. From table 10-4, the depth indicated at the downstream portal for maximum losses is only 4.43 feet, which should provide ample air space to preclude sealing from splashing or wave action. The design of the free flow portion of the tunnel and the stilling basin design are, therefore, satisfactory.

(b) *Example 2.*—The problem is to design an outlet works system similar in layout to that shown for Stateline Dam on figure 10-3, capable of discharging 50 ft^3/s at reservoir elevation 100.0 feet. The top of the downstream regulating gate is at elevation 55.0, above the maximum tailwater. The sill of the drop inlet intake is at elevation 70.0, above the 100-year silt level. The length of the pressure conduit upstream from the guard gate is 300 feet, including the vertical length and the length around the bend at the drop inlet. The length of the downstream pressure pipe is 250 feet, including the lengths of transitions. The solution is as follows:

First, an evaluation of the approximate size of the system can be obtained by estimating total losses and velocity head for the system with downstream control at $4h_v$. An average diameter of 4.9 feet is, therefore, required for the entire length of 550 feet for the available head of 45 feet. For the indicated average size, a 4- by 4-foot regulating gate might be considered. Assuming that the discharge coefficient of the regulating gate is 0.96, then $K_g = (1/C^2) - 1 = 0.09$. The head needed to discharge 500 ft/s will then be:

$$h_g = \frac{(1+K_g)}{2g}\left(\frac{Q}{a}\right)^2 = \frac{1.09}{64.4}\left(\frac{500}{16}\right)^2 = 16.5 \text{ feet}$$

This will leave 28.5 feet for all other losses.

Next, consider the pipe size downstream from the gate chamber. An area approximately 1.1 times the regulating gate area could be used, for a diameter of 56 inches. The loss through the 250 feet of length will then be, from equation (10):

$$h_f = \frac{29.1\, n^2}{r^{4/3}}\left(\frac{L}{2g}\right)\left(\frac{Q}{a}\right)^2$$

$$= \frac{29.1(0.012)^2}{1.17^{4/3}}\left(\frac{250}{64.4}\right)\left(\frac{500}{17.1}\right)^2 = 11.3 \text{ feet}$$

for an n of 0.012. This loss plus the required head for the regulating gate discharge will leave 17.2 feet for upstream and other losses.

Table 10-2.—Computation of total loss coefficients — example 1.

Element	Area, ft²	$\left(\frac{a_1}{a_x}\right)^2$	Loss type	Loss symbol	Maximum losses[1]: Loss coefficient	Maximum losses[1]: $\left(\frac{a_1}{a_x}\right)^2$ times coefficient	Minimum losses: Loss coefficient	Minimum losses: $\left(\frac{a_1}{a_x}\right)^2$ times coefficient
Trashrack	Gross, 2471; Net, 2060	0.02	Trashrack	[2]K_t	0.55	0.01	0.00	0.00
Entrance	837.0	.14	Entrance	K_e	0.20	.03	.20	.03
	837.0	.14	Friction	[3]K_f	.004		.001	
	837.0	.14	Contraction	K_c	.10	−.01	.10	−.01
Transition	400.0	.62	Contraction	K_c	.10	.06	.10	.06
	400.0	.62	Friction	[3]K_f	.015	.01	.006	.00
	400.0	.62	Contraction	K_c	.10	−.06	.10	−.06
Upstream tunnel	314.2	1.00	Contraction	K_c	.10	.10	.10	.10
	314.2	1.00	Friction	[3]K_f	.46	.46	.17	.17
	314.2	1.00	30° bend	[4]K_b	.07	.07	.07	.07
	314.2	1.00	Expansion	K_{ex}	.20	.20	.20	.20
Transition	357.1	0.77	Expansion	K_{ex}	.20	−.15	.20	−.15
	357.1	0.77	Friction	[3]K_f	.009	.01	.003	.00
	160.0	3.86	Entrance	K_e	.20	.77	.20	.77
	160.0	3.86	Friction	[3]K_f	.010	.04	.004	.02
	160.0	3.86	Contraction	K_c	.10	−.39	.10	−.39
Gates	48.0	42.85	Contraction	K_c	.10	4.28	.10	4.28
	48.0	42.85	Friction	[3]K_f	.10	4.28	.045	1.93
	48.0	42.85	Gates	[5]K_g	.09	3.86	.09	3.86
	48.0	42.85	Exit	K_v	1.00	42.85	1.00	42.85
			Total loss coefficient, K_L			56.42		53.73

[1]a_1 = area of tunnel; a_x = area of element.
[2]From equation (11), for maximum losses, K_t = 0.55 (assumed); for minimum losses, loss is neglected.
[3]Friction losses, $K_f = 29.1n^2\,(L/r^{4/3})$:

a. 31 feet × 27 ft, r = 7.22 feet, L = 10 feet, K_f = 0.004 (n = 0.013), K_f = 0.001 (n = 0.008)
b. 20 feet × 20 ft, r = 5.00 feet, L = 25.5 feet, K_f = 0.015 (n = 0.013), K_f = 0.006 (n = 0.008)
c. 20-feet dia., r = 4.00 feet, L = 800 feet, K_f = 0.46 (n = 0.013), K_f = 0.17 (n = 0.008)
d. 20-feet modified H.S., r = 5.00 feet, L = 15.5 feet, K_f = 0.009 (n = 0.013), K_f = 0.003 (n = 0.008)
e. 2 − 8 feet × 10 feet, r = 2.22 feet, L = 6 feet, K_f = 0.010 (n = 0.13), K_f = 0.004 (n = 0.008)
f. 2 − 4 feet × 6 feet, r = 1.20 feet, L = 30.5 feet, K_f = 0.10 (n = 0.012), K_f = 0.045 (n = 0.008)

[4]From figure 10-12, for R_b/D = 2.0.
[5]From C_d = 0.96. Note that when both gates are wide open, the downstream gate will not be submerged because of the top contraction of the issuing stream through the upstream gate. Therefore, it will not affect the flow.

Table 10-3.—Hydraulic computation for free flow portion of tunnel — example 1 (maximum losses).[1]

Station	ΔL	Trial d	Width	a	v	h_v	r	[2]s	$\frac{s_1+s_2}{2}$	Σh_L	Invert El.	Invert El. $+ d + h_v$	EGL $- \Sigma h_L$
20+34.5	–	2.82	20.0	46.4	117.5	214.2	1.80	0.1819	–	0	6669.9	6887.0	6887.0
22+00	165.5	2.98	20.0	49.6	109.9	187.6	1.90	.1482	0.1651	27.3	6669.0	6859.6	6859.6
24+00	200.0	3.17	20.0	53.4	102.1	162.0	2.02	.1783	.1333	26.6	6667.9	6833.0	6833.0
26+00	200.0	3.36	20.0	57.1	95.4	141.5	2.13	.0961	.1072	21.4	6666.8	6811.6	6811.5
28+00	200.0	3.54	20.0	60.8	89.7	124.8	2.24	.0795	.0878	17.6	6665.6	6794.0	6794.0
29+71	171.0	1.92	30.0	57.7	94.4	138.4	1.70	.1266	.1030	17.6	6636.0	6776.4	6776.4

[1] $n = 0.008$, $Q = 5{,}450$ ft^3/s.

[2] $s = \frac{h_f}{L} = \frac{29.1n^2v^2}{2gr^{4/3}}$

Table 10-4.—Hydraulic computation for free flow portion of tunnel — example 1 (minimum losses).[1]

Station	ΔL	Trial d	Width	a	v	h_v	r	[2]s	$\frac{s_1+s_2}{2}$	Σh_L	Invert El.	Invert El. $+ d + h_v$	EGL $- \Sigma h_L$
20+34.5	–	2.82	20.0	46.4	114.8	204.5	1.80	0.4584	–	0	6669.9	6877.2	6877.2
22+00	165.5	3.26	20.0	55.1	96.6	144.8	2.07	.2696	0.3640	60.2	6669.0	6817.0	6817.0
24+00	200.0	3.78	20.0	65.6	81.2	102.4	2.37	.1594	.2145	42.9	6667.9	6774.1	6774.1
26+00	200.0	4.29	20.0	75.8	70.3	76.7	2.64	.1033	.1313	26.3	6666.8	6747.8	6747.8
28+00	200.0	4.79	20.0	85.8	62.1	59.8	2.89	.0715	.0874	17.5	6665.6	6730.3	6730.3
28+70.5	70.5	4.42	20.0	88.5	60.2	56.2	3.07	.0621	.0668	4.7	6664.9	6725.6	6725.6

[1] $n = 0.013$, $Q = 5{,}325$ ft^3/s.

[2] $s = \frac{h_f}{L} = \frac{29.1n^2v^2}{2gr^{4/3}}$.

Next, select the conduit size upstream from the pipe. Assuming a 4- by 5-foot guard gate, a 5.5-foot-diameter conduit could be used. Assuming a steel liner is not required, the loss through the 300-foot length with an n of 0.014 is:

$$h_f = \frac{29.1(0.014)^2}{1.38^{4/3}}\left(\frac{300}{64.4}\right)\left(\frac{500}{23.76}\right)^2 = 7.7 \text{ feet}$$

This loss plus the pipe and regulating gate losses of 11.3 and 16.5 feet, respectively, total approximately 36 feet, leaving about 9 feet for other losses. This seems reasonable enough to warrant evaluation.

Assuming then, a 5.5-foot-diameter upstream conduit, a 4- by 5-foot guard gate, a 56-inch-diameter downstream pipe, and a 4- by 4-foot regulating gate, a detailed analysis of the losses can be made. The losses will be based on the maximum loss coefficients as discussed previously. Table 10-5 shows the results.

For $K_L = 2.91$, from equation (8):

$$Q = a_1\sqrt{\frac{2gH_T}{K_L}}$$

$$= 17.10\sqrt{\frac{64.4H_T}{2.91}} = 80.4\sqrt{H_T}$$

or for a 45-foot head, $Q = 539$ ft^3/s. This value is slightly higher than the design requirement, and one or more of the elements could be reduced to increase the total loss. If the downstream pipe size is decreased to 54 inches, the area designated as 1 in table 10-5 will change from 17.10 to 15.90, and the loss coefficient for item j will be increased to 0.90. Recalculating the other items, the total value of K_L becomes 2.68. Then,

$$Q = 15.90\sqrt{\frac{64.4H_T}{2.68}} = 77.9\sqrt{H_T}$$

or for a 45-foot head, $Q = 522$ ft^3/s.

The completed outlet works system should be checked to determine whether reservoir evacuation requirements can be met. The upstream conduit may have to be resized to pass a diversion flood for a specified head. After the outlet works has been sized, the stilling basin must be designed for the maximum discharge possible using the maximum head and minimum losses through the system.

Table 10-5.—Computation of total loss coefficient—example 2.

Element	Designated area subscript	Area, ft^2	$\left(\frac{a_1}{a_x}\right)^2$	Item	Loss type	Loss symbol	Loss coef-ficient	$\left(\frac{a_1}{a_x}\right)^2$ times loss coefficient
Trashrack	6	[1]Gross, 300; Net, 125	0.02	(a)	Trashrack	[3]K_t	1.09	0.02
Entrance	5	23.76	.52	(b)	Entrance	[4]K_e	0.10	.05
Upstream conduit	4	23.76	.52	(c)	Bend	[5]K_b	.14	.07
		23.76	.52	(d)	Friction	[6]K_f	1.12	.58
		23.76	.52	(e)	Contraction	K_c	0.10	−.05
Guard gate	3	20.00	.73	(f)	Contraction	K_c	.10	.07
		20.00	.73	(g)	Guard gate	K_g	.05	.04
		20.00	.73	(h)	Contraction	K_c	.10	−.07
Downstream pipe	1	17.10	1.00	(i)	Contraction	K_c	.10	.10
		17.10	1.00	(j)	Friction	[7]K_f	.85	.85
		17.10	1.00	(k)	Contraction	K_c	.10	−.10
Regulating gate	2	16.00	1.14	(l)	Contraction	K_c	.10	.11
		16.00	1.14	(m)	Reg. gate	K_g	.09	.10
		16.00	1.14	(n)	Exit	K_v	1.00	1.14
					Total loss coefficient, K_L			2.91

[1]a_l = area of downstream pipe; a_x = area of element.
[2]Assuming trashracks designed for 2-ft/s velocity and 50 percent clogged; gross area = net area × 1.2 = 300.

[3]$K_t = 1.45 - 0.45\frac{125}{300} - \left(\frac{125}{300}\right)^2 = 1.09$, from equation (11).

[4]From table 10-1, item g.
[5]From figure 10-12, for $R_b/D = 2$, 90° bend.
[6]For D = 5.5 feet and n = 0.014, from equation (10):

$$K_f = \frac{29.1n^2L}{r^{4/3}} = \frac{29.1(0.014)^2\,300}{(1.38)^{4/3}} = 1.12\,.$$

[7]For D = 56 inches = 4.67 feet, and n = 0.012, from equation (10):

$$K_f = \frac{29.1n^2L}{r^{4/3}} = \frac{29.1\,(0.012)^2\,250}{(1.17)^{4/3}} = 0.85\,.$$

D. STRUCTURAL DESIGN DETAILS

10.19. *General.*—The same types of structures may be used for either spillways or outlet works. Because spillways use open channels more often than outlet works do, the structural design details for open channels are discussed in part G of chapter 9. The details of the design of walls, open-channel linings, and floors, discussed as spillway structures in chapter 9, also apply to these structures when used for outlet works. Furthermore, the headworks of open-channel outlet works are similar to gated crest structures for spillways in regard to their structural design details.

On the other hand, closed-conduit waterways are more commonly used for outlet works than they are for spillways; therefore, their design details are discussed in this chapter. Nevertheless, these design details are the same in either case.

A closed-conduit waterway might be a cast-in-place cut-and-cover culvert or conduit, a precast or prefabricated pipe, or a tunnel bored through the abutment. Waterways for a spillway are most often free flowing; whereas, those for outlet works may either flow full under pressure or partly full. The safety of earthfill and rockfill dams depends to a large degree on the stability of the spillway and outlet structures, especially when conduits pass through the embankment. Where all or part of a conduit is under internal pressure from the reservoir head, any leakage or failure of the conduit may cause openings through the dam that may gradually be enlarged until partial or complete failure results. Seepage is also possible along the contact surfaces between the conduit and the earthfill; this can result in serious damage. Another danger is the possibility of structural collapse of the conduit, which would almost certainly result in failure for an earthfill dam. These facts emphasize the importance of using durable materials, conservative design procedures, proper design details, and construction methods that will ensure safe structures.

Replacing a conduit through either an earthfill or a rockfill dam is usually difficult and expensive. However, such an operation can be avoided by the use of durable materials, such as steel pipe encased in concrete, cast-in-place reinforced-concrete conduit, or precast concrete pipe. Conduit joints must be made watertight to prevent leakage into the surrounding embankment. Joints of concrete cast-in-place conduits must be sealed with waterstops, and rubber-gasketed joints must be used for precast concrete pipe.

When the outlet conduit consists of prefabricated pipe, the methods of bedding and backfilling the pipe should insofar as possible, preclude unequal settlement and ensure uniform distribution of load on the foundation. When backfilling near these structures, extreme care should be taken to secure tight contact between the fill and the conduit surface and to obtain the proper densities of the earthfill material (see sec. E.4). This is important not only to prevent seepage along the conduit, but also to ensure that the fill develops a lateral restraint on the structure, which will prevent excessive stresses in the conduit shell.

When the outlet consists of precast reinforced concrete, it should be set carefully on a good foundation and well bedded in concrete, as shown on figure C-2. The concrete bedding not only helps distribute the conduit load on the foundation, but also precludes uncompacted zones and void spaces under the pipe, which could induce leakage along the undersurface of the structure. Void spaces or inadequate compaction of impervious materials at the inverts of pipes have caused numerous failures of small earthfill dams. The practice of supporting pipes on piers or collars without a concrete bedding should be avoided because greater foundation reactions at the concentrated support points cause unequal stress distribution in the pipe. Furthermore, if the foundation below the conduit settles between piers, the unsupported conduit will sag and crack. If the conduit is strong enough to sustain the fill load, the earth shrinking away from the underside will leave voids that will permit the free passage of water and possible piping.

Details of designs for cut-and-cover conduits are discussed in section 10.21.

10.20. ***Tunnel Details.***—Linings are provided in tunnel waterways for both hydraulic and structural reasons. The smooth boundary surfaces reduce frictional resistance and permit a smaller diameter tunnel for a required capacity. Lining a tunnel also prevents saturation of the surrounding ground by seepage. Structural lining is used to support the tunnel walls against raveling or unstable ground.

Where the purpose of the lining is to provide a smooth surface for hydraulic flow or to reduce seepage, its thickness may be determined by requirements for shrinkage, temperature change, and concrete placement. For ordinary linings where reasonably stable ground is encountered and little tunnel support is required, an average lining thickness of between ¾ and 1 inch for each foot of tunnel diameter is ordinarily used. The minimum thickness normally provided is 6 inches. However, unstable ground or areas through water-bearing strata may require thicker linings to resist external rock loads and hydrostatic pressures. A full circular lining is the most efficient shape to withstand such external loads.

A tunnel lining that is to be reinforced must be made sufficiently thick both to accommodate the reinforcement and to provide enough room for placing the concrete in the confined space behind the forms. A minimum thickness of 6 inches is suggested for tunnel linings with a single layer of reinforcement. Where two layers of reinforcement are required, a minimum thickness of 9 inches is desirable. In either case, the contractor may need to provide additional space outside the reinforcement to accommodate the concrete placement pipe.

The portions of a tunnel that must be reinforced and the amount of reinforcement required depend on the tunnel shape, external and internal loadings, requirements for watertightness, and many geologic factors. For a nonpressure tunnel, reinforcement may be required to resist external loads from unstable ground or from grout or water pressures. Pressure tunnels with high internal hydrostatic loads must have linings reinforced sufficiently to withstand bursting where inadequate cover or unstable supporting rock prevails.

General guidelines for determining reinforcement requirements are suggested below.

a. A pressure tunnel should ordinarily be reinforced whenever the depth of cover must withstand the unbalanced internal pressure head or whenever leakage control is important. The reinforcement should be sufficient to provide the required structural strength and leakage control for the maximum internal hydrostatic and surge pressure reduced by a conservative estimate of the external hydrostatic pressure expected along the length of the tunnel. Restraint from the surrounding rock should be considered in areas of adequate cover based on the properties and quality of the surrounding media. Where there are provisions for unwatering, the external pressure head should be the maximum possible along the length of the tunnel.

b. Where a gate chamber connects a pressure and a nonpressure tunnel, the upstream and downstream tunnels should be specially reinforced. This is required for the upstream portion of the tunnel to prevent excessive cracking, which could permit leakage from the pressure portion to seep downstream and enter behind the lining of the nonpressure portion. The pressure portion should be reinforced for a distance upstream from the gate chamber equal to five times the diameter of the tunnel. The extent of the reinforcement should be based on full internal hydrostatic head with no allowance for restraint from the surrounding rock. The nonpressure portion of the tunnel should be reinforced for a distance downstream from the gate chamber equal to from two to five times the tunnel diameter. Such reinforcement should be based on an external static head equal to the internal head just upstream from the gate chamber.

c. An adequate amount of both longitudinal and circumferential reinforcement should be provided near the portals of both pressure and nonpressure tunnels to resist loads resulting from loosened rock above the tunnel or from sloughing of the portal cuts. This reinforcement should extend back from the portals for a distance equal to at least twice the tunnel diameter.

d. Except at the portals and at the transition from pressure to nonpressure, a concrete tunnel lining in competent rock may be unreinforced where the rock cover can withstand the unbalanced internal pressure head. If it is in unstable ground, the lining should be reinforced to support probable rock loadings. Methods of estimating loadings for tunnel supports given in [8] may be used to estimate requirements for reinforced lining. However, other methods may also be used. Where the properties of the rock are known, the theoretical stresses in the rock surrounding the excavated tunnel can be determined analytically. Permanent supports and concrete lining, either acting separately or in combination, can then be designed. Figure 10-18 shows typical initial supports used for the outlet works tunnel at Ruedi Dam, Colorado.

Permanent tunnel supports are made of steel ribs, steel lagging, steel liner plates, shotcrete, reinforcement sheets, rock bolts with or without chain link fabric, or a combination of these. The choice of one or a combination of these materials should depend upon geologic conditions, ground-water levels, excavation methods to be used, length of elapsed time between excavating and placing permanent lining, and economic factors.

Ribs, rock bolts, or other support materials must be capable of supporting large blocks of loosened material that may result from tunnel excavation. The lagging must be closely spaced where the rock is highly fractured or slacks off in small pieces; elsewhere it may be more widely spaced or even omitted. Methods of assuming and computing the size of

Figure 10-18.—Typical supports for an outlet works tunnel. Ruedi Dam, Colorado. P382–706–699NA.

supports are given in [8]; however, any other accepted state-of-the-art method may also be used. Loadings should be based on the nature of the ground encountered. If the exact underground conditions are not known, the design of the ground-support system can only be approximate. The designed size and spacing of supports are often adjusted depending on the actual ground conditions encountered during excavation. All spaces outside of liner plates used for initial support should be filled as completely and compactly as possible with clean gravel and thoroughly grouted after the lining has been placed. In some cases, the grouting may be required immediately after installation of the liner plates as the excavation advances.

For tunnels through jointed rock or where seepage is to be minimized, the areas surrounding the tunnel are usually grouted. This is done both to consolidate the material and to fill the open fissures in the rock and the voids between the lining and the rock. This grouting is accomplished by drilling holes through the lining (or through pipes placed in the lining for this purpose) into the surrounding rock and then injecting grout under pressure, as described in part E of appendix G. Permissible grouting pressures depend on the nature of the surrounding material and on the lining thickness. For small tunnels, rings of grout holes should be spaced at about 20-foot centers, depending on the nature of the rock. Each ring consists of grout holes distributed at about 90° around the periphery, with alternate rings placed on vertical and 45° axes.

Drainage holes are often provided in tunnels other than pressure tunnels to relieve external pressures caused by seepage along the outside of the tunnel lining. Like grout holes, drainage holes should be spaced at about 20-foot centers, at intermediate locations between the grout hole rings. At successive sections, one vertical hole should be drilled near the crown and two horizontal holes drilled, one in each sidewall. In free flow tunnels, all drainage holes should be above the water surface; if flow through the tunnel is conveyed in a separate pipe, these holes should be drilled near the invert of the tunnel.

Typical tunnel supports for circular, horseshoe, modified horseshoe, and miscellaneous tunnels are shown on figures 10-19, 10-20, and 10-21. The "A" lines shown on the typical sections are lines within which no unexcavated material of any kind, no timbering, and no metallic or other supports are permitted to remain. The "B" lines are the outside limits to which the excavation is measured for payment.

Suggested "A" line to "B" line dimensions are shown on figure 10-22. Specifications for tunnels are given in part D of appendix G.

10.21. *Cut-and-Cover Conduit Details.*—

(a) *General.*—The design of a cut-and-cover conduit to be constructed through or under an earthfill embankment must include details that will provide for movement and settlement without excessive cracking or leakage. To obtain a safe structure, the following actions must be taken:

(1) Provide ways to minimize seepage along the contact of the conduit and the impervious embankment.
(2) Provide details to forestall cracking that might result in leakage of water into the fill surrounding a pressure conduit and to prevent piping of embankment material into a free flow conduit.
(3) Select and treat the foundation to minimize differential settlement, which is a cause of cracking.
(4) Provide a structure to safely carry the loads to which the conduit will be subjected.

Selection of the designs and details to accomplish these is discussed in this section.

(b) *Cutoff Collars.*—The Bureau of Reclamation has traditionally utilized cutoff collars around conduits to minimize seepage. This policy has been reevaluated, and other approaches are now being used to mitigate the seepage problem. Each engineer or organization should make their own decision as to the viability and effectiveness of the use of cutoff collars. Current Bureau policy and criteria are available on request.

The foundation preparation and compaction around conduits must be equivalent to the foundation preparation for the dam and compaction of the impervious earthfill. Projecting fins or cutoff collars minimize seepage along the contact between the outside surface of the conduit and the embankment. These collars should be made of reinforced concrete, generally from 2 to 3 feet high, 12 to 18 inches wide, and spaced from 7 to 10 times their height along the portion of the conduit within the impervious zone of the dam. Such cutoff collars increase the length of the percolation path along the contact by 20 to 30 percent. Figure 10-23 shows typical cutoff collars used on the outlet works at Silver Jack Dam, Colorado.

For a conduit on an earth foundation, the collar should completely encircle the conduit barrel. Where the foundation is sound rock, good contact along the base may be expected and the collars need extend only enough to be keyed into the rock foundation. The collars should be separated from the conduit to avoid introducing concentrated stresses into the conduit walls, which would alter the normal stress in the barrel. This is accomplished by adding watertight fillers between the collars and the barrel. The structural separation permits lateral slipping of the collar on the barrel, eliminates secondary stresses in the conduit that would otherwise be caused by the stiffening effect of the collars, and avoids the introduction of torsional stresses in the conduit if horizontal movement or displacement of the embankment should occur. The joint filler material may be several layers of graphite-coated paper if only slight movement is expected, or premolded bituminous fillers where greater movement is expected.

Although cutoff collars are usually located between joints in the conduit, some collars have been constructed to span the joints. When so located, they also serve as watertight covers for the joints. If the collar is not placed at a conduit joint or it is placed over a joint that is restrained from movement by keyways or by reinforcement extending across it, the collar ordinarily will not be subjected to large lateral loadings. In such cases, it will need to be only strong enough to resist the superimposed fill load. When a collar covers a joint designed to permit differential movement, either the collar must be designed sufficiently strong to restrain

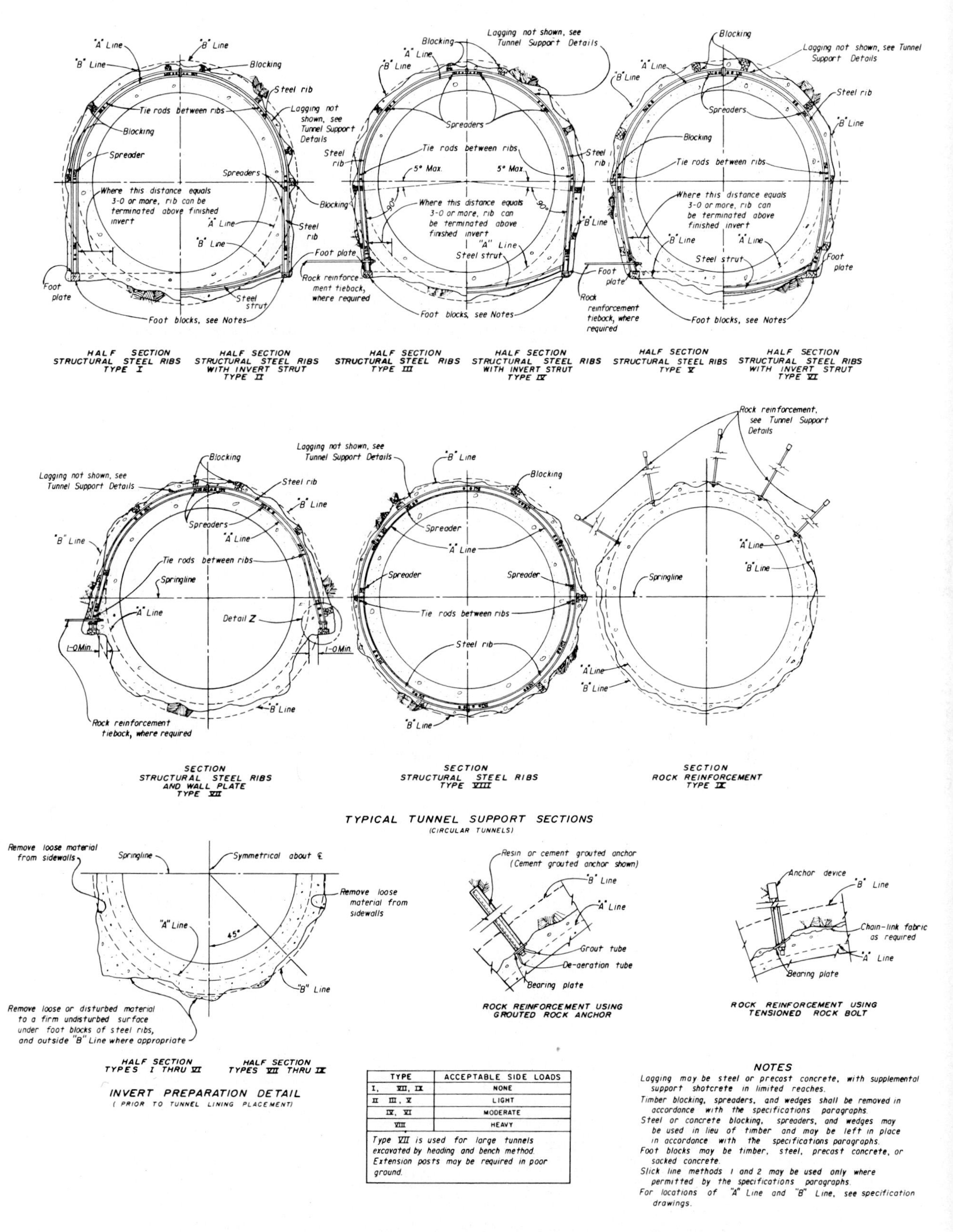

TYPE	ACCEPTABLE SIDE LOADS
I, VII, IX	NONE
II, III, V	LIGHT
IV, VI	MODERATE
VIII	HEAVY

Type VII is used for large tunnels excavated by heading and bench method. Extension posts may be required in poor ground.

NOTES

Lagging may be steel or precast concrete, with supplemental support shotcrete in limited reaches.
Timber blocking, spreaders, and wedges shall be removed in accordance with the specifications paragraphs.
Steel or concrete blocking, spreaders, and wedges may be used in lieu of timber and may be left in place in accordance with the specifications paragraphs.
Foot blocks may be timber, steel, precast concrete, or sacked concrete.
Slick line methods 1 and 2 may be used only where permitted by the specifications paragraphs.
For locations of "A" Line and "B" Line, see specification drawings.

Figure 10-19.—Sections and details for circular tunnels. 103–D–1839.

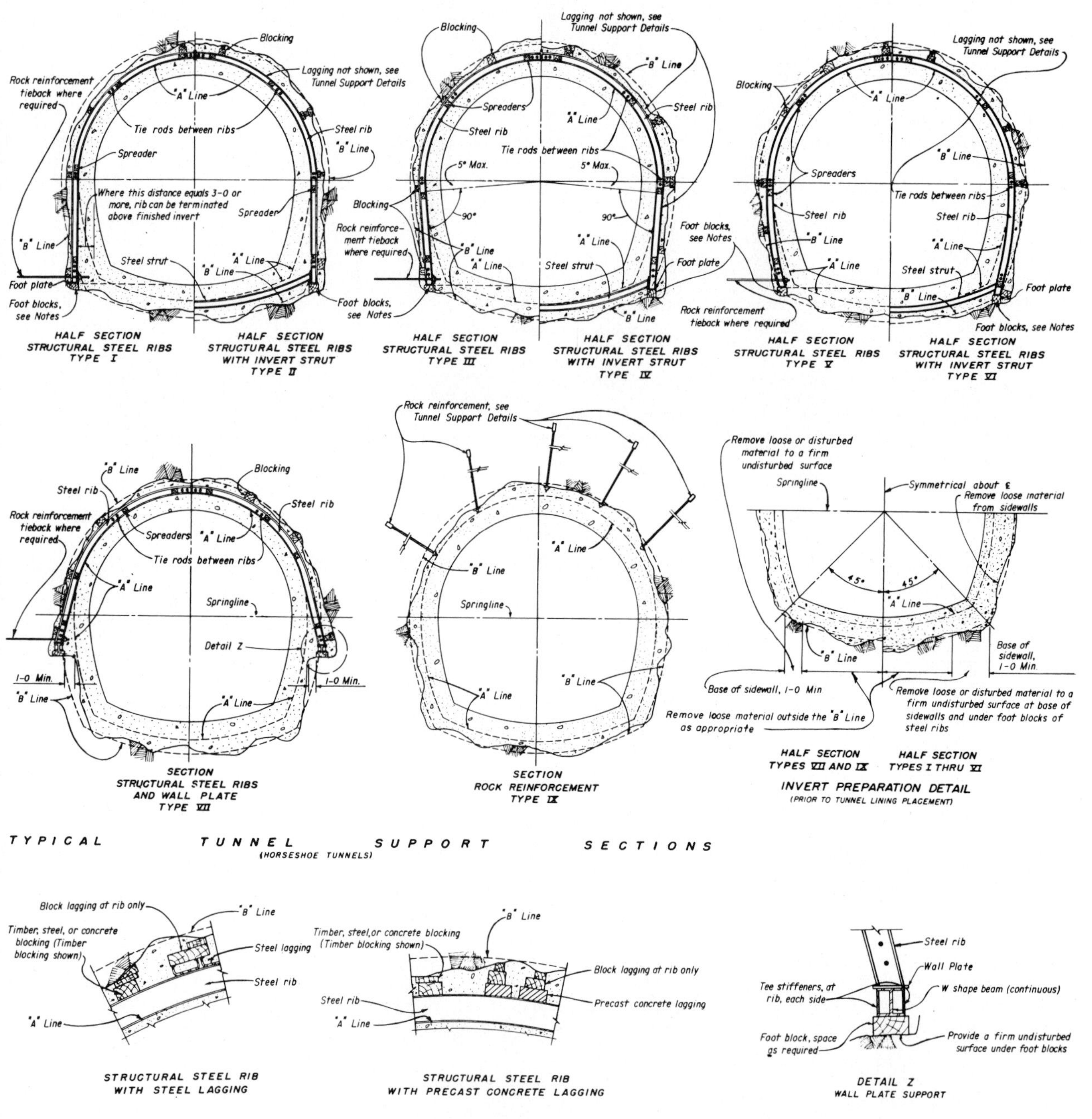

TYPE	ACCEPTABLE SIDE LOADS
I, III, VII, IX	NONE
II, V	LIGHT
IV	MODERATE
VI*	INTERMEDIATE
For heavy side loads, use circular shape and structural steel supports. Type VII is used for large tunnels excavated by heading and bench method. Extension posts may be required in poor ground.	

NOTES

Lagging may be steel or precast concrete, with supplemental support shotcrete in limited reaches.
Timber blocking, spreaders, and wedges shall be removed in accordance with the specifications paragraphs.
Steel or concrete blocking, spreaders, and wedges may be used in lieu of timber and may be left in place in accordance with the specifications paragraphs.
Foot blocks may be timber, steel, precast concrete, or sacked concrete.
Slick line methods 1 and 2 may be used only where permitted by the specifications paragraphs.
For locations of "A" Line and "B" Line, see specification drawings.

Figure 10-20.—Sections and details for horseshoe tunnels. 103–D–1840.

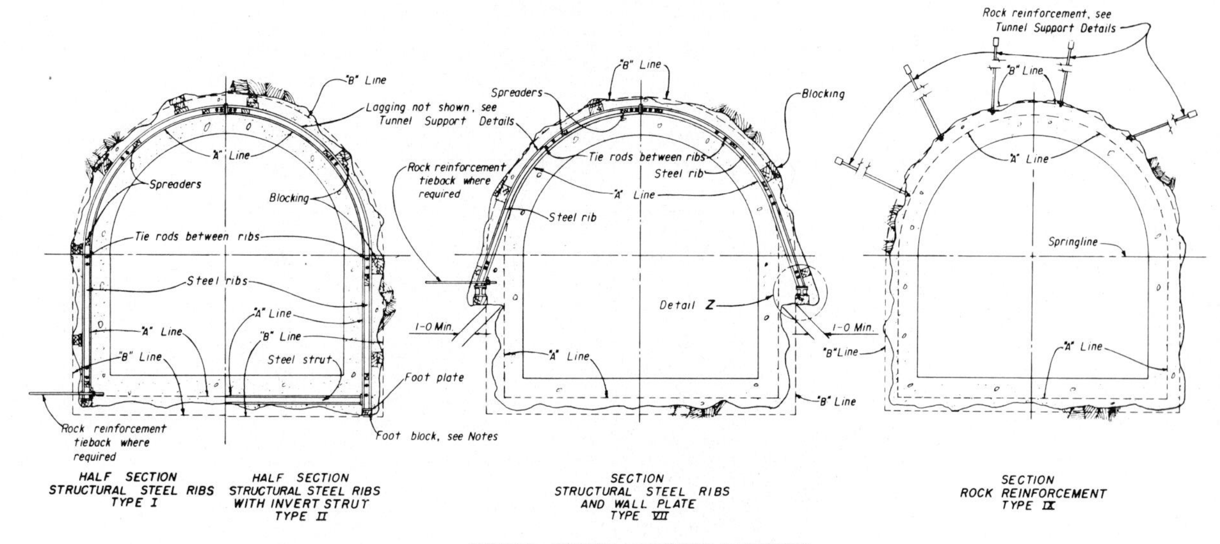

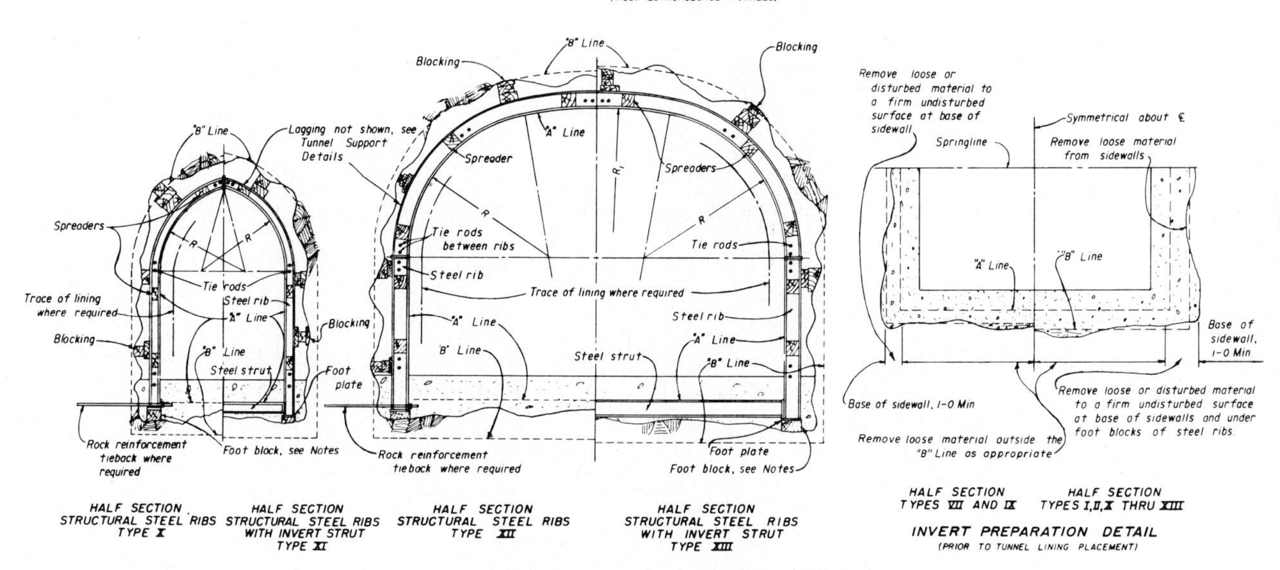

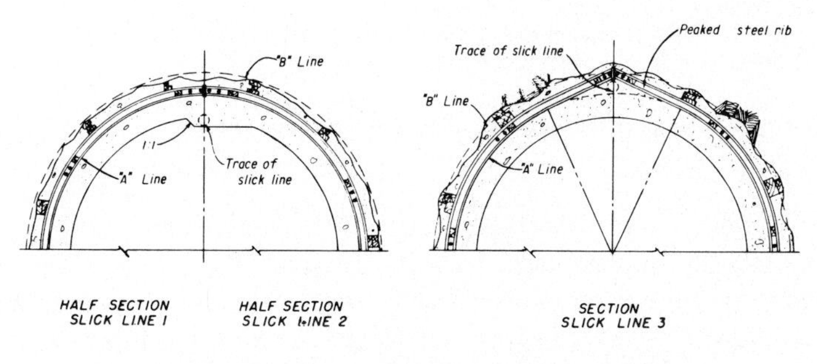

TYPE	ACCEPTABLE SIDE LOADS
I, VII, IX, X, XII	NONE
II, XI, XIII	LIGHT

For greater side loads, use circular shapes and structural steel supports.
Type VII is used for large tunnels excavated by heading and bench method. Extension posts may be required in poor ground.

NOTES

Lagging may be steel or precast concrete, with supplemental support shotcrete in limited reaches.
Timber blocking, spreaders, and wedges shall be removed in accordance with the specifications paragraphs.
Steel or concrete blocking, spreaders, and wedges may be used in lieu of timber and may be left in place in accordance with the specifications paragraphs.
Foot blocks may be timber, steel, precast concrete, or sacked concrete.
Slick line methods 1 and 2 may be used only where permitted by the specifications paragraphs.
For locations of "A" Line and "B" Line, see specification drawings.

Figure 10-21.—Sections and details for modified horseshoe and miscellaneous tunnels. 103–D–1841.

"A" LINE TO "B" LINE DIMENSIONS

For tunnels excavated by conventional blasting method

"A" LINE DIAMETERS IN FEET AND INCHES	RIB SET SUPPORTED			UNSUPPORTED AND ROCK BOLTED (ALL SHAPES) (INCHES)
	CIRCULAR (INCHES)	HORSESHOE (INCHES)	MODIFIED HORSESHOE (INCHES)	
7'-0" TO 9'-6"	14	13	12	10
9'-7" TO 13'-6"	15	14	13	10
13'-7" TO 18'-6"	15	15	13	10
18'-7" TO 22'-0"	16	16	14	10
22'-1" TO 30'-0"	16	17	14	10
30'-1" TO 36'-0"	17	18	15	10
36'-1" TO 50'-0"	17	18	16	10

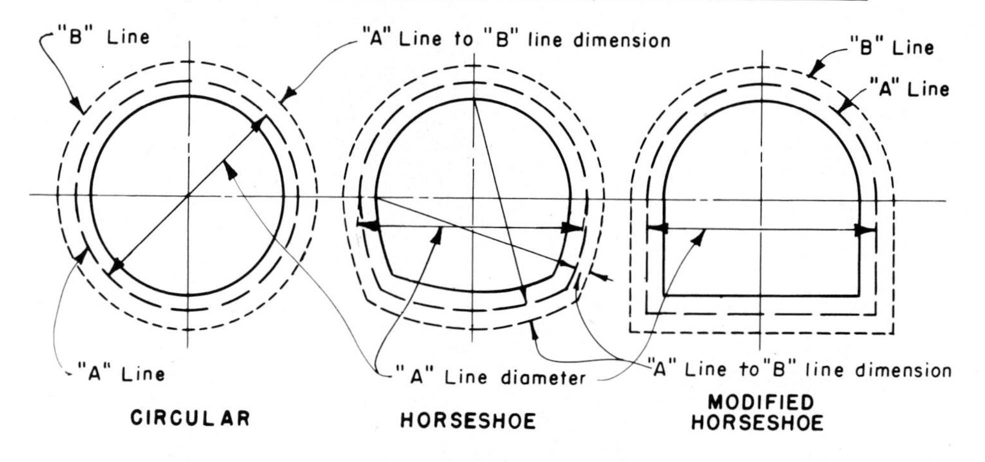

NOTE: Enter table with "A" line shape.
For strutted ribs increase table dimensions 1-inch.
For full circle ribs increase table dimensions :
1-inch for "A" line diameters from 22'-1" to 36'-0"
2-inches for "A" line diameters from 36'-1" to 50'-0"

Figure 10-22.—Definitions of "A" line and "B" line dimensions for different shapes of tunnels. 288-D-2813.

such movement, or the collar must adjust to the movement without losing the watertight contact.

(c) *Conduit Joints.*—Major cracking of cast-in-place conduit can be avoided by placing the conduit in short sections (usually 12 to 16 feet), by continuing the longitudinal reinforcement through the joints, and by placing adjoining sections of the conduit barrel after most of the shrinkage of previously placed sections has occurred. Transverse joints in cast-in-place conduits are called control joints. Waterstops should be placed across these joint provide a watertight seal. The ends of each section placed should be painted with sealing compound to prevent bonding between sections. The waterstops and

Figure 10-23.—Typical cutoff collars on an outlet works conduit. Silver Jack Dam, Colorado. P860–427–964NA.

painted joints confine any cracking from settlement to the joints to prevent leakage. The longitudinal reinforcement, which should be continuous through the conduit joints, prevents longitudinal forces from opening the joints between sections. Details of this type of joint construction are shown on figure 10-24.

Precast pipe used for outlet works or spillway conduits under or through earthfill dams should be bedded in a concrete base (see app. C). The concrete base prevents percolation along the underside of the pipe and structurally supports the precast pipe both laterally and longitudinally. The concrete base should be reinforced; its longitudinal reinforcement should be continuous through the transverse joints. Differential lateral displacement of precast pipe conduit sections and joints is ordinarily restrained by a bell-and-spigot joint or by a reinforced collar encircling a plain joint. Rubber-gasketed joints similar to those shown on figure 10-25 may be used to connect individual lengths of concrete pipe.

Specifications for pipe and the pipe joints shown on figure 10-25 can be found in the Bureau of Reclamation publication, *Standard Specifications for Reinforced Concrete Pressure Pipe* (1969).

(d) *Design Loads.*—Embankment loads on conduits vary over a wide range depending on many factors related to the foundation, method of bedding, and flexibility or rigidity of the conduit; and to the soil characteristics of the embankment, such as angle of internal friction, unit weight, homogeneity, consolidation properties, cohesiveness, and moisture content. All possible combinations of these various factors must be considered to evaluate their overall effect. The loads must be considered not only as they may occur during construction, but also as they may be altered after embankment completion, reservoir filling and embankment saturation.

The Marston theory of embankment pressures

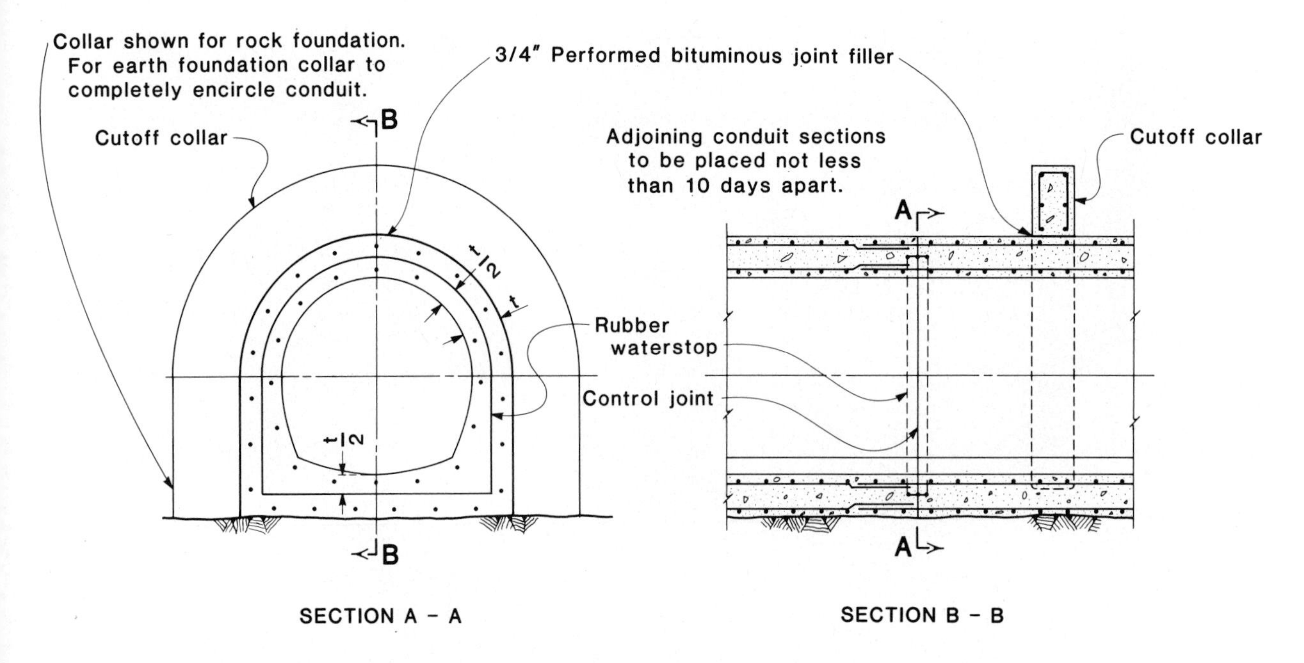

Figure 10-24.—Typical control joint and cutoff collar details. 103–D–1842.

is usually adopted for precast conduits under relatively low fills. This theory is discussed in many bulletins published by the Iowa State College Experiment Station and is summarized in various handbooks [9, 10] that contain bibliographies of relevant publications. Using Marston theory, the vertical load on a conduit is considered to be a combination of the weight of the fill directly above the conduit and the frictional forces, acting either upward or downward, from the adjacent fill. When the adjacent fill settles more than the overlying fill, downward acting frictional forces are induced; this increases the resultant load on the conduit. Conversely, a greater settlement immediately above the conduit results in an arching condition; this reduces the load on the conduit. Thus, a conduit laid in a trench excavated in a compact natural soil may never receive the full weight of the backfill above it because of the development of arching action when the backfill starts to settle. On the other hand, if the conduit is placed so that it projects, in whole or in part, above the natural ground surface, the embankment load on it can be as much as 50 percent greater than the weight of the fill directly above it.

For cast-in-place conduits under relatively high fills where the conduit is placed in cut so that neither a full trench nor a complete projecting condition exists, a loading assumption that averages the extremes noted above is assumed. For this case, the load on the conduit is assumed to be the weight of the column of fill directly above it. The load over that portion of a conduit under the upstream part of the dam includes both the weight of the saturated fill and the weight of the reservoir water above it. The conduit barrel is designed on the basis of a given safety factor, considering that the unit horizontal lateral load on the conduit is one-third of the unit vertical load. The design is then checked on the basis of a reduced safety factor considering no horizontal lateral load exists. The vertical reaction of the base of the conduit is assumed equal to the vertical load plus the weight of the conduit. On an earth foundation, the base reaction is assumed to be distributed uniformly across the width of the conduit; on a rock foundation, it is assumed to be distributed triangularly, varying from twice the average unit reaction at the outside edges to zero at the center of the base. External hydrostatic pressures are assumed to act equally in all directions, vertically downward as an increased load, upward as uplift, and laterally on the sides of the conduit.

Procedures for designing concrete box culverts and circular conduits are comprehensively discussed in *Concrete Culverts and Conduits* [11]. Ap-

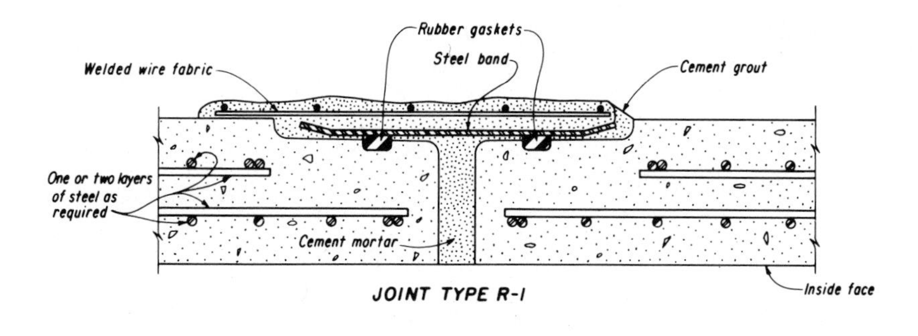

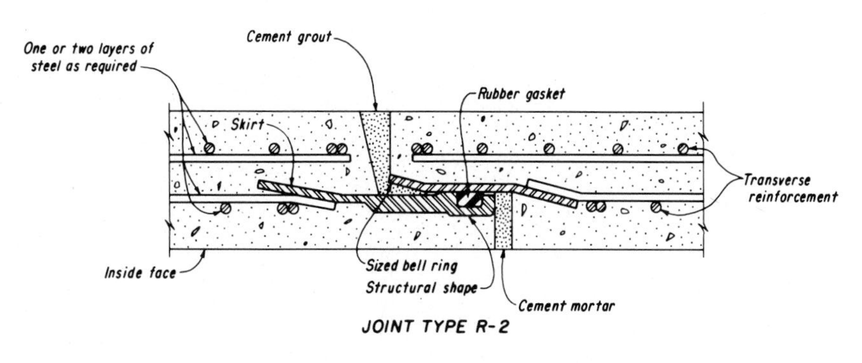

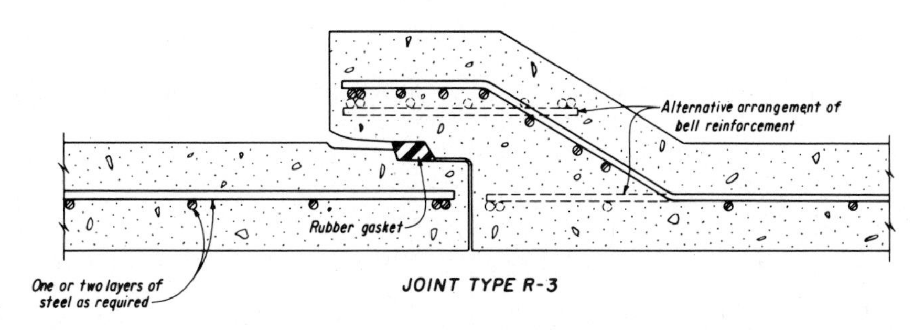

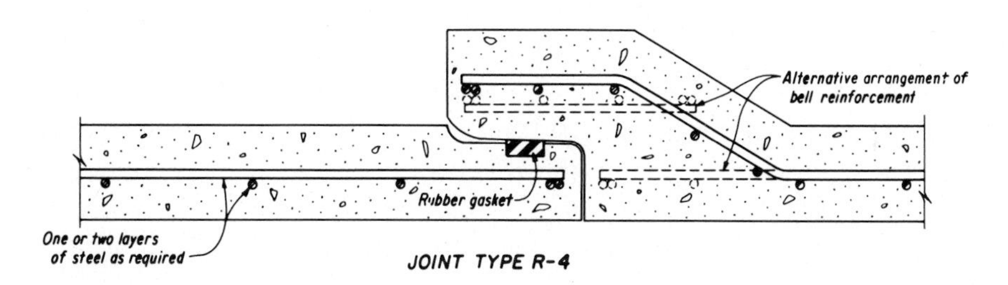

Figure 10-25.—Typical joint details for precast concrete pipe. From 288–D–2814, –2815, –2816, and –2817.

pendix C contains data for selecting precast concrete pipe for use as conduits under limited fill loads.

10.22. ***Details of Typical Structures.***—Figures 10-26 through 10-33 show arrangements for outlet works intakes, shafts, and stilling basins constructed at various Bureau of Reclamation dams. These are presented as examples that may be used as guides in the design of similar structures.

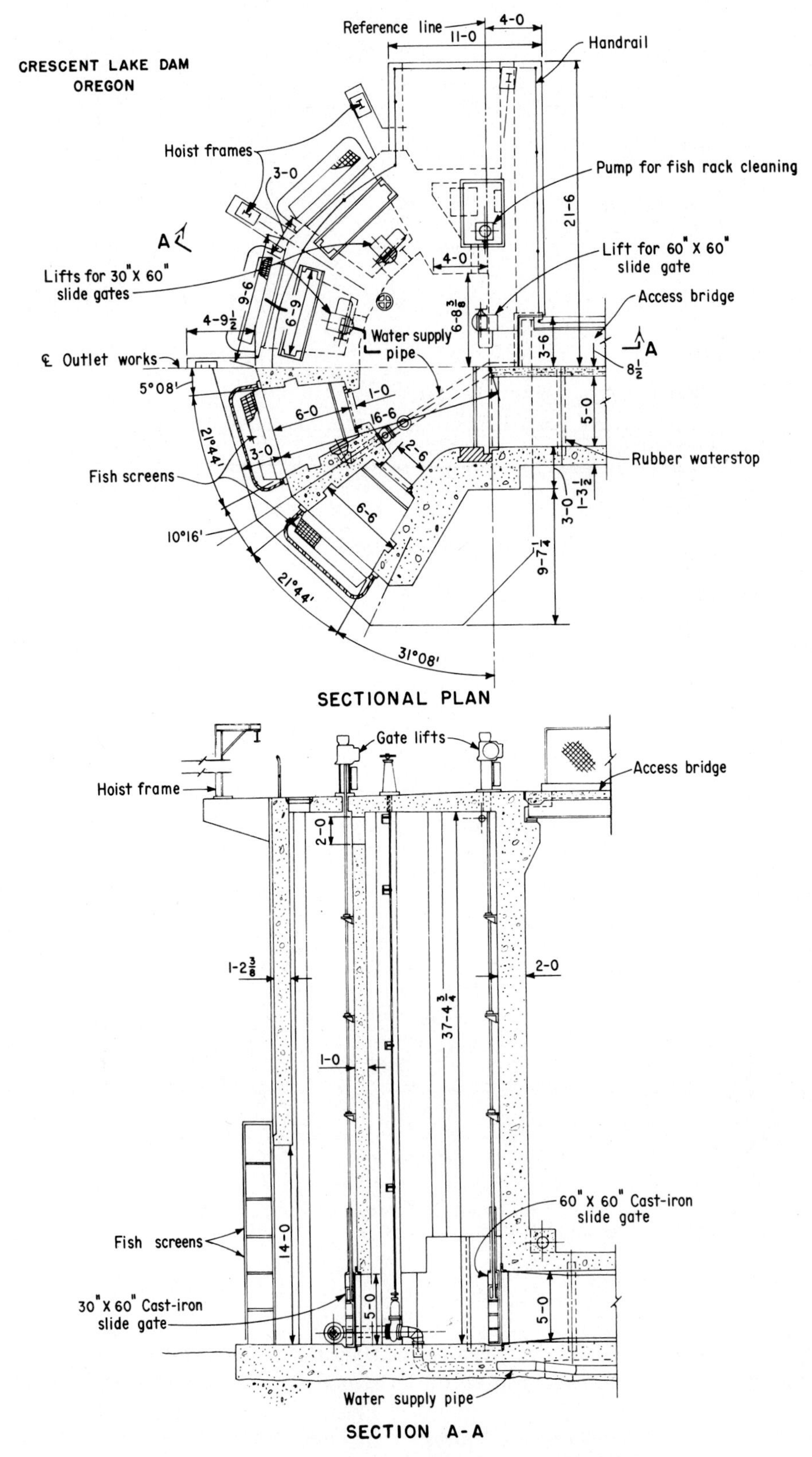

Figure 10-26.—Intake tower arrangement. 288–D–2541.

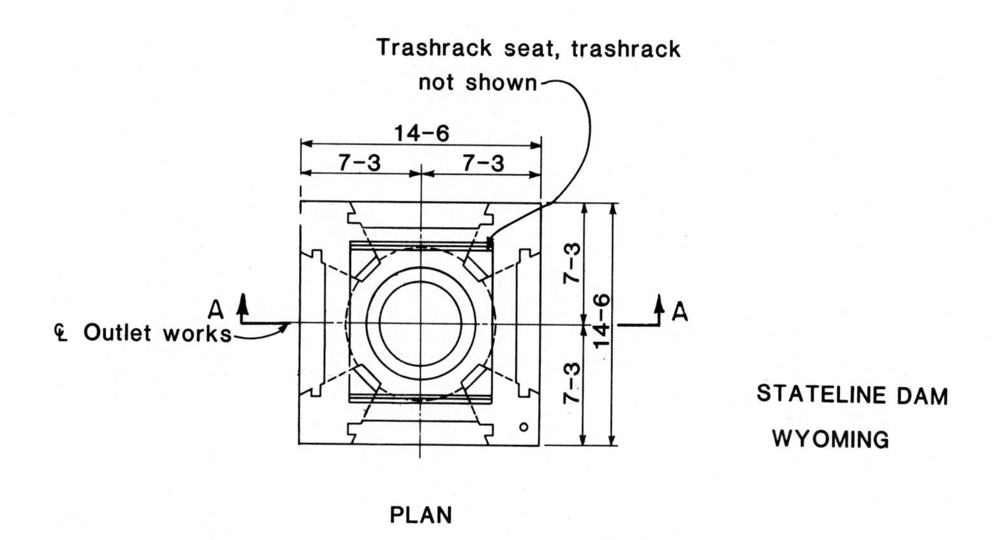

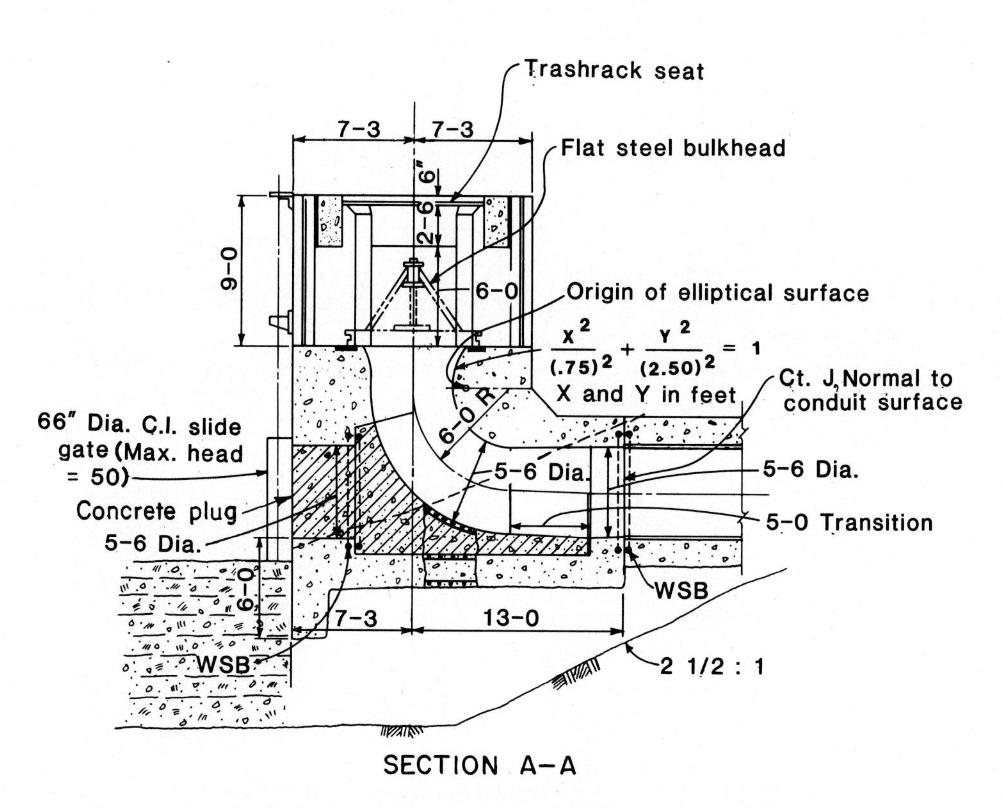

Figure 10-27.—Typical drop inlet intake. 103-D-1843.

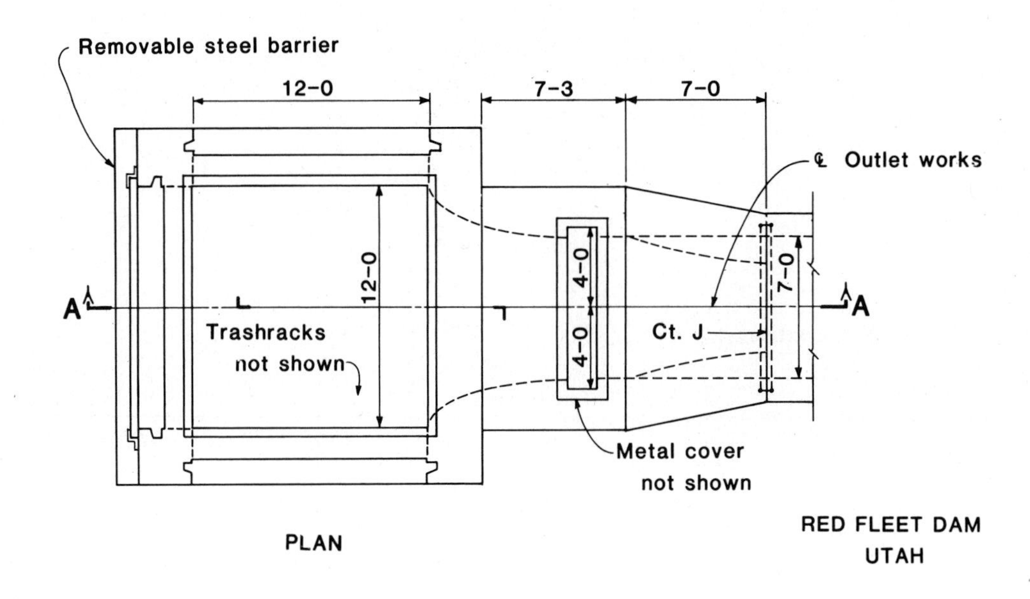

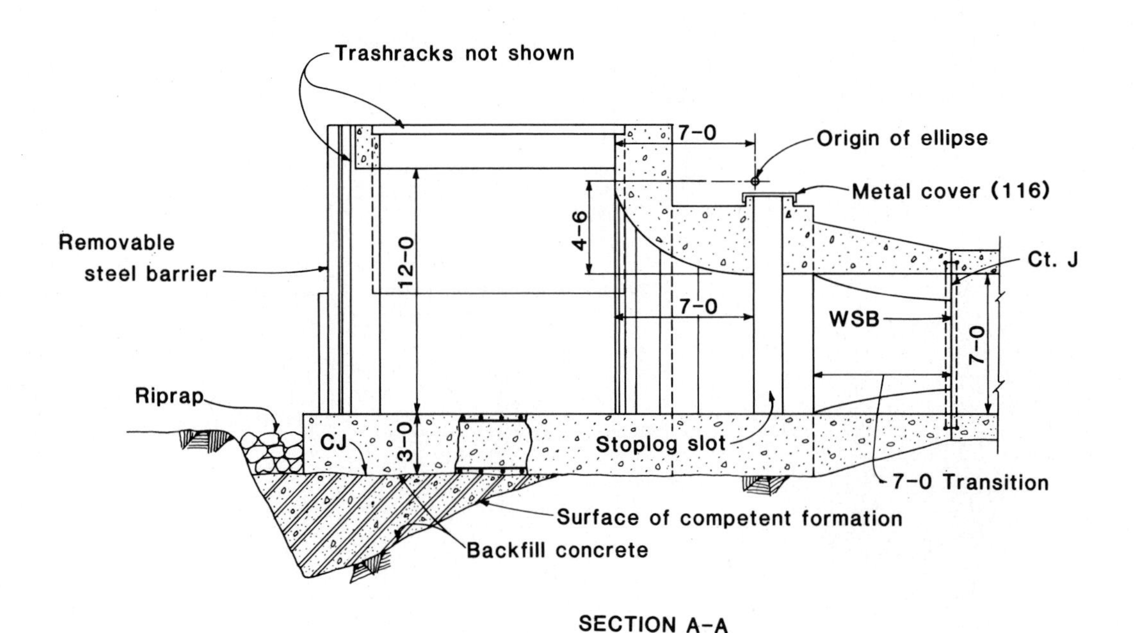

Figure 10-28.—Typical trashracked box intake. 103-D-1844.

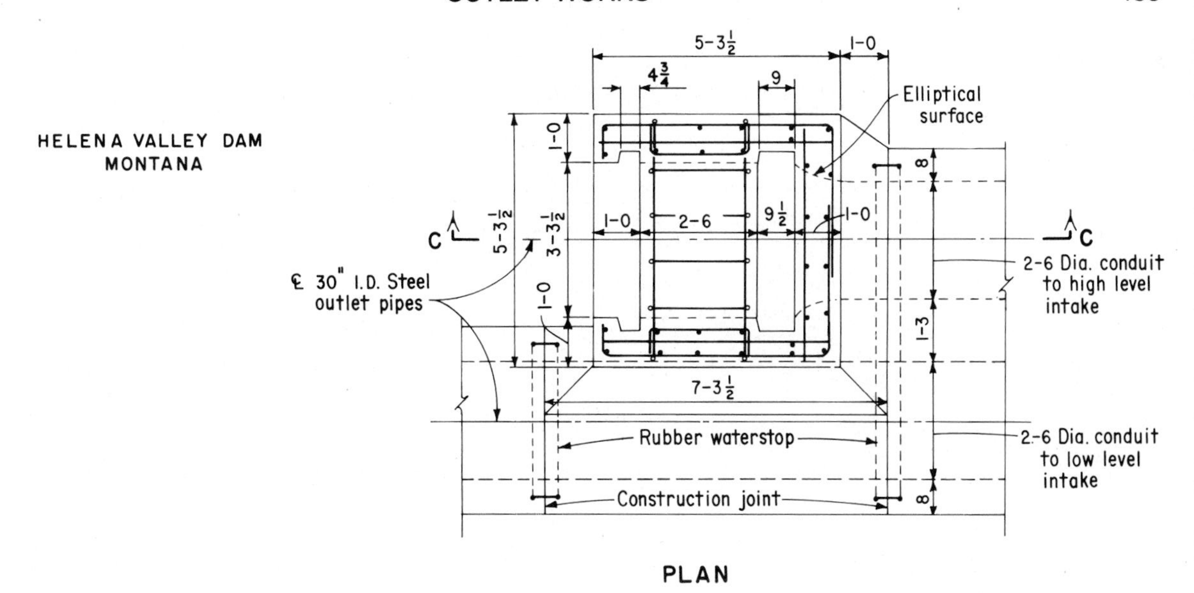

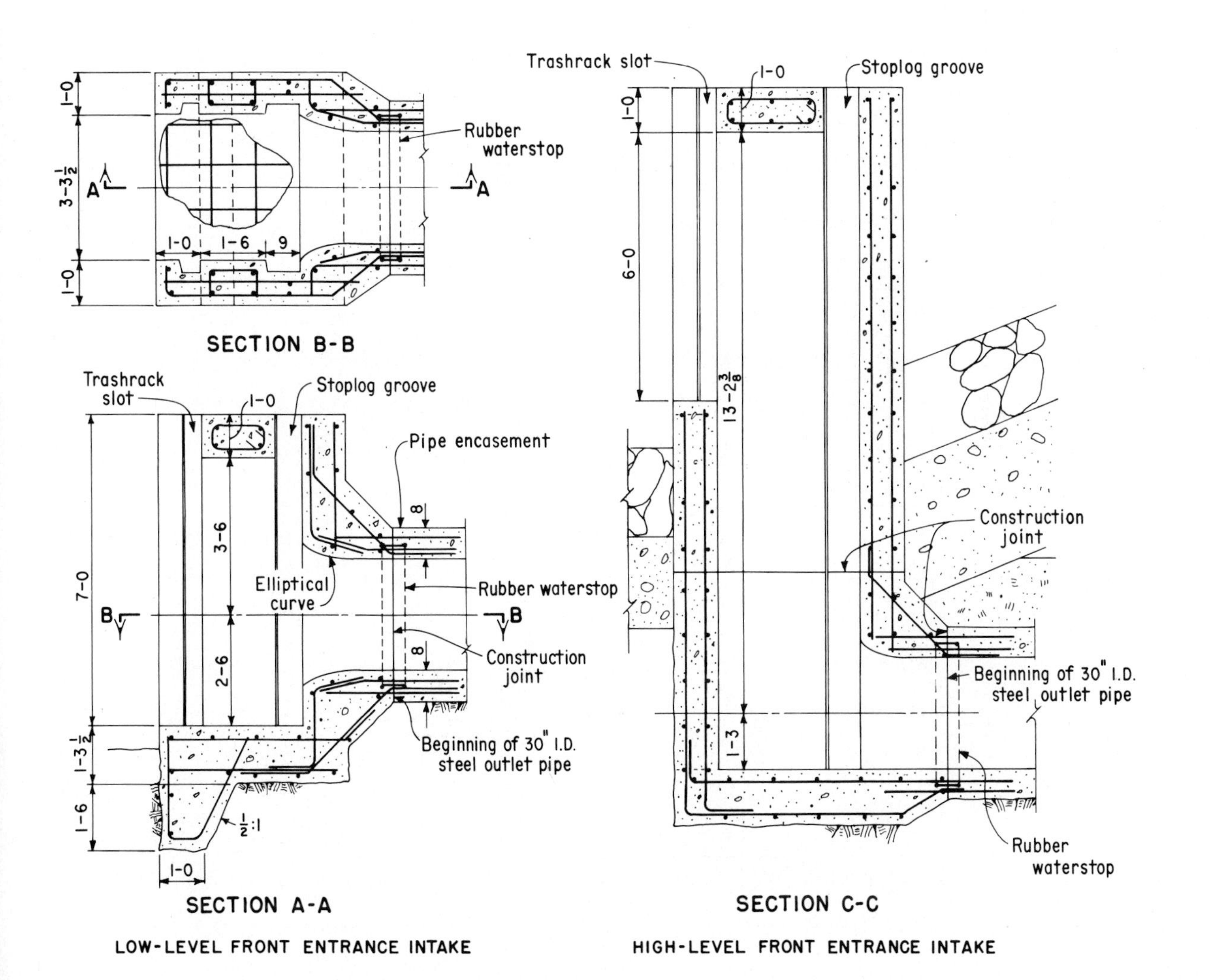

Figure 10-29.—Typical front-entrance intake structures. 288–D–2544.

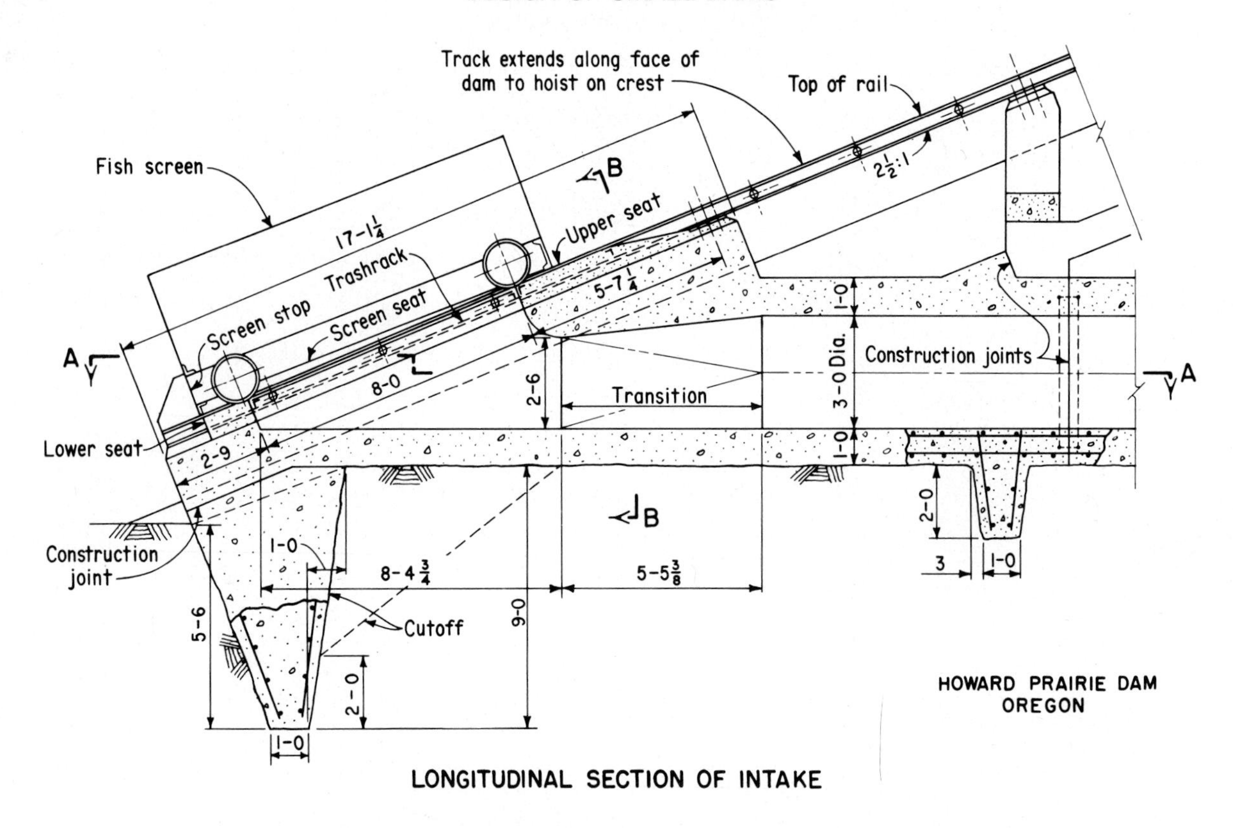

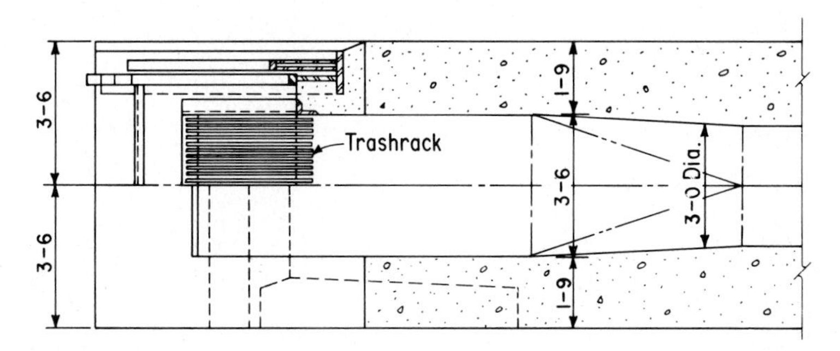

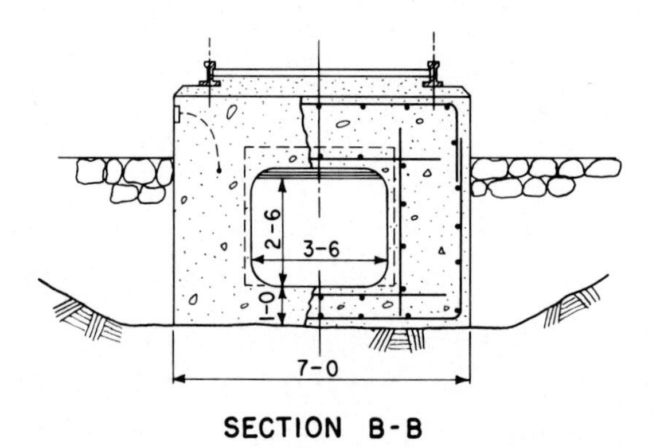

Figure 10-30.—Intake with sloping entrance. 288-D-2545.

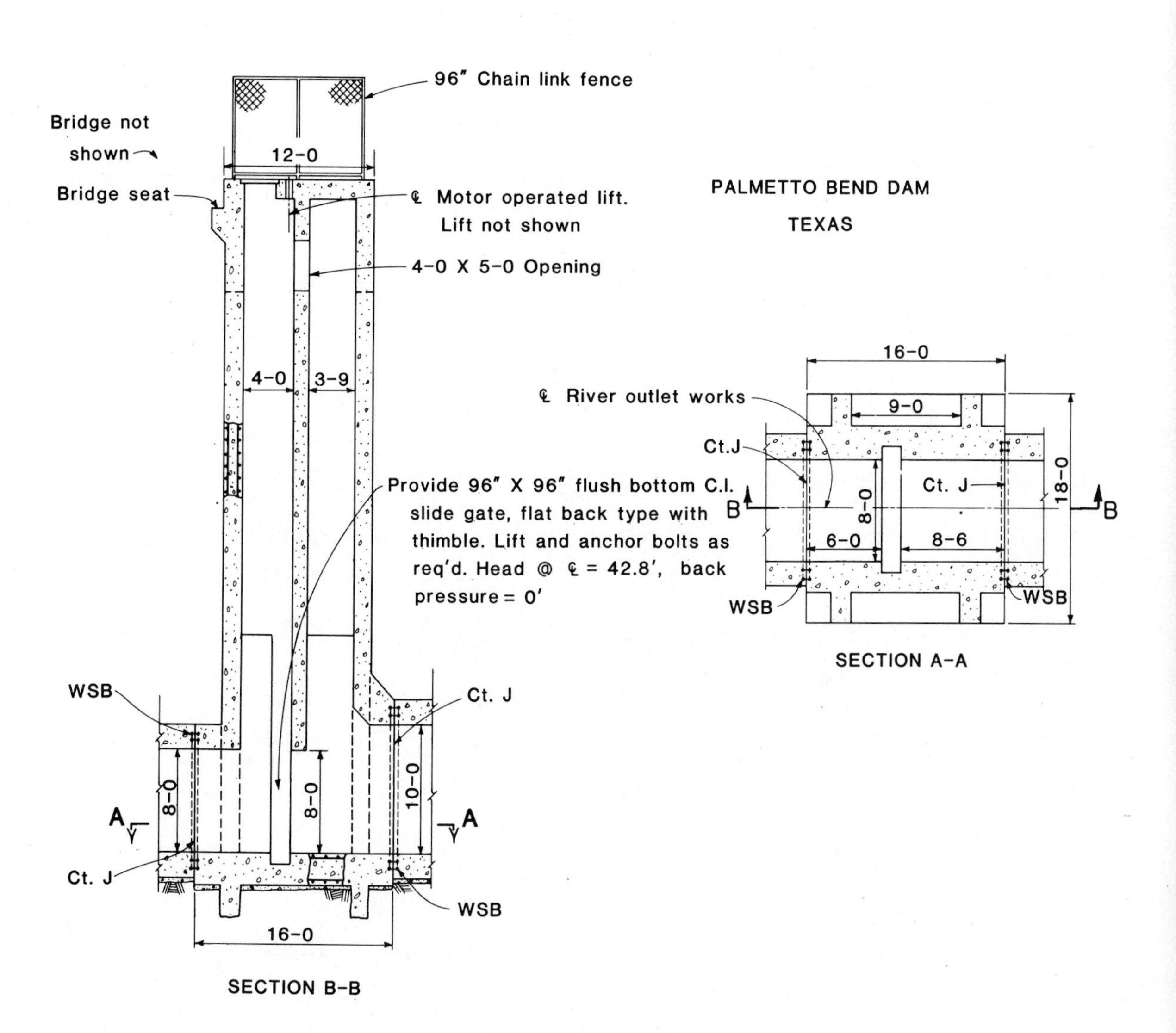

Figure 10-31.—Typical shaft for slide gate control. 103–D–1845.

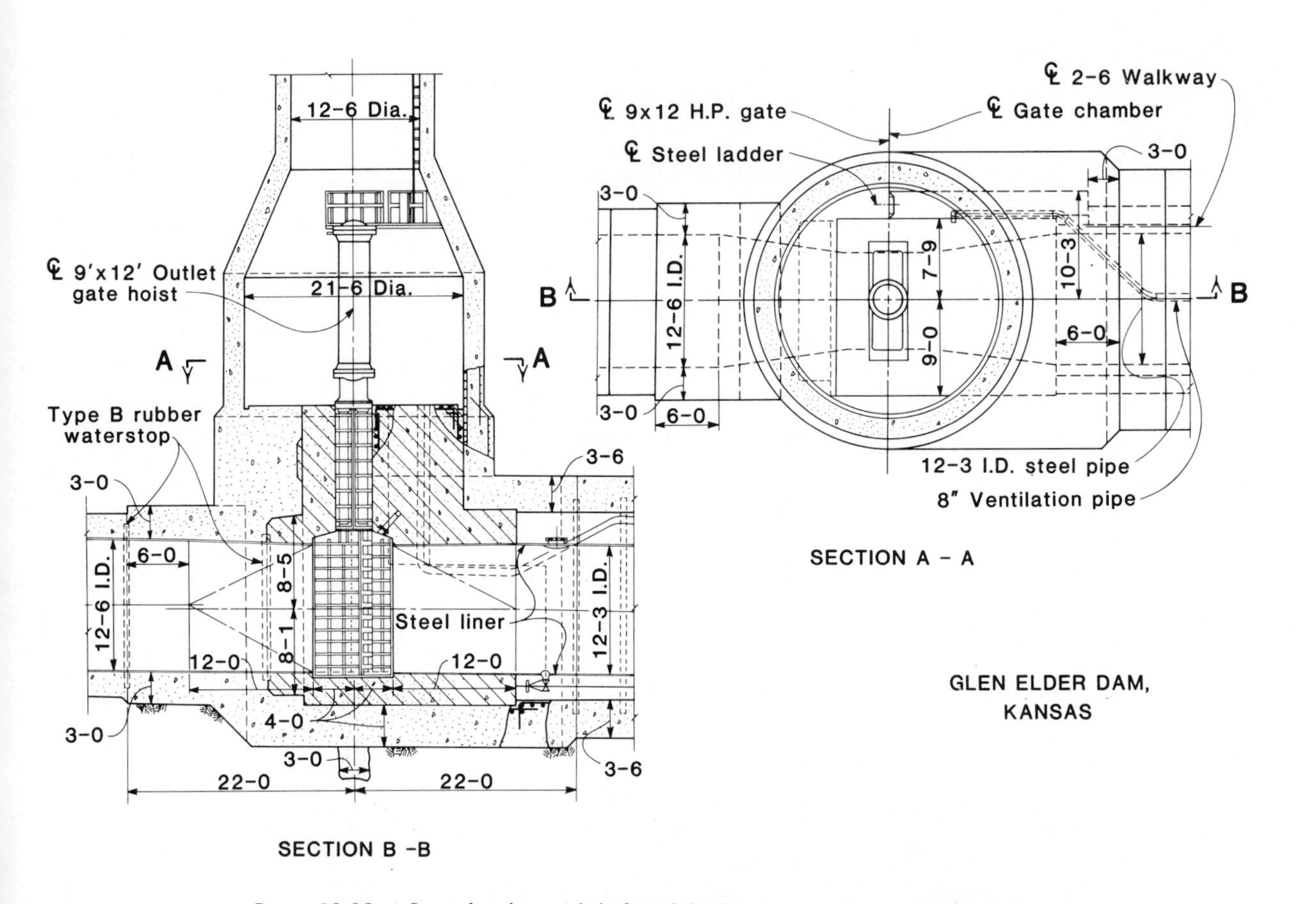

Figure 10-32.—Gate chamber and shaft with high-pressure gates. 103–D–1846.

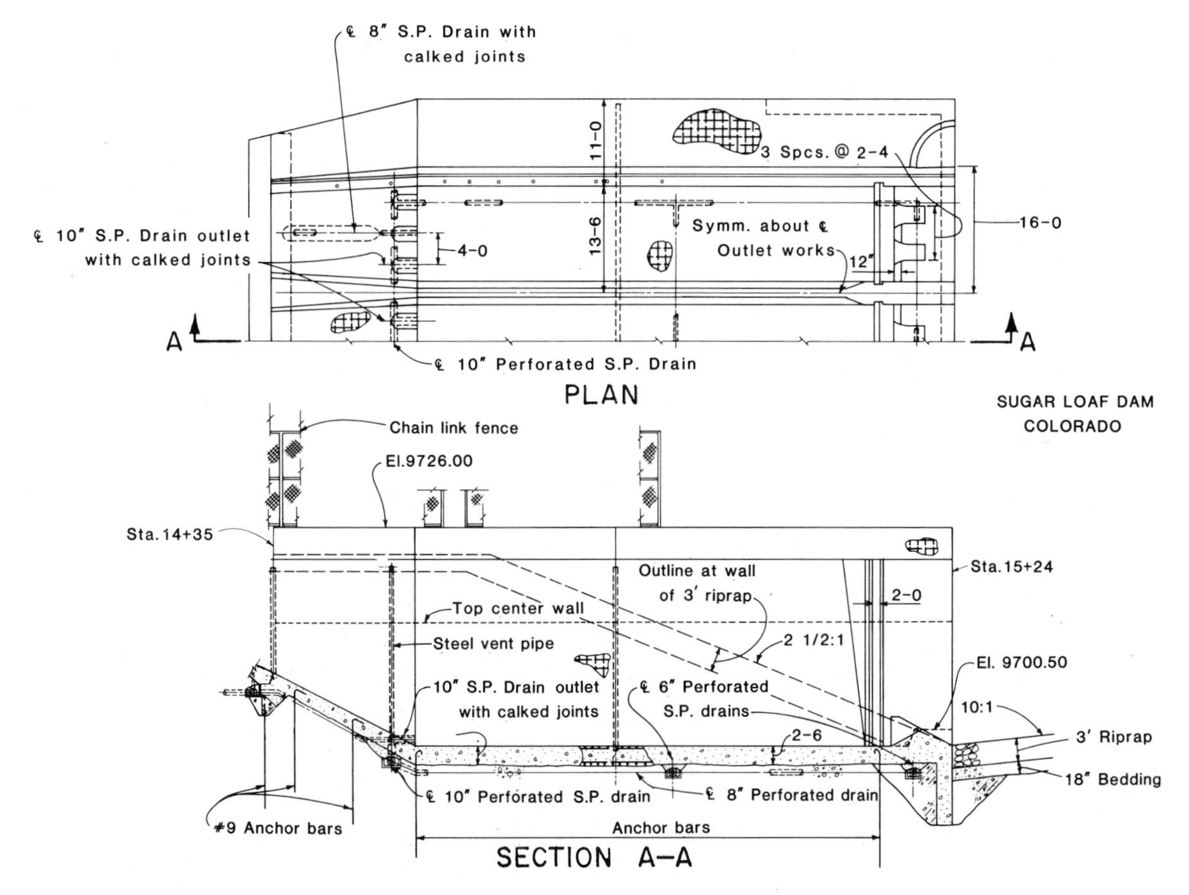

Figure 10-33.—Typical hydraulic-jump stilling basin. 103-D-1847.

E. BIBLIOGRAPHY

10.23. *Bibliography.*

[1] King, W. H., *Handbook of Hydraulics*, 6th ed., McGraw-Hill, New York, NY, 1976.

[2] Creager, W. P., and J. D. Justin, *Hydroelectric Handbook*, 2d ed., John Wiley and Sons, Inc., New York, NY, 1963.

[3] "Friction Factors for Large Conduits Flowing Full," Bureau of Reclamation, Engineering Monograph No. 7, 1977.

[4] Rouse, Hunter, *Engineering Hydraulics*, John Wiley and Sons, Inc., New York, NY, 1950.

[5] Beichley, G. L., "Hydraulic Design of Stilling Basin for Pipe or Channel Outlets," Bureau of Reclamation Research Report No. 24, 1976.

[6] Burgi, P. H., "Hydraulic Tests and Development of Multi-Jet Sleeve Valves," Bureau of Reclamation, Hydraulic Laboratory Report No. REC-ERC-77-14, 1977.

[7] Burgi, P. H., "Hydraulic Model Studies of Vertical Stilling Wells," Hydraulic Laboratory Report No. REC-ERC-73-3, 1973.

[8] Procter, R. V., and T. L. White, *Rock Tunneling with Steel Supports*, rev., Commercial Shearing & Stamping Co., Youngstown, OH, 1977.

[9] *Concrete Pipe Handbook*, rev., American Concrete Pipe Association, 228 North LaSalle Street, Chicago, IL, 1981.

[10] *Handbook of Drainage and Construction Products*, Armco Drainage & Metal Products, Inc., Middletown, OH, 1958.

[11] *Concrete Culverts and Conduits*, Portland Cement Association, 33 West Grand Avenue, Chicago, IL, 1975.

[12] Phillips, H. B., "Beggs Deformeter Stress Analysis of Single-Barrel Conduits," Bureau of Reclamation, Engineering Monograph No. 14, 1968.

Building Code Requirements for Reinforced Concrete, ACI 318-83 and 318M-83, American Concrete Institute, Detroit, MI.

"Supplement for ACI 318-63 Code," Bureau of Reclamation, Denver, CO, 1968.

Ultimate-Strength Design Handbook, Special Publication No. 17, American Concrete Institute, Detroit, MI.

Chapter 11

Diversion During Construction

A. DIVERSION REQUIREMENTS

11.1. *General.*—The design for a dam that is to be constructed across a stream channel must consider diversion of the streamflow around or through the damsite during the construction period. The extent of the diversion problem varies with the size and flood potential of the stream; at some damsites diversion may be costly and time-consuming and may affect the scheduling of construction activities; whereas, at other sites it may not present any great difficulties. Nevertheless, a diversion problem exists to some extent at all sites except those located offstream, and the selection of the most appropriate scheme for diversion during construction is important to the economy of the dam.

The diversion scheme selected ordinarily represents a compromise between the cost of the diversion facilities and the amount of risk involved. The proper diversion scheme will minimize the potential for serious flood damage to the work in progress at a minimum of expense. The following factors should be considered in a study to determine the best diversion scheme:

(1) Streamflow characteristics
(2) Size and frequency of diversion flood
(3) Methods of diversion
(4) Specifications requirements

These factors are discussed in the following sections.

11.2. *Streamflow Characteristics.*—Streamflow records provide the most reliable information regarding streamflow characteristics and should be consulted whenever available.

Depending upon the size of the drainage area and its geographical location, floods on a stream may be the result of snowmelt, rain falling on snow, seasonal rains, or cloudbursts. Because each of these types of runoff have their peak flows and their periods of low flow at different times of the year, the nature of the runoff influences the selection of the diversion scheme. A site subject only to snowmelt floods need not be provided with elaborate measures for use later in the construction season. A site where seasonal rains or rain falling on snow may occur requires only minimal diversion provisions for the rest of the year. A stream subject to a cloudburst that may occur at any time is the most unpredictable and probably requires the most elaborate diversion scheme because the construction contractor must be prepared to handle both low flows and floodflows at all times during the construction period.

11.3. *Selection of Diversion Flood.*—Usually, it is not economically feasible to plan on diverting the largest flood that has ever occurred or may be expected to occur at the site. Consequently, some lesser requirement must be decided upon. This brings up the question of how much risk is involved in the diversion scheme under consideration. In the case of an embankment dam, where considerable areas of foundation and structural excavation are exposed or where overtopping of the embankment under construction may result in serious damage or loss of partially completed work, the importance of eliminating the risk of flooding is relatively great. This consideration is not as important, however, in the case of a concrete dam because the floodwaters can, if the locations of appurtenant structures permit, overtop the dam with little or no adverse effect.

In selecting the flood to be used in the diversion designs, consideration should be given to the following:

(1) The safety of workmen and downstream inhabitants in case the failure of diversion works results in unnatural flooding
(2) The length of time the work will be under construction, to determine the number of flood seasons that will be encountered
(3) The cost of possible damage to work completed or still under construction if it is flooded
(4) The cost of delay to the completion of the

work, including the cost of forcing the contractor's equipment to remain idle while the flood damage is being repaired

After an analysis of these factors is made, the cost of increasing the protective works to handle progressively larger floods should be compared with the cost of damages resulting if such floods occurred without the increased protective work. Judgment should then be used in determerming the amount of risk that is warranted.

The 5-, 10-, or 25-year frequency flood is generally selected based on the previous analysis or on past experience for sizing the diversion works. The methods for determining floods of a specific frequency are discussed in section 3.12.

It should be considered that floods may be recurrent; therefore, if the diversion scheme involves temporary storage of cloudburst-type runoff, facilities must be provided to evacuate such storage within a reasonable period, usually a few days.

B. METHODS OF DIVERSION

11.4. *General.*—The method, or scheme, of diverting floods during construction depends on the magnitude of the flood to be diverted; the physical characteristics of the site; the type of dam to be constructed; the nature of the appurtenant works, such as the spillway, penstocks, or outlet works; and the probable sequence of construction operations. The objective is to select the optimum scheme considering practicability, cost, and the risks involved. The diversion works should be capable of being incorporated into the overall construction program with minimal impact and delay.

The common practice for diverting streams during construction involves one or more of the following provisions: tunnels driven through the abutments, conduits through or under the dam, temporary channels through the dam, or multiple-stage diversion over the tops of alternate construction blocks of a concrete dam. Outlet works conduits or tunnels are frequently constructed large enough to carry the diversion flow. On a small stream the flow may be bypassed by the installation of a temporary flume or pipeline, or the flow may be impounded behind the dam during its construction—pumps are used, if necessary, to control the water surface. Figures 11-1 and 11-2 show flumes used to divert the streamflow during the construction of an earthfill dam and a concrete dam, respectively. In any case, barriers are constructed across or along the stream channel so that the site,

Figure 11-2.—Temporary diversion flume used during construction of a concrete dam. Horsetooth Feeder Canal Tunnel No. 1. CBT 245–704–330.

or portions thereof, may be unwatered and construction can proceed without interruption.

A common problem is the meeting of downstream requirements when the entire flow of the stream is stopped during closure of the diversion works. Downstream requirements may demand that a small flow be maintained at all times. In such a case the contractor must provide the required flow until water can be released through the outlet works. An intake to a bypass pipe for this purpose is shown on the right side of figure 11-3.

Figure 11-4 shows how diversion of the river was accomplished during the construction of Folsom Dam and Powerplant on the American River in California. This photograph illustrates many of the diversion principles discussed in this chapter. The river, flowing from top to bottom in the photograph, is being diverted through a tunnel; "a" and "b" mark the inlet and outlet portals, respectively. Construction is proceeding in the original river channel between earthfill cofferdams "c" and "d." Discharge from pipe "e" at the lower left in the photograph is from unwatering of the foundation. Since it was impracticable to provide sufficient diversion tunnel capacity to handle the large anticipated spring floods, the contractor made provisions to minimize damage that would result from overtopping of the cofferdam. These provisions included the following:

(1) Placing concrete in alternate low blocks in the dam "f" to permit overflowing with a minimum of damage;

(2) Construction of an auxiliary rockfill and cellular-steel sheetpiling cofferdam "g" to protect the powerplant excavation "h" from being flooded by overtopping of the cofferdam; and

(3) Early construction of the permanent training wall "i" to take advantage of the protection it affords.

11.5. *Tunnels.*—It is usually not feasible to do a significant amount of foundation work in a narrow canyon until the stream is diverted. In this situation

Figure 11-3.—Diversion through an auxiliary stream-level conduit. Intake structure (under construction) is at upper right. Ridgway Dam. P894–427–5891 NA.

a tunnel may prove the most feasible means for diversion, either for a concrete dam or for an embankment dam. The streamflow is bypassed around the construction area through tunnels in one or both abutments. If tunnel spillways or tunnel outlet works are designed, it usually proves economical to use them in the diversion plan. If the upstream portion of the permanent tunnel is above the streambed elevation, a temporary upstream diversion adit can be provided to effect a stream-level bypass. Figure 11-5 shows such an adit, which was constructed at Seminoe Dam to permit diversion through the spillway tunnel. The diversion adit leads from the streambed to the intersection of the horizontal portion of the spillway tunnel with the inclined shaft leading from the spillway gate structure. The first stages of construction of the spillway gate structure can be seen in the upper right portion of the photograph.

When there is a river outlet works tunnel, particularly for embankment dams, it is generally used for diversion. Normally the diversion works tunnel is placed at an elevation near river level. When a tower or drop inlet intake is used, a temporary adit upstream of the base of the intake structure is necessary. After diversion, this adit is closed off by a gate or a bulkhead, and a concrete plug (see fig. 11-6) is placed in the intake structure for permanent closure. In addition, gates and second-stage concrete are added in the gate chamber and control structure, where applicable, to complete the outlet works for permanent operation.

Temporary diversion tunnels that are not part of a spillway or outlet works can be lined or unlined. The advisability of lining the diversion tunnel is influenced by (1) the cost of a lined tunnel compared with that of a larger unlined tunnel of equal carrying capacity; (2) the nature of the rock in the tunnel, specifically, whether it can stand unsupported and unprotected during the passage of the

Figure 11-4.—Diversion of the American River during construction of Folsom Dam and Powerplant. (Corps of Engineers and Bureau of Reclamation). AR–1627–CV.

diversion flows; and (3) the permeability of the material through which the tunnel is carried, because it affects the amount of leakage through or around the abutment.

Some means of shutting off the diversion flows must be provided. This can be accomplished through the use of closure devices such as bulkheads, slide gates, or stoplogs.

Permanent closure of the diversion tunnel is made by placing a concrete plug in the tunnel. Keyways may be excavated into the rock to ensure adequate shear resistance between the plug and the rock or lining. After the plug has been placed and sufficient time has elapsed for concrete shrinkage, grout is forced in through previously installed grout connections to the contact between the plug and the surrounding rock to ensure a watertight joint.

11.6. ***Conduits.***—The outlet works for an embankment dam often entails the construction of a conduit that may be used for diversion during construction of the dam. This method for handling the diversion flows is an economical one, especially if the conduit for the outlet works is large enough to carry the diversion flows. Where diversion flow requirements exceed the capacity of the completed outlet works, that capacity can be increased by delaying the installation of gates, valves, pipe, and trashracks (although trashracks should be installed if a problem with floating debris is anticipated) until the need for diversion is over. Considerations for this approach are similar to those outlined in section 11.5 "Tunnels." Increased capacity also can be obtained by increasing the height of the cofferdam, thereby increasing the head. In some instances the storage capacity of the reservoir at lower elevations may be such that much of the diversion design flood can be temporarily retained and then evacuated through a diversion conduit of smaller capacity than required to discharge the peak of the flood.

In cases where the intake to the outlet works conduit is above the level of the streambed, an auxiliary stream-level conduit may be provided to join the lower portion of the permanent conduit. Such an auxiliary conduit is shown on the lower middle

Figure 11-5.—Diversion adit and upstream cofferdam at Seminoe Dam.

of figure 11-3. The upstream side of a slide gate for closure of the diversion conduit for Ridgway Dam outlet works is shown on figure 11-7. Permanent closure of this auxiliary conduit after diversion is completed can be accomplished in the manner outlined in section 11.5. A concrete plug in an auxiliary diversion conduit is shown on figure 10-27.

Diversion conduits at stream level are sometimes installed through a concrete dam. These openings are provided with keyways, metal seals, and grouting systems. They must be permanently closed throughout their entire length, in the manner prescribed for placing tunnel plugs, if they are not used as permanent outlet works.

11.7. *Temporary Diversion Channels—Earthfill Dams.*—At sites where it may not be economical to provide a tunnel or conduit large enough to pass the diversion design flood, a temporary channel involving a gap through the embankment dam may be used to divert streamflows while the remainder of the embankment is being constructed (see fig. 11-8). This method is adaptable to wide sites; obviously it cannot be used in narrow canyons. However, in the wider valleys the diversion flows are likely to be too large to be economically carried in tunnels or conduits.

Before the stream is diverted, the foundation preparation required for the dam should be completed in the area where the temporary opening will be left through the embankment. This preparation should include excavation and refilling of a cutoff trench, if one is to be constructed. The stream is then channeled through this area, after which the foundation work in the remainder of the streambed is completed. The portion of the embankment to either side of the diversion opening may then be completed. The side slopes of the opening should not be steeper than 4:1 to facilitate filling of the gap at the end of the construction period and to decrease the danger of cracking of the embankment caused by differential settlement. The flat slope also provides a good bonding surface between the previously constructed embankment and the material to be placed.

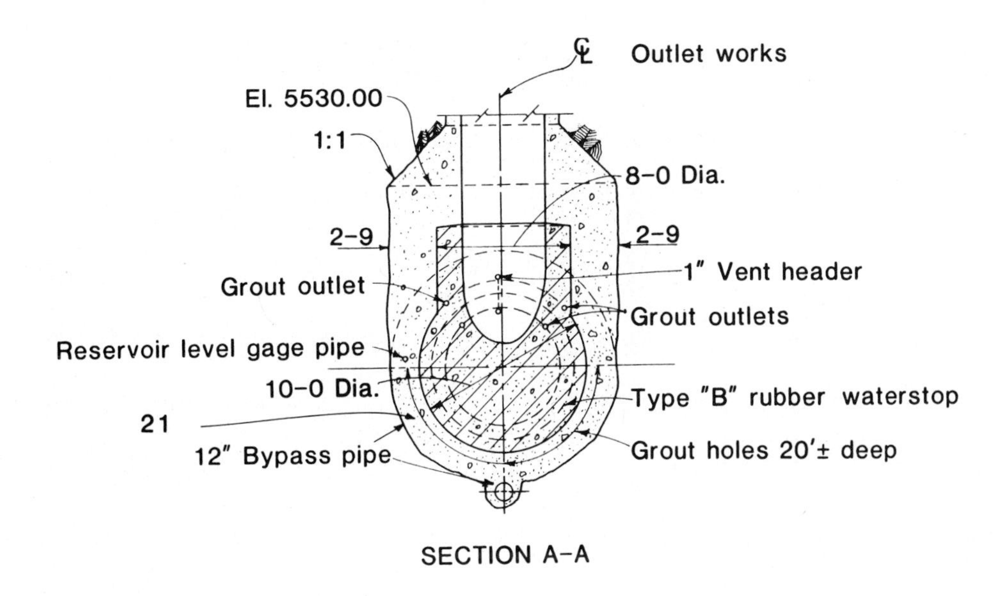

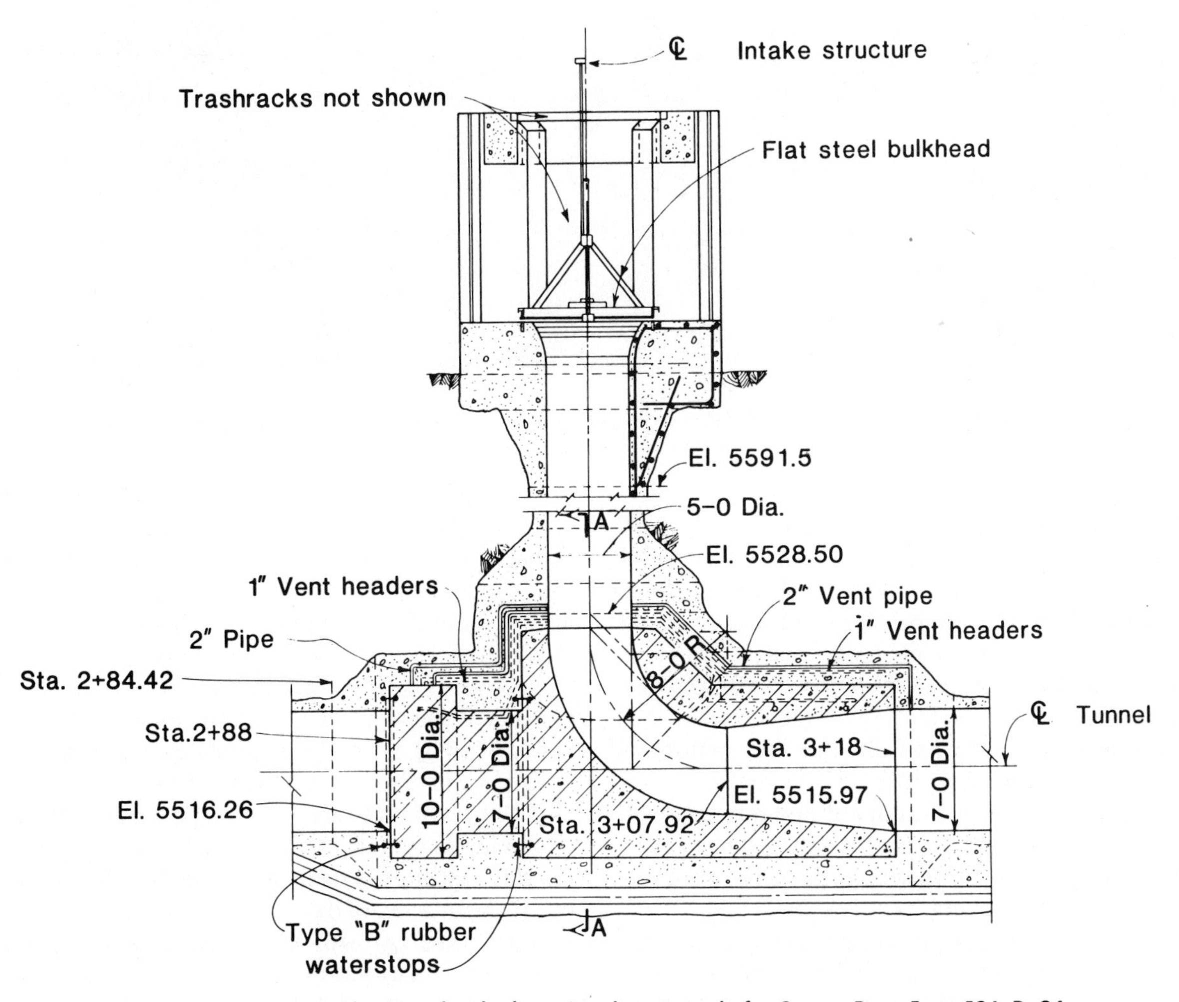

Figure 11-6.—Concrete plug (crosshatched area) in diversion adit for Causey Dam. From 526–D–24.

Figure 11-7.—Upstream side of slide gate for closure of river outlet works. View is looking downstream from inside of auxiliary conduit. Note inlet to bypass at left of photograph. Ridgway Dam, Dallas Creek Project, Colorado. C894–427–980 NA

The bottom grade of the temporary channel through the embankment should be the same as the original streambed so that erosion in the channel will be minimized. The width of opening depends on the magnitude of the diversion design flood and on the capability of the equipment for filling the gap in the time available.

The diversion is carried through the opening in the dam until sufficient progress is made on the construction of the embankment and appurtenant works that floods can be carried safely through the completed spillway or outlet works. Closure of the gap in the embankment can then be made. To reduce the risk of the rising water surface in the reservoir overtopping the embankment being placed in the closure section, this construction should be scheduled when large floods are least likely to occur. Construction equipment should be mobilized so that the gap can be filled as quickly as possible to an elevation that will permit discharge of a flood, should one occur, through the spillway and/or the outlet works. The average rate of embankment placement must be such that the gap can be filled faster than the water rises in the reservoir. The capability of the contractor to meet this requirement may be gauged by considering the average rate of embankment placing he must attain to complete the dam within the contract period, taking into account the number of days during the contract period that the weather will likely be suitable for embankment construction.

Care must be exercised during the filling of the

Figure 11-8.—Temporary diversion channel through an earthfill dam. Bonny Dam. 414–289C.

gap, so that the quality of work is not sacrificed because of the urgency of the situation. This is of great importance because the diversion gap is frequently in the highest part of the dam. Extreme care must be used to obtain required densities and thus avoid excessive settlement of the completed embankment. Special attention must also be given to bonding of the newly placed material with the previously placed earthfill.

11.8. *Multiple-Stage Diversion for Concrete Dams.*—The multiple-stage method of diversion over the tops of alternate low construction blocks or through diversion conduits in a concrete dam requires shifting of the cofferdam from one side of the river to the other during construction. During the first stage, the flow is restricted to one portion of the stream channel while the dam is constructed to a safe elevation in the remainder of the channel. In the second stage, the cofferdam (see sec. 11.9) is shifted and the stream is carried over low blocks or through diversion conduits in the constructed section of the dam while work proceeds on the unconstructed portion. The dam is then carried to its ultimate height, with diversion finally being made through the spillway, penstock, or permanent outlets. Figure 11-9 shows diversion through a conduit in a concrete dam, with excess flow over the low blocks.

11.9. *Cofferdams.*—A cofferdam is a temporary dam or barrier used to divert a stream or to enclose an area during construction. The design of an adequate cofferdam involves the problem of construction economics. When the construction is timed so that the foundation work can be executed during the low-water season, the use of cofferdams can be held to a minimum. However, where the streamflow characteristics are such that this is not practical, the cofferdam must be so designed that it is not only safe, but also of the optimum height. The height to which a cofferdam should be constructed may involve an economic study of cofferdam height versus diversion works capacity. This may include routing studies of the diversion design flood, especially when the outlet works require-

Figure 11-9.—Flows through diversion opening and over low blocks of a concrete dam. Olympus Dam.

ments are small. If outlet works requirements dictate a relatively large outlet conduit or tunnel, diversion flows ordinarily may be accommodated without a high cofferdam. It should be remembered that the floodwater accumulated behind the cofferdam must be evacuated in time to accommodate another storm. The maximum height to which it is feasible to construct the cofferdam without encroaching upon the area to be occupied by the dam must also be considered. Furthermore, the design of the cofferdam must take into consideration the effect that excavation and unwatering of the foundation of the dam will have on its stability, and it must anticipate removal, salvage, and other factors.

Generally, cofferdams are constructed of materials available at the site. The two types normally used in the construction of dams are earthfill cofferdams and rockfill cofferdams, whose design considerations closely follow those for permanent dams of the same type. Figure 11-5 shows the construction of an earth and rockfill cofferdam. Another cofferdam is shown on the middle of figure 11-10. Notice the water starting to accumulate upstream of the cofferdam and the temporary spillway consisting of six conduits on the right side of the figure. Other less common cofferdam types are concrete cribs filled with earth or rock, and cellular-steel cofferdams filled with earth or rock. Figure 11-11 shows a combination of several types. In this case, the major portion of the cofferdam consists of an earth and rock embankment, and steel sheet piling was used to effect final closure in swift water. Figure 11-4 shows the use of both earthfill cofferdams and cofferdams formed by steel-piling cells. Cellular-steel cofferdams and steel sheet piling are adaptable to confined areas where currents are swift.

If the cofferdam can be designed so that it is permanent and adds to the structural stability of the dam, it will have a decided economic advantage. In some embankment dams the cofferdam can even be incorporated into the main embankment. In such instances, the saving is twofold—the amount saved by reducing the embankment material required and the amount saved by not having to remove the cofferdam when it is no longer needed.

Figure 11-10.—Cofferdam at Ridgway Dam, Colorado. Note accumulation of water behind cofferdam and the temporary spillway that consists of six conduits on right side. P894–427–5989 NA.

C. SPECIFICATIONS REQUIREMENTS

11.10. ***Contractor's Responsibilities.***—It is general practice to require the contractor to assume responsibility for the diversion of the stream during the construction of the dam and appurtenant structures. The requirement should be defined by appropriate paragraphs in the specifications that describe the contractor's responsibilities and define the provisions incorporated in the design to facilitate construction. Usually, the specifications should not prescribe the capacity of the diversion works, nor the details of the diversion method to be used, but hydrographs prepared from available streamflow records should be included. In addition, the specifications usually require that the contractor's diversion plan be subject to the owner's approval.

In some cases, such as in constructing a concrete gravity dam in a wide canyon, the entire diversion scheme might be left in the contractor's hands, with the expectation that the resulting flexibility afforded the contractor would be reflected in low bids. Because various contractors usually present different schemes, in such instances the diversion of the river should be a lump-sum item in the bid schedule.

Figure 11-11.—Upstream cofferdam of steel sheet piling and earthfill diverting streamflow into tunnel. Green Mountain Dam. GM–283–CBT.

Sometimes it is appropriate to stipulate the contractor's construction procedures in the specifications. For example, for an embankment dam where diversion by a temporary channel is feasible or contemplated, the specifications may permit the contractor to divert the stream over the embankment placed in the completed cutoff trench, but usually would prohibit him from making final closure of the diversion works until the dam has been constructed to an elevation well above the spillway crest. In addition, the contractor may be required to have the concrete in the spillway and outlet works essentially completed before closure of the temporary channel.

These, or similar restrictions, tend to guide the contractor toward a safe diversion plan. However, to further define the contractor's responsibility, other statements should be made to the effect that the contractor shall be responsible for and shall repair (at the contractor's expense) any damage to the foundation, structures, or any other part of the work caused by flood, water, or failure of any part of the diversion or protective works.

Sample specifications regarding diversion during construction are included in appendix G.

11.11. *Designer's Responsibilities.*—For difficult diversion situations, it may prove economical for the owner to assume the responsibility for the diversion plan. One reason for this is that contractors tend to increase bid prices for diversion of the stream if the specifications contain many restrictions and there is a large amount of risk involved. Where a dam is to be constructed in a narrow gorge, a definite scheme of cofferdams and tunnels might be specified, because the loss of life and property damage might be heavy if a cofferdam were to fail.

Another point to consider is that the orderly sequence of constructing various stages of the entire project often depends on the use of a particular diversion scheme. However, if the responsibility for diversion rests with the contractor, a different diversion scheme may be used, with possible delay to the completion of the project. This could result in a delay in the delivery of water and a subsequent loss in revenue.

If the owner assumes responsibility for the diversion scheme, it is important that the diversion scheme be realistic in all respects and that it be compatible with the contractor's capabilities.

D. BIBLIOGRAPHY

11.12. *Bibliography*

[1]Stafford, J. P., "Diversion Works for Construction," ASCE National Meeting on Water Resources Engineering, New Orleans, LA, February 1969.

Chapter 12

Operation and Maintenance

A. GENERAL

12.1. ***Operation and Maintenance Program.***—
The people responsible for dam operation and maintenance should become involved with the dam during the design and construction stages. This will give O&M (operation and maintenance) personnel an opportunity to become familiar with design and construction considerations and to become aware of problems that may require special attention during the operation and maintenance of the dam. An inspection should be made at construction completion by design, construction, and operations personnel to ensure that all items are complete or deficiencies are identified for later completion. During this inspection, problems, unique operations, general maintenance requirements, etc. should be discussed and procedures established for their proper handling. Requirements for initial filling should be available and should be agreed upon. During this time extra precautions and procedures for operation should be established because unpredictable situations may occur. During the first filling the facility should be attended continuously.

Routine maintenance and inspection of dams and appurtenant facilities should be an ongoing process. All unusual conditions that may adversely affect the operation, maintenance, or safety of the dam should be reported promptly using predetermined written procedures (see sec. 12.10).

In addition to ongoing routine maintenance and inspection, periodic in-depth inspections should be made on every dam at least every 5 years. The depth and frequency of these inspections should depend on dam size, hazard, complexity, and the previous problems encountered. A qualified team, usually headed by an engineer not directly involved in the operation and maintenance of the facility, should perform these inspections. The engineer should be accompanied by operations personnel familiar with all facets of the operation and maintenance of the dam. Inspections should be scheduled, if possible, during alternate periods of high and low water to observe conditions unique to these situations. Special inspections should be scheduled when there is reason to believe that significant damage has occurred or has potential to develop. Deficiencies noted during the inspection should be identified and documented in the report, and procedures should be established for correction in a timely manner. The responsibility for correcting problems should be clearly documented. Funding schedules should be considered to ensure adequate and timely funding to accomplish the work.

Underwater inspections of facilities not normally observable, such as stilling basins, upstream face, etc., should be scheduled periodically to ensure continued performance. An underwater inspection every 6 years is recommended; however, the inspection frequency can be adjusted depending on the findings. Inspections should be scheduled during low water periods to the maximum extent possible. Underwater divers and photography may be used to good advantage in some cases; however, dewatering may be required to better evaluate the condition of facilities. A report of all such inspections should be prepared, describing the condition of facilities and citing identified deficiencies.

Written instructions should be available for use by O&M personnel to operate the dam. These instructions furnished by designers and manufacturers should include the procedures for routine servicing and the requirements for special operation and maintenance of equipment. The procedures, generally referred to as SOP's (Standing Operating Procedures) should also include emergency preparedness plans and inundation mapping, the extent and nature of inspections, hydrologic and reservoir operations, and other pertinent aspects of dam O&M. The operation and maintenance of the dam should be carried out according to these procedures. Significant deviations from these procedures by

O&M personnel should not be made without the approval of higher management or engineering personnel. A copy of these instructions should be accessible to the dam operator both during routine operation and during abnormal conditions at the dam. The Bureau of Reclamation has published a guide [1] that may be used for preparing written SOP's for the operation and maintenance of dams.

A log should be kept for each dam to record all significant actions or information, such as releases, seepage, maintenance, emergencies, etc. This book should be kept at the dam or other accessible convenient place for ready reference and use. It should become a part of the permanent records for the dam.

Dam O&M personnel should be trained before their independent operation of a dam. The degree and complexity of training should depend on the conditions and hazards at and below the dam. (See [2] and sec. 12.11 for more specific details.)

B. INSPECTION AND MAINTENANCE OF DAMS

12.2. *General Information.*—The inspection and maintenance of a dam should be performed in accordance with specific written instructions and procedures prepared for that particular dam. Nevertheless, all unusual or abnormal conditions that may adversely affect operation, maintenance, or safety should be reported promptly and according to the SOP's.

During rapid filling of a reservoir, the downstream slope, or face, of the dam and the foundation contacts should be carefully inspected at specified intervals for indications of abnormal condition. Special inspections should also be conducted after all unusual occurrences, such as earthquakes, sustained periods of high-velocity winds, or infrequent low reservoir conditions that expose features normally submerged. Low reservoir levels afford the opportunity to carefully inspect the reservoir floor for sink holes, seepage holes, unusual beaching conditions, or cracking.

During periods of sustained high reservoir level, particular attention should be given to inspecting the visible portions of the upstream face of the dam, crest, downstream face, abutments, and areas downstream from the dam for evidence of abnormal development. The frequency of inspections may be decreased after several seasons of operation if no abnormal conditions have been observed.

Appendix H contains a checklist that is useful during inspection of dams. This or a similar checklist should be used to ensure a complete inspection.

12.3. *Earthfill Embankments.*—Earth embankment dams should be inspected at regular intervals for evidence of the development of unfavorable conditions. The downstream slope should be carefully inspected for indications of cracks, slides, sloughs, subsidence, impairment of slope protection, springs, seeps, or boggy areas caused by seepage from the reservoir. The upstream slope of the embankment should be carefully inspected for adequate protection of the embankment. Extensive wave action, poor quality riprap, poor gradation, large debris, or riprap movement by visitors can contribute to conditions of inadequate protection of the embankment.

The maintenance of earthfill embankments consists of removing debris from the upstream face of the dam, replacing disintegrated riprap, repairing eroded material, proper grading of access roads, controlling undesirable vegetation and rodents, maintaining monitoring devices within the embankment and adjacent area, and controlling vandalism.

12.4. *Concrete Dams.*—Regular inspection is as important for a concrete dam as it is for an embankment dam. A periodic inspection as part of the ongoing O&M program is essential to disclose conditions that might cause disruption or failure of operation and to determine the adequacy of the dam to serve the purpose for which it was designed. A regular inspection program will document the extent of the problems and the rate of deterioration, which can be used as a basis for planning timely maintenance, repair, and rehabilitation.

Inspections of concrete dams should include close observations for detecting abnormal settlements, heaving, deflections, or lateral movement between structures. These observations should be made from inspections conducted along the exposed abutment contacts, upstream and downstream

[1]Numbers in brackets refer to entries in the bibliography (sec. 12.12).

faces of the dam, crest, parapets, galleries, construction and contraction joints, and the toe of the dam. Abnormal leakage through foundation drains, formed drains, and construction and contraction joints should be measured, and these records should be maintained to alert operation personnel of an unusual condition. The instrumentation installed in the dam should be inspected, and the maintenance required to keep it functional should be performed. Calcium carbonate deposits, which are common in drainage systems, must be removed on a regular basis to prevent excessive pressures between foundation material and the dam.

12.5. *Structures and Mechanical Equipment.*— Two principal features vital to the performance of most dams are the outlet works and spillways. In one form or another, most dams are provided with a means of releasing reservoir water downstream through an outlet works. The structure that functions as a control feature for passing floods or large releases from reservoirs is normally referred to as a spillway. All components of both of these features should be included in the inspection of each dam.

Regularly scheduled inspections of an outlet works should include observations of the external and internal metal and concrete surfaces for abnormal conditions. Deterioration of protective coatings on metal will reduce the effective life of pipe and equipment substantially. Small irregularities on the surfaces of flow passages will contribute to the phenomenon known as cavitation, which can lead to rapid deterioration of metal and concrete. Leakage of ground water into access shafts, tunnels, gate chambers, and control houses can be detrimental to equipment and metal work and can be a safety hazard to operating personnel. Cracking of concrete in tunnel linings, shafts, and gate chambers should be monitored, and any differential movement between adjoining structures should be noted.

Inspections of intake structures, trashracks, conduit upstream of emergency gates, emergency gate upstream faces, and stilling basin concrete surfaces below the tailwater surface are normally not feasible during the regularly scheduled inspections. Special inspections of those features should be performed by dewatering the structure or when operating conditions permit. Investigation of these features using experienced divers is an alternative. The frequency of such special inspections is normally based on experience derived for each specific structure. Stilling basins have been the feature requiring the most regular monitoring and major maintenance. These basins are holding ponds for rock and debris, which can cause extensive damage to their concrete surfaces. Rock and debris may enter the stilling during construction, they may be washed in, or they may be thrown in by vandals.

Spillway inlet and outlet channels should be maintained free of trees and debris that would impede flow. Restrictions in these channels affect the capacity of the spillway. Differential movement of the spillway walls, crest, chute, and stilling basin should be observed. Erosion of slopes within the spillway area should be controlled, and proper drainage should be ensured. Logbooms or boatbooms should be maintained upstream of the spillway inlet channel to prevent plugging of the spillway and to keep boats from entering the spillway. Stilling basins should be inspected in the same manner described above for outlet works.

Most outlet works and some spillway structures are dependent on the ability of mechanical equipment to perform. Regularly scheduled inspections of these structures should include inspections of all aspects of the mechanical equipment required to release flow from the reservoir. Gates, valves, pumps, controls, and auxiliary equipment should be operated and observed during the inspection, if possible. If gate operation is not possible during the inspection, the operation should be performed according to the written procedures for the dam and noted in the logbook. Mechanical equipment should be lubricated and serviced according to manufacturer's instructions.

Appendix H contains a checklist that includes typical components of outlet works and spillways. This or a similar checklist should be used to ensure a complete inspection.

C. OPERATION

12.6. *Storage Dams.*—Storage dams should be operated to provide as many benefits as feasible. They should be operated and releases made to provide optimum benefits considering contractual requirements and primary benefits. Dams discussed in this text may be used to store water to achieve benefits related to irrigation, power, municipal, industrial, recreation, fish, wildlife, flood control, and water quality. Obviously, not all dams will provide all of these benefits, but an evaluation should be made to determine the potential benefits from a dam and how management of the dam and reservoir can best achieve optimum benefits. The operational requirements should be based on these studies and on experience, and these requirements should be documented in the written instructions for dam operation.

Multiple use of reservoirs often results in conflicts among the potential beneficiaries. For example, optimum power production may result in reduced irrigation water supply and fewer recreation benefits. These conflicts should be evaluated keeping in mind the primary purposes of the facility. Quite often, multiple benefits can be achieved without significant loss to primary beneficiaries.

Obtaining accurate and timely hydrological data is critical to the proper and safe operation of a dam and reservoir. A reliable means of determining the potential water supply is essential to (1) safe operation, i.e., reservoir evacuation to pass floodflows, and (2) maximum storage for given conditions. To obtain accurate and useful data for determing the potential water supply, the entire hydrologic cycle should be considered on a basin-wide scale. Pertinent information required for efficient operation include quantity of precipitation, distribution over time, and relative uncertainty (forecast error). The technology is now available to telemeter hydrometeorological phenomena and to relay that information through ground or satellite links to computers to improve forecasting capabilities. Computer models are available to determine river flow forecasts from that data. Before installing a data-acquisition system, a study should be made to determine what other equipment is already installed in the area. A compatible telemetry scheme should be used where possible to enhance existing capabilities and to avoid redundancy.

Considerations in developing a hydrometeorological telemetry and forecasting scheme include:

- Defining issues and requirements for improved water management service and operations, and identifying how these improvements may be addressed through enhancements in measurement systems, data handling, and research
- Selecting the appropriate research in hydrologic and meterological areas to understand the key elements of the hydrologic cycle, and defining corresponding goals and approaches.
- Providing program guidance and concepts as input to complement the existing plans and programs
- Using the information gathered to govern operational processes.

Special precautions should be taken in the operation of a dam and reservoir during periods of potential high inflows. Management during these periods should be governed by forecasted inflows, potential runoff, reservoir elevation, and downstream condition. The dam should normally be attended continuously during these periods; however, discretion based on conditions should be practiced.

The written procedures for dam operations should not be arbitrarily changed without consideration of the effect of such a change. However, these procedures should not be inflexible when conditions suggest alternative operations.

The stimulation and protection of vegetation to retard erosion on the slopes of the reservoir and on the slopes of earthfill dams not otherwise protected is an important aspect that should be given frequent attention. This vegetative cover is essential to protect against erosion and sloughing of banks, which can result in costly maintenance and safety problems.

Expert advice on suppression of algal growth in reservoirs should be obtained and followed, and no chemicals should be introduced into a reservoir without competent advice.

Periodic inspections of the reservoir area should be made to detect slide areas and to monitor their progress. Corrective action should be taken in these areas at an early stage to minimize problems. Posting waring signs for slide areas should be considered if they pose a safety problem to boaters or recreationists or could lead to liability for the operator or owner.

Safety buoys should be constructed upstream of overflow spillways if there is a potential danger to boaters or others. Log booms are sometimes necessary to preclude blockage of spillways during high water periods in reservoirs that have a high volume of debris. Debris should be cleared from the reservoir areas periodically (annually if large amounts) and burned in a safe area. Burning of debris on riprapped surfaces should be avoided because it leads to rapid deterioration of the riprap.

Instructions for operating mechanical equipment should be followed closely to prevent damage to the installations through improper operation. Instructions for the control of spillway gates during floodflows into the reservoir should be followed in detail as outlined in the written operating procedures. Deviations from these instructions should not be made without approval from higher management.

Dams that are operated remotely or that depend on remote readings for proper and safe operation require periodic inspection of their facilities to ensure proper operation. For example, equipment that read reservoir elevation remotely should be checked by means of a staff gauge (or other means) periodically or when a problem is suspected.

The degree of attendance needed at a dam should be determined by evaluating such aspects as size, complexity, prior history, and downstream hazard. Reference [1] has guidelines for determining the attendance needed and for downstream warning and communication systems.

12.7. *Diversion Dams.*—Diversion dams are usually built for the purpose of raising the level of the stream and not for purposes of storage or for equalization of flow. Such dams may divert flows into canals for irrigation of lands in the stream valleys or to spreading grounds for replenishment of ground-water storage. Diversion dams are usually overflow dams or have long overflow sections. Control gates are usually supplied to maintain the required diversion level despite fluctuations in the streamflow or to pass portions of the flow as needed to satisfy downstream water rights. This mechanical equipment should be operated and maintained in accordance with the instructions furnished as a part of the design function or the instructions developed through operational experience.

Diversion dams are often founded on sandy or gravelly streambed materials. In such cases, their stability may be ensured by a broad base with cutoff walls. Such dams must be safeguarded by frequent inspections for evidence of piping or boils below the dam and of increased seepage at the downstream toe. The downstream apron is usually protected at the toe by heavy riprap. After floods, the streambed should be examined, and the riprap renewed and repaired if necessary.

Diversion dams should be operated, maintained, and inspected using the same general procedures outlined above for earthfill and concrete dams, taking into consideration the obvious inherent differences.

12.8. *Flood Detention Reservoirs.*—Flood detention reservoirs serve to reduce flood peaks by the temporary storage of the part of the flow that exceeds the capacity of the spillway or outlet works of the dam. All reservoirs or pools produce some detention effect.

Structures built for the specific purpose of flood control by detention may be built with outlets that automatically control the rate of release within safe limits. Overflow spillways are also constructed to protect the dams, even at the expense of possible flood damage below the structure, in the event of a flood larger than the one the dam was designed to control.

In addition to general inspections, the outlet works of structures should be kept free of soil deposits and debris that might affect their proper functioning.

12.9. *Changes in Operating Plan.*—A dam may be diverted from its intended use by new requirements. Such requirements may result in improper or dangerous situations and, possibly, in the complete loss of the dam by overflow in the event of excessive runoff. A change in the operation of a structure or dam should not be made without a complete appraisal of its structural and functional effects on the structures.

A dam is sometimes raised without due consideration of the relation of the resulting increased pressures to the limitations of the original design. No structural changes should be made without reference to the original plans or without the approval of a qualified engineer, preferably the designer.

The capacity of a storage reservoir should not be increased by placing stoplogs or other obstructions in an open-crest spillway without reference to the original plans and to the contemplated method of operation or without the approval of a qualified engineer. Such devices may effectively reduce the ability of the reservoir and dam to safely store and pass the predicted inflow design flood.

The ability of a dam and spillway to safely store and pass the inflow design flood should be reviewed where storm and runoff occurrence and recent developments in hydrologic technique indicate that an up-to-date inflow design flood would be significantly larger than that on which the design was based. Operational or structural modifications, such as enlargement of the spillway, should be made where necessary to provide for safe handling of a new inflow design flood.

12.10. *Emergency Preparedness Plan.*—An EPP (Emergency Preparedness Plan) should be developed for all dams and conveyance facilities whose failure would endanger human life or cause substantial property damage. The EPP should include all pertinent instructions for a dam operator to follow during an emergency. It should be written in a clear and precise manner.

During its development or upon completion, each EPP should be discussed with local community leaders or presented to the people directly responsible for the well-being of the citizenry for their comments. Heads of Federal and State agencies affected by an emergency should also be contacted. Local officials should be clearly aware of the hazard potential a dam failure would present and should be assisted in developing communications and warning procedures. Each plan should include warning systems or procedures for warning the endangered downstream population and should include the necessary inundation maps or descriptions delineating flooded areas.

12.11. *Dam Operator's Training.*—To ensure that a dam is operated in an efficient and correct manner, the owner is responsible for providing training to each dam operator. The object of the training is to acquaint the operator with the full range of operations required. It is recommended that the training be provided in two parts: general, in the classroom, and onsite, at the dam operator's work station.

The training should be specific in outlining the dam operator's responsibilities. It should also provide an awareness and working familiarity with all operating documents and emphasize the importance of accurate and complete recordkeeping. This may involve entries on forms, concise explanations in diary format, use of tape recorders, and taking quality photographs of events or conditions.

The training should provide sufficient information for the dam operator to make knowledgeable, correct, and prompt decisions concerning protection of facilities and downstream life and property. The best source of information for this is the EPP. Sound judgment is an intangible quality, which can be greatly enhanced through complete familiarity with capabilities and limitations of the physical facilities under the operator's care.

All dam operators should take a refresher course every 3 years. If possible, a prospective operator should be trained before assuming full responsibility. This can be best accomplished during tenure in an assistant's position. If this is not possible, a newly appointed operator should receive formal training as soon as possible, even if it must be accomplished in a one-to-one situation with a qualified instructor. The Bureau of Reclamation's *Training for Dam Operators—A Manual for Instructors* [2] is a useful document for guidance in training dam operators.

D. BIBLIOGRAPHY

12.12. *Bibliography.*

[1] *Guide for Preparation of Standing Operating Procedures for Dams and Reservoirs,* Bureau of Reclamation, Denver, CO, January 1986.

[2] *Training for Dam Operators—A Manual for Instructors,* Bureau of Reclamation, Denver, CO, September 1981.

Chapter 13

Dam Safety

A. INTRODUCTION

13.1. *Purpose.*—Dams are constructed to impound water for storage or to divert water for beneficial use. Unfortunately, the impoundment of water sometimes poses a potential hazard to public safety. The purpose of a dam safety program is to recognize potential hazards and reduce them to acceptable levels. Safe dams can be built, and dam safety deficiencies or potential deficiencies can usually be corrected with the proper application of current technology when adequate resources are made available.

13.2. *Scope.*—Dam safety practices apply to all dams. The degree of application of these practices requires reasonable judgments based on the size of the dam and reservoir and the hazards to people and property from failure. The safety of a dam should be accorded the highest priority throughout all phases of its development and use, including the planning, design, construction, and operation and maintenance phases.

Dam engineering is not an exact science that can completely eliminate the risk of dam failure. Therefore, the goal of dam safety is to minimize the risk of failure—making new dams as safe as practical by promoting the application of competent technical judgment and the use of state-of-the-art technology in all phases of development and use. Dam safety also requires providing emergency preparedness plans, periodic safety examinations and evaluations, and rehabilitations or modifications of existing dams.

For a dam, whether embankment or concrete, the inclusion of instruments to monitor some of the important performance-related parameters is warranted. These parameters might include uplift pressures, foundation and downstream water levels, and internal or surficial movements. Instruments located in strategic positions and monitored according to a set schedule may provide invaluable information on what could be unfavorable trends or, on the other hand, continued satisfactory performance. References on instrumentation can be found in *Design of Arch Dams* [1][1], *Design of Gravity Dams* [2], *Embankment Dam Instrumentation Manual* [3], and *Concrete Dam Instrumentation Manual* [4].

13.3. *Definitions.*—The following definitions apply to dam safety activities:

(a) *Dam.*—A barrier constructed across a water course or a topographic low area for the purpose of storage, control, or diversion of water.

(b) *Dam Failure.*—Catastrophic type of failure characterized by the sudden, rapid, and uncontrolled release of impounded water. It is recognized that there are lesser degrees of failure and that any malfunction or abnormality outside the design assumptions and parameters which adversely affect a dam's primary function of impounding water is properly considered a failure. Lesser degrees of failure can progressively lead to or increase the risk of a catastrophic failure. They are, however, normally amenable to corrective action.

(c) *Maintenance.*—The work on structures and equipment to ensure their proper operation; such as repairing equipment and minor structures and maintaining embankments, keeping them free of trees, brush, and burrowing animals.

(d) *Rehabilitation.*—The repair of deteriorated structures to restore them to their original condition or to state-of-the-art standards; such as the alteration of structures to improve the dam, spillway, or outlet-works functions, or to enlarge the reservoir capacity, or to increase the spillway and outlet works capacity; and the replacement of equipment for dam safety.

(e) *Hazard.*—A source of danger; something that has the potential for creating adverse consequences.

(f) *EPP (Emergency Preparedness Plan) or EAP*

[1]Numbers in brackets refer to entries in the bibliography (sec. 13.20).

(Emergency Action Plan).—A plan of action to be taken to reduce the potential for property damage and loss of life in an area affected by a dam failure or large flood.

(g) *Dam Safety Deficiency.*—A physical condition capable of causing dam failure.

(h) *Potential Dam Safety Deficiency.*—A condition that currently does not significantly affect the safety of the dam, but is capable of becoming a dam safety deficiency; for example, continuing erosion, tree growth, the potential adverse response of the dam to an unusual loading condition such as a PMF (probable maximum flood) or MCE (maximum credible earthquake), or a suspected problem that may exist, but cannot be definitely evaluated with existing data.

(i) *Essential Element.*—A structural or geologic feature or an item of equipment whose failure under the loading conditions or circumstances being considered would create a dam safety deficiency.

(j) *Failure Potential Assessment.*—A judgment of the potential for failure of an essential element within the expected life of the project. Five terms are used to describe these assessments: "negligible," "low," "moderate," "high," and "urgent." A rating of "negligible" reflects the judgment that failure of the essential element is regarded as very unlikely; "low" reflects the judgment that failure is unlikely; "moderate" reflects the judgment that failure is possible and further data collection and/or analyses may be required; "high" reflects the judgment that failure is very probable; and "urgent" reflects the judgment that failure is imminent.

(k) *IDF (Inflow Design Flood) or SDF (Spillway Design Flood).*—The flood hydrograph used in the design of a dam and its appurtenant works particularly for sizing the spillway and outlet works, and for determining maximum temporary storage and height of dam requirements.

(l) *PMF (Probable Maximum Flood).*—The maximum runoff condition resulting from the most severe combination of hydrologic and meteorologic conditions that are considered reasonably possible for the drainage basin under study.

(m) *Normal Loading Conditions.*—Loading conditions that occur frequently, or are expected to occur during the life of the structure; contrasted with unusual loading conditions such as an MCE or PMF, which have much less probability of occurrence.

(n) *MCE (Maximum Credible Earthquake).*—The earthquake(s) associated with specific seismotectonic structures, source areas, or provinces that would cause the most severe vibratory ground motion or foundation dislocation capable of being produced at the site under the currently known tectonic framework. It is determined by judgment based on all known regional and local geological and seismological data.

13.4. *Federal Guidelines for Dam Safety.*— The Bureau of Reclamation Safety of Dams Program substantially conforms to the *Federal Guidelines for Dam Safety* [5] with regard to planning, design, construction, operation, maintenance, and examination of dams. The guidelines establish the Federal agencies' management procedures intended to stimulate technical advances in engineering, construction, and operation to minimize the risks of dam failure. The guidelines were prepared by the Ad Hoc Interagency Committee on Dam Safety of the Federal Coordinating Council for Science, Engineering, and Technology based on a review of the procedures and criteria used by the Federal agencies responsible for dams.

B. PRINCIPLES AND CONCEPTS

13.5 *New Dams.*—(a) *Planning and Design.*—A new dam should be developed in accordance with state-of-the-art design techniques and construction practices and in a manner commensurate with its size, function, geologic setting, and potential hazard classification. Careful attention must be given to the following planning and design considerations; most of these considerations are discussed thoroughly in other chapters of this manual.

(1) Selection of the damsite
(2) Estimation of the PMF and selection of the IDF
(3) Identification of earthquake source area and structure, estimation of MCE's, and identification of earthquake-related safety concerns
(4) Development of a site-specific geotechnical exploration program

(5) Design of the foundation, dam, and appurtenant structures
(6) Design of a system of instrumentation to monitor the performance of the dam, foundation, and appurtenant structures
(7) Development of an initial reservoir-filling and surveillance plan and of reservoir-drawdown criteria
(8) Preparation of designer's operating criteria and identification of special considerations to be observed during construction and operation
(9) Provisions for the automatic, independent review by competent individuals of all design decisions, methods, procedures, and results related to dam safety
(10) Provisions to revise the design to make it compatible with conditions encountered during construction

(b) *Construction.*—Quality construction is critical to dam safety. Construction personnel must be constantly alert to recognize and recommend the possible need for adjustments in the design, construction materials, and construction practices to properly provide for actual conditions encountered. The essential aspects of the construction program include:

(1) Keeping construction engineers and inspectors informed of the design philosophies, assumptions, and intent of the designer with regard to foundation excavation and treatment, to the usage and processing of construction materials, and to the design concepts associated with the construction of embankments and concrete structures and with the installation of mechanical and electrical equipment
(2) Keeping construction engineers and inspectors informed of the field control measures and tests required to ensure quality construction
(3) Maintaining an adequately staffed and equipped materials laboratory at the damsite to meet the field testing requirements
(4) Providing a formal plan for construction inspection to ensure that each facet of essential work is accomplished in multishift operations
(5) Giving the Project Construction Engineer the authority to suspend work until all site conditions different from those anticipated are evaluated and the necessary design or construction changes are implemented
(6) Inspection and acception of critical work stages, by the appropriate engineers or geologist (design and/or technical review personnel)
(7) Keeping a job diary and documentation that provides a complete history of the work
(8) Providing mapping and photographic documentation of the construction progress and of significant events; e.g., geologic maps and photographs of final treated foundations.

13.6. *Existing Dams.*—(a) *Operation and Maintenance.*—The operation and maintenance procedure implemented should ensure the safe operation of the dam and provide for timely repair of facilities. The essential procedures include:

(1) Preparing SOP's (Standing Operating Procedures); information on the preparation of SOP's is contained in chapter 12
(2) Training personnel in both normal and emergency operation and maintenance responsibilities and in problem detection
(3) Maintaining a written record of reservoir, waterway, and mechanical equipment operations and of maintenance activities
(4) Testing full operation of spillway and outlet-works gates on a regular basis, using both primary and auxiliary power systems
(5) Providing for public safety and for security against vandalism of essential operating equipment
(6) Establishing and maintaining communication links with local governmental agencies and authorities
(7) Preparing and maintaining current EPP's; information on the preparation of EPP's is contained in chapter 12.

(b) *Periodic Examinations and Evaluations.*—The periodic examination and evaluation of dams and reservoirs is of considerable importance for public safety. The intent of conducting periodic examinations and evaluations is to disclose conditions that can disrupt operations or threaten dam safety early enough for these conditions to be corrected. Periodic examinations and evaluations are discussed in part C and in the *Safety Evaluation of Existing Dams Manual* [6].

13.7. *Documentation on Dams.*—All significant design data, computations, and engineering and management decisions should be documented and retained throughout the life of a dam. The documentation should cover investigations and design, construction plans and specifications, construction history, operation and maintenance instructions and history, instrumentation monitoring instructions, structural behavior history, damage, repairs and improvements, and periodic examinations and evaluations. Memoranda, reports, criteria, computations, drawings, and records of all major decisions regarding the design, construction, operation and maintenance, and safety of the dam should be permanently retained and accessible in a central file.

C. PERIODIC DAM SAFETY EVALUATIONS

13.8. *General.*—(a) *Purpose.*—SEED (Safety Evaluation of Existing Dams) evaluations are conducted to determine the condition of a dam relative to its structural and operational integrity. The evaluation identifies existing or potential dam safety deficiencies and confirms these deficiencies with analyses based on existing or developed data.

(b) *Phases.*—The safety evaluation process involves two major phases: the examination phase and the analysis phase. The examination phase identifies existing and potential dam safety deficiencies as determined from a review of the design, construction, operation, and performance data, and from an onsite examination of the dam. The analysis phase evaluates each recommendation identified in the examination phase to determine its significance to the safety of the dam and to identify actions that will be required to confirm or resolve all dam safety deficiencies. Additional issues may be identified and analyzed during the analysis phase.

(c) *Reports.*—Reports on each phase of the safety evaluation should contain findings, conclusions, and recommendations. These reports should be objective, comprehensive, straightforward, and prepared in a timely manner.

13.9. *Examinations.*—(a) *Types.*—Two types of onsite examinations assess the safety of dams: the formal examination and the intermediate examination. Onsite examinations are conducted every 3 years in conjunction with Review of Operation and Maintenance Examinations.

A formal SEED examination is performed every 6 years by a team of multidisciplined engineers and a geologist. It is characterized by a state-of-the-art evaluation of the dam and its appurtenant features, particularly a review of the standards for the design, construction, performance, and operating procedures.

Intermediate examinations are usually conducted between formal examinations by a single dam safety engineer. To properly assess the safety of an existing dam, it is necessary to review the Data Book and the performance data from instrumentation and other available records and to perform a comprehensive onsite examination of the dam, appurtenances, and other features that can affect its safety. The intent of reviewing the records is to understand the physical features and performance history of the dam and appurtenances and to identify any potential design, construction, performance, or operational deficiencies. After reviewing these records, the dam safety engineer should have the information and background necessary to perform the onsite examination.

The onsite examination is a comprehensive observation and evaluation of the visible features of the dam and appurtenant structures. If existing or potential deficiencies are identified, recommendations are made for correcting or further evaluating them. A written report is promptly prepared to document the results of the examination and its conclusions and recommendations. The recommendations in both formal and intermediate SEED Examination Reports are evaluated to determine whether a dam safety deficiency or potential deficiency exists. The process by which recommendations are evaluated is described in part D of this chapter.

(b) *Frequency.*—The safety of a dam must be assessed continually with periodic safety examinations throughout the life of the structure. The frequency of onsite examinations is established as every 3 years, and SEED examinations are scheduled to occur in conjunction with examinations performed in the Review of Operation and Maintenance Program.

(c) *Data Books.*—Proper assessment of dam safety involves a thorough review of design, construction, and performance records before the onsite examination. A Data Book is prepared to fulfill this need. This book is an abbreviated, convenient source of information consisting of pertinent records and history of the safety of a dam. It is prepared before the initial formal examination of each dam and is updated as the data change.

The Data Book contains all data pertinent to the safety of the dam obtained from sources such as records of design and construction for new dams and from records of design, construction, operation and maintenance, structural behavior, and previous dam safety examinations for existing dams. Copies of pertinent source records are obtained to eliminate errors in technical information and from data presented in the Data Book. A statistical summary is prepared for the dam and included in the Data Book.

To fulfill its purpose, the Data Book must be kept up-to-date. The examination team is responsible for reviewing, revising, and updating this book.

(d) *Examination Team.*—A formal examination team is normally composed of engineers and a geologist. It should have the technical knowledge and experience required to critically assess the performance of dams during both past and anticipated events. Team members are selected to accommodate the complexities of the subject dam. The teams that perform formal examinations usually include a civil engineer, a mechanical engineer, and a geologist. The engineers should be registered professionals.

Team members should have considerable experience in the design, construction, and operation of dams and their appurtenant features. Various team members should have expertise in the following disciplines: hydraulics, geotechnical engineering, rock mechanics, structural design, embankment and concrete dam design, mechanical design, materials properties evaluation, engineering geology, and instrumentation.

Field personnel familiar with the subject dam and appurtenances should accompany the team during the onsite examination to answer questions concerning the condition and the operation and maintenance of the various features, and to operate the equipment.

The team should make a comprehensive review of all data pertinent to the safety of the dam, make an onsite examination, analyze all data and findings, update the Data Book, and prepare a written Examination Report stating their findings, conclusions, and recommendations relative to the safety of the dam.

D. TECHNICAL ANALYSES

13.10. *General.*—The engineering and geologic dam safety deficiencies identified from the site examinations and from other sources are entered into a computerized SOD (Safety of Dams) data base and prioritized as to their level of seriousness. In this way, all dams are prioritized with respect to the significant issues, and studies can then be scheduled to reflect the critical nature of the identified issues. The SOD issues are analyzed by technical specialists and an Analysis Report is written. The Analysis Report is then combined with the Examination Report, the Management Summary (which includes pertinent information for managers about the dam and the overall safety classification), the Downstream Hazard Assessment, and the Structural Behavior Report (which includes plots of instrumentation readings and interpretation with regard to the structural performance) to form the SEED Report.

The types of recommendations analyzed encompass a wide range of issues that normally apply to dams. These typically include the hydrologic/hydraulic, seismotectonic, geologic, geotechnical, and structural issues. The analyses use the state-of-the-art technology and methodology available within the various disciplines. The analyses are conducted in two phases. Phase I is a technical assessment using available data and conservative assumptions to determine whether the potential problem identified is a SOD deficiency. Phase I analyses are the type typically prepared for the Analysis Report section of the SEED Report. If the results of this phase are inconclusive, a phase II study is scheduled. Phase II is a more detailed study, which may include field investigations and laboratory tests to establish the necessary design parameters for more sophisticated analyses. Phase II level analysis would be appropriate for an MDA (Modification Decision Analysis). The MDA is used to identify the need for a modification to correct safety deficiencies of the dam or appurtenant structures and to identify the scope of the modifications if a need is identified.

The scope of phase I analyses within each major area is generally as follows:

To gain background knowledge about a dam, an engineer or geologist in each discipline should thoroughly review the existing Data Book, Examination Report, operation and maintenance records, the Technical Record of Design and Construction, and any new or additional information. After this background information is studied, the technical analyses are initiated on the recommendations and problems stated in the Examination Report. During both phases of the analysis, the potential problems of seepage, stability, and seismicity often require a multidisciplinary approach and, usually, another onside examination by at least some of those doing the analyses. After the phase I analyses, the technical assessment can conclude one of the following:

(1) No further action is required because the threat to the safety of the dam is low or negligible,
(2) A threat to the safety of the dam clearly exists, and a corrective action should be determined, or
(3) Additional field or analytical (phase II) studies are required to assess the issues.

These additional studies could involve surface and subsurface exploration that may require drilling, sampling, laboratory testing, installing instrumentation, mapping, or other types of field investigations necessary to provide new data for phase II analyses.

13.11. *Overall Safety Classification.*—After the Phase I analysis is completed, an overall safety classification is assigned to the dam. The dam can be classified as SATISFACTORY, FAIR, CONDITIONALLY POOR, POOR, or UNSATISFACTORY. These terms are defined as follows:

SATISFACTORY.—No existing or potential dam safety deficiencies are recognized. Safe performance is expected under all anticipated loading conditions, including such events as the MCE and the PMF.

FAIR.—No existing dam safety deficiencies are recognized for normal loading conditions. Infrequent hydrologic and/or seismic events would probably result in a dam safety deficiency.

CONDITIONALLY POOR.—A potential dam safety deficiency is recognized for unusual loading conditions that may realistically occur during the expected life of the structure. CONDITIONALLY POOR may also be used when uncertainties exist as to critical-analysis parameters that identify a potential dam safety deficiency; further investigations and studies are necessary.

POOR.—A potential dam safety deficiency is clearly recognized for normal loading conditions. Immediate actions to resolve the deficiency are recommended; reservoir restrictions may be necessary until problem resolution.

UNSATISFACTORY.—A dam safety deficiency exists for normal conditions. Immediate remedial action is required for problem resolution.

13.12. *Downstream Hazard Assessment.*—(a) *General.*—A downstream hazard is defined as the potential loss of life or property damage downstream from a dam from floodwaters released at the dam or waters released by partial or complete failure of the dam [5].

Hazard classification is not associated with the existing condition of a dam and its appurtenant structures or with the anticipated performance or operation of a dam. Rather, hazard classification is a statement of the most realistic adverse impact on human life and downstream developments should a designated dam fail.

Dams are given a hazard classification for two reasons:

(1) The DOI (Department of the Interior) *Department Manual*, Part 753 [7], establishes that a hazard classification is to be assigned to every DOI dam.
(2) Hazard classification serves as a management tool for prioritizing and selecting levels of dam safety program activities and for scheduling the frequency of dam safety reassessments.

(b) *Determining the Loss of Life.*—The system presented in table 13-1 is currently used by the Bureau's (Bureau of Reclamation) Division of Dam Safety for hazard classification of Bureau and other DOI dams [8].

Anticipated loss of life refers to people in the downstream flood plain, either on a permanent or temporary basis, whose lives would be at risk should a dam failure occur. Permanent and temporary use are defined below.

Permanent use includes:

- Permanently inhabited dwellings (structures that are currently used for housing people and

Table 13-1.—Hazard classification.

Classification	Anticipated loss of life	Economic loss
Low	0	Minimal (undeveloped agriculture, occasional uninhabited structures, or minimal outstanding natural resources)
Significant	1-6	Appreciable (rural area with notable agriculture, industry, or worksites, or outstanding natural resources)
High	>6	Excessive (urban area including extensive community, industry, agriculture, or outstanding natural resources)

that are permanently connected to utilities; three residents per dwelling is assumed based on the 1980 National Census); this includes mobile homes

- Worksite areas that contain workers on a daily (workweek) basis. Commonly affected worksites include public utilities and vital public facilities (powerplants, water and sewage treatment plants, etc.), private industrial plants or operations including production of materials (sand, gravel, etc.), farm operations, and fish hatcheries

Temporary use includes:

- Secondary and primary roads in the channel or on the crest of the dam
- Established campgrounds and backpacker campsites
- Other recreational areas

Determining the anticipated loss of life involves many uncertainties and requires good judgment by the analyst. Analyses may indicate catastrophic flooding of a permanently occupied area with obvious loss of life to any occupants, or it may merely indicate shallow flooding (e.g., 1-2 ft) with low velocities in areas of temporary use. In the latter case, it is difficult to determine the extent of loss of life, if any, that would occur as a result of the flood. People may be safe if they remain in buildings or automobiles, or if they move to high ground. Flooding may be little more than the mere wetting of an area, such that a person may safely wade. Yet although the floodwater may be shallow, a small child could fall into a ditch or depression, or be drowned by local fast-moving water.

Other factors to consider are the proximity of the hazard and the time of day. A dam should be assumed to fail during the most inopportune time of day for warning and evacuating downstream residents (11:00 p.m. to 6:00 a.m.). However, a community may be susceptible to catastrophic flooding, but be far enough downstream from the dam to allow ample warning and evacuation of its occupants.

These scenarios are nearly endless and every case is different. Because of this and because the hazard assessment affects how a dam is managed in a dam safety program, a highly conservative approach should be used in estimating the potential loss of life.

Uncertainties and errors in predicting flood depths and human behavior also exist in the analyses. For instance, actual flood depths may be greater than analysis indicates, residents may not receive or they may ignore warnings, or they may not be able to safely evacuate from the flood plain. Therefore, in estimating the anticipated loss of life, all occupants believed to be in the area susceptible to flooding should be considered.

(c) *Determining Economic Losses.*—The hazard classification of a dam should be based on loss of life first, then on economic loss. Thus, if a dam is classified as a "low" or "significant" hazard based on loss of life, then economic loss should be evaluated to determine whether a higher hazard classification is justified (see table 13-1). Economic loss includes damage to croplands, pasturelands, residences, commercial buildings, utilities, industries, roads, highways, and railroads. Outstanding natural resources within officially declared parks, preserves, wilderness areas, or similar types of areas should also be considered. Because the dollar value of real property changes over time and varies according to the uses of the property, no attempt is made to assign estimated values as guidelines. Hazard classification based on economic loss should, therefore, be based on the judgment of the analyst.

(d) *Estimating the Inundated Area.*—Before the

loss of life or economic loss can be estimated, the extent of flooding from a dam failure must be known. This is accomplished by using one of three different methods: an existing inundation study, engineering judgment, or a dam break inundation analysis.

(1) *Existing Inundation Study.*—Many dams have comprehensive inundation studies associated with them. These inundation studies identify the flood plain resulting from the flood releases. Such should be used as the basis for hazard classification. Frequently, these inundation studies have been performed by water resources specialists using state-of-the-art analytical techniques and are usually the most accurate studies available.

(2) *Engineering Judgment.*—Sometimes, where the hazards are obvious, the hazard classification may be based solely on field inspection or on current topographic maps. Consider the following examples:

a. A community located in the flood plain immediately downstream from a dam
b. A flood plain completely unoccupied and undeveloped downstream to a point where the failure flood reaches a large body of water (e.g., a large reservoir or ocean) without threatening human life or causing economic loss

In example *a*, the dam would be an obvious high-hazard facility, but in example *b*, the dam would be an obvious low-hazard facility. No detailed technical analysis would be necessary in either case.

(3) *Performing a Dam Break Inundation Analysis.*—If a comprehensive inundation study does not exist, or the hazard classification is not obvious, then a dam break inundation analysis should be performed to define the inundated area. Many methods with different levels of sophistication are available for performing such an analysis. A technical discussion on how to perform a dam break inundation analysis is beyond the scope of this section. Instead, the subject will be discussed in general terms with reference to state-of-the-art methods.

The following discussion includes a simple method for performing a preliminary analysis. This method is useful when technical personnel with knowledge of dam break flood routing procedures or computer facilities are not available.

The three phases in a dam break inundation analysis involve determining breach size and discharge, routing the breach discharge downstream, and determining flood depths at possible hazard sites.

a. Determining Breach Size and Discharge.—If the breach size, slope, and time to develop are known, the breach discharge can be determined using hydraulic principles. However, unless a major structural weakness and obvious failure condition are known, determining the breach parameters must be based on experience and engineering judgment.

Many assumptions can be made, and scenarios envisioned regarding a dam failure: A dam could fail from overtopping by a large inflow flood or from piping on a clear day. A thin arch dam may burst in its entirety, or just a section of it may fail. The complete breaching of an earth dam may require as little as 30 minutes or more than 2 hours, and the breach may vary greatly in size and shape. The reservoir may be half full or at its maximum capacity. Factors such as these can only be speculated before a dam failure. Because of these uncertainties a "reasonable maximum" breach discharge should be predicted for hazard classification purposes.

The type of dam and the type of assumed failure should be considered when estimating a peak breach discharge. The type of assumed failure may involve overtopping from a large flood or a normally full reservoir "sunny day" failure. If an overtopping failure is assumed, the size, duration, and depth of overtopping must be accounted for (combined with the breach discharge). If a failure is assumed to occur when the reservoir is full, a failure mechanism must be considered. This failure mechanism could involve piping, seepage, earthquake, slope instability, structural weakness, or landslide.

The type of dam has a significant effect on breach configuration and peak breach discharge. The dam may be a well-constructed or poorly constructed earth dam, a concrete gravity or arch dam, a tailings dam (mine waste), or one of many other types.

A reasonable maximum breach discharge can be estimated based on information from historical dam failures or on assumptions of breach parameters and application of hydraulic principles.

One approach for using information from historical dam failures is application of the Bureau's envelope curve equation of maximum breach discharge [9]. This equation was developed from data collected on the historical peak breach discharge and the depth of water behind the dam at the time of failure:

$$Q = 75D^{1.85} \quad (1)$$

where:

Q = peak discharge at the dam, in cubic feet per second, and
D = depth of the water behind the dam at time of breaching, in feet.

Another peak breach discharge equation based on historical data that also includes storage behind the dam at the time of failure has been developed by the Subcommittee on Emergency Action Planning of ICODS (Interagency Committee on Dam Safety) [10]:

$$Q = 370(HS)^{0.5} \quad (2)$$

where:

Q = peak discharge at the dam, in cubic feet per second
H = height of water in the reservoir measured from streambed, in feet, and
S = reservoir storage capacity corresponding to H, in acre-feet.

The values derived from equations (1) and (2) can be used directly as input to a channel-routing analysis or indirectly in determining breach parameters for a deterministic computer model. The model input variables are chosen such that the computed breach discharge will be approximately the value obtained from the peak discharge equation.

Commonly used computer dam break models that use physically based procedures for computing breach outflow are DAMBRK [11], SMPDBK [12], and HEC-1 [13]. The equations and guidance presented in their respective manuals are excellent for predicting breach discharge. However, selection of the model parameters requires a strong knowledge of dam failure mechanics.

Historical data can be used as a basis for determining breach discharge. If a failed dam and its reservoir are similar in dimensions and structure to the subject dam, their peak breach discharges may be assumed to be similar. MacDonald and Langridge-Monopolis [14] present a good data base on historical dam failures.

MacDonald and Langridge-Monopolis also present a deterministic approach for predicting breach parameters for use as input variables on dam break models. They use data from historical dam failures to develop graphical relationships for predicting breach characteristics for erosion-type breaches. They also develop a relationship for estimating the peak discharge from dam failures. Parameters determined from the procedures described herein can be used as input to commonly used computer dam break models [11, 12, 13].

Additional information regarding breach assumptions is contained in appendix 4C of *Safety of Existing Dams: Evaluation and Improvement* [15].

Determining a peak breach discharge for use in hazard classification is very subjective—there is no "cookbook" method or single procedure that is applicable for all situations. Therefore, it is very helpful to use several different methods (including data from dams that have failed), compare the results, and choose the peak breach discharge that seems most reasonable. The engineer performing the analysis should have a strong knowledge of dam failure mechanisms and hydraulics and be very familiar with historical dam failures. Only then can the engineer use good judgment in determining a reasonable peak breach discharge.

Fortunately, there is room for error in choosing the peak breach discharge because the difference in flood depths computed from routing different breach discharges downstream diminishes with distance downstream from the dam and eventually becomes negligible. This distance is dependent on the discharge at the dam, on the reservoir storage, and on the configuration, slope, and roughness of the channel.

b. Routing the Breach Discharge Downstream.—

The dam break discharge will attenuate (i.e., gradually decrease) as it travels downstream from the dam. To determine the amount of attenuation of the peak discharge at selected points of interest, the dam break flood is routed downstream. Normally, for the purpose of hazard classification, only the peak discharge is routed.

Many factors affect the attenuation of the dam break flood wave peak:

Small attenuation	*Large attenuation*
Large reservoir volume	Small reservoir
Small channel and overbank storage	Large channel and overbank storage
Steep channel slope	Gentle channel slope
Little frictional resistance to flow	Large frictional resistance to flow
Supercritical flow	Subcritical flow

A simple routing procedure is based on using a "decay rate" equation (3a) or (3b) determined from historical dam failures [9].

The decay rate equation is:

$$Q_x = 10(\log[75D^{1.85}] - aX), \text{ if } S/D > 40, \text{ or} \quad (3a)$$

$$Q_x = 10(\log [370 (DS)^{0.5}] - aX), \text{ if } S/D < 40 \quad (3b)$$

where:

Q_x = peak discharge at mile X, in cubic feet per second.
S = storage, for the resevoir at crest of dam, in acre-feet,
D = depth of water behind the dam as measured from crest of dam to streambed, in feet,
a = 0.01 for reservoir storage > 1,500 acre-feet,
a = 0.04 for storage between 800 and 1,500 acre-feet, and
a = 0.1 for storage < 800 acre-feet.

A sophisticated and complex procedure, such as the "dynamic wave method," is used by DAMBRK [11]. The DAMBRK method is based on the equations of unsteady nonuniform flow.

SMPDBK [12] routes the dam break flood peak by storing the flood volume in the channel as the flood progresses downstream using channel geometry data and attenuation curves developed from DAMBRK [11]. This method is physically based, accurate, relatively easy to use, and not very time consuming. It is an excellent model for hazard classification purposes when complicated channel hydraulics are not involved and the highest degree of accuracy is not needed.

If more accuracy is needed, or more hydraulic detail should be accounted for, DAMBRK is a recommended model. This model employs the dynamic wave method of flood routing. Only the dynamic wave method accounts for the acceleration effects associated with dam break flood waves and the influence of downstream unsteady backwater effects produced by channel constrictions, dams, bridge-road embankments, and tributary inflows. DAMBRK routes the complete hydrograph, not just the peak flow, downstream. The DAMBRK manual [11] states:

> "The hydrograph is modified (attenuated, lagged, and distorted) as it is routed through the valley due to the effects of valley storage, frictional resistance to flow, flood wave acceleration components, and downstream obstructions and/or flow control structures. Modifications to the dambreak flood wave are manifested as attenuation of the flood peak elevations, spreading-out or dispersion of the flood wave volume, and changes in the celerity (translation speed) or travel time of the flood wave. If the downstream valley contains significant storage volume such as a wide flood plain, the flood wave can be extensively attenuated and its time of travel greatly increased."

HEC-1 [13] uses simple semiempirical hydrologic routing techniques. It is recommended for preliminary studies when time and funds are limited and the highest degree of accuracy is not necessary.

c. Determining Flood Depths.—The end product of a dam break inundation analysis performed for hazard classification is inundation boundaries. Inundation boundaries can readily be determined if flood depths (maximum water surface elevations) are known at the area of concern. This is accomplished by defining the maximum water surface elevation on both sides of the channel on topographic maps. The area between the maximum water surface elevation boundaries is the inundation area.

Almost all popular widely used procedures for determining flood depth are based upon Manning's equation:

$$Q = \frac{1.48}{n} AR^{2/3} S^{1/2} \quad (4)$$

where:

$Q = Q_x$ = peak discharge, in cubic feet per second,
A = hydraulic cross-sectional area, in square feet,
R = hydraulic radius, in feet,
S = slope of the energy gradient, and
n = Manning's roughness coefficient.

The hydraulic radius and the cross-sectional area are variables dependent on the depth of flow. This equation is solved for depth given all the other variables. The major difference among methods of solving Manning's equation is in the detail of computing cross-sectional area and hydraulic radius.

Modern dam break flood routing methods and models are very sophisticated and accurate, but they also have limitations and many sources of error. Some of these are listed below:

- What is the reservoir inflow at the time of failure?
- What is the breach size, shape, and time of formation?
- What is the flow resistance (Manning's n) of the downstream channel or valley?
- What will be the effects of debris and sediment on the channel capacity and roughness and on the flood wave propagation?
- Do the equations adequately model the flood wave?
- How much of the flood volume is lost to off-channel storage and infiltration?
- Is there personal bias in choosing model parameters?

However, the effects of these errors are not as severe as they may appear. As stated by Fread [16]:

> "The errors associated with the breach characteristics do dampen as the flood propagates downstream, and the degree of dampening depends on the cross-sectional shape and the reservoir volume. Also, the percent error in the computed flow depth is less than the percent error in routed discharge, cross-sectional area, and/or flow resistance. Also, there is a dampening of the error in the wave celerity caused by error in the resistance coefficient. These error properties aid in producing the accuracy that is now achievable with dam-breach flood routing models."

The aforementioned errors and limitations are presented to emphasize that dam break inundation analyses are not exact. Therefore, the engineer must be very cautious when basing important decisions regarding hazard classification on the results of an analysis. For instance, if the results of a study indicate that water levels from a dam failure will flood a community by less than 1 foot, a "low" hazard classification should not necessarily be concluded. Sensitivity of various parameters should be checked to determine whether the flood depths at the community would be significantly greater given the right combination of circumstances and model variable values.

A dam break flood routing needs to be performed downstream from the dam only until the hazard classification can be ascertained or until "adequate floodwater disposal" is reached. For example, if it is determined that a community located 1 mile downstream from a dam would be inundated by a dam failure flood, resulting in a "high" hazard classification, then additional downstream analysis is not necessary.

Adequate floodwater disposal is defined as that point below which the potential for loss of life and for significant property damage caused by routed floodflows appears limited.

This includes such situations as:

- No human occupancy
- No anticipated future development
- Floodflows being contained in a large downstream reservoir
- Floodflows being confined within the channel
- Floodflows entering a bay, ocean, or large channel

13.13. ***Analyses of Hydrologic/Hydraulic Issues.***—(a) *General.*—The analyses of hydrologic/hydraulic issues may include the review of existing operation and examination reports, of flood routing studies with recently approved PMF, of reservoir evacuation studies, and of the probable structural and hydraulic performance of the spillway and outlet works under large discharges.

(b) *Flood Routing.*—The selected hydrograph should be routed through the reservoir using conservative routing assumptions as noted in ACER (Assistant Commissioner-Engineering and Research) Technical Memorandum No. 1, "Criteria for Selecting and Accommodating Inflow Design Floods for Storage Dams and Guidelines for Applying Criteria to Existing Storage Dams" [17]. For phase I level studies, the evaluation flood should be equated to the PMF for significant and high hazard dams.

(1) If it is determined that overtopping will occur, the peak discharge, maximum reservoir water surface, and duration of overtopping (assuming no dam failure) should be ascertained.

(2) If the evaluation flood threatens the safety of the dam, return-period flood hydrographs (i.e., 200-year, 100-year) should be routed

through the dam to provide additional information on the hydrologic/hydraulic adequacy of the dam and its appurtenances. Floods equal to various percentages of the PMF peak and the PMF volume should be routed through the dam, and the impacts on the dam, appurtenances, and downstream channel determined. For an embankment dam, the percentage of the routed flood that can be contained without overtopping and with 3 feet of freeboard should be determined.

(3) If overtopping does not occur with the selected inflow hydrograph, the amount of freeboard, the maximum spillway discharge, and the duration of operation above the maximum design discharge (or similar information) should be determined. The required freeboard should be determined for the new maximum reservoir water surface according to ACER Technical Memorandum No. 2, "Freeboard Criteria and Guidelines for Computing Freeboard Allowances for Storage Dams" [18].

(c) *Reservoir Evacuation Studies.*—Reservoir evacuation studies should determine compliance with the criteria contained in ACER Technical Memorandum No. 3, "Criteria and Guidelines for Evacuating Storage Reservoirs and Sizing Low-Level Outlet Works" [19]. The evacuation study will require that the investigator determine the discharge capacity and reliability of the outlet, safe reservoir drawdown rates, the maximum safe downstream discharge, and the maximum average reservoir inflows for the evacuation periods considered.

(d) *Spillway and Outlet Works Performance.*—The spillway and outlet works should be evaluated for hydrologic/hydraulic concerns.

(1) The reliability of the spillway or outlet works should be determined if it is used for flood routings or if its failure to operate under normal conditions would endanger the dam. This is of particular concern when the appurtenant structures are automated.

(2) The safe capacity and performance of the appurtenant structures should be evaluated when they are used to route the selected flood. The design capacity of the appurtenance may be exceeded in such a way that the structure does not operate as designed; however, unless this operation or failure endangers the dam it may be treated as an acceptable risk.

(3) The cavitation and scour potential for some structures should be evaluated. Increased peak discharges, extended flood operation durations, and structural deterioration may effect the performance or integrity of the appurtenant structures in such a way to endanger the dam.

(4) The geology and foundation for and around the appurtenant structures should be evaluated to ensure that they will not adversely affect the performance of the structure and endanger the dam.

13.14. *Analyses of Seismotectonic Issues.*— The purpose of this analysis is to estimate the earthquake loading to which the structure may be subjected.

The analysis to determine the seismicity of a site requires the review of records and reports dealing with the seismicity and remote-sensing interpretation. Either of two general approaches may be used, determined basically by whether the damsite is east or west of the eastern boundary of the Rocky Mountains Seismotectonic Province. West of the Rocky Mountains, a deterministic approach is generally possible, but probabilistic methods may be used alone or together with deterministic methods. A deterministic approach uses fault characteristics and historic seismicity combined with potential epicentral distances for each fault to determine the potential earthquake loading. East of the Rocky Mountains Seismotectonic Province, a probabilistic approach is usually most appropriate. It uses recurrence rates based on historical seismicity to predict epicentral distances for the MCE in each source area, and predicts events of lesser magnitude and distance for a given probability of occurrence. These probabilistic events are then used to estimate potential earthquake loadings. Other considerations used to assess performance during an earthquake include the potential for fault offsets in the dam foundation and abutments, relative movement (relocation) of the reservoir basin, and earthquake seiche in the reservoir.

Initially, a damsite is evaluated using available information and, possibly, a brief site reconnaissance. The initial evaluation uses conservative distances. If the geotechnical analysis using these conservative parameters does not identify potential dam deficiencies, no further seismotectonic investigations may be necessary. However, if potential deficiencies are identified, further seismotectonic analysis is warranted and a comprehensive state-of-the-art seismotectonic study, including fault mapping, fault trenching, dating of past activity, microseismic monitoring of significant structures, and other techniques, may be necessary.

13.15. *Analyses of Geologic Issues.*—

(a) *General.*—The main areas of geologic concern are stability of the reservoir rim, abutment, and foundation; foundation seepage; and landslide hazards. Geologic analysis must often locate or establish detailed information on rock structure, seismicity and seismic-related effects, and geophysical properties of embankments and foundations. The analysis should consist of (1) a review of construction geology reports, all drill data, geophysical data, instrumentation records, and reports of past seepage and ground-water movements; (2) the study of the properties of materials and of structures; and (3) and the remote-sensing interpretations of aerial photography.

The geologic contribution frequently includes an interpretive discussion on the review of geologic records, reports, and geologic mapping. This provides information regarding landslide masses and rock-structure characteristics, such as bedding, joints, faults, foliation, and in some instances, volcanic hazard. In addition, the results of new remote-sensing studies are included in the geologic analyses.

(b) *Phase II Analyses.*—For recommended phase II analyses, geologists need intimate involvement in the definition of field investigative programs to collect additional data or samples. Phase II analyses can include both drilling and geophysical methods.

Drilling methods of exploration generally involve the same methods of drilling and sampling used for investigating a damsite for design purposes, although special attention should also be paid to installing piezometers and collecting hydrostatic pressure and seepage information. In addition, a special investigation of potentially liquefiable foundation soils may be necessary.

Two specialized geophysical programs are used extensively in the SEED Program. One program involves identifying anomalies along an earth dam or foundation. If such anomalies exist, the usual procedure is to recommend further exploration, such as drilling, to define the properties of the materials. The other program involves the use of shear-wave velocities derived from seismic surveys for seismic-stability analyses.

The various geophysical techniques and how their implications are used for SEED investigations follow:

(1) Seismic Refraction and Reflection.—This method measures layered compressional and ground-roll velocities. If there are any changes in the earth materials of a dam, a velocity anomaly will be generated. The ground-roll velocity approximate shear-wave velocity and can be used as a parameter in the determination of the dynamic response of an earth dam when shear-wave velocities are not available.

(2) Seismic Shear-Wave Velocity Investigations.—Shear waves are measured by down-hole, cross-hole, and up-hole methods, using a standard refraction seismograph as the recorder. Shear-wave velocities are used as one of the key parameters in the determination of the dynamic response of an earth dam.

(3) Radar Surveys.—Radar surveys measure reflections from any interface that has a contrast in its complex dielectric properties. Radar is used to locate voids in concrete and behind tunnel walls, and to evaluate soils near the surface.

(4) Resistivity Surveys.—Resistivity surveys measure the electrical properties of soil and rock. Resistivity is primarily used to locate the phreatic surface through earth embankments.

The information obtained from the analysis of geologic issues is generally needed for the analysis of geotechnical issues. In some instances, the geologic analysis may indicate a need for additional geotechnical analysis, or it may, by itself, identify a dam safety deficiency. An example of such a case is a landslide hazard, which may necessitate the installation of an extensive landslide monitoring instrumentation and warning system and the modification of the SOP's for the dam.

13.16. *Analyses of Geotechnical Issues.*—

(a) *General.*—The analyses of geotechnical issues may include an evaluation of the available data, static stability analyses, seepage analyses, dynamic stability (deformation) analyses, and liquefaction analyses.

The performance of the structure under prior

maximum loading conditions often provides a partial basis for assessment. The quality of performance is judged on the visual condition of the structure, as described in the Examination Reports, and on available instrumentation records (Structural Behavior Report).

All available instrumentation data from the Structural Behavior Report and other sources are reviewed during the geotechnical evaluation. If no data or only limited data are available, a determination is made on whether additional instrumentation is required to assess a potential dam safety problem.

An assessment of the structural stability and seepage-control integrity of the embankment and foundation under static loads is made for each dam. The extent of the assessment should vary in each case, depending on the following factors:

(1) Visual condition of the embankment and foundation
(2) Operation and performance record
(3) Structural and hydraulic height of the embankment
(4) Embankment zoning and exterior slope steepness
(5) Reservoir capacity, operational procedures, and evacuation capability
(6) Hazard classification
(7) Relevant engineering and geologic information available

(b) *Static Stability Analyses.*—The static stability of the embankment and foundation should be analyzed, see USBR Design Standards No. 13, chapter 4, "Static Stability Analyses." Data such as geologic maps, drill logs, laboratory tests, phreatic surface estimates, and construction methods should be used when available. Shear-strength assumptions for analysis are based on material types, gradations, and compaction methods, and usually assume that a long-term, consolidated, drained-strength condition has been established. Phreatic surfaces are estimated using available piezometric data, or they are assumed based on embankment-zoning and slope configurations. Stability analyses are normally performed for a steady-state seepage condition. Sudden drawdown analyses are performed on a case-by-case basis, as determined from such factors as the location of the storage dam (whether it is "onstream" or "offstream"), the drawdown (reservoir evacuation) capability of appurtenances, the drainage capability of the embankment zones, and the potential of the reservoir to refill quickly after a flood and before a drawdown slide could be repaired.

(c) *Seepage Stability Analyses.*—The seepage stability of the embankment and foundation should be assessed. This analysis focuses on such factors as increased seepage with time and the presence of sinkholes, cavities, and sandboils. Existing information and records are used in the evaluation. Seepage analyses of items like critical gradients, flow-net construction, and finite elements are performed as required when sufficient data are available. The seepage-control integrity of filters, drains, blankets, and transition-zone materials should also be assessed.

(d) *Dynamic Stability (Deformation) Analyses.*—A dynamic stability (deformation) analysis of the embankment and foundation should be performed, see USBR Design Standards No. 13, chapter 13, "Dynamic Stability Analyses." The dynamic stability of the dam should be evaluated for the earthquakes developed in the seismotectonic review. If the embankment is shown not to be susceptable to liquefaction, analyses incorporating the time-dependence of the ground acceleration and the dynamic response should be conducted. This analysis is more sophisticated than the pseudostatic analysis. The initial step should be a simplified SEED analysis using the NRC (Nuclear Regulatory Commission) response spectrum. Local site effects are not considered in the determination of the spectral amplitudes. Results include the following:

- The permanent displacments along assumed failure surfaces extending through the top one-fourth, the top one-half, and the full height of the embankment resulting from the critical MCE's or appropriate probabilistic earthquakes.
- The epicentral distances for events with magnitudes of M = 6½, 7½, and 8¼ that would cause a 3-foot permanent deformation along a failure surface extending through a critical section of the embankment (more sophisticated phase II analyses would then be conducted as needed). The more sophisticated analyses are usually staged (i.e., progressively more exact) until the dam is determined to be safe or is determined to be unsafe, which is usually more difficult.
- Liquefaction Analyses.—Liquefaction analyses should be conducted for all foundations and embankments where an initial assessment indicates the presence of potentially liquefiable

materials. The initial liquefaction analyses should be made by simplified methods. Phase II analyses should be performed to the extent required.

- Fault Offsets through the Dam Foundation and Abutments.—The effects of fault offsets should be assessed on a case-by-case basis because some sites have a low potential for offset faulting in the foundation or abutments and some embankments are designed with crack stopping zones.
- Seiche.—The effects of seiche arising from ground accelerations (i.e., not from faults, displacements, or landslides in the reservoir) should be investigated with ground oscillations perpendicular to and parallel to the dam. If the earthquakes under consideration have significant energy content at these periods, then a simplified modal superposition analysis should be conducted, and the resultant wave amplitudes estimated. Additional phase II analyses should be made as needed and should include analyzing the effects of overtopping.
- Landslides and Fault-Displacement Waves.—The effects of landslides and of fault-offset generated waves in the reservoir are assessed on a case-by-case basis because some reservoir areas have a low potential for landslides or offset faulting.

(e) *Phase II Analyses.*—Phase II analyses requirements should be identified when results of phase I static and dynamic stability and seepage stability analyses indicate a low or marginal safety factor.

Additional investigations or studies may be advisable when items such as increased seepage with time or the presence of sinkholes, cavities, or sandboils are identified. Phase II requirements may include field drilling, sampling, laboratory testing, installing and monitoring instrumentation, and analyzing the results of these functions.

13.17. *Analyses of Structural Issues.*— (a) *General.*—The analyses of structural issues may include static and dynamic analyses of concrete arch dams, concrete gravity dams, and appurtenant structures to all dams. The descriptions of dam structural analyses presented in this section are brief. Additional criteria and procedures are presented in chapter 8, in *Design of Arch Dams* [1], and in *Design of Gravity Dams* [2].

(b) *Analyses of Concrete Arch Dams.*—

(1) *General.*—The static and dynamic analyses of concrete arch dams is based on three-dimensional computer simulations of the response of the dam and foundation to a series of load combinations. The computer model may be a trial load or finite element type for static analysis or a finite element program for dynamic analysis. The dam is considered to be homogeneous, elastic, and isotropic, and the foundation is considered generally heterogeneous, inelastic, and anisotropic. For a phase I analyses, the properties of materials should be estimated from the best available data. If specific concrete data are not available, average values from [1] and [20] should be used. The properties of foundation materials should be the average values from the original design data or construction documentation.

Instrumentation and examination reports should be reviewed to analyze how the structure has responded to loading during its history; i.e., foundation uplift pressure or dam cracking.

(2) *Loading.*—The loading combinations that should be considered are "usual," "unusual," "extreme," and "other" loading combinations.

a. Usual Loading Combinations.—Because concrete arch dams may be as responsive to temperature variation as they are to reservoir loads, the usual loading combinations should include the minimum and maximum usual concrete temperature load with the loads from the most probable reservoir elevations that would occur at the time of the minimum and maximum usual concrete temperatures. Appropriate dead loads, tailwater, ice, and silt loads should be included in the loading combinations. Loads from the normal and minimum design reservoir elevations should be combined with usual concrete temperature loads that occur at the time of the normal and minimum reservoir loadings for additional usual loading combinations. Appropriate dead, tailwater, ice, and silt loads should be included in the loading combinations.

b. Unusual Loading Combinations.—The load from the maximum reservoir elevation and the associated mean concrete temperature load are combined with the appropriate dead loads and tailwater and silt loads to produce the unusual loading combination. The maximum reservoir elevation will probably result during the routing of the PMF.

c. Extreme Loading Combination.—The extreme loading combines the effects of the MCE with any of the usual loading combinations.

d. Other Loadings and Investigations.—Any of the other loading combinations may be combined with hydrostatic pressures within the foundation for foundation stability analysis. In addition, any other loading combinations that the investigator considers significant should be analyzed.

(3) *Seismic Analyses.*—The seismic analysis of an arch dam should be performed for ground motions that act in the vertical, cross-canyon, and upstream/downstream directions. A response spectrum for the site should be determined for each MCE, which should be provided as described in section 13.14. The required accelerograms may be developed by appropriate adjustments of existing or artifically generated accelerograms for the three ground-motion directions. The response spectrums generated from the accelerograms must correspond to the design response spectrum. The accelerogram or time history can then be applied to the finite element model as part of the extreme loading combination. Additional seismic analyses may need to be performed with OBE (operating basis earthquake) and DBE (design basis earthquake) to determine the critical loading combination.

(4) *Safety Factors.*—The safety factors indicate the capability of the structure to resist applied loads; it is the specified or known strength of the dam or foundation material divided by the stress resulting from the applied loads. Criteria for safety factors are presented in detail in *Design of Arch Dams* [1] and "Design Criteria for Concrete Arch and Gravity Dams" [20]. Safety factors are established for compressive stresses, shear stress, shear friction, and sliding. The allowable safety factors decrease in value from the usual to the unusual to the extreme loading conditions. The foundation safety factors have higher values because of the strength variation common in foundation materials.

The tensile stresses developed from the applied loads are evaluated with specific stress criteria, which are presented in [1] and [20]. The allowable tensile stress in the dam increases from the usual to the unusual to the extreme loading combinations. A determination of the tensile strength of the rock is seldom required because unhealed joints, shears, and faults cannot transmit tensile stress within the foundation.

A phase II structural analysis would be necessary if the phase I study indicated that the application of the loading combinations resulted in low safety factors, or if a phase II seismotectonic investigation yielded greater MCE's than the phase I study. For a phase II investigation, critical areas of the dam and foundation may be sampled to allow the actual properties of materials to be determined.

(c) *Analyses of Concrete Gravity Dams.*—

(1) *General.*—The static and dynamic analyses for concrete gravity dams is similar to the analyses for arch dams, except the structure and foundation is modeled two-dimensionally and internal hydrostatic pressure is used in the computation of stresses. This section highlights areas where the analyses of gravity dams differs from the analyses of arch dams (sec. 13.17(b)). A more complete description of the analyses of gravity dams is presented in chapter 8 and in [2] and [20].

(2) *Loading.*—The loading combinations that should be considered are "usual," "unusual," "extreme," and "other" loading combinations.

a. Usual Loading Combinations.—The load from the normal design reservoir elevation is combined with appropriate dead loads, the uplift, and the silt, ice, and tailwater loads for the usual loading combinations. If temperature loads are applicable, the minimum usual temperature loads occuring at the time of the normal design reservoir elevation should be used.

b. Unusual Loading Combinations.—The load from the maximum reservoir elevation is combined with the appropriate dead loads, the uplift, the silt and tailwater loads, and the associated minimum usual temperature occuring at the time of the maximum reservoir elevation, if applicable for the unusual loading combination.

c. Extreme Loading Combination.—The extreme loading combines the effects of the MCE with the usual loading.

d. Other Loadings and Investigations.—The usual and unusual loadings should be combined with the effects of inoperative drains. In addition, any other loading combination considered significant by the investigator should be analyzed.

(3) *Seismic Analyses.*—The seismic analyses of a gravity dam should be performed for ground motions that act in both the vertical and in the upstream/downstream directions. The MCE response spectrums and accelerograms are developed as described for arch dams (sec. 13.17(b)(3)). The OBE and DBE may also be derived and applied to the dam and foundation model.

(4) *Safety Factors.*—As with arch dams, the

safety factors of gravity dams are an evaluation of their ability to resist the applied loads. Safety factors are presented for compressive stresses, tensile stresses, and shear friction in [2] and [20]. To keep from exceeding the allowable tensile stresses, the minimum allowable compressive stresses computed without internal hydrostatic pressure should be determined. The highest safety factors are established for the usual loading combinations, reduced for the unusual loading combinations, and further reduced for the extreme loading combinations. Higher safety factors are established for the foundation material than for the concrete.

(d) *Analyses of Appurtenant Structures.*—

(1) *General.*—The levels of analyses vary from a simple qualitative assessment to more detailed response-spectrum dynamic analyses, depending on the importance of the appurtenant structure to the overall safety of the dam.

(2) *Failure Impacts.*—The impacts of the failure of appurtenant structures must be assessed to determine whether such a failure, under any loading condition, would constitute a dam safety concern. A dam safety concern would arise if the failure of some component of the appurtenance lead to a failure of the dam. In some cases the secondary impacts of the failure of an appurtenance must be evaluated to determine whether they constitute a dam safety concern. For instance, a spillway stilling basin that fails may not directly effect the dam because the spillway can still route the design flood; however, because of a changed stilling action, spillway discharges may erode the downstream toe of the dam, thus placing the dam at risk.

(3) *Structural Analysis.*—Preliminary evaluations of the structural competency of appurtenant structures can be determined by inspecting how the structures have performed throughout their loading history. Other factors, such as the structure foundation and adjacent slope stability, may have an impact on the performance of the structure and should be evaluated.

If higher discharge rates and higher water surfaces result from flood routings of the new PMF and interval floods, then structural analysis should be performed to determine the effects of the increased static and dynamic loads on the structures. The investigator must determine the allowable overstress for periodic and dynamic loading conditions.

The type and detail of the seismic analyses that should be performed on a structure vary according to the way the structure responds to ground accelerations. Pseudostatic analyses, where the MCE is converted to a gravitational force acting in a single direction, may be adequate for simple structures such as stilling basins. However, finite element modeling and response-spectrum analyses may be necessary to adequately model complex responding structures such as an outlet works intake tower. The investigator must determine the allowable overstress for the dynamic loading conditions.

(e) *Miscellaneous Evaluations.*—A wide variety of other issues, which do not fall into the above categories, may be identified at storage and diversion dams. These issues typically consist of the need to examine underwater features, install emergency power, test spillway gates, and other items. The level of analysis and the urgency for the accomplishment of these items must be identified on a case-by-case basis. Detailed guidance for this wide range of issues is beyond the scope of this manual; nevertheless, engineers making technical analyses must be aware of these issues.

E. CORRECTION OF DAM SAFETY DEFICIENCIES

13.18. *Responsibility.*—The owners of dams are responsible for correcting the dam safety deficiencies. Necessary corrective measures are usually prioritized in accordance with the probability of occurrence of the event causing failure and with the potential downstream consequences from dam failure.

13.19. *Basis for Dam Safety Corrections.*—Corrective solutions should:

(a) Preserve the structural safety of the dam
(b) Place importance on the prevention of loss of human life
(c) Provide corrective measures at the lowest practical cost while retaining project and environmental benefits
(d) Provide optimum protection to project facilities and public and private property through the use of risk-based decision anal-

ysis, as presented in ACER Technical Memorandum No. 7, "Guidelines to Decision Analysis" [21]

(e) Consider nonstructural solutions and combinations of nonstructural and structural modifications to minimize the cost of required modifications

(f) Apply state-of-the-art design standards and construction practices

F. BIBLIOGRAPHY

13.20. Bibliography

[1] *Design of Arch Dams*, Bureau of Reclamation, 882 pp., Denver, CO, 1977.

[2] *Design of Gravity Dams*, Bureau of Reclamation, 553 pp., Denver, CO, 1976.

[3] *Embankment Dam Instrumentation Manual*, Bureau of Reclamation, Denver, CO, January 1987.

[4] *Concrete Dam Instrumentation Manual*, Bureau of Reclamation, Denver, CO, Currently (1987) in preparation.

[5] *Federal Guidelines for Dam Safety*, Federal Coordinating Council for Science, Engineering, and Technology, June 25, 1979.

[6] *Safety Evaluation of Existing Dams*, rev. reprint, Bureau of Reclamation, 1983.

[7] *Departmental Manual, Part 753*, "Dam Safety Program," U.S. Department of the Interior, January 1981.

[8] "Dam Safety Hazard Classification Guidelines", Bureau of Reclamation, Denver, CO, October 1983.

[9] "Guidelines for Defining Inundated Areas Downstream from Bureau of Reclamation Dams," Bureau of Reclamation, Denver, CO, June 1982.

[10] "Dam Safety Emergency Action Planning Guidelines," Subcommittee on Emergency Action Planning of ICODS (Interagency Committee on Dam Safety), January 1983.

[11] Fread D.L., "DAMBRK: The NWS-Dam Break Flood Forecasting Model," Office of Hydrology, National Weather Service, Silver Spring, MD, July 18, 1984.

[12] Wetmore, Jonathan N., and D.L. Fread, "The NWS Simplified Dam Break Flood Forecasting Model for Desk-Top and Hand-Held Microcomputers," Hydrologic Research Laboratory, Office of Hydrology, National Weather Service, National Oceanic and Atmospheric Administration, Silver Spring, MD.

[13] "HEC-1, Flood Hydrograph Package, USER's Manual," Hydrologic Engineering Center, U.S. Army Corps of Engineers, Davis, CA, September 1981.

[14] MacDonald, Thomas C., and Langridge-Monopolis, Jennifer, "Breaching Characteristics of Dam Failures," *Journal of Hydraulic Engineering*, vol. 110, No. 5, May 1984.

[15] *Safety of Existing Dams: Evaluation and Improvement,"* Committee on the Safety of Existing Dams, Water Science and Technology Board, Commission on Engineering and Technical Systems, National Research Council, National Academy Press, Washington, D.C., 1983.

[16] Fread, D.L., "Some Limitations of Dam-Breach Flood Routing Models," ASCE Fall Convention, St. Louis, MO, October 26-30, 1981.

[17] "Criteria for Selecting and Accommodating Inflow Design Floods for Storage Dams and Guidelines for Applying Criteria to Existing Storage Dams," ACER Technical Memorandum No. 1, Bureau of Reclamation, Denver, CO, November 1981.

[18] "Freeboard Criteria and Guidelines for Computing Freeboard Allowances for Storage Dams," ACER Technical Memorandum No. 2, Bureau of Reclamation, Denver, CO, December 1981.

[19] "Criteria and Guidelines for Evacuating Storage Reservoirs and Sizing Low-Level Outlet Works," ACER Technical Memorandum No. 3, Bureau of Reclamation, Denver, CO, January 1982.

[20] *Design Criteria for Concrete Arch and Gravity Dams*, Engineering Monograph No. 19, rev., 67 pp., Bureau of Reclamation, Denver, CO, 1977.

[21] "Guidelines to Decision Analysis," ACER Technical Memorandum No. 7, Bureau of Reclamation, Denver, CO, March 1986.

Reservoir Sedimentation

A.1. ***General.***—All reservoirs formed by dams on natural water courses are subject to some degree of sediment inflow and deposition. The problem confronting the project planner is to estimate the rate of deposition and the period of time before the sediment will interfere with the useful functioning of the reservoir. At the time of design, provisions should be made for sufficient sediment storage in the reservoir so as not to impair the reservoir functions during the useful life of the project or during the period of economic analysis. The replacement cost of storage lost to sediment accumulation in American reservoirs amounts to millions of dollars annually [1][1].

There are a series of basic principles for studying the sedimentation processes in reservoirs: Sediment transported by the upstream river system into a reservoir is deposited and transported at a reduced rate farther into the reservoir, the deposition location depends on the decrease in the water velocity. As sediment accumulates in the reservoir, storage capacity is reduced. Continuous deposition develops distribution patterns within the reservoir that are greatly influenced by both operations of the reservoir and timing of large flood inflows. Deposition of the coarser sediments occurs in the upper, or delta, reaches; whereas, finer sediments may reach the dam and influence the design of the outlet works. A major secondary effect is the downstream degradation of the river channel caused by the releases of clearer water.

These guidelines cover the essential sedimentation characteristics to be considered in the design of a dam and reservoir. The sediment-related features requiring study are the sediment inflow, deposition, and degradation processes. Sedimentation processes in a reservoir are quite complex because of the wide variation in many of the influencing factors. The most important of these factors are (1) hydrological fluctuations in water and sediment inflow, (2) sediment particle size variation, (3) reservoir operation cycle, and (4) physical controls, or the size and shape of the reservoir. Other factors that may be quite important for some reservoirs are vegetative growth in upper reaches, turbulence and density currents, erosion of deposited sediments and shoreline deposits, and operation for sluicing of sediment through the dam.

The procedures described in this appendix represent a combination of the state of the art together with methods that are practical, technically sound, and sufficiently varied to fit the complexity of the problem. It is because of this complexity that empirical relationships developed from surveys of existing reservoirs are used to define sediment depositional patterns. Many mathematical models are being developed to simulate the physical processes of sediment transport and deposition in reservoirs. To date, the models have not been easily adapted to solving problems of reservoir sedimentation without some simplifications in defining the four most important factors previously described. With more research and additional reservoir survey data for verification of the mathematical models, they may become useful for predicting sediment deposition. Changes in these guidelines can also be expected in many of the empirical relationships with the continuing surveys of existing reservoirs. Further support to update these guidelines will occur as loss of storage capacity and the economic and social changes affecting future reservoir uses become more severe.

In recent years, critical sediment problems have occurred in some reservoirs in all climatic regions of the world; Complete loss of dependable storage has resulted from sediment deposition. Sediment control methods are being planned and, in many cases, construction has been completed on up-

[1]Numbers in brackets refer to entries in the bibliography (sec. A.5).

stream sediment traps, bypass channels, special outlets for sluicing sediment, and mechanical dredging techniques. In many situations, sediment yields are high and conservation or erosion control measures in the drainage area are important for a reduction in the long-term sediment production. In the United States, these measures are usually carried out under the direction of the Soil Conservation Service, Department of Agriculture, in cooperation with landowners and with the encouragement of the Bureau (Bureau of Reclamation).

A.2. *Methods of Determining Sediment Inflow.*—Sediment is the end product of erosion, or wearing away, of the land surface by the action of water, wind, ice, and gravity. Water resource development projects are affected most by sediment that is transported by water. The total amount of onsite sheet and gully erosion in a watershed is known as the gross erosion. However, all the eroded material does not enter the stream system; some of the material is deposited at natural or manmade barriers within the watershed, and some may be deposited within the channels and their flood plains. The portion of eroded material that does travel through the drainage network to a downstream measuring or control point is referred to as the sediment yield. The sediment yield per unit of drainage area is the sediment yield rate.

Most methods for predicting sediment yields are either directly or indirectly based on the results of measurements. Direct measurements of sediment yields are considered the most reliable method for determination of sediment yields. This is accomplished by either surveying a reservoir or sampling the sediment load of a river. Both methods are described in subsequent sections of these guidelines. Other methods for predicting sediment yields depend on measurements to derive empirical relationships or use empirically checked procedures such as the sediment yield rate weighting factors or the Universal Soil-Loss equation [2].

(a) *Sediment Yield Rate Factors.*—The factors that determine the sediment yield of a watershed can be summarized as follows:

(1) Rainfall amount and intensity
(2) Soil type and geologic formation
(3) Ground cover
(4) Land use
(5) Topography
(6) Upland erosion (nature of the drainage network-density, slope, shape, size, and alignment of channels)
(7) Runoff
(8) Sediment characteristics—grain size, mineralogy, etc.
(9) Channel hydraulic characteristics

Some researchers have considered it necessary to include some additional factors; however, even the nine above are interrelated. As an example, a heavy vegetative cover is dependent upon at least a moderate amount of rainfall; however, the ground cover conditions could be upset by tillage practices, overgrazing, or fire. Sediment transported from the drainage basin to a reservoir is controlled by the sediment transport characteristics of the river, which is influenced by the first six factors, but reflects a more direct combination of items 7, 8, and 9.

Systems of weighting the individual sediment influencing factors have been devised [3] to arrive at a sediment yield rate for an individual drainage basin. This type of analysis is best applied to preliminary planning studies and has its greatest reliability when the yield rates can be correlated with a measured sediment yield from an adjacent basin or subbasin.

An example of the techniques for weighting of the nine factors that is similar but not identical to those used in [3] is given in table A-1. The weighted values apply to the Pacific Southwest area, but because they are interrelated, could be used for other parts of the United States.

In computing the sediment yield of a drainage area above a dam or reservoir, a field inspection by a trained sedimentation specialist is needed to evaluate the factors in table A-1 for weighting the significance of the nine factors affecting sediment

Table A-1.—Weighting values of factors affecting sediment yield.

Factors	Sediment yield level		
	High	Moderate	Low
(1) Rainfall amount and intensity	10	5	0
(2) Soil type and geological information	20	10	0
(3) Ground cover	10	0	−10
(4) Land use	10	0	−10
(5) Topography	20	10	0
(6) Upland erosion	25	10	0
(7) Runoff	10	5	0
(8) Sediment characteristics } (9) Channel hydraulics	25	10	0

yield. After this inspection, recommended procedures will be given on (1) available data and methods for analyzing data, (2) techniques available for predicting sediment yields in gauged as well as ungauged drainage basins, and (3) additional measurements required to compute sediment yields.

A well-known method for determination of sediment yields from small drainage areas is the empirical relationship developed by Wischmeieir and Smith, 1965 [2], most commonly referred to as the Universal Soil-Loss equation. It should be recognized that gross erosion determined by this empirical method is, at best, an approximation and is considered a rough estimate. The equation is normally applied to areas of less than about 4 mi^2 and sometimes may have to be corrected by a sediment delivery ratio when converting gross erosion to sediment reaching a main river channel.

(b) *Reservoir Resurvey Data.*—Measurement of the sediment accumulation in a reservoir is considered by many engineers as the best method for determining the sediment yield. Surveys of existing reservoirs for determining loss of storage space and distribution of sediment deposits provide data on sediment yield rates as well as for operations purposes. It is important that when construction is completed on a dam, a plan be established for surveying or monitoring the sediment accumulation. Even before construction of the dam is completed, a decision is needed on the basic method selected for future surveys and the technique for analyzing sediment accumulation [4].

The main purpose of a reservoir resurvey is to compare the storage capacity with that of an earlier survey (usually the original survey); the difference is the sediment accumulation. The storage volume computations are made from an area-capacity computer program involving computation of capacities corresponding to each elevation in the area-elevation data set and fitting the capacity-elevation relationship using either the cubic-spline or least-square set of equations (Bureau of Reclamation ACAP Program). The end product of the area-capacity computations is a plot of the areas and capacities for the original and new surveys. An example of this plot is shown on figure A-1.

A comparison of capacities between the two surveys, as shown on figure A-1, gives the measured volume of sediment accumulation. It is important in this sediment volume computation that the

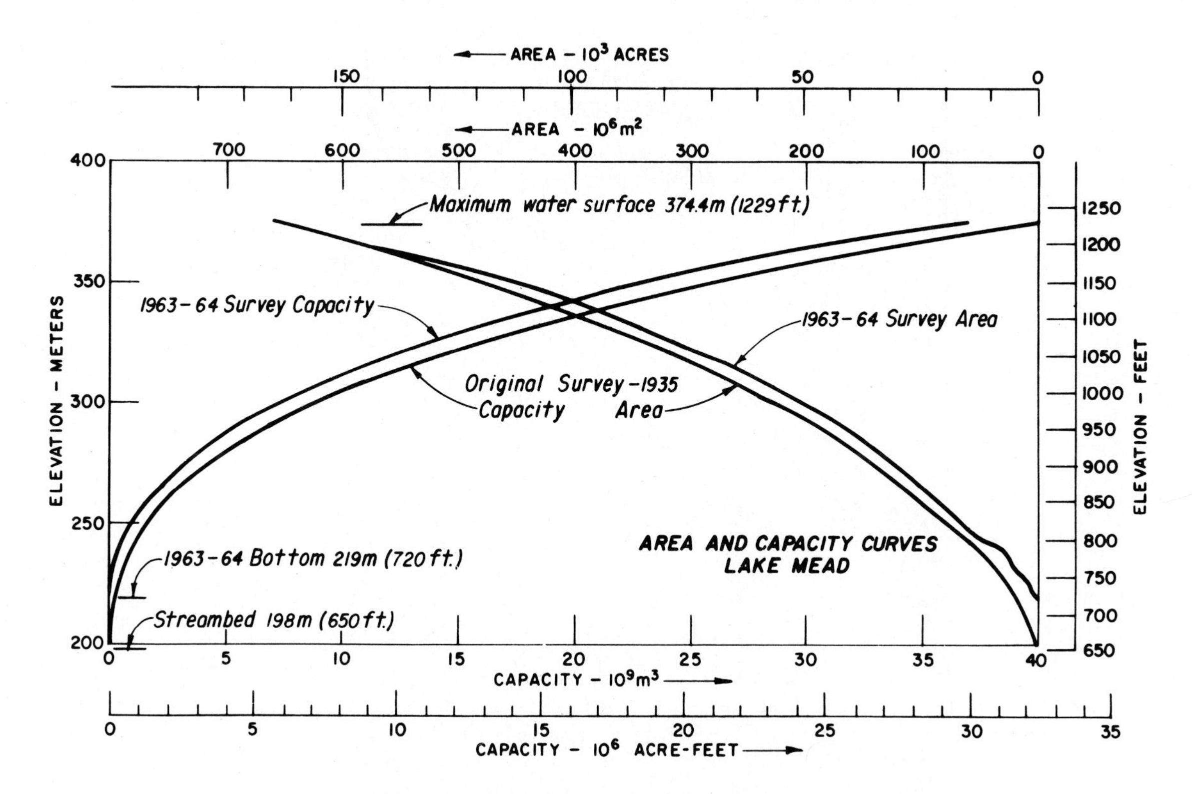

Figure A-1.—Area and capacity curves for Lake Mead. 103–D–1803.

method selected to compute capacities from contour areas be the same for both of the surveys being compared. That is, if the ACAP method is used for the original capacity computations, it should also be used for computing the resurveyed reservoir capacity. This would help eliminate any differences in technique having undue influence on the sediment volume computations. All information from the survey should be documented in the Reservoir Sedimentation Data Summary sheet, which is presented to the Subcommittee on Sedimentation, Interagency Advisory Committee on Water Data for use in the periodically published summary on reservoir surveys [5].

Other worthwhile analyses of data from reservoir sedimentation surveys involve plotting percent reservoir depth versus percent sediment deposit or plotting a sediment deposition profile throughout the length of the reservoir. The plot of percent depth versus percent sediment (fig. A-2) has been used in developing design curves in predicting the distribution of sediment deposits in planning studies. The deposition profile provides valuable information for defining the delta, foreset slopes for possible density currents, and depth of sediment depositions at the dam. An example of a dimensionless plot of a sediment deposition profile for Lake Mead is shown on figure A-3.

At the time of the reservoir survey, data are also needed on some of the characteristics of the sediments that are deposited and moving through the reservoir. Samples of deposited sediments should be spaced throughout the reservoir area to be representative of deposits in the topset and foreset slopes of the delta as well as at the bottomset slopes in the deeper parts of the reservoir. Analysis of the samples collected consists of density, particle-size distribution, and mineralogic composition. These data on deposited sediments are used for a better understanding of the source of incoming sediments, for the study of density currents or the study of sluicing capabilities through outlet works, for verification of models being developed on movement of sediment through reservoirs, and for development of empirical relationships to be used in the planning and design of other reservoirs. In addition to the above uses, data on sediment characteristics when combined with survey data on depths of sediment near the dam can be used to identify future problems of sediment deposition associated with inflow to powerplant intakes or plugging of outlet works. A unique sediment deposition problem to be

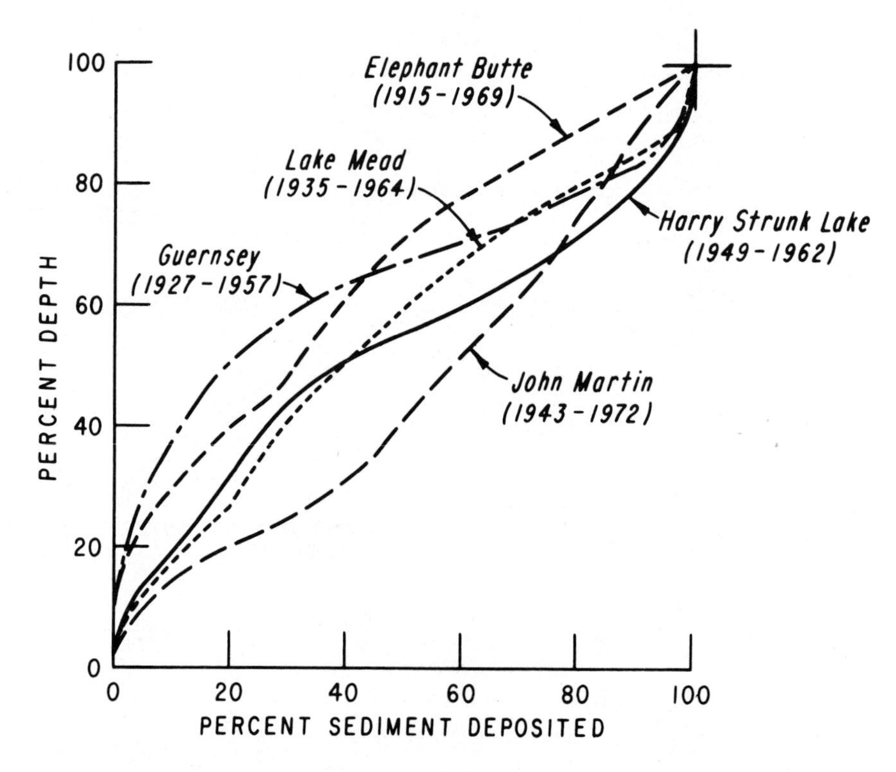

Figure A-2.—Sediment distribution from reservoir surveys. 103-D-1804.

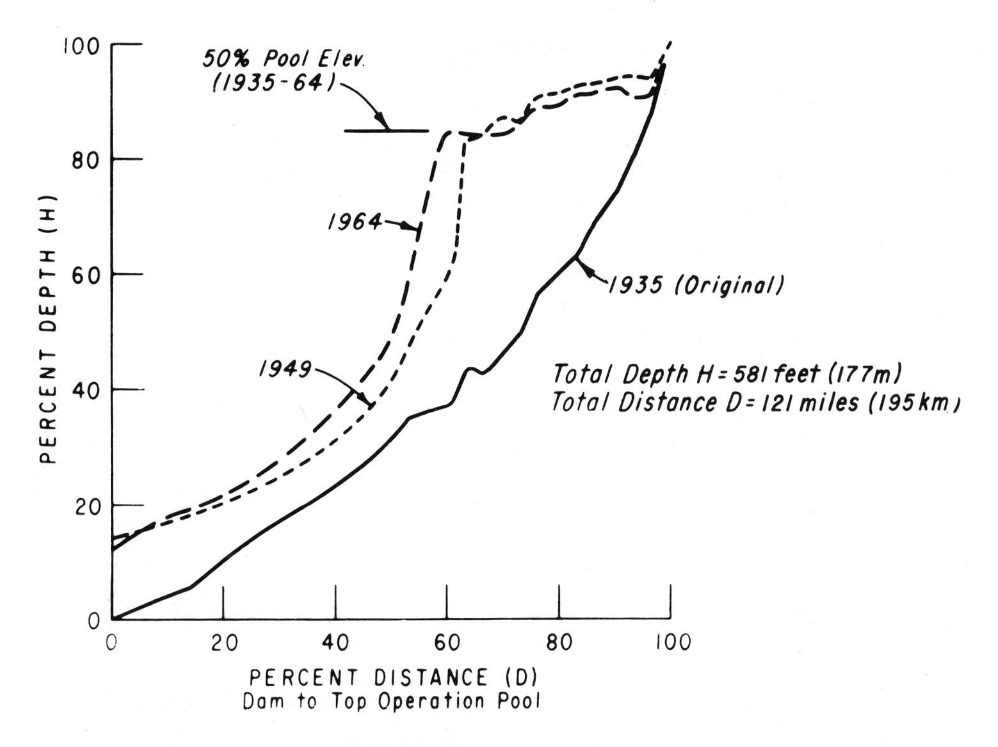

Figure A-3.—Lake Mead sediment deposition profile. 103–D–1805.

evaluated in reporting the results of the survey data involves the effects of bank sloughing, landslides, and valley wall erosion by wave action or unstable slopes.

Reservoir survey data [5] provide an excellent source for determining sediment yield rates for any part of the United States. Adjustments in the sediment yield rate are usually necessary to account for variation in drainage area characteristics. One of the most important variations is the size of the drainage basin. Some investigators have found that the sediment yield varies with the 0.8 power of the drainage area size [1] (equivalent to sediment yield rate varying with −0.2 power of the drainage area). Figure A-4 is a plot of sediment yield rate versus drainage area that was developed from selected reservoir resurvey data in the semiarid climate of the southwestern United States. In using the drainage area versus sediment yield relationship as shown on figure A-4, it is best to make a calibration with a known sediment yield and evaluate the nine sediment contributing factors. This calibration, along with an identification of similar sediment contributing characteristics, permits drawing a line parallel to that shown on figure A-4 through any measured data point.

(c) *Sediment Sampling Data.*—Sampling is the surest method of accurately determining the suspended sediment load being carried by a stream at a particular location. Suspended sediment sampling in combination with total load computations is the preferred method used for planning studies in determining the sediment inflow to a proposed reservoir. The objective of a sediment sampling program on a river is to collect sufficient samples of sediment carried both as suspended load and as bedload to define the total sediment being transported. For suspended sediment sampling it is essential to measure the water discharge, Q_w, in cubic feet (cubic meters) per second, which is combined with the suspended sediment concentration, C, in milligrams per liter, to give the suspended sediment load Q_s in tons per day by the equation:

$$Q_s = 0.0027CQ_w \text{ (English units)}$$
$$\text{or } Q_s = 0.0864CQ_w \text{ (SI units)} \quad (1)$$

Suspended sediment sampling equipment and techniques for collecting can vary considerably depending on program objectives and field conditions. Suspended sediment sampling devices are designed to collect a representative sample of the water-sediment mixture. A thorough discussion of sediment samplers and techniques for sampling is given

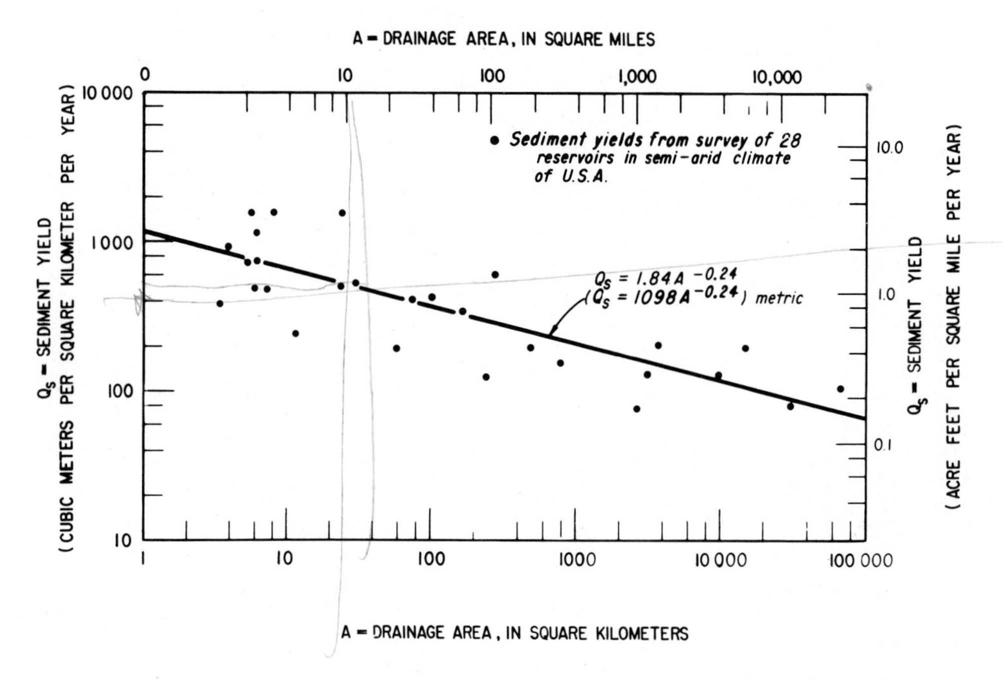

Figure A-4.—Average annual sediment yield rate versus drainage area size. 103–D–1806.

in both the series of reports prepared by U.S. Interagency Sedimentation Project [6] and the *U.S. Government Handbook* [7]. An example of the sampler designed by the U.S. Interagency Sedimentation Project is shown on figure A-5.

In the collection of suspended sediment samples, it is important that samples are integrated with the depth from the water surface to the streambed and the width across the channel. Although other methods for sampling are described in the *U.S. Government Handbook* [7], the EWI (equal-width-increment) method provides the most representative sample of the total suspended sediment load. This method is accomplished by sampling at equally spaced widths, or increments, across the cross section and maintaining a constant travel rate in each of the verticals sampled. In this method, a composite sample is made of all verticals sampled for only one laboratory analysis of sediment concentration (in milligrams per liter) and particle-size distribution.

The sediment sampling program should vary from one river to another, depending on temporal variations in the sediment load and particle-size distribution of the suspended and bed material sediments. The frequency of sampling suspended sediments will usually vary from every day to once or twice a month; but samples should always be taken during the flood events. In many situations, the collection and analysis of suspended sediment samples is an expensive process. Because daily sampling yields much duplication through a base flow period, sampling once or twice a month or at miscellaneous intervals, which includes sampling of flood flows, is more common and economical.

The objective of any suspended sediment sampling program is to develop a correlation between water discharge and sediment load. This correlation is commonly called a suspended sediment rating curve. This rating curve is normally a plot on logarithmic paper of water discharge, Q_w, in cubic feet (cubic meters) per second, versus sediment load, Q_s in tons per day from equation (1). These curves can best be computed by a least-squares analysis in which water discharge is the independent variable usually defined by one to three such relationships. When two or three equations are computed from the plotted points, the extrapolation beyond the observed data, especially at high flows, is considered more reliable because the skewing effect of the data points at the other extreme has been eliminated. In this extrapolation it is important that maximum concentrations of sediment be considered to avoid the potential hazard of extrapolating beyond either an observed high value for the stream being sampled or no greater than about 50 to 60 percent concentration by weight.

The one to three equation procedure can also be

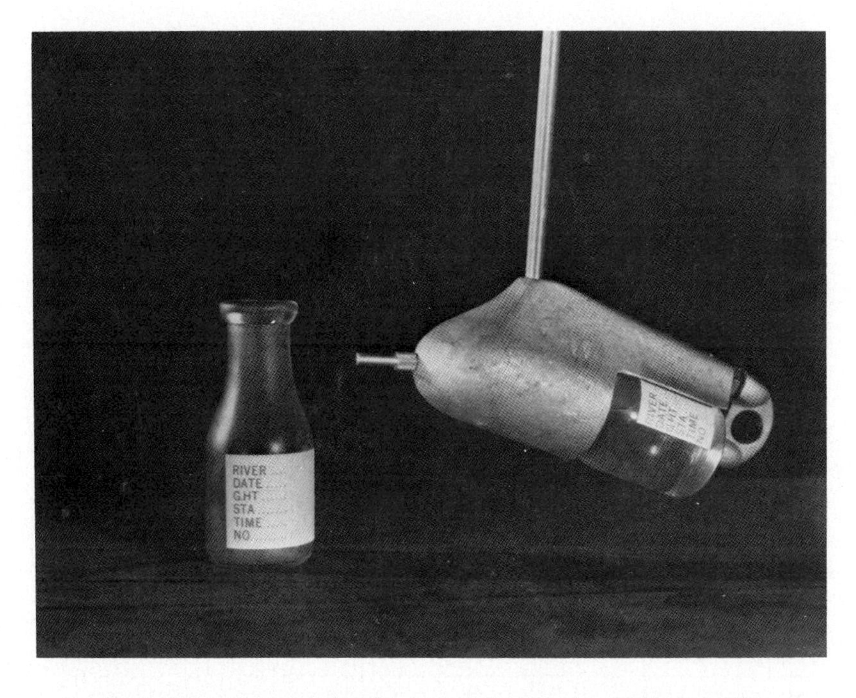

Figure A-5.—Suspended sediment sampler DH-48. P-801-D-80126

adjusted so that a second, parallel set of curves will produce the sediment load equal to the sum of the observed data points. The result of this procedure for computing suspended sediment rating curves is shown on figure A-6 where the equation for any segment is in the form:

$$Q_s = aQ_w^b \tag{2}$$

where:

Q_s = suspended transport, in tons per day,
Q_w = discharge, in cubic feet (cubic meters) per second,
a = coefficient, and
b = exponent.

An approximately 5-year sampling period may be needed to adequately cover the full range in water discharges and to avoid extreme curve extrapolation. However, a shorter period may be possible if the range in flows is adequately covered. The upper portion of the rating curve is most critical; it significantly affects the rate of sediment transport because of the extremely large sediment loads carried during flood periods. Another variation in rating curves, described by Miller [8], occurs when the source of runoff can be a combination of either snowmelt or rainstorms. Runoff from thunderstorms usually transports sediment at higher concentrations than runoff from snowmelt in the higher elevations. It may be necessary to develop individual sediment-rating curves for each of the seasons.

Suspended sediment rating curves can be combined with available water discharge records to determine the long-term average sediment yield. The longer the period of discharge records, the more reliable the results. One technique for gauging station records that cover a long period is to construct a flow-duration curve from the daily water discharges. This curve is really a cumulative frequency plot that shows the percent of time that specific discharges are equaled or exceeded for the period of record. For some streams, where only short-term discharge records are available, a long-term flow-duration curve can be computed from a correlation of short-term to long-term records at a gauging station on either the same stream or a nearby stream. If the flow-duration curve is representative of the long-term flow of the stream, it may be considered a probability curve and used to represent future conditions. With this assumption, it is combined with the suspended sediment-rating curve as described by Miller [8] to determine the long-term average suspended sediment yield for any projected period, such as 100 years. An example of the flow-duration curve for the same station used to develop the sediment rating curve on figure A-6 is illustrated on figure A-7. The Bureau of Reclamation's

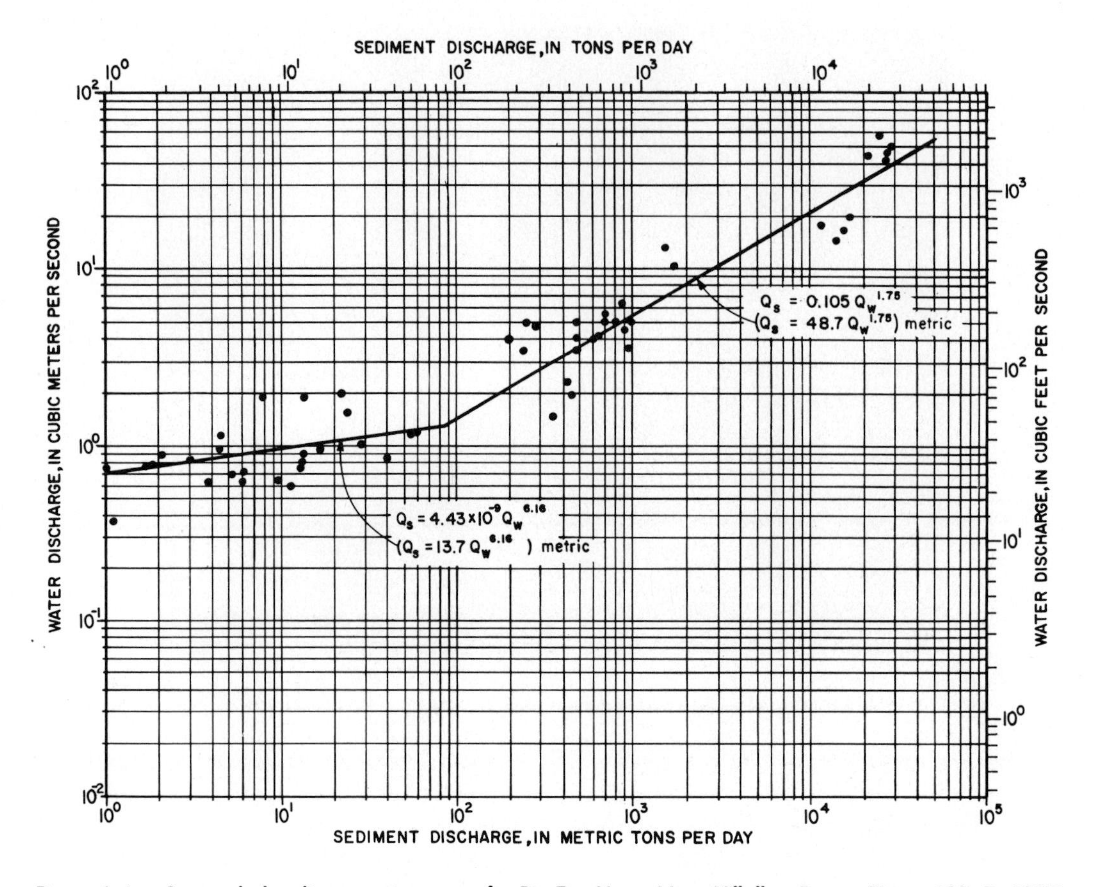

Figure A-6.—Suspended sediment rating curve for Rio Toa Vaca. Near Villalba, Puerto Rico. 103–D–1807.

computer facility is linked up with that of the USGS in Reston, Virginia, for obtaining flow-duration data for any desired period of flow record. Table A-2 shows the computation of suspended sediment load at the gauge based on combining the sediment rating curve with the flow-duration curve.

(d) *Unmeasured Sediment Load.*—To analyze the unmeasured portion of the total sediment load requires a knowledge of the following terms:

Bed material—The sediment mixture of which the streambed is composed.

Bedload—Sediment that moves by saltation, rolling, or sliding on or near the streambed.

Bed material load—The part of the sediment load that consists of grain sizes represented in the bed.

Wash load—The part of the sediment load that consists of grain sizes finer than those of the bed.

Suspended load—Particles moving outside the bed layer.

Unsampled zone—The 3 or 4 inches (76 to 102 mm) from the streambed up to the lowest point of the sampling vertical. Most suspended sediment samplers cannot sample within this zone.

The suspended sediment load as computed in table A-2 represents only a portion of the total sediment load. The unmeasured load consists of bedload plus suspended sediments in the unsampled zone between the sampler nozzle and the streambed. When the sediment sampling program is established, a preliminary appraisal should be made on the percentage that the unmeasured load is of the total load. A useful guide for evaluating the unmeasured load is the bedload correction shown in table A-3. Five conditions are given for defining bedload dependent upon suspended sediment concentration and size analysis of streambed and suspended materials. As shown in table A-3, either condition 1 or 2 may result in significant bedload, which would require a special sampling program to compute the unmeasured sediment load. Conditions 3, 4, and 5 usually indicate a 2 to 15 percent correction factor, which would not require any special bedload sampling program.

A special sampling program to be undertaken

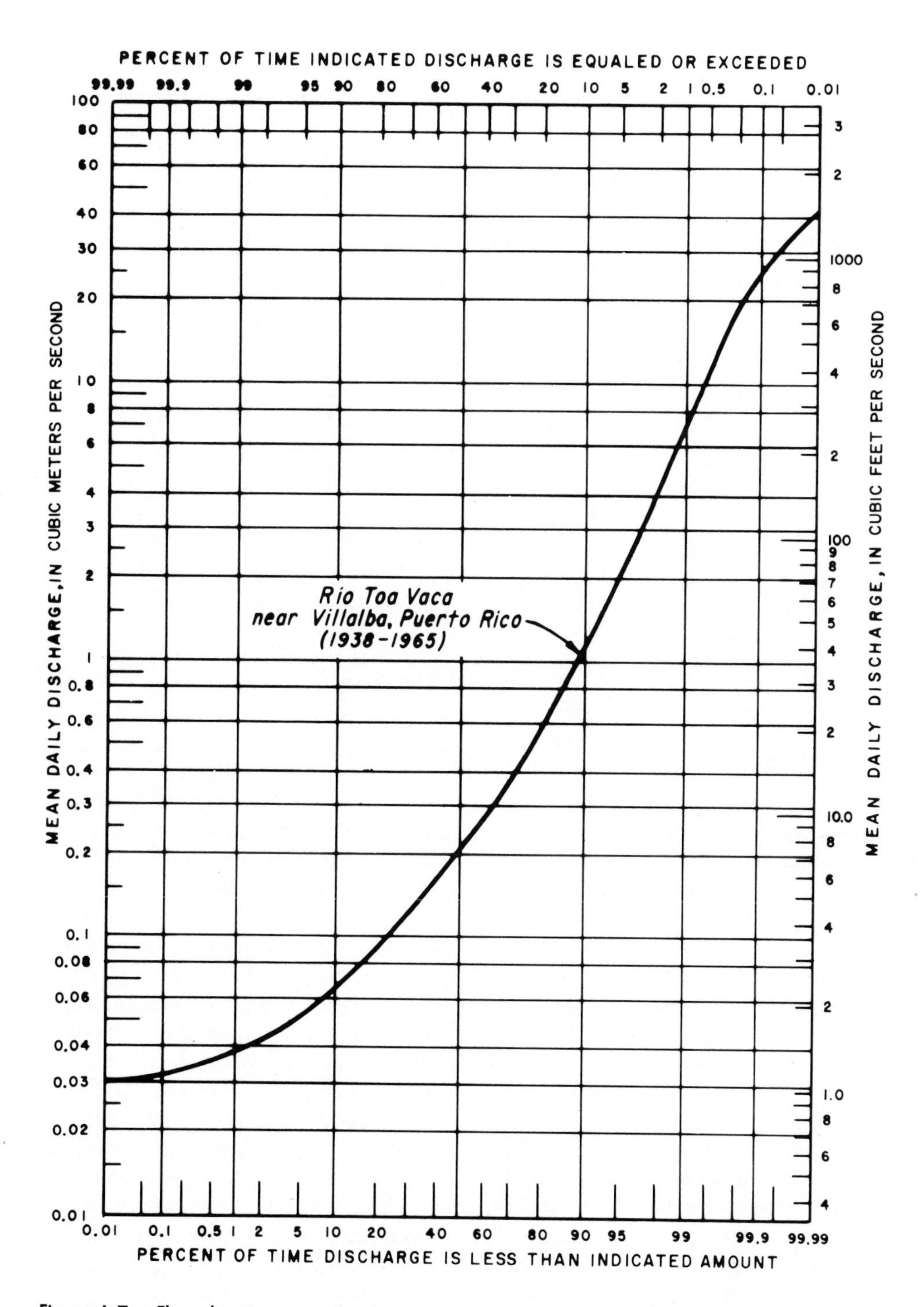

Figure A-7.—Flow duration curve for Rio Toa Vaca. Near Villalba, Puerto Rico. 103–D–1808.

Table A-2.—Sediment load computations for Rio Toa Vaca. Near Villalba, Puerto Rico.

Project: Puerto Rico
Stream: Rio Toa Vaca
Period of record: Streamflow 1938-1965
Computed by:

Reservoir: Toa Vaca
Section:
Sediment: 1963-1967
Checked by:

Date: May 1968

(1) Limits, %	(2) Interval	(3) Middle ordinate	(4) Q_w		(5) Q_s		(6) $Q_w = \frac{col.(2) \times col.(4)}{100}$		(7) $Q_s = \frac{col.(2) \times col.(5)}{100}$	
			ft³/s	m³/s	ton/d	t/d	ton/d	t/d	ton/d	t/d
0.00-0.02	0.02	0.01	1,412.0	40.0	34,151	30,984	0.282	0.008	6.83	6.20
0.02-0.1	.08	.06	1,037.8	29.4	19,925	18,077	0.830	.024	15.94	14.46
0.1-0.5	.4	.3	617.8	17.5	8,038	7,292	2.47	.070	32.15	29.17
0.5-1.5	1.0	1.0	250.6	7.1	1,657	1,504	2.51	.071	16.57	15.04
1.5-5.0	3.5	3.25	115.4	3.27	426.6	387	4.039	.114	14.93	13.55
5-15	10	10	44.1	1.25	59.7	54.2	4.410	.125	5.97	5.42
15-25	10	20	20.8	0.59	0.583	0.531	2.080	.059	0.058	0.053
25-35	10	30	14.1	.40	.053	.049	1.410	.040	.005	.005
35-45	10	40	10.6	.30	.009	.008	1.060	.030	.001	.001
45-55	10	50	8.1	.23	.002	.002	0.810	.023	.0002	.0002
55-65	10	60	6.4	.18	.0004	.0004	.640	.018		
65-75	10	70	4.6	.13			.460	.013		
75-85	10	80	3.5	.10			.350	.010		
85-95	10	90	2.4	.068			.240	.007		
95-96.5	3.5	96.75	1.7	.048			.060	.002		
98.5-99.5	1.0	99.0	1.3	.038			.013	.0004		
99.5-99.9	0.4	99.7	1.2	.034			.005	.0001		
99.9-99.98	.08	99.94	1.1	.030			.001			
99.98-100	.02	99.99	1.1	.030			.0002			
						Total	21.67	0.615	92.45	83.90

Annual discharge = Total Q_w = 21.67 × 365 × 1.9835 = 15,700 acre-ft/yr = Total Q_w = 0.615 × 365 × 86.4 × 10^3 = 19.4 10^6 m³/yr

Annual sediment load = Total Q_s = 92.45 × 365 = 33,700 ton/yr = Total Q_s = 83.90 × 365 = 30,600 t/yr

$$\text{Average concentration, } C = \frac{Q_s}{Q_w \times 0.0027} = \frac{92.45}{21.67 \times 0.0027} = 1580 \text{ mg/L} = \left[\frac{Q_s}{Q_w \times 0.0864} = \frac{83.90}{0.615 \times 0.0864} = 1580 \text{ mg/L}\right]$$

under conditions 1 and 2 in table A-3 is usually established for total sediment transport computations by use of the Modified Einstein procedure [9, 10, 11]. Modified Einstein computations require the collection of the following data for at least 5 to 10 discharges covering the range of flows with as many measurements at higher discharges as possible:

- *Discharge measurements*—Cross-section area, channel width, depth, mean channel velocity, and streamflow.
- *Sediment samples*—Suspended sediment samples analyzed for concentration and size distribution, bed material samples analyzed for size distribution, and water temperature.

The Modified Einstein procedure is quite different from the original Einstein [12] method. Unlike many formulas for computing sediment transport, the Modified Einstein procedure is not a method for predicting sediment transport under future flow conditions. The unique requirement for a discharge measurement and collection of depth-integrated, suspended sediment samples as a base in the computations makes the Modified Einstein procedure serve two main purposes: (1) it yields the unmeasured load to be added to the suspended load, and (2) it provides a check or verification on the most reliable predictive formula. An example of the Modified Einstein computation results is shown in table A-4, which is taken from a printout from the computer program developed by the Bureau. The computer program developed by the Bureau follows the same procedure given in the Bureau's report [10] except for the suspended load exponent, or computation of z, which is described in [11].

There are situations where other methods for computing the unmeasured load are needed to either supplement or to replace the Modified Einstein procedure. This usually happens at the higher water discharges, when sampling is difficult, or with bimodal transport (usually under condition 4 or 5 in table A-3) where streambed material is unlike the suspended material.

Several methods or formulas for computing the

Table A-3.—Bedload correction.

Condition	Suspended sediment concentration, mg/L	Streambed material	Texture of suspended material	Percent bedload in terms of suspended load
[1]1	<1000	Sand	20 to 50% sand	25 to 150
[1]2	1000 to 7500	Sand	20 to 50% sand	10 to 35
3	>7500	Sand	20 to 50% sand	5
[2]4	Any concentration	Compacted clay gravel, cobbles, or boulders	Small amount up to 25% sand	5 to 15
5	Any concentration	Clay and silt	No sand	<2

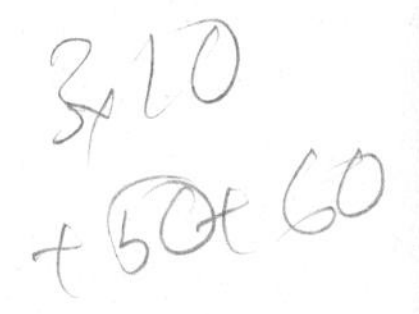

[1]Special sampling program for Modified Einstein computations required under these conditions.
[2]A bedload sampler such as the Helley-Smith bedload sampler may be used, or computations made by use of two or more of the bedload equations when bed material is gravel or cobble size.

Table A-4.—Modified Einstein procedure computations.

OUTPUT
DETERMINATION OF TOTAL SEDIMENT LOAD IN A STREAM

Job Ident Niobrara River— River Range 5
Method of Computation Modified Einstein Date of Computation 03/26/82

Date of Sample = 06/13/79 Temperature = 73.0°F (22.2°C) Slope of Energy Gradient = 0.00130 ft/ft
Discharge = 850 ft³/s (24.1 m³/s) Concentration in p/m = 296 Sampled Sediment = 679 tons/d (616 t/d)
D_{65} = 0.3080 mm D_{35} = 0.2360 mm
Area = 538 ft² (50 m²) Top Width = 705.0 ft. (215 m) Equiv. Depth = 0.00 ft Equiv. Slope = 0.00000 ft/ft
Velocity = 1.58 ft/s (0.482 m/s) Equiv. Width = 0.0 ft Average Bottom Depth = 0.76 ft (0.232 m) Hydr. Radius = 0.76 ft (0.232 m)
Distance Between Sampler and Bed (DSUBN) = 0.30 ft (.0914 m) Average Depth From Sample Verticals (DSUBS) = 0.76 ft (0.232 m)

Size fraction, mm		Percent of material		IBQB,	QPRIME Subs,	z-Values		Computational factors		Computed Total Load	
		Suspended	Bed	ton/d	ton/d	Computed	Fitted	F(J)	F(I)+1	ton/d	t/d
0.0160	0.0625	16.90	0.26	0.01	74.0	0.00	0.23	0.00	1149.56	114.8	104.2
.0625	.1250	15.20	1.84	.19	66.5	.00	.42	.00	162.95	103.3	93.7
.1250	.2500	34.00	39.50	11.28	148.8	.57	.58	.00	48.77	550.3	499.2
.2500	.5000	30.90	50.34	40.67	135.2	.74	.72	.00	18.47	751.3	681.6
.5000	1.0000	3.00	6.11	7.34	13.1	.83	.84	.00	11.87	87.1	79.0
1.0000	2.0000	0.00	0.99	0.07	0.0	.00	.94	.00	7.64	0.5	0.5
2.0000	4.0000	.00	.74	.00	.0	.00	1.05	.00	5.53	.0	
4.0000	8.0000	.00	.17	.00	.0	.00	1.17	.00	4.18	.0	
8.0000	16.0000	.00	.05	.00	.0	.00	1.29	.00	3.21	.0	
Totals		100.0	100.0		437.7					1607.3	1458.2

bedload or total bed material load have been advanced by various investigators over the years. Most of these formulas are based on the principle that the capability of the stream to transport bed materials varies directly with the differences between the shear stress acting on the bed particles and the critical shear stress required for initiation of particle motion [13]. One of the better known formulas is that of Einstein [12], which applied a stochastic approach to sediment transport. Statistical and probability theories are used as a basis for formulas, and experimental results are used to establish values for various constants and indexes. Of the various refinements of Einstein's original work, the

Bureau has had the most success in predicting sediment transport in streams having graded bed material size by using the Velocity-Xi Adjustment to the Einstein formula, as described by Pemberton [14]. Other formulas that are often compared with the Modified Einstein method are described in Meyer-Peter and Muller [15, 16], Schoklitsch [17], Ackers and White [18], Engelund and Hansen [19], and Yang [20].

A description of the theory and development of the above formulas are much beyond the scope of this narrative, and the reader is directed to the listed references for this information.

The recommended approach for extending the range of completed total sediment loads is to compute total sediment load using the Modified Einstein procedure for as wide a range of discharges as possible, then to compare these results with those of the predicative formulas. The formula yielding results most comparable with the Modified Einstein computations is then used to extend the range to higher discharges. When data are not available for Modified Einstein computations, a predicative formula should be selected that has given good comparative results for streams having similar hydraulic properties and bed material size distributions.

If the bed material is predominately coarse sand greater than about 0.5 mm, gravel- or cobble-size material, a special sampling program may be used either independently or as a check on the bedload formula. This involves measuring the bedload by a direct measuring sampler such as the Helley-Smith bedload sampler described by Emmett [21]. The sampling procedure can be quite extensive, depending on dunes and irregular streambed patterns. Several samples at 10 to 20 equally spaced verticals in the cross section are necessary to adequately describe the spatial and temporal variations in transport rate.

Once the rate of unmeasured sediment movement has been determined from either the Modified Einstein computations or bedload formulas, an unmeasured load rating curve is drawn. A log-log plot of water discharge versus unmeasured load for these special samples can be analyzed by least-squares analysis. A computation of unmeasured load from the correlation of water discharge to unmeasured load is similar to the suspended load computations shown in table A-2. Total load is obtained by combining the results of the suspended load and unmeasured load computations.

(e) *Adjustment to Damsite.*—Any direct measurement of sediment yield, either from reservoir surveys or from sediment sampling, requires an adjustment in the yield rate from the specific location to that at the damsite. In many cases the sediment yields, in acre-feet or tons per square mile derived from the reservoir survey or at the gauging station can be applied directly to the drainage area above the damsite. If the yield rates are not directly applicable to the drainage area above a damsite, the nine factors shown in table A-1 can be used in a calibration technique for adjustment to the damsite.

A.3. *Reservoir Sediment Deposition.*—Once the estimated sediment inflow to a reservoir has been established, attention must be given to the effect the deposition of this sediment will have upon the life and daily operation of the reservoir. The mean annual sediment inflow, the trap efficiency of the reservoir, the ultimate density of the deposited sediment, and the distribution of the sediment within the reservoir, all must be considered in the design of the dam.

To prevent premature loss of usable storage capacity, an additional volume of storage equal to the sediment deposition anticipated during the economic life of the reservoir is usually included in the original design. The Bureau of Reclamation requires that provisions be made for sediment storage space whenever the anticipated sediment accumulation during the period of project economic analysis exceeds 5 percent of the total reservoir capacity. A 100-year period of economic analysis and sediment accumulation is typically used for a reservoir; however, less than 100 years of sediment accumulation may be used if the economic analysis justifies a lesser allocation. The allocated sediment space is provided to prevent encroachment on the required conservation storage space for the useful life of the project.

A schematic diagram of anticipated sediment deposition (fig. A-8) shows the effect of sediment on storage. A distribution study with 100-year area and capacity curves similar to that shown on the left side of figure A-8 is needed whenever the 100-year sediment accumulation is more than 5 percent of the total reservoir capacity. In operational studies of a reservoir for determining the available water supply to satisfy projected water demands over an economic life, an average (50 years for a 100-year economic analysis) of the sediment accumulation

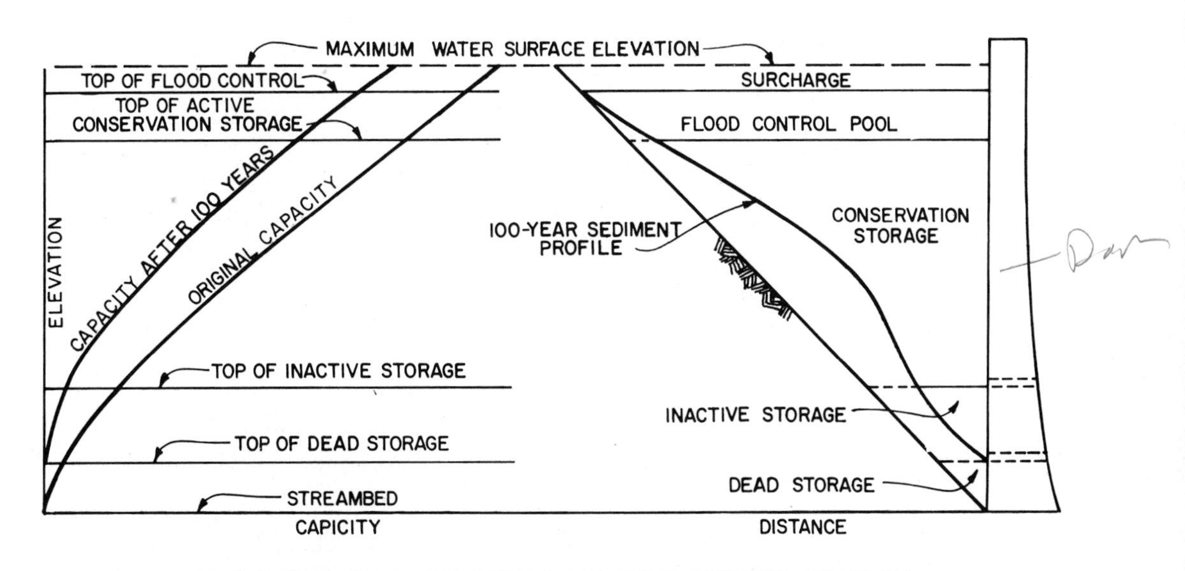

Figure A-8.—Schematic diagram of reservoir allocations and sediment deposition. 103–D–1809.

during the economic life period can be used. However, the total sediment deposition is used for design purposes to set the sediment elevation at the dam to determine loss of storage caused by sediment in any assigned storage space and to be used in determining total storage requirements.

(a) *Trap Efficiency*.—The trap efficiency of a reservoir is defined as the ratio of the quantity of deposited sediment to the total sediment inflow. It is dependent primarily upon the sediment particle fall velocity and on the rate of flow through the reservoir. Particle fall velocity may be influenced by the size and shape of the particles, the viscosity of the water, and the chemical composition of the water. The rate of flow through the reservoir is determined by the volume of inflow with respect to available storage and by the rate of outflow.

Methods for estimating reservoir trap efficiency are empirically based upon measured sediment deposits in a large number of reservoirs. Brune [22] has presented a set of envelope curves for use with normal ponded reservoirs using the capacity-inflow relationship of the reservoirs. The Brune medium curve is reproduced on figure A-9.

Using data from Tennessee Valley Authority reservoirs, M. A. Churchill [23] developed a relationship between the percent of incoming sediment passing through a reservoir and the sedimentation index of the reservoir. The sedimentation index is defined as the ratio of the period of retention to the mean velocity through the reservoir. The Churchill curve has been converted to a dimensionless expression by multiplying the sedimentation index by g, the acceleration due to gravity.

The following definitions are helpful in using the Churchill curve:

Capacity—Capacity of the reservoir in the mean operating pool for the period to be analyzed, in cubic feet (cubic meters).

Inflow—Average daily inflow rate during the study period, in cubic feet (cubic meters) per second.

Period of retention—Capacity divided by inflow rate.

Length—Reservoir length, in feet (meters) at mean operating pool level.

Velocity—Mean velocity, in feet (meters) per second, arrived at by dividing the inflow by the average cross-sectional area in square feet (square meters). The average cross-sectional area can be determined from the capacity divided by the length.

Sedimentation index—Period of retention divided by velocity.

Figure A-9 provides a good comparison of the Brune and Churchill methods for computing trap efficiencies [24]. A general guideline is to use the Brune method for large storage or normal ponded reservoirs and the Churchill curve for settling basins, small reservoirs, flood retarding structures,

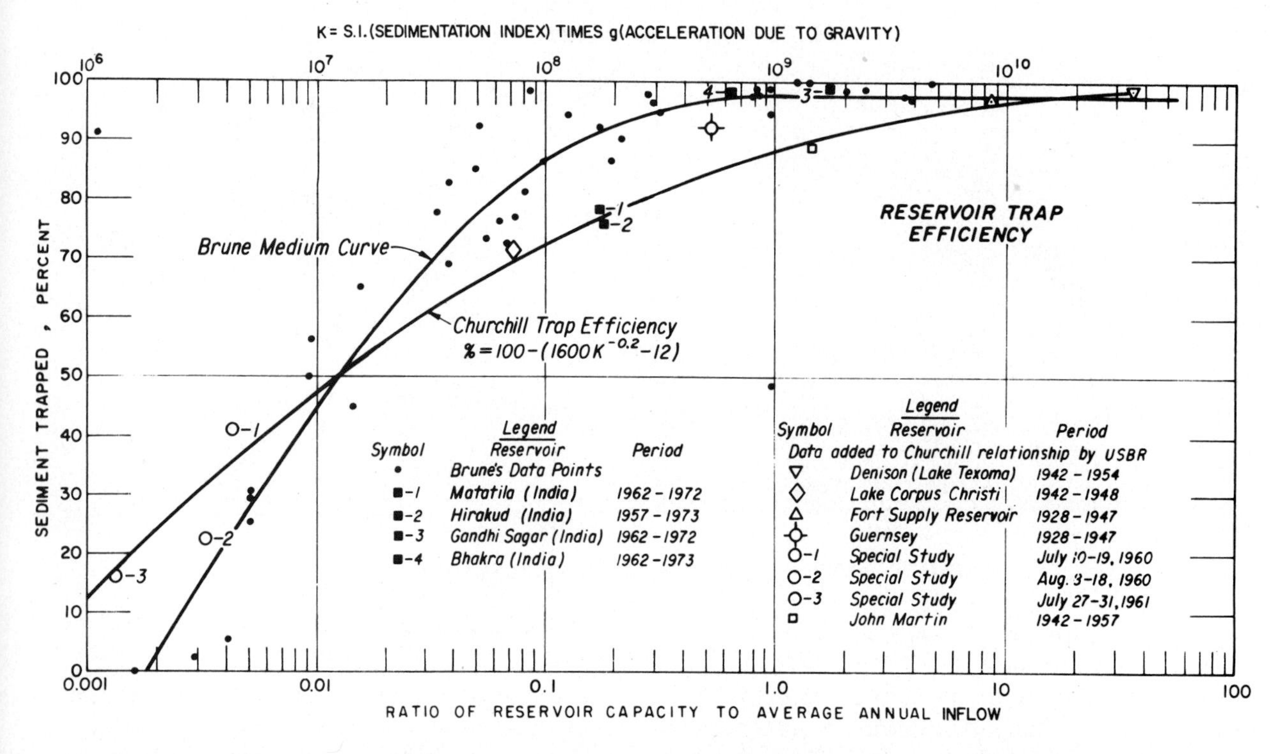

Figure A-9.—Trap efficiency curves. From Brune [22] and Churchill [23]. 103-D-1810.

semidry reservoirs or reservoirs that are continuously sluiced.

When the anticipated sediment accumulation is larger than one-fourth of the reservoir capacity, the trap efficiency must be analyzed for incremental periods of the reservoir life. Theoretically, the reservoir trap efficiency will decrease continuously once storage is begun; however, for most reservoirs it is not practical to analyze the trap efficiency in intervals of less than 10 years. The variability of the annual sediment inflow is sufficient reason not to use shorter periods of analysis.

(b) *Density of Deposited Sediment.*—Samples of deposited sediments in reservoirs have provided useful information on the density of deposits. The density of deposited material in terms of dry mass per unit volume is used to convert total sediment inflow to a reservoir from a mass to a volume. The conversion is necessary when total sediment inflow is computed from a measured suspended- and bed-material sediment sampling program. Basic factors influencing density of sediment deposits in a reservoir are (1) the manner in which the reservoir is operated, (2) the texture and size of deposited sediment particles, and (3) the compaction or consolidation rate of deposited sediments.

The reservoir operation is probably the most influential of these factors. Sediments that have deposited in reservoirs subjected to considerable drawdown may be exposed for long periods and, therefore, undergo greater consolidation. However, reservoirs operating with a fairly stable pool do not allow the sediment deposits to dry out and consolidate as much.

The size of the incoming sediment particles has a significant effect upon density. Sediment deposits composed of silt and sand have higher densities than those in which clay predominates. The classification of sediment according to size proposed by the American Geophysical Union is as follows:

Sediment type	*Size range in millimeters*
Clay	<0.004
Silt	0.004 to 0.062
Sand	0.062 to 2.0

The accumulation of new sediment deposits on top of previously deposited sediments changes the density of the earlier deposits. This consolidation affects the average density over the estimated life of the reservoir, such as for a 100-year period. A good example of consolidation of deposited sediments is shown on figure A-10, which is taken from the report by Lara and Sanders [25] for unit weights (densities) in Lake Mead at a sampling location with all clay-size material.

The method that takes into account all three factors in determining the density of deposited sediment is demonstrated in these guidelines. The influence of reservoir operation is most significant because of the amount of consolidation or drying that can occur in the clay fraction of the deposited material when a reservoir is subjected to considerable drawdown. The size of sediment particles entering the reservoir also effects the density, as shown by the variation in initial masses. Some 1,300 samples were statistically analyzed by Lara and Pemberton [26] for determining mathematical equations for variation of the density (sometimes termed unit weight or specific weight) of the deposits with the type of reservoir operation. Additional data on density of deposited material from reservoir resurveys have supported the Lara and Pemberton [26] equation (eq. 3), which is slightly different from the Lane and Koelzer [27] equations.

Reservoir operations were classified according to operation as follows:

Operation	*Reservoir operation*
1	Sediment always submerged or nearly submerged
2	Normally moderate to considerable reservoir drawdown
3	Reservoir normally empty
4	Riverbed sediments

Selection of the proper reservoir operation number usually can be made from the operation study prepared for the reservoir.

Once the reservoir operation number has been selected, the density of the sediment deposits can be estimated using the following equation:

$$W = W_c p_c + W_m p_m + W_s p_s \qquad (3)$$

where:

W = unit weight in pounds per cubic foot (kilograms per cubic meter),

p_c, p_m, p_s = percentages of clay, silt, and sand, respectively, of the inflowing sediment, and

W_c, W_m, W_s = coefficients of unit weight for clay, silt, and sand, respectively.

These coefficients can be obtained from the following tabulation:

Reservoir operation	*Initial unit weight (mass) in lb/ft³ (kg/m³)* W_c	W_m	W_s
1	26 (416)	70 (1120)	97 (1550)
2	35 (561)	71 (1140)	97 (1550)
3	40 (641)	72 (1150)	97 (1550)
4	60 (961)	73 (1170)	97 (1550)

As an example, the following data are known for a proposed reservoir:

Reservoir operation: 1

Size analysis: 23 percent clay, 40 percent silt, and 37 percent sand

Therefore:

$$W = 26\ (0.23) + 70\ (0.40) + 97\ (0.37)$$
$$= 6 + 28 + 36 = 70\ \text{lb/ft}^3 = 1120\ \text{kg/m}^3$$

In determining the density of sediment deposits in reservoirs after a period of reservoir operation, it is recognized that part of the sediment will deposit in the reservoir in each of the T years of operation, and each year's deposits will have a different compaction time. Miller [28] developed an approximation of the integral for determining the average density of all sediment deposited in T years of operation as follows:

$$W_T = W_1 + 0.4343K \left[\frac{T}{T-1}(\log_e T) - 1 \right] \qquad (4)$$

where:

W_T = average density after T years of reservoir operation,

W_1 = initial unit weight (density) derived from equation (3), and

K = a constant based on type of reservoir operation and sediment size analysis, obtained from the following tabulation:

Reservoir operation	*K values for English (SI) units* *Sand-*K_s	*Silt-*K_m	*Clay-*K_c
1	0	5.7 (91)	16.0 (256)
2	0	1.8 (29)	8.4 (135)
3	0	0.0 (0)	0.0 (0)

and $K = K_c p_c + K_m p_m + K_s p_s$

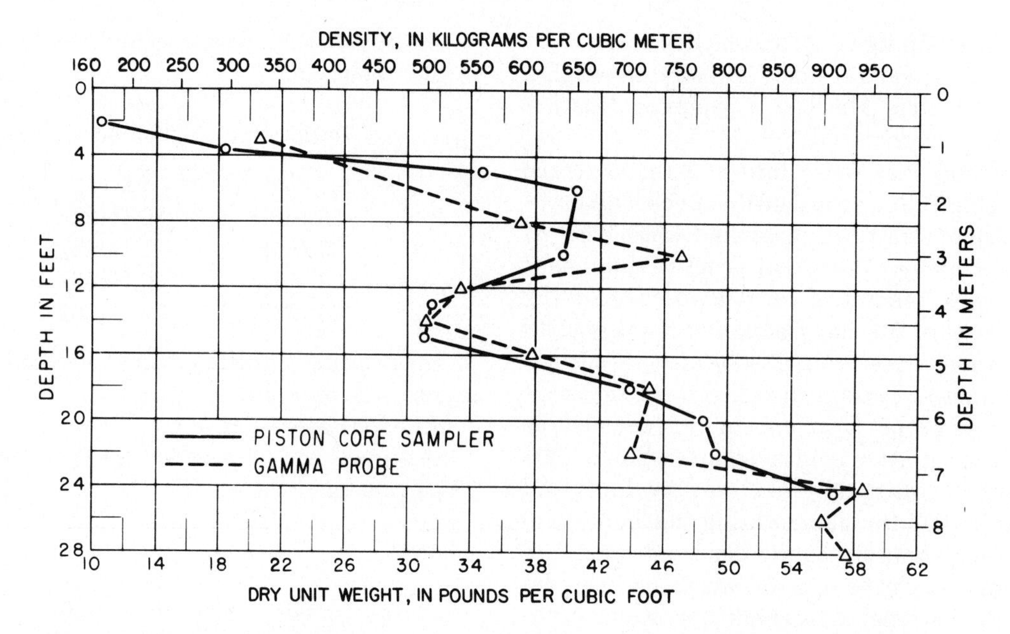

Figure A-10.—Comparison of densities on Lake Mead. At sampling location 5. 103–D–1811.

Using the same example used for the initial unit weight (density) computation, the 100-year average values to include compaction are computed as follows:

$$K = 16\ (0.23) + 5.7\ (0.40) + 0\ (0.37)$$
$$= 3.68 + 2.28 + 0 = 5.96$$

$$W_{100} = 70 + 0.4343\ (5.96) \left[\frac{100}{99} (4.61) - 1 \right]$$
$$= 70 + 2.59\ (3.66) = 79\ \text{lb/ft}^3 = 1270\ \text{m}^3$$

This value may then be used to convert the initial units weights (masses) of incoming sediment to the volume it will occupy in the reservoir after 100 years.

(c) *Sediment Distribution within a Reservoir.*—The data obtained from surveys of existing reservoirs [5], as described in section A.2 (b) "Reservoir Resurvey Data," have been extensively used to develop empirical relationships for predicting sediment distribution patterns in reservoirs. The two most common distribution techniques are illustrated on figures A-2 and A-3, where sediment is distributed by depth and by longitudinal profile distance, respectively. Both methods clearly show that sediment deposition is not necessarily confined to the lower storage increments of the reservoir.

Sediment accumulations in a reservoir are usually distributed below the top of the conservation pool, or normal water surface. However, if the reservoir has a flood control pool and it is anticipated that the water surface will be held within this pool for significant periods of time, a portion of the sediment accumulation may be deposited within this pool. Figure A-11 is a plot of data from 11 Great Plains reservoirs in the United States, which may be used as a guide in estimating the portion of the total sediment accumulation that will deposit above the normal water surface. This plot should be regarded as a rough guide only, and the estimate obtained from it should be tempered with some judgment based upon the proposed reservoir operation and the nature of the incoming sediment. This curve is based on a limited amount of data and may be revised as more information becomes available.

The flood pool index is the ratio of the flood control pool depth to the depth below the pool, multiplied by the percent of time the reservoir water surface will be within the flood control pool. For a proposed reservoir, this information must be obtained from the reservoir operation study.

Once the quantity of sediment that will deposit below the normal water surface has been established, the empirical area-reduction method may be used to estimate the distribution. This method, which was first developed from data gathered in the resurvey of 30 reservoirs, is described by Borland and Miller [29] and revised by Lara [30]. The method recognizes that distribution of sediment is dependent upon (1) the manner in which the reservoir is to be operated, (2) the texture and size of deposited sediment particles, (3) the shape of the reservoir, and (4) the volume of sediment deposited in the reservoir. However, the shape factor (3) was adopted as the major criteria for development of empirically derived design curves for use in distributing sediment. The shape of the reservoir is defined by the depth to capacity relationship where m is the reciprocal of the slope of the depth versus capacity plot on a logarithmic scale. The classification of reservoirs on this basis is as follows:

Reservoir type	*Classification*	m
I	Lake	3.5 to 4.5
II	Flood plain-foothill	2.5 to 3.5
III	Hill	1.5 to 2.5
IV	Normally empty	—

To predict the future distribution with depth, the Bureau now uses the design curves shown on figure A-12. With equal weight applied to reservoir operation and shape, a distribution type is selected from table A-5. In those cases where a choice of two types are given, a judicious decision should be made on whether the reservoir operation or shape is more influential. The texture and size of deposited sediments could be considered in this judgment analysis from the following guidelines:

Predominant size	*Type*
Sand or coarser	I
Silt	II
Clay	III

The size of sediments in most river systems, a mixture of clay, silt, and sand, has been found to be the least important factor in selecting the design type curve from figure A-12. Only for those cases with two possible type distributions should size of sediment be considered in selecting the design type curve.

Lara [30] details distributing sediment in a reservoir by the empirical-area reduction method. The appropriate design type curve is selected using the weighting procedure shown in table A-5. A computer program written by Hudspeth and Trietsch [31] can be also used for distributing sediment by either the empirical area-reduction method or the

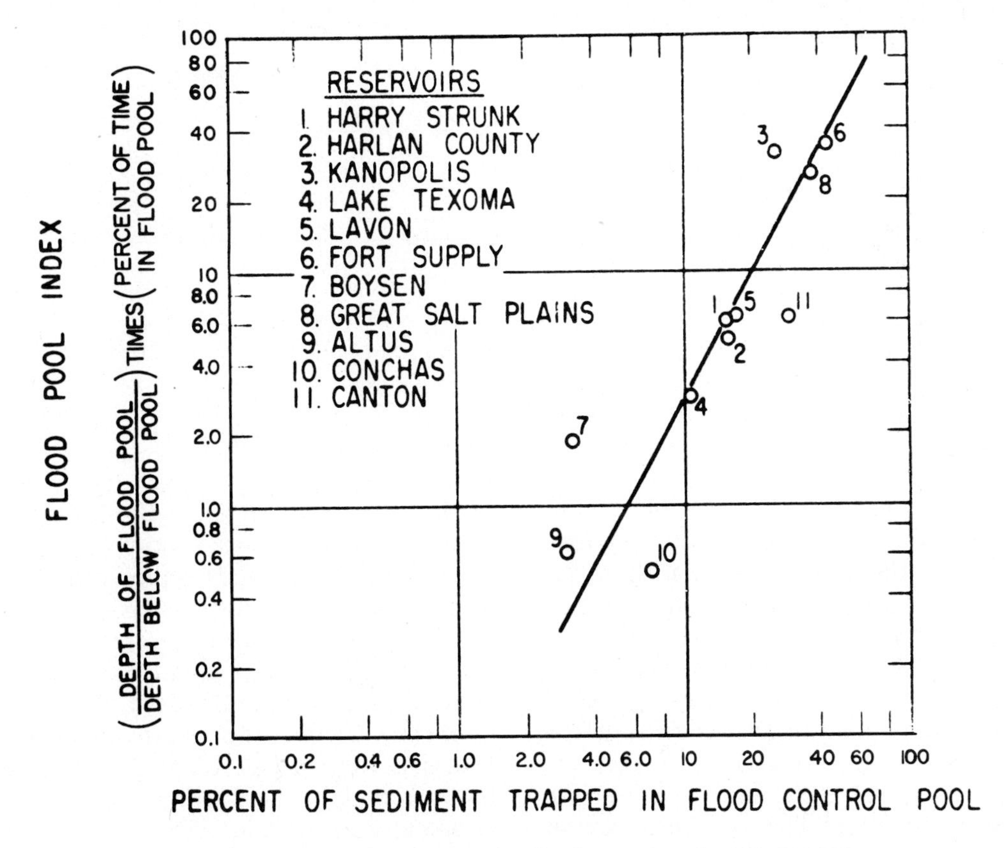

Figure A-11.—Sediment deposited in flood control pool. 103–D–1812.

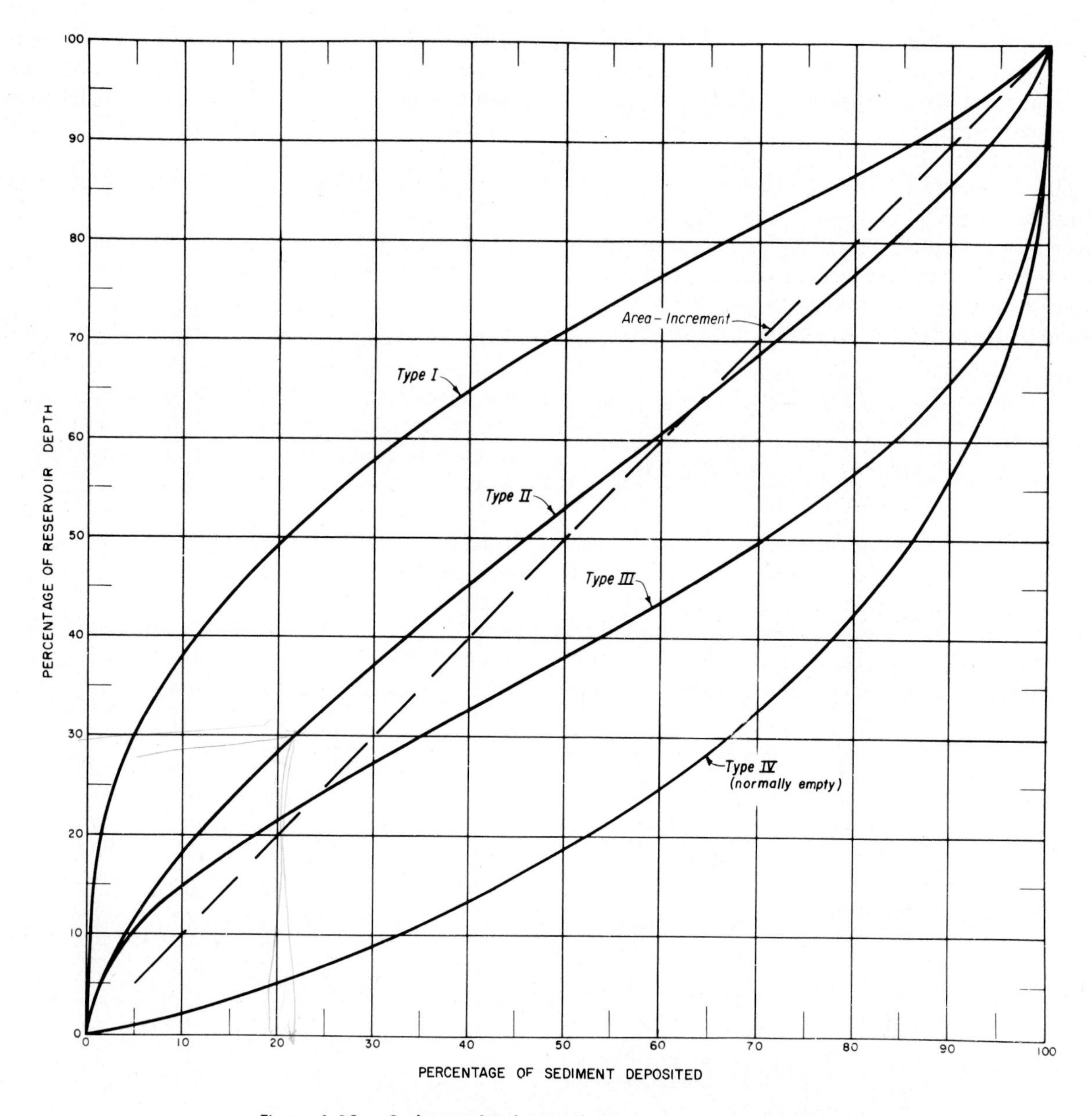

Figure A-12.—Sediment distribution design curves. 103–D–1813.

area-increment method. The area-increment method is based on the assumption that the area of sediment deposition remains constant throughout the reservoir depth. It is almost identical to the type II design curve and is often used to estimate the new zero capacity elevation at the dam.

An example of a sediment distribution study is given for Theodore Roosevelt Dam located on the Salt River in Arizona. Construction of the dam was completed in 1909, and a complete survey of the reservoir made in 1981. The reservoir had an original total capacity of 1,530,500 acre-feet (1888×10^6 m^3) at elevation 2136.0 feet (651.0 m), the top of the active conservation pool. The purpose of this example is to (1) compare the actual 1981 survey with the distribution procedures, (2) show all of the steps involved in a distribution study, and (3) provide changes in capacity and projected sediment depths at the dam for 100, 200 and 300 years.

Table A-6 gives the pertinent area-capacity data necessary to evaluate the actual 1981 survey and to use as a base in the distribution study. The total sediment accumulation in Theodore Roosevelt Lake determined from the 1981 survey was 193,765 acre-

Table A-5.—Design type curve selection.

Reservoir operation		Shape		Weighted
Class	Type	Class	Type	type
Sediment submerged	I	Lake	I	I
		Flood plain-foothill	II	I or II
		Hill and gorge	III	II
Moderate drawdown	II	Lake	I	I or II
		Flood plain-foothill	II	II
		Hill and gorge	III	II or III
Considerable drawdown	III	Lake	I	II
		Flood plain-foothill	II	II or III
		Hill and gorge	III	III
Normally empty	IV	All shapes		IV

feet (239×10^6 m^3). In the 72.4 years from closure of the dam in May 1909, until the survey in September 1981, the average annual sediment deposited was 2676 acre-feet (3.301×10^6 m^3) per year. The survey data from table A-6 were used to draw the sediment distribution design curve on figure A-13. To check the most appropriate design curve by the empirical area-reduction method, the volume of sediment accumulated in Theodore Roosevelt Lake from 1909 to 1981 was distributed by both a type II and III distribution, as shown on figure A-13. This comparison indicates that type II more closely resembles the actual survey. A plot of the area and capacity data from table A-6 is shown on figure A-14.

The first step in the distribution study for the 100-, 200-, and 300-year period is a determination of the rate of sediment accumulation. In the case of Theodore Roosevelt Lake, the rate determined from the 1981 survey used for future projections (with the assumption that the compaction or density of deposits will not change) is:

Years	*Sediment volume*	
	10^3 acre-ft	10^6 m^3
72.4 (1981)	193.765	239.009
100	267.600	330.100
200	535.200	660.200
300	802.800	990.300

There were no data on trap efficiency to apply to the above projections. The use of the rate from the 1981 survey results assumes that the trap efficiency for the first 72.4 years will remain the same through 300 years. In cases where sediment accumulation is determined from the total sediment load at a gauging station, the trap efficiency from figure A-9 and the densities from equations (3) and (4) are needed for computing the volume of sediment accumulation.

To complete this example, a logarithmic plot of the depth-capacity relationship for the original (1909) survey (fig. A-15) for Theodore Roosevelt Lake provided the shape factor for type classification. Although the lower portion of the reservoir falls slightly in the type III, the upper portion and overall slope indicates a type II classification. When assigning a type classification for either an existing reservoir or in distributing sediment on top of previous sediment deposits, it is important that the stage-capacity relationship be plotted only for the original survey. Studies have shown that a reservoir does not change type with continued sediment depositions. Once a reservoir has been assigned a type by shape, this classification will not change. However, it is possible that a change in reservoir operation could produce a new weighted type (see table A-5).

The next step in the distribution study is computation of the elevation of sediment deposited at the dam. A set of computations for determining the depth of sediment at the dam is shown in table A-7. The relative depth and a dimensionless function from the original area and capacity curves for Theodore Roosevelt Lake are computed as shown in table A-7 for the function:

$$F = \frac{S - V_h}{HA_h} \tag{5}$$

where:

F = dimensionless function of total sediment deposition, capacity, depth, and area,
S = total sediment deposition,
V_h = reservoir capacity at a given elevation h,
H = original depth of reservoir, and
A_h = reservoir area at a given elevation h.

A plot of the data points from table A-7 is superimposed on figure A-16 and the p value (relative depth) at which the line for any year crosses; the appropriate type curve will give the relative depth, p_0, equal to the new zero elevation at the dam. Figure A-16 contains plotted curves of the full range

Table A-6.—Reservoir area and capacity data, Theodore Roosevelt Lake.

Elevation		Original survey (1909)				Actual survey (1981)			
		Area		Capacity		Area		Capacity	
ft	m	acres	hectares	10^3 acre-ft	10^6 m^3	acres	hectares	10^3 acre-ft	10^6 m^3
2136.0	651.0	17,785	7198	1530.5	1888	17,337	7016	1336.7	1649
2130.0	649.2	17,203	6962	1425.5	1758	16,670	6783	1234.3	1523
2120.0	646.2	16,177	6547	1258.5	1552	15,617	6320	1072.4	1323
2110.0	643.1	15,095	6109	1102.2	1360	14,441	5844	922.3	1138
2100.0	640.1	14,104	5708	956.5	1180	13,555	5486	782.6	965
2090.0	637.0	13,247	5361	819.3	1011	12,746	5158	650.5	802
2080.0	634.0	11,939	4832	693.3	855	11,331	4586	530.0	654
2070.0	630.9	10,638	4305	580.6	716	9,842	3983	424.0	523
2060.0	627.9	9,482	3837	479.9	592	8,230	3331	333.8	412
2050.0	624.8	8,262	3344	391.2	483	6,781	2744	258.9	319
2040.0	621.8	7,106	2876	314.6	388	5,569	2254	197.6	244
2030.0	618.7	6,216	2516	248.0	306	4,847	1962	145.6	180
2020.0	615.7	5,286	2139	190.3	235	4,212	1705	100.3	124
2010.0	612.6	4,264	1726	142.9	176	3,387	1371	61.6	76.0
2000.0	609.6	3,544	1434	103.8	128	2,036	824	35.0	43.2
1990.0	606.6	2,744	1110	72.3	89.2	1,304	528	18.7	23.0
1980.0	603.5	1,985	803	48.9	60.3	903	365	7.6	9.4
1970.0	600.5	1,428	578	31.9	39.4	382	155	0.8	1.0
1960.0	597.4	1,020	413	19.7	24.4	[1]0	[1]0	[1]0.0	[1]0.0
1950.0	594.4	677	274	11.3	14.0				
1940.0	591.3	419	170	5.9	7.3				
1930.0	588.3	227	91.9	2.7	3.4				
1920.0	585.2	117	47.3	1.1	1.3				
1910.0	582.2	52	21.0	0.2	0.3				
1902.0	579.7	0	0.0	.0	.0				

[1]Sediment elevation at dam for 1981 survey was 1966.0 feet (599.2 m).

of F values for all four reservoir types and the area-increment method as developed from the capacity and area design curves. For Theodore Roosevelt Dam, the intersect points for type II as well as for the area-increment method curves gave the sediment depths shown in table A-8. The area-increment method is often selected because it always intersects the F curve and, in many cases, gives a good check on the new zero capacity elevation at the dam. In the case of Theodore Roosevelt Dam, the 1981 survey had an observed elevation at the dam of 1966.0 feet (599.2 m), which was in better agreement with the area-increment method value than any of the type curves. Data from table A-8 can be used to predict useful life of a reservoir or projection beyond the 300 years.

The final step in the distribution study is to distribute a specified volume of sediment. For the example selected this involved the 72.4-, 100-, 200-, and 300-year volumes in Theodore Roosevelt Lake by the type II design curve. The results of this distribution, using procedures described by Lara [30] or the computer program by Hudspeth and Trietsch [30], are shown on figure A-14. An example of the computer results for the 100-year distribution by use of the empirical area-reduction method and type II design curves is shown in tables A-9 and A-10. Although the example given is for type II, the equations for the relative sediment area, a, for each type follows:

Type	*Equation*	
I	$a = 5.074\, p^{1.85}(1-p)^{0.35}$	(6)
II	$a = 2.487\, p^{0.57}(1-p)^{0.41}$	(7)
III	$a = 16.967\, p^{1.15}(1-p)^{2.32}$	(8)
IV	$a = 1.486\, p^{-0.25}(1-p)^{1.34}$	(9)

where:

a = relative sediment area, and
p = relative depth of reservoir measured from the bottom.

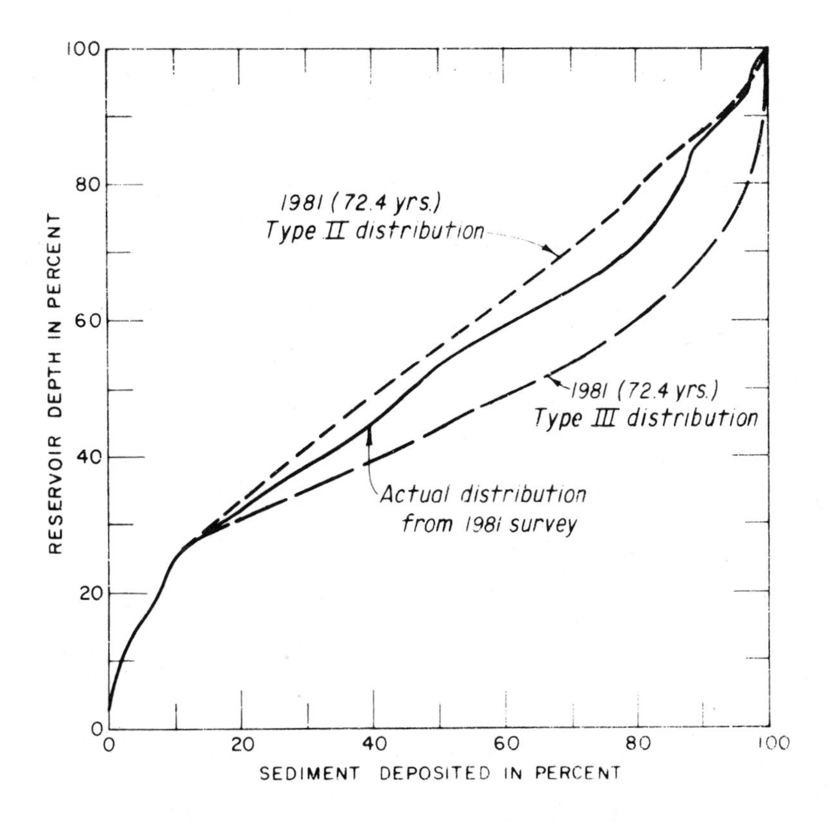

Figure A-13.—Sediment distribution for Theodore Roosevelt Lake. 103–D–1814.

(d) *Delta Deposits.*—Another phenomenon of reservoir sediment deposition is the distribution of sediment longitudinally, as illustrated on figure A-3 for Lake Mead. The extreme upstream portion of the deposition profile is the formation of delta deposits. The major consequence of these delta deposits is the raising of the backwater elevations in the channel upstream from a reservoir. Therefore, the delta may cause a flood potential that would not be anticipated from preproject channel conditions and proposed reservoir operating water surfaces. Predicting the delta development within a reservoir is a complex problem because of variables such as operation of the reservoir, sizes of sediment, and hydraulics (in particular, the width of the upper reaches of the reservoir). Sediments deposited in the delta are continually being reworked into the downstream storage during low reservoir stage and extreme flood discharges.

A delta study is needed for situations involving the construction of railroad or highway bridges in the delta area. The study should define inundated property, such as urban or farmland, and the protective structures needed to control inundation of property. The two phases of the delta study are (1) physically locating the delta and (2) with the delta located, computing the backwater through the upstream channel to define the lands that would be inundated as a result of the presence of a downstream reservoir and delta. The 100-year flood peak discharge is often used for inundation comparison in the flood plain; a 50-year delta represents the average conditions for the 100-year event. If structures such as bridges or levees to protect homes are being designed in the headwater area, then the delta should represent 100 years of sediment deposits to sustain no damage for at least a 100-year period.

The prediction of delta formation is still an empirical procedure based upon observed delta deposits in existing reservoirs. A typical delta profile is shown on figure A-17. It is defined by a topset slope, foreset slope, and a pivot point between the two slopes at the median, or 50 percent, reservoir operating level. The quantity of material to be placed in the delta is assumed equal to the volume of sand-size material or coarser (>0.062 mm) entering the reservoir for the 50- or 100-year period. A trial and error method, using survey or topographic data and

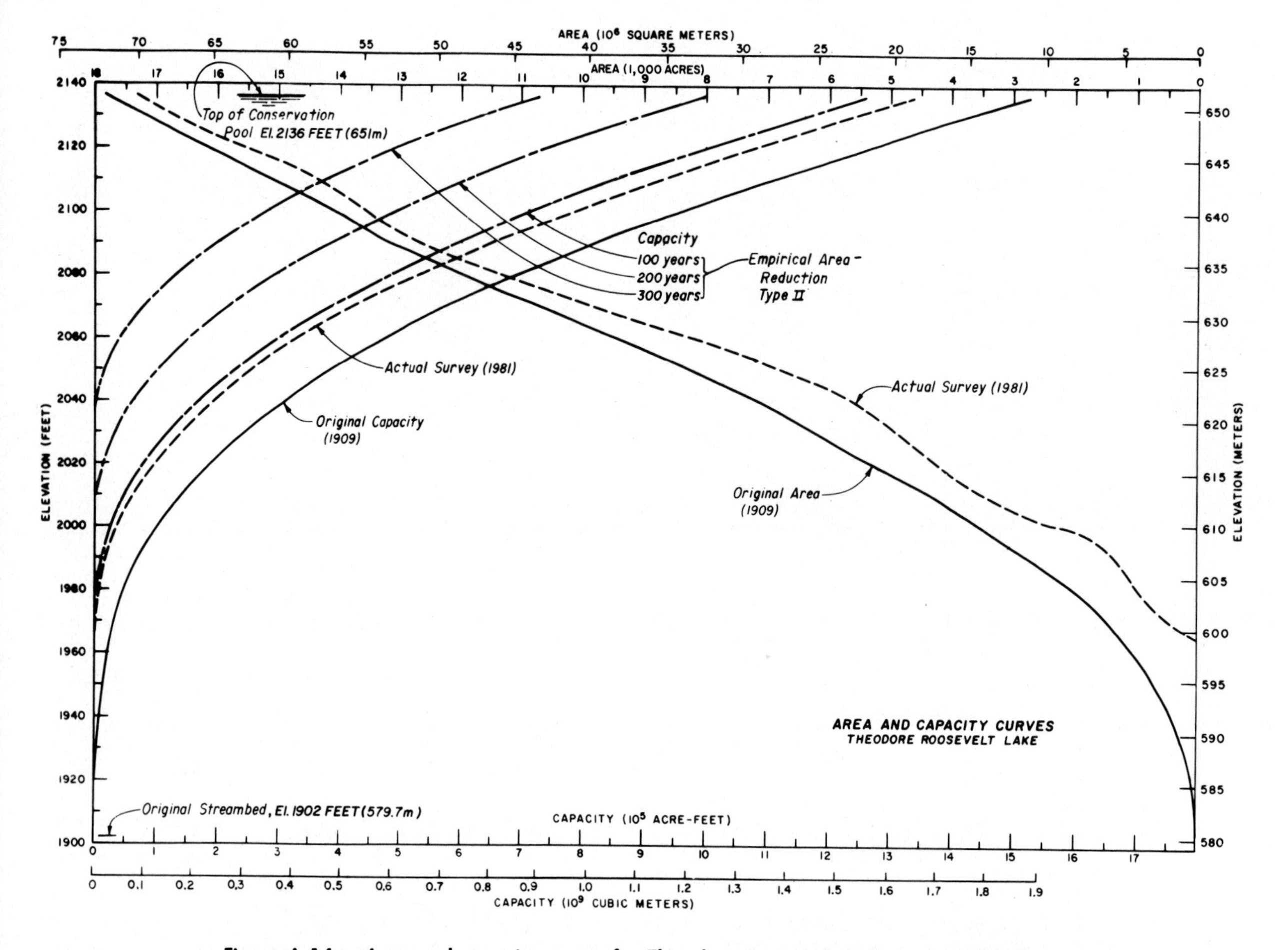

Figure A-14.—Area and capacity curves for Theodore Roosevelt Lake. 103–D–1815.

volume computations by the average end-area method, is used to arrive at a final delta location.

The topset slope of the delta is computed by one or more of several methods: (1) a statistical analysis of existing delta slopes that supports a value equal to one-half of the existing channel slope (fig. A-18), (2) topset slope from a comparable existing reservoir, or (3) zero bedload transport slope from a bedload equations such as the Meyer-Peter, Muller [15, 16] or Schoklitsch [17]. An example of the topset slope computed by the Meyer-Peter, Muller beginning transport equation for zero bedload transport is given by:

$$S = K \frac{\frac{Q}{Q_B}\left[\frac{n_s}{(D_{90})^{1/6}}\right]^{3/2} D}{d} \qquad (10)$$

where:

S = topset slope,

K = coefficient equal to 0.19 (English units) or 0.058 (SI units),

Q/Q_B = ratio of the total flow in cubic feet (cubic meters) per second to the flow over the bed of the stream, in cubic feet (cubic meters) per second. Discharge is referred to as dominant discharge and is usually determined by either channel bank full flow or by the mean annual flood peak,

D = diameter of bed material on topset slope (usually determined as weighted mean diameter in millimeters),

D_{90} = diameter of bed material for 90 percent finer than, in millimeters,

d = maximum channel depth at dominant discharge, in feet (meters), and

n_s = Manning's roughness coefficient for the bed of channel (sometimes computed as $(D_{90})^{1/6}/26$).

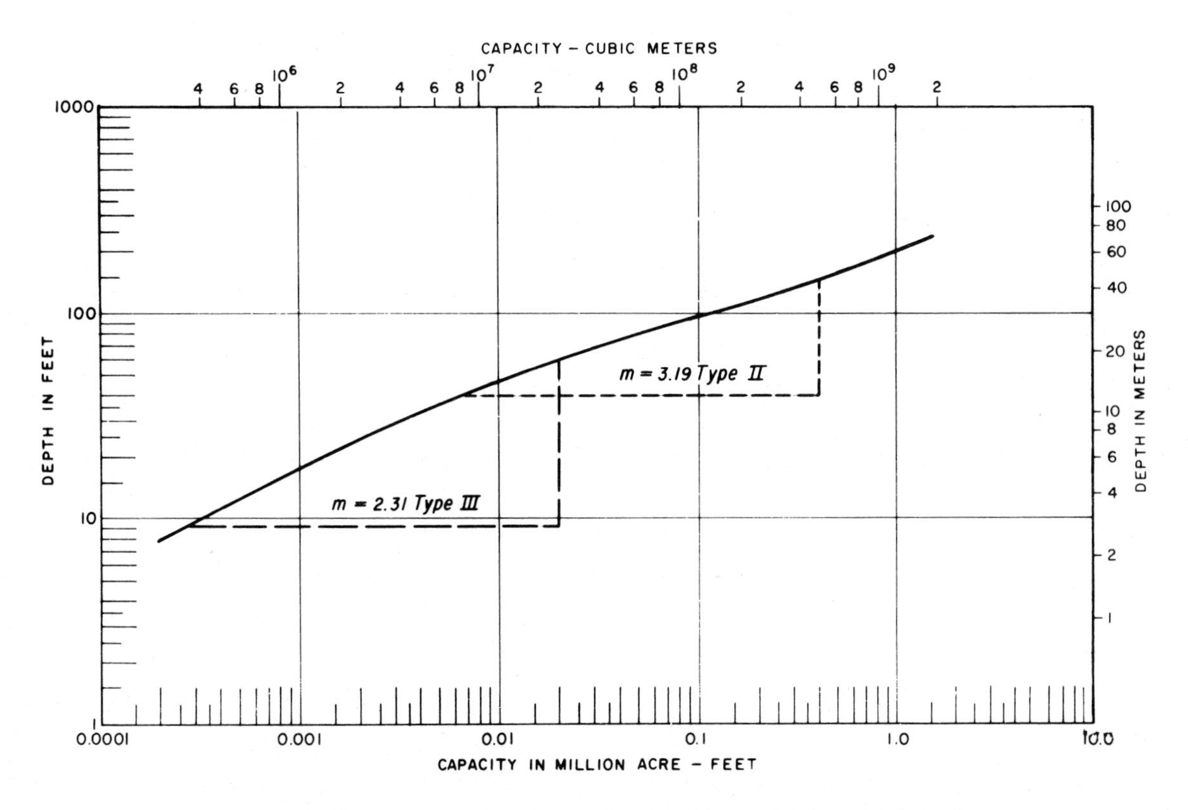

Figure A-15.—Depth versus capacity for Theodore Roosevelt Lake. 103–D–1816.

The Meyer-Peter, Muller equation or any other equation selected for zero transport will yield a slope at which the bed material will no longer be transported. This is necessary for the delta to form.

The location of the pivot point between the topset and foreset slopes depends primarily on the operation of the reservoir and on the existing channel slope in the delta area. If the reservoir is operated near the top of the conservation pool a large portion of the time, the elevation of the top of the conservation pool will be the pivot point elevation. Conversely, if the reservoir water surface has frequent fluctuations and a deeply entrenched inflow channel, a mean operating pool elevation should be used to establish the pivot point. In the extreme situation when a reservoir is emptied every year during the floodpeak flows for sluicing sediment, there will be no pivot point.

The upstream end of the delta is set at the intersection of the maximum water surface and the original streambed, and the topset slope is projected from that point to the anticipated pivot point elevation to begin the first trial computations of delta volume.

The average of foreset slopes observed in Bureau of Reclamation reservoir resurveys is 6.5 times the topset slope. However, some reservoirs exhibit a foreset slope considerably greater than this; e.g., Lake Mead's foreset slope is 100 times the topset. By adopting a foreset slope of 6.5 times the topset, the first trial delta fit can be completed.

The volume of sediment computed from the channel cross sections with the delta imposed on them should agree with the volume of sand-sized or larger material anticipated to come from the delta stream. The quantity of sediment in the delta above normal water surface elevation should also agree with that estimated to deposit above the normal operating level, as shown on figure A-11. If the adjustment necessary to attain agreement is minor, it can usually be accomplished by a small change in the foreset slope. If a significant change in delta size is needed, the pivot point can be moved forward or backward in the reservoir while maintaining the previously determined elevation of the point. The topset slope is then projected backward from the new pivot point location, and the delta volume is again computed. The intersection of the delta topset and the original streambed may fall above the maximum water surface elevation. This condition

Table A-7.—Determination of sediment elevation at Theodore Roosevelt Dam.

	Years	S (total sediment deposition)	H (original depth of reservoir)
1981 survey	72.4	193,765 acre-ft (239×10[6] m[3])	234 ft (71.3 m)
	100	267,600 acre-ft (330×100[6] m[3])	
	200	535,200 acre-ft (660×10[6] m[3])	
	300	802,800 acre-ft (990×10[6] m[3])	

Elevation		Relative depth,	Original survey (1909)						72.4 years			100 years			200 years			300 years		
			V_h (capacity)		A_h (area)		HA_h 10^6		$S-V_h$		$\frac{S-V_h}{HA_h}$[1]	$S-V_h$		$\frac{S-V_h}{HA_h}$[1]	$S-V_h$		$\frac{S-V_h}{HA_h}$[1]	$S-V_h$		$\frac{S-V_h}{HA_h}$[1]
ft	m	p	acre-ft	10^6 m^3	acres	10^6 m^3	acre-ft	10^6 m^3	acre-ft	10^6 m^3		acre-ft	10^6 m^3		acre-ft	10^6 m^3		acre-ft	10^6 m^3	
2080.0	634.0	0.761	693,315	855	11,939	48.3	2.79	3440	-	-	-	-	-	-	-	-	-	109,485	135	0.0392
2070.0	630.9	.718	580,590	716	10,638	43.1	2.49	3070	-	-	-	-	-	-	-	-	-	222,210	274	.0892
2060.0	627.9	.675	479,928	592	9,482	38.4	2.22	2700	-	-	-	-	-	-	55,272	68.2	0.0249	322,872	398	.145
2050.0	624.8	.632	391,207	483	8,262	33.4	1.93	2380	-	-	-	-	-	-	143,993	178	.0746	411,593	508	.213
2040.0	621.8	.590	314,623	388	7,106	28.8	1.66	2050	-	-	-	-	-	-	220,577	272	.133	488,177	602	.294
2030.0	618.7	.547	248,009	306	6,216	25.2	1.45	1800	-	-	-	19,591	24.2	0.0135	287,191	354	.198	554,791	684	.383
2020.0	615.7	.504	190,334	235	5,286	21.4	1.24	1530	-	-	-	77,266	95.3	.0623	344,866	425	.278	612,466	755	.494
2010.0	612.6	.462	142,903	176	4,264	17.3	0.998	1230	50,862	62.7	0.0510	124,697	154	.125	392,297	484	.393	659,897	814	.661
2000.0	609.6	.419	103,787	128	3,544	14.3	.829	1020	89,978	111	.109	163,813	202	.198	431,413	532	.520	699,013	862	.843
1990.0	606.6	.376	72,347	89.2	2,744	11.1	.642	791	121,418	149.8	.189	195,253	241	.304	462,853	571	.721	730,453	901	1.138
1980.0	603.5	.333	48,867	60.3	1,985	8.03	.464	573	144,898	178.7	.312	218,733	270	.471	486,333	600	1.048	753,933	930	1.625
1970.0	600.5	.291	31,935	39.4	1,428	5.78	.334	412	161,830	199.6	.485	235,665	291	.706	503,265	621	1.507	770,865	951	2.308
1960.0	597.4	.248	19,743	24.4	1,020	4.13	.239	294	174,022	214.6	.730	247,857	306	1.037	515,457	636	2.157	783,057	966	3.276
1950.0	594.4	.205	11,328	14.0	677	2.74	.158	195	182,437	225	1.155	256,272	316	1.622	523,872	646	3.316	791,472	976	5.009

[1] $F = \frac{S-V_h}{HA_h}$

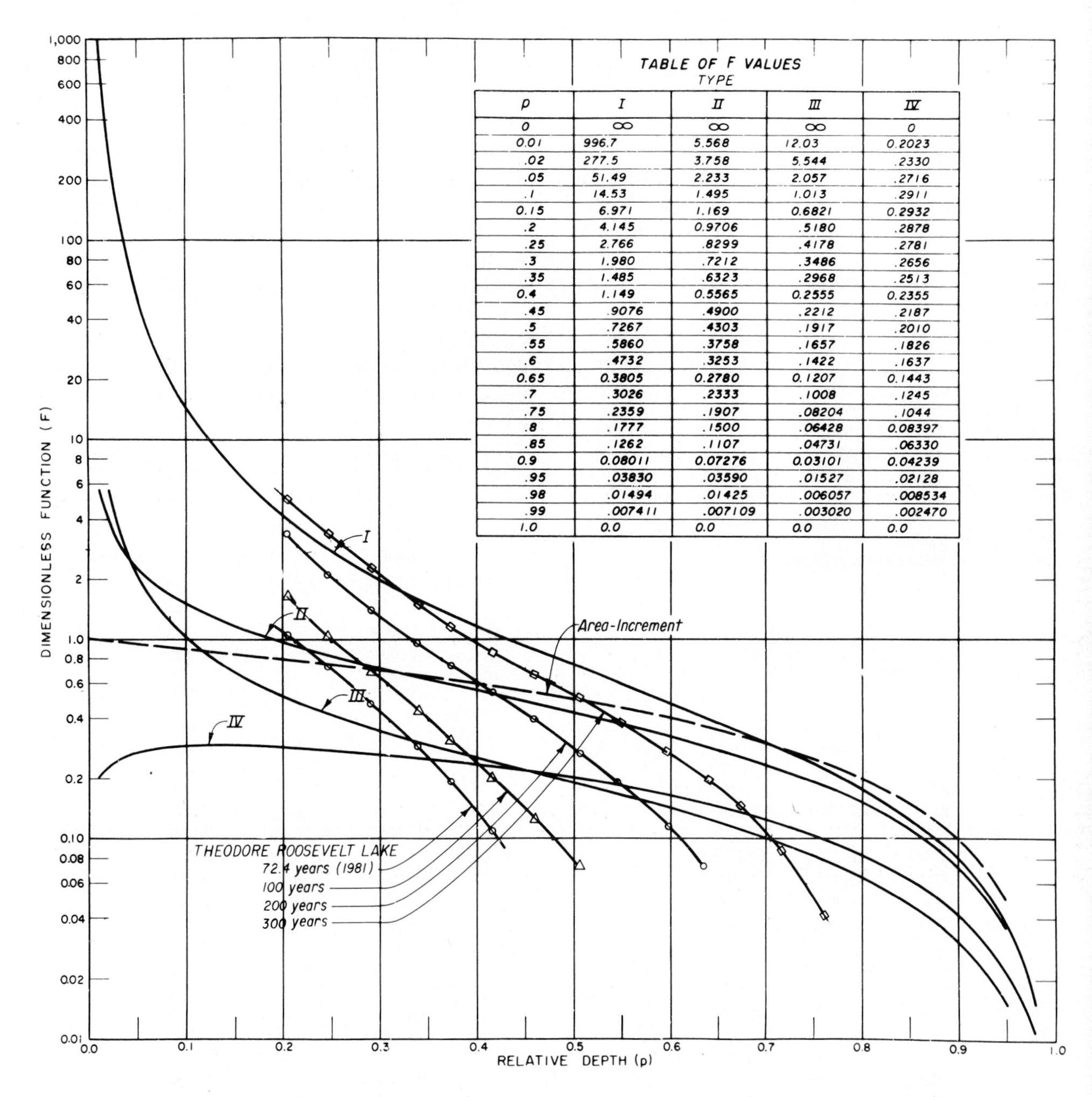

TABLE OF F VALUES

p	TYPE I	II	III	IV
0	∞	∞	∞	0
0.01	996.7	5.568	12.03	0.2023
.02	277.5	3.758	5.544	.2330
.05	51.49	2.233	2.057	.2716
.1	14.53	1.495	1.013	.2911
0.15	6.971	1.169	0.6821	0.2932
.2	4.145	0.9706	.5180	.2878
.25	2.766	.8299	.4178	.2781
.3	1.980	.7212	.3486	.2656
.35	1.485	.6323	.2968	.2513
0.4	1.149	0.5565	0.2555	0.2355
.45	.9076	.4900	.2212	.2187
.5	.7267	.4303	.1917	.2010
.55	.5860	.3758	.1657	.1826
.6	.4732	.3253	.1422	.1637
0.65	0.3805	0.2780	0.1207	0.1443
.7	.3026	.2333	.1008	.1245
.75	.2359	.1907	.08204	.1044
.8	.1777	.1500	.06428	0.08397
.85	.1262	.1107	.04731	.06330
0.9	0.08011	0.07276	0.03101	0.04239
.95	.03830	.03590	.01527	.02128
.98	.01494	.01425	.006057	.008534
.99	.007411	.007109	.003020	.002470
1.0	0.0	0.0	0.0	0.0

Figure A-16.—Curves to determine the depth of sediment at Theodore Roosevelt Dam. 103–D–1817.

has been observed in small reservoirs.

A.4. *Downstream Channel Effects.*— (a) *General Degradation.*—The trapping of sediment in a reservoir accompanied with clear water releases from the dam upsets the regime, or state of quasi-equilibrium, of the downstream river channel. A natural flowing stream transporting sediment is usually in equilibrium, or in regime [32], with no long-term trend toward aggradation or degradation. The release of clear water either through the outlets, powerplant, or spillway will upset this natural, stable condition with degradation of the channel bed and banks. The degradation process progressively moves downstream until it reaches a point where the quantities of the sediment being transported results in a stable channel, or equilibrium. Some reservoirs that have lower trap efficiencies may release water with colloidal clay material

(<0.004 mm), but these releases will usually have a minor influence on retarding the downstream degradation. The one exception to a clear water release would be a reservoir that has planned sluicing with low-level outlets having a capacity equal to the high river discharges for moving large amounts of sediment into the downstream channel. Any sediment sluiced through a dam, especially of sand-size material (>0.062 mm), would reduce the expected downstream channel degradation.

The techniques for computing degradation below a dam vary considerably depending on the size of sediments in the bed and banks, release discharges at the dam, and sophistication desired in the results. Sophisticated mathematical modeling solutions for computing degradation [33, 34] by computer are becoming available. An example is the STARS (Sediment Transport and River Simulation) model being developed by the Bureau and scheduled for completion in 1987. Such models simulate the behavior of an alluvial channel by combining a steady-state backwater computation for defining channel hydraulics with a sediment transport model. Computers can simulate flows over any selected time frame to reflect continual changes in both water surface and the corresponding bed surface profiles to help predict a span of 50 to 100 years. The models, still undergoing development, are being used on many river channels, but are con-

Table A-8.—Elevation of sediment at Theodore Roosevelt Dam.

Years	Type II design curve				Area-increment method			
			Elevation[2]				Elevation[2]	
	p_0	p_0H[1]	ft	m	p_0	p_0H	ft	m
[3]72.4	0.23	54	1956.0	596.2	0.247	58	1960.0	597.4
100	.284	66	1968.0	599.8	.290	68	1970.0	600.5
200	.418	98	2000.0	609.6	.4	94	1996.0	608.4
300	.553	129	2031.0	619.0	.506	118	2020.0	615.7

[1] H = 234 feet (71.3 m).
[2] Original streambed elevation plus p_0H.
[3] 1981.

Table A-9.—Theodore Roosevelt Lake, type II reservoir sediment deposition study. Empirical area reduction method. Sediment inflow = 267,600 acre-ft. (English units).

Elevation, ft	Original Area, acres	Original Capacity, acre-ft	Relative Depth	Relative Area	Sediment Area, acres	Sediment Volume, acre-ft	Revised Area, acres	Revised Capacity acre-ft
2136.0	17,785.0	1,530,499	1.000	0.000	0.0	267,600	17,785.0	1,262,899
2130.0	17,203.0	1,425,512	0.974	0.546	699.1	265,503	16,503.9	1,160,009
2120.0	16,177.0	1,258,547	.932	0.795	1018.8	256,914	15,158.2	1,001,633
2110.0	15,095.0	1,102,215	.889	0.945	1210.3	245,768	13,884.7	856,447
2100.0	14,104.0	956,455	.846	1.050	1344.8	232,993	12,759.2	723,462
2090.0	13,247.0	819,272	.803	1.127	1443.6	219,051	11,803.4	600,221
2080.0	11,939.0	693,315	.761	1.184	1516.9	204,248	10,422.1	489,067
2070.0	10,638.0	580,590	.718	1.225	1570.0	188,814	9,068.0	391,776
2060.0	9,482.0	479,928	.675	1.254	1606.3	172,932	7,875.7	306,996
2050.0	8,262.0	391,207	.632	1.271	1628.0	156,761	6,634.0	234,446
2040.0	7,106.0	314,623	.590	1.277	1636.5	140,438	5,469.5	174,185
2030.0	6,216.0	248,009	.547	1.274	1632.8	124,092	4,583.2	123,917
2020.0	5,286.0	190,334	.504	1.263	1617.6	107,840	3,668.4	82,494
2010.0	4,264.0	142,903	.462	1.242	1591.0	91,797	2,673.0	51,106
2000.0	3,544.0	103,787	.419	1.212	1553.1	76,076	1,990.9	27,711
1990.0	2,744.0	72,347	.376	1.174	1503.8	60,792	1,240.2	11,555
1980.0	1,985.0	48,867	.333	1.126	1443.0	46,057	542.0	2,810
1970.0	1,428.0	31,935	.291	1.068	1381.5	31,935	46.5	33
1968.6	1,369.7	29,983	.284	1.059	1369.7	29,983	0.0	0
1960.0	1,020.0	19,743	.248	0.999	1020.0	19,743	.0	0
1950.0	677.0	11,328	.205	.918	677.0	11,328	.0	0
1940.0	419.0	5,893	.162	.821	419.0	5,893	.0	0
1930.0	227.0	2,735	.120	.704	227.0	2,735	.0	0
1920.0	117.0	1,059	.077	.558	117.0	1,059	.0	0
1910 0	52.0	211	.034	.358	52.0	211	.0	0
1902.0	0.0	0	.000	.000	0.0	0	.0	0

Table A-10.—Theodore Roosevelt Lake, type II reservoir sediment deposition study. Empirical area reduction method. Sediment inflow = 330 085×10^6 m^3. (SI units).

Elevation, m	Original Area, hectares	Original Capacity, 10^6 m^3	Relative Depth	Relative Area	Sediment Area, hectares	Sediment Volume, 10^6 m^3	Revised Area, hectares	Revised Capacity, 10^6 m^3
651.05	7197.6	1887.871	1.000	0.000	0.0	330.085	7197.6	1557.786
649.22	6962.1	1758.369	0.974	.546	282.9	327.498	6679.1	1430.871
646.18	6546.8	1552.418	.932	.795	412.3	316.903	6134.5	1235.515
643.13	6108.9	1359.582	.889	.945	489.8	303.155	5619.1	1056.427
640.08	5707.9	1179.787	.846	1.059	544.2	287.397	5163.7	892.391
637.03	5361.1	1010.572	.803	1.127	534.2	270.199	4776.8	740.373
633.98	4831.7	855.204	.761	1.184	613.9	251.940	4217.8	603.264
630.94	4305.2	716.158	.718	1.225	635.4	232.901	3669.8	483.256
627.89	3837.4	591.991	.675	1.254	650.1	213.311	3187.3	378.680
624.84	3343.6	482.554	.632	1.271	658.8	193.364	2684.8	289.190
621.79	2875.8	388.087	.590	1.277	662.3	173.230	2213.5	214.858
618.74	2515.6	305.919	.547	1.274	660.8	153.066	1854.8	152.853
615.70	2139.2	234.777	.504	1.263	654.6	133.019	1484.6	101.758
612.65	1725.6	176.271	.462	1.242	643.9	113.230	1081.8	63.041
609.60	1434.3	128.021	.419	1.212	628.5	93.839	805.7	34.183
606.55	1110.5	89.249	.376	1.174	608.6	74.985	501.9	14.255
603.50	803.3	60.277	.333	1.126	584.0	56.810	219.4	3.468
600.46	577.9	39.392	.291	1.068	559.0	39.392	19.0	42
600.92	554.1	36.967	.284	1.059	554.1	36.967	0.0	0
597.41	412.8	24.353	.248	0.999	412.8	24.353	.0	0
594.36	274.0	13.973	.205	.918	274.0	13.973	.0	0
591.31	169.6	7.269	.162	.821	169.6	7.269	.0	0
588.26	91.9	3.374	.120	.704	91.9	3.374	.0	0
585.22	47.3	1.306	.077	.558	47.3	1.306	.0	0
582.17	21.0	260	.034	.358	21.0	260	.0	0
579.73	0.0	0	.000	.000	0.0	0	.0	0

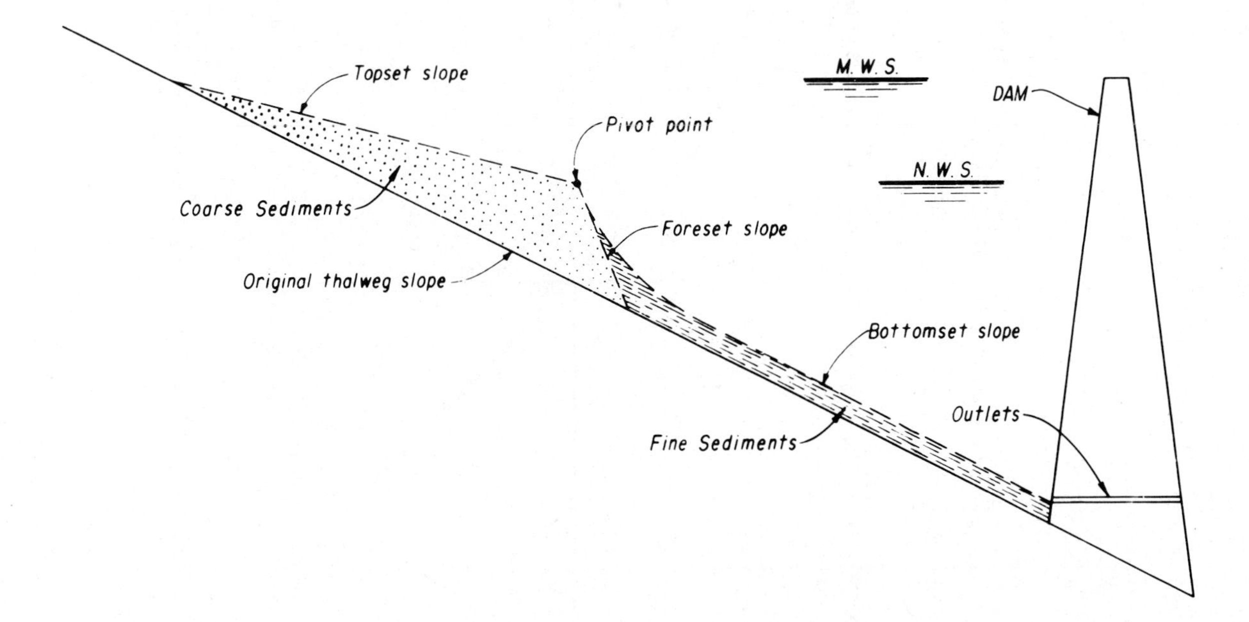

Figure A-17.—Typical sediment deposition profile. 103-D-1818.

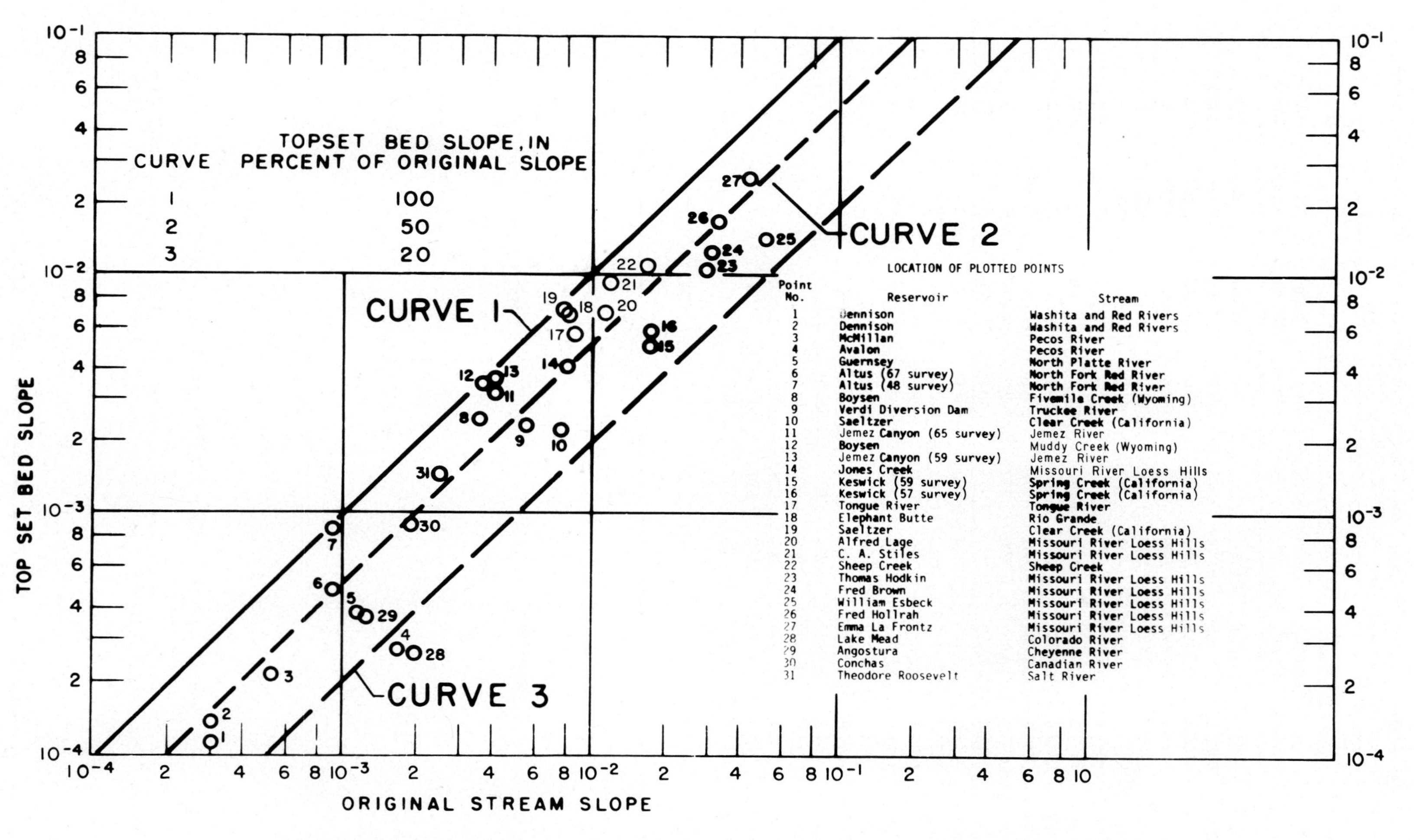

Point No.	Reservoir	Stream
1	Dennison	Washita and Red Rivers
2	Dennison	Washita and Red Rivers
3	McMillan	Pecos River
4	Avalon	Pecos River
5	Guernsey	North Platte River
6	Altus (67 survey)	North Fork Red River
7	Altus (48 survey)	North Fork Red River
8	Boysen	Fivemile Creek (Wyoming)
9	Verdi Diversion Dam	Truckee River
10	Saeltzer	Clear Creek (California)
11	Jemez Canyon (65 survey)	Jemez River
12	Boysen	Muddy Creek (Wyoming)
13	Jemez Canyon (59 survey)	Jemez River
14	Jones Creek	Missouri River Loess Hills
15	Keswick (59 survey)	Spring Creek (California)
16	Keswick (57 survey)	Spring Creek (California)
17	Tongue River	Tongue River
18	Elephant Butte	Rio Grande
19	Saeltzer	Clear Creek (California)
20	Alfred Lage	Missouri River Loess Hills
21	C. A. Stiles	Missouri River Loess Hills
22	Sheep Creek	Sheep Creek
23	Thomas Hodkin	Missouri River Loess Hills
24	Fred Brown	Missouri River Loess Hills
25	William Esbeck	Missouri River Loess Hills
26	Fred Hollrah	Missouri River Loess Hills
27	Emma La Frontz	Missouri River Loess Hills
28	Lake Mead	Colorado River
29	Angostura	Cheyenne River
30	Conchas	Canadian River
31	Theodore Roosevelt	Salt River

Figure A-18.—Topset slope versus original stream slope from existing reservoirs. 103-D-1819.

sidered more applicable to the more uniform width-depth-type river channels in the United States, such as the Missouri, Sacramento, or Mississippi rivers.

Until the mathematical models prove adaptable to all river conditions, the Bureau's approach to degradation below dams is to apply either a stable slope or an armoring analysis. Both of these two distinct approaches for estimating the depth or amount of degradation that will occur downstream from a dam or similar structure depend on the type of material forming the bed of the river channel [35].

When the streambed is composed of transportable material that extends to depths greater than that to which the channel can be expected to degrade, the most useful approach involves computing the stable channel, or limiting, slope; estimating the volume of expected degradation; and then determining a three-slope channel profile that fits these values. However, if large or coarse material that cannot be transported by normal river discharges exists in sufficient quantities, an armor layer will develop as the finer material is sorted out and transported downstream. Vertical degradation will proceed at a progressively slower rate until the armor is deep enough to inhibit further degradation.

(b) *Armoring Method.*—A less detailed procedure, which should be tested first, for computing degradation below a dam is the armoring control method. This method is especially applicable if there is large or coarse material in the channel bottom that cannot be transported by normal river discharge and there is enough of this material to develop an armor layer. This occurred on the Colorado River below Glen Canyon Dam, and was described by Pemberton [36]. In the armoring process, the finer, transportable material is sorted out, and vertical degradation proceeds at a progressively slower rate until the armor is deep enough to control further degradation. An armoring layer can usually be anticipated if approximately 10 percent or more of the bed material is armoring size or larger. The armoring computations assume that an armoring layer will form (as shown on fig. A-19) as follows:

$$y_a = y - y_d \qquad (11)$$

where:

y_a = thickness of the armoring layer,
y = depth from original streambed to bottom of the armoring layer,
y_d = depth from the originalstreambed to top of the armoring layer, or the depth of degradation.

By definition:

$$y_a = (\Delta p)y \qquad (12)$$

where:

Δp = decimal percentage of material larger than the armoring size.

Equations (11) and (12) are combined to yield:

$$y_d = y_a\left(\frac{1}{\Delta p} - 1\right) \qquad (13)$$

The depth of the armoring layer, y_a, varies with the size of particle needed, but for use in design is usually assumed to vary by three armoring particle diameters, or 0.5 feet (0.15 m), whichever is smaller. Although armoring has been observed to occur with less than three particle diameters, variability of channel bed material and occurrence of peak design discharges dictate the use of a thicker armor layer.

The sediment particle sizes required for armoring can be computed by several methods, and each is regarded as a check on the others. Each method will indicate a different armoring size; therefore, experience and judgment are required to select the most appropriate. The basic data to make the particle-size computations require (1) samples of the streambed material through the reach involved and at a depth through the anticipated scour zone; (2) selection of a dominant discharge, usually approximately a 2-year frequency peak discharge; and (3) average channel hydraulic properties for the selected dominant discharge obtained from steady flow backwater computations through the selected reach of river. The methods used to compute a nontransportable particle size that will form the armorning layer are usually based on some form of a sediment transport equation or relationship, as described in reports by the Bureau of Reclamation [35], ASCE [37], and Yang [20], such as those of:

Method	*References*
(1) Meyer-Peter, Muller	[15, 16]
(2) Competent bottom velocity	[38]
(3) Critical tractive force	[39]
(4) Shields diagram	[35, 37]
(5) Yang incipient motion	[20]

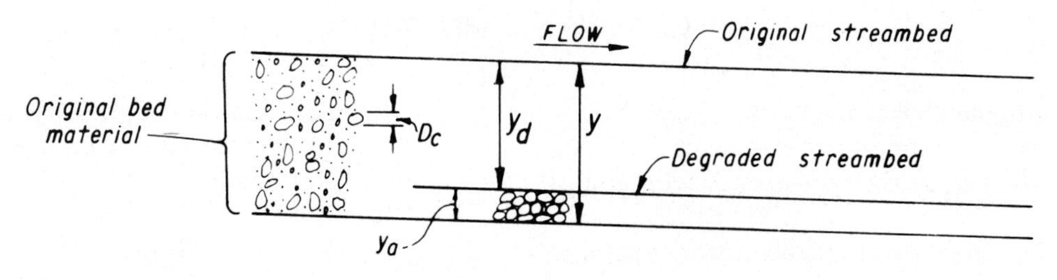

y = Depth to bottom of the armoring layer

y_d = Depth of degradation

y_a = Armoring layer

D_c = Diameter of armor material

Δ_p = Decimal percentage of original bed material larger than D_c

Figure A-19.—Armoring definitions. 103–D–1820.

An example of a degradation (limited by armoring) computation using the above methods is given below. For this example, a channel downstream of a storage dam, the following data are known:

Dominant discharge = Q = 500 ft³/s (14.2 m³/s)
Channel width = B = 60 feet (18.3 m)
Mean channel depth = d = 4 feet (1.22 m)
Mean channel velocity = V = 3.4 ft/s (1.04 m/s)
Stream gradient = S = 0.0021
Armoring size = D = diameter, in millimeters

(1) Meyer-Peter, Muller [15, 16]:

$$D = \frac{Sd}{K\left[\dfrac{n_s}{(D_{90})^{1/6}}\right]^{3/2}} \qquad (14)$$

where:

K = 0.19 English units (0.058 SI units),
n_s = 0.03 (assumed for this example), and
D_{90} = 34 millimeters (assumed for this example).

Therefore:

$$D = \frac{0.0021\ (4.0)}{0.19\left[\dfrac{0.03}{34^{1/6}}\right]^{3/2}} = \frac{0.0048}{0.000409} = 20 \text{ mm}$$

and in SI units:

$$D = \frac{0.0021\ (1.22)}{0.058\ (0.002\ 15)} = \frac{0.002\ 56}{0.000\ 125} = 20 \text{ mm.}$$

(2) Competent bottom velocity [38]:

$$V_b = 0.51\ D^{1/2} \text{ ft/s} = 0.155\ D^{1/2} \text{ m/s} \qquad (15)$$

where:

V_b = competent bottom velocity = $0.7V_m$,
V_m = mean velocity, in feet per second (meters per second), and
D = diameter, in millimeters.

Therefore:

$$D = 3.84\ V_b^2 \text{(English units)}$$
$$= 41.6\ V_b^2 \text{(SI units)}$$
$$D = 3.84\ (0.7 \times 3.4)^2 = 22 \text{ mm}$$
$$= [41.6\ (0.7 \times 1.04)^2 = 22 \text{ mm}].$$

(3) Critical tractive force [39]:

$$t.f. = \gamma_w dS \qquad (16)$$

where:

$t.f.$ = tractive force, in pounds per square foot (grams per square meter),
γ_w = unit weight (mass) of water, 62.4 lb/ft³ (1.0 t/m³),
d = mean water depth, in feet (meters), and
S = stream gradient.

Therefore:

$$t.f. = 62.4 \times 4.0 \times 0.0021 = 0.524 \text{ lb/ft}^2$$
$$= [10^6 \text{ g/m}^3 \times 1.22 \times 0.0021 = 2560 \text{ g/m}^2]$$

From figure A-20: D = 31 mm.

(4) Shields diagram [35, 37] for material >1.0 millimeter and Reynold's number $R^*>500$.

$$\frac{T_c}{(\gamma_s - \gamma_w) D} = 0.06 \quad (17)$$

where:

T_c = critical shear stress = $\gamma_w dS$, in pounds per square foot (metric tons per square meter),
γ_s = unit weight (mass) of the particle = 165 lb/ft³ (2.65 t/m³),
γ_w = unit weight (mass) of water = 62.4 lb/ft³ (1.0 t/m³),
d = mean water depth, in feet (meters),
S = slope, and
D = diameter of particle, in feet (meters).

Therefore:

$$D = \frac{62.4\ (4.0)\ (0.0021)}{0.06\ (165 - 62.4)} = 0.0848 \text{ ft} = 26 \text{ mm}$$

$$D = \frac{1.0\ (1.22)\ (0.0021)}{0.06\ (1.65)} = 0259 \text{ m} = 26 \text{ mm.}$$

(5) Yang [20] incipient motion criteria for shear velocity Reynold's number $R^*>70$:

$$\frac{V_{cr}}{w} = 2.05 \quad (18)$$

where:

V_{cr} = critical average water velocity at incipient motion, in feet (meters) per second, and
w = terminal fall velocity, feet (meters) per second.

With Rubey's settling velocity [41] for materials larger than about 2 millimeters in diameter, the fall velocity can be approximated by:

$$w = 6.01\ D^{1/2} \text{ (English units), and} \quad (19)$$
$$w = 3.32\ D^{1/2} \text{ (SI units)}$$

Equations (18) and (19) can be combined to give:

$$D = 0.00659\ V_{cr}^2 \text{ (English units), and} \quad (20)$$
$$D = 0.0216\ V_{cr}^2 \text{ (SI units)}$$

Therefore in the example problem:

$$D = 0.00659\ (3.4)^2 = 0.0762 \text{ ft} = 23 \text{ mm}$$
$$D = 0.216\ (1.04)^2 = 0.0233 \text{ m} = 23 \text{ mm.}$$

The mean result of the above five methods for computing armoring size is 24 millimeters, which was adopted as a representative armoring size. From equation (13), assuming three layers of non-transportable material to form an armor and assuming 17 percent of bed material larger than 24 millimeters (from size analysis of streambed material), the depth of degradation is:

$$y_a = 3D = 3(24) = 72 \text{ mm} = 0.236 \text{ ft}$$
$$= (0.072 \text{ m})$$
$$y_d = 0.236 \left[\frac{1}{0.17} - 1\right] = 1.15 \text{ ft}$$
$$y_d = 0.072 \left[\frac{1}{0.17} - 1\right] = 0.35 \text{ m}$$

(c) *Stable Slope Method.*—The method of computing a stable slope to define degradation below a dam is used when there is not enough coarse material to develop an armoring layer. The method is used when the primary purpose is to compute a depth of scour immediately below the dam for design of the dam and downstream protection against vertical scour of the streambed. It is also used in early planning stages with a limited amount of field data and when costs for the more detailed study are prohibitive. The more detailed computer solutions [33] or (their predecessor) the desk calculator method by Lane [34] is used when data are available to verify the mathematical model, when channel hydraulics can be easily synthesized, and when degradation results influence the channel morphology for 10 or more miles below the dam.

The stable slope method is illustrated by the sketch on figure A-21. The stable slope is defined as the slope of the stream at which the bed material will no longer be transported. As shown by figure

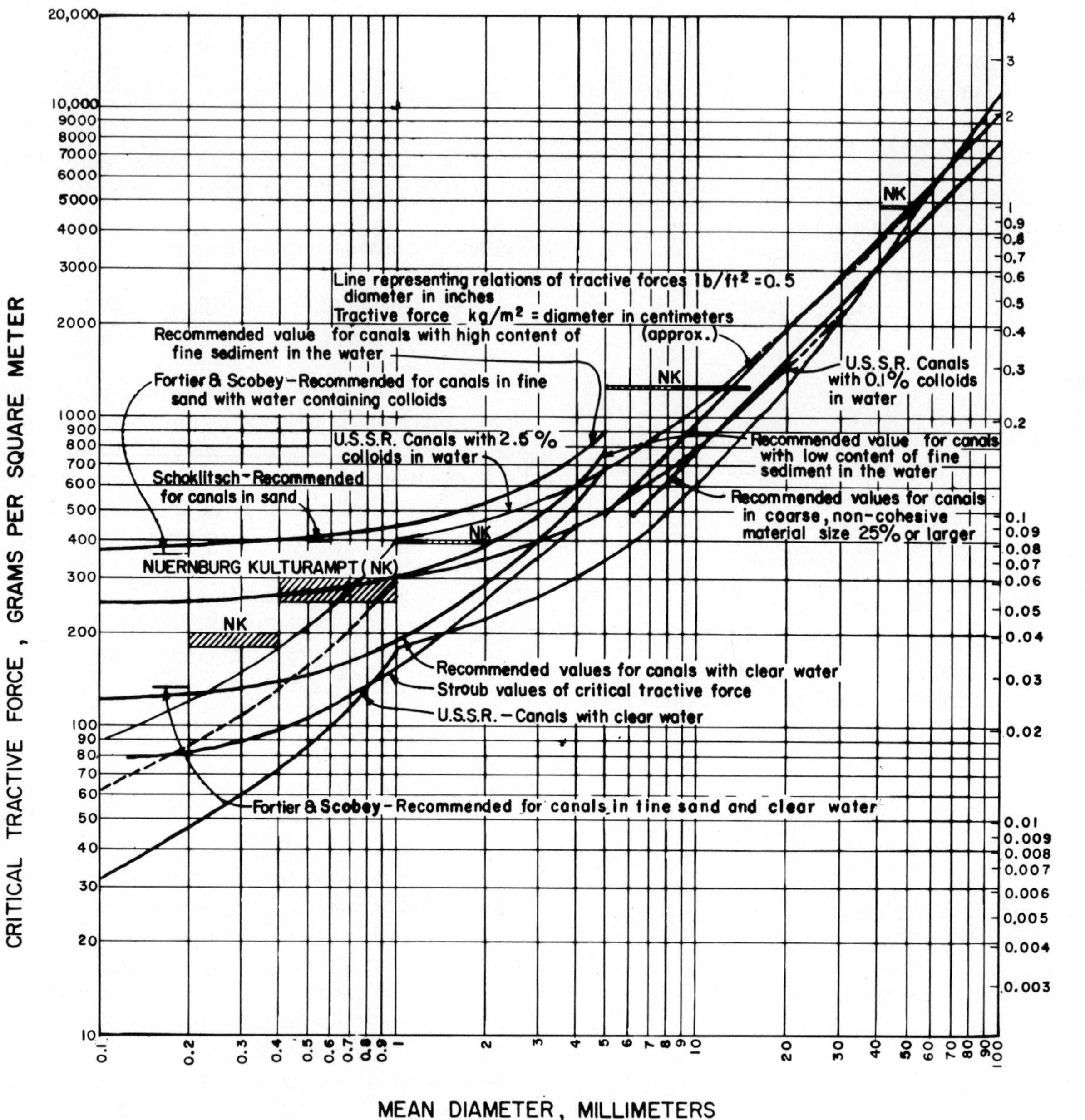

Figure A-20.—Tractive force versus transportable sediment size. 103–D–1821.

A-21, the method is also identified as the three-slope method because of the variation in slope expected between the stable slope and the existing slope farther downstream. The computations of stable slope can be made by applying several methods such as (1) the Schoklitsch [17] bedload equation for conditions of zero bedload transport, (2) the Meyer-Peter, Muller [15, 16] bedload equation for beginning transport, (3) Shields's [35, 37] diagram for no motion, and (4) Lane's [39] relationship for critical tractive force assuming clear water flow in canals. The discharge to be used in any of the above methods is the dominant discharge and is usually determined by the channel bankfull flow or the 2-year flood peak discharge. With regulation of the streamflow by an upstream dam, the problem becomes more complex because detailed data on future releases are usually not available. If the

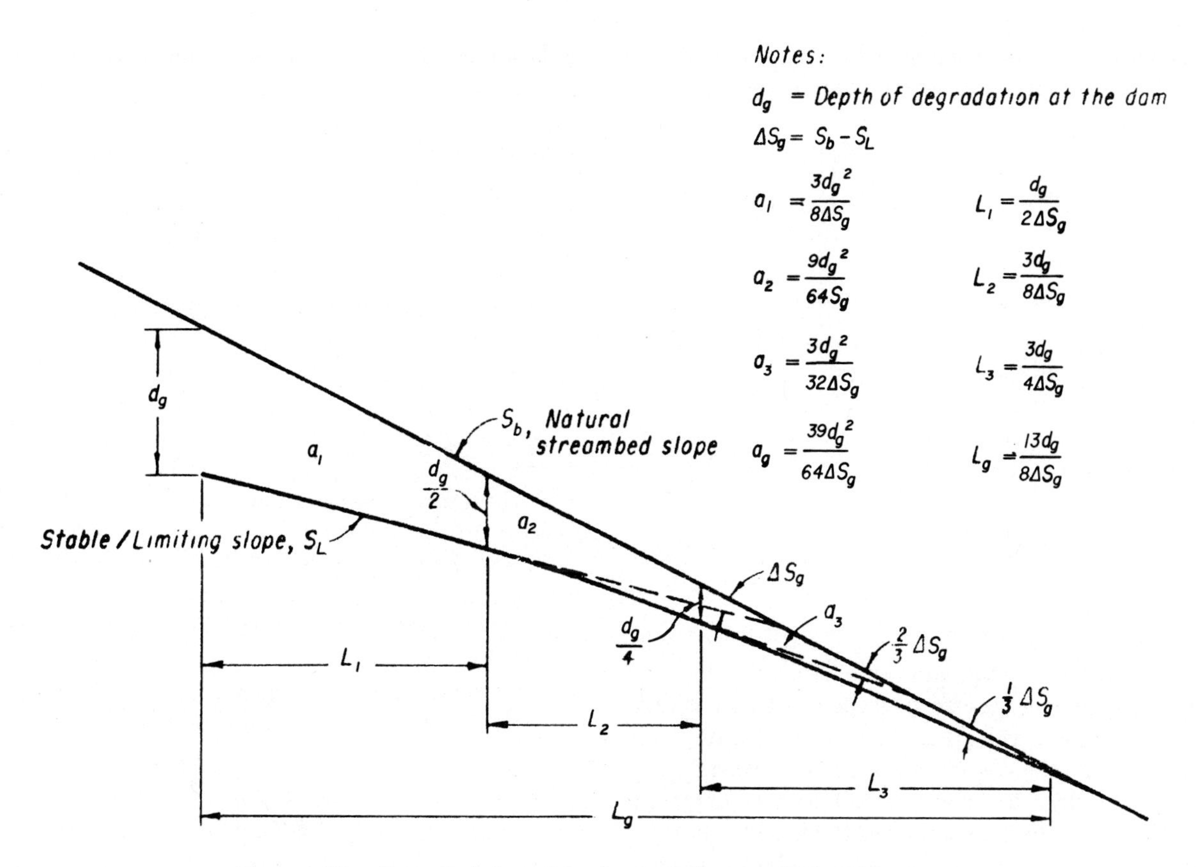

Figure A-21.—Degraded channel by the three-slope method. 103–D–1822.

releases from the reservoir are fairly uniform, and flood discharges are relatively rare, the average daily discharge may be used as the dominant discharge. However, if the releases are subject to considerable fluctuation because of floods, the peak discharge that is equaled or exceeded on the average of once every 2 years would be considered the dominant discharge.

The next step in degradation computations by the stable slope method is determining the average channel hydraulic properties for the dominant discharge. These data can usually be obtained from the tailwater study that has been prepared for the dam. The properties of all the tailwater cross sections when carrying the dominant discharge are averaged to arrive at a generalized cross section that will be representative of the degradation reach. The water surface slope may be assumed equal to the hydraulic gradient.

The volume of material to be removed by the stable slope method can be determined in several ways. From figure A-21 it may be expressed by:

$$V_g = a_g B_d \tag{21}$$

where:

V_g = volume of material to be degraded, in cubic feet (cubic meters),
a_g = longitudinal area of degradation, in square feet (square meters), and
B_d = degraded channel width, in feet (meters).

If there are no downstream controls or no limit to the length (L_g) for degradation, the two methods used to compute the volume are (1) assume the river will pick up a load of coarse (>0.062 mm) sediment equal to that portion of the historic sediment load larger than 0.062 mm, and (2) compute the overflow from the degraded reach by a sediment-rating curve, flow-duration curve method. In the second case, the sediment-rating curve would be defined by use of one or more of the bedload equations and the flow-duration curve of anticipated reservoir releases.

By rearranging equation (21) the longitudinal area may be found:

$$a_g = \frac{V_g}{B_d} \tag{22}$$

Once a value has been found for a_g, the depth of degradation may be computed using the following equation:

$$d_g = \left[\frac{64 a_g \, \Delta S_g}{39} \right]^{1/2} \qquad (23)$$

where:

ΔS_g = the difference between the existing slope and the stable slope.

And the length of the degraded reach can be computed by:

$$L_g = \frac{13 d_g}{8 \Delta S_g} \qquad (24)$$

If it is anticipated that lateral degradation will be a significant factor, additional study will be necessary to determine the degraded channel width. Because part of the material will be coming from the streambanks, the extent of vertical degradation will ordinarily not be as great. Lateral movement should always be suspect when the banks are composed of the same material as the bed and there is not a great deal of vegetation to hold them. References [35, 39, 41] are recommended as guides when these conditions prevail.

If a permanent control exists at some point within the degradation reach, equation (24) may be used to solve for the depth of degradation directly.

The three-slope or stable slope method for computing the depth of degradation at the dam and the degraded channel profile are based on satisfying the following assumptions:

1. The degradation reach is sufficiently uniform to permit the use of average cross sections and slope throughout the reach.
2. The bed and bank material throughout the reach is uniform enough that an average composition can be used and that no nonerodible barriers exist in the bed or banks to prevent the stream from attaining the average section at the stable slope.
3. The degradation will be such that the vertical component will predominate and horizontal movement will be limited to bank sloughing resulting from vertical degradation.

The Meyer-Peter, Muller equation for beginning transport is used in an example problem for degradation computations by the stable slope method. Computations by use of the other more commonly used methods for computing a stable slope are described in [34]. The following data are known about a river channel below a diversion dam:

Dominant discharge = Q = 780 ft³/s (22.1 m³/s)
Channel width = B = 350 feet (107 m)
Mean channel depth = d = 1.05 feet (0.32 m)
Existing stream gradient = S = 0.0014
Bed material $D_m = D_{50}$ = 0.3 millimeters
D_{90} = 0.96 millimeters
Manning's n for bed of stream, n_s = 0.027

Preliminary studies show that 2,160 acre-feet (2.66×10^6 m³) of sand would deposit behind the diversion dam during the 100-year economic life of the structure. Investigations indicate that an equal volume of sand could be eroded from the downstream channel.

The stable slope computation by the Meyer-Peter, Muller equation for beginning transport is:

$$S_L = K \frac{\dfrac{Q}{Q_B} \left[\dfrac{n_s}{(D_{90})^{1/6}} \right]^{3/2}}{d} D \qquad (25)$$

where:

S_L = limiting slope,
K = coefficient equal to 0.19 (English units) or 0.058 (SI units),
Q/Q_B = ratio of the total flow, in cubic feet (cubic meters) per second to the flow over the bed of the stream, in cubic feet (cubic meters) per second. Usually defined at the dominant discharge, where $Q/Q_B = 1$ for wide channels. See equation (10) for other definitions.

Therefore:

$$S_L = 0.19 \frac{\left[\dfrac{0.027}{0.96^{1/6}} \right]^{3/2}}{1.05} (0.3) = 0.00024$$

$$S_L = \frac{0.058 \, (0.004\,48)}{0.32} (0.3) = 0.000\,24$$

The difference between the existing and degraded slope, ΔS_g, is 0.00116. The longitudinal degradation area by equation (22) is:

$$a_g = \frac{43{,}560\ (2160)}{350} = 269{,}000\ \text{ft}^2$$

$$a_g = \frac{2.66 \times 10^6}{107} = 24\,900\ \text{m}^2$$

The depth of degradation at the dam by equation (23) is:

$$d_g = \left[\frac{64\ (269{,}000)\ (0.00116)}{39}\right]^{1/2} = 22.6\ \text{ft}$$

$$d_g = \left[\frac{64\ (24\,900)\ (0.001\,16)}{39}\right]^{1/2} = 6.88\ \text{m}$$

And the length by equation (24) of the degradation reach is:

$$L_g = \frac{13\ (22.6)}{8\ (0.00116)} = 31{,}700\ \text{ft}$$

$$L_g = \frac{13\ (6.88)}{8\ (0.001\,16)} = 9640\ \text{m}$$

A.5. *Bibliography.*

[1] Chow, Ven Te, editor-in-chief, *Handbook of Applied Hydrology*, McGraw-Hill, New York, NY, 1964.

[2] Wischmeier, W. H., and D. D. Smith, "Predicting Rainfall Erosion Losses from Cropland East of the Rocky Mountains," USDA, ARS, Agric. Handbook 282, 1965.

[3] "Factors Affecting Sediment Yield and Measures for the Reduction of Erosion and Sediment Yield," Pacific Southwest Interagency Committee, October 1968.

[4] Blanton, J. O., "Procedures for Monitoring Reservoir Sedimentation," Bureau of Reclamation, October 1982.

[5] "Sediment Deposition in U.S. Reservoirs, Summary of Data Reported Through 1975," Miscellaneous Publication No. 1362, USDA, Agriculture Research Service, February 1978.

[6] "A Study of Methods Used in Measurement and Analysis of Sediment Loads in Streams," Reports No. 1 through 14 and A through W, Subcommittee on Sedimentation—Interagency Advisory Committee on Water Data, 1940 to 1981.

[7] *U.S. Government Handbook*, Chapter 3—"Sediment, National Handbook of Recommended Methods for Water-Data Acquisition," prepared cooperatively by agencies of the U.S. Government, 1978.

[8] Miller, C. R., "Analysis of Flow-Duration, Sediment-Rating Curve Method of Computing Sediment Yield," Bureau of Reclamation, Denver, CO, 1951.

[9] Colby, B. R., and C. H. Hembree, "Computations of Total Sediment Discharge, Niobrara River near Cody, Nebraska," USDI, Geological Survey Water Supply Paper No. 1357, 1955.

[10] "Step Method for Computing Total Sediment Load by the Modified Einstein Procedure," Bureau of Reclamation, Denver, CO, July 1955.

[11] "Computation of 'Z's' for Use in the Modified Einstein Procedure," Bureau of Reclamation, Denver, CO, June 1966.

[12] Einstein, Hans Albert, "The Bed-Load Function for Sediment Transportation in Open Channel Flows," USDA, SCS Technical Bulletin No. 1026, September 1950.

[13] Herbertson, John G., "A Critical Review of Conventional Bed-Load Formulae," *Journal of Hydrology*, vol. VIII, No. 1, May 1969.

[14] Pemberton, E. L., "Einstein's Bed-Load Function Applied to Channel Design and Degradation," Chapter 16, "Sedimentation," Symposium to honor Prof. H. A. Einstein, H. W. Shen, editor, 1972.

[15] Meyer-Peter, E., and R. Muller, "Formulas for Bed-Load Transport," The Second Meeting of the International Association for Hydraulic Structure Research, June 1948.

[16] Sheppard, John R., "Investigation of Meyer-Peter, Muller Bed-Load Formulas," Bureau of Reclamation, June 1960.

[17] Shulits, Samuel, "The Schoklitsch Bed-Load Formula," *Engineering*, vol. 139, 1935.

[18] Ackers, P., and W. R. White, "Sediment Transport: New Approach and Analysis," *Journal of the Hydraulics Division*, ASCE, vol. 99, No. HY 11, November 1973.

[19] Engelund, F., and E. Hanson, "A Monograph on Sediment Transport in Alluvial Streams," *Teknisk Forlag*, Denmark, 1972.

[20] Yang, C. T., "Incipient Motion and Sediment Transport," ASCE, vol. 99, No. HY 10, October 1973.

[21] Emmett, W. W., "A Field Calibration of the Sediment-Trapping Characteristics of the Helley-Smith Bed-Load Sampler," USGS Prof. paper No. 1139, 1980.

[22] Brune, Gunnar M., "Trap Efficiency of Reservoirs," *Transactions of American Geophysical Union*, vol. 34, No. 3, June 1953.

[23] Churchill, M. A., Discussion of "Analysis and Use of Reservoir Sedimentation Data," by L. C. Gottschalk, pp. 139-140, *Proceedings of Federal Interagency Sedimentation Conference*, Denver, CO, January 1948.

[24] Murphy, B. N., "Life of Reservoir," Technical Report No. 19, Central Board of Irrigation and Power, New Delhi, reprinted September 1980.

[25] Lara, J. M., and H. I. Sanders, "The 1963-64 Lake Mead Survey," Bureau of Reclamation, 1970.

[26] Lara, J. M., and E. L. Pemberton, "Initial Unit Weight of Deposited Sediments," *Proceedings of Federal Interagency Sedimentation Conference, 1963*, Miscellaneous Publication No. 970, pp. 818-845, USDA, Agriculture Research Service, June 1965.

[27] Lane, E. W., and V. A. Koelzer, "Density of Sediments Deposited in Reservoirs," A Study of Methods Used in Measurement and Analysis of Sediment Loads in Streams, Report No. 9, Interagency Committee on Water Resources, 1943.

[28] Miller, Carl R., "Determination of the Unit Weight of Sediment for Use in Sediment Volume Computations," Bureau of Reclamation, Denver, CO, 1953.

[29] Borland, W. M., and C. R. Miller, "Distribution of Sediment in Large Reservoirs," *Transactions*, ASCE, vol. 125, 1960.

[30] Lara, J. M., "Revision of the Procedure to Compute Sediment Distribution in Large Reservoirs," Bureau of Reclamation, May 1962.

[31] Hudspeth, C. L., and J. W. Trietsch, "User's Manual—SWE1, Computer Program for Sediment Distribution," unpublished report by Bureau of Reclamation, SW Region, Amarillo, TX, January 1978.

[32] Lane, E. W., "The Importance of Fluvial Morphology in Hydraulic Engineering," *Proceedings of ASCE Hydraulic Division*, vol. 81, July 1955.

[33] U.S. Army Corps of Engineers, "Scour and Deposition on Rivers and Reservoirs—HEC-6," *User's Manual for a Generalized Computer Program*, Exhibit 3, 1977.

[34] Lane, E. W., "An Estimate of the Magnitude of the Degradation which Will Result in the Middle Rio Grande Channel from the Construction of the Proposed Sediment Storage Basins and Contraction Works," Bureau of Reclamation, Hyd 290, 1948.

[35] Pemberton, E. L. and J. M. Lara, "Guide for Computing Degradation," Bureau of Reclamation, Denver, CO, December 1982.

[36] Pemberton, E. L., "Channel Changes in the Colorado River Below Glen Canyon Dam," *Proceedings of the Third Federal Interagency Sedimentation Conference*, 1976.

[37] "Sedimentation Engineering," American Society of Civil Engineering Manual No. 54, V. A. Vanoni, editor, 1975.

[38] Mavis, F. T., and L. M. Laushey, "A Reappraisal of the Beginning of Bed-Movement-Competent Velocity," International Association for Hydraulic Research, Second Meeting, Stockholm, June 1948.

[39] "Progress Report on Results of Studies on Design of Stable Channels," Bureau of Reclamation, Hydraulic Laboratory Report Hyd 352, Denver, CO, June 1952.

[40] Rubey, W. W., "Settling Velocities of Gravel, Sand, and Silt Particles", *American Journal of Science*, 1933.

[41] "Stable Channel Profiles," Bureau of Reclamation, Hydraulic Laboratory Report No. Hyd. 325, Denver, CO, September 1951.

Hydraulic Computations

A. HYDRAULIC FORMULAS

B-1. ***Lists of Symbols and Conversion Factors.***— The following list includes symbols used in hydraulic formulas given in chapters 9 and 10 and in this appendix. Standard mathematical notations and symbols having only very limited applications have been omitted.

Symbol	*Description*
A, a	An area; area of a surface; cross-sectional area of flow in an open channel; cross-sectional area of a closed conduit
a_g	Gross area of a trashrack
a_n	Net area of a trashrack
B	Width of a siphon throat
b	Bottom width of a channel
C	A coefficient; coefficient of discharge
C_d	Coefficient of discharge through an orifice
C_i	Coefficient of discharge for an ogee crest with inclined upstream face
C_o	Coefficient of discharge for a nappe-shaped ogee crest designed for an H_o head
C_s	Coefficient of discharge for a partly submerged crest
D	Diameter; conduit diameter; height of a rectangular conduit or passageway; height of a square orifice
$\overline{D}$	"Drop number" parameter for defining the dimensions of a straight drop spillway, $\overline{D}=\frac{q^2}{gY^3}$
d	Depth of flow in an open channel; height of an orifice or gate opening
d_c	Critical depth
d_f	Depth of the pool under a free overfall nappe
d_H	Depth for high (subcritical) flow stage (alternate to d_L)
d_i	Height of a hydraulic jump (difference in the conjugate depths)
d_L	Depth for low (supercritical) flow stage (alternate to d_H)
d_m	Mean depth of flow
d_{m_c}	Critical mean depth
d_n	Depth of flow measured normal to channel bottom
d_s	Depth of scour below tailwater in a plunge pool
d_t	Depth of flow in a chute at tailwater level
E	Energy
E_m	Energy of a particle of mass
F	Froude number parameter for defining flow conditions in a channel, $F=\frac{v}{\sqrt{gd}}$
F_t	Froude number parameter for flow in a chute at the tailwater level
f	Friction loss coefficient in the Darcy-Weisbach formula, $h_f=\frac{fL}{D}\frac{v^2}{2g}$
G	Drop in water surface level in a reach of a natural channel
g	Acceleration due to the force of gravity
H	Head over a crest; head on center of an orifice opening; head on the bottom of a culvert entrance; head difference at a gate (between the upstream and downstream water surface levels)
H_A	Absolute head above a datum plane, in channel flow
H_{AT}	Probable minimum atmospheric pressure at the site under consideration
H_a	Head above a section in the transition of a drop inlet spillway
H_1	Head measured to bottom of an orifice opening
H_2	Head measured to top of an orifice opening
h	Head; height of baffle block; height of end sill
h_a	Approach velocity head
h_b	Head loss due to bend
h_c	Head loss due to contraction
H_D	Head from reservoir water surface to water surface at a given point in the downstream channel
h_d	Difference in water surface level, measured from reservoir water surface to the downstream channel water surface
H_E	Specific energy head
H_{E_c}	Specific energy head at critical flow
H_e	Total head on a crest, including velocity of approach

Symbol	*Description*
h_e	Head loss due to entrance
h_{ex}	Head loss due to expansion
h_f	Head loss due to friction
Δh_f	Incremental head loss due to friction
h_g	Head loss due to gates or valves
h_L	Head losses from all causes
Σh_{L_u}	Sum of head losses upstream from a section
Δh_L	Incremental head loss from all causes
$\Sigma(\Delta h_L)$	Sum of incremental head losses from all causes
H_o	Design head over ogee crest
h_o	Head measured from the crest of an ogee to the reservoir surface immediately upstream, not including the velocity of approach (crest shaped for design head H_o)
h_r	Reduction of pressure head due to inlet contraction
H_s	Total head over a sharp-crested weir
h_s	Head over a sharp-crested weir, not including velocity of approach
h_S	Priming head on a siphon spillway
h_{SA}	Subatmospheric pressure head
H_T	Total head from reservoir water surface to tailwater, or to center of outlet of a free-discharging pipe
h_t	Head loss due to trashrack
h_v	Velocity head; head loss due to exit
h_{v_c}	Critical velocity head
h_{vS}	Velocity head at throat of siphon spillway
h_{v_t}	Velocity head at tailwater level
K	A constant factor for various equations; a coefficient
k	A constant
K_a	Abutment contraction coefficient
K_b	Bend loss coefficient
K_c	Contraction loss coefficient
K_d	Conveyance capacity factor in the Manning formula, $K_d=\frac{1.486}{n}ar^{2/3}$
K_e	Entrance loss coefficient
K_{ex}	Expansion loss coefficient
K_g	Gate or valve loss coefficient
K_L	A summary loss coefficient for losses due to all causes
K_p	Pier contraction coefficient
K_r	Coefficient of pressure reduction due to inlet contraction
K_t	Trashrack loss coefficient
K_v	Velocity head loss coefficient
L	Length; length of a channel or a pipe; effective length of a crest; length of a hydraulic jump; length of a stilling basin; length of a transition
ΔL	Incremental length; incremental channel length
L_I, L_{II}, L_{III}	Stilling basin lengths for different hydraulic jump stilling basins
L'	Net length of a crest
L_B	Length of a basin for a straight drop spillway; length of a slotted grating dissipator basin
L_d	Distance from the upstream face of an overflow weir to the start of a hydraulic jump in a straight drop spillway stilling basin
L_G	Length of a slotted grating dissipator
L_m	Length of a meandering reach in a natural channel
L_p	Distance from the upstream face of an overflow weir to the point of impingement on the basin floor of a straight drop spillway
L_s	Length of a straight reach in a natural channel
M	Momentum
M_d	Momentum in a downstream section
M_u	Momentum in an upstream section
ΔM	Difference in momentum between successive sections
m	Mass
N	Number of piers on an overflow crest; number of slots in a slotted grating dissipator
n	Exponential constant used in equation for defining crest shapes; coefficient of roughness in the Manning equation
P	Approach height of an ogee weir; hydrostatic pressure of a water prism cross section
p	Unit pressure intensity; unit dynamic pressure on a spillway floor; wetted perimeter of a channel or conduit cross section
Q	Discharge; volume rate of flow
ΔQ	Incremental change in rate of discharge
q	Unit discharge
Q_c	Critical discharge
q_c	Critical discharge per unit of width
Q_i	Average rate of inflow
Q_o	Average rate of outflow
R	Radius; radius of a cross section; crest profile radius; vertical radius of curvature of the channel floor profile; radius of a terminal bucket profile
r	Hydraulic radius; radius of abutment rounding; radius of rounding of a culvert inlet opening
R_b	Radius of a bend in a channel or pipe
R_c	Radius of curvature at the crest of a siphon throat
R_s	Radius of curvature at the summit of a siphon throat; radius of a circular sharp-crested weir
S	Storage
ΔS	Increment of storage

Symbol	*Description*
s	Friction slope in the Manning equation; spacing
s_b	Slope of the channel floor, in profile
s_{ws}	Slope of the water surface
T	Tailwater depth; width at the water surface in a cross section of an open channel
T_{max}	Limiting maximum tailwater depth
T_{min}	Limiting minimum tailwater depth
t	Time
Δt	Increment of time
T_s	Tailwater sweep-out depth
$T.W.$	Tailwater; tailwater depth
U	A parameter for defining flow conditions in a closed waterway, $U=\frac{v}{\sqrt{gD}}$
v	Velocity
Δv	Incremental change in velocity
v_a	Velocity of approach
v_c	Critical velocity
v_S	Velocity at the crest of a siphon throat
v_t	Velocity of flow in a channel or chute, at tailwater depth
W	Weight of a mass; width of a stilling basin
w	Unit weight of water; width of a culvert entrance; width of a slot for a slotted grating dissipator; width of chute and baffle blocks in a stilling basin
x	A coordinate for defining a crest profile; a coordinate for defining a channel profile; a coordinate for defining a conduit entrance
Δx	Increment of length
x_c	Horizontal distance from the break point, on the upstream face of an ogee crest, to the apex of the crest
x_s	Horizontal distance from the vertical upstream face of a circular sharp-crested weir to the apex of the undernappe of the overflow sheet
Y	Drop distance measured from the crest of the overflow to the basin floor, for a free overfall spillway
y	A coordinate for defining a crest profile; a coordinate for defining a channel profile; a coordinate for defining a conduit entrance
$\overline{y}$	Depth from water surface to the center of gravity of a water prism cross section
Δy	Difference in elevation of the water surface profile between successive sections in a side channel trough
y_c	Vertical distance from the break point, on the upstream face of an ogee crest, to the apex of the crest
y_s	Vertical distance from the crest of a circular sharp-crested weir to the apex of the undernappe of the overflow sheet
Z	Elevation above a datum plane
ΔZ	Elevation difference of the bottom profile between successive sections in an open channel
z	Ratio, horizontal to vertical, of the slope of the sides of a channel cross section
α	A coefficient; angular variation of the side wall with respect to the structure centerline
θ	Angle from the horizontal; angle from vertical of the position of an orifice; angle from the horizontal of the edge of the lip of a deflector bucket

Table B–1 presents conversion factors most frequently used by the designer of small dams to convert from one set of units to another—for example, to convert from cubic feet per second to acre-feet. Also included are some basic conversion formulas such as the ones for converting flow for a given time to volume.

B-2. Flow in Open Channels.—(a) *Energy and Head.*—If it is assumed that streamlines of flow in an open channel are parallel and that velocities at all points in a cross section are equal to the mean velocity v, the energy possessed by the water is made up to two parts: kinetic energy and potential energy. Referring to figure B–1, if W is the weight of a mass m, the mass possesses Wh_2 foot-pounds of energy with reference to the datum. Also, it possesses Wh_1 foot-pounds of energy because of the pressure exerted by the water above it. Thus, the potential energy of the mass m is $W(h_1+h_2)$. This value is the same for each particle of mass in the cross section. Assuming uniform velocity, the kinetic energy of m is $W\left(\frac{v^2}{2g}\right)$.

Thus, the total energy of each mass particle is:

$$E_m=W\left(h_1+h_2+\frac{v^2}{2g}\right) \qquad (1)$$

Applying the above relationship to the whole discharge Q of the cross section in terms of the unit weight of water w,

$$E=Qw\left(d+Z+\frac{v^2}{2g}\right) \qquad (2)$$

where E is total energy per second at the cross section.

Table B-1.—Conversion factors and formulas.

[To reduce units in column 1 to units in column 4, multiply column 1 by column 2]
[To reduce units in column 4 to units in column 1, multiply column 4 by column 3]

CONVERSION FACTORS

Column 1	Column 2	Column 3	Column 4
LENGTH			
In.	2.54	0.3937	Cm.
	0.0254	39.37	M.
Ft.	0.3048	3.2808	M.
Miles	1.609	0.621	Km.
AREA			
Sq. in.	6.4516	0.1550	Sq. cm.
Sq. m.	10.764	.0929	Sq. ft.
Sq. miles	27.8784×10^{6}	0.3587×10^{-7}	Sq. ft.
	640.0	$.15625\times10^{-2}$	Acres (1 section).
	30.976×10^{5}	$.3228\times10^{-6}$	Sq. yd.
	2.59	.386	Sq. km.
Acre	43,560.0	0.22957×10^{-4}	Sq. ft.
	4,046.9	$.2471\times10^{-3}$	Sq. m.
	4,840.0	$.2066\times10^{-3}$	Sq. yd.
VOLUME			
Cu. ft.	1,728.0	0.5787×10^{-3}	Cu. in.
	7.4805	.13368	Gal.
	6.2321	.16046	Imperial gal.
Cu. m.	35.3145	0.028317	Cu. ft.
	1.3079	.76456	Cu. yd.
Gal.	231.0	0.4329×10^{-2}	Cu. in.
	3.7854	.26417	Liters.
Million gal.	133,681.0	0.74805×10^{-5}	Cu. ft.
	3.0689	.32585	Acre-ft.
Imperial gal.	1.2003	0.83311	Gal.
Acre-in.	3,630.0	$.27548\times10^{-3}$	Cu. ft.
Acre-ft.	1,233.5	0.81071×10^{-3}	Cu. m.
	43,560.0	$.22957\times10^{-4}$	Cu. ft.
In. on 1 sq. mile	232.32×10^{4}	0.43044×10^{-6}	Cu. ft.
	53.33	.01875	Acre-ft.
Ft. on 1 sq. mile	278.784×10^{5}	0.3587×10^{-7}	Cu. ft.
	640.0	$.15625\times10^{-2}$	Acre-ft.
VELOCITY AND GRADE			
Miles/hr.	1.4667	0.68182	Ft./sec.
M./sec.	3.2808	.3048	Ft./sec.
	2.2369	.44704	Miles/hr.
Fall in ft./mile	189.39×10^{-6}	5.28×10^{3}	Fall/ft.

CONVERSION FACTORS

Column 1	Column 2	Column 3	Column 4
FLOW			
Cu. ft./sec. (second-feet) (sec.-ft.).	60.0	0.016667	Cu. ft./min.
	86,400.0	$.11574\times10^{-4}$	Cu. ft./day.
	31.536×10^{6}	$.31709\times10^{-7}$	Cu. ft./yr.
	448.83	$.2228\times10^{-2}$	Gal./min.
	646,317.0	$.15472\times10^{-5}$	Gal./day.
	1.98347	.50417	Acre-ft./day.
	723.98	$.13813\times10^{-2}$	Acre-ft./365 days.
	725.78	$.13778\times10^{-2}$	Acre-ft./366 days.
	55.54	.018005	Acre-ft./28 days.
	57.52	.017385	Acre-ft./29 days.
	59.50	.016806	Acre-ft./30 days.
	61.49	.016262	Acre-ft./31 days.
	50.0	.020	Miner's inch in Idaho, Kans., Nebr., N. Mex., N. Dak., S. Dak., and Utah.
	40.0	.025	Miner's inch in Ariz., Calif., Mont., Nev., and Oreg.
	38.4	.026042	Miner's inch in Colo.
	35.7	.028011	Miner's inch in British Columbia.
	0.028317	35.31	Cu. m./sec.
	1.699	.5886	Cu. m./min.
	0.99173	1.0083	Acre-in./hr.
Cu. ft./min.	7.4805	0.13368	Gal./min.
	10,772.0	$.92834\times10^{-4}$	Gal./day.
10^{6} gal./day	1.5472	0.64632	Cu. ft./sec.
	694.44	$.1440\times10^{-2}$	Gal./min.
	3.0689	.32585	Acre-ft./day.
In. depth/hr.	645.33	0.15496×10^{-2}	Sec.-ft./sq. mile.
In. depth/day	26.889	0.03719	Sec.-ft./sq. mile.
	53.33	.01878	Acre-ft./sq. mile.
Sec.-ft./sq. mile	1.0413	0.96032	In. depth/28 days.
	1.0785	.92720	In. depth/29 days.
	1.1157	.89630	In. depth/30 days.
	1.1529	.86738	In. depth/31 days.
	13.574	.073668	In. depth/365 days.
	13.612	.073467	In. depth/366 days.
Acre-ft./day	226.24	0.442×10^{-2}	Gal./min.
	20.17	.0496	Miner's inch in Calif.
	19.36	.0517	Miner's inch in Colo.
Gal./sec.	5.347	0.187	Miner's inch in Calif.
	5.128	.195	Miner's inch in Colo.
PERMEABILITY			
Meinzer (gal./day through 1 sq. ft. under unit gradient).	48.8	0.02049	Bureau of Reclamation (cu. ft./yr. through 1 sq. ft. under unit gradient).

Table B-1.—Conversion factors and formulas.-Continued

CONVERSION FACTORS

Column 1	Column 2	Column 3	Column 4
POWER AND ENERGY			
Hp.	555.0	0.18182×10^{-2}	Ft.-lb./sec.
	0.746	1.3405	Kw.
	6,535.	0.15303×10^{-3}	Kw.-hr./yr.
	42.4	.0236	B.t.u./min.
	1.0	1.0	Sec.-ft. falling 8.8 ft.
Hp.-hr.	0.746	1.3405	Kw.-hr.
	198.0×10^{4}	0.505×10^{-6}	Ft.-lb.
	2.545.0	$.393 \times 10^{-3}$	B.t.u.
Kw.	8,760.0	0.11416×10^{-3}	Kw.-hr./yr.
	737.56	$.1354 \times 10^{-2}$	Ft.-lb./sec.
	11.8	.0846	Sec.-ft. falling 1 ft.
	3,412.0	$.29308 \times 10^{-3}$	B.t.u./hr.
Kw.-hr.	0.975	1.025	Acre-ft. falling 1 ft.
B.t.u.	778.0	0.1285×10^{-2}	Ft.-lb.
	0.1×10^{-3} to $.834 \times 10^{-4}$	10,000 to 12,000	Lb. of coal.
PRESSURE			
Ft. water at max. density	62.425	0.01602	Lb./sq./ft.
	0.4335	2.3087	Lb./sq. in.
	.0295	33.93	Atm.
	.8826	1.133	In. Hg at 30° F.
	773.3	0.1293×10^{-2}	Ft. air at 32° F. and atm. pressure.
Ft. avg. sea water	1.026	0.9746	Ft. pure water.
Atm., sea level, 32° F	14.697	.06804	Lb./sq. in.
Millibars	295.299×10^{-4}	33.863	In. Hg.
	75.008×10^{-2}	1.3331	Mm. Hg.
Atm.	29.92	33.48×10^{-3}	In. Hg.
WEIGHT			
P.p.m.	0.00136	735.29	Tons/acre-ft.
	.0584	17.123	Gr./gal.
	8.345	0.1198	Lb./10^6 gal.
Lb.	7.0×10^{3}	0.14286×10^{-3}	Gr.
Gm.	15.432	.064799	Gr.
Kg.	2.2046	.45359	Lb.
Lb. water at 39.1° F	27.6812	0.03612	Cu. in.
	0.11983	8.345	Gal.
	.09983	10.016	Imperial gal.
	.453617	2.204	Liters.
	.01602	62.425	Cu. ft. pure water.
	.01560	64.048	Cu. ft. sea water.
Lb. water at 62° F	0.01604	62.355	Cu. ft. pure water.
	.01563	63.976	Cu. ft. sea water.

FORMULAS

VOLUME

Average depth in inches, or acre-inch per acre

$$= \frac{\text{(cu. ft./sec.) (hr.)}}{\text{acres}}$$

$$= \frac{\text{(gal./min.) (hr.)}}{\text{450 (acres)}}$$

$$= \frac{\text{(miner's in.) (hr.)}}{\text{(40*) (acres)}}$$

*Where 1 miner's in. = 1/40 sec.-ft.

Use 50 where 1 miner's in. = 1/50 sec.-ft.

Conversion of inches depth on area to sec.-ft.

$$\text{sec.-ft.} = \frac{\text{(645) (sq. miles) (in. on area)}}{\text{(time in hr.)}}$$

POWER AND ENERGY

$$\text{hp.} = \frac{\text{(sec.-ft.) (head in ft.)}}{8.8}$$

$$= \frac{\text{(sec.-ft.) (pressure in lb./sq. in.)}}{3.8}$$

$$= \frac{\text{(gal./min.) (head in ft.)}}{3{,}960}$$

$$= \frac{\text{(gal./min.) (pressure in lb./sq. in.)}}{1{,}714}$$

$$\text{b. hp.} = \frac{\text{water hp.}}{\text{pump efficiency}}$$

kw.-hr./1,000 gal. pumped/hr.

$$= \frac{\text{(head in ft.) (0.00315)}}{\text{(pump efficiency) (motor efficiency)}}$$

Kw.-hr. = (plant efficiency) (1.025) (head in ft.) (water in acre-ft.)

$$\text{Load factor} = \frac{\text{(kw.-hr. in time t)}}{\text{(kw. peak load) (time t in hr.)}}$$

SEDIMENTATION

Tons/acre-ft. = (unit weight/cu. ft.) (21.78)

Tons/day = (sec.-ft.) (p.p.m.) (0.0027)

TEMPERATURE

$$°\text{C.} = \frac{5}{9}(°\text{F.} - 32°) \qquad °\text{F.} = \frac{9}{5}°\text{C.} + 32°$$

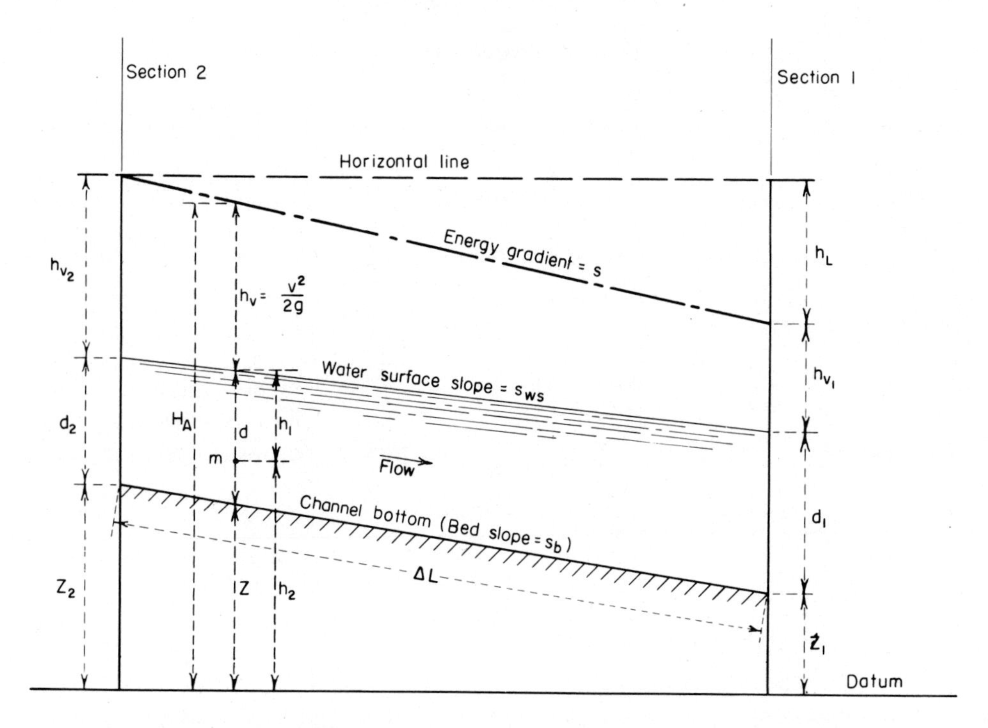

Figure B-1.—Characteristics of open-channel flow. 288-D-2550.

The portion of equation (2) in the parentheses is termed the absolute head, and is written:

$$H_A = d + Z + \frac{v^2}{2g} \tag{3}$$

Equation (3) is called the Bernoulli equation.

The energy in the cross section, with respect to the bottom of the channel, is termed the specific energy. The corresponding head is referred to as the specific energy head and is expressed as:

$$H_E = d + \frac{v^2}{2g} \tag{4}$$

Where $Q = av$, equation (4) can be stated:

$$H_E = d + \frac{Q^2}{2ga^2} \tag{5}$$

For a trapezoidal channel where b is the bottom width and z defines the side slope, if q is expressed as $\frac{Q}{b}$ and a is expressed as $d(b+zd)$, equation (5) becomes:

$$H_E = d + \frac{q^2}{2gd^2\left(1+\frac{zd}{b}\right)^2} \tag{6}$$

Equation (5) is represented in diagrammatic form on figure B–2 to show the relationships between discharge, energy, and depth of flow in an open channel. The diagram is drawn for several values of unit discharge in a rectangular channel.

It can be seen that there are two values of d, d_H and d_L, for each value of H_E, except at the point where H_E is minimum, where only a single value exists. The depth at energy $H_{E_{min}}$ is called the critical depth, and the depths for other values of H_E are called alternate depths. Those depths lying above the trace through the locus of minimum depths are in the subcritical flow range and are termed subcritical depths, while those lying below the trace are in the supercritical flow range and are termed supercritical depths.

Figure B–3 plots the relationships of d to H_E as stated in equation (6), for various values of unit discharge q and side slope z. The curves can be used to quickly determine alternate depths of flow in open channel spillways.

(b) *Critical Flow.*—Critical flow is the term used to describe open channel flow when certain relationships exist between specific energy and discharge and between specific energy

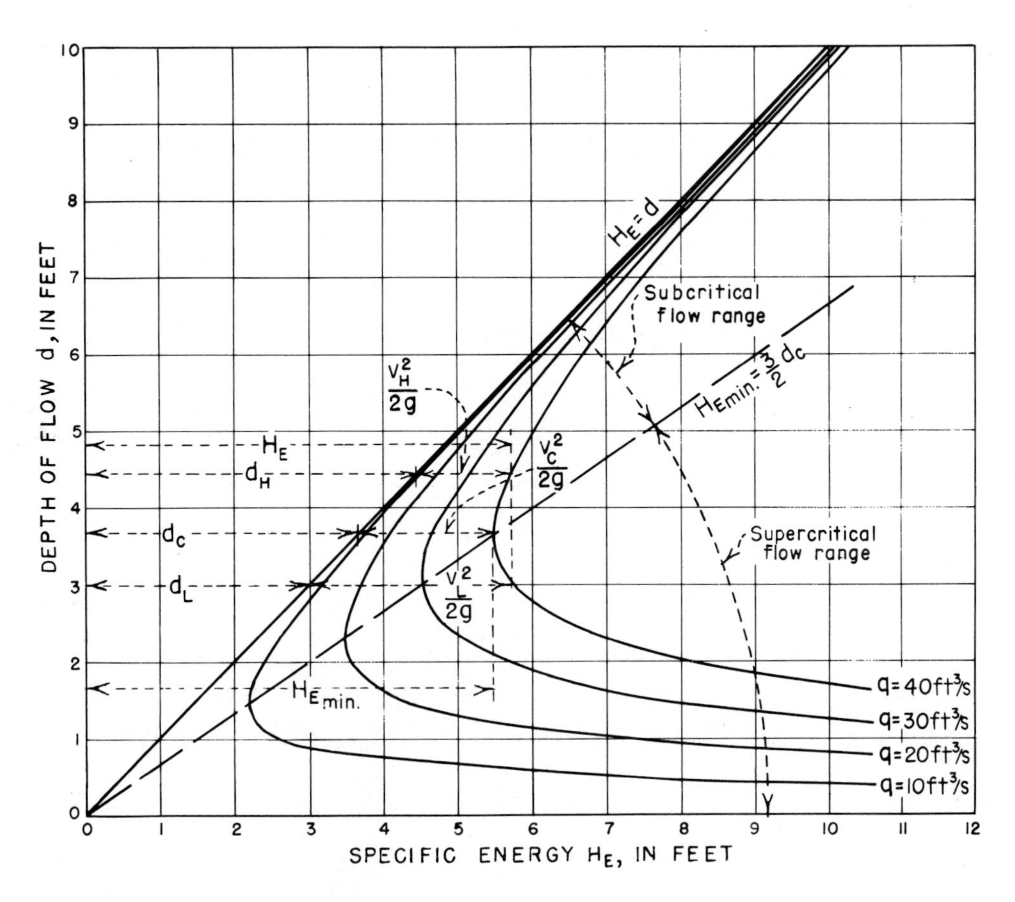

$$H_E = d + \frac{v^2}{2g} = d + \frac{q^2}{2gd^2} \quad \text{where } q = \text{discharge per unit width.}$$

$$d_c = \left(\frac{q_c}{\sqrt{g}}\right)^{\frac{2}{3}} = \frac{2}{3} H_{E_{min.}} \quad \text{where } d_c = \text{critical depth}$$

q_c = critical discharge per unit width

$H_{E_{min.}}$ = minimum energy content.

Figure B–2.—Depth of flow and specific energy for a rectangular section in open channel. 288–D–2551.

and depth. As indicated in section B–2(a) and as demonstrated on figure B–2, critical flow terms can be defined as follows:

(1) *Critical discharge.*—The maximum discharge for a given specific energy, or the discharge which will occur with minimum specific energy.

(2) *Critical depth.*—The depth of flow at which the discharge is maximum for a given specific energy, or the depth at which a given discharge occurs with minimum specific energy.

(3) *Critical velocity.*—The mean velocity when the discharge is critical.

(4) *Critical slope.*—That slope which will sustain a given discharge at uniform critical depth in a given channel.

(5) *Subcritical flow.*—Those conditions of flow for which the depths are greater than critical and the velocities are less than critical.

(6) *Supercritical flow.*—Those conditions of flow for which the depths are less than critical and the velocities are greater than critical.

More complete discussions of the critical

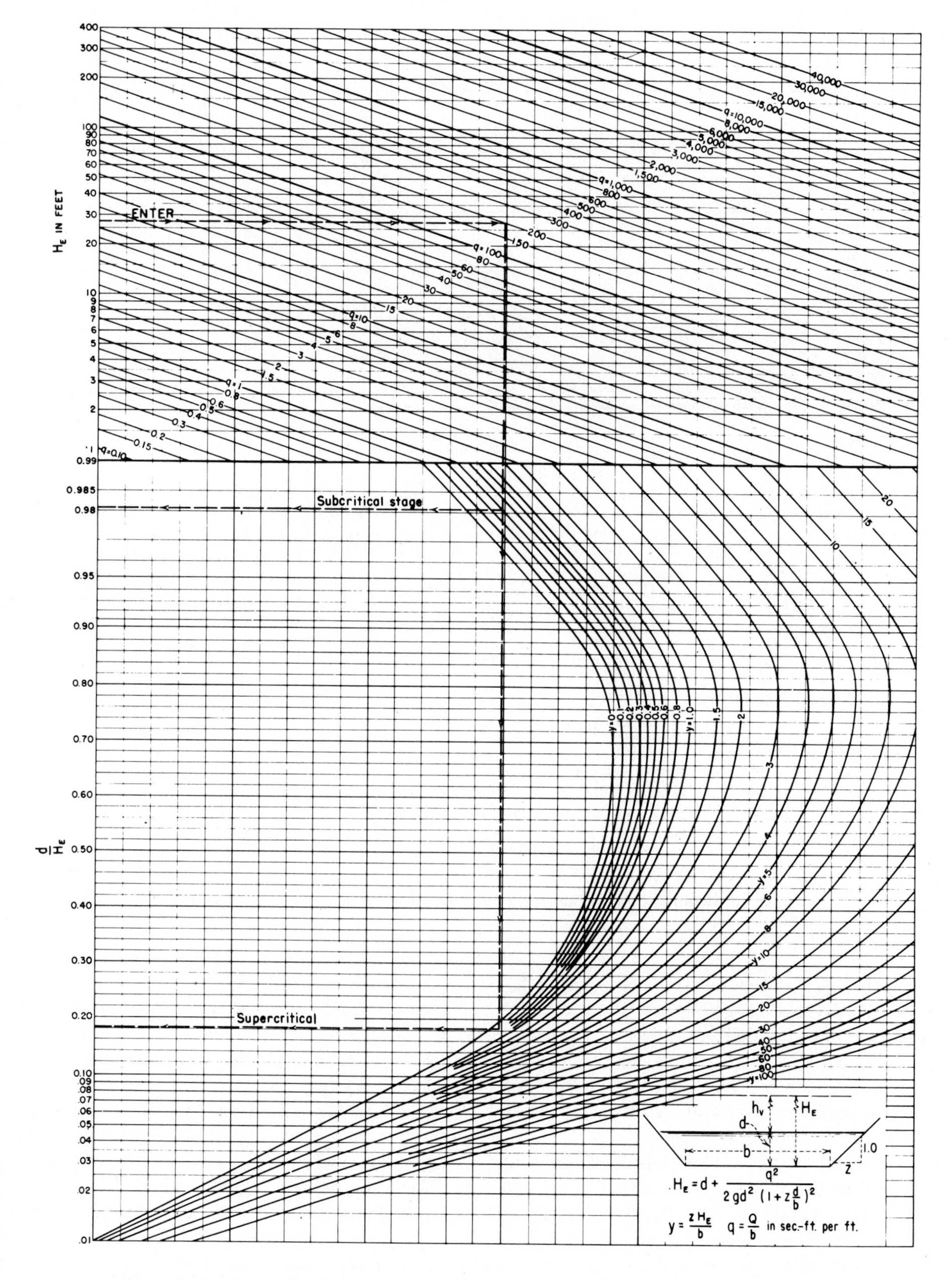

Figure B-3.—Energy-depth curves for rectangular and trapezoidal channels. 288-D-2907.

flow theory in relationship to specific energy are given in most hydraulic textbooks [1, 2, 3, 4].[1] The relationship between cross section and discharge which must exist in order that flow may occur at the critical stage is:

$$\frac{Q^2}{g}=\frac{a^3}{T} \quad (7)$$

where:

a=cross-sectional area, and
T=water surface width.

Since $Q^2=a^2v^2$, equation (7) can be written:

$$\frac{v_c^2}{2g}=\frac{a}{2T} \quad (8)$$

Also, since $a=d_mT$, where d_m is the mean depth of flow at the section, and $\frac{v_c^2}{2g}=h_{v_c}$, equation (8) can be rewritten:

$$h_{v_c}=\frac{d_{m_c}}{2} \quad (9)$$

Then equation (4) can be stated

$$H_E=d_c+\frac{d_{m_c}}{2} \quad (10)$$

From the foregoing, the following additional relations can be stated:

$$d_{m_c}=\frac{v_c^2}{g} \quad (11)$$

$$d_{m_c}=\frac{Q_c^2}{a^2g} \quad (12)$$

$$v_c=\sqrt{gd_{m_c}} \quad (13)$$

$$v_c=\sqrt{\frac{ag}{T}} \quad (14)$$

$$Q_c=a\sqrt{gd_{m_c}} \quad (15)$$

For rectangular sections, if q is the discharge per unit width of channel, the various critical flow formulas are:

$$H_{E_c}=\frac{3}{2}d_c \quad (16)$$

$$d_c=\frac{2}{3}H_{E_c} \quad (17)$$

$$d_c=\frac{v_c^2}{g} \quad (18)$$

$$d_c=\sqrt[3]{\frac{q_c^2}{g}} \quad (19)$$

$$d_c=\sqrt[3]{\frac{Q_c^2}{b^2g}} \quad (20)$$

$$v_c=\sqrt{gd_c} \quad (21)$$

$$v_c=\sqrt[3]{gq_c} \quad (22)$$

$$v_c=\sqrt[3]{\frac{gQ_c}{b}} \quad (23)$$

$$q_c=d_c^{3/2}\sqrt{g} \quad (24)$$

$$Q_c=bd_c^{3/2}\sqrt{g} \quad (25)$$

$$Q_c=0.544\ bH_{E_c}^{3/2}\sqrt{g} \quad (26)$$

The critical depth for trapezoidal sections is given by the equation:

$$d_c=\frac{v_c^2}{g}-\frac{b}{2z}+\sqrt{\frac{v_c^4}{g^2}+\frac{b^2}{4z^2}} \quad (27)$$

where z=the ratio, horizontal to vertical, of the slope of the sides of the channel.

Similarly, for the trapezoidal section,

$$v_c=\sqrt{\left(\frac{b+zd_c}{b+2zd_c}\right)d_cg} \quad (28)$$

and

$$Q_c=d_c^{3/2}\sqrt{\frac{g(b+zd_c)^3}{b+2zd_c}} \quad (29)$$

The solutions of equations (25) and (29) are simplified by use of figure B-4.

A general equation for critical depth cannot be expressed for natural channels. However, a check for the existence of critical flow in these channels is discussed in part B of this appendix.

(c) *Manning Formula.*—The formula developed by Manning for flow in open channels

[1]Numbers in brackets refer to items in the bibliography, section B-11.

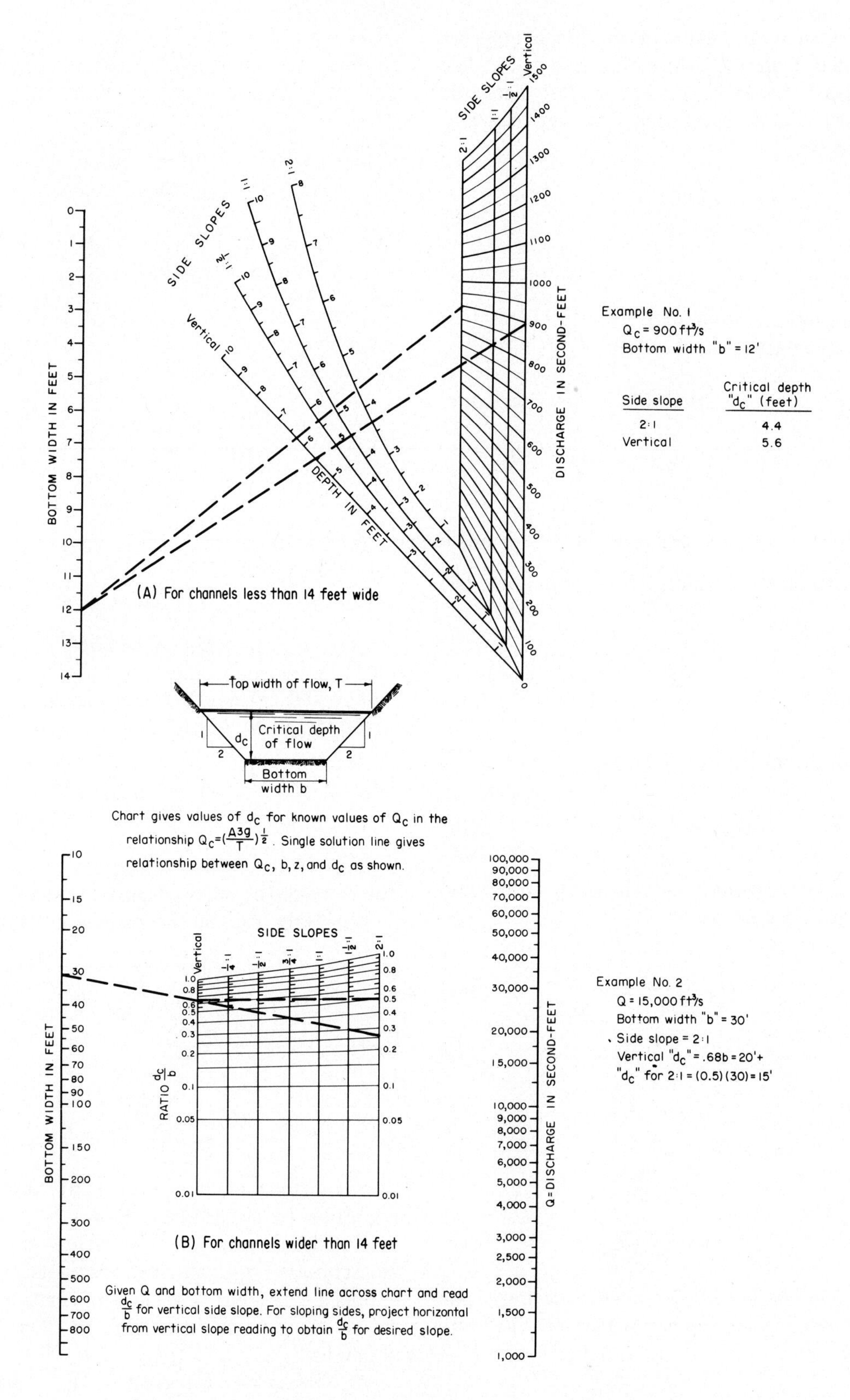

Example No. 1

Q_c = 900 ft³/s

Bottom width "b" = 12'

Side slope	Critical depth "d_c" (feet)
2:1	4.4
Vertical	5.6

Example No. 2

Q = 15,000 ft³/s

Bottom width "b" = 30'

Side slope = 2:1

Vertical "d_c" = .68b = 20'+

"d_c" for 2:1 = (0.5)(30) = 15'

Figure B-4.—Critical depth in trapezoidal sections. 288-D-2825.

is used in most of the hydraulic analyses discussed in this text. It is a special form of Chezy's formula; the complete development is contained in most textbooks on elementary fluid mechanics. The formula is written as follows:

$$v=\frac{1.486}{n}r^{2/3}s^{1/2} \tag{30}$$

or

$$Q=\frac{1.486}{n}ar^{2/3}s^{1/2} \tag{31}$$

where:

Q=discharge in cubic feet per second,
a=the cross section of flow area in square feet,
v=the velocity in feet per second,
n=a roughness coefficient,
r=the hydraulic radius= $\frac{\text{area } (a)}{\text{wetted perimeter } (p)}$, and
s=the slope of the energy gradient.

The value of the roughness coefficient, n, varies according to the physical roughness of the sides and bottom of the channel and is influenced by such factors as channel curvature, size and shape of cross section, alinement, and type and condition of the material forming the wetted perimeter.

Values of n commonly used in design of artificial channels are as follows:

Description of channel	Values of n		
	Minimum	Maximum	Average
Earth channels, straight and uniform	0.017	0.025	0.022
Dredged earth channels	.025	.033	.028
Rock channels, straight and uniform	.025	.035	.033
Rock channels, jagged and irregular	.035	.045	.045
Concrete lined	.012	.018	.014
Neat cement lined	.010	.013	.011
Grouted rubble paving	.017	.030	.025
Corrugated metal	.023	.025	.024

The determination of n values for natural channels is discussed in part B of this appendix.

(d) *Bernoulli Theorem.*—The Bernoulli theorem, which is the principle of conservation of energy applied to open channel flow, may be stated: The absolute head at any section is equal to the absolute head at a section downstream plus intervening losses of head. Expressed in terms of equation (3), from figure B–1:

$$Z_2+d_2+h_{v_2}=Z_1+d_1+h_{v_1}+h_L \tag{32}$$

where h_L represents all losses in head between section 2 (subscript 2) and section 1 (subscript 1). Such head losses will consist largely of friction loss, but may include minor other losses such as those due to eddy, transition, obstruction, impact, etc.

When the discharge at a given cross section of a channel is constant with respect to time, the flow is steady. If steady flow occurs at all sections in a reach, the flow is continuous and

$$Q=a_1v_1=a_2v_2 \tag{33}$$

Equation (33) is termed the equation of continuity. Equations (32) and (33), solved simultaneously, are the basic formulas used in solving problems of flow in open channels.

(e) *Hydraulic and Energy Gradients.*—The hydraulic gradient in open channel flow is the water surface. The energy gradient is above the hydraulic gradient a distance equal to the velocity head. The fall of the energy gradient for a given length of channel represents the loss of energy, either from friction or from friction and other influences. The relationship of the energy gradient to the hydraulic gradient reflects not only the loss of energy, but also the conversion between potential and kinetic energy. For uniform flow the gradients are parallel and the slope of the water surface represents the friction loss gradient. In accelerated flow the hydraulic gradient is steeper than the energy gradient, indicating a progressive conversion from potential to kinetic energy. In retarded flow the energy gradient is steeper than the hydraulic gradient, indicating a conversion from kinetic to potential energy. The Bernoulli theorem defines the progressive relationships of these energy gradients.

For a given reach of channel ΔL, the average slope of the energy gradient is $\frac{\Delta h_L}{\Delta L}$, where Δh_L is the cumulative losses through the reach. If these losses are solely from friction, Δh_L will become Δh_f and

$$\Delta h_f=\left(\frac{s_2+s_1}{2}\right)\Delta L \tag{34}$$

Expressed in terms of the hydraulic properties at each end of the reach and of the roughness coefficient,

$$\Delta h_f=\frac{n^2}{4.41}\left[\left(\frac{v_2}{r_2^{2/3}}\right)^2+\left(\frac{v_1}{r_1^{2/3}}\right)^2\right]\Delta L \tag{35}$$

If the average friction slope, s_f, is equal to $\frac{s_2+s_1}{2}=\frac{\Delta h_f}{\Delta L}$, and s_b is the slope of the channel floor, by substituting $s_b\Delta L$ for Z_2-Z_1, and H_E for $(d+h_v)$, equation (32) may be written:

$$\Delta L=\frac{H_{E_1}-H_{E_2}}{s_b-s_f} \tag{36}$$

(f) *Chart for Approximating Friction Losses in Chutes.*—Figure B-5 is a nomograph from which approximate friction losses in a channel can be evaluated. To generalize the chart so that it can be applied for differing channel conditions, several approximations are made. First, the depth of flow in the channel is assumed equal to the hydraulic radius; the results will therefore be most applicable to wide, shallow channels. Furthermore, the increase in velocity head is assumed to vary proportionally along the length of the channel. Thus, the data given in the chart are not exact and are intended to serve only as a guide in estimating channel losses.

The chart plots the solution of the equation $s=\frac{dh_f}{dx}$, integrated between the limits from zero to L, or

$$h_f=\int_0^L s\,dx,$$

where, from the Manning equation,

$$s=\frac{v^2}{\left(\frac{1.486}{n}\right)^2 r^{4/3}}$$

B-3. Flow in Closed Conduits.—(a) *Part Full Flow in Conduits.*—The hydraulics of part full flow in closed conduits is similar to that in open channels, and open channel flow formulas are applicable. Hydraulic properties for different flow depths in circular and horseshoe conduits are tabulated in tables B-2 through B-5 to facilitate hydraulic computations for these sections.

Tables B-2 and B-4 give data for determining critical depths, critical velocities, and hydrostatic pressures of the water prism cross section for various discharges and conduit diameters. If the area at critical flow, a_c, is represented as k_1D^2 and the top width of the water prism, T, for critical flow is equal to k_2D, equation (7) can be written:

$$\frac{Q_c^2}{g}=\frac{(k_1D^2)^3}{k_2D},\ \text{or}\ Q_c=k_3D^{5/2} \tag{37}$$

Values of k_3, for various flow depths, are tabulated in column 3. The hydrostatic pressure, P, of the water prism cross section is $wa\bar{y}$, where $\bar{y}$ is the depth from the water surface to the center of gravity of the cross section. If $a_c=k_1D^2$ and $\bar{y}=k_4D$, then

$$P=k_5D^3 \tag{38}$$

Values of k_5, for various flow depths, are tabulated in column 4. Column 2 gives the values of h_{v_c} in relation to the conduit diameter, for various flow depths.

The use of tables B-2 and B-4 can be illustrated by an example. Suppose that it is desired to find the critical depth for 650 second-feet flowing free in a 9-foot-diameter circular conduit. For this case, $\frac{Q}{D^{5/2}}=\frac{650}{243}=2.675$. From column 3, by interpolation, the corresponding value in column 1 is $\frac{d}{D}=0.701$. The critical depth is then $9\times0.701=6.31$ feet. The critical velocity from column 2 is $h_{v_c}=0.3212\times 9=2.89$ feet, which gives a critical velocity of 13.6 feet per second.

Column 4 gives hydrostatic pressure upon the cross section of the water prism. The tabular value multiplied by D^3 gives pressure in cubic units of water. The pressure in pounds is 62.4 times the tabular value. For this example, $P = (62.4)(9^3)(0.1822) = 8{,}300$ pounds.

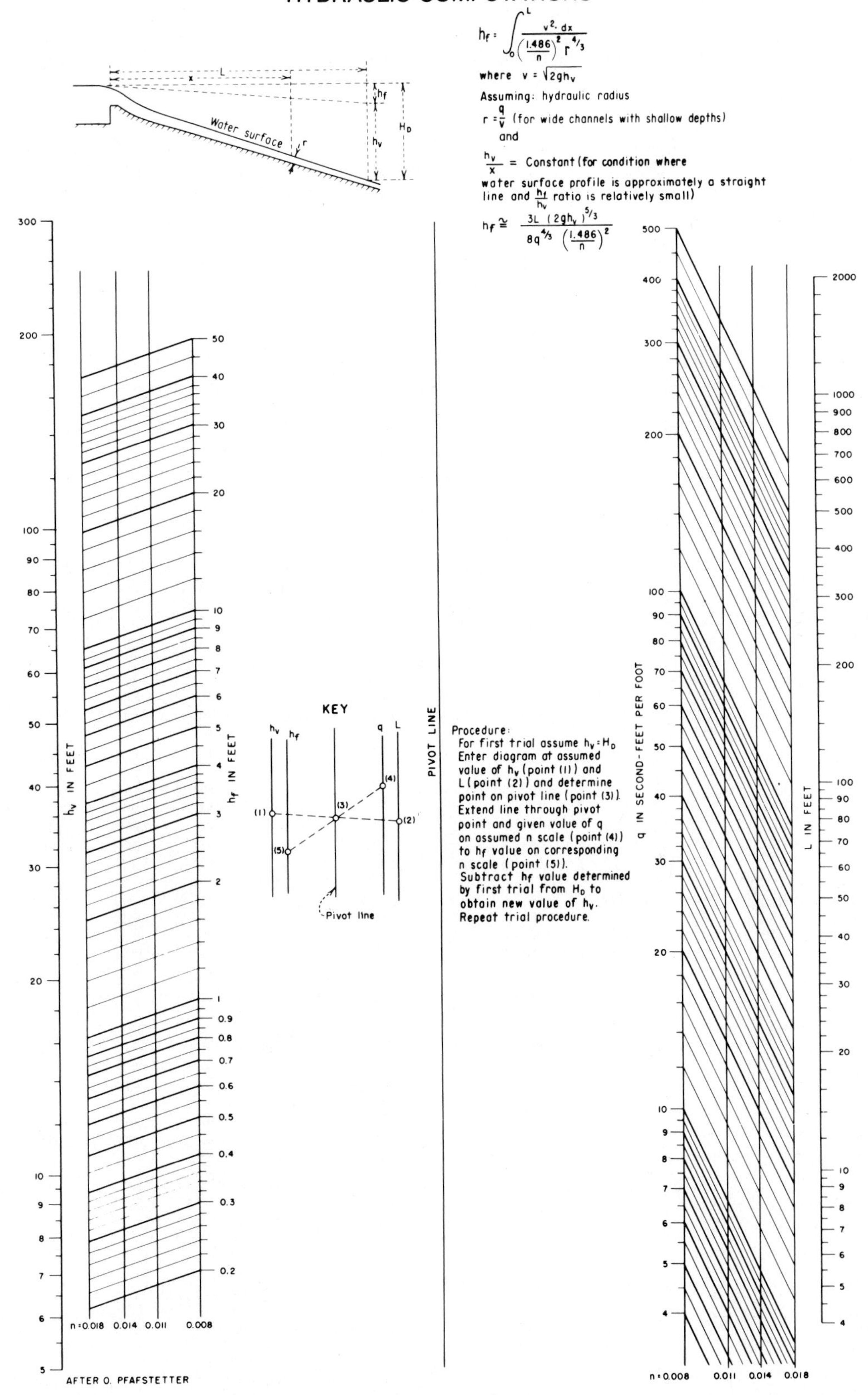

Figure B-5.—Approximate losses in chutes for various values of water surface drop and channel length. 288-D-2826.

Table B-2.—Velocity head and discharge at critical depths and static pressures in circular conduits partly full.

D = Diameter of pipe.
d = Depth of flow.
h_{v_c} = Velocity head for a critical depth of d.
Q_c = Discharge when the critical depth is d.
P = Pressure on cross section of water prism in cubic units of water. To get P in pounds, when d and D are in feet, multipy by 62.4.

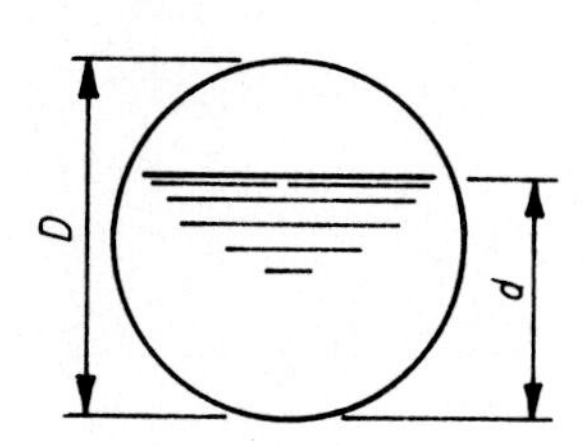

$\frac{d}{D}$	$\frac{h_{v_c}}{D}$	$\frac{Q_c}{D^{5/2}}$	$\frac{P}{D^3}$	$\frac{d}{D}$	$\frac{h_{v_c}}{D}$	$\frac{Q_c}{D^{5/2}}$	$\frac{P}{D^3}$	$\frac{d}{D}$	$\frac{h_{v_c}}{D}$	$\frac{Q_c}{D^{5/2}}$	$\frac{P}{D^3}$
1	2	3	4	1	2	3	4	1	2	3	4
0.01	0.0033	0.0006	0.0000	0.34	0.1243	0.6657	0.0332	0.67	0.2974	2.4464	0.1644
.02	.0067	.0025	.0000	.35	.1284	.7040	.0356	.68	.3048	2.5182	.1700
.03	.0101	.0055	.0001	.36	.1326	.7433	.0381	.69	.3125	2.5912	.1758
.04	.0134	.0098	.0002	.37	.1368	.7836	.0407	.70	.3204	2.6656	.1816
.05	.0168	.0153	.0003	.38	.1411	.8249	.0434	.71	.3286	2.7414	.1875
.06	.0203	.0220	.0005	.39	.1454	.8671	.0462	.72	.3371	2.8188	.1935
.07	.0237	.0298	.0007	.40	.1497	.9103	.0491	.73	.3459	2.8977	.1996
.08	.0271	.0389	.0010	.41	.1541	.9545	.0520	.74	.3552	2.9783	.2058
.09	.0306	.0491	.0013	.42	.1586	.9996	.0551	.75	.3648	3.0607	.2121
.10	.0341	.0605	.0017	.43	.1631	1.0458	.0583	.76	.3749	3.1450	.2185
.11	.0376	.0731	.0021	.44	.1676	1.0929	.0616	.77	.3855	3.2314	.2249
.12	.0411	.0868	.0026	.45	.1723	1.1410	.0650	.78	.3967	3.3200	.2314
.13	.0446	.1016	.0032	.46	.1769	1.1899	.0684	.79	.4085	3.4112	.2380
.14	.0482	.1176	.0038	.47	.1817	1.2399	.0720	.80	.4210	3.5050	.2447
.15	.0517	.1347	.0045	.48	.1865	1.2908	.0757	.81	.4343	3.6019	.2515
.16	.0553	.1530	.0053	.49	.1914	1.3427	.0795	.82	.4485	3.7021	.2584
.17	.0589	.1724	.0061	.50	.1964	1.3955	.0833	.83	.4638	3.8061	.2653
.18	.0626	.1928	.0070	.51	.2014	1.4493	.0873	.84	.4803	3.9144	.2723
.19	.0662	.2144	.0080	.52	.2065	1.5041	.0914	.85	.4982	4.0276	.2794
.20	.0699	.2371	.0091	.53	.2117	1.5598	.0956	.86	.5177	4.1465	.2865
.21	.0736	.2609	.0103	.54	.2170	1.6164	.0998	.87	.5392	4.2721	.2938
.22	.0773	.2857	.0115	.55	.2224	1.6735	.1042	.88	.5632	4.4056	.3011
.23	.0811	.3116	.0128	.56	.2279	1.7327	.1087	.89	.5900	4.5486	.3084
.24	.0848	.3386	.0143	.57	.2335	1.7923	.1133	.90	.6204	4.7033	.3158
.25	.0887	.3667	.0157	.58	.2393	1.8530	.1179	.91	.6555	4.8725	.3233
.26	.0925	.3957	.0173	.59	.2451	1.9146	.1227	.92	.6966	5.0603	.3308
.27	.0963	.4259	.0190	.60	.2511	1.9773	.1276	.93	.7459	5.2726	.3384
.28	.1002	.4571	.0207	.61	.2572	2.0409	.1326	.94	.8065	5.5183	.3460
.29	.1042	.4893	.0226	.62	.2635	2.1057	.1376	.95	.8841	5.8118	.3537
.30	.1081	.5225	.0255	.63	.2699	2.1716	.1428	.96	.9885	6.1787	.3615
.31	.1121	.5568	.0266	.64	.2765	2.2386	.1481	.97	1.1410	6.6692	.3692
.32	.1161	.5921	.0287	.65	.2833	2.3067	.1534	.98	1.3958	7.4063	.3770
.33	.1202	.6284	.0309	.66	.2902	2.3760	.1589	.99	1.9700	8.8263	.3848
								1.00	------	------	.3927

Tables B–3 and B–5 give areas and hydraulic radii for partially full conduits and coefficients which can be applied in the solution of the Manning equation. If $A=k_6\frac{\pi D^2}{4}$ and $r=k_7D$, Manning's equation can be written:

$$Q'=\frac{1.486}{n}\left(k_6\frac{\pi D^2}{4}\right)(k_7D)^{2/3}\,s^{1/2},$$

or

$$\frac{Qn}{D^{8/3}s^{1/2}}=k_6\frac{1.486\pi}{4}(k_7)^{2/3}=k_8 \qquad (39)$$

Table B-3.—Uniform flow in circular sections flowing partly full.

d=Depth of flow.
D=Diameter of pipe.
A=Area of flow.
r=Hydraulic radius.

Q=Discharge in second-feet by Manning's formula.
n=Manning's coefficient.
s=Slope of the channel bottom and of the water surface.

$\frac{d}{D}$	$\frac{A}{D^2}$	$\frac{r}{D}$	$\frac{Qn}{D^{8/3}s^{1/2}}$	$\frac{Qn}{d^{8/3}s^{1/2}}$	$\frac{d}{D}$	$\frac{A}{D^2}$	$\frac{r}{D}$	$\frac{Qn}{D^{8/3}s^{1/2}}$	$\frac{Qn}{d^{8/3}s^{1/2}}$
1	2	3	4	5	1	2	3	4	5
0.01	0.0013	0.0066	0.00007	15.04	0.51	0.4027	0.2531	0.239	1.442
.02	.0037	.0132	.00031	10.57	.52	.4127	.2562	.247	1.415
.03	.0069	.0197	.00074	8.56	.53	.4227	.2592	.255	1.388
.04	.0105	.0262	.00138	7.38	.54	.4327	.2621	.263	1.362
.05	.0147	0325	.00222	6.55	.55	.4426	.2649	.271	1.336
.06	.0192	.0389	.00328	5.95	.56	.4526	.2676	.279	1.311
.07	.0242	.0451	.00455	5.47	.57	.4625	.2703	.287	1.286
.08	.0294	.0513	.00604	5.09	.58	.4724	.2728	.295	1.262
.09	.0350	.0575	.00775	4.76	.59	.4822	.2753	.303	1.238
.10	.0409	.0635	.00967	4.49	.60	.4920	.2776	.311	1.215
.11	.0470	.0695	.01181	4.25	.61	.5018	.2799	.319	1.192
.12	.0534	.0755	.01417	4.04	.62	.5115	.2821	.327	1.170
.13	.0600	.0813	.01674	3.86	.63	.5212	.2842	.335	1.148
.14	.0668	.0871	.01952	3.69	.64	.5308	.2862	.343	1.126
.15	.0739	.0929	.0225	3.54	.65	.5404	.2882	.350	1.105
.16	.0811	.0985	.0257	3.41	.66	.5499	.2900	.358	1.084
.17	.0885	.1042	.0291	3.28	.67	.5594	.2917	.366	1.064
.18	.0961	.1097	.0327	3.17	.68	.5687	.2933	.373	1.044
.19	.1039	.1152	.0365	3.06	.69	.5780	.2948	.380	1.024
.20	.1118	.1206	.0406	2.96	.70	.5872	.2962	.388	1.004
.21	.1199	.1259	.0448	2.87	.71	.5964	.2975	.395	0.985
.22	.1281	.1312	.0492	2.79	.72	.6054	.2987	.402	.965
.23	.1365	.1364	.0537	2.71	.73	.6143	.2998	.409	.947
.24	.1449	.1416	.0585	2.63	.74	.6231	.3008	.416	.928
.25	.1535	.1466	.0634	2.56	.75	.6319	.3017	.422	.910
.26	.1623	.1516	.0686	2.49	.76	.6405	.3024	.429	.891
.27	.1711	.1566	.0739	2.42	.77	.6489	.3031	435	.873
.28	.1800	.1614	.0793	2.36	.78	.6573	.3036	.441	.856
.29	.1890	.1662	.0849	2.30	.79	.6655	.3039	.447	.838
.30	.1982	.1709	.0907	2.25	.80	.6736	.3042	.453	.821
.31	.2074	.1756	.0966	2.20	.81	.6815	.3043	.458	.804
.32	.2167	.1802	.1027	2.14	.82	.6893	.3043	.463	.787
.33	.2260	.1847	.1089	2.09	.83	.6969	.3041	.468	.770
.34	.2355	.1891	.1153	2.05	.84	.7043	.3038	.473	.753
.35	.2450	.1935	.1218	2.00	.85	.7115	.3033	.477	.736
.36	.2546	.1978	.1284	1.958	.86	.7186	.3026	.481	.720
.37	.2642	.2020	.1351	1.915	.87	.7254	.3018	.485	.703
.38	.2739	.2062	.1420	1.875	.88	.7320	.3007	.488	.687
.39	.2836	.2102	.1490	1.835	.89	.7384	.2995	.491	.670
.40	.2934	.2142	.1561	1.797	.90	.7445	.2980	.494	.654
.41	.3032	.2182	.1633	1.760	.91	.7504	.2963	.496	.637
.42	.3130	.2220	.1705	1.724	.92	.7560	.2944	.497	.621
.43	.3229	.2258	.1779	1.689	.93	.7612	.2921	.498	.604
.44	.3328	.2295	.1854	1.655	.94	.7662	.2895	.498	.588
.45	.3428	.2331	.1929	1.622	.95	.7707	.2865	.498	.571
.46	.3527	.2366	.201	1.590	.96	.7749	.2829	.496	.553
.47	.3627	.2401	.208	1.559	.97	.7785	.2787	.494	.535
.48	.3727	.2435	.216	1.530	.98	.7817	.2735	.489	.517
.49	.3827	.2468	.224	1.500	.909	.7841	.2666	.483	.496
.50	.3927	.2500	.232	1.471	1.00	.7854	.2500	.463	.463

Table B-4.—Velocity head and discharge at critical depths and static pressures in horseshoe conduits partly full.

D=Diameter of horseshoe.
d=Depth of flow.
h_{v_c}=Velocity head for a critical depth of d.
Q_c=Discharge when the critical depth is d.
P = Pressure on cross section of water prism in cubic units of water. To get P in pounds, when d and D are in feet, multipy by 62.4.

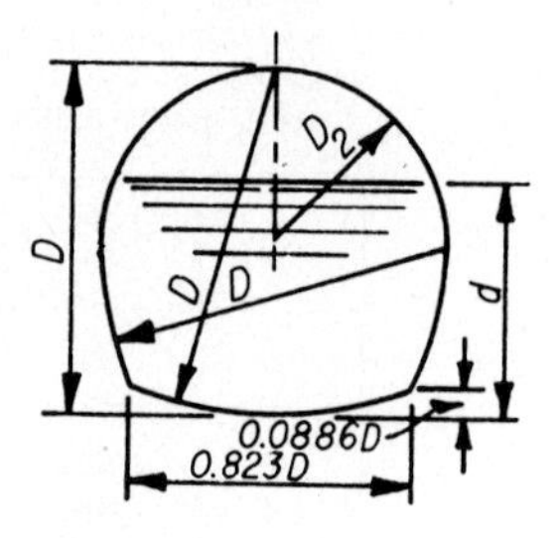

$\frac{d}{D}$	$\frac{h_{v_c}}{D}$	$\frac{Q_c}{D^{5/2}}$	$\frac{P}{D^3}$	$\frac{d}{D}$	$\frac{h_{v_c}}{D}$	$\frac{Q_c}{D^{5/2}}$	$\frac{P}{D^3}$	$\frac{d}{D}$	$\frac{h_{v_c}}{D}$	$\frac{Q_c}{D^{5/2}}$	$\frac{P}{D^3}$
1	2	3	4	1	2	3	4	1	2	3	4
0.01	0.0033	0.0009	0.0000	0.35	0.1472	0.8854	0.0449	0.69	0.3362	2.8922	0.1999
.02	.0067	.0035	.0000	.36	.1518	.9296	.0478	.70	.3443	2.9702	.2062
.03	.0100	.0079	.0001	.37	.1563	.9746	.0508	.71	.3528	3.0499	.2125
.04	.0134	.0139	.0002	.38	.1609	1.0205	.0540	.72	.3615	3.1311	.2190
.05	.0168	.0217	.0004	.39	.1655	1.0673	.0572	.73	.3707	3.2140	.2255
.06	.0201	.0312	.0007	.40	.1702	1.1148	.0605	.74	.3802	3.2987	.2321
.07	.0235	.0425	.0010	.41	.1749	1.1633	.0639	.75	.3902	3.3853	.2385
.08	.0269	.0554	.0014	.42	.1795	1.2125	.0675	.76	.4006	3.4740	.2457
.09	.0305	.0703	.0018	.43	.1843	1.2626	.0711	.77	.4116	3.5650	.2525
.10	.0351	.0879	.0024	.44	.1890	1.3135	.0748	.78	.4232	3.6584	.2595
.11	.0397	.1069	.0030	.45	.1938	1.3652	.0786	.79	.4354	3.7544	.2666
.12	.0443	.1272	.0037	.46	.1986	1.4178	.0825	.80	.4484	3.8534	.2737
.13	.0489	.1487	.0045	.47	.2035	1.4712	.0865	.81	.4623	3.9557	.2809
.14	.0534	.1714	.0054	.48	.2084	1.5253	.0907	.82	.4771	4.0616	.2882
.15	.0579	.1953	.0063	.49	.2133	1.5803	.0949	.83	.4930	4.1716	.2956
.16	.0624	.2203	.0074	.50	.2183	1.6361	.0992	.84	.5102	4.2863	.3030
.17	.0669	.2465	.0085	.51	.2234	1.6928	.1036	.85	.5289	4.4063	.3105
.18	.0714	.2736	.0098	.52	.2285	1.7505	.1081	.86	.5494	4.5325	.3181
.19	.0758	.3019	.0111	.53	.2337	1.8092	.1127	.87	.5719	4.6660	.3258
.20	.0803	.3312	.0125	.54	.2391	1.8688	.1174	.88	.5969	4.8080	.3335
.21	.0847	.3615	.0140	.55	.2445	1.9294	.1223	.89	.6251	4.9605	.3413
.22	.0891	.3928	.0156	.56	.2500	1.9911	.1272	.90	.6570	5.1256	.3492
.23	.0936	.4251	.0173	.57	.2557	2.0537	.1322	.91	.6939	5.3065	.3572
.24	.0980	.4583	.0191	.58	.2615	2.1174	.1373	.92	.7371	5.5077	.3653
.25	.1024	.4926	.0210	.59	.2674	2.1821	.1425	.93	.7889	5.7354	.3733
.26	.1069	.5277	.0229	.60	.2735	2.2479	.1478	.94	.8528	5.9996	.3813
.27	.1113	.5638	.0250	.61	.2797	2.3148	.1532	.95	.9345	6.3157	.3894
.28	.1158	.6009	0271	.62	.2861	2.3828	.1587	.96	1.0446	6.7114	.3976
.29	.1202	.6389	.0294	.63	.2926	2.4519	.1643	.97	1.2053	7.2417	.4058
.30	.1247	.6777	.0317	.64	.2994	2.5221	.1700	.98	1.4742	8.0892	4140
.31	.1292	.7175	.0342	.65	.3063	2.5936	.1758	.99	2.0804	9.5780	.4223
.32	.1337	.7582	.0367	.66	.3134	2.6663	.1817	1.00	----------	----------	.4306
.33	.1382	.7997	.0393	.67	.3208	2.7402	.1877				
.34	.1427	.8421	.0421	.68	.3283	2.8155	.1937				

Values of k_8, for various flow depths, are tabulated in column 4. If $D=k_9d$, equation (39) can be written:

$$\frac{Qn}{d^{8/3}s^{1/2}}=\frac{1.486\pi}{4}k_6(k_7)^{2/3}(k_9)^{8/3}=k_{10} \qquad (40)$$

Values of k_{10}, for various flow depths, are tabulated in column 5.

(b) *Pressure Flow in Conduits.*—Since factors affecting head losses in conduits are independent of pressure, the same laws apply to flow in both closed conduits and open channels,

Table B-5.—Uniform flow in horseshoe sections flowing partly full.

d=Depth of flow.
D=Diameter.
A=Area of flow.
r=Hydraulic radius.

Q=Discharge in second-feet by Manning's for…
n=Manning's coefficient.
s=Slope of the channel bottom and of the water surface.

$\frac{d}{D}$	$\frac{A}{D^2}$	$\frac{r}{D}$	$\frac{Qn}{D^{8/3}s^{1/2}}$	$\frac{Qn}{d^{8/3}s^{1/2}}$	$\frac{d}{D}$	$\frac{A}{D^2}$	$\frac{r}{D}$	$\frac{Qn}{D^{8/3}s^{1/2}}$	$\frac{Qn}{d^{8/3}s^{1/2}}$
1	2	3	4	5	1	2	3	4	5
0.01	0.0019	0.0066	0.00010	21.40	0.51	0.4466	0.2602	0.2705	1.629
.02	.0053	.0132	.00044	14.93	.52	.4566	.2630	.2785	1.593
.03	.0097	.0198	.00105	12.14	.53	.4666	.2657	.2866	1.558
.04	.0150	.0264	.00198	10.56	.54	.4766	.2683	.2946	1.524
.05	.0209	.0329	.00319	9.40	.55	.4865	.2707	.303	1.490
.06	.0275	.0394	.00473	8.58	.56	.4965	.2733	.311	1.458
.07	.0346	.0459	.00659	7.92	.57	.5064	.2757	.319	1.427
.08	.0421	.0524	.00876	7.37	.58	.5163	.2781	.327	1.397
.09	.0502	.0590	.01131	6.95	.59	.5261	.2804	.335	1.368
.10	.0585	.0670	.01434	6.66	.60	.5359	.2824	.343	1.339
.11	.0670	.0748	.01768	6.36	.61	.5457	.2844	.351	1.310
.12	.0753	.0823	.02117	6.04	.62	.5555	.2864	.359	1.283
.13	.0839	.0895	.02495	5.75	.63	.5651	.2884	.367	1.257
.14	.0925	.0964	.02890	5.47	.64	.5748	.2902	.374	1.231
.15	.1012	.1031	.0331	5.21	.65	.5843	.2920	.382	1.206
.16	.1100	.1097	.0375	4.96	.66	.5938	.2937	.390	1.181
.17	.1188	.1161	.0420	4.74	.67	.6033	.2953	.398	1.157
.18	.1277	.1222	.0467	4.52	.68	.6126	.2967	.405	1.133
.19	.1367	.1282	.0516	4.33	.69	.6219	.2981	.412	1.109
.20	.1457	.1341	.0567	4.15	.70	.6312	.2994	.420	1.087
.21	.1549	.1398	.0620	3.98	.71	.6403	.3006	.427	1.064
.22	.1640	.1454	.0674	3.82	.72	.6493	.3018	.434	1.042
.23	.1733	.1508	.0730	3.68	.73	.6582	.3028	.441	1.021
.24	.1825	.1560	.0786	3.53	.74	.6671	.3036	.448	1.000
.25	.1919	.1611	.0844	3.40	.75	.6758	.3044	.454	0.979
.26	.2013	.1662	.0904	3.28	.76	.6844	.3050	.461	.958
.27	.2107	.1710	.0965	3.17	.77	.6929	.3055	.467	.938
.28	.2202	.1758	.1027	3.06	.78	.7012	.3060	.473	.918
.29	.2297	.1804	.1090	2.96	.79	.7094	.3064	.479	.898
.30	.2393	.1850	.1155	2.86	.80	.7175	.3067	.485	.879
.31	.2489	.1895	.1220	2.77	.81	.7254	.3067	.490	.860
.32	.2586	.1938	.1287	2.69	.82	.7332	.3066	.495	.841
.33	.2683	.1981	.1355	2.61	.83	.7408	.3064	.500	.822
.34	.2780	.2023	.1424	2.53	.84	.7482	.3061	.505	.804
.35	.2878	.2063	.1493	2.45	.85	.7554	.3056	.509	.786
.36	.2975	.2103	.1563	2.38	.86	.7625	.3050	.513	.768
.37	.3074	.2142	.1635	2.32	.87	.7693	.3042	.517	.750
.38	.3172	.2181	.1708	2.25	.88	.7759	.3032	.520	.732
.39	.3271	.2217	.1781	2.19	.89	.7823	.3020	.523	.714
.40	.3370	.2252	.1854	2.13	.90	.7884	.3005	.526	.696
.41	.3469	.2287	.1928	2.08	.91	.7943	.2988	.528	.678
.42	.3568	.2322	.2003	2.02	.92	.7999	.2969	.529	.661
.43	.3667	.2356	.2079	1.973	.93	.8052	.2947	.530	.643
.44	.3767	.2390	.2156	1.925	.94	.8101	.2922	.530	.625
.45	.3867	.2422	.2233	1.878	.95	.8146	.2893	.529	.607
.46	.3966	.2454	.2310	1.832	.96	.8188	.2858	.528	.589
.47	.4066	.2484	.2388	1.788	.97	.8224	.2816	.525	.569
.48	.4166	.2514	.2466	1.746	.98	.8256	.2766	.521	.550
.49	.4266	.2544	.2545	1.705	.99	.8280	.2696	.513	.527
.50	.4366	.2574	.2625	1.667	1.00	.8293	.2538	.494	.494

.he formulas for each take the same general n. Thus, the equation of continuity, equa-.on (33), $Q=a_1v_1=a_2v_2$, also applies to pressure flow in conduits.

A mass of water as such does not have pressure energy. Pressure energy is acquired by contact with other masses and is, therefore, transmitted to or through the mass under consideration. The pressure head $\frac{p}{w}$ (where p is the pressure intensity in pounds per square foot and w is unit weight in pounds per cubic foot), like velocity and elevation heads, also expresses energy. Thus for pressure pipe flow, the Bernoulli equation for flow in open channels, equation (3), can be written:

$$H_A=\frac{p}{w}+Z+\frac{v^2}{2g} \tag{41}$$

The Bernoulli theorem for flow in a reach of pressure pipe (as shown on fig. B–6) is:

$$\frac{p_1}{w}+Z_1+h_{v_1}=\frac{p_2}{w}+Z_2+h_{v_2}+\Delta h_L \tag{42}$$

where Δh_L represents the head losses within the reach from all causes. If H_T is the total head and v is the velocity at the outlet, Bernoulli's equation for the entire pipe is:

$$H_T=\Sigma(\Delta h_L)+h_v \tag{43}$$

As in open channel flow, the Bernoulli theorem and the continuity equation are the basic formulas used in solving problems of pressure conduit flow.

(c) *Energy and Pressure Gradients.*—If piezometer stand pipes were to be inserted at various points along the length of a conduit flowing under pressure, as illustrated on figure B–6, water would rise in each pipe to a level equal to the pressure head in the conduit at those points. The level may be equal to the pipe grade or be above or below it; that is, the pressure at that point may be equal to, greater than, or less than the local atmospheric pressure. The height to which the water would rise in a piezometer is termed the pressure gradient. The energy gradient is above the pressure gradient a distance equal to the velocity head. The fall of the energy gradient for a given length of pipe represents the loss of energy, either from friction or from friction and other influences. The relationship of the energy gradient to the pressure gradient reflects the variations between kinetic energy and pressure head.

(d) *Friction Losses.*—Many empirical formulas have been developed for evaluating the flow of fluids in pipes. Those in most common use are the Manning equation, which, written in terms of the pipe length and diameter (in feet), is:

$$h_f=185n^2\frac{L}{D^{4/3}}\frac{v^2}{2g} \tag{44}$$

and the Darcy-Weisbach equation, which, written in similar terms, is:

$$h_f=\frac{fL}{D}\frac{v^2}{2g} \tag{45}$$

The Manning equation assumes that the energy loss depends only on the velocity, the dimensions of the conduit, and the magnitude of wall roughness as defined by the friction coefficient n. The n value is related to the physical roughness of the conduit wall and is independent of the size of the pipe or of the density and viscosity of the water.

The Darcy-Weisbach equation assumes the loss to be related to the velocity, the dimensions of the conduit, and the friction factor f. The factor f is a dimensionless variable based on the viscosity and density of the fluid and on the roughness of the conduit walls as it relates to the size of the conduit. Data and criteria for determining f values for large pipe are given in a Bureau of Reclamation engineering monograph [5].

(e) *Design Charts for Flow in Culverts.*—Figures B–7 through B–12 are nomographs prepared by the Bureau of Public Roads, presenting data which can be used for determining flow in circular and box culvert conduits. Figures B–7 and B–8 give discharges for pipes for conditions where the control is at the inlet; these charts are based on experimental data. Figures B–9 and B–10 give discharges for pipes flowing full, with friction losses based on the Manning equation. Similarly, figure B–11 gives discharges through box culverts with entrance control, based on discharge coefficients determined experimentally. Figure B–12 gives discharges for box culverts flowing full, using the Manning equation to determine losses.

B-4. *Hydraulic Jump*.—The hydraulic jump is an abrupt rise in water surface which may occur in an open channel when water flowing at high velocity is retarded. The formula for the hydraulic jump is obtained by equating the unbalanced forces acting to retard the mass of flow to the rate of change of the momentum of flow. The general formula for this relationship is:

$$v_1^2 = g\frac{a_2\bar{y}_2 - a_1\bar{y}_1}{a_1\left(1-\frac{a_1}{a_2}\right)} \qquad (46)$$

where:

v_1=the velocity before the jump,

a_1 and a_2=the areas before and after the jump, respectively, and

$\bar{y}_1$ and $\bar{y}_2$=the corresponding depths from the water surface to the center of gravity of the cross section.

The general formula expressed in terms of discharge is:

$$Q^2 = g\frac{a_2\bar{y}_2 - a_1\bar{y}_1}{\frac{1}{a_1}-\frac{1}{a_2}} \qquad (47)$$

or:

$$\frac{Q^2}{ga_1}+a_1\bar{y}_1=\frac{Q^2}{ga_2}+a_2\bar{y}_2 \qquad (48)$$

For a rectangular channel, equation (46) can be reduced to $v_1^2=\frac{gd_2}{2d_1}(d_2+d_1)$, where d_1 and d_2 are the flow depths before and after the jump, respectively. Solving for d_2:

$$d_2=-\frac{d_1}{2}+\sqrt{\frac{2v_1^2d_1}{g}+\frac{d_1^2}{4}} \qquad (49)$$

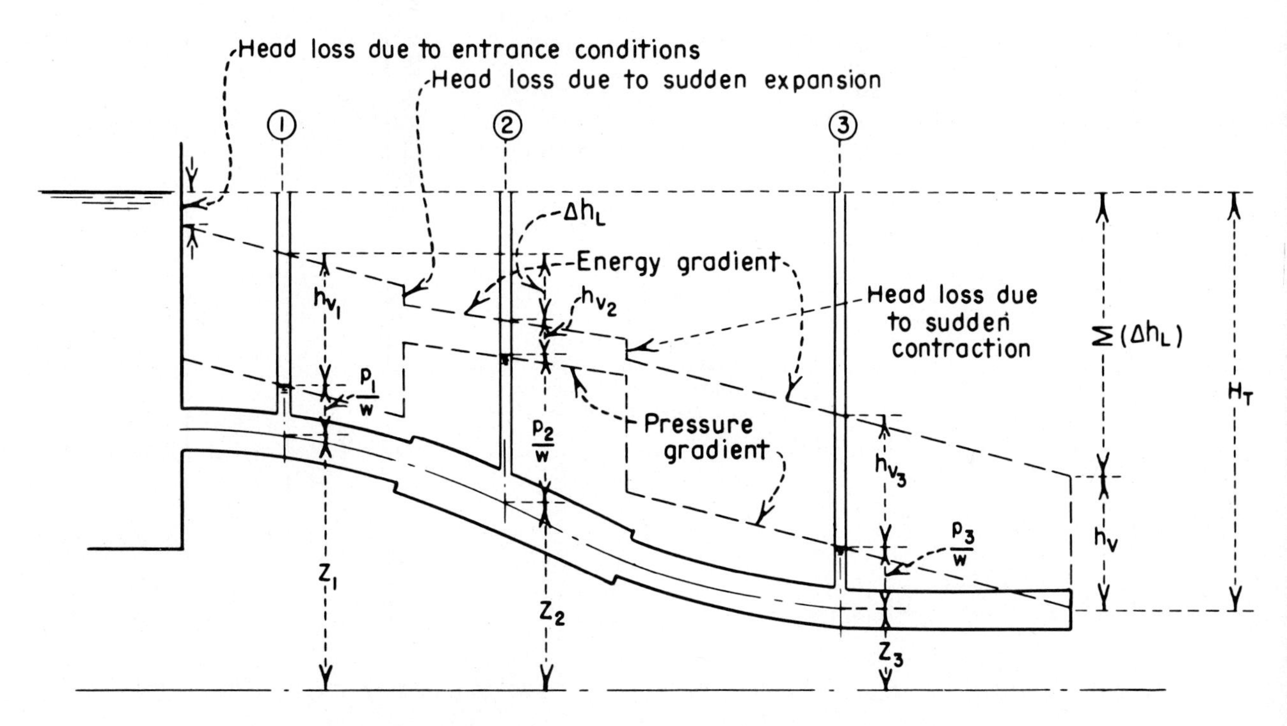

Figure B–6.—Characteristics of pressure flow in conduits. 288–D–2555.

To use scale (2) or (3), project horizontally to scale (1), then use straight inclined line through D and Q scales, or reverse as illustrated.

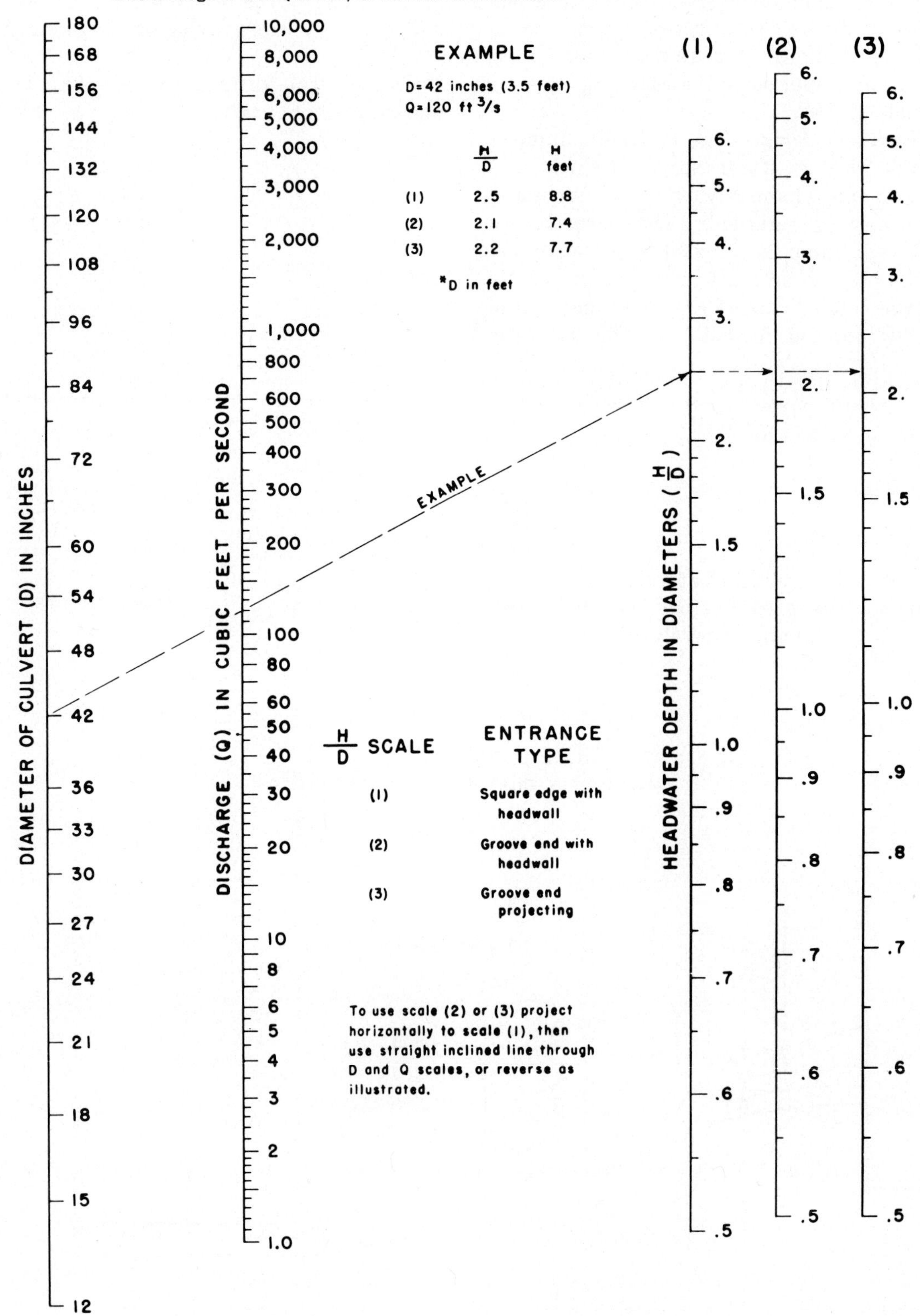

Figure B–7.—Headwater depth for concrete pipe culverts with entrance control. From FHWA. 288–D–2908.

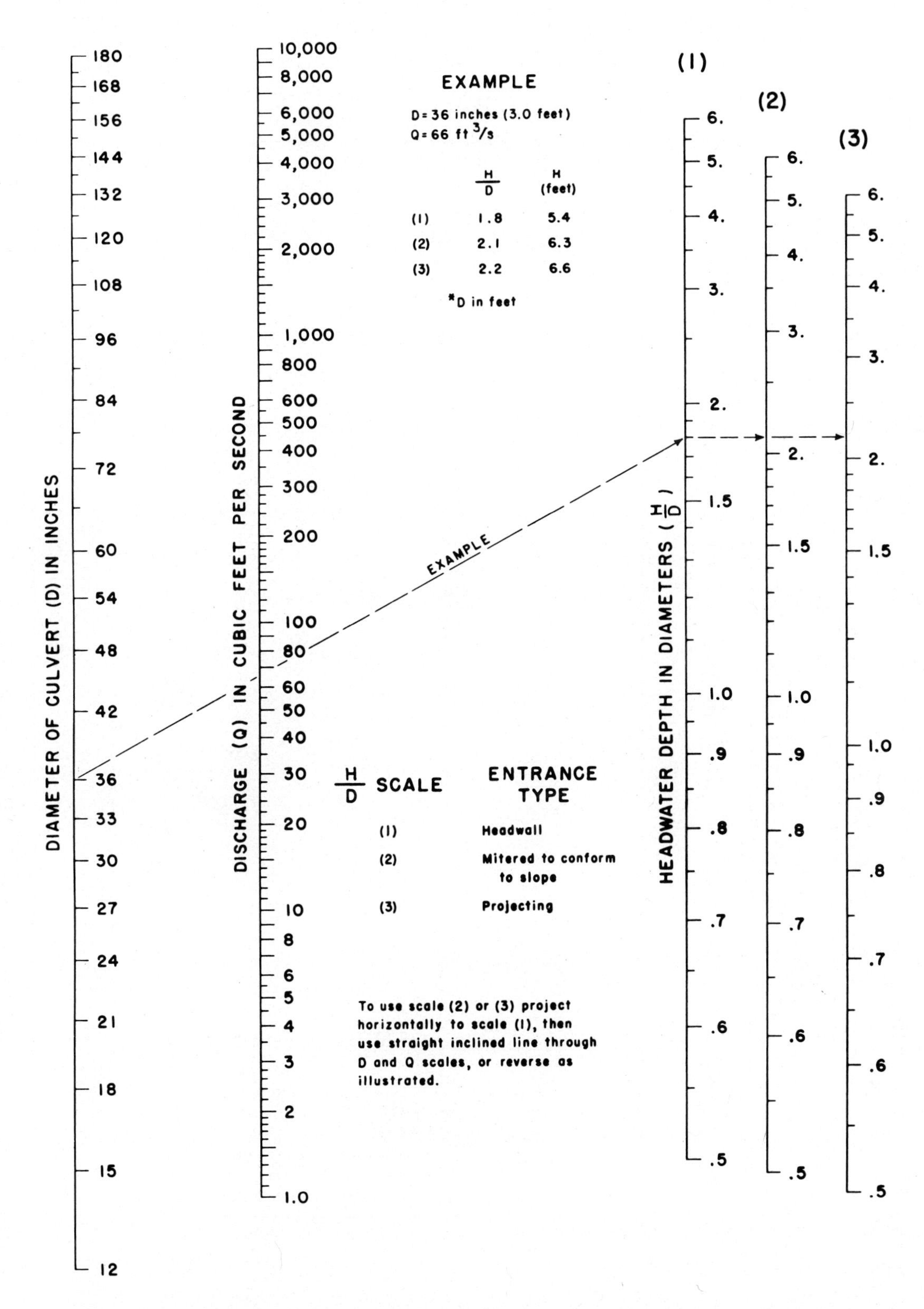

Figure B–8.—Headwater depth for corrugated-metal pipe culverts with entrance control. From FHWA. 288–D–2909.

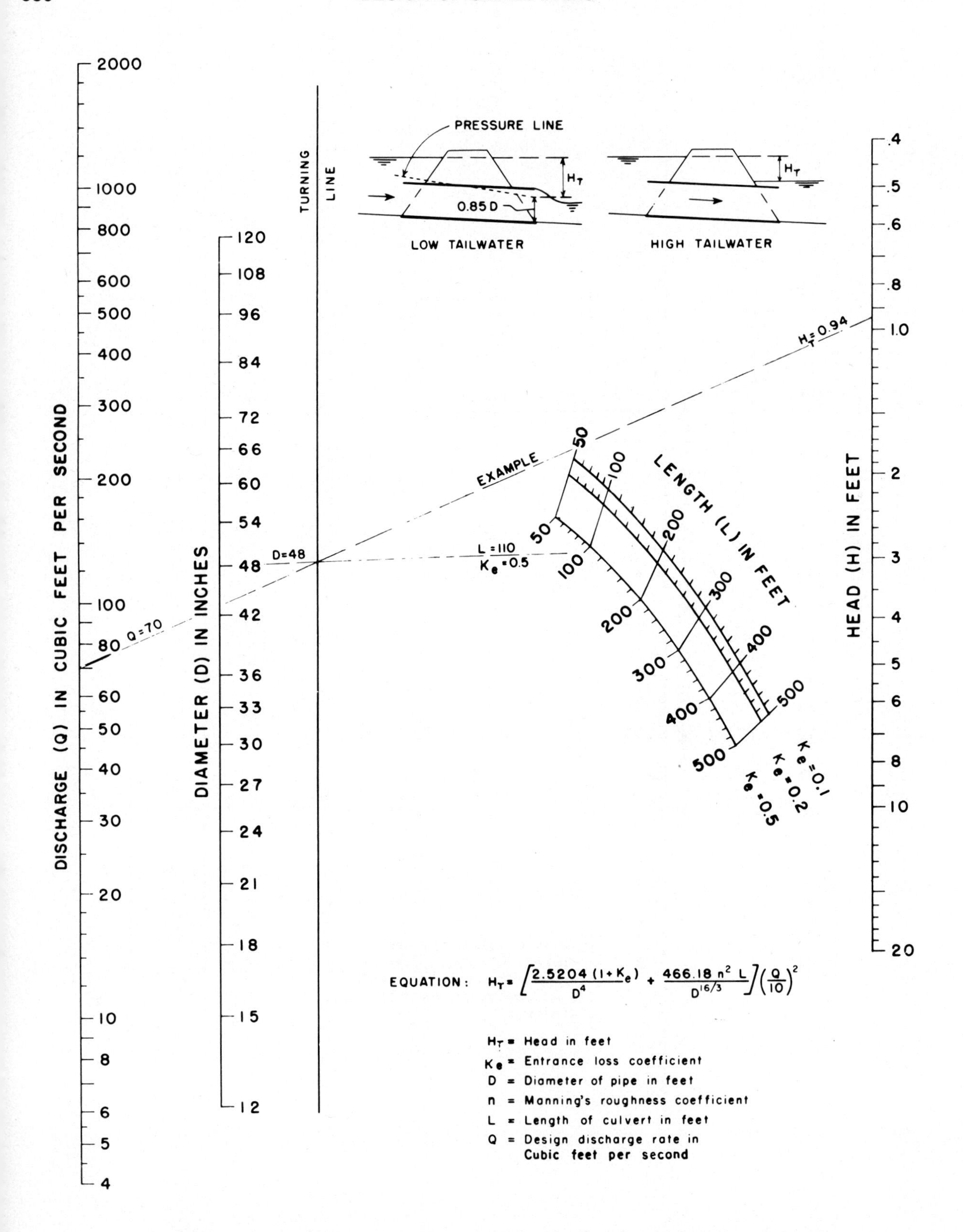

$$H_T = \left[\frac{2.5204\,(1+K_e)}{D^4} + \frac{466.18\,n^2\,L}{D^{16/3}}\right]\left(\frac{Q}{10}\right)^2$$

Figure B-9.—Head for concrete pipe culverts flowing full, *n*= 0.012. From FHWA. 288-D-2910.

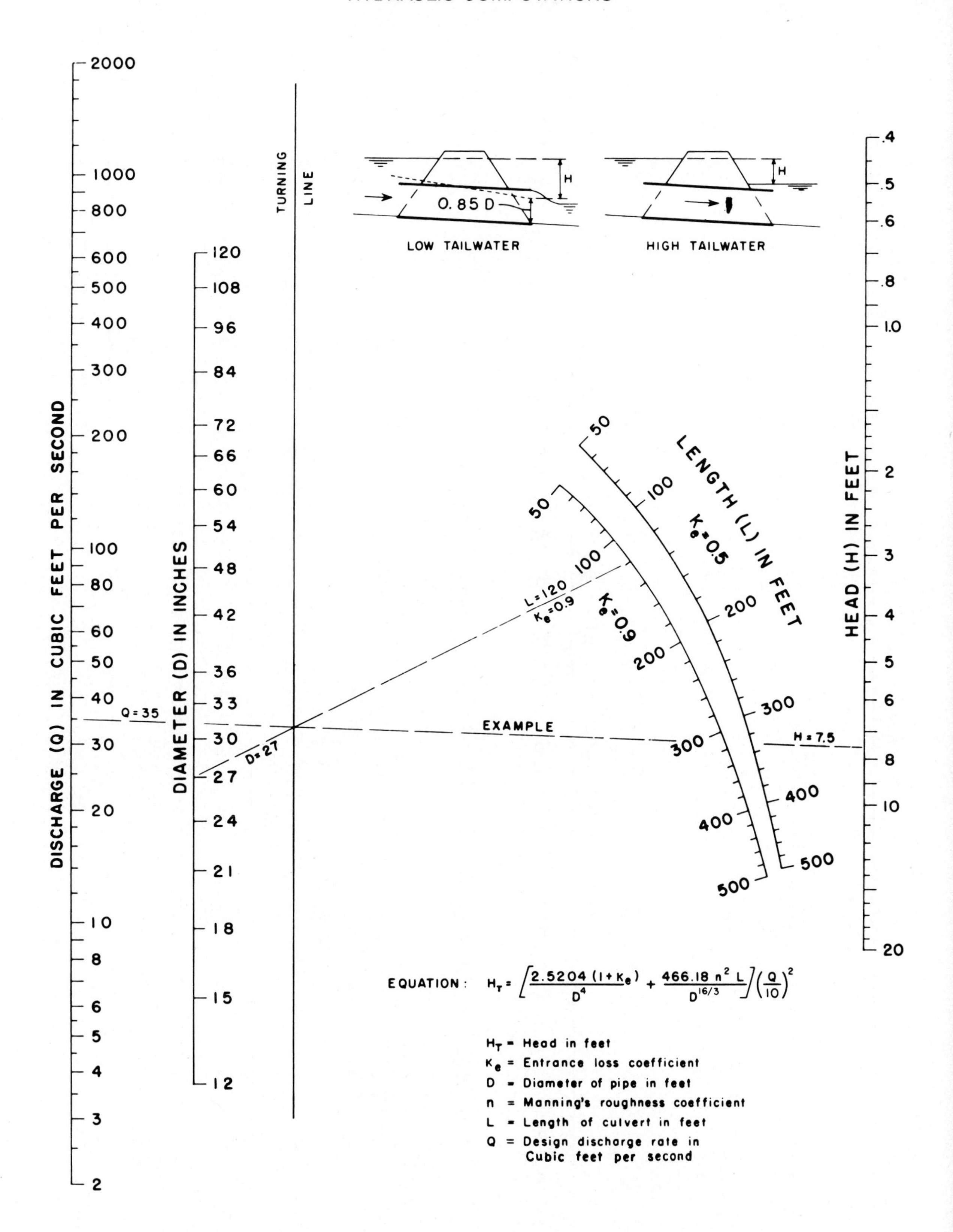

Figure B-10.—Head for corrugated-metal pipe culverts flowing full, *n*=0.024. From FHWA. 288-D-2911.

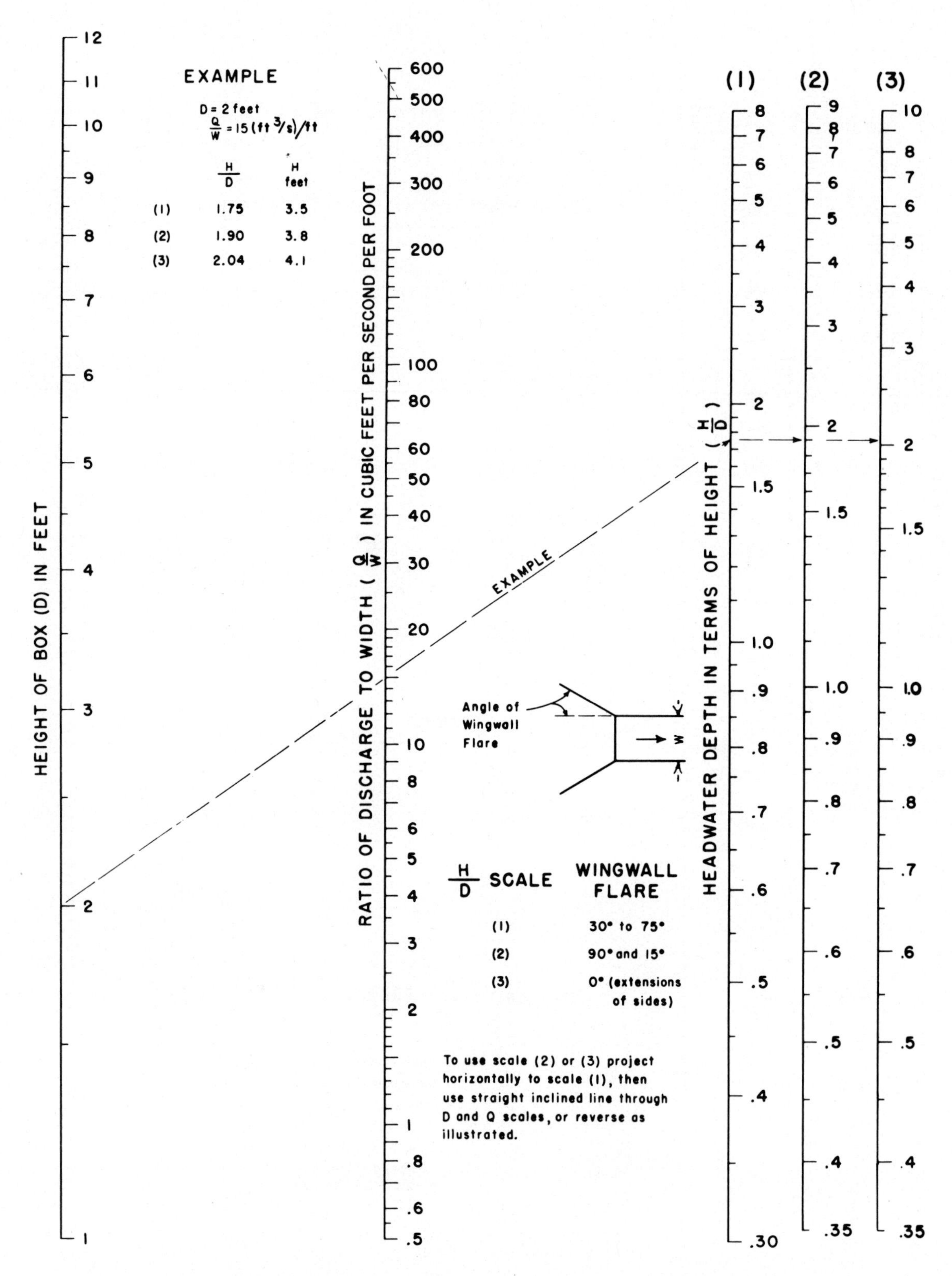

Figure B-11.—Headwater depth for box culverts with entrance control. From FHWA. 288-D-2912.

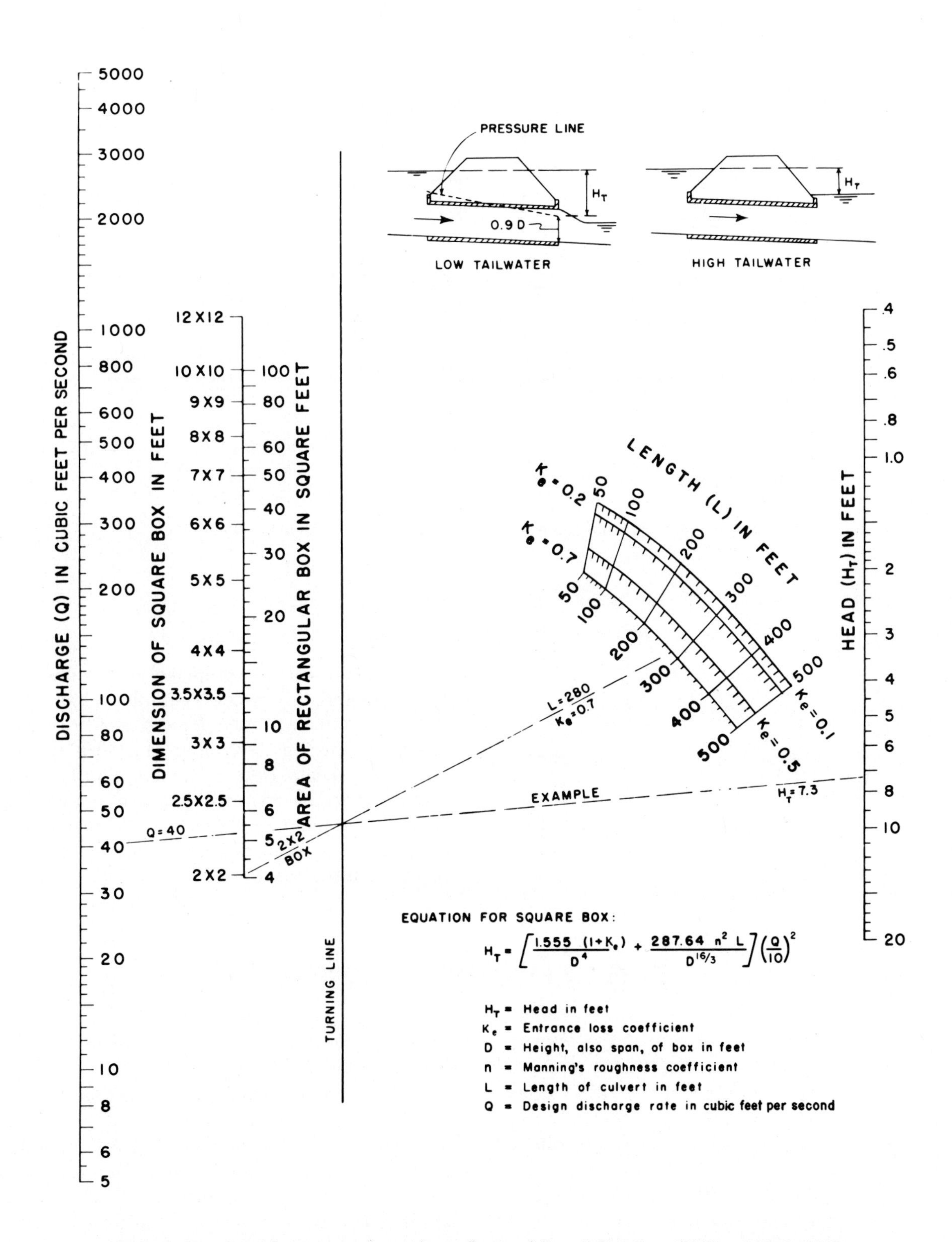

Figure B-12.—Head for concrete box culverts flowing full, n=0.013. From FHWA. 288-D-2913.

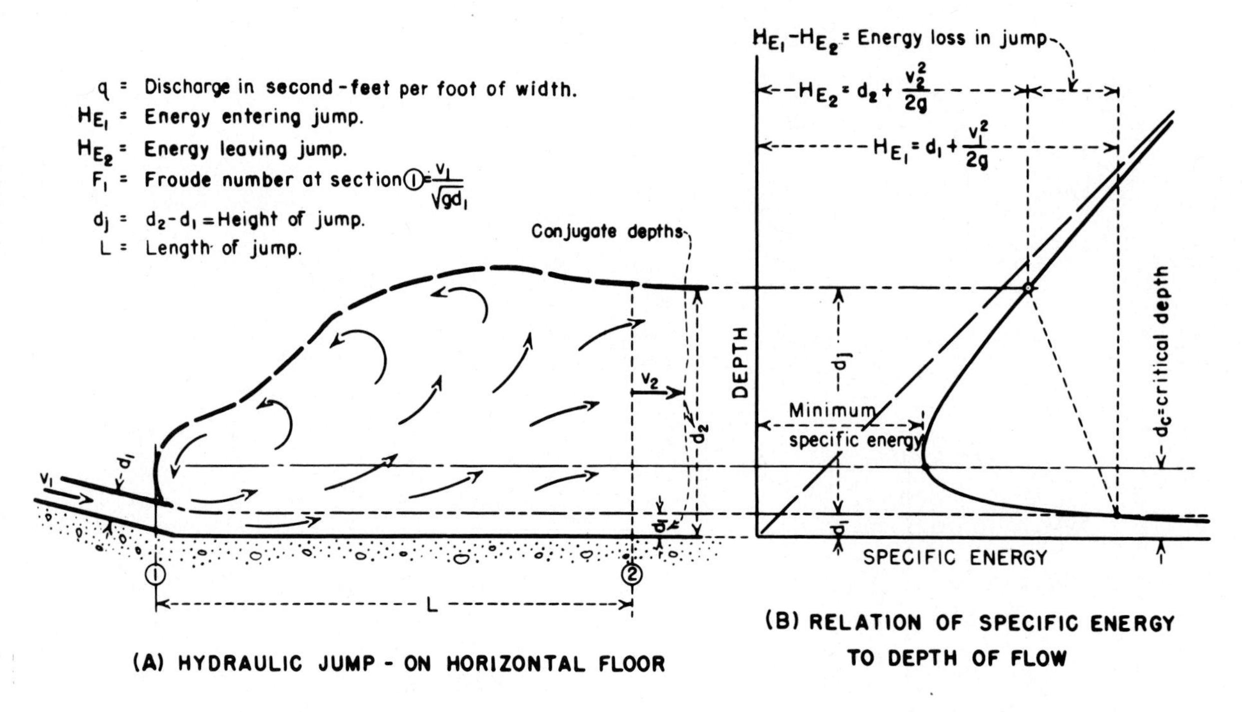

Figure B-13.—Hydraulic jump symbols and characteristics. 288-D-2557.

Similarly, expressing d_1 in terms of d_2 and v_2:

$$d_1=-\frac{d_2}{2}+\sqrt{\frac{2v_2^2d_2}{g}+\frac{d_2^2}{4}} \qquad (50)$$

A graphic solution of equation (49) is shown on figure B-15.

If the Froude number $F_1=\frac{v_1}{\sqrt{gd_1}}$ is substituted in the equation (49) :

$$\frac{d_2}{d_1}=\frac{1}{2}(\sqrt{8F_1^2+1}-1) \qquad (51)$$

Figure B-13 shows a graphical representation of the characteristics of the hydraulic jump. Figure B-14 shows the hydraulic properties of the jump in relation to the Froude number, as determined from experimental data. Data are for jumps on a flat floor with no chute blocks, baffle piers or end sills. Ordinarily, the jump length can be shortened by incorporation of such devices in the designs of a specific stilling basin.

B. FLOW IN NATURAL CHANNELS

B-5. *General.*—This portion of the appendix presents briefly the hydraulic theory and analyses of natural stream channel flow as related to the design of small dams. These analyses are all directed toward the goal of establishing rating curves (stage-discharge relation) at some desired location within the stream channel. One of the more important uses of the rating curve is in connection with establishing tailwater conditions in the design of stilling basins.

The hydraulic conditions discussed herein involve only the conditions of steady and nonuniform flow. A steady flow condition is said to prevail when the discharge is the same at all sections along the channel and remains constant with respect to time. The flow is defined as nonuniform when the grade of the water

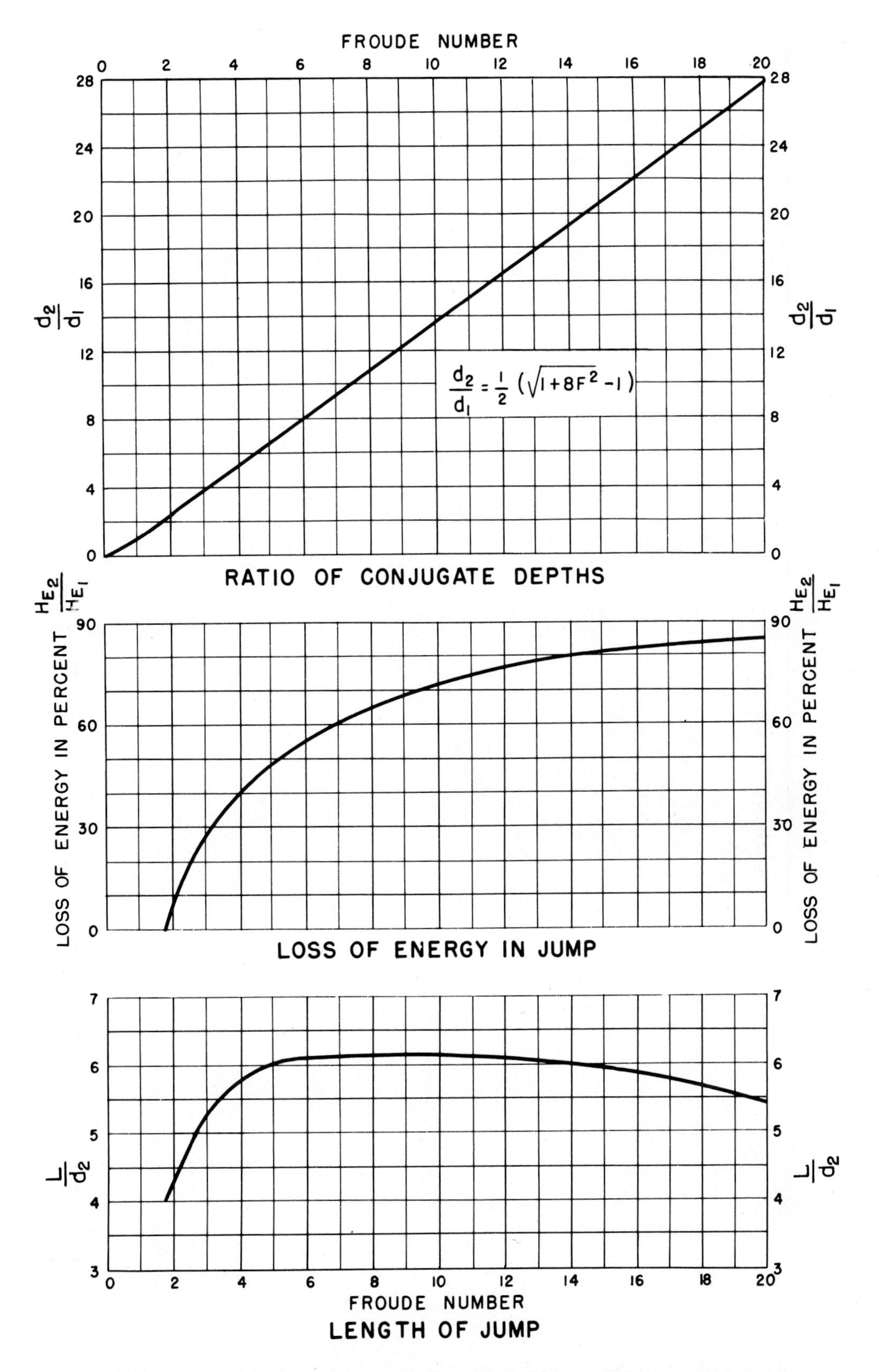

Figure B-14.—Hydraulic jump properties in relation to Froude number. 288-D-2558.

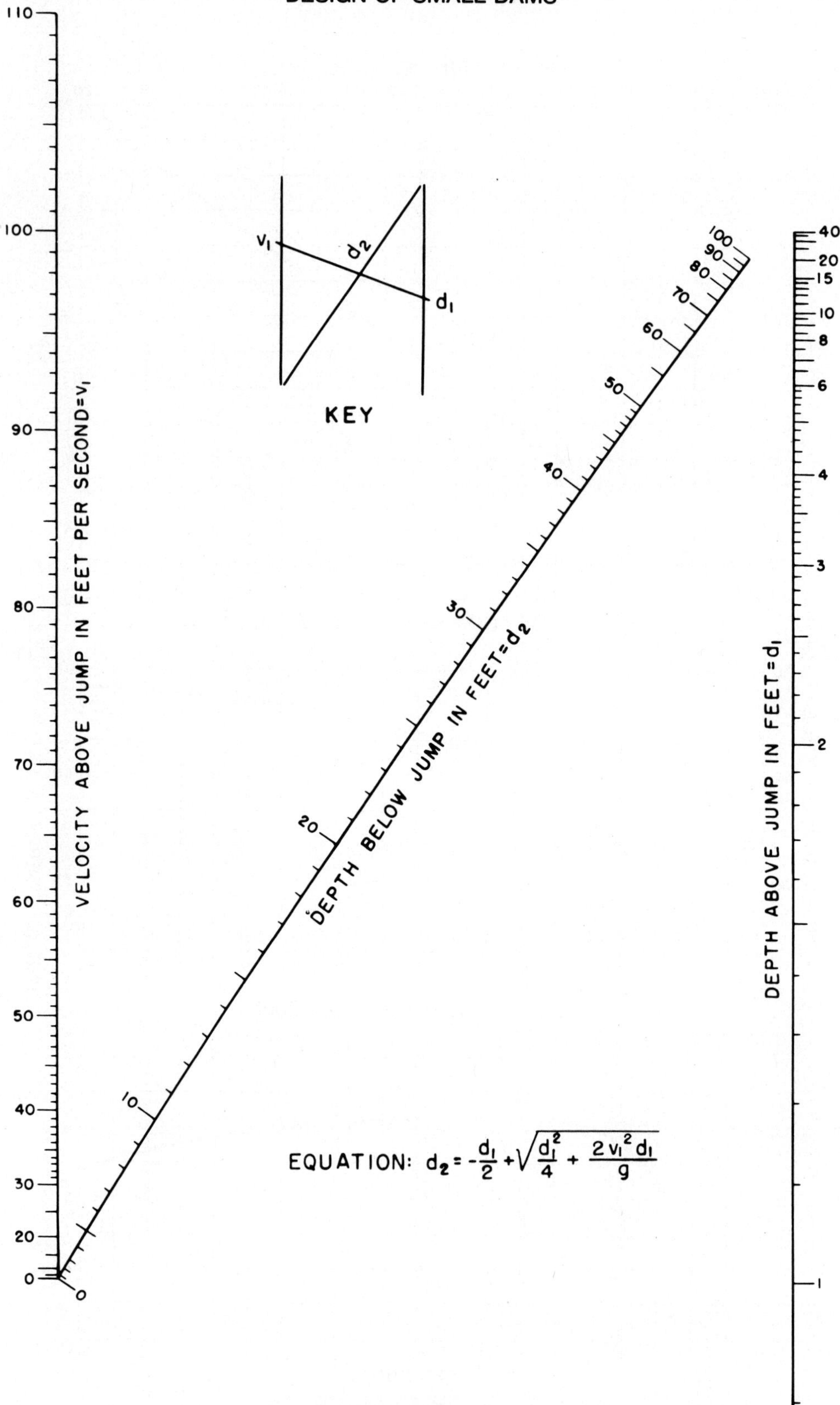

Figure B–15.—Relation between variables in the hydraulic jump. 288–D–2559.

surface is different from that of the channel bottom, which implies accelerating or decelerating flow. Both conditions generally prevail in natural channels. The flows may be confined to the main channel portion of the stream, but generally overbank or flood plain discharge will occur at design discharges.

Suggested procedures are given for the collection of an adequate set of field data to define each of the components in Manning's formula or Bernoulli's theorem which are used in the hydraulic computations. The accuracy of the results is very much dependent on gathering the field data representative of the prevailing hydraulic conditions and analyzing them through reasonable assumptions and interpretations. An accuracy of 0.5 foot is ordinarily a reasonable limit for the computation of water surfaces for low flows. The degree of accuracy expected for higher discharges involving overbank flow is about 1.0 foot. The loss in accuracy for overbank flow conditions is due to more difficult definition of overbank n values and flow distances between sections.

B-6. Collection of Data.—(a) *Streamflow Records.*—Records of streamflow taken from established U.S. Geological Survey (USGS) gaging stations furnish valuable information for the required hydraulic analysis. A check of the USGS water supply papers and the water resources data published annually for each State will show the available streamflow data for each station. Detailed descriptions of gaging stations can be studied in publications of the U.S. Geological Survey [9].

Damsites are occasionally located near gaging stations. The rating curve of a station can be transposed to a cross section at or near the damsite if the hydraulic conditions of the reach between the damsite and the station are relatively uniform. A reasonable distance between the damsite and the gaging station for transposing the curve probably should not exceed 1,000 feet. Extreme changes in grade of the streambed, cross-sectional dimensions, and n values destroy the uniformity of the channel reach and consequently reduce the accuracy of the transposed rating curve.

(b) *Topographic Maps and Aerial Photographs.*—A topographic map and aerial photographs, if available, also provide useful information for rating curve development or water surface profile computation. For rough studies, the hydraulic properties of the stream at the damsite can be determined for a cross section as plotted from the topographic map. An example is included in section B-8 showing how this is done. The topographic map is also useful in studies involving water surface profile computations, where it can be used to locate a series of cross sections below the damsite. Flow distances between such cross sections can be measured from the map.

Aerial photographs can be used to assist in selecting the location of the cross sections. Further, the n coefficients can be evaluated by observing the areal coverage of vegetation and the meandering pattern of the stream.

(c) *Field Surveys.*—The field work required to define the hydraulic dimensions of a single cross section is relatively simple and generally inexpensive. Essentially, the procedure involves setting up a level or transit in direct line with the cross section and taking intermittent soundings and distance measurements across the section. Concurrently, levels can be run along the stream thalweg (lowest points in the streambed) or water surface (intermittent shots may be taken at water's edge along both banks) to define a slope for use in Manning's formula; a distance of 200 to 300 feet downstream and upstream from the cross section will usually be sufficient. Elevations to the nearest tenth of a foot are satisfactory for cross-sectional data; however, it may be necessary to establish water surface elevations to the nearest hundredth of a foot on streams having relatively flat gradients. Horizontal distances measured to the nearest foot are usually adequate for the other cross-sectional coordinate.

If water surface profiles are to be computed for a more precise determination of a rating curve, a series of cross sections downstream from the dam will be needed. The sections should be spaced so that there will be a drop of no more than 2 feet in water surface between cross sections and a total drop of 8 to 10 feet in the study reach.

High water marks may be used to define the

water surface slope. Field observations of these marks should be made immediately following the occurrence of any flows of sufficient magnitude to leave discernible high water marks. An example of their use in a slope-area computation is shown in the next section.

(d) *Determination of* n *Values.*—The selection of n values for use in the Manning formula requires considerable judgment. Table B-6 gives values of n for average channels of various conditions. Table B-7 presents a procedure for computing a mean n value by systematically considering the factors which are involved.

The following publications will serve as guides in the proper selection of n values:

1. "Hydraulic and Excavation Tables," Bureau of Reclamation, eleventh edition, 1957, U.S. Government Printing Office, Washington, D.C.
2. "Handbook of Hydraulics," King, H. W. and Brater, E. F., sixth edition, 1976, McGraw-Hill, New York, N.Y.
3. "Hydrologic and Hydraulic Analyses, Computation of Backwater Curves in River Channels," Part CXIV, ch. 9, Engineering Manual, Civil Works Construction, May 1952, Department of the Army, Corps of Engineers, Office of the Chief of Engineers.
4. "Open Channel Hydraulics," Chow, Ven Te, 1959, McGraw-Hill, New York, N.Y.
5. "Flow of Water in Irrigation and Similar Canals," Scobey, F. C., Bureau of Agricultural Engineering, U.S. Department of Agriculture, Washington, D.C., February 1939.
6. "Design Criteria for Interrelated Highway and Agricultural Drainage and Erosion Control," Tentative ASAE Recommendation, Agricultural Engineers Yearbook, 1958, American Society of Agricultural Engineers.
7. "Roughness Characteristics of Natural Channels," Water Supply Paper 1849, U.S. Department of the Interior, Geological Survey, 1967.

B-7. *Slope-Area Method of Computing Streamflow.*—The slope-area method is utilized primarily to determine the discharge of a stream from specific field data. However, if the discharge is known, the method can be used to compute the value of n. Field procedures required to obtain needed data for the slope-area method include:

1. Selecting a representative reach of river channel: (a) The length of the reach should be at least 75 times the mean depth in the channel.
   (b) The fall in the reach should be equal to or greater than the velocity head or at least 0.50 foot.
2. Defining channel cross sections:
   (a) A minimum of three cross sections is recommended.
3. Measuring the water surface slopes from observed high water marks:
   (a) Average the elevations on both banks at each cross section.
4. Selecting a suitable roughness factor, n.

With these data, the discharge can be determined by Manning's formula,

$$Q=\frac{1.486}{n}ar^{2/3}s^{1/2} \tag{52}$$

where:

Q=total discharge in cubic feet per second,
n=a roughness coefficient,
a=the cross-sectional area of the channel in square feet,
r=hydraulic radius in feet, and
s=energy gradient.

This procedure involves combining such factors as the area, hydraulic radius, and n to compute the conveyance capacity, K_d, for each section, defined by the equation:

$$K_d=\frac{1.486}{n}ar^{2/3} \tag{53}$$

From equations (52) and (53), it can be seen that

$$Q=K_d\,s^{1/2} \tag{54}$$

The Manning equation was developed for conditions of uniform flow, but it has been assumed that the equation is also valid for nonuniform reaches that are characteristic of natural channels, if the energy gradient is modified to reflect only the

Table B–6.—Coefficient of roughness, average channels.

Value of n	*Channel condition*
0.016–0.017	Smoothest natural earth channels, free from growth, with straight alinement.
0.020	Smooth natural earth channels, free from growth, little curvature.
0.0225	Average, well-constructed, moderate-sized earth channels in good condition.
0.025	Small earth channels in good condition, or large earth channels with some growth on banks or scattered cobbles in bed.
0.030	Earth channels with considerable growth. Natural streams with good alinement, fairly constant section. Large floodway channels, well maintained.
0.035	Earth channels considerably covered with small growth. Cleared but not continuously maintained floodways.
0.040–0.050	Mountain streams in clean loose cobbles. Rivers with variable section and some vegetation growing in banks. Earth channels with thick aquatic growths.
0.060–0.075	Rivers with fairly straight alinement and cross section, badly obstructed by small trees, very little underbrush or aquatic growth.
0.100	Rivers with irregular alinement and cross section, moderately obstructed by small trees and underbrush. Rivers with fairly regular alinement and cross section, heavily obstructed by small trees and underbrush.
0.125	Rivers with irregular alinement and cross section, covered with growth of virgin timber and occasional dense patches of bushes and small trees, some logs and dead fallen trees.
0.150–0.200	Rivers with very irregular alinement and cross section, many roots, trees, bushes, large logs, and other drift on bottom, trees continually falling into channel due to bank caving.

Table B–7.—A method of computing mean *n* value for a channel.

(Used by U.S. Soil Conservation Service)

Steps

1. Assume basic *n*
2. Select modifying *n* for roughness or degree of irregularity
3. Select modifying *n* for variation in size and shape of cross section
4. Select modifying *n* for obstructions such as debris deposits, stumps, exposed roots, and fallen logs
5. Select modifying *n* for vegetation
6. Select modifying *n* for meandering
7. Add items 1 through 6

Aids in Selecting Various n Values

1. Recommended basic *n* values

Channels in earth	0.010	Channels in fine gravel	0.014
Channels in rock	0.015	Channels in coarse gravel	0.028

2. Recommended modifying *n* value for degree of irregularity

Smooth	0.000	Moderate	0.010
Minor	0.005	Severe	0.020

3. Recommended modifying *n* value for changes in size and shape of cross section

Gradual	0.000	Frequent	0.010 to 0.015
Occasional	0.005		

4. Recommended modifying *n* value for obstructions such as debris, roots, etc.

Negligible effect	0.000	Appreciable effect	0.030
Minor effect	0.010	Severe effect	0.060

5. Recommended modifying *n* values for vegetation

Low effect	0.005 to 0.010	High effect	0.025 to 0.050
Medium effect	0.010 to 0.025	Very high effect	0.050 to 0.100

6. Recommended modifying *n* value for channel meander

L_s=Straight length of reach L_m=Meander length of reach

L_m/L_s	n
1.0–1.2	0.000
1.2–1.5	0.15 times n_s
>1.5	0.30 times n_s

where n_s=items 1+2+3+4+5

losses due to boundary friction. Figure B-16 is a definition sketch of a two-section slope-area reach, from which the energy equation can be written:

$$Z_2+d_2+h_{v_2}=Z_1+d_1+h_{v_1}+h_f+k(\Delta h_v) \quad (55)$$

where:

Z=channel bottom elevation,
d=depth of water,
h_v=velocity head $=\frac{\alpha V^2}{2g}$,
h_f=energy loss due to boundary friction,
Δh_v=upstream velocity head minus the downstream velocity head, and
$k(\Delta h_v)$=energy loss due to acceleration or deceleration in a contracting or expanding reach.

Adding $Z+d$ gives the water surface elevation, h, and equation (55) may be written:

$$h_2+h_{v_2}=h_1+h_{v_1}+h_f+k(\Delta h_v) \quad (56)$$

The friction slope may now be solved:

$$s=\frac{h_f}{L}=\frac{\Delta h+\Delta h_v-k(\Delta h_v)}{L} \quad (57)$$

where Δh is the difference in water surface elevation at the two sections and L is the length of the reach.

The reach discharge can now be computed using the friction slope and the geometric mean of the cross-section conveyances, or

$$Q=\sqrt{K_{d_1}\cdot K_{d_2}\cdot s} \quad (58)$$

The velocity head (h_v) at each section is computed as

$$h_v=\frac{\alpha V^2}{2g} \quad (59)$$

where V is the mean velocity in the section and α is the velocity-head coefficient. The value

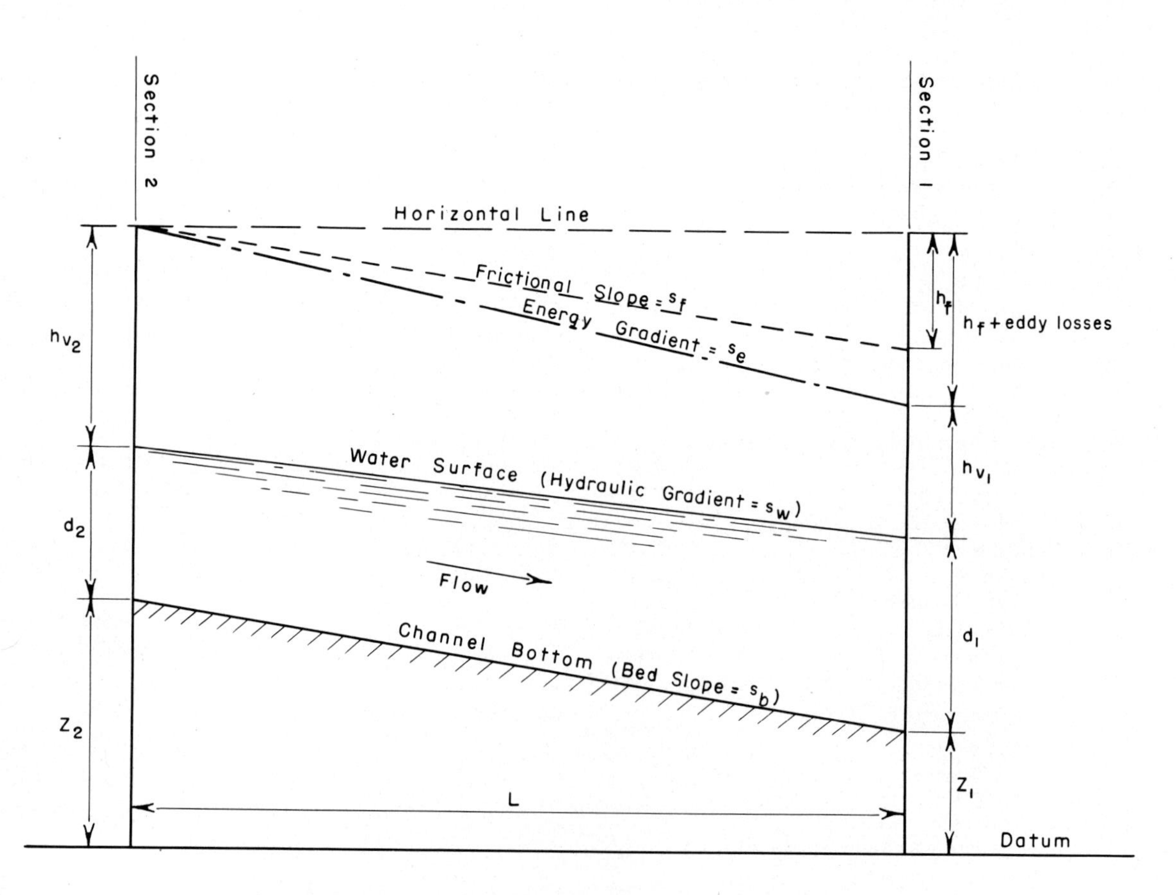

Figure B-16.—Energy of open-channel flow. 288-D-2827.

of α is assumed to be 1.0 if the section is not subdivided. The value of α in subdivided channels is computed as

$$\alpha = \frac{\Sigma (K_{d_i}^3/a_i^2)}{K_{d_T}^3/a_T^2} \quad (60)$$

where the subscript i refers to the conveyance or area of the individual subsections and T to the area or conveyance of the entire cross section.

The energy loss due to contraction or expansion of the channel in the reach is assumed to be equal to the difference in velocity heads at the two sections (Δh_v) times a coefficient, k. The value of k has been set at zero for contracting reaches and 0.5 for expanding reaches by the U.S. Geological Survey [10]. The value of Δh_v is computed as the upstream velocity head minus the downstream velocity head; therefore, the friction slope to be used in the Manning equation is computed algebraically as

$$s = \frac{\Delta h + (\Delta h_v/2)}{L} \text{ (when } \Delta h_v \text{ is positive)} \quad (61)$$

and

$$s = \frac{\Delta h + \Delta h_v}{L} \text{ (when } \Delta h_v \text{ is negative)} \quad (62)$$

The U.S. Geological Survey publication [10] contains discharge equations for slope-area computations developed from the above basic equations. The general equation and the equation for a two-section reach are presented here.

Two sections:

$$Q = K_{d_1}\sqrt{\frac{\Delta h}{\frac{K_{d_1}}{K_{d_2}}L + \frac{K_{d_1}^2}{2gA_1^2}\left[-\alpha_2\left(\frac{A_1}{A_2}\right)^2(1-k) + \alpha_1(1-k)\right]}} \quad (63)$$

where:

Q=Total discharge in cubic feet per second, and

A=Total cross-sectional area in square feet.

Multiple sections (n=number of sections):

$$Q = K_{d_1}\sqrt{\frac{\Delta h}{X+Y}} \quad (64)$$

where:

$$X = K_{d_1}^2 \frac{L_{[n-(n-1)]}}{K_{d_n} K_{d_{(n-1)}}} + K_1^2 \frac{L_{[(n-1)-(n-2)]}}{K_{d_{(n-1)}} K_{d_{(n-2)}}} + \cdots$$

$$\frac{K_{d_1}^2 L_{3-2}}{K_{d_3} K_{d_2}} + \frac{K_{d_1}^2 L_{2-1}}{K_{d_2} K_{d_1}}, \text{ and}$$

$$Y = \frac{K_{d_1}^2}{A_1^2 2g}\Bigg[-\alpha_n\left(\frac{A_1}{A_n}\right)^2(1-k_{n-(n-1)}) +$$

$$\alpha_{n-1}\left(\frac{A_1}{A_{n-1}}\right)^2(k_{(n-1)-(n-2)} - k_{n-(n-1)}) +$$

$$\alpha_{(n-2)}\left(\frac{A_1}{A_{n-2}}\right)^2(k_{(n-2)-(n-3)} - k_{(n-1)-(n-2)}) + \cdots + $$

$$\alpha_2\left(\frac{A_1}{A_2}\right)^2(k_{2-1} - k_{3-2}) + \alpha_1(1-k_{2-1})\Bigg].$$

Using the data from the USGS publication [10] (see figures B–17, B–18, and B–19), the following procedure is used to compute the discharge. The conveyance (K_d), the velocity head coefficient for each cross section (α), and the weighted conveyance (K_w) of each subreach are computed and tabulated on the form shown in figure B–20. It should be noted that the subscripting is in reverse order of that used in the definition sketch and discharge formulas. Next, use the two-section formula given above to compute directly the discharge for each two-section subreach. The computed values will most likely differ for each subreach. Then, using the appropriate discharge as the "assumed" value on the form, complete for each subreach the computation of the various heads, slope, and "computed" discharge. The "computed" discharge must agree exactly with the "assumed" if all computations have been made correctly.

Using the multiple section equation, the final value of discharge can then be computed for the total reach. After this value is determined, it is used to compute the subsection discharges for subdivided sections, the corresponding velocities, and the mean velocities for all sections. Enter the computations in the two columns at the right of the computation form (fig. B–20). Gross errors can be often recognized if velocities are greatly different from those

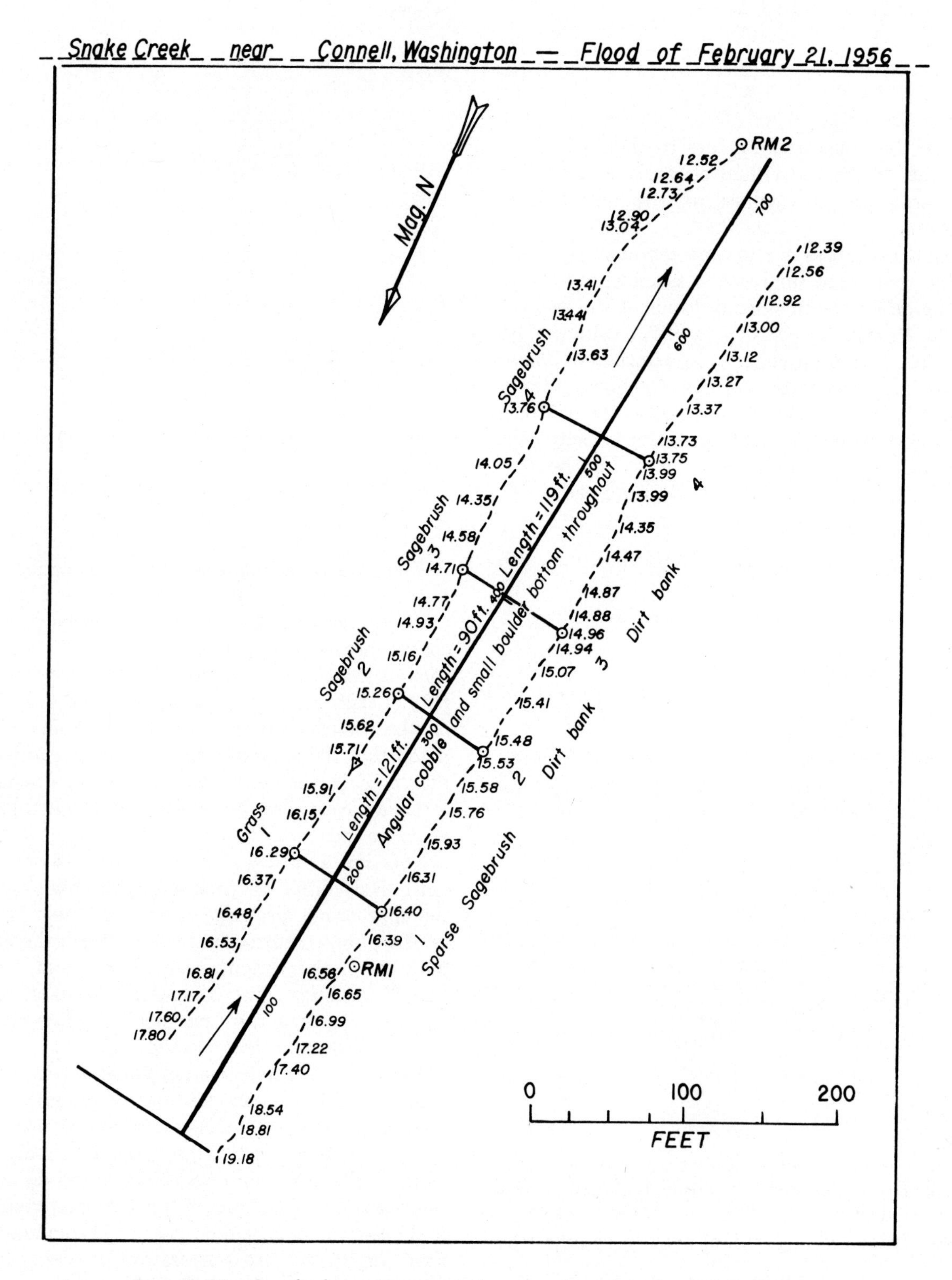

Figure B-17.—Sample slope-area computation, plan view of reach. 288-D-2828.

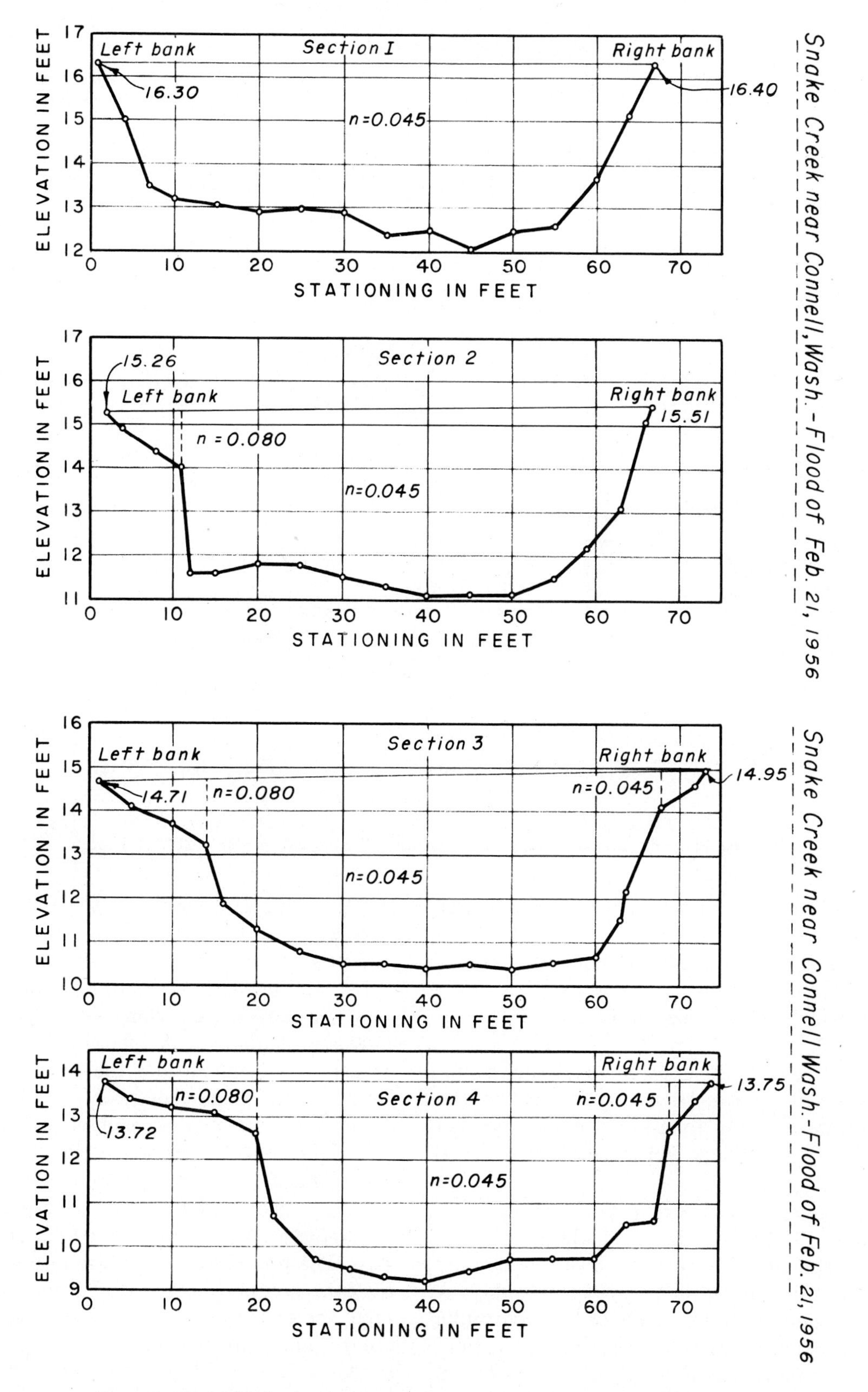

Figure B–18.—Sample slope-area computation, cross sections. 288–D–2829.

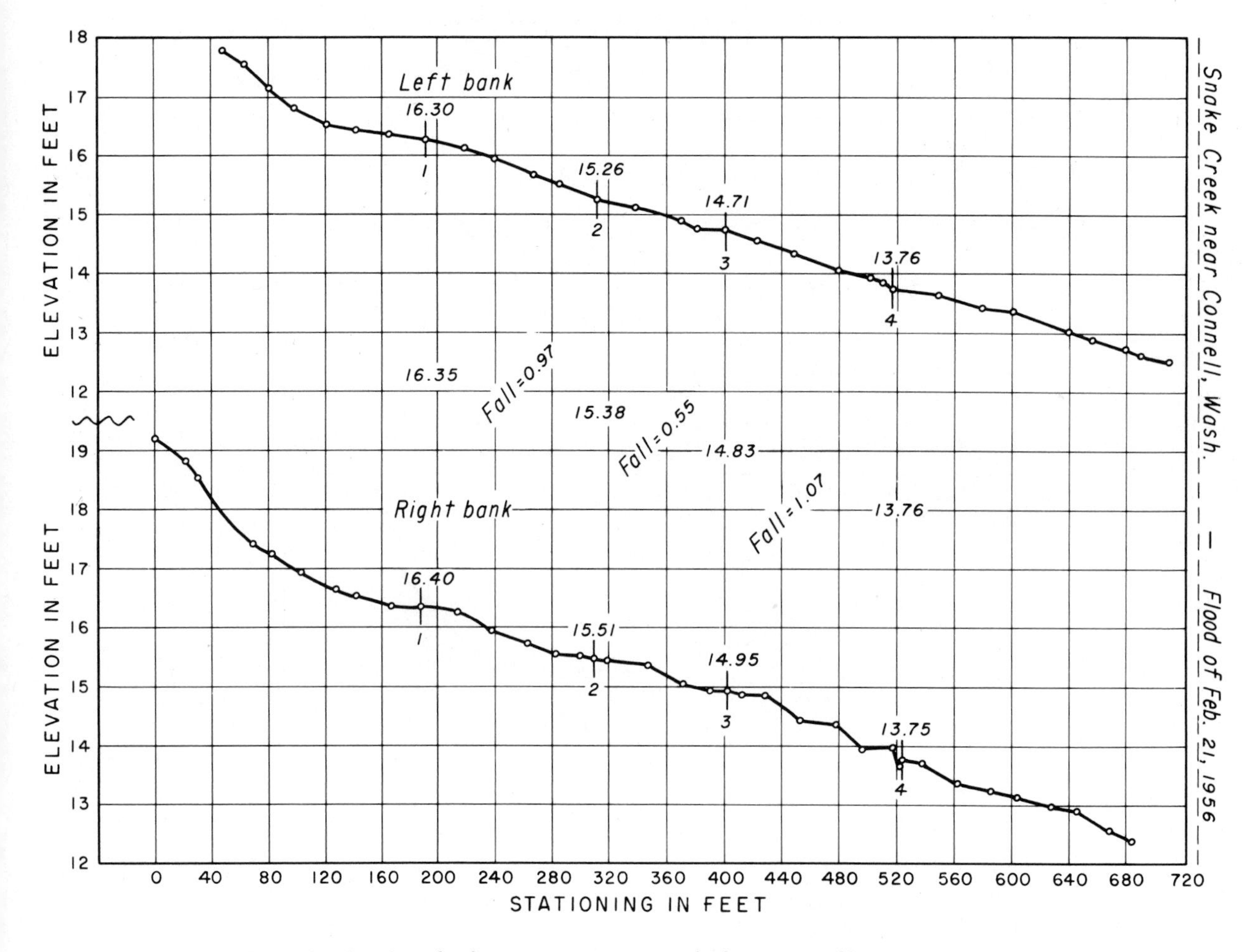

Figure B-19.—Sample slope-area computation, high-water profile. 288-D-2830.

anticipated based on inspection of the channel after the flood.

A check should be made for critical or supercritical flow conditions at each section. This matter will be discussed in further detail in section B-9.

If the discharge is known, an analysis similar to the above can be used to arrive at the appropriate n value to assign to the channel sections. A trial and error solution will be necessary.

B-8. Development of Rating Curves.—(a) *Approximate Method.*—The field data required for development of a rating curve are similar to those used in a slope-area analysis. A determination must be made of the hydraulic properties for the section under consideration. Data required include channel cross-section geometry, channel bottom or water surface slope, and assignment of n value(s) to the affected area.

When economics or time will not permit detailed field measurements to be taken, the curve must be developed from whatever pertinent data are available. A topographic map might be used for determining the cross section and possibly the channel bed profile. Other sources of information, such as photographs, may provide data from which a selection of an n value can be made.

Figures B-21 and B-22 and table B-8 illustrate the preparation of a rating curve from a topographic map. The procedures shown are also applicable if the cross section is established from a field survey. First, the centerline of the dam was located on the topographic map available for the area, as shown in (A) of figure B-21. The cross section in (B) was then developed by scaling the distances between

9-193
Slope-area measurement
December 1960

UNITED STATES DEPARTMENT OF THE INTERIOR
GEOLOGICAL SURVEY
WATER RESOURCES DIVISION

File ________

Meas. No. ________

Slope-area measurement of Snake Creek near Connell, Wash. (Miscellaneous site for flood of Feb. 21, 1956

Reach between sections	1-2	2-3	3-4
Length of reach (L), ft	121	90	119
Fall in reach (Δh), ft	0.97	0.55	1.07

Gage height, —— ft
Discharge[1] 1,380 cfs
Drainage area, 115 sq mi

SECTION PROPERTIES

Section	n	$\frac{1.486}{n}$	a	r	$r^{2/3}$	$K=\frac{1.486}{n}ar^{2/3}$	K^3/a^2	[2] α	[3] q	v
1 Sta. 1-67	.045	33.0	208	3.09	2.12	14,550		1.00	1,380	6.64
2 2-11	.080	18.6	6.1	.68	.77	90	0.196		8	1.31
11-67	.045	33.0	203	3.47	2.29	15,340	876		1,370	6.75
			209.1			15,430	876 .196	1.04		
							842			
3 1-14	.080	18.6	10.0	.77	.84	160	.410		13	1.30
14-68	.045		212	3.83	2.45	17,140	1 122		1,360	6.42
68-73	.045		2.6	.51	.64	50	.185		4	1.54
			224.6			17,350	1 122 .595	1.08		
							1 035			
4 2-20	.080	18.6	11.1	.62	.73	150	.274		13	1.17
20-69	.045		193	3.79	2.43	15,480	996		1,360	7.05
69-74	.045		2.8	.55	.67	60	.275	1.10	4	1.43
			206.9			15,690	996 .549			
							901			

Weighted conveyance[4] (K_w), 1-2: 14,930 | 2-3: 16,360 | 3-4: 16,500

COMPUTATION OF DISCHARGE

Reach	Assumed Q	[5] h_v	[6] Δh_v	[7] h_f	$s = h_f/L$	$s^{1/2}$	Computed Q $=K_w s^{1/2}$
1-2	1,330	Upstr. .636 Dwnstr. .655	-0.019	0.951	0.00786	0.0887	1,330
2-3	1,320	Upstr. .645 Dwnstr. .580	.065	.582	.00647	.0804	1,320
3-4	1,460	Upstr. .710 Dwnstr. .852	-.142	.928	.00780	.0883	1,460

[1] DISCHARGE (by formula) 1,380, or

FORMULAS

2. $\alpha = \Sigma (K^3/a^2) \div K^3_{total}/A^2_{total}$
3. $q = Q\,(K/K_{total})$
4. $K_w = \sqrt{K_{Upstr.} \times K_{Dwnstr.}}$
5. $h_v = \alpha\, V^2/2g$
6. $\Delta h_v =$ Upstr. $h_v -$ Dwnstr. h_v
7. When Δh_v is positive, $h_f = \Delta h + \frac{1}{2}\Delta h_v$; When Δh_v is negative, $h_f = \Delta h + \Delta h_v$

Summary of factors influencing measuring conditions (floodmarks, surge, scour, fill, channel configuration, angle of flow, selection of n, etc.): ______

Sheet No. 11 of 13 Sheets. Prepared by E.L.S. Date 3-19-56 Checked by E.G.P. Date 5-14-56

Figure B-20.—Sample slope-area computation, discharge. 288-D-2831.

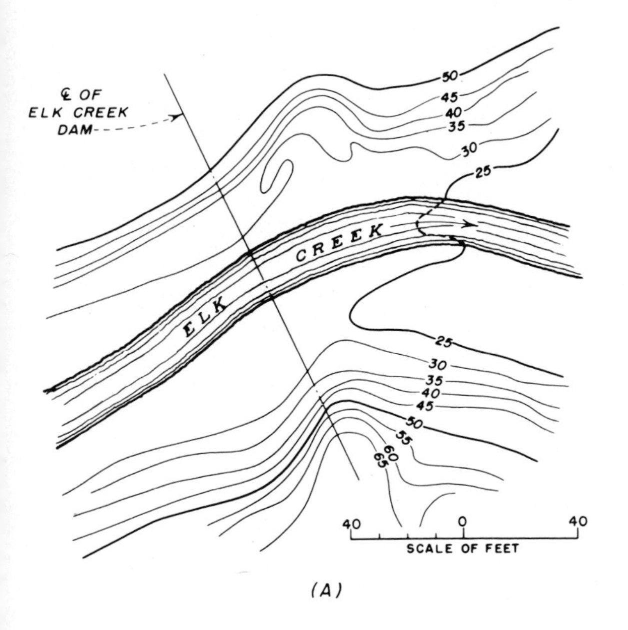

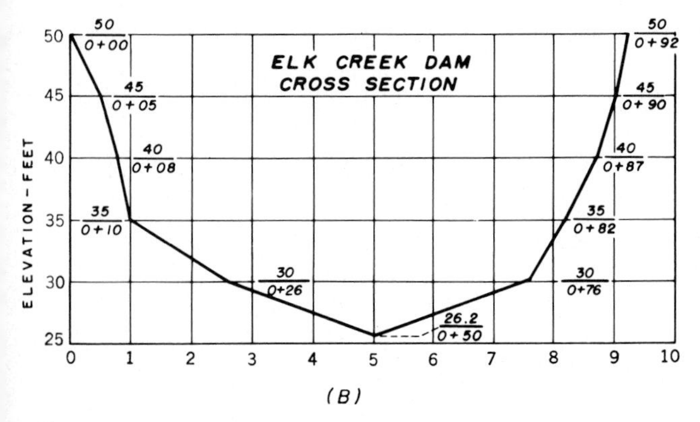

Figure B–21.—Plan and cross section of Elk Creek Dam site. 288–D–2832.

contour on the map. The low point in the streambed was determined by interpolating between contours. The mean bed slope of the stream was obtained from map-scaled measurements of distances between contours crossing the stream channel. A value of n of 0.030 was selected on the basis of various descriptions and field observations that considerable growth of vegetation was present in a stream of relatively straight alinement. The computations were then performed as shown in table B–8.

The conveyance capacity method illustrated under the slope-area discussion has been utilized in the computations. From the geometric properties of the section and an n of 0.030, the conveyance capacity, K_d, is computed for various elevations. These values are multiplied by the one-half power of the mean bed slope to compute the discharge at each elevation. The tailwater rating curve derived from the computations is shown in figure B–22.

(b) *Water Surface Profile Method.*—In studies where more exact tailwater curves are required, water surface profiles may be developed for a range of discharges. The computations in such studies are more involved and require a series of cross sections downstream from the damsite.

Several methods [1, 7, 8] have been developed for computing water surface profiles; however, this discussion will be limited to Bureau of Reclamation Method A. This method is adaptable to irregular channels having various roughness segments and large variations in cross-section geometry. It is limited to the assumption that flow paths between cross sections are equal in length for all roughness segments. Other methods [7, 8] must be used for variable travel distances.

In Method A, a number of cross sections are selected at intervals below the damsite. The selection of the cross-section locations is probably the most important factor in preparing a good study. The sections should be located so the average area, hydraulic radius, and n values of any two sections will be representative of the reach length between them. Channels that are alternately wide and narrow should have sections located in the narrow and wide points so the average condition can be defined. Special attention should also be given to locating a section at each point that indicates a definite change in grade or a control such as a natural constriction or bridge. The cross sections should be surveyed and segmented according to roughness (n) characteristics. A minimum of five cross sections should be selected, with no more than 2 feet of fall between the sections.

Reference is again made to figure B–16 and the basic hydraulic equations presented in section B–7. Equation (54) can be rearranged to give

$$s_f=\left(\frac{Q}{K_d}\right)^2 \tag{65}$$

in which K_d is the total conveyance capacity of the main channel and overbank areas. Now

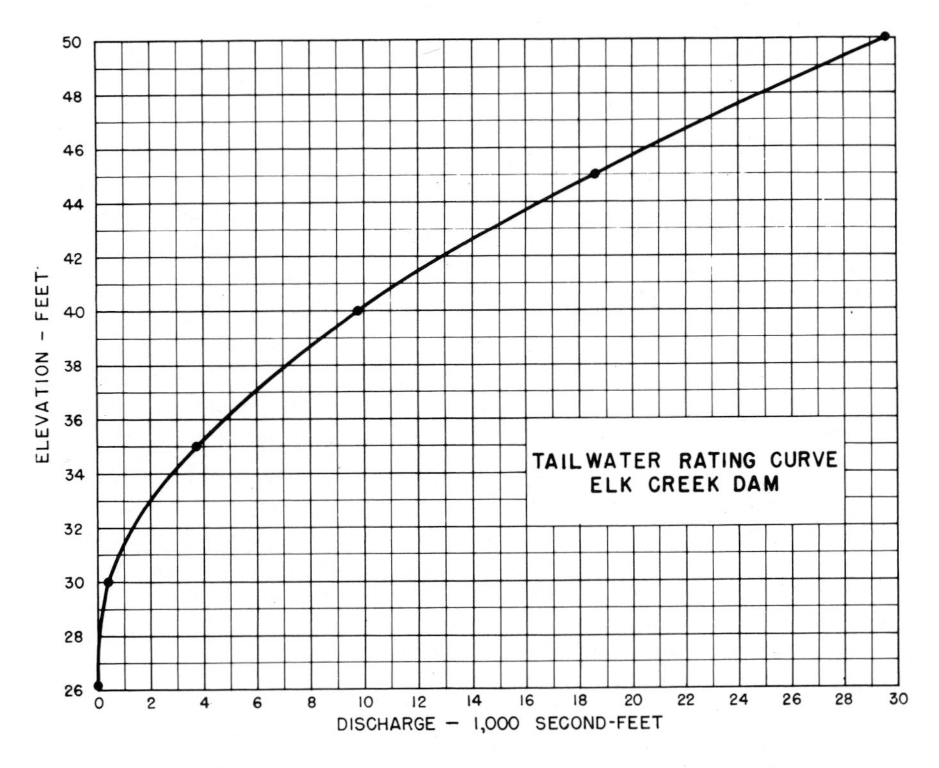

Figure B-22.—Tailwater rating curve for Elk Creek Dam. 288-D-2560.

Table B-8.—Computations for tailwater rating curve.

ELK CREEK DAM

Data: $n=0.030$ s_b=mean bed slope=0.00395

$C=\frac{1.486}{n}=49.53$ $s_b^{1/2}=0.0628$

Elevation	a	p	r	$r^{2/3}$	C	K_d	$s_b^{1/2}$	Q
26.2......	0	0	0	0	......	....	....	....
30........	95	50.6	1.88	1.523	49.53	7,170	0.0628	450
35........	400	75.1	5.32	3.047	49.53	60,400	.0628	3,790
40........	753	87.6	8.60	4.198	49.53	156,000	.0628	9,800
45........	1160	99.2	11.70	5.154	49.53	296,000	.0628	18,600
50........	1610	111.7	14.40	5.919	49.53	472,000	.0628	29,600

the discharge in each subdivision of the cross section can be determined as follows:

$$Q=K_d\ s_f^{1/2} \quad (66)$$

and $$Q_s=K_{d_s}\ s_f^{1/2} \quad (67)$$

where:

Q=total discharge

s_f=slope of the friction gradient

K_d=total conveyance

and Q_s and K_{d_s}=corresponding elements for partial discharge and conveyance capacity of the subdivision under consideration.

Dividing one equation by the other

$$\frac{Q}{Q_s}=\frac{K_d}{K_{d_s}}$$

and solving for Q_s:

$$Q_s=\frac{Q\cdot K_{d_s}}{K_d} \quad (68)$$

The friction head, h_f, is determined by averaging the computed friction slopes at sections 1 and 2 and multiplying by the length as below:

$$h_f=L\left(\frac{s_{f_1}+s_{f_2}}{2}\right) \quad (69)$$

The velocity head, h_v, is derived by a weighting process using the partial discharges occurring in each subdivision of the cross section. Velocities in each segment are computed by the equation $V_s=Q_s/a_s$ where a_s is the area of the segment. The velocity head results from the following equation:

$$h_v = \frac{\Sigma(V_s^2 Q_s)}{2gQ} \quad (70)$$

It should be noted that this equation gives the same result as equation (59).

Method A deviates slightly at this point from the slope-area computation in that a coefficient of 0.1 is used to determine the eddy losses in contracting reaches. A coefficient of 0.5 is also used here to compute losses in expanding reaches.

The following example shows the procedure required to establish a rating curve by Method A:

(1) Seven cross sections designated by numbers 1 through 7 were selected from figure B–23, and their geometric properties were determined by field survey.
(2) Area and hydraulic radius curves were developed for each cross section, similar to the one shown in figure B–24. It should be noted that a separate curve is drawn for each subsection.
(3) A set of conveyance curves was developed for each section similar to the one shown in figure B–25.
(4) A rating curve for the lowermost cross section, section 1 (fig. B–26), was determined by the approximate method described in section B–8(a) of this appendix.
(5) Water surface profiles were computed for several discharges to define the required tailwater rating curve. The computations shown in table B–9 are for Q=11,100 cubic feet per second.
(6) Section 1 is the starting point of the profile computation. The starting elevation 5714.0 in column 2 was taken from the rating curve in figure B–26. The area values in column 3 were read from the area curve for section 1 (not shown). The distance between sections 1 and 2 was entered in column 4 and the K_d values were read from the conveyance capacity curve for section 1 (not shown) at elevation 5714.0
(7) Next, the s_f value was computed for section 1 using equation (65).
(8) Q_s values were computed for each subsection of section 1 using equation (68).
(9) The velocity in each subsection was computed using $V=Q/A$, and the values V^2Q were computed and placed in column 11 and totaled.
(10) The h_v value was next derived for section 1 using equation (70).
(11) The elevation 5714.0 was repeated in column 17.
(12) A trial water surface elevation was then placed in column 2 for section 2 and steps 6 and 7 were repeated based on the data for section 2.
(13) A mean friction slope was computed for the reach by averaging the friction slopes computed for sections 1 and 2.
(14) The friction head loss, h_f, between sections 1 and 2 was then arrived at by multiplying the mean friction slope by the distance L.
(15) Steps 8, 9, and 10 were then repeated for section 2 data.
(16) The algebraic difference in velocity head was then entered in column 13. The upstream velocity head is subtracted from the downstream value.
(17) The eddy loss is assumed to be 0.1 and 0.5 of the absolute value of the difference in velocity heads for contracting and expanding reaches, respectively. Thus, if the Δh_v is –1.0 foot, the eddy loss is 0.5 foot and if the Δh_v is +1.0 foot, the eddy loss is 0.1 foot. The eddy loss value was placed in column 14.
(18) The total loss is equal to the friction head loss plus the eddy loss. The ΔH value is the algebraic sum of the total head loss and the change in velocity head.
(19) The water surface elevation in column 17 is the sum of the water surface elevation at section 1 and the ΔH. If the computed water surface elevation in column 17 agrees with the assumed elevation within a tenth of a foot, the computation is completed and computations are begun for the next upstream section.

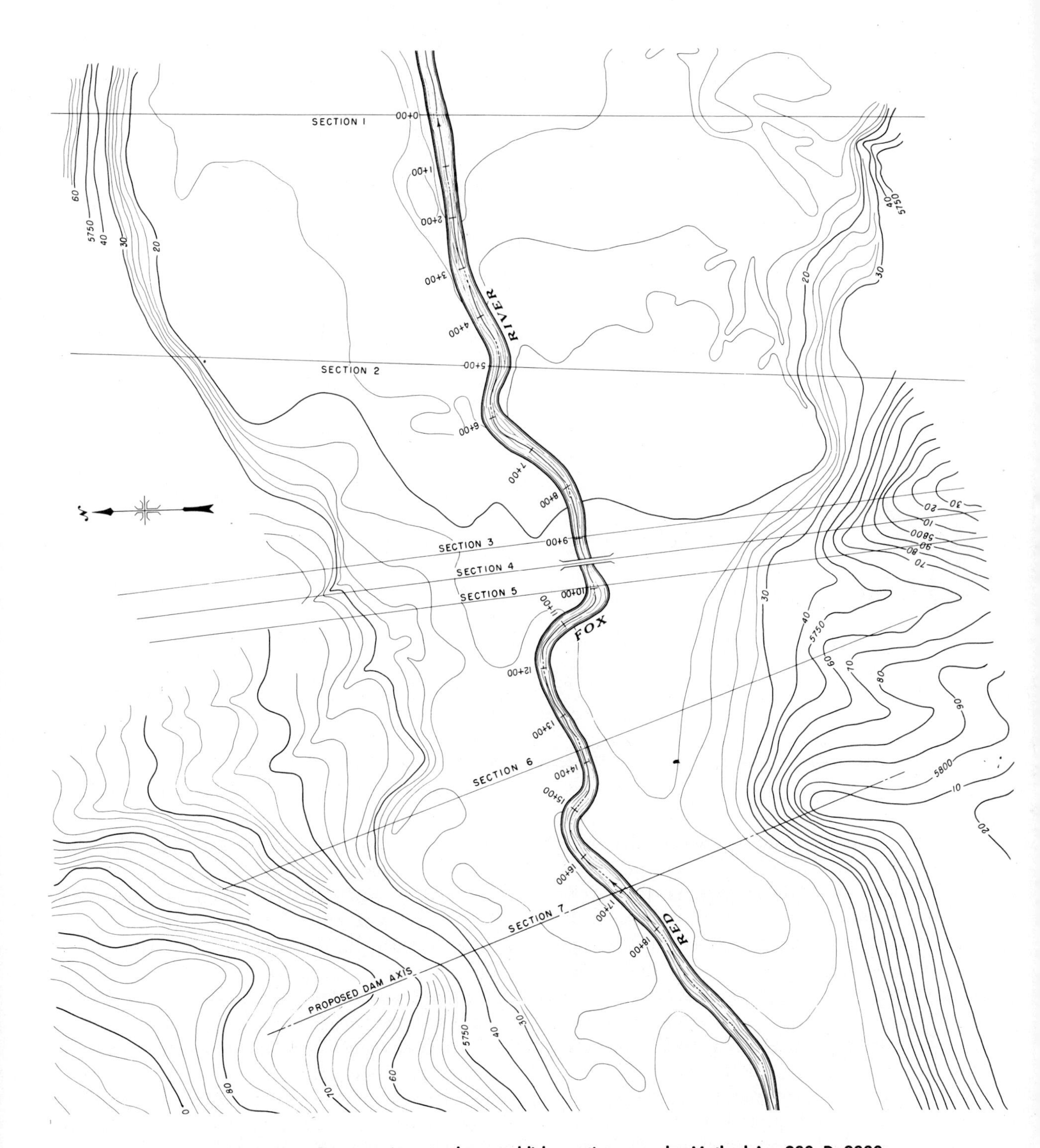

Figure B-23.—Cross sections used to establish a rating curve by Method A. 288-D-2833.

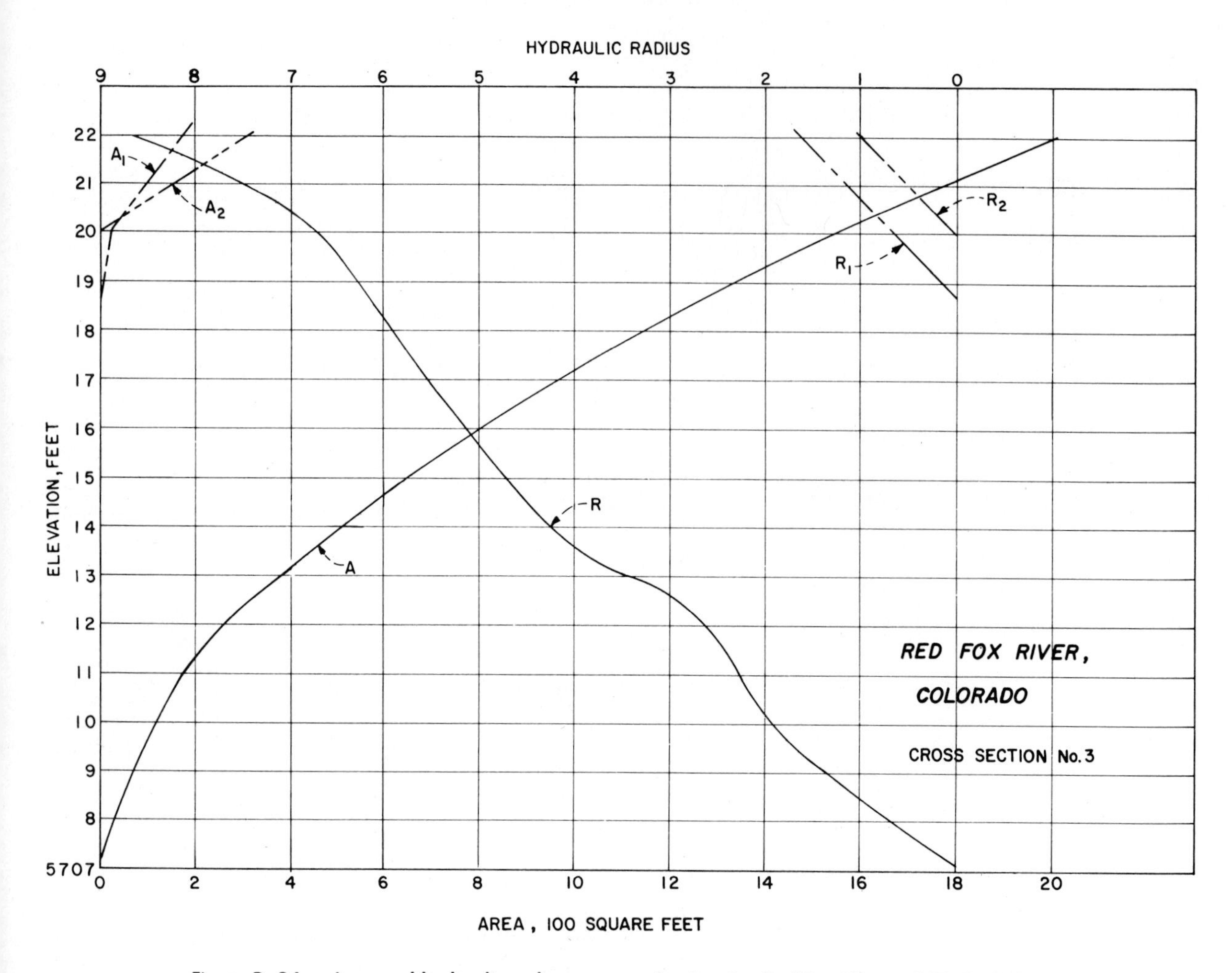

Figure B-24.—Area and hydraulic radius curves—Section 3—Red Fox River. 288-D-2834.

When a sufficient number of profiles have been computed, a rating curve can be developed from the computed water surface elevations at any given section. This method is more reliable than the approximate method previously described, because if the first section does not typify the average stream channel hydraulics the variations are recognized as the profiles are continued upstream. This may be proven by changing the starting elevation at the first section and computing a new profile. It will be found that a considerable change in the starting elevation at section 1 will make much less difference in the computed elevation for section 7.

B-9. *Critical Flow*.—The hydraulic analysis of flow in open channels becomes more complex when critical conditions can occur at some point along the river reach under consideration. The conditions of critical flow can be commonly observed at a "control" section in the channel. Such controls occur at locations where there is a material change in the cross section causing a constriction of the flow. These constrictions may be natural, or artificial such as bridges. Another cause may be a significant change in bottom grade. Vortices, eddies, cross currents, and large standing waves are some of the characteristics indicating critical flow conditions. A field reconnaissance of the hydraulic reach under investigation should include the location of any critical sections.

Whenever a computed velocity appears very high, a check should be made to see if the velocity exceeds critical velocity. This is true if the elevation has been arrived at by the approximate method or by an energy balance. Equation (14) of this appendix,

$$V_c = 5.67\sqrt{\frac{a}{T}}, \tag{14}$$

can be used to determine the critical velocity and, when the velocity at the computed elevation exceeds critical, it may be assumed that a control exists. Other methods may be used for checking critical flow but they are not discussed because all are based on different ways of analyzing equation (7)

$$\frac{Q^2}{g} = \frac{a^3}{T} \tag{7}$$

When the depth of flow is greater than critical depth throughout the reach under study and a control point is not evident at some relatively close distance downstream from the reach, the computed water surface profiles are acceptable. If a control point is located downstream from the reach, the reach should be extended to the control, and profile computations started at that point. When the control point is encountered within the study reach, the critical depth elevation is determined and the profile computation is started again at the critical discharge elevation. Generally, in most streams, supercritical flow conditions will occur only in the immediate vicinity of a control section.

The above discussion involves the analysis of critical flow as applied to water surface profile computations. It may be required to develop a critical rating curve for a control section which is located at or near a damsite. In this event the critical velocities are computed by equation (14) and multiplied by the area to

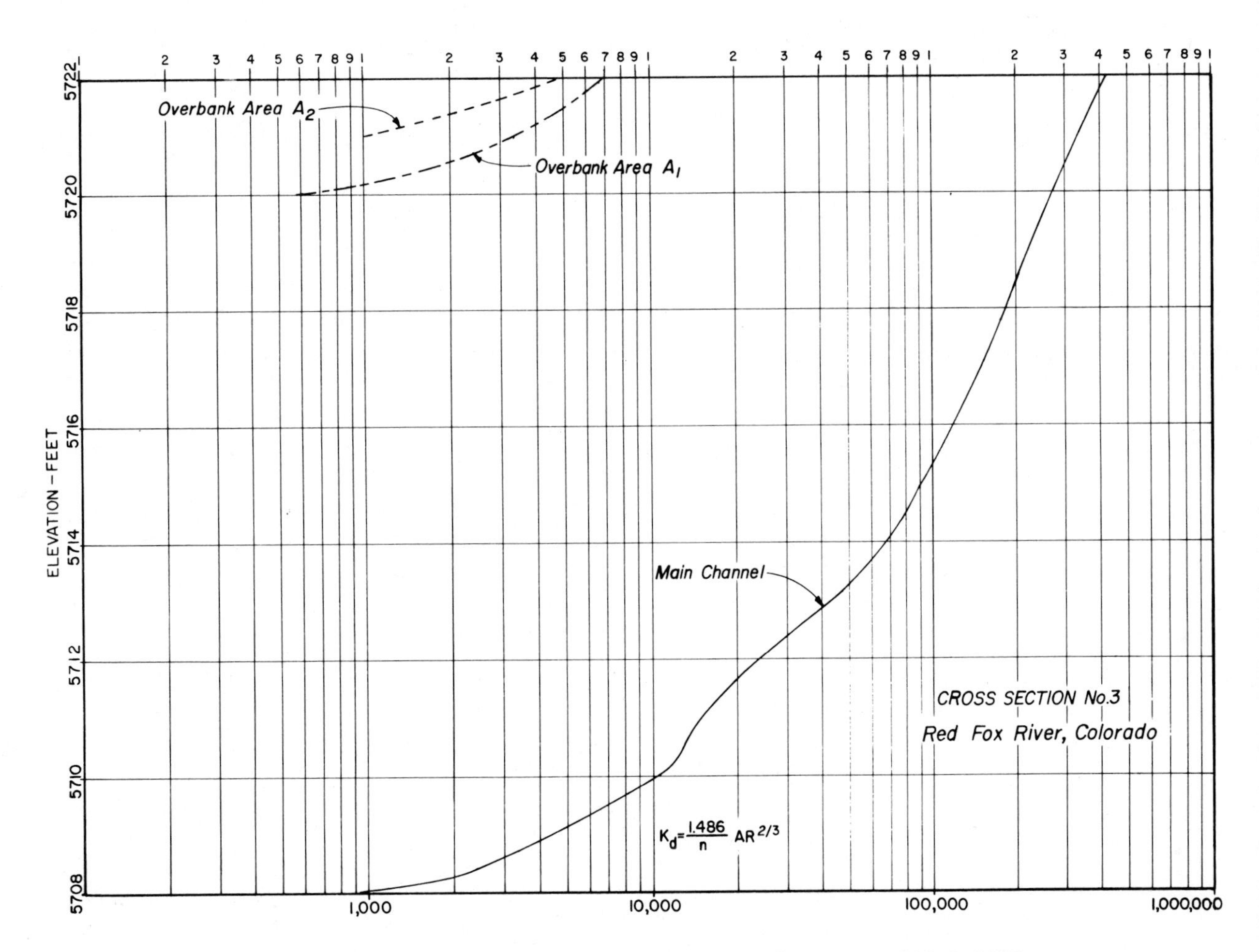

Figure B-25.—Conveyance (K_d) curves—Section 3—Red Fox River. 288-D-2835.

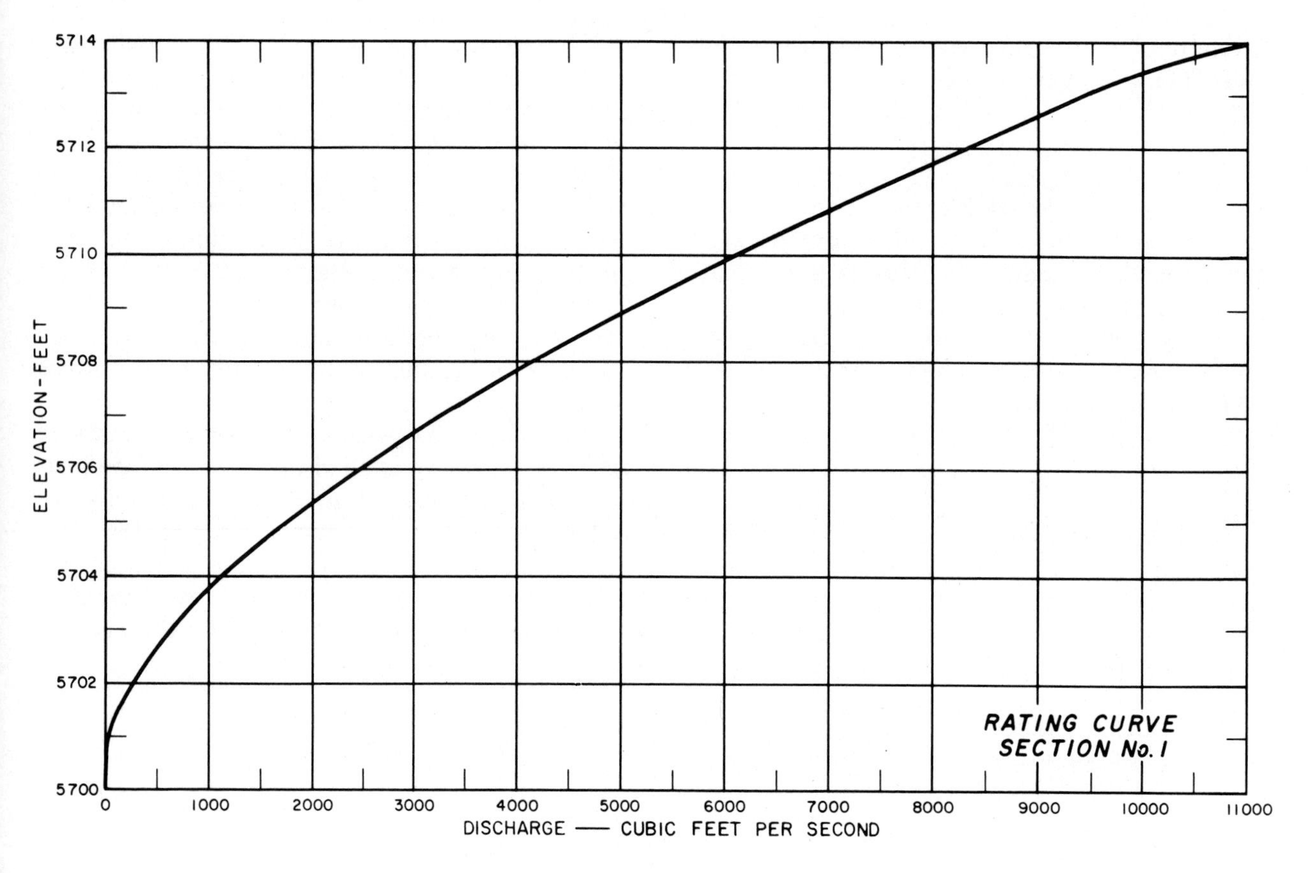

Figure B-26.—Rating curve—Section 1. 288-D-2836.

determine the discharge. This is done for several elevations and a curve of critical flow stage versus discharge plotted.

It is advisable to consider only the main channel portion of subdivided cross sections because the overbank areas will tend to lower the mean cross-section velocity and not depict the velocities attained in the channel itself.

B-10. *Computer Applications.*—The necessary trial-and-error solution of the energy balance equation involving iterative processes is ideally suited to digital computer applications. The Bureau of Reclamation has made use of several computer programs for computing water surface profiles; however, all are based upon an energy balance procedure and differ only in degree of sophistication.

Table B-9.—Water surface profile computations—Method A. 288-D-2859.

WATER SURFACE PROFILE COMPUTATIONS - METHOD A

SUBJECT: Red Fox River, Colorado Discharge = 11,100 cfs

COMPUTED BY: ___ DATE: ___ CHECKED BY: ___ DATE: ___ SHEET ___ OF ___

1	2	3	4	5	6	7	8	9	10	11	12	13	14	15	16	17
STATION	Assumed Water Surface Elev.	Area a	Dist. L	$K_d = \frac{1.486}{n} ar^{2/3}$	$s_f = \left(\frac{Q}{K_d}\right)^2$	Mean s_f	Mean $s_f \times L = h_f$	Q	V	V^2Q	h_v	$h_{v_1} - h_{v_2}$	Eddy Loss	Total Loss	ΔH	W.S. El.
Section 1	5714.0	594		125,000				10,700	18.0	3,460,000						
		192		4,150				400	2.08	1,730						
				129,150	0.00735			11,100		3,461,730	4.85					5714.0
			500													
Section 2	5720.9	863		230,000				5,960	6.80	276,000						
		1,170		130,000				3,370	2.88	28,000						
		1,000		25,000				650	0.65	274						
		1,500		43,000				1,120	0.75	630						
				428,000	0.000673	0.00401	2.00	11,100		304,904	0.43	+4.42	0.44	2.44	6.86	5720.86
			400													
Section 3	5721.2	1,832		360,000				11,000	6.00	396,000						
		115		2,700				70	0.61	26						
		185		1,250				30	0.16	8						
				363,950	0.00108	0.000877	0.35	11,100		396,034	0.56	-0.13	0.07	0.42	0.29	5721.15
			100													
Section 4	5721.2	1,300		158,000	0.00493	0.00301	0.30	11,100	8.54		1.13	-0.57	0.27	0.57	0.00	5721.20
			100													
Section 5	5722.1	1,681		220,000	0.00254	0.00374	0.37	11,100	6.60		0.68	+0.45	0.05	0.42	0.87	5722.07
			400													
Section 6	5722.8	1,018		174,000				10,900	10.7	1,250,000						
		130		3,380				190	1.46	405						
		20		161				10	0.50	3						
				177,541	0.00391	0.00328	1.31	11,100		1,250,408	1.75	-1.07	0.54	1.85	0.78	5722.85
			500													
Section 7	5725.3	844		124,000				10,500	12.5	1,640,000						
		98		1,400				110	1.12	138						
		220		5,800				490	2.23	2,440						
				131,200	0.00714	0.00553	2.77	11,100		1,642,578	2.30	-0.55	0.28	3.05	2.50	5725.35

C. BIBLIOGRAPHY

B-11. ***Bibliography.***—

[1] King, H. W., and Brater, E. F., "Handbook of Hydraulics," 6th edition, McGraw-Hill Book Co., Inc., New York, N.Y., 1976.

[2] Chow, Ven Te., "Open Channel Hydraulics," McGraw-Hill Book Co., New York, N.Y., 1959.

[3] Streeter, V. L., "Fluid Mechanics," 4th edition, McGraw-Hill Book Co., New York, N.Y. 1966.

[4] Rouse, Hunter, "Engineering Hydraulics," John Wiley & Sons, Inc., New York, N.Y. 1950.

[5] "Friction Factors for Large Conduits Flowing Full," Engineering Monograph No. 7, Bureau of Reclamation, 1977.

[6] Bureau of Reclamation, "Hydraulic Design of Stilling Basins and Energy Dissipators," Engineering Monograph No. 25, May 1984.

[7] "Guide for Computing Water Surface Profiles," Bureau of Reclamation, November 1957.

[8] "Hydrologic and Hydraulic Analyses—Computation of Backwater Curves in River Channels," Engineering Manual, Department of the Army, Corps of Engineers, pt. CXIV, ch. 9, May 1952.

[9] "Techniques of Water-Resources Investigations," Book 3, Chapters A6, A7, A8, U.S. Geological Survey, 1968.

[10] Dalrymple, Tate, and Benson, M.A., "Measurement of Peak Discharge by the Slope-Area Method," Techniques of Water Resources Investigations of the U.S. Geological Survey—ch. A2, U.S. Department of the Interior, Geological Survey, 1967.

[11] "Water Measurement Manual," Bureau of Reclamation, Second edition, revised reprint, 1984.

Structural Design Data

C.1. *Introduction.*—This appendix presents structural design data peculiar to hydraulic structures for the design of concrete appurtenances to embankment dams. It is presumed that the user of this text is familiar with reinforced concrete design, or will consult other texts for information on this subject. A major portion of this appendix is concerned with the design of reinforced concrete conduits for use as spillways or outlet works under or through embankment dams.

C.2. *Earth Pressures on Retaining Walls.*—Figure C-1 presents a method for determining the active earth loads on retaining walls when the properties of the fill material behind the wall are known. The curves are based on Coulomb's theory of active earth pressure against retaining walls [1][1]. In applying Coulomb's theory, the angle of friction between the earth and the back of the wall is assumed to be zero. The effect of fill cohesion has been omitted because its contribution is uncertain and relatively unimportant for most situations [2]. Detailed discussions of methods available for determining earth pressure and for designing retaining walls can be found in many texts [1, 2, 3, 4, 5].

C.3. *Earthquake Loads on Retaining Walls.*—The design of retaining walls should include the effects of dynamic fill and water loads in addition to static loads. Earthquakes impart accelerations to structures that may significantly increase the effective loadings. The values of accelerations used for design are selected based on the proximity of the structure to major faults, on seismic records, on site geology, and on the function of the structure. Higher allowable stresses and reduced safety factors for stability are generally allowed for earthquake designs. A discussion of the general procedures and methods that may be used for earthquake design can be found in "Design Criteria for Concrete Retaining Walls" [2].

[1]Numbers in brackets refer to entries in the bibliography (sec. C.7).

C.4. *Allowable Bearing Values for Structure Footings.*—Table C-1 gives suggested allowable bearing values for footings of structures appurtenant to small dams. These values are based on an evaluation of several sources of published data [1, 2, 6, 7], in light of the problems peculiar to hydraulic structures, and may be used when laboratory tests defining the compressive and shear strength of a material are not available. The allowable bearing values listed for foundations of soils are smaller than those generally given in building codes. Except for the gravels, these values vary according to the relative density and relative consistency of cohesionless and cohesive soils, respectively, rather than with the soil classifications group.

C.5. *Precast Concrete Pipe Conduits.*—

(a) *General.*—When precast concrete pipes are used as conduits for outlet works (or for spillways) under or through embankment dams, they should be bedded in a concrete base, as shown on figure C-2. One of the purposes of the concrete base is to prevent percolation along the underside of the pipe where tightly compacted earth bedding is difficult to obtain. For this reason the concrete base should be placed concurrently with the pipe or after the pipe is in position.

Another purpose of the concrete base is to provide a 90° "bedding angle" for the precast concrete pipe. This is discussed in more detail in subsection (b).

Cutoff collars should be provided to prevent percolation along the pipe. These collars should be identical to those used with cast-in-place concrete conduits, as discussed in section 10.21(b).

Precast concrete pipe joints should have rubber gaskets, as shown on figure 10-25. To provide flexibility for settlement caused by superimposed embankment loads, pipe with types R-3 and R-4 joints should be installed with the joint space between the

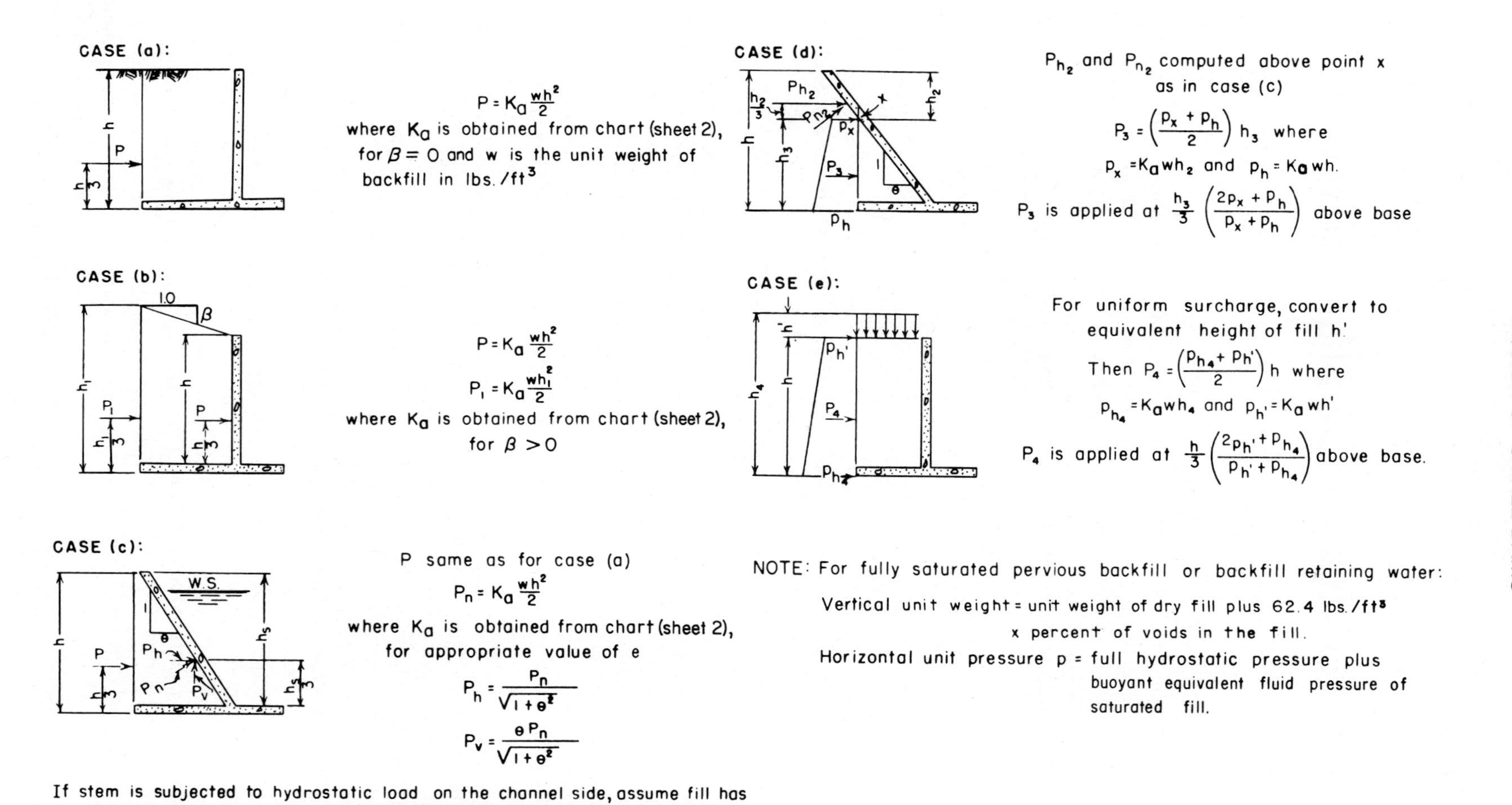

Figure C-1.—Earth pressures on retaining walls. (sheet 1 of 2).

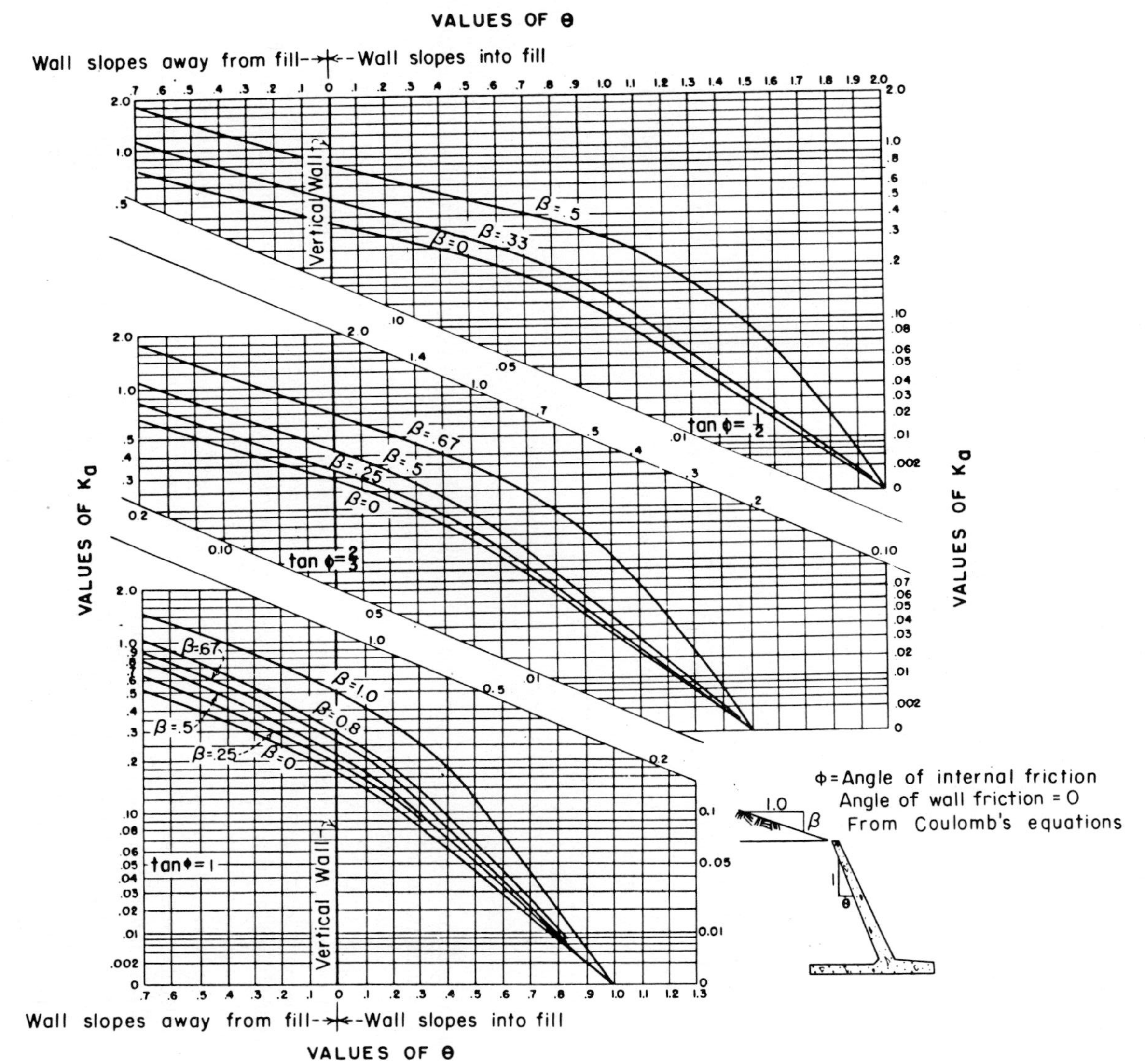

Figure C-1.—Earth pressures on retaining walls. (sheet 2 of 2).

Table C-1.—Suggested allowable bearing values for footings of structures appurtenant to small dams.

Material	Condition, relative density, or relative consistency	Average standard penetration values in fine-grained soils		Allowable bearing pressure, tons/ft²
		Effective overburden pressure, lb/in²	Number of blows per foot	
Massive igneous, metamorphic, or sedimentary hard rock	Sound (minor cracks allowed)			60
Hard laminated rock such as slate or schist	Sound (minor cracks allowed)			40
Intensely weathered bedrock of any kind except shale (shale is treated as clay)				10
Gravel (GW, GP, GM, GC)				4 to 6
Clay				3 to 5
Cohesionless sands (SW, SP)	Loose	0 20 40	4 12 17	[2]
	Medium	0 20 40	4 to 8 12 to 24 17 to 40	1 to 2
	Dense	0 20 40	8 24 40	2 to 4
Saturated [1]sands, silts, and clays (SM, SC, ML, CL, MH, CH)	Soft Medium Stiff Hard		4 4 to 10 11 to 20 20	0.25 0.5 1.0 1.5

[1]Values are for foundations that are almost or completely saturated during the construction period. Bearing values can be increased by one-third if the foundation is relatively dry, provided that the criteria on figure 6-34 for "no treatment required" are met.
[2]Requires compaction.

end of the spigot and the face of the bell, a minimum of ¼ inch and a maximum of ½ inch.

(b) *Design of Precast Concrete Pipe.*— When precast concrete pipe is used for outlet works, it should be designed for internal pressure, for superimposed embankment loads, and for a combination of the two as conditions require. The live loads (with impact) from the operation of construction equipment on the embankment above pipe with shallow cover should also be considered. The embankment loads are usually computed in accordance with Marston's theory, as described in section 10.21(d). The precast concrete pipe should be assumed to be a rigid conduit. In determining embankment loads for design purposes, the projection condition is most likely to govern.

The various conditions of densities of material and settlements in the foundation and embankment must be given due consideration. It is important to remember that even where the natural ground and the constructed embankment have equal densities, the embankment will settle more than the natural foundation.

Precast concrete pipe shells and reinforcement should be designed in accordance with the formulas of this section and using the ultimate strength design methods, with a load factor of 1.8 and without consideration of compressive reinforcement. To ensure watertightness, a hypothetical case for bursting caused by hydrostatic head should be calculated, and the unit stresses in the reinforcement should not exceed the following values:

Hydrostatic head, feet	f_s due only to head, lb/in²
0 to 50	16,000
50.1 to 75	14,000
75.1 to 150	12,500

Note: The maximum internal pressure head for reinforced concrete pressure pipe is 150 feet.

The supporting strength of precast concrete pipe under superimposed loads is highly dependent upon the bedding angle provided for the pipe during installation. The bedding angle is defined as the angle formed by the arc of the pipe that is in firm complete contact with the material beneath the pipe and across which superimposed loads are transmitted from the wall of the pipe to the material below. As mentioned previously, one of the purposes of the concrete base beneath the pipe is to provide a 90° bedding angle. This 90° angle is shown on figure C-2 as the sum of the two 45° angles on either side of the vertical centerline of the pipe. To illustrate the importance of the bedding angle: A pipe laid on a flat, horizontal surface with line bearing on the bottom (0° bedding angle) can support only half the load that the same pipe can support when it is installed with a 90° bedding angle.

The formulas given below are based on a bulb-like distribution of applied forces and reactions [9]. The coefficients in the formulas and the locations of the critical sections shown on figure C-3 are valid only for a 90° bedding angle.

Section 1: $M = -115r^2t - 24rr_i^2 - 0.126rW$ (1)

$T = +195rt - 53r_i^2 + 0.324W - 62.4r_iH$ (2)

Section 2: $M = +83r^2t + 17rr_i^2 + 0.089rW$ (3)

$T = +280rt - 12r_i^2 + 0.539W - 62.4r_iH$ (4)

Section 3: $S = -244rt - 51r_i^2 - 0.273W$ (5)

where:

r, r_i, t, and H are dimensions, in feet,
W = total earth load on the pipe, in pounds per linear foot,
M = moment, in foot pounds
S = shear, in pounds, and
T = thrust in pounds.

Table C-2 gives the minimum circumferential reinforcement and nominal wall thicknesses for reinforced concrete pressure pipe from 12 to 108 inches in diameter, for an internal pressure head of 25 feet of water or less, and for overfills of up to 20 feet above the top of the pipe. In each case, the internal pressure is measured to the centerline of the pipe. This table was developed for the design of precast concrete pressure pipelines with a bedding angle of 90°.

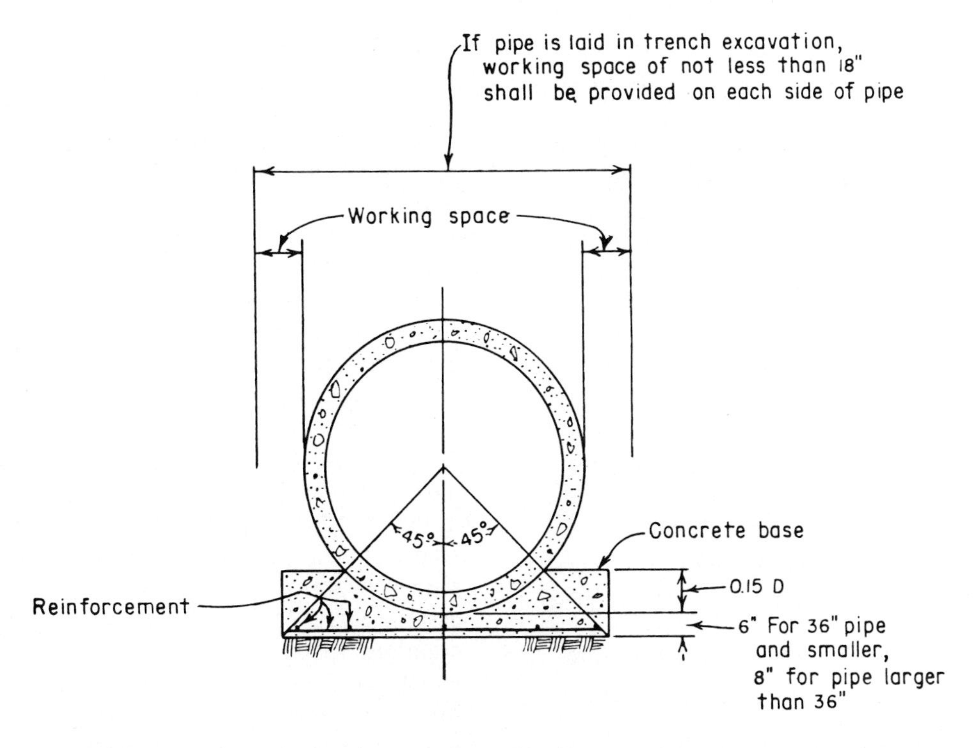

Figure C-2.—Precast concrete pipe on concrete base for conduit under or through embankment dams.

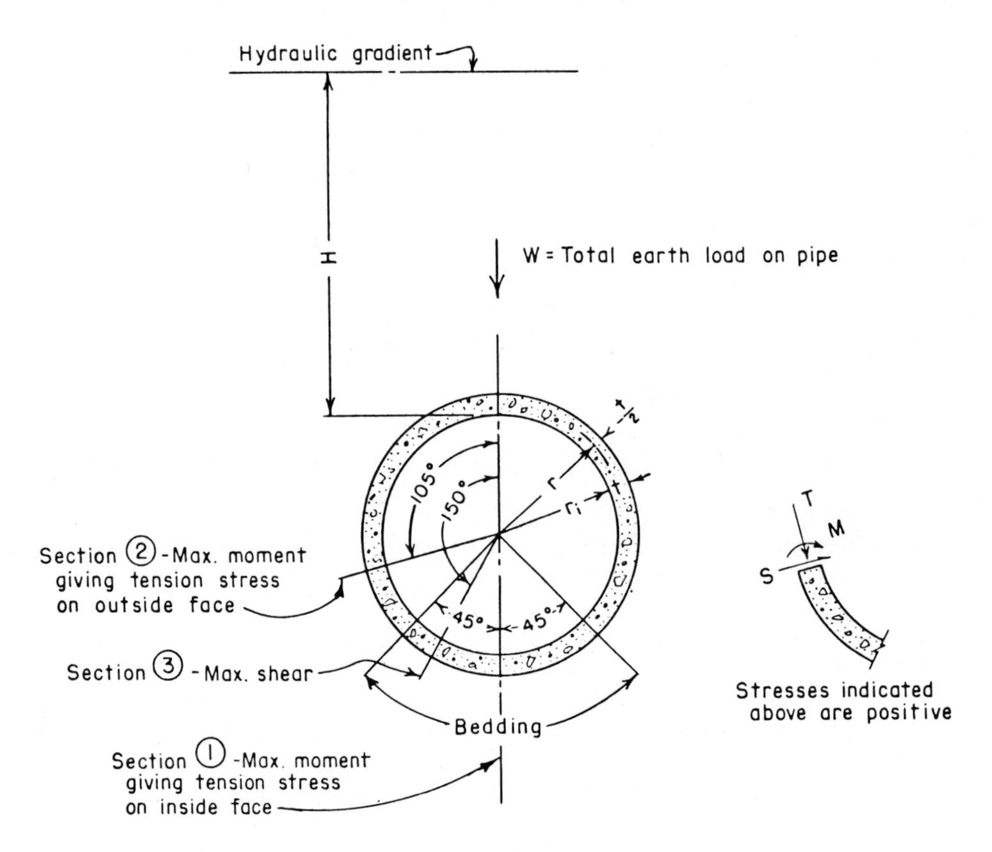

Figure C-3.—Location of critical sections in design of precast concrete pressure pipe. For a 90° bedding angle. 288-D-2915.

Marston's equations for earth loads were not used in the development of table C-2. Instead, the total weight of the vertical prism of soil above the pipe was used [9] with an empirical relationship for the effective unit weight of the earth cover above the pipe. The formula used for the unit weight of earth cover is:

$$W_e = 100 + 20\frac{h}{D_o} \qquad (6)$$

where:

W_e = the effective unit weight of the earth cover above the top of the pipe, in pounds per cubic foot (150 lb/ft³ maximum),

h = height of the earth cover above the top of the pipe, in feet, and

D_o = the outside diameter of the pipe, in feet.

Formula (6) provides reasonably accurate approximations to loads computed by Marston's equations, but is generally somewhat low for the projection conditions. Many miles of concrete pipelines have been satisfactorily installed using the designs listed in table C-2, and this table may be used, as appropriate, for the designs of precast concrete conduits under embankment dams.

Concrete pipe should be manufactured in accordance with Bureau of Reclamation publication, "Standard Specifications for Reinforced Concrete Pressure Pipe"[10]. Table C-2 is excerpted from the table of pipe designs in the standard specifications [10]. The designs in this table are based on a 4,500 lb/in² design concrete compressive strength and on tensile strengths of 40,000 lb/in² ultimate and 33,000 lb/in² yield for the reinforcing steel. Industry standard wall thicknesses were used. Should design requirements indicate the need for wall thicknesses greater than those shown in table C-2 and in the standard specifications, some manufacturers can supply a "thick-wall" pipe by using the inner form for the nominal pipe size and an outer form for the next larger size pipe. A manufacturer should be consulted for the wall thicknesses of thick-wall pipe.

Table C-2.—Reinforcement and wall thicknesses for 12- through 108-inch reinforced concrete pressure pipe. For a 90° bedding angle.

	Minimum circumferential reinforcement in square inches per linear foot of pipe											
Internal diameter of pipe in inches	12		15		18				21			
Type of reinforcement	Circular		Circular		Circular		Elliptical		Circular		Elliptical	
Nominal wall thickness, inches	2	3	2	3	2¼	3	2¼	3	2⅜	3	2⅜	3
Layers of reinforcement	Single	Single	Single	Single	Single	Single	Single	Single	Single	Single	Single	Single
CLASS												
A-25	0.07	0.06	0.10	0.08	0.12	0.11	0.12	0.12	0.15	0.13	0.14	0.14
B-25	.10	.08	.14	.11	.18	.15	.16	.12	.23	.19	.19	.14
C-25	.13	.09	.19	.14	.25	.19	.21	.14	.32	.26	.27	.19
D-25	.16	.11	.25	.17	.32	.24	.28	.17	.42	.33	.35	.23

	Minimum circumferential reinforcement in square inches per linear foot of pipe											
Internal diameter of pipe in inches	24				27							
Type of reinforcement	Circular		Elliptical		Circular						Elliptical	
Nominal wall thickness, inches	2½	3	2½	3	2⅝	3⅛	3¼		4¼		2⅝	3¼
Layers of reinforcement	Single	Single	Single	Single	Single	Single	Inner	Outer	Inner	Outer	Single	Single
CLASS												
A-25	0.18	0.16	0.16	0.16	0.21	0.19	0.13	0.09	0.11	0.07	0.18	0.18
B-25	.29	.25	.23	.18	.35	.30	.20	.11	.15	.08	.27	.20
C-25	.40	.33	.32	.24	.49	.41	.27	.14	.20	.09	.37	.27
D-25	.54	.43	.41	.30	–	.54	.34	.16	.24	.10	.49	.34

	Minimum circumferential reinforcement in square inches per linear foot of pipe									
Internal diameter of pipe in inches	30									
Type of reinforcement	Circular								Elliptical	
Nominal wall thickness, inches	2¾	3⅛	3¼		3½		4¾		2¾	3½
Layers of reinforcement	Single	Single	Inner	Outer	Inner	Outer	Inner	Outer	Single	Single
CLASS										
A-25	0.24	0.23	0.16	0.10	0.15	0.10	0.12	0.08	0.20	0.20
B-25	.41	.37	.25	.14	.22	.13	.17	.09	.31	.22
C-25	.60	.51	.33	.17	.30	.15	.21	.10	.43	.30
D-25	–	.69	.43	.21	.38	.19	.26	.11	.59	.38

	Minimum circumferential reinforcement in square inches per linear foot of pipe									
Internal diameter of pipe in inches	33									
Type of reinforcement	Circular								Elliptical	
Nominal wall thickness, inches	2⅞	3⅛	3¼		3¾		4¾		2⅞	3¾
Layers of reinforcement	Single	Single	Inner	Outer	Inner	Outer	Inner	Outer	Single	Single
CLASS										
A-25	0.28	0.26	0.18	0.12	0.16	0.11	0.13	0.09	0.22	0.22
B-25	.48	.44	.29	.17	.25	.14	.19	.10	.35	.25
C-25	–	.64	.40	.22	.33	.17	.25	.12	.50	.33
D-25	–	–	.53	.27	.43	.21	.32	.14	.67	.43

Table C-2.—Reinforcement and wall thicknesses for 12- through 108-inch reinforced concrete pressure pipe. For a 90° bedding angle.— Continued

	Minimum circumferential reinforcement in square inches per linear foot of pipe								
Internal diameter of pipe in inches	36								
Type of reinforcement	Circular							Elliptical	
Nominal wall thickness, inches	3⅛	3¼		4		5		3⅛	4
Layers of reinforcement	Single	Inner	Outer	Inner	Outer	Inner	Outer	Single	Single
CLASS									
A-25	0.31	0.21	0.14	0.17	0.12	0.15	0.10	0.24	0.24
B-25	.53	.34	.20	.27	.15	.22	.12	.36	.27
C-25	–	.49	.26	.37	.19	.28	.14	.52	.37
D-25	–	.64	.33	.46	.23	.35	.16	.69	.46

	Minimum circumferential reinforcement in square inches per linear foot of pipe															
Internal diameter of pipe in inches	39								42							
Type of reinforcement	Circular						Elliptical		Circular						Elliptical	
Nominal wall thickness, inches	3½		4¼		5¼		3½	4¼	3¾		4½		5½		3¾	4½
Layers of reinforcement	Inner	Outer	Inner	Outer	Inner	Outer	Single	Single	Inner	Outer	Inner	Outer	Inner	Outer	Single	Single
CLASS																
A-25	0.22	0.15	0.19	0.13	0.16	0.11	0.26	0.26	0.24	0.16	0.20	0.14	0.17	0.12	0.28	0.28
B-25	.37	.22	.29	.17	.24	.13	.37	.29	.40	.23	.32	.18	.26	.14	.40	.32
C-25	.52	.28	.40	.21	.31	.15	.52	.40	.54	.30	.43	.22	.34	.17	.54	.43
D-25	.67	.35	.50	.25	.39	.18	.67	.50	.73	.38	.55	.27	.43	.20	.73	.55

	Minimum circumferential reinforcement in square inches per linear foot of pipe															
Internal diameter of pipe in inches	45								48							
Type of reinforcement	Circular						Elliptical		Circular						Elliptical	
Nominal wall thickness, inches	3⅞		4¾		5¾		3⅞	4¾	4⅛		5		5¾		4⅛	5
Layers of reinforcement	Inner	Outer	Inner	Outer	Inner	Outer	Single	Single	Inner	Outer	Inner	Outer	Inner	Outer	Single	Single
CLASS																
A-25	0.26	0.18	0.22	0.15	0.19	0.13	0.30	0.30	0.28	0.19	0.24	0.16	0.21	0.14	0.31	0.31
B-25	.43	.25	.34	.19	.28	.15	.43	.34	.45	.27	.36	.21	.32	.18	.45	.36
C-25	.60	.33	.46	.24	.37	.19	.60	.46	.66	.36	.51	.27	.44	.22	.66	.51
D-25	.80	.42	.59	.30	.47	.22	.80	.59	.86	.45	.65	.33	.54	.26	.86	.65

	Minimum circumferential reinforcement in square inches per linear foot of pipe															
Internal diameter of pipe in inches	51								54							
Type of reinforcement	Circular						Elliptical		Circular						Elliptical	
Nominal wall thickness, inches	4¼		5¼		6		4¼	5¼	4½		5½		6¼		4½	5½
Layers of reinforcement	Inner	Outer	Inner	Outer	Inner	Outer	Single	Single	Inner	Outer	Inner	Outer	Inner	Outer	Single	Single
CLASS																
A-25	0.30	0.20	0.25	0.17	0.23	0.15	0.33	0.33	0.32	0.21	0.27	0.18	0.25	0.16	0.35	0.35
B-25	.49	.29	.38	.22	.34	.19	.49	.38	.50	.30	.40	.23	.36	.20	.50	.40
C-25	.72	.40	.54	.29	.47	.24	.72	.54	.75	.41	.58	.31	.50	.26	.75	.58
D-25	.97	.50	.69	.35	.58	.28	–	.69	1.00	.52	.74	.37	.63	.30	–	.74

Table C–2.—Reinforcement and wall thicknesses for 12- through 108-inch reinforced concrete pressure pipe. For a 90° bedding angle.—Continued

Minimum circumferential reinforcement in square inches per linear foot of pipe																
Internal diameter of pipe in inches	57								60							
Type of reinforcement	Circular						Elliptical		Circular						Elliptical	
Nominal wall thickness, inches	4¾		5¾		6½		4¾	5¾	5		6		6¾		5	6
Layers of reinforcement	Inner	Outer	Inner	Outer	Inner	Outer	Single	Single	Inner	Outer	Inner	Outer	Inner	Outer	Single	Single
CLASS																
A-25	0.34	0.22	0.29	0.19	0.26	0.17	0.37	0.37	0.35	0.23	0.30	0.20	0.28	0.18	0.39	0.39
B-25	.53	.32	.43	.25	.38	.22	.53	.43	.55	.33	.45	.26	.41	.23	.55	.45
C-25	.78	.43	.61	.33	.53	.28	.78	.61	.82	.45	.65	.35	.56	.29	.82	.65
D-25	1.03	.55	.78	.40	.67	.33	–	.78	1.09	.57	.82	.43	.71	.35	–	.82

Minimum circumferential reinforcement in square inches per linear foot of pipe														
Internal diameter of pipe in inches	63								66					
Type of reinforcement	Circular						Elliptical		Circular				Ellipitcal	
Nominal wall thickness, inches	5¼		6¼		7		5¼	6¼	5½		6½		5½	6½
Layers of reinforcement	Inner	Outer	Inner	Outer	Inner	Outer	Single	Single	Inner	Outer	Inner	Outer	Single	Single
CLASS														
A-25	0.37	0.25	0.32	0.22	0.30	0.20	0.41	0.41	0.39	0.26	0.34	0.23	0.43	0.43
B-25	.58	.35	.48	.28	.43	.25	.58	.48	.60	.36	.50	.30	.60	.50
C-25	.87	.48	.69	.37	.60	.31	.87	.69	.89	.49	.72	.38	.89	.72
D-25	1.15	.60	.88	.46	.76	.38	–	.88	1.19	.63	.94	.48	–	.94

Minimum circumferential reinforcement in square inches per linear foot of pipe												
Internal diameter of pipe in inches	69						72					
Type of reincforcement	Circular				Circular		Circular				Elliptical	
Nominal wall thickness, inches	5¾		6¾		5¾	6¾	6		7		6	7
Layers of reinforcement	Inner	Outer	Inner	Outer	Single	Single	Inner	Outer	Inner	Outer	Single	Single
CLASS												
A-25	0.41	0.28	0.36	0.24	0.45	0.45	0.46	0.30	0.40	0.26	0.48	0.47
B-25	.62	.37	.53	.31	.63	.53	.69	.41	.58	.34	.69	.58
C-25	.91	.51	.74	.40	.91	.74	1.01	.56	.81	.44	1.01	.81
D-25	1.23	.66	.98	.50	–	.98	1.39	.73	1.08	.56	–	1.08

Minimum circumferential reinforcement in square inches per linear foot of pipe												
Internal diameter of pipe in inches	78				84				90			
Type of reincforcement	Circular				Circular				Circular			
Nominal wall thickness, inches	6½		7½		7		8		7½		8	
Layers of reinforcement	Inner	Outer	Inner	Outer	Inner	Outer	Inner	Outer	Inner	Outer	Inner	Outer
CLASS												
A-25	0.49	0.33	0.44	0.29	0.53	0.35	0.48	0.32	0.57	0.38	0.54	0.36
B-25	.73	.44	.63	.37	.78	.47	.68	.40	.83	.50	.77	.46
C-25	1.06	.59	.87	.48	1.10	.62	.94	.51	1.16	.66	1.07	.59
D-25	1.47	.78	1.17	.61	1.54	.82	1.26	.66	1.61	.85	1.44	.77

Table C-2.—Reinforcement and wall thicknesses for 12- through 108-inch reinforced concrete pressure pipe. For a 90° bedding angle.—Continued

	Minimum circumferential reinforcement in square inches per linear foot of pipe											
Internal diameter of pipe in inches	96				102				108			
Type of reinforcement	Circular				Circular				Circular			
Nominal wall thickness, inches	8		8½		8½		9		9		9½	
Layers of reinforcement	Inner	Outer	Inner	Outer	Inner	Outer	Inner	Outer	Inner	Outer	Inner	Outer
CLASS												
A-25	0.62	0.41	0.59	0.39	0.67	0.44	0.64	0.42	0.71	0.47	0.68	0.45
B-25	.88	.53	.83	.50	.94	.56	.88	.53	.99	.60	.94	.56
C-25	1.23	.69	1.13	.64	1.29	.73	1.19	.67	1.35	.77	1.27	.71
D-25	1.67	.90	1.51	.81	1.73	.94	1.60	.85	1.79	.98	1.67	.90

Note: Designations A, B, C, and D for class of pipe denote 5, 10, 15 and 20 feet of cover, respectively. The number 25 for class of pipe denotes design hydrostatic pressure head in feet measured to centerline of pipe.

The requirements for reinforcing steel and concrete materials, mixing, placing, and curing can be found in the standard specifications [10].

C.6. *Cast-in-Place Concrete Conduits.*—Conduits used in conjunction with earthfill or rockfill dams can vary considerably in size and shape. For high fill and water loads, the interior and exterior surfaces are curved to better handle the applied loads.

Flat-bottom conduits with straight sides and curved top sections, or rectangular shapes, are often used where shallow loads exist. The flat bottom makes foundation excavation easier, the flat sides make backfilling and compaction easier, and the straight sides make forming less expensive. In addition, the rectangular shapes provide good cross sections for open channel waterways through shallow embankments. They also provide good transitions where a conduit connects to a flat-bottom chute.

Examples of typical cast-in-place single-barrel conduits used by the Bureau of Reclamation are shown on figure C-4.

Configuration details and Beggs deformeter coefficients for analysis of these shapes for different loadings is covered in [11]. Other methods such as finite element computer programs are also available for analysis of these conduit shapes.

The loads for cut-and-cover cast-in-place conduit sections normally consist of dry or saturated fill loads, external and internal hydrostatic loads, and construction equipment loads.

For large earthfill and rockfill dams, there is a limit to the fill height for which a conduit, especially a large conduit, can be economically designed. This height limit is generally about 200 feet depending on the conduit shape selected. Generally, the thickness of a conduit is designed to take the maximum allowable shear stress at the critical area around the section. This is done to keep cracking of the section to a minimum. This consideration is particularly critical where the conduit extends through the impervious core of an earthfill dam.

To limit cracking from shrinkage and temperature changes, transverse control joints are normally placed in the conduit at less than 15-foot intervals. The control joint should be painted to prevent bonding and should have a transverse waterstop to prevent leakage. The longitudinal reinforcement should extend through the control joints.

Normally, two mats of reinforcement are placed in the inside and outside faces of the cross section to satisfy design requirements. A typical reinforced cross section is shown on figure C-5. The reinforcement sizes will vary widely based on design considerations, and the locations of splices may vary depending on construction considerations and moment concentrations.

Conduits are sometimes constructed on soil foundations. In such cases, a steel liner is often used and, depending on the type of foundation, some of the material under the conduit may be replaced with well-compacted select material to minimize foundation deformation potential.

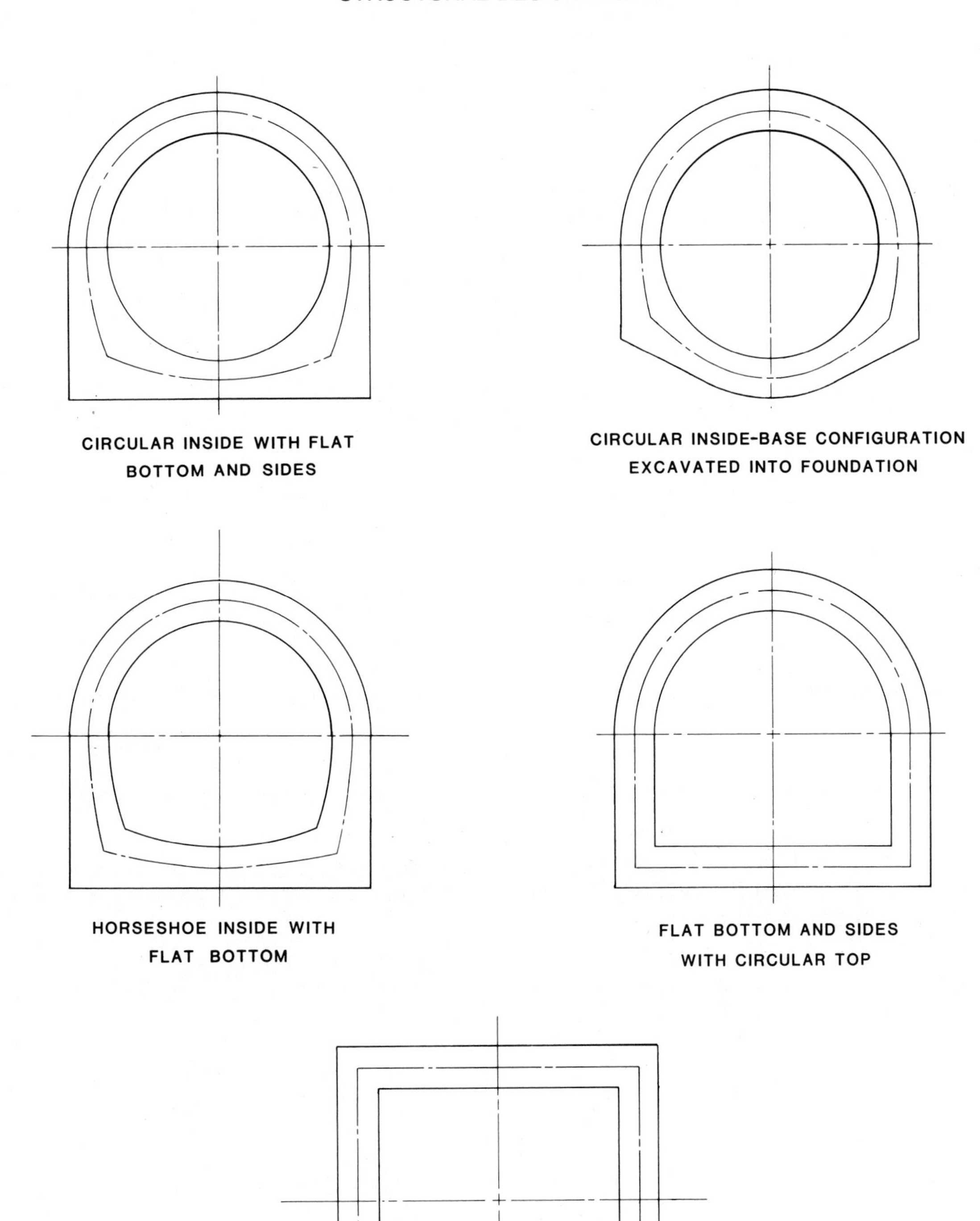

Figure C-4.—Typical cast-in-place, single-barrel conduits. 103-D-1791.

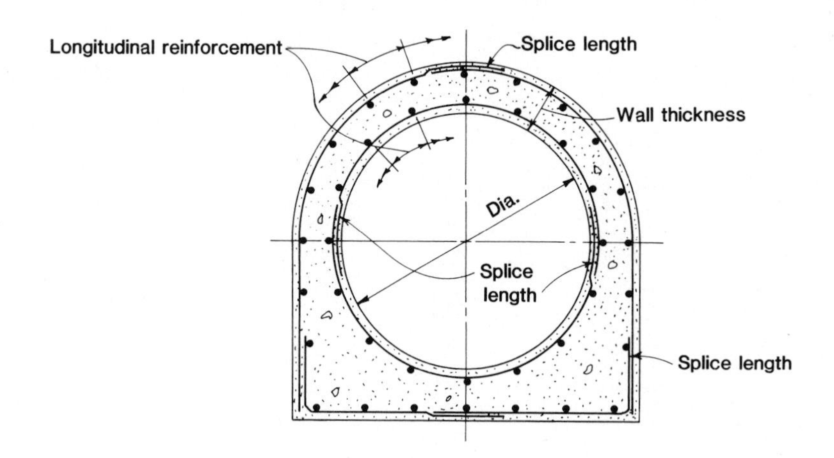

Figure C-5.—Typical reinforcement pattern for cast-in-place conduits. 103-D-1792.

C.7. *Bibliography.*

[1] Terzaghi, Karl, *Theoretical Soil Mechanics,* John Wiley and Sons, Inc., New York, NY, 1943.

[2] "Design Criteria for Concrete Retaining Walls," Report of the task committee on Design Criteria for Retaining Walls, Bureau of Reclamation, Denver, CO, 1977.

[3] Terzaghi, Karl, and Peck, R. B., *Soil Mechanics in Engineering Practices,* John Wiley and Sons Inc., New York, NY, 1967.

[4] Tschebotarioff, G. P., *Soil Mechanics, Foundations, and Earth Structures,* McGraw-Hill, New York, NY, 1951.

[5] Huntington, W. C., *Earth Pressures and Retaining Walls,* John Wiley and Sons, Inc., New York, NY, 1957.

[6] "Final Revised and Adopted Form of Part 29 Excavation and Foundations of the Boston Building Code," *Journal of the Boston Society of Civil Engineers,* vol. 50, No. 3, pp. 149-171, July 1963.

[7] Gibbs, H. J., and Holtz, W. G., "Research on Determining the Density of Sands by Spoon Penetration Testing," *Proceedings,* Fourth International Conference on Soil Mechanics and Foundation Engineering, vol. I, London, 1957.

[8] "Ultimate Strength Design Data for 3750 psi Concrete," Bureau of Reclamation, Denver, CO, 1968.

[9] Olander, H. C., *Stress Analysis of Concrete Pipe,* Bureau of Reclamation, Engineering Monograph No. 6, Denver, CO, October 1950.

[10] "Standard Specifications for Reinforced Concrete Pressure Pipe," Bureau of Reclamation, Denver, CO, March, 1984.

[11] Phillips, H. B., and I. E. Allen, *Beggs Deformeter Stress Analysis of Single-Barrel Conduits,* Bureau of Reclamation, Engineering Monograph No. 14, Denver, CO, June 1965.

Building Code Requirements for Reinforced Concrete, ACI 318-83, American Concrete Institute, Detroit, MI, 1983.

"Design Handbook in Accordance with the Strength Design Method of ACI 318-83," Special publication No. 17(83), American Concrete Institute, Detroit, MI, 1983.

Soil Mechanics Nomenclature

D.1. ***Introduction.***—The following definitions of terms and symbols were selected from ASTM Designation D 653, "Standard Definition of Terms and Symbols Relating to Soil and Rock Mechanics," prepared by Subcommittee G-3 on Nomenclature and Definitions of ASTM Committee D-18 on Soil and Rock for Engineering Purposes, in cooperation with the Committee on Glossary of Terms and Definitions in Soil Mechanics of the Soil Mechanics and Foundations Division of the American Society of Civil Engineers. The list that follows is an abbreviated version of the ASTM designation, in which most of the cross-references and terms which have little or no relation to the subject matter of this text were omitted.

Units, where applicable, are indicated in capital letters on the right-hand side, under the item, and immediately above the definition. The letters denote:

F, force, such as pound-force, ton, newton, kilonewton.

L, length, such as inch, foot, meter.

T, time, such as second, minute.

D, dimensionless.

M, mass, such as pound-mass, gram, kilogram.

Positive exponents designate multiples in the numerator.

Negative exponents designate multiples in the denominator.

Degrees of angles are indicated as "degrees" (°). Expressing the unit either in the SI-metric or inch-pound system has been purposely omitted to leave the choice of the system and specific unit to the engineer and the particular application. For example, FL^{-2} may be expressed in pound-force per square inch, kilonewtons per square meter, tons per square foot, etc.; LT^{-1} may be expressed in feet per minute, meters per second, etc. No significance should be placed on the order in which symbols are presented where two or more are given.

The following letters of the Greek alphabet are used in this nomenclature:

Greek letter	*Greek name*	*Greek letter*	*Greek name*
α	Alpha	μ	Mu
β	Beta	σ	Sigma
γ	Gamma	τ	Tau
Δ, δ	Delta	ϕ	Phi
ε	Epsilon	ψ	Psi
θ	Theta		

D.2. ***Definitions, Symbols, and Units.***

ABSORBED WATER:

Water held mechanically in a soil mass and having physical properties not substantially different from ordinary water at the same temperature and pressure.

ADHESION:

Unit: c_a — FL^{-2}

Total: C_a — F or FL^{-1}

Shearing resistance between soil and another material under zero externally applied pressure.

ADSORBED WATER:

Water in a soil or rock mass, held by physicochemical forces, having physical properties substantially different from absorbed water or chemically combined water, at the same temperature and pressure.

AEOLIAN DEPOSITS:

Wind-deposited material such as dune sands and loess deposits.

AIRSPACE RATIO:

G_a — D

Ratio of (1) volume of water that can be drained from a saturated soil or rock under the action of force of gravity to (2) total volume of voids.

AIR-VOID RATIO:

G_v D

The ratio of (1) the volume of airspace to (2) the total volume of voids in a soil mass.

ALLOWABLE BEARING VALUE (ALLOWABLE SOIL PRESSURE):

q_a, p_a FL^{-2}

The maximum pressure that can be permitted on foundation soil, giving consideration to all pertinent factors, with adequate safety against rupture of the soil mass or movement of the foundation of such magnitude that the structure is impaired.

ALLOWABLE PILE BEARING LOAD:

Q_a, P_a F

The maximum load that can be permitted on a pile with adequate safety against movement of such magnitude that the structure is endangered.

ALLUVIUM:

Soil, the constituents of which have been transported in suspension by flowing water and subsequently deposited by sedimentation.

ANGLE OF EXTERNAL FRICTION (ANGLE OF WALL FRICTION):

δ Degrees (°)

Angle between the abscissa and the tangent of the curve representing the relationship of shearing resistance to normal stress acting between soil and surface of another material.

ANGLE OF INTERNAL FRICTION (ANGLE OF SHEAR RESISTANCE):

ϕ Degrees (°)

The angle between the axis of normal stress and the tangent to the Mohr envelope at a point representing a given failure-stress condition for solid material.

ANGLE OF OBLIQUITY:

α, B, θ, ψ Degrees (°)

The angle between the direction of the resultant stress or force acting on a given plane and the normal to that plane.

ANGLE OF REPOSE:

α Degrees (°)

Angle between the horizontal and the maximum slope that a soil assumes through natural processes. For dry granular soils, the effect of the height of slope is negligible; for cohesive soils, the effect of height of slope is so great that the angle of repose is meaningless.

ANISOTROPIC MASS:

A mass having different properties in different directions at any given point.

AQUIFER:

A water-bearing formation that provides a ground-water reservoir.

ARCHING:

The transfer of stress from a yielding part of a soil or rock mass to adjoining less-yielding or restrained parts of the mass.

AREA OF INFLUENCE OF A WELL:

a L^2

Area surrounding a well within which the piezometric surface has been lowered when pumping has produced a maximum steady rate of flow.

AREA RATIO OF A SAMPLING SPOON, SAMPLER, OR SAMPLING TUBE:

A_r D

$A_r = \frac{D_e^2 - D_i^2}{D_i^2}$ (100) where D_e represents the maximum external diameter of the sampling spoon and D_i represents the minimum internal diameter of the sampling spoon at the cutting edge. The area ratio is an indication of the volume of soil displaced by the sampling spoon (tube).

BASE COURSE (BASE):

A layer of specified or selected material of planned thickness constructed on the subgrade or subbase for the purpose of serving one or more functions such as distributing load, providing drainage, minimizing frost action, etc.

BASE EXCHANGE:

The physicochemical process whereby one species of ions adsorbed on soil particles is replaced by another species.

BEARING CAPACITY (OF A PILE):

Q_p, P_p F

The load per pile required to produce a condition of failure.

BEDROCK (LEDGE):
Rock of relatively great thickness and extent in its native location.

BENTONITIC CLAY:
A clay with a high content of the mineral montmorillonite, usually characterized by high swelling on wetting.

BERM:
A shelf that breaks the continuity of a slope.

BINDER (SOIL BINDER):
Portion of soil passing a No. 40 United States standard sieve.

BOULDER:
A particle of rock that will not pass a 12-inch-square opening.[1]

BOULDER CLAY:
A geological term used to designate glacial drift that has not been subjected to the sorting action of water and therefore contains particles from boulders to clay sizes.

BULKING:
The increase in volume of a material due to manipulation. Rock bulks upon being excavated; damp sand bulks if loosely deposited, as by dumping, because the "apparent cohesion" prevents movement of the soil particles to form a reduced volume.

CALIFORNIA BEARING RATIO:
CBR D
The ratio of (1) the force per unit area required to penetrate a soil mass with a 3-inch-square circular piston (approximately 2 inches in diameter) at the rate of 0.05 inch per minute to (2) that required for corresponding penetration of a standard material. The ratio is usually determined at 0.1-inch penetration, although other penetrations are sometimes used. Original California procedures required determination of the ratio at 0.1-inch intervals to 0.5 inch. Corps of Engineers' procedures require determination of the ratio at 0.1 and 0.2 inch. Where the ratio at 0.2 inch is consistently higher than at 0.1 inch, the ratio at 0.2 inch is used.

CAPILLARY ACTION (CAPILLARITY):
The rise or movement of water in the interstices of a soil or rock due to capillary forces.

CAPILLARY FRINGE ZONE:
The zone above the free water elevation in which water is held by capillary action.

CAPILLARY HEAD:
h L
The potential, expressed in head of water, that causes the water to flow by capillary action.

CAPILLARY MIGRATION (CAPILLARY FLOW):
The movement of water by capillary action.

CAPILLARY RISE (HEIGHT OF CAPILLARY RISE):
h_c L
The height above a free water elevation to which water will rise by capillary action.

CAPILLARY WATER:
Water subject to the influence of capillary action.

CLAY (CLAY SOIL):
Fine-grained soil or the fine-grained portion of soil that can be made to exhibit plasticity (putty-like properties) within a range of water contents, and which exhibits considerable strength when air-dry. The term has been used to designate the percentage finer than 0.002 mm (0.005 mm in some cases), but it is strongly recommended that this usage be discontinued because there is ample evidence that, from an engineering standpoint, the properties described in the above definition are many times more important.

CLAY SIZE:
That portion of the soil finer than 0.002 mm (0.005 mm in some cases). (See discussion under Clay)

COBBLE (COBBLESTONE):
A particle of rock that will pass a 12-inch-square opening and be retained on a 3-inch U.S. Standard sieve.[2]

[1]New definition from ASTM D 2487.

[2]New definition from ASTM D 2487.

COEFFICIENT OF COMPRESSIBILITY (COEFFICIENT OF COMPRESSION):

a_v L^2F^{-1}

The secant slope, for a given pressure increment, of the pressure-void ratio curve. Where a stress-strain curve is used, the slope of this curve is equal to $\frac{a_v}{1+e}$.

COEFFICIENT OF CONSOLIDATION:

c_v L^2T^{-1}

A coefficient utilized in the theory of consolidation, containing the physical constants of a soil affecting its rate of volume change.

$$c_v = \frac{k(1+e)}{a_v \cdot \gamma_w}, \text{ where}$$

k= coefficient of permeability, LT^{-1}
e= void ratio, D
a_v= coefficient of compressibility, L^2F^{-1}
γ_w= unit weight of water, FL^{-3}

NOTE.—In the literature published prior to 1935, the coefficient of consolidation, usually designated c, was defined by the equation $c = \frac{k}{a_v \cdot \gamma_w (1+e)}$. This original defintion of the coefficient of consolidation may be found in some more recent papers and care should be taken to avoid confusion.

COEFFICIENT OF EARTH PRESSURE:

K D

The principal stress ratio at a point in a soil mass.

ACTIVE:

K_A D

The minimum ratio of (1) the minor principal stress to (2) the major principal stress. This is applicable where the soil has yielded sufficiently to develop a lower limiting value of the minor principal stress.

AT REST:

K_o D

The ratio of (1) the minor principal stress to (2) the major principal stress. This is applicable where the soil mass is in its natural state without having been permitted to yield or without having been compressed.

PASSIVE:

K_p D

The maximum ratio of (1) the major principal stress to (2) the minor principal stress. This is applicable where the soil has been compressed sufficiently to develop an upper limiting value of the major principal stress.

COEFFICIENT OF INTERNAL FRICTION:

The tangent of the angle of internal friction. (See Internal Friction)

COEFFICIENT OF PERMEABILITY (PERMEABILITY):

k LT^{-1}

The rate of discharge of water under laminar flow conditions through a unit cross-sectional area of a porous medium under a unit hydraulic gradient and standard temperature conditions (Usually 20° C).

COEFFICIENT OF SUBGRADE REACTION (MODULUS OF SUBGRADE REACTION):

k, k_s FL^{-3}

Ratio of (1) load per unit area of horizontal surface of a mass of soil to (2) corresponding settlement of the surface. It is determined as the slope of the secant, drawn between the point corresponding to zero settlement and the point of 0.05-inch settlement, of a load settlement curve obtained from a plate load test on a soil using a 30-inch or greater diameter loading plate. It is used in the design of concrete pavements by the Westergaard method.

COEFFICIENT OF UNIFORMITY:

C_u D

The ratio D_{60}/D_{10}, where D_{60} is the particle diameter corresponding to 60 percent finer on the grain-size curve, and D_{10} is the particle diameter corresponding to 10 percent finer on the grain-size curve.

COEFFICIENT OF VISCOSITY (COEFFICIENT OF ABSOLUTE VISCOSITY):

μ FTL^{-2}

The shearing force per unit area required to maintain a unit difference in velocity between two parallel layers of a fluid a unit distance apart.

COEFFICIENT OF VOLUME COMPRESSIBILITY (MODULUS OF VOLUME CHANGE):

m_v L^2F^{-1}

The compression of a soil layer per unit of original thickness due to a given unit increase in pressure. It is numerically equal to the coefficient of compressibility, divided by one, plus the original void ratio: $\frac{a_v}{1+e}$

COHESION:

c FL^{-2}

The portion of the shear strength of a soil indicated by the term c in Coulomb's equation, $s=c+\bar{\sigma}\tan\varphi$

APPARENT COHESION:

Cohesion in granular soils due to capillary forces.

COHESIONLESS SOIL:

A soil that when unconfined has little or no strength when air-dried, and that has little or no cohesion when submerged.

COHESIVE SOIL:

A soil that when unconfined has considerable strength when air-dried, and that has significant cohesion when submerged.

COLLOIDAL PARTICLES:

Soil particles that are so small that the surface activity has an appreciable influence on the properties of the aggregate.

COMPACTION:

The densification of a soil by means of mechanical manipulation.

COMPACTION CURVE (PROCTOR CURVE) (MOISTURE-DENSITY CURVE):

The curve showing the relationship between the dry unit weight and the moisture content of a soil for a given compactive effort.

COMPACTION TEST:

A laboratory compacting procedure whereby a soil at a known moisture content is placed in a specified manner into a mold of given dimensions, subjected to a compactive effort of controlled magnitude, and the resulting unit weight determined. The procedure is repeated for various moisture contents sufficient to establish a relation between moisture content and unit weight.

COMPRESSIBILITY:

Property of a soil pertaining to its susceptibility to decrease in volume when subjected to load.

COMPRESSION INDEX:

C_c D

The slope of the linear portion of the pressure-void ratio curve on a semilog plot.

COMPRESSIVE STRENGTH (UNCONFINED OR UNIAXIAL COMPRESSIVE STRENGTH):

p_c, q_u, c_o FL^{-2}

The load per unit area at which an unconfined cylindrical specimen of soil or rock will fail in a simple compression test. Commonly, the failure load is the maximum that the specimen can withstand in the test.

CONCENTRATION FACTOR:

n D

A parameter used in modifying the Boussinesq equations to describe various distributions of vertical stress.

CONSISTENCY:

The relative ease with which a soil can be deformed.

CONSISTENCY INDEX:

See Relative Consistency.

CONSOLIDATED DRAINED TEST (SLOW TEST):

A soil test in which essentially complete consolidation under the confining pressure is followed by additional axial (or shear) stress applied in such a manner that even a fully saturated soil of low permeability can adapt itself completely (fully consolidate) to the changes in stress due to the additional axial (or shear) stress.

CONSOLIDATED UNDRAINED TEST (CONSOLIDATED QUICK TEST):

A test in which complete consolidation under the vertical load (in a direct shear test) or under the confining pressure (in a triaxial test) is followed by a shear at constant moisture content.

CONSOLIDATION:

The gradual reduction in volume of a soil mass resulting from an increase in compressive stress.

INITIAL CONSOLIDATION (INITIAL COMPRESSION):

A comparatively sudden reduction in volume of a soil mass under an applied load due principally to expulsion and compression of gas in the soil voids preceding primary consolidation.

PRIMARY CONSOLIDATION (PRIMARY COMPRESSION) (PRIMARY TIME EFFECT):

The reduction in volume of a soil mass caused by the application of a sustained load to the mass and due principally to a squeezing out of water from the void spaces of the mass and accompanied by a transfer of the load from the soil water to the soil solids.

SECONDARY CONSOLIDATION (SECONDARY COMPRESSION) (SECONDARY TIME EFFECT):

The reduction in volume of a soil mass caused by the application of a sustained load to the mass and due principally to the adjustment of the internal structure of the soil mass after most of the load has been transferred from the soil water to the soil solids.

CONSOLIDATION RATIO:

U_z D

The ratio of (1) the amount of consolidation at a given distance from a drainage surface and at a given time to (2) the total amount of consolidation obtainable at that point under a given stress increment.

CONSOLIDATION TEST:

A test in which the specimen is laterally confined in a ring and is compressed between porous plates.

CONSOLIDATION-TIME CURVE (TIME CURVE) (CONSOLIDATION CURVE) (THEORETICAL TIME CURVE):

A curve that shows the relation between (1) the degree of consolidation and (2) the elapsed time after the application of a given increment of load.

CREEP:

Slow movement of rock debris or soil usually imperceptible except to observations of long duration. Time-dependent strain or deformation, for example, continuing strain with sustained stress.

CRITICAL CIRCLE (CRITICAL SURFACE):

The sliding surface assumed in a theoretical analysis of a soil mass for which the factor of safety is a minimum.

CRITICAL DENSITY:

The density of a saturated granular material below which it will lose strength and above which it will gain strength when subjected to rapid deformation. The critical density of a given material is dependent on many factors.

CRITICAL HEIGHT:

H_c L

The maximum height at which a vertical or sloped bank of soil will stand unsupported under a given set of conditions.

CRITICAL SLOPE:

The maximum angle with the horizontal at which a sloped bank of soil or rock of given height will stand unsupported.

DEFLOCCULATING AGENT (DEFLOCCULANT) (DISPERSING AGENT):

An agent that prevents fine soil particles in suspension from coalescing to form flocs.

DEFORMATION:

Change in shape or size.

DEGREE OF CONSOLIDATION (PERCENT CONSOLIDATION):

U D

The ratio, expressed as percentage, of (1) the amount of consolidation at a given time within a soil mass, to (2) the total amount of consolidation obtainable under a given stress condition.

DENSITY:

ρ ML^{-3}

Mass per unit volume.

(See Unit Weight)

NOTE.—Although it is recognized that density is defined as mass per unit volume, in the field of soil mechanics the term is frequently used in place of unit weight.

DEVIATOR STRESS:

Δ, σ, σ_1-σ_3 FL^{-2}

The difference between the major and minor principal stresses in a triaxial test.

DILATANCY:

The expansion of cohesionless soils when subject to shear deformation.

DIRECT SHEAR TEST:

A shear test in which soil or rock under an applied normal load is stressed to failure by moving one section of the soil container (shear box) relative to the other section.

DISCHARGE VELOCITY:

v LT^{-1}

Rate of discharge of water through a porous medium per unit of total area perpendicular to the direction of flow.

DRAWDOWN:

L

Vertical distance the free water elevation is lowered or the reduction of the pressure head due to the removal of free water.

EARTH PRESSURE:

Unit: p FL^{-2}

Total: P F or FL^{-1}

The pressure or force exerted by soil on any boundary.

ACTIVE EARTH PRESSURE:

P_A, p_A

The minimum value of earth pressure. This condition exists when a soil mass is permitted to yield sufficiently to cause its internal shear resistance along a potential failure surface to be completely mobilized.

EARTH PRESSURE AT REST:

P_o, p_o

The value of the earth pressure when the soil mass is in its natural state without having been permitted to yield or without having been compressed.

PASSIVE EARTH PRESSURE:

P_P, p_P

The maximum value of earth pressure. This condition exists when a soil mass is compressed sufficiently to cause its internal shear resistance along a potential failure surface to be completely mobilized.

EFFECTIVE DIAMETER (EFFECTIVE SIZE):

D_{10}, D_e L

Particle diameter corresponding to 10 percent finer on the grain-size curve.

EFFECTIVE FORCE:

$\bar{F}$ F

The force transmitted through a soil or rock mass by intergranular pressures.

EFFECTIVE POROSITY (EFFECTIVE DRAINAGE POROSITY):

n_e D

The ratio of (1) the volume of the voids of a soil or rock mass that can be drained by gravity to (2) the total volume of the mass.

ELASTIC STATE OF EQUILIBRIUM:

State of stress within a soil mass when the internal resistance of the mass is not fully mobilized.

EQUIPOTENTIAL LINE:

See Piezometric Line.

EQUIVALENT DIAMETER (EQUIVALENT SIZE):

D L

The diameter of a hypothetical sphere composed of material having the same specific gravity as that of the actual soil particle and of such size that it will settle in a given liquid at the same terminal velocity as the actual soil particle.

EQUIVALENT FLUID:

A hypothetical fluid having a unit weight such that it will produce a pressure against a lateral support presumed to be equivalent to that produced by the actual soil. This simplified approach is valid only when deformation conditions are such that the pressure increases linearly with depth and the wall friction is neglected.

EXCHANGE CAPACITY:

The capacity to exchange ions as measured by the quantity of exchangeable ions in a soil or rock mass.

FILL:

Manmade deposits of natural soils or rock products and waste materials.

FILTER (PROTECTIVE FILTER):

A layer or combination of layers of pervious materials designed and installed in such a manner as to provide drainage, yet prevent the movement of soil particles due to flowing water.

FINES:
Portion of soil finer than a No. 200 United States standard sieve.

FLOC:
Loose, open-structured mass formed in a suspension by the aggregation of minute particles.

FLOCCULATION:
The process of forming flocs.

FLOW CHANNEL:
The portion of a flow net bounded by two adjacent flow lines.

FLOW CURVE:
The locus of points obtained from a standard liquid limit test and plotted on a graph representing moisture content as ordinate on an arithmetic scale and the number of blows as abscissa on a logarithmic scale.

FLOW FAILURE:
Failure in which a soil mass moves over relatively long distances in a fluidlike manner.

FLOW INDEX
F_w, I_f D
The slope of the flow curve obtained from a liquid limit test, expressed as the difference in moisture contents at 10 and 100 blows.

FLOW LINE:
The path that a particle of water follows in its course of seepage under laminar flow conditions.

FLOW NET:
A graphical representation of flow lines and equipotential (piezometric) lines used in the study of seepage phenomena.

FLOW SLIDE:
The failure of a sloped bank of soil in which the movement of the soil mass does not take place along a well-defined surface of sliding.

FLOW VALUE:
N_ϕ D
A quantity equal to $\tan^2\left(45^\circ + \frac{\phi}{2}\right)$

FOOTING:
Portion of the foundation of a structure that transmits loads directly to the soil.

FOUNDATION:
Lower part of a structure that transmits the load to the soil or rock.

FOUNDATION SOIL:
Upper part of the earth mass carrying the load of the structure.

FREE WATER (GRAVITATIONAL WATER) (GROUND WATER) (PHREATIC WATER):
Water that is free to move through a soil or rock mass under the influence of gravity.

FREE WATER ELEVATION (WATER TABLE) (GROUND-WATER SURFACE) (FREE WATER SURFACE) GROUND-WATER ELEVATION):
Elevations at which the pressure in the water is zero with respect to the atmospheric pressure.

FROST ACTION:
Freezing and thawing of moisture in materials and the resultant effects on these materials and on structures of which they are a part or with which they are in contact.

FROST BOIL:
(1) Softening of soil occurring during a thawing period due to the liberation of water from ice lenses or layers.
(2) The hole formed in flexible pavements by the extrusion of soft soil and melt waters under the action of wheel loads.
(3) Breaking of a highway or airfield pavement under traffic and the ejection of subgrade soil in a soft and soupy condition caused by the melting of ice lenses formed by frost action.

FROST HEAVE:
The raising of a surface due to the accumulation of ice in the underlying soil or rock.

GLACIAL TILL (TILL):
Material deposited by glaciation, usually composed of a wide range of particle sizes, which has not been subjected to the sorting action of water.

GRADATION (GRAIN SIZE DISTRIBUTION) (TEXTURE):

The proportions by mass of a soil or fragmented rock distributed in specified particle-size ranges.

GRAIN SIZE ANALYSIS (MECHANICAL ANALYSIS) (PARTICLE-SIZE ANALYSIS):

The process of determining grain-size distribution.

GRAVEL:

Particles of rock that will pass a 3-inch sieve and be retained on a No. 4 U.S. Standard sieve.[3]

HARDPAN:

A hard impervious layer, composed chiefly of clay, cemented by relatively insoluble materials, that does not become plastic when mixed with water and definitely limits the downward movement of water and roots.

HEAVE:

Upward movement of soil caused by expansion or displacement resulting from phenomena such as moisture absorption, removal of overburden, driving of piles, frost action, and loading of an adjacent area.

HOMOGENEOUS MASS:

A mass that exhibits essentially the same physical properties at every point throughout the mass.

HORIZON (SOIL HORIZON):

One of the layers of the soil profile, distinguished principally by its texture, color, structure, and chemical content.

A HORIZON:

The uppermost layer of a soil profile from which inorganic colloids and other soluble materials have been leached. Usually contains remnants of organic life.

B HORIZON:

The layer of a soil profile in which material leached from the overlying A horizon is accumulated.

C HORIZON:

Undisturbed parent material from which the overlying soil profile has been developed.

[3]New definition from ASTM D 2487.

HUMUS:

A brown or black material formed by the partial decomposition of vegetable or animal matter; the organic portion of soil.

HYDRAULIC GRADIENT:

i, s D

The loss of hydraulic head per unit distance of flow, $\frac{dh}{dL}$

CRITICAL HYDRAULIC GRADIENT:

i_c D

Hydraulic gradient at which the intergranular pressure in a mass of cohesionless soil is reduced to zero by the upward flow of water.

HYDROSTATIC PRESSURE:

u_o FL^{-2}

A state of stress in which all the principal stresses are equal (and there is no shear stress), as in a liquid at rest; the product of the unit weight of the liquid and the difference in elevation between the given point and the free water elevation.

EXCESS HYDROSTATIC PRESSURE (HYDROSTATIC EXCESS PRESSURE):

$\bar{u}$, u FL^{-2}

The pressure that exists in pore water in excess of the hydrostatic pressure.

HYGROSCOPIC CAPACITY (HYGROSCOPIC COEFFICIENT):

w_e D

Ratio of (1) the mass of water absorbed by a dry soil or rock in a saturated atmosphere at a given temperature to (2) the mass of the oven-dried soil or rock.

HYGROSCOPIC WATER CONTENT:

w_H D

The moisture content of an air-dried soil or rock.

INTERNAL FRICTION (SHEAR RESISTANCE):

FL^{-2}

The portion of the shearing strength of a soil or rock indicated by the terms $\bar{\sigma} \tan \phi$ in Coulomb's equation $s = c + \bar{\sigma} \tan \phi$. It is usually considered to be due to the interlocking of the soil or rock grains and the resistance to sliding between the grains.

ISOCHROME:
A curve showing the distribution of the excess hydrostatic pressure at a given time during a process of consolidation.

ISOTROPIC MASS:
A mass having the same property (or properties) in all directions.

KAOLIN:
A variety of clay containing a high percentage of kaolinite.

LAMINAR FLOW (STREAMLINE FLOW) (VISCOUS FLOW):
Flow in which the head loss is proportional to the first power of the velocity.

LANDSLIDE (SLIDE):
The failure of a sloped bank of soil or rock in which the movement of the mass takes place along a surface of sliding.

LEACHING:
The removal of soluble soil material and colloids by percolating water.

LINE OF CREEP (PATH OF PERCOLATION):
The path that water follows along the surface of contact between the foundation soil and the base of a dam or other structure.

LINE OF SEEPAGE (SEEPAGE LINE) (PHREATIC LINE):
The upper free water surface of the zone of seepage.

LINEAR EXPANSION:
L_E D
The increase in one dimension of a soil mass, expressed as a percentage of that dimension at the shrinkage limit, when the moisture content is increased from the shrinkage limit to any given moisture content.

LINEAR SHRINKAGE:
L_S D
Decrease in one dimension of a soil mass, expressed as a percentage of the original dimension, when the moisture content is reduced from a given value to the shrinkage limit.

LIQUEFACTION (SPONTANEOUS LIQUEFACTION):
The sudden large decrease of the shearing resistance of a cohesionless soil. It is caused by a collapse of the structure by shock or other type of strain and is associated with a sudden but temporary increase of the pore-filled pressure. It involves a temporary transformation of the material into a fluid mass.

LIQUID LIMIT:
LL, L_w, w_L D
(1) The moisture content corresponding to the arbitrary limit between the liquid and plastic states of consistency of a soil.
(2) The moisture content at which a pat of soil, cut by a groove of standard dimensions, will flow together for a distance of 1/2 inch under the impact of 25 blows in a standard liquid limit apparatus.

LIQUIDITY INDEX (WATER PLASTICITY RATIO) (RELATIVE WATER CONTENT):
B, R_w, I_L D
The ratio, expressed as a percentage, of (1) the natural moisture content of a soil minus its plastic limit to (2) its plasticity index.

LOAM:
A mixture of sand, silt, or clay, or a combination of any of these, with organic matter (see Humus). It is sometimes called topsoil in contrast to the subsoils that contain little or no organic matter.

LOESS:
A uniform aeolian deposit of silty material having an open structure and relatively high cohesion due to cementation of clay or calcareous material at grain contacts. A characteristic of loess deposits is that they can stand with nearly vertical slopes.

MODULUS OF ELASTICITY (MODULUS OF DEFORMATION):
E, M FL^{-2}
The ratio of stress to strain for a material under given loading conditions; numerically equal to the slope of the tangent or the secant of a stress-strain curve. The use of the term Modulus of Elasticity is recommended for materials that deform in accordance with Hooke's law; the term Modulus of Deformation for materials that deform otherwise.

MOHR CIRCLE:

A graphical representation of the stresses acting on the various planes at a given point.

MOHR ENVELOPE (RUPTURE ENVELOPE) (RUPTURE LINE):

The envelope of a series of Mohr circles representing stress conditions at failure for a given material. According to Mohr's rupture hypothesis, a rupture envelope is the locus of points, the coordinates of which represent the combinations of normal and shear stresses that will cause a given material to fail.

MOISTURE CONTENT (WATER CONTENT):

w D

The ratio, expressed as a percentage of (1) the mass of water in a given soil mass to (2) the mass of solid particles.

MOISTURE EQUIVALENT:

CENTRIFUGE MOISTURE EQUIVALENT:

W_c, *CME* D

The moisture content of a soil after it has been saturated with water and then subjected for one hour to a force equal to 1,000 times that of gravity.

FIELD MOISTURE EQUIVALENT:

FME

The minimum moisture content, expressed as a percentage of the mass of the oven-dried soil, at which a drop of water placed on a smoothed surface of the soil will not immediately be absorbed by the soil but will spread out over the surface and give it a shiny appearance.

MUCK:

Stone, dirt, debris, or useless material; or an organic soil of very soft consistency.

MUD:

A mixture of soil and water in a fluid or weakly solid state.

MUSKEG:

Level, practically treeless areas supporting dense growth consisting primarily of grasses. The surface of the soil is covered with a layer of partially decayed grass and grass roots which is usually wet and soft when not frozen.

NORMALLY CONSOLIDATED SOIL DEPOSIT:

A soil deposit that has never been subjected to a pressure greater than the existing overburden pressure.

OPTIMUM MOISTURE CONTENT (OPTIMUM WATER CONTENT):

OMC, W_o D

The moisture content at which a soil can be compacted to the maximum dry unit weight by a given compactive effort.

ORGANIC CLAY:

A clay with sufficient organic content to influence the soil properties.[4]

ORGANIC SILT:

A silt with sufficient organic content to influence the soil properties.[4]

ORGANIC SOIL:

Soil with a high organic content. In general, organic soils are very compressible and have poor load-sustaining properties.

OVERCONSOLIDATED SOIL DEPOSIT:

A soil deposit that has been subjected to pressure greater than the present overburden pressure.

PARENT MATERIAL:

Material from which a soil has been derived.

PEAT:

A soil composed of vegetable tissue in various stages of decomposition with an organic odor, a dark brown to black color, a spongy consistency, and a texture ranging from fibrous to amorphous.[4]

PENETRATION RESISTANCE (STANDARD PENETRATION RESISTANCE) (PROCTOR PENETRATION RESISTANCE):

p_R, N FL^{-2} or blows L^{-1}

(1) Number of blows of a hammer of specified mass falling a given distance required to produce a

[4]New definition from ASTM D 2487.

given penetration into soil of a pile, casing, or sampling tube.

(2) Unit load required to maintain constant rate of penetration into soil of a probe or instrument.

(3) Unit load required to produce a specified penetration into soil at a specified rate of a probe or instrument. For a Proctor needle, the specified penetration is 2.5 inches and the rate is 0.5 in/s.

PENETRATION RESISTANCE CURVE (PROCTOR PENETRATION CURVE):

The curve showing the relationship between (1) the penetration resistance and (2) the moisture content.

PERCENT COMPACTION:

The ratio, expressed as a percentage, of (1) dry unit weight of a soil to (2) maximum unit weight obtained in a laboratory compaction test.

PERCENT SATURATION (DEGREE OF SATURATION):

S_r D

The ratio, expressed as a percentage of (1) the volume of water in a given soil or rock mass to (2) the total volume of intergranular space (voids).

PERCHED WATER TABLE:

A water table usually of limited area maintained above the normal free water elevation by the presence of an intervening relatively impervious confining stratum.

PERCOLATION:

The movement of gravitational water through soil. (see Seepage.)

PERMAFROST:

Perennially frozen soil.

pH

pH D

An index of the acidity or alkalinity of a soil in terms of the logarithm of the reciprocal of the hydrogen ion concentration.

PIEZOMETER:

An instrument for measuring pressure head.

PIEZOMETRIC LINE (EQUIPOTENTIAL LINE):

A line along which water will rise to the same elevation in piezometric tubes.

PIEZOMETRIC SURFACE:

The surface at which water will stand in a series of piezometers.

PILE:

Relatively slender structural element which is driven, or otherwise introduced, into the soil, usually for the purpose of providing vertical or lateral support.

PIPING:

The progressive removal of soil particles from a mass by percolating water leading to the development of channels.

PLASTIC EQUILIBRIUM:

State of stress within a soil or rock mass, or a portion thereof, which has been deformed to such an extent that its ultimate shear resistance is mobilized.

ACTIVE STATE OF PLASTIC EQUILIBRIUM:

Plastic equilibrium obtained by an expansion of a mass.

PASSIVE STATE OF PLASTIC EQUILIBRIUM:

Plastic equilibrium obtained by a compression of a mass.

PLASTIC FLOW (PLASTIC DEFORMATION):

The deformation of a plastic material beyond the point of recovery, accompanied by continuing deformation with no further increase in stress.

PLASTICITY:

The property of a soil or rock which allows it to be deformed beyond the point of recovery without cracking or appreciable volume change.

PLASTICITY INDEX:

I_p, PI, I_w D

Numerical difference between the liquid limit and the plastic limit.

PLASTIC LIMIT:

w_p, PL, P_w D

(1) The moisture content corresponding to an arbitrary limit between the plastic and the semisolid state of consistency of a soil.

(2) Moisture content at which a soil will just begin to crumble when rolled into a thread about 1/8 inch in diameter.

PLASTIC SOIL:
A soil that exhibits plasticity.

PLASTIC STATE (PLASTIC RANGE):
The range of consistency within which a soil or rock exhibits plastic properties.

PORE PRESSURE (PORE FLUID PRESSURE):
See Neutral Stress under Stress.

POROSITY:
n D
The ratio, usually expressed as a percentage, of (1) the volume of voids of a given soil mass to (2) the total volume of the soil mass.

POTENTIAL DROP:
Δh L
The difference in total head between two equipotential lines.

PRECONSOLIDATION PRESSURE (PRESTRESS):
p_c FL^{-2}
The greatest pressure to which a soil has been subjected.

PRESSURE:
p FL^{-2}
The load divided by the area over which it acts.

PRESSURE BULB:
The zone in a loaded soil or rock mass bounded by an arbitrarily selected isobar of stress.

PRESSURE—VOID RATIO CURVE (COMPRESSION CURVE):
A curve representing the relationship between effective pressure and void ratio of a soil as obtained from a consolidation test. The curve has a characteristic shape when plotted on a semilog paper with pressure on the log scale. The various parts of the curve and extensions to the parts have been designated as recompression, compression, virgin compression, expansion, rebound, and other descriptive names by various authorities.

PRINCIPAL PLANE:
Each of three mutually perpendicular planes through a point in a soil mass on which the shearing stress is zero.
INTERMEDIATE PRINCIPAL PLANE:
The plane normal to the direction of the intermediate principal stress.
MAJOR PRINCIPAL PLANE:
The plane normal to the direction of the major principal stress.
MINOR PRINCIPAL PLANE:
The plane normal to the direction of the minor principal stress.

PROCTOR COMPACTION CURVE:
See Compaction Curve.

PROCTOR PENETRATION CURVE:
See Penetration Resistance Curve.

PROCTOR PENETRATION RESISTANCE:
See Penetration Resistance.

PROGRESSIVE FAILURE:
Failure in which the ultimate shearing resistance is progressively mobilized along the failure surface.

QUICK CONDITION (QUICKSAND):
Condition in which water is flowing upward with sufficient velocity to reduce significantly the bearing capacity of the soil through a decrease in intergranular pressure.

QUICK TEST:
See Unconsolidated Undrained Test.

RADIUS OF INFLUENCE OF A WELL:
Distance from the center of the well to the closest point at which the piezometric surface is not lowered when pumping has produced the maximum steady rate of flow.

RELATIVE CONSISTENCY:
I_c, C_r D
Ratio of (1) the liquid limit minus the natural moisture content to (2) the plasticity index.

RELATIVE DENSITY:
D_d, I_D D
The ratio of (1) the difference between the void ratio of a cohesionless soil in the loosest state and

any given void ratio to (2) the difference between its void ratios in the loosest and in the densest states.

REMOLDED SOIL:
Soil that has had its natural structure modified by manipulation.

REMOLDING INDEX:
I_R D
The ratio of (1) the modulus of deformation of a soil in the undisturbed state to (2) the modulus of deformation of the soil in the remolded state.

REMOLDING SENSITIVITY (SENSITIVITY RATIO):
S_t D
The ratio of (1) the unconfined compressive strength of an undisturbed specimen of soil to (2) the unconfined compressive strength of a specimen of the same soil after remolding at unaltered moisture content.

RESIDUAL SOIL:
Soil derived inplace by weathering of the underlying material.

ROCK:
Natural solid mineral matter occurring in large masses of fragments.

ROCK FLOUR:
See Silt.

SAND:
Particles of rock that will pass a No. 4 United States standard sieve and be retained on a No. 200 sieve.

SAND BOIL:
The ejection of sand and water resulting from piping.

SEEPAGE (PERCOLATION):
The slow movement of gravitational water through the soil or rock.

SEEPAGE FORCE:
J F
The force transmitted to the soil or rock grains by seepage.

SEEPAGE VELOCITY:
v_s, v_l LT^{-1}
The rate of discharge of seepage water through a porous medium per unit area of void space perpendicular to the direction of flow.

SENSITIVITY:
The effect of remolding on the consistency of a cohesive soil.

SHAKING TEST:
A test used to indicate the presence of significant amounts of rock flour, silt, or very fine sand in a fine-grained soil. It consists of shaking a pat of wet soil, having a consistency of thick paste, in the palm of the hand; observing the surface for a glossy or livery appearance; then squeezing the pat; and observing if a rapid apparent drying and subsequent cracking of the soil occurs.

SHEAR FAILURE (FAILURE BY RUPTURE):
Failure in which movement caused by shearing stresses in a soil or rock mass is of sufficient magnitude to destroy or seriously endanger a structure.

GENERAL SHEAR FAILURE:
Failure in which the ultimate strength of the soil or rock is mobilized along the entire potential surface of sliding before the structure supported by the soil or rock is impaired by excessive movement.

LOCAL SHEAR FAILURE:
Failure in which the ultimate shearing strength of the soil or rock is mobilized only locally along the potential surface of sliding at the time the structure supported by the soil is impaired by excessive movement.

SHEAR STRENGTH:
s, T_f FL^{-2}
The maximum resistance of a soil or rock to shearing stresses.

SHEAR STRESS (SHEARING STRESS) (TANGENTIAL STRESS):
See Stress.

SHRINKAGE INDEX:
SI D
The numerical difference between the plastic and shrinkage limits.

SHRINKAGE LIMIT:
SL, w_s D
The maximum moisture content at which a reduction in moisture content will not cause a decrease in volume of the soil mass.

SHRINKAGE RATIO:
R D
The ratio of (1) a given volume change, expressed as a percentage of the dry volume, to (2) the corresponding change in moisture content above the shrinkage limit, expressed as a percentage of the weight of the oven-dried soil.

SILT (INORGANIC SILT) (ROCK FLOUR):
Material passing a No. 200 United States standard sieve that is nonplastic or very slightly plastic and that exhibits little or no strength when air-dried.

SILT SIZE:
That portion of the soil finer than 0.02 mm and coarser than 0.002 mm (0.05 and 0.005 mm in some cases).

SKIN FRICTION:
f FL_{-2}
The frictional resistance developed between soil and an element of a structure.

SLAKING:
The process of breaking up or sloughing when an indurated soil is immersed in water.

SLOW TEST:
See Consolidated-Drained Test.

SOIL (EARTH):
Sediments or other unconsolidated accumulations of solid particles produced by the physical and chemical disintegration of rocks, and which may or may not contain organic matter.

SOIL CEMENT:
A tightly compacted mixture of pulverized soil, portland cement, and water that, as the cement hydrates, forms a hard, durable, low-cost paving material.

SOIL MECHANICS:
The application of the laws and principles of mechanics and hydraulics to engineering problems dealing with soil as an engineering material.

SOIL PHYSICS:
The organized body of knowledge concerned with the physical characteristics of soil and with the methods employed in their determinations.

SOIL PROFILE (PROFILE):
Vertical section of a soil, showing the nature and sequence of the various layers, as developed by deposition or weathering, or both.

SOIL STABILIZATION:
Chemical or mechanical treatment designed to increase or maintain the stability of a mass of soil or otherwise to improve its engineering properties.

SOIL STRUCTURE:
The arrangement and state of aggregation of soil particles in a soil mass.

FLOCCULENT STRUCTURE:
An arrangement composed of flocs of soil particles instead of individual soil particles.

HONEYCOMB STRUCTURE:
An arrangement of soil particles having a comparatively loose, stable structure resembling a honeycomb.

SINGLE-GRAINED STRUCTURE:
An arrangement composed of individual soil particles; characteristic structure of coarse-grained soils.

SOIL SUSPENSION:
Highly diffused mixture of soil and water.

SOIL TEXTURE:
See Gradation.

SPECIFIC GRAVITY:

SPECIFIC GRAVITY OF SOLIDS:
G, G_s, S_s D
Ratio of (1) the mass in air of a given volume of solids at a stated temperature to (2) the mass in air of an equal volume of distilled water at a stated temperature.

APPARENT SPECIFIC GRAVITY:
G_a, S_a D
Ratio of (1) the mass in air of a given volume of the impermeable portion of a permeable material (that is the solid matter including its impermeable pores or voids) at a stated temperature to (2) the mass in air of an equal volume of distilled water at a stated temperature.

BULK SPECIFIC GRAVITY (SPECIFIC MASS GRAVITY):

G_m, S_m D

Ratio of (1) the mass in air of a given volume of a permeable material (including both permeable and impermeable voids normal to the material) at a stated temperature to (2) the mass in air of an equal volume of distilled water at a stated temperature.

SPECIFIC SURFACE:

L^{-1}

The surface area per unit of volume of soil particles.

STABILITY FACTOR (STABILITY NUMBER):

N_s D

A pure number used in the analysis of the stability of a soil embankment, as defined by the following equation:

$$N_s = \frac{H_c \cdot \gamma_e}{c}$$

where: H_c = critical height of the sloped bank,
γ_e = the effective unit weight of the soil, and
c = the cohesion of the soil.

Note.—Taylor's stability number is the reciprocal of Terzaghi's stability factor.

STICKY LIMIT:

T_w D

The lowest moisture content at which a soil will stick to a metal blade drawn across the surface of the soil mass.

STRAIN:

ε D

The change in length per unit of length in a given direction.

STRESS:

σ, p, f FL^{-2}

The force per unit area acting within the soil mass.

EFFECTIVE STRESS (EFFECTIVE PRESSURE) (INTERGRANULAR PRESSURE):

$\bar{\sigma}$, $\bar{f}$ FL^{-2}

The average normal force per unit area transmitted from grain to grain of a soil mass. It is the stress that is effective in mobilizing internal friction.

NEUTRAL STRESS (PORE PRESSURE) (PORE WATER PRESSURE):

u, u_w FL^{-2}

Stress transmitted through the pore water (water filling the voids of the soil).

NORMAL STRESS:

σ, p FL^{-2}

The stress component normal to a given plane.

PRINCIPAL STRESS:

σ_1, σ_2, σ_3 FL^{-2}

Stress acting normal to three mutually perpendicular planes intersecting at a point in a body on which the shear stress is zero.

MAJOR PRINCIPAL STRESS:

σ_1 FL^{-2}

The largest (with regard to sign) principal stress.

MINOR PRINCIPAL STRESS:

σ_3 FL^{-2}

The smallest (with regard to sign) principal stress.

INTERMEDIATE PRINCIPAL STRESS:

σ_2 FL^{-2}

The principal stress whose value is neither the largest nor the smallest (with regard to sign) of the three.

SHEAR STRESS (SHEARING STRESS) (TANGENTIAL STRESS):

τ, s FL^{-2}

The stress component tangential to a given plane.

TOTAL STRESS:

σ, f FL^{-2}

The total force per unit area acting within a mass of soil. It is the sum of the neutral and effective stresses.

SUBBASE:

A layer used in a pavement system between the subgrade and base course, or between the subgrade and portland-concrete pavement.

SUBGRADE:

The soil prepared and compacted to support a structure or a pavement system.

SUBGRADE SURFACE:

The surface of the earth or rock prepared to support a structure or a pavement system.

SUBSOIL:

(1) Soil below a subgrade or fill.

(2) That part of a soil profile occurring below the A horizon.

TALUS:

Rock fragments mixed with soil at the foot of a natural slope from which they have been separated.

THIXOTROPHY:

The property of a material that enables it to stiffen in a relatively short time on standing but, upon agitation or manipulation, to change to a very soft consistency or to a fluid of high viscosity, the process being completely reversible.

TILL:

See Glacial Till.

TIME FACTOR:

T_r, T D

Dimensionless factor, utilized in the theory of consolidation, containing the physical constants of a soil stratum influencing its time-rate of consolidation, expressed as follows:

$$T = \frac{k(1+e)t}{a_v \gamma_w \cdot H^2} = \frac{c_v t}{H^2}$$

where: k = coefficient of permeability (LT^{-1}),
e = void ratio (dimensionless),
t = elapsed time that the stratum has been consolidated (T),
a_v = coefficient of compressibility (L^2F^{-1}),
γ_w = unit of weight of water (FL^{-3}),
H = thickness of stratum drained on one side only, if stratum is drained on both sides, its thickness equals $2H$ (L), and
c_v = coefficient of consolidation (L^2T^{-1}).

TOPSOIL:

Surface soil usually containing organic matter.

TORSIONAL SHEAR TEST:

A shear test in which a relatively thin test specimen of solid circular or annular cross section, usually confined between rings, is subjected to an axial load and to shear in torsion. Inplace torsion shear tests may be performed by pressing a dentated solid circular or annular plate against the soil and measuring its resistance to rotation under a given axial load

TOUGHNESS INDEX:

I_T, T_w

The ratio of (1) the plasticity index to (2) the flow index.

TRANSFORMED FLOW NET:

A flow net whose boundaries have been properly modified (transformed) so that a net consisting of curvilinear squares can be constructed to represent flow conditions in an anisotropic porous medium.

TRANSPORTED SOIL:

Soil transported from the place of its origin by wind, water, or ice.

TRIAXIAL SHEAR TEST (TRIAXIAL COMPRESSION TEST):

A test in which a cylindrical specimen of soil or rock encased in an impervious membrane is subjected to a confining pressure and then loaded axially to failure.

TURBULENT FLOW:

That type of flow in which any water particle may move in any direction with respect to any other particle, and in which the head loss is approximately proportional to the second power of the velocity.

ULTIMATE BEARING CAPACITY:

q_o, q_{ult} FL^{-2}

The average load per unit of area required to produce failure by rupture of a supporting soil or rock mass.

UNCONFINED COMPRESSIVE STRENGTH:

See Compressive Strength.

UNCONSOLIDATED-UNDRAINED TEST (QUICK TEST):

A soil test in which the moisture content of the test specimen remains practically unchanged during the application of the confining pressure and the additional axial (or shearing) force.

UNDERCONSOLIDATED SOIL DEPOSIT:

A deposit that is not fully consolidated under the existing overburden pressure.

UNDISTURBED SAMPLE:

A soil sample that has been obtained by methods in which every precaution has been taken to minimize disturbance to the sample.

UNIT WEIGHT:

γ FL^{-3}

Weight per unit volume.

DRY UNIT WEIGHT (UNIT DRY WEIGHT):

γ_d, γ_0 FL^{-3}

The weight of soil or rock solids per unit of total volume of soil mass.

EFFECTIVE UNIT WEIGHT:

γ_e FL^{-3}

That unit weight of a soil or rock which, when multiplied by the height of the overlying column of soil or rock, yields the effective pressure due to the weight of the overburden.

MAXIMUM UNIT WEIGHT:

γ_{max} FL^{-3}

The dry unit weight defined by the peak of a compaction curve.

SATURATED UNIT WEIGHT:

γ_G, γ_{sat} FL^{-3}

The wet unit weight of a soil mass when saturated.

SUBMERGED UNIT WEIGHT (BUOYANT UNIT WEIGHT):

γ_m, γ', γ_{sub} FL^{-3}

The weight of the solids in air minus the weight of water displaced by the solids per unit of volume of soil or rock mass; the saturated unit weight minus the unit weight of water.

UNIT WEIGHT OF WATER:

γ_w FL^{-3}

The weight per unit volume of water; nominally equal to 62.4 lbf/ft^3 or 9.807 kN/m^3.

WET UNIT WEIGHT (MASS UNIT WEIGHT):

γ_m, γ_{wet} FL^{-3}

The weight (solids plus water) per unit of total volume of soil or rock mass, irrespective of the degree of saturation.

ZERO AIR VOIDS UNIT WEIGHT:

γ_z FL^{-3}

The weight of solids per unit volume of a saturated soil mass.

UPLIFT:

Unit: u FL^{-2}

Total: U F or FL^{-1}

The upward water pressure on a structure.

VANE SHEAR TEST:

An inplace shear test in which a rod with thin radial vanes at the end is forced into the soil and the resistance to rotation of the rod is determined.

VARVED CLAY:

Alternating thin layers of silt (or fine sand) and clay formed by variations in sedimentation during the various seasons of the year, often exhibiting contrasting colors when partially dried.

VOID:

Space in a soil or rock mass not occupied by solid mineral matter. This space may be occupied by air, water, or other gaseous or liquid material.

VOID RATIO:

e D

The ratio of (1) the volume of void space to (2) the volume of solid particles in a given soil mass.

CRITICAL VOID RATIO:

e_c D

The void ratio corresponding to the critical density.

VOLUMETRIC SHRINKAGE (VOLUMETRIC CHANGE):

V_s D

The decrease in volume, expressed as a percentage of the soil mass when dried, of a soil mass when the moisture content is reduced from a given percentage to the shrinkage limit.

WALL FRICTION:

f' FL^{-2}

Frictional resistance mobilized between a wall and the soil or rock in contact with the wall.

WATER CONTENT:

See Moisture Content.

WATER-HOLDING CAPACITY:

D

The smallest value to which the moisture content of a soil can be reduced by gravity drainage.

ZERO AIR VOIDS CURVE (SATURATION CURVE):

The curve showing the zero air voids unit weight as a function of moisture content.

ZERO AIR VOIDS DENSITY (ZERO AIR VOIDS UNIT WEIGHT):

See Unit Weight.

Construction of Embankments

E.1. ***General.***—The need to control the construction of embankments that impound water has been recognized for many years. In 1932, Justin [1][1] wrote:

> "An entirely safe and substantial design may be entirely ruined by careless and shoddy execution, and the f ilure of the structure may very possibly be the result. Careful attention to the details of construction is, therefore, fully as important as the investigation and design."

The consequences of ignoring construction control are exemplified by the large number of earthfill dams built in the United States during the first quarter of this century that did not survive the first filling of the reservoir. Records show that most of these dams were constructed without moistening the soil and without applying special compactive effort.

The rapid increase in knowledge of soil mechanics since 1925 has resulted in substantial progress toward understanding the factors involved in transforming loose earth into structural material. During this same period, however, the development of large economical earthmoving machines has increased the placing rate of earthfill many times, thereby intensifying the problem of quality control. Successful earthwork depends not only on the application of sound geotechnical design principles, but also on the inspector's insistence on good construction practices in accordance with proper specifications and on the inspector's ability to understand and conscientiously apply sound control techniques.

Construction is controlled by inspection, testing, and reports. The inspector of foundations and earthwork is responsible for ensuring that the work he/she is assigned to cover is performed in compliance with the specifications. To discharge this responsibility efficiently, the inspector should be fully informed of the designs and specifications relating to the work. Fairness, courtesy, firmness, initiative, and good judgement are highly desirable in an inspector. The inspector's diary, containing data on the conditions and progress of the work and records of conversations and instructions given to the contractor, is a valuable document that should be carefully compiled and preserved.

Proper control of earthwork requires the use of laboratory facilities. For small dams these facilities can be portable, or a small field laboratory can be set up near the site. In most cases commercial laboratory facilities can be used. The control procedures recommended in this text will minimize the cost of the control testing needed to ensure a satisfactory job.

Discoveries of remnants of earthfill dams indicate that man's first engineering structures were probably made of earth. The ancient earthfill dams were constructed by armies of workers carrying baskets loaded with soil. Excavation was done manually, and some incidental compaction of the fill was obtained by the tramping feet of the porters. Available records do not indicate that there was any intentional moistening or compacting of soil before the 19th century. The importance of earthfill compaction was first realized in England where, by 1820, cattle and sheep were used for this purpose. By the middle of the 19th century, heavy, smooth rollers made of concrete or metal had been used in Europe and in the United States.

The first sheepsfoot roller, the "Petrolithic" roller, was patented in the United States in 1906, for use in compacting oil-treated road surfacing. The most notable early use of the sheepsfoot roller for compaction of fills started in 1912, in the construction of storage reservoirs by oil companies of

[1] Numbers in brackets refer to entries in the bibliography (sec. E.10).

southern California. The sheepsfoot roller was found to be the only roller that compacted the fill in lifts and gave uniform compaction without producing laminations. Largely because of the development of the automobile and the airplane, which require roadbeds and airport subgrades of great strength, larger and heavier rollers were developed by the construction industry during the first half of the 20th century.

Published material on moisture control for rolled fills dates back to 1907, when Bassell [2], wrote:

> "Too much or too little (water) is equally bad and is to be avoided. It is believed that only by experience is it possible to determine just the proper quantity of water to use with different classes of materials and their varying conditions. In rolling and consolidating of the bank, all portions that have a tendency to quake must be removed at once . . ."

It was not until 1933, that a definite procedure for moisture and compaction control was established. In a series of articles published in 1933, Proctor [3] gave the principles of soil compaction and their application. Figure 5-74 shows the Proctor (or laboratory) compaction curve, which indicates that for a given compactive effort there is one moisture content, called the optimum moisture content, that produces the maximum dry unit weight, or smallest total volume of voids, for a given cohesive soil. Greater compactive efforts on the same soil produce different moisture-unit weight curves whose optimum points occur at smaller moisture contents and at greater unit weights than for lesser compactive efforts.

Figure E-1 shows embankment placing operations at Ridgway Dam. Although Ridgway is not a small dam, the photograph illustrates current placement, spreading, disking, and compaction equipment applicable to any earthfill dam.

E.2. *Soil Mechanics of Compaction.*—The compaction of cohesive soils has definitely been proved to follow the principles stated by Proctor. Although many kinds of compactive effort are used as compaction standards and for compacting cohesive soils, the effect of varying the moisture content on the unit weight of the compacted soil is similar for all methods. Each compactive effort has its own optimum moisture content. The laboratory standard of compaction used by the Bureau (Bureau of Reclamation) has the same intensity of effort as ASTM D 698 (see sec. 5.49(e)). This compaction has been found to approximate the actual field compaction achieved by 12 passes of the 20-ton dual-drum tamping roller, as specified in section G.29, on 8- to 9-inch loose lifts (6-inch compacted lifts). The relation between the moisture-unit weight curve for this roller effort on the fill and the standard laboratory compaction curve varies for different soils, but it is close enough that the standard laboratory curve can be used for control purposes. Figure E-2 shows the average roller curves for three very different soils used in Bureau dams with their respective standard laboratory curves [4].

In compacted cohesive soils, permeability, shear strength, and compressibility are of major concern. It has been shown, both theoretically and experimentally, that an increase in dry unit weight reduces the permeability of a given soil because of the corresponding reduction in the volume of voids in the soil mass. Therefore, to achieve the greatest impermeability, it is desirable to obtain the maximum practicable compaction. Extreme impermeability, however, is not always required in the design and, especially for clays, only moderate compactive effort is needed to ensure impermeability. On the other hand, well-graded sands and gravels and even formation rock, can be made quite impermeable by the crushing and compacting effort of heavy tamping rollers.

The embankment designs given in chapter 6 are based on the angles of internal friction and the cohesion determined by laboratory tests on typical soils. Compaction control attempts to secure a dry unit weight of soil in the fill sufficient to obtain a shear strength comparable with that used in the design. Although the unit weight affects cohesion less than the moisture content does, test data indicate that the angle of internal friction of a soil varies with the unit weight of that soil. The angle of internal friction varies among soils because of differences in mineral composition and differences in the size, shape, and gradation of the soil grains.

For cohesive soils, pore pressures produced by compaction increase rapidly with increase in moisture content in the vicinity of the peak of the compaction curve. Compaction of the soil at moisture contents less than the optimum results in relatively lower pore pressure and subsequently higher unconsolidated undrained shear strength. The reduction of shear strength caused by reduction of unit

Figure E-1.—Embankment placing operations. In impervious fill, sand and gravel chimney drain, and gravel-cobble zones. Ridgway Dam, Dallas Creek Project, Colorado. P894–427–6045 NA.

weight (dry of optimum) is more than compensated for by the increase of shear strength caused by the reduction of pore pressure. Therefore, the maximum undrained shear strength for cohesive soils with respect to a compaction method occurs at a moisture content slightly less than the optimum moisture content.

The compressibility of a soil is the relation between effective stress on the soil skeleton and the volume change. Impermeable soils vary in compressibility, depending on the amount and character of the fines (silts and clays) and according to the amount and gradation of coarse particles (sands and gravels) they contain. For a particular soil at a given moisture content, the greater the unit weight the lower its compressibility will be. The relation between compressibility and development of construction pore-water pressure is such that, for a particular air and moisture content, the pore pressure increases rapidly with an increase in compressibility. In general, a very compressible cohesive soil will develop high pore pressures when loaded, unless there is an appreciable amount of air in the compacted soil. The most efficient means of keeping air in the soil and still having a fairly high unit weight is to compact the soil at a moisture content slightly less than optimum. However, this must be balanced against the need to have a deformable impervious zone that will not crack. A soil compacted at optimum moisture content will be more likely to provide this characteristic.

Coarse-grained, permeable soils, also known as

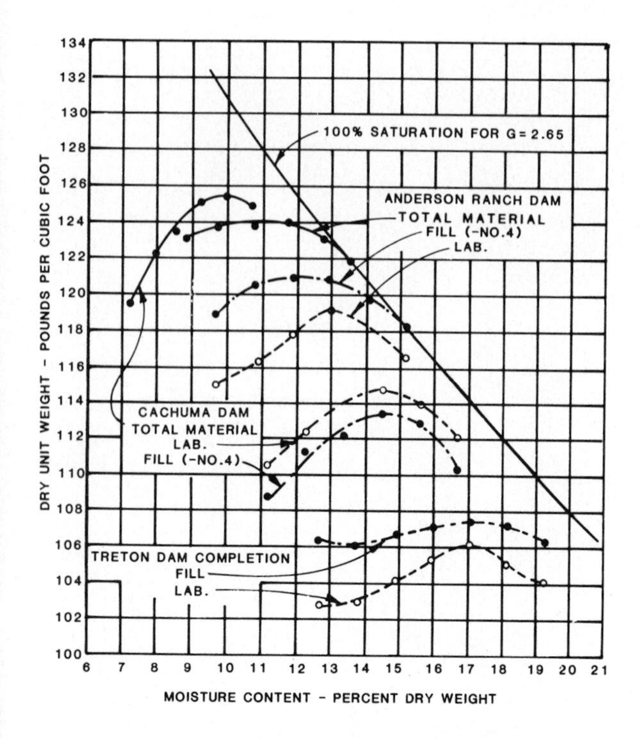

Figure E-2.—Average field and laboratory compaction curves for three dam embankment soils. 101–D–248.

cohesionless or free-draining soils, are commonly used as major zones in earthfill dams and as backfill around conduits or behind retaining walls. This type of soil is also used as filter material for drainage in wells and around hydraulic structures. These soils are inherently permeable and have fairly high shear strengths when compacted. However, in the uncompacted state they are compressible and may be subject to liquefaction if they are saturated. The desirable properties of high strength and low compressibility can be greatly improved by the compaction of permeable soils. Although permeability is thereby decreased, the reduction is usually allowable from a design standpoint.

The most efficient method of compacting cohesionless soil is by vibrating the material when it is either perfectly dry or nearly saturated with water. The latter method is usually the only practicable one in the field, because perfectly dry material is seldom encountered. The shear strength of permeable materials, such as fairly clean sands and gravels or rockfills, depends almost entirely on the angle of internal friction. Cohesion is negligible, and pore-water pressures are never greater than hydrostatic pressure because of free drainage of the soil. The angle of internal friction is a function of the size, shape, and gradation of the grains, but for a given cohesionless soil its magnitude varies significantly with the void ratio. The state of compactness of soils is given by their relative density, which is defined in section 5.49(f).

E.3. *Preparation of Foundations.*—Foundation design features are discussed in chapter 6, part C. The weak points in earthfill dams are generally within the foundation and at the contact of the foundation with the placed embankment. Construction of foundation seepage control and stability features must be carefully supervised by the inspection force to ensure conformance with the design and specifications. Dewatering methods used in connection with excavating cutoff trenches or stabilizing the foundations should be carefully checked to ensure that fine material is not washed out of the foundation because of improper screening of wells. Whenever possible, well points and sumps should be located outside the area to be excavated to avoid loosening of soil or creation of a "live" bottom caused by the upward flow of water. Sumps and associated drainage trenches within the impervious zone should be avoided because of difficulty in properly grouting them after fill placement and the danger of damaging the impervious zone-foundation contact.

Concrete footings for cutoff walls or concrete grout caps should be founded in unfractured rock. Blasting for the excavation of these structures should be prohibited or strictly controlled, in accordance with the specifications, to avoid shattering the foundation. In recent years the use of grout caps and concrete cutoff walls has declined because of the difficulty in constructing them without damaging the rock. An alternative is to leave the foundation high and to set grout nipples through the highly weathered zone. Excavation to final foundation grade is performed after grouting. In poor rock, long grout nipples may be necesssary. In hard, sound rock, neither a group cap nor a high foundation may be necessary.

When overburden is stripped to rock foundations, the rock surface including all pockets or depressions should be carefully cleaned of soil and rock fragments before the embankment is placed on it. This may require handwork and compressed-air cleaning. Rock surfaces that disintegrate rapidly on exposure must be protected or covered immediately with embankment material. Foundation rock should be shaped to remove overhangs and steep surfaces. High rock surfaces must be stable during construction and should be cut back to maintain a smooth continuous profile to minimize differential settlement and stress concentration within the embankment. Slopes should be 0.5:1 (horizontal to vertical) or flatter. Beneath the impervious zone, all overhangs should be removed, stepped surfaces steeper than 0.5:1 and higher than 1 foot should be excavated or treated with dental concrete (conventional concrete used to shape surfaces, fill irregularities, and protect poor rock) to a slope of 0.5:1 or flatter. Outside the impervious zone, all overhangs should be removed, and stepped surfaces steeper than 0.5:1 and higher than 5 feet should be excavated or treated with dental concrete to a slope of 0.5:1 or flatter.

Slush grout or joint mortar should be used to fill narrow cracks in the foundation. However, they should not be used to cover exposed areas of the foundation. Slush grout and joint mortar are composed of portland cement and water or, in some cases, portland cement, sand and water.

Dental concrete should be used to fill potholes and grooves created by bedding planes and other irregularities such as previously cleaned shear zones and large joints or channels in rock surfaces. Formed dental concrete can be used to fillet steep slopes and fill overhangs. Figures E-3 and E-4 illustrate foundation cleanup and the use of dental concrete.

Care should be used during all blasting to excavate or to shape rock surfaces. Smooth blasting techniques, such as line drilling and presplitting, should be used.

When the foundation is earth, all organic or other unsuitable materials, such as stumps, brush, sod, and large roots, should be stripped and wasted. Stripping operations should be performed carefully to ensure the removal of all material that may be rendered unstable by saturation, of all material that may interfere with the creation of a proper bond between the foundation and the embankment, and of all pockets of soils significantly more compressible than the average foundation material. Stripping of pervious materials under the pervious or semipervious zones of an embankment should be limited to the removal of surface debris and grass roots. Test pits for further exploration should be excavated if the stripping operations indicate the presence of unstable or otherwise unsuitable material,

Figure E-3.—Cleanup of foundation rock. Dental concrete is used to fill an irregular surface in rock beneath the impervious zone. McGee Creek Dam, southeastern Oklahoma. P801-D-81035

Figure E-4.—Use of formed dental concrete to fillet steep, rough rock. Special compaction against the steep surface. Ridgway Dam, Dallas Creek Project, Colorado. P801–D–81036

and an inspection should be made by an experienced engineer.

Before placing the first layer of embankment on an earth foundation, moistening and compacting the surface by rolling with a tamping roller is necessary to obtain proper bond. Rock foundation surfaces should be moistened, but no standing water should be permitted when the first lift is placed. Sometimes an earth foundation surface requires scarification by disks or harrows to ensure proper bonding; however, no additional scarification is usually necessary if it is penetrated by tamping rollers. Where a rock foundation would be injured by penetration of the tamping roller feet, it is permissible to make the first compacted lift thicker than that specified. However, the first lift should never exceed 15 inches loose for 9-inch-long tamper feet, and additional roller passes are required, in such a case, to ensure proper compaction. Special compaction methods, such as hand tamping, should be used in pockets that cannot be compacted by the specified roller, instead of permitting an unusually thick initial lift to obtain a uniform surface for compaction.

An alternative to using thick lifts is using a pneumatic-tire roller or pneumatic-tire equipment and disking or scarifying the lift surfaces to obtain bond between lifts. Use of the tamping roller can begin when the fill is sufficiently thick to protect the foundation from the tamping feet. Unit weight and moisture should be carefully monitored in the foundation contact zone, and placing and compacting operations should be carefully inspected.

Figures E-4, E-5, and E-6 show special compaction techniques along the contact surface between the earthfill portion of a dam and the rock abutments or structures. Irregular surfaces of the rock may prevent proper compaction by rollers, and hand-compaction techniques may be necessary. However, where the foundations surfaces permit, a pneumatic-tire roller or pneumatic-tire equipment should be used near foundation contact surfaces. On steep surfaces, ramping the fill aids compaction; about a 6:1 slope should be used for ramping the fill. The surfaces of structures should be sloped (battered) at about 1:10 to facilitate compaction.

The use of very wet soil for the first lift against the foundations should generally be avoided; rather, the foundation should be properly moistened. On steep, irregular rock abutments, material slightly wetter than optimum may be necessary or desirable to obtain good workability and a suitable bond. However, such material should be used only with the approval of the contracting authority. Care

(a) First lift of zone 1 against rock. P801–D–81037.

(b) Zone 1B against outlet conduit. P801–D–81038.

Figure E-5.—Pneumatic-tire front-end loader being used for compaction. McGee Creek Dam, Oklahoma.

Figure E-6.—Vibratory plate being used for special compaction adjacent to conduit. McGee Creek Dam, Oklahoma. P801-D-81039.

must be exercised when special compaction is used to ensure that suitable bonds are created between successive layers of material. This may require light scarification between lifts of tamped material. Appendix G contains sample specifications pertinent to items of work required for the preparation of foundations. Bureau of Reclamation Design Standards No. 13, chapter 3, should also be referred to for foundation surface treatment.

E.4. *Earthfill.*—Specifications for the control of placement, moisture content, and compaction of earthfill are given in appendix G. Procedures should be established to ensure these specifications are followed. For the construction of small dams within the scope of this text, the plan of control for embankments of cohesive soil is to place the material at the optimum moisture content and at the maximum laboratory unit weight. The optimum moisture content, rather than a moisture content slightly less than optimum, is selected for the reasons given in section 6.15. The most important variables affecting construction of earthfill embankments are the distribution, placement, and moisture content of the soils, the uniformity of moisture throughout the spread material, the moisture content of the borrow material, the methods used for correcting the moisture content of borrow material (if too wet or too dry), roller characteristics, the number of roller passes, the thickness of lifts, the maximum size and quantity of gravel sizes in the material, the condition of the lift surfaces after rolling, and the effectiveness of power tamping in places inaccessible or undesirable for roller operation.

Figure E-7 shows the placing, leveling, and compacting of the semipervious zone of the embankment at Olympus Dam. Compacting was done by tamping rollers because the material was not permeable enough to permit compaction as a pervious fill in the manner described in section E.5. The maximum section of this dam is shown on figure 6-74, and a photograph of the completed structure is shown on figure 4-4.

Adequate inspection and laboratory testing are essential to the control of earthfill construction. It is impossible even for an experienced soils engineer to visually determine the unit weight of cohesive soil, especially when it is dryer than optimum. The apparent cohesion of these soils makes them firm and gives them the appearance of denseness that disappears when they become saturated. There is no satisfactory substitute for control testing to determine the unit weight of these soils. The testing must include all critical areas where seepage or loss of shear strength could induce failure.

Borrow pit inspection includes controlling and

Figure E-7.—Placing, leveling, and compacting the fill at Olympus Dam. A combination earthfill and concrete gravity dam on the Big Thompson River in Colorado. 375–EPA–PS.

recording all earthwork operations that take place before the material is placed on the embankment. Areas to be excavated are selected, depths of cut are determined, and the zone of the dam in which a particular material is to be placed should be predetermined. The borrow pit inspector should check the adequacy of all mixing or separation methods used by the contractor. As required, the inspector cooperates with the contractor in determining the amount of water to be added to the borrow pit by irrigation or to be removed by drainage to attain the proper moisture content of the materials before placing. The rapid method of compaction control described in USBR 7240 of the *Earth Manual* [5] can be used to determine the status of natural moisture conditions in the borrow pit. Quicker but less accurate methods (within 1 percent of the actual moisture content) are USBR 5310, Determining Moisture Content of Soils Using the Calcium Carbide Reaction Device, and USBR 5315, Determining Moisture Content of Soils by the Microwave Oven Method. Every effort should be made to get the excavated material as close as possible to the optimum moisture content before it is delivered to the embankment.

The embankment inspector should be provided with a means for determining the location and elevation of tests made on the embankment and for reporting the location of the contractor's operations. Horizontal control by means of coordinates or stations and offsets should be established. It has been found effective to establish vertical control by benchmarks and by the use of stadia rods, from which the inspector can determine the elevation anywhere on the fill with a hand level. When materials are brought on the embankment, the inspector should check that they are placed in the proper zones. The previous lift should be properly compacted and scarified or disked, if necessary, to ensure a good bond with the next lift. The inspector should also be alert for smooth areas caused by equipment travel and ensure that they are disked or scarified to provide a good bond with the next lift. If a zoned embankment is being constructed, lines of demarcation may be painted on rock abutments or marked by flags. Within a particular zone the objective is to direct the placing of materials so that the most impermeable soils are located in the center of the impervious zone and the coarser, more permeable soils are placed toward the slopes of the embankment, so that the permeability and stability of materials will increase toward the outer slopes. In general, when materials differ in dry unit weight but have about the same permeability, the material having the greater dry unit weight should be placed in the outer sections of the zone or of the dam, as the case may be.

After the materials are placed in their proper locations, the embankment inspector should determine whether they contain the proper amount of moisture before compaction. This is of utmost importance. The rapid compaction control method or the Proctor needle value should be used for this determination. If the materials arrive on the embankment too dry, it is necessary to condition them by sprinkling and disking before, during, or after spreading. Contractors' operations in sprinkling and mixing the moisture with the soil vary, but it is of paramount importance that the proper moisture content be uniformly distributed throughout the spread lift before compaction. The use of a heavy disk plow to break down and mix impermeable fill before compaction has become almost routine in the construction of embankment dams.

Another important inspection task is the determination of the thickness of the compacted lift. A lift that is spread too thick will not provide the desired unit weight for given compaction conditions. Initial placing operations should be used to determine the proper loose thickness of a lift that will compact to the specified thickness. This is usually 8 to 9 inches for a 6-inch compacted lift of earthfill. A method of determining the average thickness of compacted lifts is to plot daily a cross section of the fill at a reference station. The inspector's report for that day should contain the number of lifts placed at that station; from this and the elevation, the average thickness can be determined.

The removal of oversized rock from the earthfill embankment material when the oversized rock content is greater than about 1 percent is most efficiently done before the soil is delivered to the embankment. This procedure was used at Crescent Lake Dam, as shown on figure E-8. The shovel at the left in the photograph is excavating and mixing the borrow material. The scoopmobile transports the material to electrically operated screens that separate the oversize rock from the soil; trucks are loaded by conveyor belt. Figure E-9 shows borrow operations in an impervious borrow area at Ridgway Dam, which was completed in 1986, and illustrates more modern equipment.

Smaller amounts of oversize rock can be removed by hand picking or, under favorable conditions, by various kinds of rock rakes. Oversize rock that had been overlooked before rolling can generally be detected by the inspector during rolling by observing the bounce that occurs when the roller passes over the hidden rock. The inspector should ensure that all such rocks are removed from the fill.

The inspector is responsible for ensuring that the specified number of roller passes is made on each lift. An oversight in maintaining the proper number of passes may result in a considerable decrease in the unit weight. The insistence on orderly placing and compacting operations and the establishment of routine construction operations will minimize the possibility of trouble from too few roller passes.

The final check on the unit weight attained can be done by the rapid method of compaction control given in USBR 7240 in the *Earth Manual* [5] or by other methods that compare laboratory maximum unit weight to placement unit weight. If the field dry unit weight of the material passing the No. 4 sieve is above the minimum allowable unit weight, as given in section E.9, and if the moisture content is within the allowable limits, the embankment will be ready for the next lift after the scarifying or disking and moistening necessary to secure a good bond between the lifts. It is good procedure to periodically check the rapid method of compaction control against the standard Proctor compaction test, USBR 5500 in the *Earth Manual*.

Mechanical tamping should be minimized and compaction by equipment with rollers should be used as much as practicable. When mechanical tamping is used around structures, along abutments, and in other areas inaccessible to rolling equipment, it should be watched closely and checked by frequent unit weight tests. The mechanical tamping procedures followed depend on the type of tamper used. Some of the factors affecting unit weight are the thickness of the lift being

Figure E-8.—Removal of oversize rock by screening pit-run material. Impermeable borrow area for a small earthfill storage dam on Crescent Creek in Oregon. P806-126-55.

placed, time of tamping, air pressure (if air tampers are used), moisture content of the material, and mass of the tamping unit.

An important function of inspection is to determine when and where to make field unit weight tests. These tests should be made (1) in areas where the unit weight is doubtful, (2) in areas where embankment operations are concentrated, and (3) for every 2,000 yd^3 when (1) and (2) do not apply. Areas susceptible to insufficient compaction include those near junctions between mechanically tamped and rolled embankments (along abutments and near structures); areas where rollers turn during compaction operations; areas where the lift compacted was too thick; areas where the material has improper moisture content; and areas where less than the specified number of roller passes were made. When embankment operations are concentrated in a small area (i.e., many lifts of material are being placed in a single day), tests should be taken on every third or fourth lift to ensure that the desired unit weight is being attained. If there are no areas of doubtful compaction and no tests are required because of concentrated areas, at least one field unit weight test should be taken for each 2,000 yd^3 of compacted embankment. The area selected for this test should be representative of the unit weight being obtained.

E.5. *Pervious Fill.*—Permeable materials are used in rolled earthfill dams to provide an outer shell of high shear strength to support the impervious core, to secure favorable hydraulic drainage conditions, and to act as filters and drains between materials having wide variations in grain sizes or between the foundation and the fill. Controlling the construction of zones of sand and gravel is necessary to ensure that (1) the material is formed into a homogeneous mass free from large voids, (2) the soil mass is free draining, (3) the material will not consolidate excessively under the weight of superimposed fill, and (4) the soil has a high angle of internal friction.

Figure E-9.—Borrow area operation at Ridgway Dam. P894-427-7299 NA.

The workability and permeability of a permeable soil is reduced considerably by the inclusion of even small amounts of silt or clay; hence, every effort should be made to ensure that the contractor's operations in the borrow pits and on the fill minimize the contamination of the permeable soil. As the fill material is brought to the embankment, it should be directed to the proper zone. Within the pervious zone, individual loads should be placed so that the more coarse material will be placed toward the outer slopes. When compacted thicknesses are specified, the thickness of loose lifts should be determined by the inspector during the initial stages of construction. Because the field unit weight will be tested relatively infrequently after satisfactory placing procedures have been established, the proper thickness of the loose lifts must be maintained within close limits throughout the job. The specified thickness of compacted lifts is usually made large enough to accommodate the size of rock encountered in the borrow area. Where cobbles or rock fragments larger than the specified lift thickness occur, provisions are usually made for special embedding, removal to outer slopes of the pervious zone, or removal to other zones. To secure the best compaction, the inspector should ensure that the specified requirements for the disposal of oversize rock are followed.

After the material has been placed and spread to the desired lift thickness and oversize cobbles or rock fragments have been disposed of, the next important step is the application of water. Thorough and uniform wetting of materials during or immediately before compaction is essential for best results. The most appropriate method of adding and distributing water to the fill should be determined during the initial placement. It has been found that relaxation of the requirements for thorough wetting may result in unit weights far below the minimum, even with excessive compactive effort.

Different permeable materials require different amounts of water for thorough wetting and best compaction. In general, it is desirable to add as much water to the material as it will readily absorb. An extremely permeable soil can take large amounts of water; however, permeable soils containing small amounts of silt or clay can become temporarily boggy if an excessive amount of water is used. For these soils care must be exercised when adding water. The contractor's operations should be carefully controlled to avoid excessive wetting of the impermeable zone adjacent to the permeable material being compacted.

When compacting a permeable soil by the treads of a crawler-type tractor, it is desirable to have the tractor operate at the highest practicable speed. High speed is conducive to greater vibration, which aids in the compaction. When inspecting compaction operations using tractor treads, it is important to ensure that the tractor covers the entire area to be compacted before making subsequent passes. Different lift widths require different numbers of tractor trips to obtain the same number of passes of the treads. The proper number of trips should be determined and enforced. Today, smooth-drum vibratory rollers have almost replaced compaction by crawler-type tractors.

It is recommended that relative density tests and gradation analyses be made during the initial placing operation at a frequency of about one test for each 1,000 yd^3 placed. The procedure for making relative density tests is given in sections 5.47 and 5.49(f). If a material has a fines content approaching 10 percent passing a No. 200 sieve, the Proctor compaction test, USBR 5500 [5], may be a more appropriate control test. After placement procedures have proved satisfactory, one relative density test for every 10,000 yd^3 of material placed will suffice, unless significant changes in gradation occur. If the gradation of the borrow material changes significantly, more field tests may be needed to ensure satisfactory compaction of the variable materials.

E.6. *Rockfill and Riprap.*—Rockfill zones are used in earthfill dams to provide stability for the embankment and to protect exposed surfaces of the fill. Rockfill is generally placed in lifts 2 to 4 feet thick, sprinkled with water, and compacted by vibratory rollers. High permeability is desirable in rockfills; therefore, the amount of fines permitted is limited. On the other hand, large unfilled voids are undesirable. The outer portion of a rockfill zone should contain the largest available rock to secure slope protection. There may be some occasions when rockfill is dumped without compaction. If this is the case where very large rockfill sections are used, excessive settlement may be a problem, and sluicing may be required to compact the fill.

Riprap is a relatively thin layer of specially selected and graded rock used for protecting earth slopes from erosion by water currents and waves. Riprap is not compacted, but is dumped or placed to interlock the angular fragments. The most desirable riprap surface is well-keyed but rough to resist wave action effectively.

Inspection may be necessary both at the rock source and at the rockfill to ensure that the material used does not have an excessive amount of fines. Breakage in handling and transporting should be taken into account. Placing operations should be inspected to see that segregation is avoided and that no large voids are left in the rockfill. Inspection of rockfill placement and compaction basically consists of visual observation to ensure that the specified rolling and wetting of the fill is accomplished and that adequate unit weight is obtained. Occasionally, large-diameter unit weight tests are taken to check density, but are used sparingly because they are difficult to perform and time consuming. Test fills are useful at the beginning of construction to establish procedures. If sluicing is required, the contractor's operations should be carefully controlled to avoid excessive wetting of the impermeable zone and to ensure that enough water is being used uniformly.

Inspection of riprap placement consists of visual observation of the operation and of the finished surface to ensure that a dense, rough surface of well-keyed graded rock fragments of the specified quality and sizes is obtained. Typical specifications for placing rockfill and riprap are contained in appendix G.

E.7. *Miscellaneous Fills.*—Dam embankments on saturated fine-grain foundations may require toe support fills, the weight of which improves stability. These fills are discussed in section 6.13. Excavation for the foundation of a dam or for appurtenant structures often produces material unsuitable for or in excess of the requirements for the structural zones of a dam. Such excavated material can be used for stabilizing fills at the toe of the dam. In localities where good quality riprap is very expensive, fill materials from structural excavations have been used to flatten the upstream slope of the dam to permit the use of poor quality rock or, in some cases, the omission of rock. In a few cases, excess required excavation has been used in an isolated zone in the downstream portion of a dam merely to replace material that otherwise would have had to be borrowed at greater expense.

The permeability of stabilizing fills is not important in the design, and such fills usually are not purposely compacted by compaction equipment. However, full use should be made of the compaction obtainable by routing the hauling and placing equipment over lifts of the material. Sometimes the nature of the available materials or the design requires some compactive effort other than the routing of the hauling equipment. For example, sheepsfoot rolling has been used to break up fairly large chunks of soft rocks to avoid excessive settlement. Compaction may also be required when the miscellaneous fill is designed to serve as an impervious blanket.

Inspection of miscellaneous fills is usually entirely visual; ordinarily, no control tests are taken. The main objectives of inspecting miscellaneous fills is to ensure that the specified lift thickness is not exceeded and that the hauling equipment is not channelized by a roadway, but is spread as far as practicable over the entire placement area.

E.8. *Records and Reports.*—Daily reports should be made by the inspector covering the activities for each shift. These reports should record the progress of construction, provide pertinent information for the inspector about to go on shift (including shutdowns and orders given to the contractor), and furnish data for use in compiling reports. The form of the daily report varies to suit the requirements of the job, but all information required on summary progress reports should be based on daily records.

A systematic method of identifying field unit weight tests made on the embankment is desirable. A suggested scheme is to designate each test by the date, shift, number on that shift, and purpose. For example, "8-2-70-a-2-D" would define a field unit weight test made August 2, 1970, on the first shift, the second test made on that shift, for the purpose of checking an area of doubtful compaction. The legend is as follows: a = first shift; b = second shift; c = third shift; C = concentrated area; D = doubtful area; R = representative. The results of daily tests on the embankment should be reported on the appropriate forms.

E.9. *Control Criteria.*—Determination of the quality of embankment being placed can be made by a simple statistical analysis of the test results as given by Davis [6]. Figures E-10 and E-11 show work sheets and curves for dry unit weight control and moisture control, respectively, for compacted cohesive soils in an earthfill dam. From this analysis, the frequency distribution of the test results is obtained; from this, statistical parameters, such as the mean, standard deviation, and the percentage of tests falling outside specified limits, can be determined.

Various criteria for quality control have been proposed. Table E-1 lists suggested limits of unit weight and moisture control based on experience gained in compacting 44 cohesive soils and 18 cohesionless soils in Bureau of Reclamation earthfill dams. The soils were compacted by the equipment and methods specified in appendix G; therefore, the values in the table may not be possible with other methods of compaction or with less compactive effort. It is recognized that the normal frequency distribution curve for any desired average value permits a small percentage of very low tests. However, because of the relatively small number of samples tested, the values listed in table E-1 as "minimum acceptable" are suggested as a basis for requiring recompaction of all areas represented by lower values.

The effect of gravel content in cohesive soils is discussed in several papers [4, 5, 8]. Available data indicate that lower percentages of unit weight on the minus No. 4 basis are required for gravelly cohesive soils than for soils containing little or no gravel. This fact is reflected in table E-1.

Example DAM ZONE 1

$D = \frac{\text{FILL DRY UNIT WEIGHT}}{\text{MAXIMUM LABORATORY DRY UNIT WEIGHT}} \times 100$ (MINUS NO. 4 MATERIAL)

D	F (PREV)	THIS PERIOD: FREQUENCY OF OCCURRENCE	THIS PERIOD: F	THIS PERIOD: CUM F	THIS PERIOD: CUM %	TO DATE: F	TO DATE: CUM F	TO DATE: CUM %
93.0-93.9								
94.0-94.9								
95.0-95.9								
96.0-96.9		||||	4	4	8			
97.0-97.9		||||	4	8	16			
98.0-98.9		𝍸 ||||	9	17	34			
99.0-99.9		𝍸 ||	7	24	48			
100.0-100.9		𝍸 |||	8	32	64			
101.0-101.9		𝍸 𝍸	10	42	84			
102.0-102.9		𝍸	5	47	94			
103.0-103.9		|||	3	50	100			
104.0-104.9								
105.0-105.9								
TOTALS			50					

	PREV.	THIS PERIOD	TO DATE
Average fill lab γ_D (lb/ft^3)		117.1	
Average fill γ_D (lb/ft^3)		117.1	
Mean variation from max. lab γ_D (lb/ft^3)		0.0	
Average rock content (% of plus No. 4 by dry mass)		2.6	

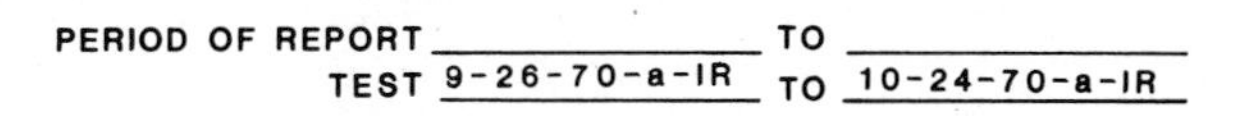

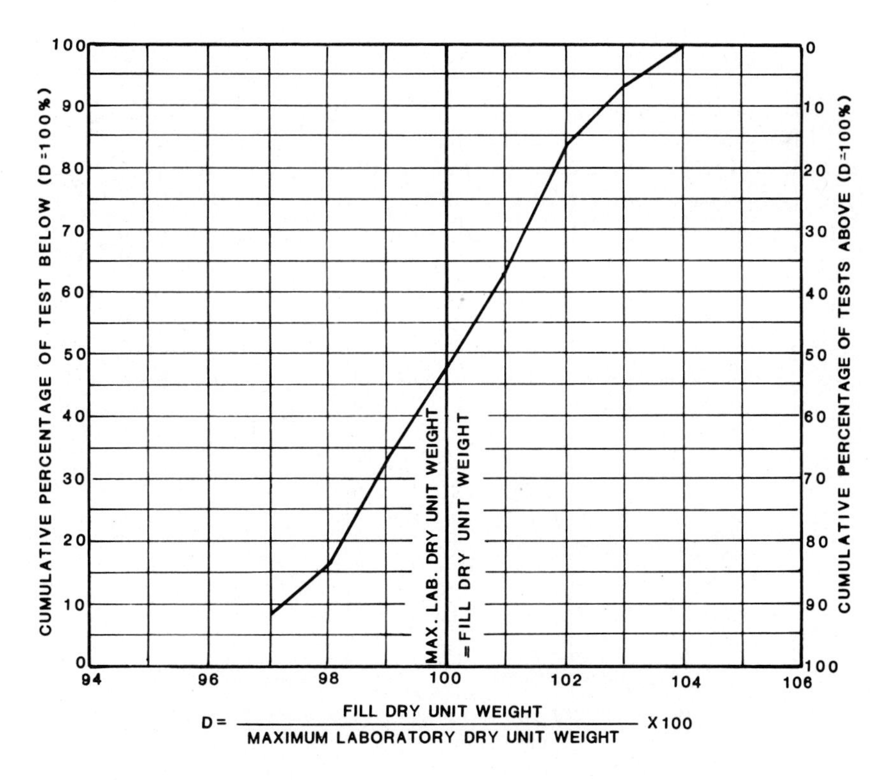

Figure E-10.—Statistical analysis of field unit weight tests for compaction control. 288–D–2567.

Example DAM ZONE 1

OPTIMUM MOISTURE CONTENT MINUS FILL MOISTURE CONTENT ($W_o - W_f$) IN PERCENT OF DRY MASS

		F (PREV)	THIS PERIOD				TO DATE		
			FREQUENCY OF OCCURRENCE	F	CUM F	CUM %	F	CUM F	CUM %
W_f IS BELOW OPTIMUM	3.3-3.7								
	2.8-3.2								
	2.3-2.7		𝍸 |	6	6	12			
	1.8-2.2		𝍸	5	11	22			
	1.3-1.7		𝍸 |	6	17	34			
	0.8-1.2		𝍸 𝍸 |	11	28	56			
	0.3-0.7		𝍸 𝍸	10	38	76			
	-0.2 to -0.2		𝍸 ||	7	45	90			
W_f IS ABOVE OPTIMUM	0.3-0.7		|||	3	48	96			
	0.8-1.2		|	1	49	98			
	1.3-1.7								
	1.8-2.2								
	2.3-2.7		|	1	50	100			
	2.8-3.2								
	3.3-3.7								
	TOTALS			50					

	PREV.	THIS PERIOD	TO DATE
Average optimum moisture content %		13.7	
Average fill moisture content %		12.8	
Mean variation from optimum moisture content		0.9	

PERIOD OF REPORT ______ TO ______

TESTS 9-26-70-a-IR TO 10-24-70-a-IR

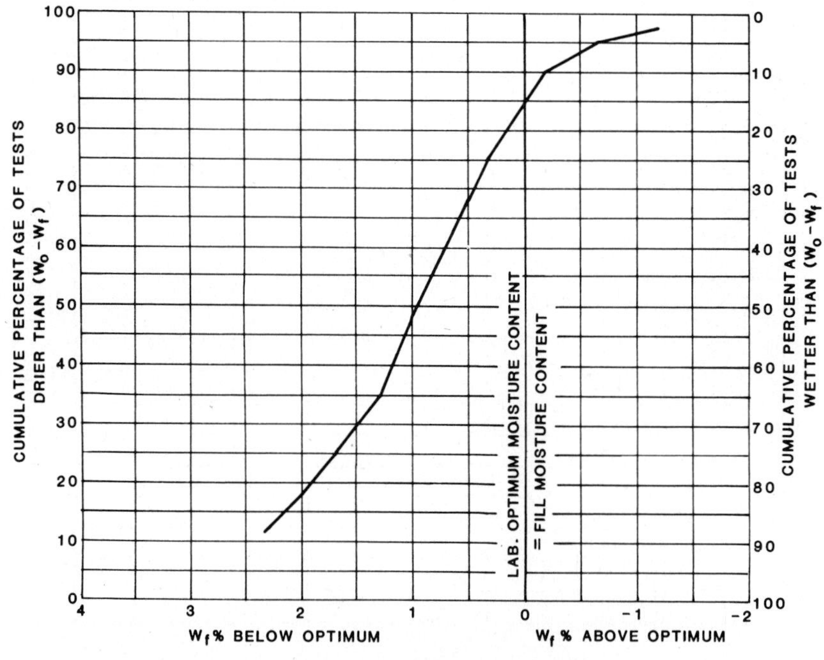

Figure E-11.—Statistical analysis of field unit weight tests for moisture control. 288–D–2568.

Table E.1.—Criteria for control of compacted dam embankments.

Type of material	Percentage of plus No. 4 fraction by mass of total material	Percentage based on minus No. 4 fraction: Minimum acceptable unit weight	Desirable average unit weight	Moisture limits, $w_o - w_f$
Cohesive soils controlled by compaction test	0 to 25	D = 95	D = 98	−2 to +2
	26 to 50	D = 92.5	D = 95	
	>50[1]	D = 90	D = 93	
Cohesionless soils controlled by relative unit weight test	Fine sands with 0 to 25	D_d = 75	D_d = 90	Soils should be very wet
	Medium sands with 0 to 25	D_d = 70	D_d = 85	
	Coarse sands and gravels with 0 to 100	D_d = 65	D_d = 80	

$w_o - w_f$ is the difference between optimum moisture content and fill moisture content in percent of dry mass of soil.
D is fill dry unit weight divided by maximum dry unit weight, in percent.
D_d is relative density, as defined in appendix D, in percent.
[1]Cohesive soils containing more than 50 percent gravel sizes should be tested for permeability of the total material if used as a water barrier.

E.10. *Bibliography.*

[1] Justin, J. D., *Earth Dam Projects*, John Wiley and Sons, Inc., p. 188, New York, NY, 1932.

[2] Bassell, Burr, *Earth Dams*, Engineering News Publishing Co., New York, NY, 1907.

[3] Proctor, R. R., "The Design and Construction of Rolled Earth Dams," *Engineering News-Record*, August 31, September 7, 21, and 28, 1933.

[4] Hilf, J. W., "Compacting Earth Dams With Heavy Tamping Rollers," ASCE Proceedings, *Journal of the Soil Mechanics and Foundations Division*, vol. 83, No. SM2, paper No. 1205, April 1957.

[5] *Earth Manual*, vol. 2, "Test Designations," Bureau of Reclamation, Denver, CO, 1987.

[6] Davis, F. J., "Quality Control of Earth Embankments," 3rd International Conference on Soil Mechanics and Foundations Engineering, vol. 1, p. 218, Switzerland, 1953.

[7] Walker, F. C., and W. G. Holtz, "Control of Embankment Material by Laboratory Testing," Transactions ASCE, vol. 118, p. 1, 1953.

[8] Holtz, W. G., and C. A. Lowitz, "Compaction Characteristics of Gravelly Soils," Conference on Soils for Engineering Purposes, ASTM Committee D-18 and Sociedae Mexicana de Mecanica de Suelos, ASTM Special Technical Publication No. 232, American Society for Testing Materials, p. 123, Philadelphia, PA, December 9-13, 1957.

Concrete in Construction

A. CONCRETE AND CONCRETE MATERIALS

F.1. ***Important Properties of Concrete.***—Concrete is one of the most durable and versatile of construction materials. It is composed of sand, gravel, crushed rock, or other aggregates held together by a hardened paste of hydraulic cement and water. The selection, testing, and evaluation of these materials, together with their processing and proportioning are the subject of this appendix. Specifications for concrete are included in appendix G. For complete coverage of concrete as a construction material, the reader is referred to the Bureau of Reclamation's *Concrete Manual* [1].[1]

The characteristics of concrete discussed in the following sections should be considered on a relative basis and in terms of the quality required for the construction purpose. In addition to being adequately designed, a structure must be properly constructed with concrete that is strong enough to carry the design loads and yet economical, not only in first cost but also in terms of its ultimate service. In addition to strength, concrete must have the properties of workability and durability.

F.2. ***Workability.***—Workability has been defined as the ease with which a given set of materials can be mixed into concrete and subsequently handled, transported, and placed with a minimal loss of homogeneity. Workability is dependent on the proportions of the constituent materials as well as on their individual characteristics. The degree of workability required for proper placement and consolidation of concrete is governed by the dimensions and shape of the structure and by the spacing and size of the reinforcement. For example, concrete having suitable workability for a pavement slab could be difficult or impossible to economically place in a thin, heavily reinforced section.

F.3. ***Durability.***—Durable concrete will withstand, to a satisfactory degree, the effects of service conditions such as weathering, chemical action, and wear.

(a) *Weathering Resistance.*—Disintegration of concrete by weathering is caused mainly by the disruptive action of freezing and thawing and by expansion and contraction under restraint, resulting from temperature variations and alternate wetting and drying. Concrete with excellent resistance to the effects of such exposures can be made if careful attention is given to the selection of materials and to all other phases of job control. The purposeful entrainment of small bubbles of air helps to greatly improve concrete durability. It is also important that, where practicable, provision be made for adequate drainage of exposed concrete surfaces. In general, the more watertight the concrete, the more difficult it is for water to gain entrance and to fill the voids, and the greater the resistance to frost action.

(b) *Resistance to Chemical Deterioration.*—The common causes of chemical deterioration of concrete include alkali-aggregate reactivity, in which alkalies in the cement react chemically with mineral constituents of concrete aggregates; sulfate attack, in which salts (principally soluble sulfates) in the ground water or the soil touching the concrete attack the cement paste; and deterioration resulting from contact with other various chemical agents.

Alkali-aggregate reactivity is characterized by the following observable conditions: cracking, usually in a random pattern on a fairly large scale (see fig. F-1); excessive internal and overall expansion; cracks that may be very large at the concrete surfaces (openings up to 1½ inches have been observed), but that extend into the concrete only 6 to 18 inches; gelatinous exudations and whitish amorphous deposits, both on the surface and within the mass of the concrete, especially in voids and adjacent to some affected aggregate; peripheral zones of reactivity, alteration, or infiltration in the aggre-

[1]Numbers in brackets refer to entries in the bibliography (sec. F.29.).

Figure F-1.—Typical pattern cracking on the exposed surface of concrete affected by alkali-aggregate reaction. TC-8-16.

gate, particularly opal and certain types of acidic and intermediate volcanic rocks; and dull chalky appearance of the freshly fractured concrete.

Use of low-alkali cement, that is, cement having a total alkali content expressed as sodium oxide of not more than 0.6 percent as determined by summation of the percentage of sodium oxide and 0.658 times the percentage of potassium oxide, provides an effective means of controlling expansive alkali-aggregate reaction, generally at little increase in cost. The use of a suitable pozzolan in concrete provides another effective method of obtaining such control and provides added insurance when used in combination with low-alkali cement. However, the efficiency of different pozzolans in controlling expansive alkali-aggregate reaction varies widely, and it is therefore necessary to test pozzolan sources individually to evaluate their effectiveness.

Tests to evaluate reactive combinations of aggregate and cement are complex and expensive. Therefore, for jobs with a limited budget, inspection of existing concrete structures near the jobsite and determination of the source of the aggregate and cement used in these structures may provide valuable information regarding the quality of local materials to be used in construction. In addition, the need for protective measures frequently can be determined by examination of the prospective aggregate by an experienced petrographer.

Most prominent among the aggressive substances that affect concrete structures are the sulfates of sodium, magnesium, and calcium. These salts are frequently encountered in the "alkali" soils and ground waters of the Western States. The sulfates react chemically with certain compounds in the cement to produce considerable expansion and disruption of the paste. The result of such action is shown on figure F-2. Sulfate attack is reduced by using the type of cement indicated in table F-1 for varying degrees of sulfate concentration. While

Figure F-2.—Disintegration of concrete caused by sulfate attack. PX-D-32050.

use of the type of cement indicated in table F-1 is preferable, further increase in resistance of concrete to sulfate attack can be obtained by decreasing the water-cement ratio and by using a suitable fly ash or other effective pozzolan.

Where white surface deposits of salt occur, it is advisable to examine existing concrete structures near the proposed work to determine whether protection against sulfate attack will be necessary. The presence of these white deposits often indicates the need for testing the soil and ground water to determine whether harmful sulfate concentrations are present. Testing is desirable because the white deposits may contain chloride salts which, compared with sulfate salts, are relatively harmless to hardened concrete.

(c) *Resistance to Erosion.*—The principal causes of erosion of concrete surfaces are cavitation, movement of abrasive material by flowing water, abrasion and impact of traffic, wind blasting, and impact of floating ice.

Cavitation is one of the most destructive of these causes and one to which concrete or any other construction material offers very little resistance regardless of its quality. On concrete surfaces subjected to high-velocity flow, an obstruction or abrupt change in surface alignment causes a zone of severe subatmospheric pressure to be formed against the surface immediately downstream from the obstruction or abrupt change. This zone is

Table F-1.—Attack on concrete by soils and waters containing various sulfate concentrations.

Relative degree of sulfate attack	Water-soluble sulfate (as SO_4) in soil samples, percent	Sulfate (as SO_4) in water samples, mg/L
Negligible	0.00 to 0.10	0 to 150
Moderate[1]	0.10 to 0.20	150 to 1,500
Severe[2]	0.20 to 2.00	1,500 to 10,000
Very severe[3]	2.00 or more	10,000 or more

[1]Use type II cement.
[2]Use type V cement or approved combination of portland cement and pozzolan that has been shown by tests to provide comparable sulfate resistance when used in concrete.
[3]Use type II or V cement plus approved pozzolan that has been shown by tests to improve sulfate resistance when used in concrete with this type cement.

promptly filled with turbulent water interspersed with small, fast-moving bubblelike cavities of water vapor. The cavities of water vapor form at the upstream edge of the zone, pass through it, and then collapse from an increase in pressure within the waterflow at a point just downstream. Water from the boundaries of the cavities rushes toward their centers at high speed when the collapse takes place, thus concentrating a tremendous amount of energy. The entire process, including the formation, movement, and collapse, or implosion, of these cavities, is known as cavitation.

It may seem surprising that the collapse of a small vapor cavity can create an impact sufficiently severe and concentrated not only to disintegrate concrete but also to erode the hardest metals; however, there is abundant evidence proving that this occurs commonly. The impact of the collapse has been estimated to produce pressures as high as 100,000 lb/in^2. Repetition of these high-energy blows eventually forms the pits or holes known as cavitation erosion. Cavitation may occur in clear water flowing at high velocities when the divergence between the natural path of the water and the surface of the channel or conduit is too abrupt, or when there are abrupt projections or depressions on the surface of the channel or conduit, such as might occur on concrete surfaces because of poor formwork or inferior finishing. Cavitation may occur on horizontal or sloping surfaces over which water flows or on vertical surfaces past which waterflows. Figure F-3 is an illustration of cavitation erosion on surfaces on and adjacent to a stilling basin dentate. The collapse of the cavities is often accompanied by popping and crackling noises (crepitation).

Although most small dams have insufficient head to cause cavitation, cavitation damage can occur when the flow velocity approaches 40 ft/s. It is best to design flow surfaces to avoid offsets and abrupt changes in alignment, which cause low pressures and subsequent cavitation. However, where low pressures cannot be avoided, critical areas are sometimes protected by facing the concrete with metal or other appropriate materials that have better resistance to cavitation. Introduction of air into the streamflow upstream has also been effective in reducing the occurrence of cavitation and diminishing its effects on some structures.

Erosion damage to concrete caused by abrasive materials in water can be as severe as cavitation damage. The hydraulic-jump sections of spillway and sluiceway stilling basins, where turbulent flow conditions occur, are particularly vulnerable to abrasion damage. The water action in these areas tends to sweep cobbles, gravel, and sand from the downstream riverbed back into the concrete-lined stilling basin where the action becomes one of a grinding ball mill. Even the best concrete cannot withstand this severe wearing action. Figure F–4 shows the abrasion erosion that occurred to the dentates, walls, and floor areas of the Yellowtail Afterbay Dam sluiceway stilling basin. Characteristic of this type of erosion is the badly worn reinforcing steel and aggregate. Contrast this with the cavitation damage, shown on figure F–3, which reflects little or no wearing of the aggregate particles. Although the most severe cases of abrasion damage occur in the areas just described, similar damage could be expected in diversion tunnels, canals, and pipelines carrying water containing large amounts of sediment.

Use of concrete of increased strength and wear resistance offers some relief against the forces of erosion caused by movement of abrasive material in flowing water, abrasion and impact of traffic, sandblasting, and floating ice. However, as is evident with cavitation erosion, the most worthwhile relief from these forces is the prevention, elimination, or reduction of the causes by the proper design, construction, and operation of the concrete structures.

F.4. *Effects of Curing on Strength.*—Experience has demonstrated that when the maximum permissible water-cement ratio has been established on the basis of durability requirements, as shown in table F–2, concrete will usually develop adequate compressive strength if properly placed and cured. Figure F–5 shows the compressive strength development of concrete cured for various lengths of time and subsequently stored or dried. Concrete exposed to dry air from the time it is placed is only about 50 percent as strong at 6 months as concrete moist-cured 14 days before being exposed to dry air.

F.5. *Effects of Entrained Air on the Properties of Concrete.*—Except for compressive strength, all properties of concrete, including workabiltiy, durability, permeability, drying shrinkage, bleeding, etc., are materially improved by the purposeful entrainment of from 2 to 6 percent air; the optimum amount depends on the maximum size aggregate used. Supplementary benefits in the form of reduced water and cement requirements and an increase in ease of finishing may also be realized. Figure F–6 shows the effects of air content on the durability, compressive strength, and required water content of concrete. Note that the durability increases rapidly to a maximum with the initial addition of air, then decreases as the air content is further increased; whereas, compressive strength and water content continue to decrease with increases in air content. Figure F–7 shows the strength in relation to the water-cement ratio for both air-entrained and nonair-entrained concrete. Note that the strength decreases with an increase in water-cement ratio, and that the use of air entrainment also decreases the strength.

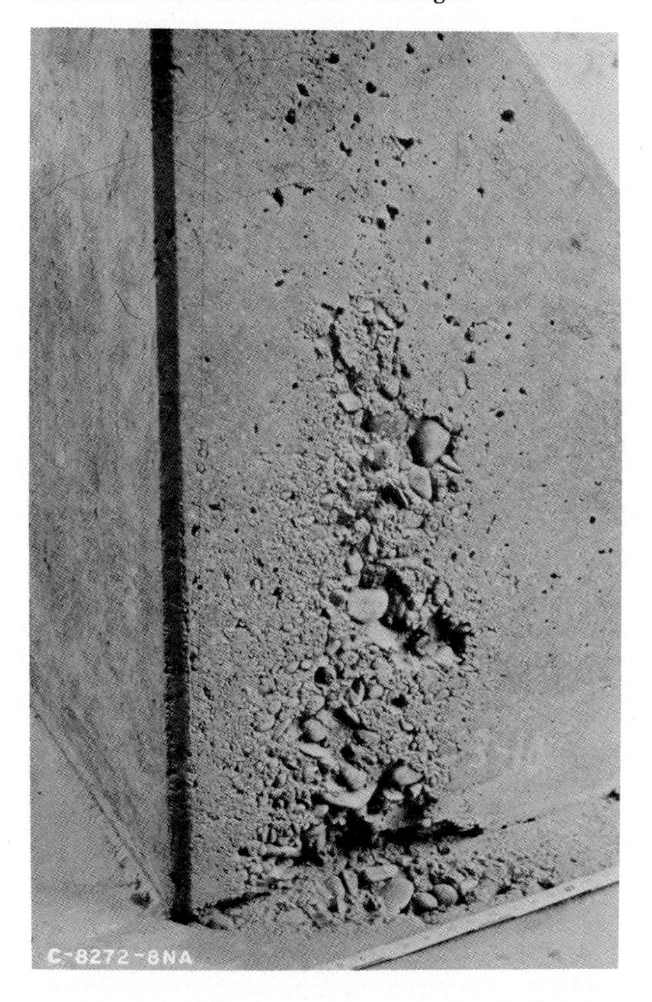

Figure F–3.—Cavitation erosion of concrete on and adjacent to a dentate in the Yellowtail Afterbay Dam spillway stilling basin. Fast-moving water during a floodflow caused a pressure phenomenon at the concrete suface that triggered the cavitation damage shown here. P459–D–68902.

Figure F–4.—Abrasion erosion of concrete in the dentates, walls, and floor of the Yellowtail Afterbay Dam sluiceway stilling basin. The "ball-mill" action of cobbles, gravel, and sand in turbulent water abraded the concrete, thus destroying the integrity of the structure. P459–D–68905.

F.6. *Types of Portland Cement.*—Because of their size and exposure to sulfate deterioration, structures often require the use of cements having special properties to ensure adequate durability and economic life. There are five main types of portland cement, which will be briefly discussed. The differences in types are the result of changes in the relative proportions of the four predominating chemical compounds.

Type I cement is for use in general concrete construction when the special properties of the other types of cement are not required. This type of cement is suitable for use when there is no exposure to sulfates in the soil or ground water. Usually, it is more economical than type II cement.

Type II cement is used where moderate heat generation is desired or where moderate sulfate attack may occur. Concrete made with type II cement possesses all the good qualities inherent in that containing type I cement.

Type III cement is used where rapid strength development of concrete is essential, as in emergency construction and repairs, and in the construction of machine bases and gate installations. Where this type of cement is used, curing and protection of the concrete may be discontinued at an earlier age.

Type IV cement generates less heat than the other types and at a slower rate. It was developed to reduce the cracking resulting from high temperature rise and subsequent contraction with temperature drop that, in general, accompanies the use of type I or type II cements in massive concrete structures. In addition, concrete containing type IV cement has greater resistance to sulfate attack than that containing type I or type II, and has less rapid strength development but equal strength at advanced ages (particularly in the case of mass concrete). Type IV cement is not currently being produced in the United States, but some properties of type IV cement can be obtained by specifying type II or type V, low heat of hydration cement, or by a combination of portland cement and pozzolan.

Type V cement is especially beneficial where structures such as canal linings, culverts, and siphons will be in contact with soils and ground waters containing soluble sulfates in such concentrations as would cause serious deterioration of the concrete if other types of cement were used. Concrete containing type V cement is more resistant to sulfate attack than concretes containing the other types of cement. Type V cement also has a relatively low heat generation during hydration. Compressive strength development, though generally not so rapid, ultimately is approximately equal to that developed by other types.

Table F-2.—Allowable maximum net water-cement plus pozzolan ratios for durability of concrete subjected to various degrees of exposure.

Type or location of concrete or structure, and degree of exposure	Water-cement + pozzolan ratio, W/(C+P), by mass	
	Severe climate, wide range of temperature, long periods of freezing or frequent freezing and thawing	Mild climate, rainy or arid, rarely snow or frost
A. Concrete in portions of structures subjected to exposure of extreme severity, such as the top 2 feet of walls, boxes, piers, and parapets; all of curbs, sills, ledges, copings, corners, and cornices; and concrete in the range of fluctuating water levels or spray. These are parts of dams, spillways, wasteways, blowoff boxes, tunnel inlets and outlets, tailrace walls, valve houses, canal structures, and other concrete work.	0.45±0.02	0.55±0.02

Table F-2.—Allowable maximum net water-cement plus pozzolan ratios for durability of concrete subjected to various degrees of exposure.—Continued

Type or location of concrete or structure, and degree of exposure	Water-cement + pozzolan ratio, W/(C+P), by mass	
	Severe climate, wide range of temperature, long periods of freezing or frequent freezing and thawing	Mild climate, rainy or arid, rarely snow or frost
B. Concrete in exposed structures and parts of structures where exposure is less severe than in A, such as portions of tunnel linings and siphons subjected to freezing, the exterior of mass concrete, and the other exposed parts of structures not covered by A.	0.50±0.02	0.55±0.02
C. Concrete in structures or parts of structures to be covered with backfill, or to be continually submerged or otherwise protected from the weather, such as cutoff walls, foundations, and parts of substructures, dams, trashracks, gate chambers, outlet works, and control houses. (If severe exposure during construction appears likely to last several seasons, reduce W/(C+P) for parts most exposed by 0.05.)	0.58±0.02	0.58±0.02
D. Concrete that will be subjected to attack by sulfate alkalies in soil and ground waters, and will be placed during moderate weather.	- -	0.50±0.02
E. Concrete that will be subjected to attack by sulfate alkalies in soil and ground waters, but will be placed during freezing weather, when calcium chloride would normally be used in mix. Do not use $CaCl_2$, but decrease W/(C+P) to the value shown.	0.45±0.02	- -
F. Concrete deposited by tremie in water	0.45±0.02	0.45±0.02
G. Canal lining	0.53±0.02	0.58±0.02
H. Concrete for the interior of dams	The W/(C+P) of this concrete will be governed by the strength, thermal properties, and volume change requirements established for each structure.	

The five types described above may be purchased to meet the low-alkali provisions of ASTM C 150. Air-entraining cement may also be purchased under these specifications.

F.7. *Abnormal Set of Portland Cement.*—Abnormal set, or premature stiffening, of cement impedes or prevents proper placing and consolidation of concrete. A normal setting concrete may be defined as one that retains its workability long enough to permit proper placing and consolidation. The period of time required between completion of mixing and completion of consolidation may be as short as 10 minutes or may extend up to 2 hours. The loss of workability during the interval is called slump loss and can be measured either by the slump test or by ASTM C 403, Time of Setting of Concrete Mixtures by Penetration Resistance. In the laboratory, abnormal setting is measured by the decrease of penetration of a 10-mm diameter, 400-gram Vicat needle in a mortar, following the method of ASTM C 359.

Abnormal set may be due to one or more causes.

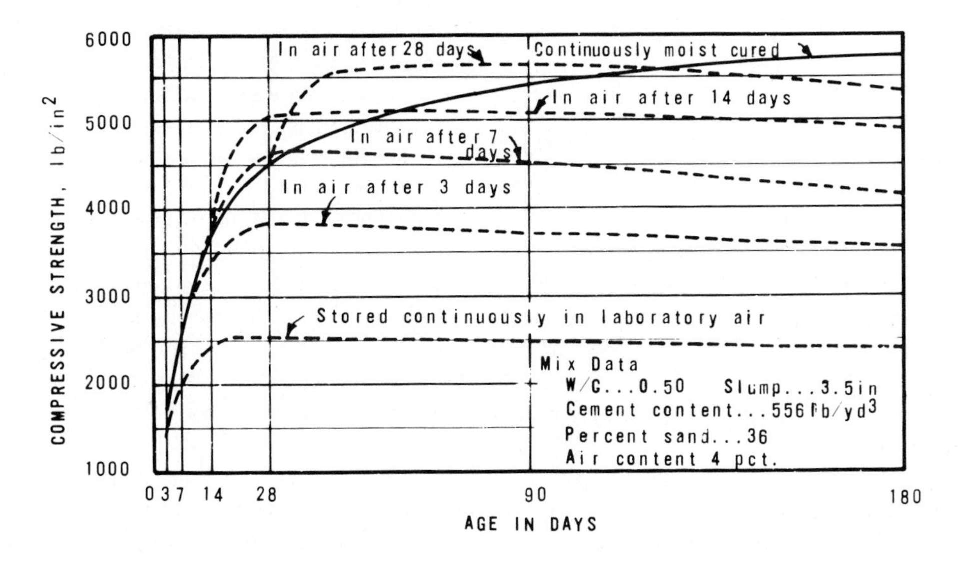

Figure F-5.—Compressive strength of concrete dried in laboratory air after preliminary moist curing. 288-D-2644.

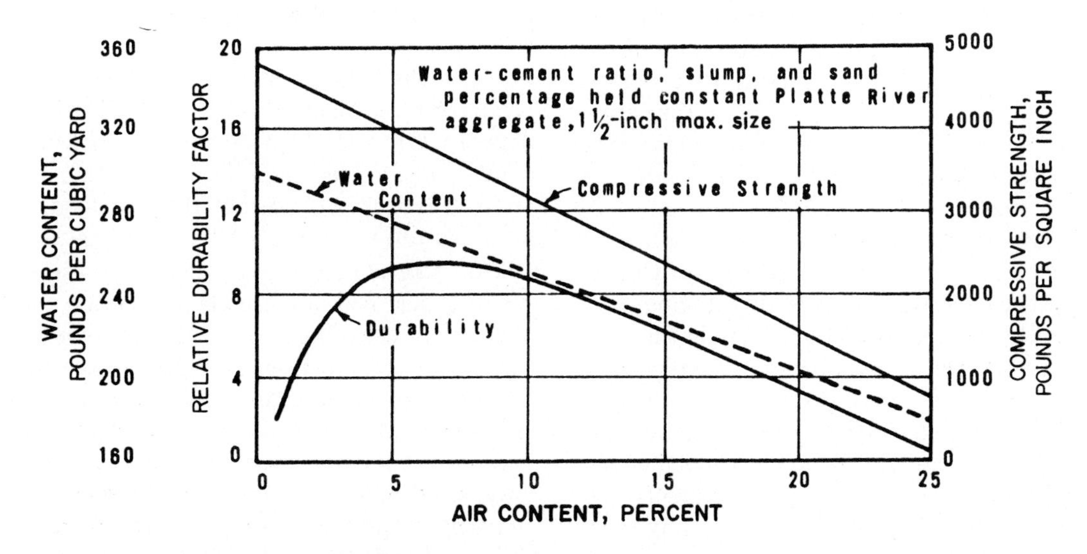

Figure F-6.—Effects of air content on durability, compressive strength, and required water content of concrete. 288-D-1520.

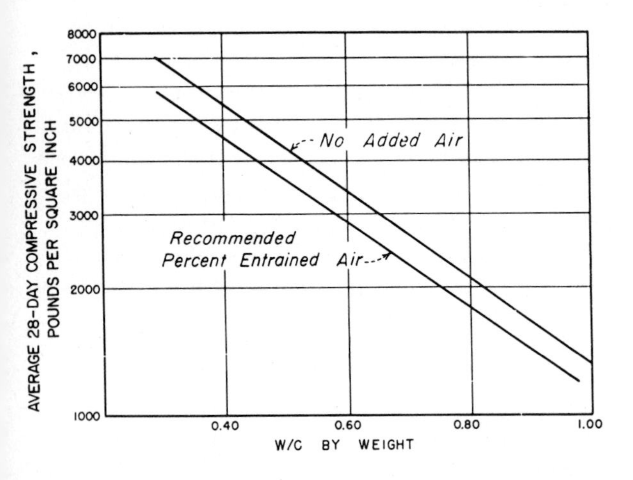

Figure F-7.—Strength in relation to water-cement ratio for air-entrained and non-air-entrained concrete. 288-D-1524.

Different types of set are known (or designated) as false, delayed false, quick, delayed quick, and thixotropic. In the following definitions, paste, mortar, and concrete are interchangeable words. According to ASTM C 359, "False set is the rapid development of rigidity in a mixed portland cement paste, mortar, or concrete without evolution of much heat, which rigidity can be dispelled and plasticity regained by further mixing without addition of water." False set as described is often caused by recrystallization of gypsum in the immediate postmixing period (which has been dehydrated during grinding). This type of false set can be prevented by maintaining enough gypsum in the cement during manufacture to cause total precipitation of dehydrated gypsum during the mixing of concrete. False set is also occasionally caused by continuation of ettringite precipitation for several minutes in the postmixing period. Ettringite ($C_3A \cdot 3CS \cdot H_{32}$) is formed by the reaction of the C_3A, gypsum, and water. In a normal-setting cement, ettringite precipitates as a slightly pervious coating over the exposed surfaces of C_3A crystals and temporarily stops the fast hydration of C_3A. This is the generally accepted theory explaining gypsum as a set retarder.

Delayed false set is phenomenologically and chemically the same as false set except that the recrystallization of gypsum (and infrequently ettringite precipitation) occurs after the remixing at 11 minutes in ASTM C 359. Both false set and delayed false set can be dispelled by further mixing.

According to ASTM C 359, "Quick set is the rapid development of rigidity in a mixed portland cement paste, mortar, or concrete, usually with the evolution of considerable heat, which rigidity cannot be dispelled nor can plasticity be regained by further mixing without addition of water." Quick set is caused by rapid and uninterrupted precipitation of ettringite. However, it has not been encountered in Bureau work for several years. Delayed quick set occurs when the ettringite reaction has temporarily stopped during mixing, but is reactivated during remixing at 11 minutes or shortly thereafter. Pastes or mortars exhibiting delayed ettringite precipitation continue to set; therefore, this set is not dispelled by further mixing. The dispelling or nondispelling of delayed sets is the criterion for calling one delayed false set and the other delayed quick set.

Thixotropic set may be defined as a very rapid and pronounced development of rigidity of a cement paste immediately upon cessation of mixing. This rigidity is dispelled without recurrence by additional mixing up to 2 minutes, but infrequently longer mixing may be required. This type of set was determined in the Bureau laboratories to be caused by interaction of opposite electrostatic surface charges on different compounds in ground cement clinker. Such charges, detected in a few cements obtained from different projects, were probably induced by aeration. It has been found that electrostatic charges can be caused by aeration of ground clinker or cement at 50 percent relative humidity. An instrument called a thixometer (adapted from a Stormer paint viscometer) has been developed to measure the relative strengths of bonds between particles in a cement-benzene slurry. The difference between the total load required to shear the set slurry and the load required to maintain free flow after set is broken divided by the total load provides an index ratio to express thixotropic set.

F.8. ***Use of Pozzolans.***—Pozzolans are siliceous or siliceous and aluminous materials, which in themselves usually possess little or no cementitious value, but will, in finely divided form and in the presence of moisture, chemically react with calcium hydroxide (lime) at ordinary temperatures to form compounds possessing cementitious properties. In concrete the lime required for this reaction is provided by the portland cement. Materials having pozzolanic properties are some clays and shales, volcanic materials (including pumice, pumicite, etc.) and fly ash, a product of some coal-burning boilers.

Pozzolans may be used to improve the workability and the quality of concrete, to effect economy, or to protect against disruptive expansion caused by alkali-aggregate reaction or sulfate attack. In addition to improving the workability of concrete, most pozzolans reduce heat generation and thermal volume change of the concrete when they are used to replace a portion of the cement. Concrete bleeding and permeability are also reduced when pozzolans are used. Compressive strength development normally occurs at a slower rate than that of portland cement, but the ultimate strength developed is usually greater, so long as curing continues.

F.9. *Quality and Gradation of Aggregates.*— The procedures for quality and gradation tests of concrete aggregates are outlined in the Bureau of Reclamation's *Concrete Manual* [1], and are found in volume 04.02 of *ASTM Book of Standards*. Concrete aggregate usually consists of natural sand and gravel, crushed rock, or mixtures of these materials. Natural sands and gravels are the most common and are used whenever they are of satisfactory quality and can be obtained economically in sufficient quantity. Crushed rock is widely used for coarse aggregate and occasionally is processed to produce sand when suitable materials from natural deposits are not economically available. Production of workable concrete using sharp, angular, crushed fragments usually requires more cement and water than does concrete made with well-rounded sand and gravel. However, the difficulty of making workable concrete with crushed aggregate may be greatly reduced through the extra workability imparted by entrained air.

Aggregate is commonly contaminated by silt, clay, mica, coals, humus, wood fragments or other organic matter, chemical salts, surface coatings or encrustations. Some contaminating substances in concrete act in a variety of ways to cause unsoundness, decreased strength and durability, and unsightly appearance; their presence complicates processing and mixing operations. Fortunately, excesses of contaminating substances may frequently be removed by simply washing the aggregate.

An aggregate is considered to be physically sound if it is adequately strong and is capable of resisting the agencies of weathering without disruption or decomposition. Aggregate that are physically weak, extremely absorptive, easily cleavable, or that swell when saturated are susceptible to breakdown through exposure to natural weathering processes. The use of such materials in concrete reduces strength or leads to premature deterioration by weakening the bond between the aggregate and the cement paste, or by inducing cracking, spalling, or popouts. Shales, friable sandstones, some micaceous rocks, clayey rocks, some very coarsely crystalline rocks, and various cherts are examples of physically unsound aggregate materials.

Chemical soundness of an aggregate is also important. In many instances, excessive expansion causing premature deterioration of concrete has been associated with chemical reaction between the reactive aggregate and the alkalies in cement. Known reactive substances are the silica minerals (opal, chalcedony, tridymite, cristobalite), zeolite, heulandite (and probably ptilolite), glassy to cryptocrystalline rhyolites, dacites and andesites and their tuffs, and certain phyllites.

An aggregate should and usually does have sufficient strength to develop the full strength of the cementing matrix. Generally, resistance of concrete to abrasion is directly related to its compressive strength regardless of the type of aggregate employed. Usually, quartz, quartzite, and many dense volcanic and siliceous rocks are well adapted for making strong and, therefore, wear-resistant concrete.

Volume change in aggregate resulting from wetting or drying is a common source of injury to concrete. Shales, clays, and some rock nodules are examples of materials that expand when they absorb water and shrink as they dry.

Flat or elongated particles of aggregate have a detrimental effect on the workability of concrete and require more highly sanded mixes with consequent use of more cement and water. A moderate percentage of flat or elongated fragments in the larger sizes of coarse aggregate has little effect on the workability or cost of concrete.

Specific gravity [2] is a useful, quick indicator of aggregate quality. Low specific gravity frequently indicates porous, weak, and absorptive material, and high specific gravity often indicates good quality. However, such indications are not infallible and should be confirmed by other tests. Specific gravity of aggregate in itself is of direct importance only in those cases where design or structural considerations require that the concrete have minimum or maximum weight. When lightness is desired, artificially prepared aggregates of low density are frequently used in place of natural rock.

The particle-size distribution of aggregate as determined by separation with standard sieves is known as its gradation [3]. Aggregate grading is important principally because of its effect on water-cement ratio and paste-aggregate ratio, which affect economy and placeability of concrete. A grading chart, similar to that shown on figure F–8, is useful for depicting the size distribution of the aggregate particles.

F.10. ***Quality of Mixing and Curing Water.***—Mixing and curing water for concrete should be reasonably clean and free from objectionable quantities of silt, organic matter, alkali, salts, and other impurities. Preparatory to its use in concrete, water from a stream carrying an excessive quantity of suspended solids should be allowed to stand in settling basins or should be clarified by other means. Except for possible discoloration, moderate amounts of salts in water do not appear to have any harmful effects, and water containing not more than 3,000 parts per million of soluble sulfates may be used for mixing and curing concrete.

F.11. ***Use of Admixtures.***—The early strength of concrete can be materially increased by inclusion of an accelerator such as calcium chloride in the concrete mix. Increased early strength during cold weather affords better protection against damage of concrete from freezing at the end of the specified protection period. In addition, high early strengths may be desirable for expediting form removal or to permit early loading of anchor devices. However, calcium chloride should not be used in concrete in which aluminum or galvanized metalwork is to be embedded, nor in prestressed concrete because of the possibility of corrosion.

Air-entrainment is a requirement for Bureau of Reclamation concrete [4]. The most important benefit of purposefully entraining air in concrete is that it greatly increases the resistance to the disintegrating action of freezing and thawing. In addition, entrainment of air reduces bleeding and segregation, greatly facilitates the handling and placing of concrete, and permits the use of a wider range of aggregate gradations. It reduces sand and water requirements, and the curtailed bleeding permits finishing of concrete surfaces earlier and with less effort. Resistance to chemical attack is improved and permeability is decreased by the reduction in capillarity produced by air entrainment. Among the factors that influence the amount of air entrained in concrete, for a given amount of air-entraining admixture, are the gradation and particle shape of the aggregate, richness of mix, mixing time, slump, and concrete temperature. Recommended percentages of entrained air are shown in table F–3. In mild climates these values may be reduced about one-fourth if strength development is critical and satisfactory workability can be maintained.

Chemical or WRA (water-reducing admixtures) and/or set-controlling admixtures are commonly required in Bureau concrete to further reduce water requirements and extend the length of time concrete can be consolidated by vibration [5]. Cement savings usually result from water reductions and the risk of obtaining cold joints is reduced by using a set-retarding WRA.

F.12. ***Field Control.***—After concrete materials have been selected and the relative proportions determined, their use should be controlled closely. This field control governs the quality, uniformity, and ultimate economy of the concrete structure. Much of the potential value of first-class materials and optimum proportioning may be lost through ineffective control in batching, mixing, handling, placing, and curing. The poorer the quality of the ingredients, the greater the need for rigid control to attain satisfactory durability and strength and, therefore, the maximum serviceable life for the structure.

The degree of uniformity of concrete strength is a measure of success in attaining adequate field control. Without adequate control of concrete manufacturing operations, wide variations in strength will occur and extra cement will be needed to ensure that the quality of the concrete will meet minimum requirements.

SIEVE SIZE	% RETAINED		COMB % RET	
	INDI-VIDUAL	CUMU-LATIVE	INDI-VIDUAL	CUMU-LATIVE
6 Inch	0	0	0	0
3 inch	28	28	21	21
1½ inch	26	54	20	41
¾ inch	22	76	16	57
⅜ inch	16	92	12	69
No. 4	8	100	6	75
No. 4	0	0	0	
No. 8	12	12	3	78
No. 16	20	32	5	83
No. 30	24	56	6	89
No. 50	24	80	6	95
No. 100	16	96	4	99
PAN	4	100	1	100
F M		2.76		
PERCENT SAND (clean separation) 25				
(Sieve sizes are based on square openings)				

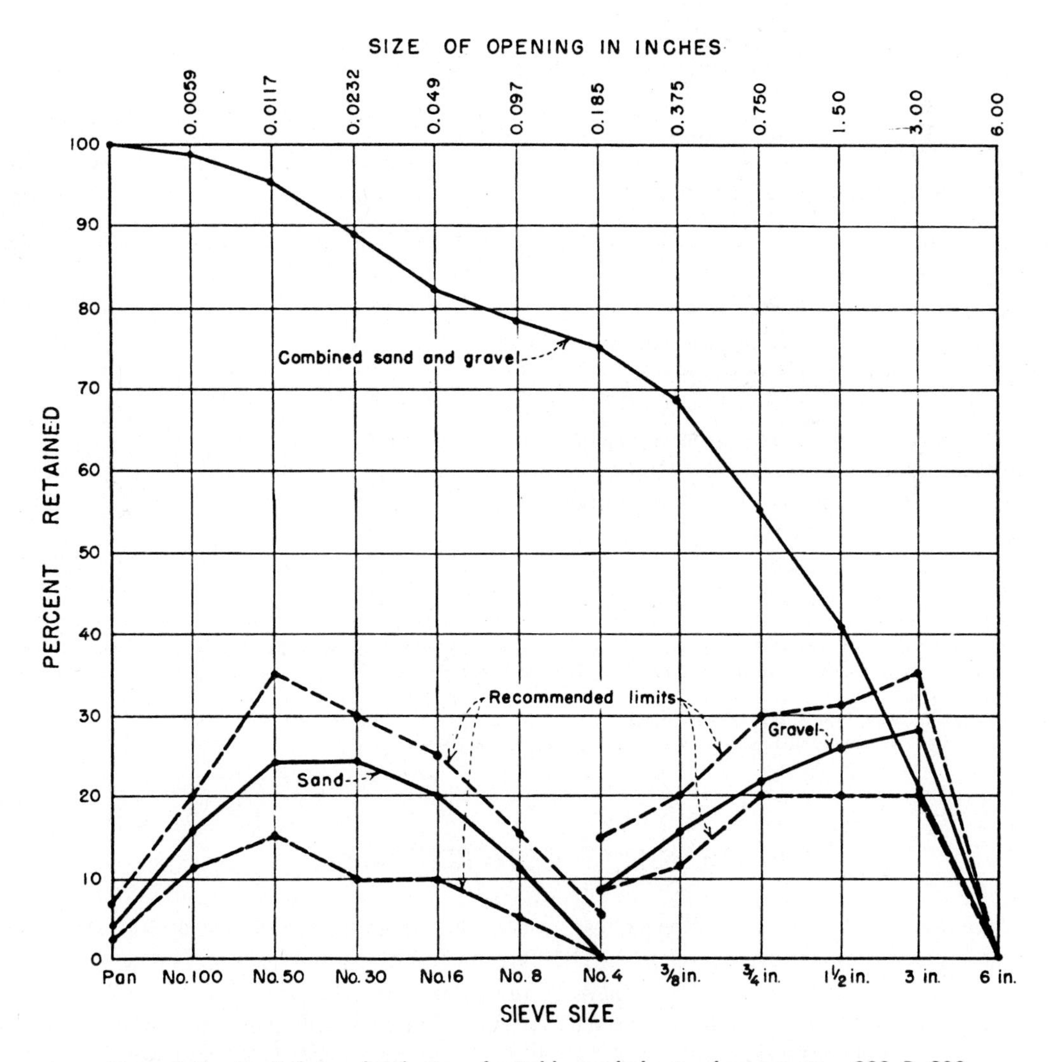

Figure F-8.—Typical size distribution of suitably graded natural aggregate. 288-D-803.

Table F-3.—Approximate air and water contents per volume of concrete; and proportions of fine and coarse aggregate.[1]

Max. size of coarse aggregate, inches	Recommended total air content, ±1 percent	Sand, percent of total aggregate by solid volume	Percent of dry-rodded or dry-jigged density of coarse aggregate per unit volume of concrete	Air-entrained concrete, average water content, lbm/yd³
3/8	7.0	60	41	320
1/2	6.0	50	52	305
3/4	5.5	42	62	280
1	5.5	37	67	265
1½	5.0	34	73	245
2	4.5	30	76	230
3	4.0	28	81	200
4	4.0	26	84	185
6	3.5	24	87	165

Adjustment of values for other conditions[2]

Changes in materials or proportions	Water content, percent	Percentage of sand	Percentage of dry-rodded or dry-jigged coarse aggregate
When WRA[3] is used	−5	+2	—
When HRWRA[4] is used	−12	+5	—
Each 0.2 increase or decrease in fineness modulus of sand	—	±1	∓2
Each 1-inch increase or decrease in slump	±3	—	—
Each 10°F increase or decrease in concrete temperature	±2	—	—
Each 1 percent increase or decrease in air content	∓3	∓1	—
Each 0.05 increase or decrease in W/(C+P)	—	±1	—
Each 1 percent increase or decrease in sand content	±1	—	∓2
Each 10 percent increase or decrease in fly ash	∓3	∓1	±2
When manufactured sand is used	+5	+2	—
When flat, elongated, or angular coarse aggregate is used	+8	+4	—

[1]For 70 °F, concrete containing natural sand with a fineness modulus of 2.75, average coarse aggregate, and a slump of 3 to 4 inches at the mixer.
[2]If aggregates are proportioned by the percentage of sand method, use first and second columns; if by the dry-rodded or dry-jigged density method, use first and third columns.
[3]WRA = water reducing admixture (Type A or D, ASTM C 494).
[4]HRWRA = high-range water reducing admixture (Type F or G admixtures, ASTM C 494).

B. DESIGN OF CONCRETE MIXES

F.13. *Introduction.*—Concrete is composed essentially of water, cement, pozzolan, aggregate, and purposefully entrained air. The proportions of these ingredients should be selected to make the most economical use of available materials and produce concrete of the required workability, durability and strength. Mix proportions should be selected to produce concrete with:

(1) The stiffest consistency (lowest slump) that can be efficiently placed and consolidated by

vibration into a homogeneous mass,

(2) The lowest sand-aggregate ratio that is reasonably possible,

(3) The largest maximum size of aggregate economically available that is consistent with placement and strength requirements,

(4) Adequate durability to satisfactorily withstand weathering and other destructive agencies to which it may be exposed, and

(5) Sufficient strength to withstand the loads to be imposed without danger of failure.

F.14. ***Estimate of Water Requirement.***—Overwet concrete should always be avoided; it is difficult to place without segregation and it is certain to be weak and lacking in durability. Adequate consistency, as determined by the slump test [6], for placing and consolidating concrete in various types of structures is shown in table F–4.

The quantity of water per unit volume of concrete required to produce a mix of desired consistency is influenced by the maximum size, particle shape, and gradation of the aggregate and by the amount of entrained air. Within the normal range of mixes, the water requirement is relatively unaffected by the quantity of cement. The quantities of water given in table F–3 are of sufficient accuracy for preliminary estimates of proportions. They are the averages that may be expected for various maximum sizes of fairly well-shaped and well-graded aggregate. Flat-shaped aggregates with excess fines will require more water, and very round-shaped, well-graded aggregates will not require as much water as shown in table F–3. The weight of water throughout the normal range of placing temperatures may be assumed to be 62.4 lb/ft^3.

Table F-4.—Recommended slumps for various types of construction.[1]

Type of construction	Slump, inches	
	maximum	minimum
Footings, caissons, and substructures	3	1
Beams and reinforced walls	4	1
Sidewalls and arch in tunnel linings	4	1
Tops of walls, piers, parapets, curbs	2	1
Pavements, slabs, and tunnel inverts[2]	2	1
Canal linings[3]	3	1
Mass concrete, mass construction	2	1
Building columns	4	1
Other structures	3	1

[1]The maximum slumps are for concrete after placement and before consolidation, and for mixes having air contents given on table F–3. For certain applications, the use of a HRWRA (high-range water reducing admixture) is allowed. If mix is properly designed to prevent segregation, a HRWRA can be used to produce flowing concrete with a maximum slump of 9 inches; however, each use or application must be allowed in the specifications or approved by contracting officer.

[2]The slump of tunnel inverts placed monolithically with sidewalls and arch may be increased to a maximum of 4 inches.

[3]On machine-placed canal lining less than 3 inches thick, the slump may be increased to a maximum of 4 inches.

F.15. ***Estimate of Cement Requirement.***—A fundamental rule for designing plastic concrete mixes is that the strength and the durability of hardened concretes, with the same air content, vary inversely with the ratio of the weight of water to the weight of cement. Table F–2 is a guide to selecting maximum permissible water-cement ratios for different severities of exposure when proper use is made of air entrainment.

Table F–5 shows an approximation of the minimum strengths to be expected for air-entrained concrete with different water-cement ratios. This table can be used in estimating the strength of concrete until verified by tests of compressive strength specimens.

The cement content is calculated using the lowest water-cement ratio selected from table F–2 or table F–5 and the water requirement from table F–3. The calculation is accomplished by dividing the water requirement by the water-cement ratio. If a minimum cement content is specified, the corresponding water-cement ratio for estimating strength can be computed by dividing the water content by the cement content.

The term "cement" refers to portland cement or a combination of portland cement and pozzolan fully meeting the requirements of applicable Bureau of Reclamation specifications.

F.16. ***Estimate of Admixture Requirement.***—When calcium chloride is used as an accelerator, it is normally not used in excess of 1 percent by weight

Table F-5.—Approximate strength of concrete (containing good aggregate) for various water-cement ratios.

Water-cement ratio by mass	Compressive strength at 28 days: Air-entrained concrete, lbf/in^2	Compressive strength at 28 days: Air-entrained concrete with WRA, lbf/in^2
0.40	5,700	6,500
.45	4,900	5,600
.50	4,200	4,800
.55	3,600	4,200
.60	3,100	3,600
.65	2,600	3,100
.70	2,200	2,700

of cement and pozzolan and should never be used in excess of 2 percent. Calcium chloride should be added to the batch in solution as a part of the mixing water. If proprietary accelerators are used, the manufacturer's recommendations should be followed. However, use of an accelerator may cause greater temperature rise in massive sections.

The amount of air-entraining admixture required to produce a desired percentage of entrained air varies with the materials used, temperature of the concrete, richness of mix, and consistency of the fresh concrete. Decreasing the slump or increasing the temperature or cement content of concrete will usually require larger amounts of admixture to maintain the desired air content. The manufacturer's recommendations should be used for the initial mix. More or less admixture may be added to subsequent mixes based on fresh concrete tests. Admixtures should be added as a solution to the mix water, either before the mixer is charged or during charging. Some cements are manufactured with an air-entraining admixture integrally blended with cement. However, if a uniform air content is to be maintained under varying conditions, the air-entraining admixture should be added at the batch plant so that the amount added may be readily adjusted. Control of the amount of air is necessary for adequately uniform strength of concrete because a high air content will decrease the compressive strength.

Batch quantities of water-reducing, set-retarding admixtures are based on the weight of cementitious material; that is, fluid ounces of WRA per pound of cement plus pozzolan. Again, the manufacturer's recommended dosage should be used for initial tests and then the dosage may be adjusted to obtain the desired results. Actual results are affected by the materials used and the ambient temperature. The amount of water reduction and set-retardation increases as the WRA dosage increases.

F.17. *Estimate of Aggregate Requirement.*—Estimates for the fine aggregate content by the sand percentage method and for the coarse aggregate content by the dry-rodded or dry-jigged density method are presented in this section. Concretes of comparable workability can be expected with aggregates of comparable size and gradation provided the volume of mortar is the same. The solid volume of cement, pozzolan, water, air, and sand may be interchanged to maintain a constant mortar content. The percentage of sand in a concrete mix has been used extensively as a means of identifying the proportions of sand and coarse aggregate. Recommended percentages of sand for each maximum size of coarse aggregate are listed in table F-3.

It is demonstrated below that aggregates can be proportioned by computing the total solid volume of sand and coarse aggregate in the concrete mix and multiplying this total volume by the recommended percentage of sand, or by estimating quantity of coarse aggregate and paste initially, then determining amount of sand. Either method is satisfactory and results in about the same proportions for most conditions. However, basing the amount of coarse aggregate on a fixed percentage of the dry-rodded or dry-jigged density automatically makes allowances for differences in aggregate shapes. For example, angular aggregates have a higher void content, and therefore require more mortar than rounded aggregates. The higher void content results in a lower dry-rodded or dry-jigged density and therefore decreases the amount of coarse aggregate obtained from the fixed percentage, which automatically produces a greater amount of mortar.

(a) *Percentage of Sand Method.*—Example 1 in section F.18 uses the percentage of sand method. To use this method, first calculate the volume of water, cement, pozzolan, and air per cubic yard of concrete. Then, calculate the total volume of aggregate by subtracting the volume of paste initially calculated. The volume of sand is obtained by multiplying total volume of aggregate by percentage of sand recommended in table F-3. The volume of coarse aggregate is determined last, by subtracting volume of paste and sand from unity. If more than one nominal size fraction of coarse aggregate is used, it is desirable to determine the optimum proportion of each by density comparisons of various proportions of the combined nominal size fractions. Then, the volume of each nominal size of coarse aggregate is computed using the optimum percentages obtained by the comparison. Finally, the mass of each size aggregate is determined by multiplying volume of aggregate by bulk density of aggregate.

(b) *Dry-Rodded or Dry-Jigged Density of Coarse Aggregate Method.*—Initially, determine dry-rodded or dry-jigged density of the coarse aggregate. If more than one nominal size fraction of coarse aggregate is used, determine the optimum proportion of each by density comparisons of various proportions of the combined nominal size fractions. Then, select the percentage of dry-rodded or dry-jigged density of coarse aggregate per unit volume of concrete from table F–3. Calculate the mass of coarse aggregate per cubic yard or per cubic meter of concrete by multiplying this percentage by the optimum dry-rodded or dry-jigged density of the coarse aggregate. The volume of coarse aggregate is obtained by dividing this mass by the bulk density. To obtain the volume of sand, add the volume of coarse aggregate to the volume of paste and subtract from unity. The mass of the sand is obtained by multiplying the volume of sand by the bulk density of sand.

F.18. *Computations of Proportions.*—The computations of proportions for concrete mixes can best be explained by specific examples. Computations are initially based on SSD (saturated-surface-dry) aggregates and later adjusted for actual moisture conditions. The following materials shall be used for the computations:

- Water with a specific gravity of 1.00 and density of 1685 lbm/yd³.
- Type II portland cement with a specific gravity of 3.15.
- Sand with a specific gravity of 2.63, fineness modulus of 2.75, and moisture content of 5.0 percent wet of SSD.
- Coarse aggregate with a specific gravity of 2.68. The No. 4 to ¾-inch size fraction has a moisture content of 1.0 percent wet of SSD, and the ¾- to 1½-inch size fraction has a moisture content of 0.5 percent wet of SSD. The optimum combination of No. 4 to 1½-inch aggregate is 45 percent ¾-inch nominal MSA (maximum size aggregate) and 55 percent 1½-inch nominal MSA.
- A neutralized, vinsol resin, air-entraining admixture. The manufacturer recommends 2 fluid ounces per 100 pounds of cementitious materials.

(a) *Example.*—The example on table F–6 uses the percentage of sand method. This example is a 1½-inch nominal MSA concrete mix for a reinforced retaining wall having a minimum thickness of 12 inches and a minimum rebar spacing of 2.5 inches. The concrete will be exposed to severe climatic conditions (many cycles of freezing and thawing) but will not often be saturated, which puts it into class B of table F–2. The structural design is based on 90 percent of the standard 6- by 12-inch test cylinders having 28-day compressive strengths greater than 4,000 lbf/in². Average Bureau control, which is considered as having a coefficient of variation no more than 15 percent, requires average 28-day strength of 4,980 lbf/in², see table F–7. When designing a mix with new materials or for a new batch plant or contractor, a coefficient of variation of 20 percent should be assumed, similar to the recommendations in ACI 214.

F.19. *Batch Mass Computations.*—The trial-mix computations in section F–18 provided batch quantities for 1 cubic yard of concrete. It is seldom possible to mix concrete in exactly one unit batches; therefore, these quantities must be converted to the size batch to be used. Table F–8 illustrates a convenient form for recording computations when converting design masses to batch masses. This conversion can be accomplished by multiplying the unit quantity of each ingredient by the volume of batch. For example, assume that a 0.10-cubic yard mixer is available for laboratory trial mixes, and use the trial mix design of the example in section F.18. The batch proportions would be:

Water	(0.10) (245) = 24.5 lbm
Cement	(0.10) (557) = 55.7 lbm
Sand	(0.10) (1,055) = 105.5 lbm
No. 4 to ¾-inch	(0.10) (939) = 93.9 lbm
¾- to 1½-inch	(0.10) (1,147) = 114.7 lbm

Aggregates were assumed to be in SSD condition for initial computations. Under field conditions, the aggregates would generally be moist (because of sprinkling stockpiles and the use of spray bars on rescreens), and quantities to be batched must be adjusted accordingly. Assume tests show sand contains 5.0 percent free moisture; No. 4 to ¾-inch aggregate contains 1.0 percent free moisture; and ¾- to 1½-inch aggregate contains 0.5 percent free moisture. Since the quantity of SSD sand required is 105.5 lbm, the amount of moist sand that must be determined is 110.8 lbm (105.5)(1.05). Similarly, the mass of moist coarse aggregate that must be determined is 94.8 lbm (93.9)(1.01) and 115.3 lbm (114.7)(1.005), respectively. Coarse aggregate is sometimes drier than SSD. Assuming the ¾- to 1½-inch aggregate contains −0.5 percent free moisture (aggregate will absorb 0.5 percent moisture to reach SSD condition), the amount of dry aggregate that must be determined is 114.1 lbm (114.7)(0.995).

Table F-6.—Example of trial mix computation using percentage of sand method.

Mix ingredients	Mass, lbm/yd³	Conversion of mass to volume	Conversion of volume to mass	Solid volume, yd³/yd³ of concrete
Water:				
Estimated value from table F-3 for a 3- to 4-inch slump at mixer = 245	245	$\frac{245}{1,685}$	–	0.145
Cement:				
W/C for durability, class B, from table F-2 = 0.50				
W/C for strength, from table F-5 = 0.44				
(Strength controls, use 0.44)				
Cement = $\frac{\text{water}}{\text{W/C}} = \frac{245}{0.44} = 557$	557	$\frac{557}{(3.15)(1,685)}$	–	0.105
Air:				
From table F-3 = 5% = 0.050	–	–	–	0.050
Sand:				
From table F-3 = 34% of volume of aggregate = [1.000−(0.145+0.105+0.050)](0.34) = (0.700)(0.34) = 0.238	1,055	–	(0.238)(2.63)(1,685)	0.238
Coarse Aggregate:				
Volume of all ingredients except coarse aggregate = 0.145+0.105+0.050+0.238 = 0.538				
Coarse aggregate = 1.000−0.538 = 0.462				
¾-inch nominal MSA = 45% of coarse aggregate volume = (0.45)(0.462) = 0.208	939	–	(0.208)(2.68)(1,685)	0.208
1½-inch nominal MSA = 55% of coarse aggregate volume = (0.55)(0.462) = 0.254	1,147	–	(0.254)(2.68)(1,685)	0.254
Totals	3,943	–	–	1.000

Note: W/C = water-cement ratio
MSA = maximum size aggregate

Free water in the aggregate must be considered as part of the mixing water and theoretically removed from the quantity of water to be batched. Conversely, in the case of dry aggregate, water must be added to allow for absorption. In this example, free water (mixing water) in the sand is 5.3 lbm (110.8 – 105.5); the No. 4 to ¾-inch aggregate contains 0.9 lbm (94.8 – 93.9); and the ¾- to 1½-inch aggregate contains 0.6 lbm (115.3 – 114.7). If the ¾- to 1½-inch aggregate were dry, as mentioned previously, 0.6 lbm (114.7 – 114.1) of water would have to be added to the batch water to allow for absorption.

F.20. ***Adjustments to Trial Mix.***—When working with materials that the personnel involved have little or no experience with, several trial mixes will usually be necessary to establish the correct quantities, especially for the water and the air-entraining

Table F-7.—Average strength that must be maintained to meet design requirements.

Design strength (f_c'), lbf/in²	Percent of strength greater than design strength	Average strength required (f_{cr}) in lbf/in² so that 75, 80, 85, or 90 percent of tests are greater than design strength (f_c') — Coefficient of variation, percent: 5	10	15	20	25
2,000	75	2,070	2,150	2,230	2,320	2,410
	80	2,090	2,190	2,290	2,410	2,540
	85	2,110	2,240	2,380	2,530	2,720
	90	2,140	2,300	2,490	2,710	2,980
2,500	75	2,590	2,680	2,790	2,900	3,010
	80	2,610	2,730	2,870	3,010	3,180
	85	2,640	2,790	2,970	3,170	3,400
	90	2,680	2,880	3,110	3,390	3,720
3,000	75	3,110	3,220	3,340	3,470	3,620
	80	3,130	3,280	3,440	3,620	3,810
	85	3,170	3,350	3,560	3,800	4,070
	90	3,210	3,450	3,730	4,070	4,460
3,500	75	3,620	3,760	3,900	4,050	4,220
	80	3,660	3,830	4,010	4,220	4,450
	85	3,690	3,910	4,160	4,440	4,750
	90	3,750	4,030	4,360	4,740	5,210
4,000	75	4,140	4,290	4,460	4,630	4,820
	80	4,180	4,370	4,590	4,820	5,090
	85	4,220	4,470	4,750	5,070	5,430
	90	4,280	4,600	4,980	5,420	5,950
4,500	75	4,660	4,830	5,010	5,210	5,430
	80	4,700	4,920	5,160	5,430	5,720
	85	4,750	5,030	5,350	5,700	6,110
	90	4,820	5,180	5,600	6,100	6,690
5,000	75	5,180	5,370	5,570	5,790	6,030
	80	5,220	5,470	5,730	6,030	6,360
	85	5,280	5,590	5,940	6,340	6,790
	90	5,350	5,750	6,220	6,780	7,440
5,500	75	5,690	5,900	6,130	6,370	6,630
	80	5,750	6,010	6,310	6,630	6,990
	85	5,810	6,150	6,530	6,970	7,470
	90	5,890	6,330	6,850	7,450	8,180
6,000	75	6,210	6,440	6,680	6,950	7,240
	80	6,270	6,560	6,880	7,240	7,630
	85	6,330	6,710	7,130	7,600	8,150
	90	6,420	6,910	7,470	8,130	8,930

Table F-8.—Typical trial computations for concrete mix.

MIX NAME: **DATE:** 7/3/85

INGREDIENTS	DESCRIPTION - SOURCE AND TYPE, ETC.	SPECIFIC GRAVITY	BULK DENSITY lbm/yd³
WATER	Tap	1.00	1686
CEMENT	Ideal - Type II, LA	3.15	5308
POZZOLAN			
SAND	Clear Creek	2.63	4432
COARSE AGGREGATE NO. 1	" "	2.68	4516
COARSE AGGREGATE NO. 2	" "	2.68	4516
COARSE AGGREGATE NO. 3			
COARSE AGGREGATE NO. 4			
ADMIXTURES	AEA Protex AES 2oz/100# Cement	OTHER	None
AIR METER: NO. White 3	VOLUME .009 yd³	MASS	8.03 lbm

MIX DESIGN CONSIDERATIONS

DESIGN STRENGTH: 4000 lbf/in² 90 % MUST EXCEED DESIGN STRENGTH WITH 15 % COEFFICIENT OF VARIATION

AVERAGE STRENGTH REQUIRED: 4980 lbf/in²

DURABILITY: $\frac{W}{C+P}$ = 0.50 STRENGTH: $\frac{W}{C+P}$ = 0.44 MSA: 1-1/2 in

SAND F.M.: 2.75 DESIRED SLUMP: 3 to 4 inches % AIR: 5.0

AGGREGATE DATA	SAND	COARSE AGGREGATE (1)	(2)	(3)	(4)
NOMINAL SIZE		4.75mm TO 19mm	19 mm TO 37.5 mm	mm TO mm	mm TO mm
DRY-RODDED DENSITY lbm/yd³		—	—		
PERCENT MOISTURE	+5.0	+1.0	+0.5		
COARSE AGGREGATE DISTRIBUTION (%)		45	55		

APPROXIMATE SAND OR DRY-RODDED C.A. CONTENT: 34 % ADJUSTMENTS: —

APPROXIMATE WATER CONTENT: 245 lbm ADJUSTMENTS: —

TRIAL MIX DESIGN

ESTIMATED QUANTITIES PER CUBIC YARD

TRIAL MIX NO.	$\frac{W}{C+P}$ BY MASS	% SAND OR DRY-RODDED DENSITY OF COARSE AGGREGATE		AIR 5.0 %	WATER	CEMENT	POZZOLAN % OF TOTAL CEMENTITIOUS MATERIAL	SSD SAND	SSD COARSE AGGREGATE (1)	(2)	(3)	(4)	TOTAL	ADMIXTURES AEA mL	ADMIXTURES OTHER
Example 1	0.44	34	lbm		245	557	—	1055	939	1147			3943	329	—
			yd³	.050	.145	.105		.238	.208	.254			1.000		
Redesigned Example 1	0.44	34	lbm		252	573	—	1042	930	1134			3931	416	—
			yd³	.050	.150	.108		.235	.206	.251			1.000		

BATCH COMPUTATION

TRIAL MIX NO.	VOLUME OF BATCH yd³	WATER lbm	CEMENT lbm	POZZOLAN lbm	SSD SAND lbm	SSD COARSE AGG. (1) lbm	(2)	(3)	(4)	TOTAL	ADMIXTURES AEA mL	ADMIXTURES OTHER	AGG. WATER (± SSD) SAND lbm	C.A. (1) lbm	(2)	(3)	(4)	ADJUSTED WATER lbm	ADJUSTED SAND lbm	ADJUSTED C.A. (1) lbm	(2)	(3)	(4)
Batch 1	0.100	24.5	55.7	—	105.5	93.9	114.7			394.3	32.9	—	5.3	0.9	0.6			17.7	110.8	94.8	115.3		
Batch 2	0.100	25.2	57.3	—	104.2	93.0	113.4			393.1	41.6	—	5.2	0.9	0.6			18.5	109.4	93.9	114.0		

TESTS OF FRESH CONCRETE

TRIAL MIX NO.	TEMP. °F	SLUMP in.	% AIR PRESSURE METER	SAMPLE MASS - LB GROSS / NET	DENSITY lbm/yd³
Batch 1	70	2	4.1	43.92 / 35.89	3988
Batch 2	71	3 1/2	5.1	43.38 / 35.35	3928

ACTUAL COMPOSITION OF TRIAL MIX

ACTUAL QUANTITIES PER CUBIC YARD

TRIAL MIX NO.	YIELD VOL. OF BATCH yd³		WATER	CEMENT	POZZOLAN	SSD SAND	SSD C.A. (1)	(2)	(3)	(4)	SUB-TOTAL	AIR GRAVIMETRIC	ADMIXTURES AEA mL	ADMIXTURES OTHER	% AIR GRAVIMETER	$\frac{W}{C+P}$ BY MASS	% SAND OR DRY RODDED DENSITY OF C.A.	TEST SPECIMEN NUMBERS AND AGES
Batch 1	.989	lbm	248	563	—	1067	949	1160					333	—	3.9	.44	34	Wasted-low slump & air
		yd³	.147	.106		.241	.210	.257			.961	.039						
Batch 2	1.001	lbm	252	572	—	1041	929	1133					416	—	5.0	.44	34	1 thru 6 7 and 28 d
		yd³	.150	.108		.235	.206	.251			.950	.050						

MIX NOTES:

admixture. After the actual water requirement is established for the job materials, the mix must be redesigned by repeating the computations previously discussed, beginning with the amount of cement. Table F–8 illustrates a convenient form for recording trial mix data. The data presented conform to the trial batches of the example in section F.18 with appropriate adjustments made to the mix after testing the slump, entrained air content, and yield.

(a) *Adjustment of Water.*—After performing tests on the fresh concrete and calculating the actual composition of the batch based on the yield, the mix should be redesigned. Assume the first trial batch had only a 2-inch slump and 4.0 percent air. Table F–3 indicates that to increase the slump by the desired 1.5 inches, an increase in water content of 4.5 percent is necessary (1.5 × 3 percent). Similarly, when increasing air content 1.0 percent, an adjustment in water content must be made. Because entrained air improves workability and consequently increases slump, this adjustment will be a decrease in water content of 3.0 percent (1.0 × 3 percent). These two adjustments occur simultaneously and result in a net increase of 1.5 percent to the actual quantity of batch water used, (1.015)(2.48) = 2.5 lbm.

(b) *Adjustment of Air-Entraining Admixture.*—The percentage of entrained air in the mix can be measured directly with an airmeter or obtained by computing the difference between the calculated (theoretical) volume of air and the measured volume. It is advantageous to record both air contents because any marked difference indicates an error and may lead to discovery of mistakes in mix design, trial mix computations, or test methods. A difference in the indicated air contents of as much as 0.3 percent is considered normal. The amount of air-entraining admixture required to produce the desired 5.0 percent can be easily calculated by assuming a straight-line adjustment of the dosage. Since 333 mL produced 4.0 percent air and 5.0 percent is desired, then (5.0/4.0)(333) or 416 mL should be used in trial batch number 2.

(c) *Adjustment of Aggregate Proportions.*—It is usually necessary to adjust the aggregate proportions. This adjustment is a judgment based on the intended use of the concrete mix and the method of placement. If the concrete mix appears too harsh or does not consolidate or finish well, the sand and fines may have to be increased. If the mix appears too fat or is sticky, the mortar may have to be decreased.

(d) *Adjustment of Water-Cementitious Materials Ratio.*—Once concrete strengths are known by testing cylinders cast from the trial mix, it will be necessary to adjust the water-cement plus pozzolan ratio to achieve the proper strength level consistent with the coefficient of variation. The average strengths obtained from the test cylinders may need to be increased by redesigning the mix with a lower f_{cr} (average strength required) ratio. Conversely, if strengths are above the average strength required (f_{cr}), the ratio may need to be higher to improve the economy of the mix. The field mix need not be adjusted for minor fluctuations in the ratio. A difference of ±0.02 is considered normal and usually results from maintaining a constant slump. However, this variation should be considered when selecting the ratio so that, with the usual variation, the specified maximum is not exceeded.

F.21. *Mixes for Small Jobs.*—For small jobs, where time and personnel are not available to determine the proportions in accordance with the recommended procedure, mixes in table F–9 will provide concrete that is amply strong and durable if the amount of water added at the mixer is not large enough to make the concrete overwet. These mixes have been predetermined in accordance with recommended procedure by assuming conditions applicable to the average small job and the use of aggregate of average specific gravity. Three mixes are given for each maximum size of coarse aggregate. Mix B for each size of coarse aggregate is intended for use as a starting mix in table F–9. If this mix is undersanded, change to mix A; if it is oversanded, change to mix C. Note that the mixes listed in the table apply where the sand is dry. If the sand is moist or very wet, make the corrections in batch weight prescribed in footnote 2.

The approximate cement content in bags per cubic yard of concrete listed in the table will be helpful in estimating cement requirements for the job. These requirements are based on concrete that contains just enough water to permit ready working into the forms without objectionable separation. Concrete should slide, not run, off a shovel.

C. MANUFACTURE, PLACEMENT, CURING, AND INSPECTION OF CONCRETE

F.22. *Aggregate Production and Control.*—The control of production and handling of concrete aggregates is often complicated by lack of uniformity in sources of supply and difficulty in maintaining uniformity in the finished production. It is a problem that requires the constant vigilance of the construction engineer. Deleterious materials are ordinarily removed by washing. Unsatisfactory gradation requires correction by wasting surplus sizes or by supplying deficient sizes, or both. Breakage must be minimized and the moisture content of the aggregate should be kept as uniform as practicable.

The gradation of sand as it comes from the pit often does not conform to the specifications, and some form of processing is required. Defects in gradation may be corrected by adding suitable blending sand, by crushing a portion of the excess of larger sizes, by removing portions of sizes present in excessive amounts, or by a combination of methods.

Table F-9.—Concrete mixes for small jobs.[1]

Maximum size of aggregate, inches	Mix designation	Approximate bags cement per cubic yard of concrete	Pounds of aggregate per 1-bag batch: Sand[2] Air-entrained concrete[3]	Sand[2] Concrete without air	Gravel or crushed stone
½	A	7.0	235	245	170
	B	6.9	225	235	190
	C	6.8	225	235	205
¾	A	6.6	225	235	225
	B	6.4	225	235	245
	C	6.3	215	225	265
1	A	6.4	225	235	245
	B	6.2	215	225	275
	C	6.1	205	215	290
1½	A	6.0	225	235	290
	B	5.8	215	225	320
	C	5.7	205	215	345
2	A	5.7	225	235	330
	B	5.6	215	225	360
	C	5.4	205	215	380

[1]Procedure: Select the proper maximum size of aggregate. Then, using mix B, add just enough water to produce a sufficiently workable consistency. If the concrete appears to be undersanded, use mix A; if it appears to be oversanded, use mix C.

[2]Weights are for dry sand. If damp sand is used, increase the weight of sand 10 pounds for a 1-bag batch; if very wet sand is used, add 20 pounds for a 1-bag batch.

[3]Air-entrained concrete is specified for all Bureau of Reclamation work. In general, air-entrained concrete should be used in all structures that will be exposed to alternate cycles of freezing and thawing.

Wet processing is more common than dry processing for this purpose, because sand is usually damp when it is excavated from the deposit.

Use of sand manufactured by crushing or grinding rock or gravel may result in a harsh mix. This type of sand should be used only when it is not practicable to obtain suitable natural sand at a reasonable cost. Because the angular shape of crushed sand is its only disadvantage, it is important that the crushing machines and equipment used produce the best shape of particles from the material to be crushed. Sand produced by crushing in rollers is generally unsatisfactory because of the high percentage of thin and elongated particles. The product of a rod mill is much better in this respect. If the material is not too hard, as in the case of limestone, good results may be obtained with equipment of the impact type, more commonly known as the hammer mill, which excels in producing particles that approach a cubical shape.

Natural river gravels are usually well shaped by stream action, and satisfactory coarse aggregate with the desired gradation can be produced with a minimum of plant equipment. However, in some cases where natural coarse aggregate is not economically available, crushed aggregate is used. Although the shape of the individual particles is important, it is not so critical for coarse aggregate as it is for sand. Use of corrugated roll crushers to produce smaller sizes of coarse aggregate and of gyratory crushers to produce the large sizes generally results in the least amount of flat and elongated pieces. Because of the segregation and breakage that can result, handling should be kept to a minimum during stockpiling operations. Figure F-9 shows correct and incorrect methods of stockpiling.

Since some breakdown of materials will occur regardless of the care exercised in stockpiling, it is desirable to finish-screen coarse aggregates at the batch plant to ensure production of uniform concrete.

Periodic analysis of aggregate materials should be made to determine the specific gravity and moisture content of the aggregate and to determine the relative percentages of the various size fractions. The frequency of these tests should be sufficient to ensure that the aggregates meet specifications.

F.23. *Batching Methods and Facilities at Concrete Mixing Plants.*—For full advantage of accurate weigh batching to be realized, the weighed materials must be properly and carefully handled so that the batches reaching the mixer will be uniform and complete when released by the measuring equipment.

Tilting mixers are generally more efficient than other types because they can be discharged quickly with a minimum of segregation. Regardless of the type of mixer, to maintain efficiency the mixing blades should be properly spaced, inspected frequently, and repaired when worn, and the interior of the drum should be kept clean and free of deposits of hardened concrete or mortar.

More attention and effort are usually required to obtain uniform slump and mix proportions at minimum water content from truck mixers than from stationary mixers. There is often considerable slump loss in truck-mixed concrete, especially in warm weather. Such loss can be kept to a minimum by avoiding overmixing. Other precautions that can be taken in warm weather are as follows:

(1) Mixer drums should be painted white and kept white.
(2) Materials should be kept as cool as practicable by shading and by light spraying to promote evaporative cooling.
(3) Water should be as cold as practicable and kept cold by shading and by painting tanks and surface lines white.
(4) Delays before discharge and placement of the concrete should be avoided by organizing the work for prompt handling.

F.24. *Production of Quality Concrete.*—The assurance of uniform and economical concrete is largely dependent on inspection at the batching and mixing plants. Mix adjustments are made using results of aggregate gradation and moisture tests, and fresh concrete tests for consistency, temperature, air content, and density. Concrete cylinders are made for the compressive strength tests necessary for quality control. The frequency of sampling and testing the concrete should vary with the type and size of job. In general, slump and air tests should be performed on a routine basis to help ensure that a uniform product is being provided. However, it is sufficient to perform the full complement of tests (concrete and concrete materials testing used for monthly records) only once during each shift for each class of concrete used during that shift. The samples should be representative of materials used and concrete placed during that shift.

F.25. *Preparations Preliminary to Placing.*—Before concrete is ordered for placing, adequate inspection should be performed to ensure that (1) foundations are properly prepared and ready to receive the concrete, (2) construction joints are clean and free from defective concrete, (3) forms are grout-tight, amply strong, and set to line and grade, (4) all reinforcement steel and embedded parts are clean, in their correct position, and securely held in place, and (5) adequate concreting equipment and facilities are on the job, ready to go, and capable of completing the placement without additional unplanned construction joints. Detailed requirements for these items are given in the "Concrete Specifications" portion of appendix G.

F.26. *Transporting.*—Even though the concrete may be carefully designed and properly mixed, its quality may be seriously impaired by the use of improper or careless methods in transporting and placing. Buckets, when designed for the job conditions and properly operated, are a satisfactory means for handling and placing concrete. They should not, however, be used where they have to be hauled so far by truck or railroad that there will be noticeable separation or bleeding caused by settlement, or there will be a loss of slump greater than 1 inch.

Dumpcrete trucks are convenient for the distribution of concrete from a central mixer to small and medium size structures. Care must be taken to avoid segregation during the filling and discharging of these units. No free water should be on the surface of the concrete as delivered, nor should there be an objectionable amount of settlement of coarse aggregate or caking at the bottom of the load. Such stratification or settlement can be reduced considerably by the use of agitator bodies mounted on trucks or, preferably, by mixing the concrete near the point of placement in portable mixers supplied by dry-batch trucks.

As ordinarily used, chutes are unsatisfactory devices for transporting concrete because they result in objectionable segregation and slump loss. To avoid these conditions, the following requirements must be fulfilled:

(1) The chute must be on a slope sufficiently steep to handle concrete of the least slump that can be worked and vibrated. The chute must be supported so that its slope will be constant for varying loads.
(2) If more than about 10 feet long, the chute

INCORRECT METHODS OF STOCKPILING AGGREGATES CAUSE SEGREGATION AND BREAKAGE

PREFERABLE

Crane or other means of placing material in pile in units not larger than a truck load, that remain where placed and do not run down slopes.

OBJECTIONABLE

Methods that permit aggregate to roll down the slope as it is added to the pile, or that permit hauling equipment to operate over the same level repeatedly.

PERMISSIBLE BUT NOT PREFERABLE

Pile built radially in horizontal layers by bulldozer working from materials as dropped from conveyor belt. A rock ladder may be needed in this setup.

Bulldozer stacking progressive layers on slope not flatter than 3:1.

STOCKPILING OF COARSE AGGREGATE WHEN PERMITTED

(STOCKPILED AGGREGATE SHOULD BE FINISH SCREENED AT BATCH PLANT. WHEN THIS IS DONE, NO RESTRICTIONS ON STOCKPILING ARE REQUIRED)

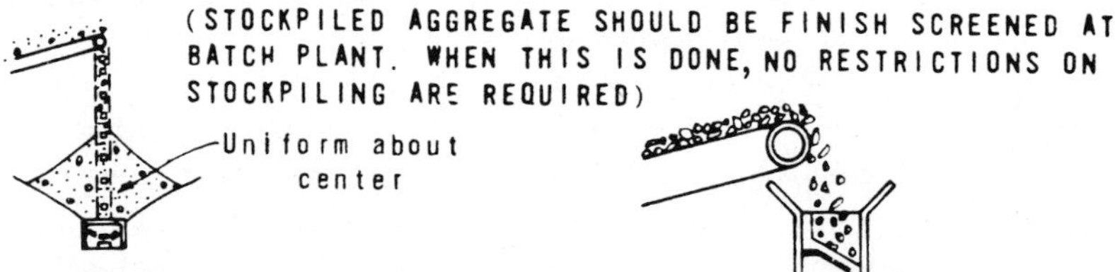

CORRECT

Chimney surrounding material falling from end of conveyor belt to prevent wind from separating fine and coarse materials. Openings provided as required to discharge materials at various elevations on the pile.

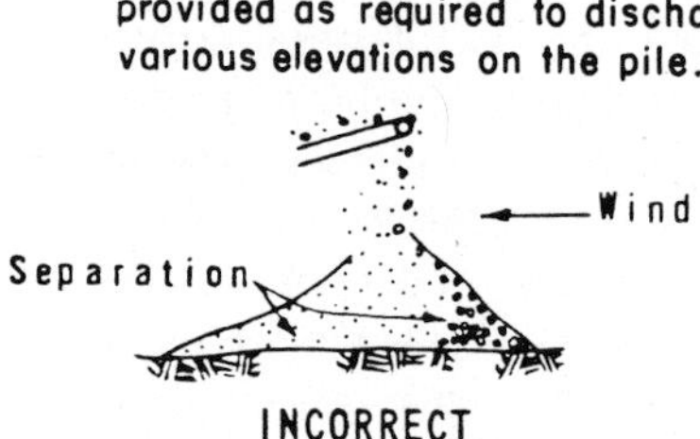

INCORRECT

Free fall of material from high end of stacker permitting wind to separate fine from coarse material.

UNFINISHED OR FINE AGGREGATE STORAGE (DRY MATERIALS)

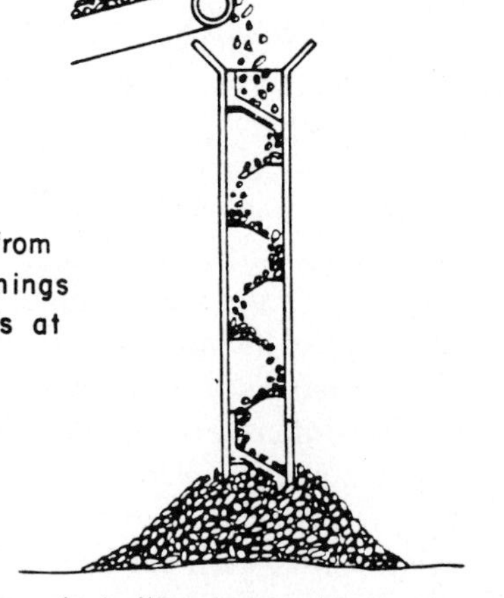

When stockpiling large-sized aggregates from elevated conveyors, breakage is minimized by using a rock ladder.

FINISHED AGGREGATE STORAGE

Figure F-9.—Methods of stockpiling aggregates. 288–D–2655.

must be protected from wind and sun to prevent slump loss.

(3) Effective end control that will produce a vertical drop and prevent separation of the concrete ingredients must be provided, preferably in the form of two sections of metal drop chutes, as shown on figure F–10.

(4) With pneumatic methods, separation of coarse aggregate will result from the impact of violently discharged concrete unless the end of the discharge line is always buried in fresh concrete. Specifications should therefore require that pneumatic equipment used in placing concrete permit introduction of the concrete into the forms without high-velocity discharge. A further objection to the pneumatic method is a loss of slump that occurs in the shooting process. Slump losses as great as 3½-inches between mixer and forms have been observed, and a loss of 2 to 3 inches is not uncommon.

There is no objection to the use of belt conveyors if segregation and objectionable slump losses are prevented and there is no loss of mortar on the return belt. Segregation, which occurs chiefly at transfer points and at the end of the conveyor, may be avoided by using suitable hoppers and drop chutes, as shown on figure F–10. Slump loss is largely preventable by protecting the belt from the sun and wind. A rubber or other suitable scraper should be placed on the return belt to prevent the loss of mortar and to feed the mortar into the concrete-receiving hopper.

Pumping through steel pipelines is one of the most satisfactory methods of transporting concrete where space is limited, such as in tunnels, bridge decks, powerhouses, and buildings. Although pump lines longer than 1,000 feet are not recommended, concrete has been pumped through straight, horizontal pipe under the most favorable conditions as far as 1,300 feet. Curves, lifts, and harsh concrete material reduce the maximum pumping distance. For example, a 90° bend is equivalent to about 40 feet of straight, horizontal line, and each foot of head is equivalent to about 8 feet of line. Although manufacturers rate their largest equipment as capable of handling concrete containing aggregate up to 3 inches in size, experience indicates that operating difficulties will be materially lessened if the maximum size aggregate pumped through such equipment is limited to about 2½ inches. A pump will make good progress handling concrete with a slump of 3 to 4 inches and containing 2 to 3 percent more sand than required for concrete to be transported and placed by gravity methods. Normal rated capacities range from 15 to 65 cubic yards per hour.

F.27. *Placing.*—Properly placed concrete is free of segregation, and its mortar is intimately in contact with the coarse aggregate, the reinforcement and other embedded parts. If any detail of the placing inspector's many duties deserves special emphasis, it is guarding against objectionable segregation during concrete placement. Separation of coarse aggregate from the mortar may be minimized by avoiding or controlling the lateral movement of concrete during handling and placing operations, as illustrated on figures F–10, F–11, and F–12. The concrete should be deposited as nearly as practicable in its final position. Placing methods that cause the concrete to flow in the forms should be avoided. Such methods result in concentrations of less durable mortar in the ends of walls and corners where durability is most important. They also encourage the use of a mix that is wetter than necessary. The concrete should be placed in horizontal layers, and each layer should be thoroughly vibrated. Practicable depths of layers for concrete range from 12 to 20 inches.

Hoppers for drop chutes should have throat openings of sufficient area to readily pass concrete of the lowest slump that is practicable to work and vibrate. If drop chutes are discharged directly through form ports, considerable separation results and rock pockets and honeycombs will probably be formed. Provision for an outside pocket below each port, as shown on figure F–13, will check the fall of the concrete and permit it to flow in the form with a minimum of separation.

Concrete in the top 2 feet of walls, piers, and columns is very susceptible to weathering and should be of the lowest slump that can be adequately vibrated. After initial vibration, the concrete should be left for 1 or 2 hours to settle and complete the bleeding process. The surfaces should then be topped off with additional concrete as required, and the top 2 feet revibrated to close bleeding channels.

When placing an unformed slab on a slope, there is a tendency to place the concrete using a stiff mix that will not slough. Drill cores have shown that the placement of such low-slump concrete without thorough vibration usually results in considerable

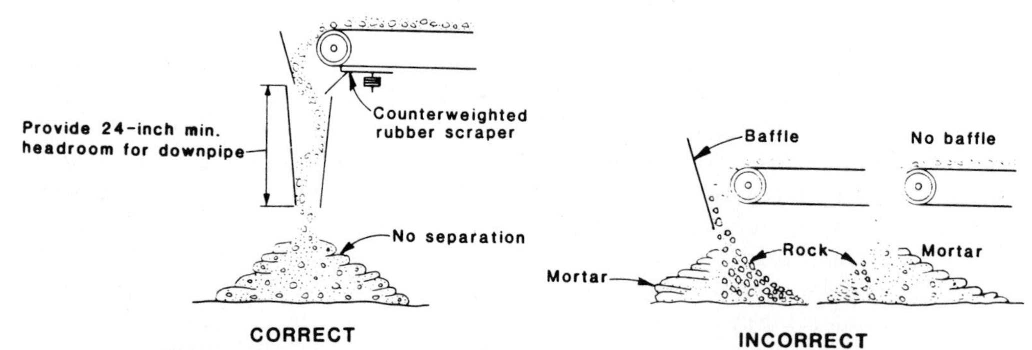

The above arrangement prevents separation of concrete whether it is being discharged into hoppers, buckets, cars, trucks, or forms.

Improper or complete lack of control at end of belt. Usually, a baffle or shallow hopper merely changes the direction of separation.

CONTROL OF SEPARATION OF CONCRETE AT END OF CONVEYOR BELT

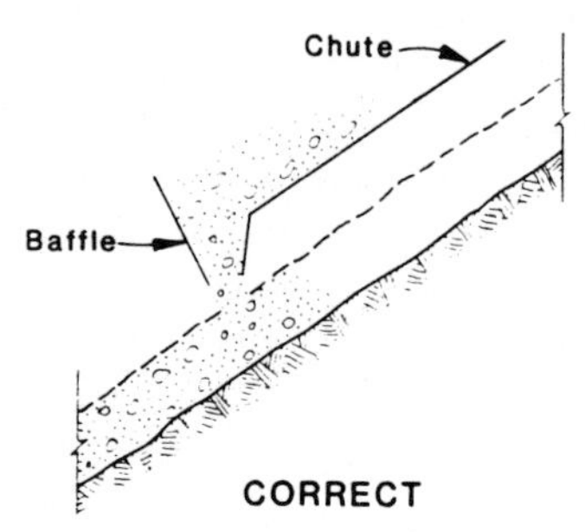

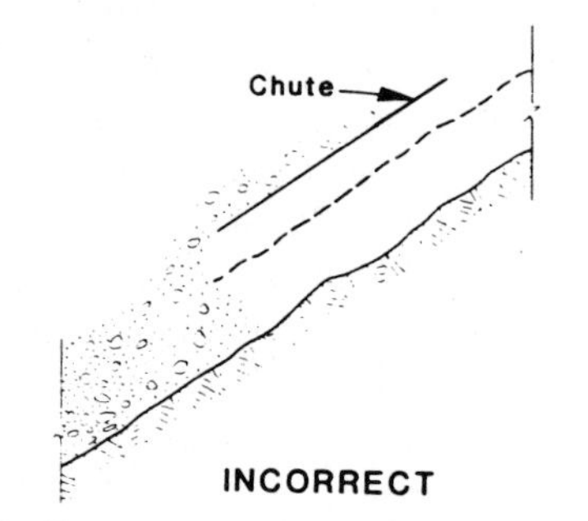

INCORRECT

Place baffle and drop at end of chute so that separation is avoided and concrete remains on slope.

To discharge concrete from a free-end chute on a slope to be paved. Rock is separated and goes to bottom of slope. Velocity tends to carry concrete down slope.

PLACING CONCRETE ON A SLOPING SURFACE

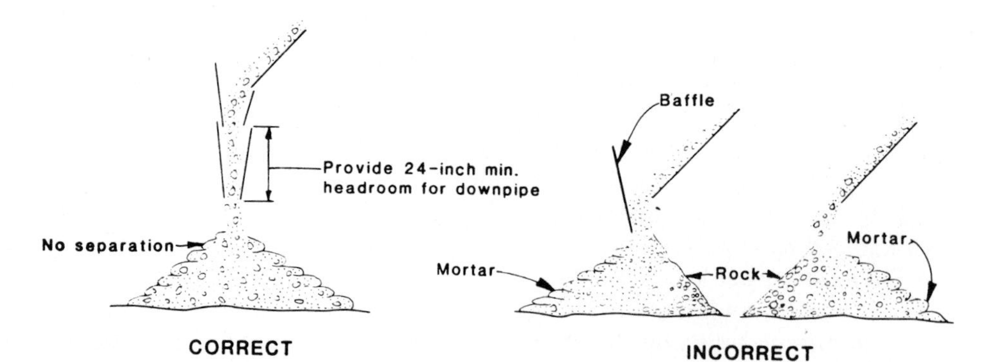

INCORRECT

The above arrangement prevents separation, no matter how short the chute, whether concrete is being discharged into hoppers, buckets, cars, trucks, or forms.

Improper or lack of control at end of any concrete chute, no matter how short. Usually, a baffle merely changes direction of separation.

CONTROL OF SEPARATION AT THE END OF CONCRETE CHUTES

This applies to sloping discharges from mixers, truck mixers, etc. as well as to longer chutes, but not when concrete is discharged into another chute or onto a conveyor belt.

Figure F-10.—Methods of handling concrete at ends of conveyors and chutes. 288-D-854.

honeycombing on the underside. To avoid such results, the consistency for this purpose should not be stiffer than a 2½-inch slump. Concrete with this consistency will barely stay on the slope, but it should not be drier. After spreading, the concrete should be thoroughly and systematically vibrated, preferably just ahead of a weighted steel-faced slip-form screed working up the slope, as shown on figure F–14.

F.28. ***Curing.***—Early drying must be prevented or concrete will not reach its full potential. Bureau specifications require all concrete to be cured. The contractor generally has the option of providing water curing or maintaining polyethylene film for

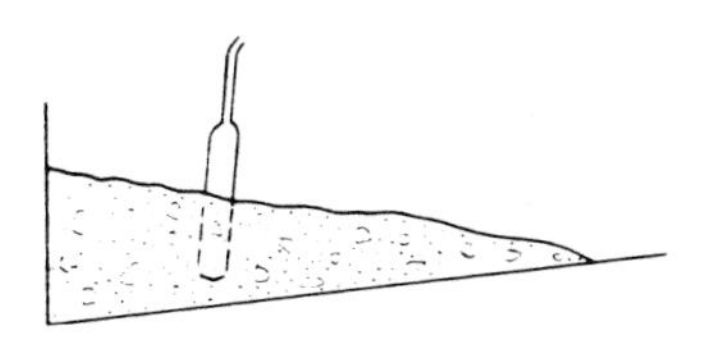

CORRECT

Start placing at bottom of slope so that compaction is increased by weight of newly added concrete as vibration consolidates.

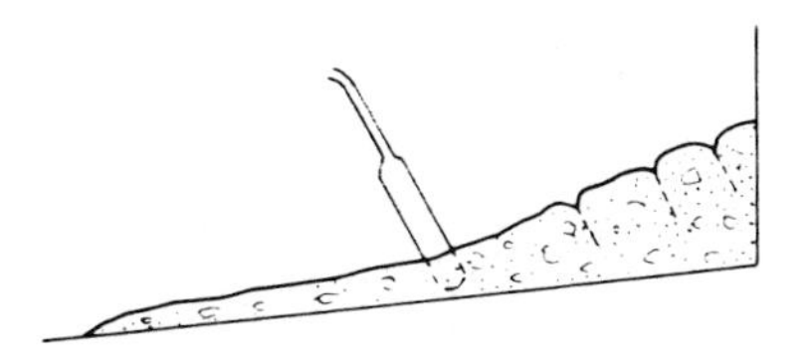

INCORRECT

To begin placing at top of slope. Upper concrete tends to pull apart, especially when vibrated below, as vibration starts flow and removes support from concrete above.

WHEN CONCRETE MUST BE PLACED IN A SLOPING LIFT

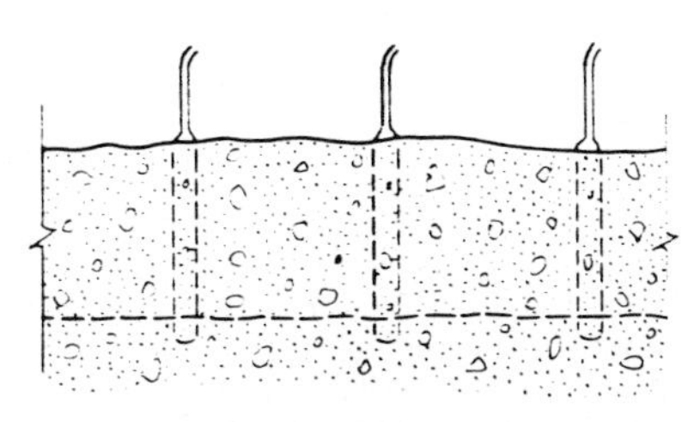

CORRECT

Vertical penetration of vibrator a few inches into previous lift (which should not yet be rigid) at systematic regular intervals results in adequate consolidation.

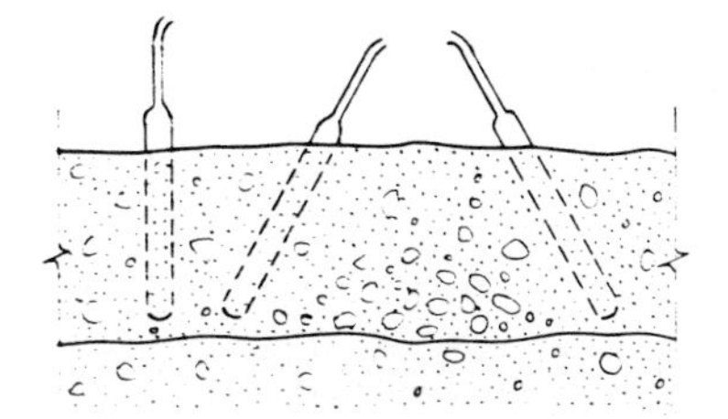

INCORRECT

Haphazard random penetration of the vibrator at all angles and spacings without sufficient depth to assure monolithic combination of the two layers.

SYSTEMATIC VIBRATION OF EACH NEW LIFT

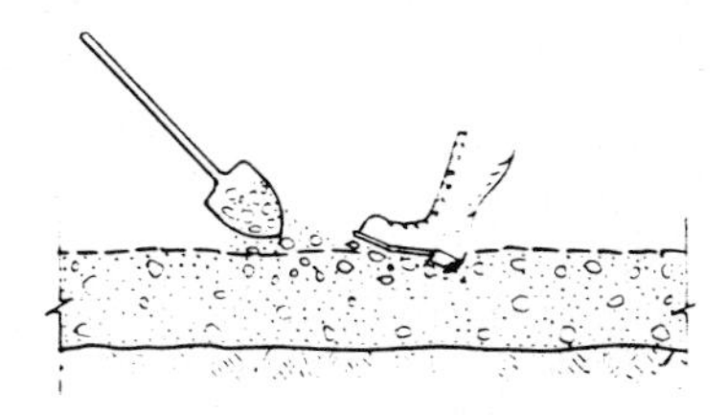

CORRECT

Shovel rocks from rock pocket onto softer, amply sanded area and tramp or vibrate.

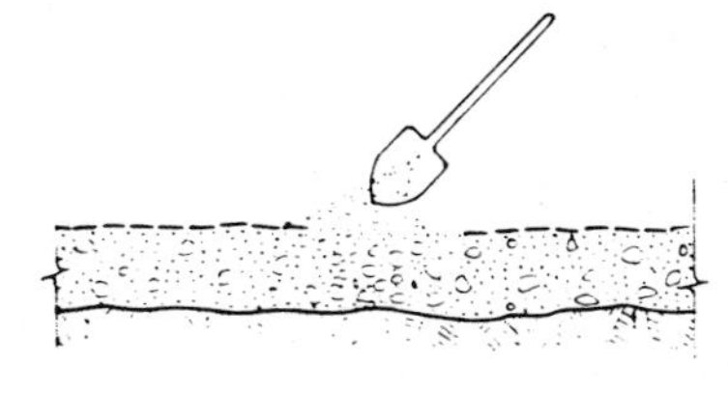

INCORRECT

Attempting to correct rock pocket by shoveling mortar and soft concrete on it.

TREATMENT OF ROCK POCKET WHEN PLACING CONCRETE

Figure F-11.—Methods of vibrating and of working concrete. 288–D–856.

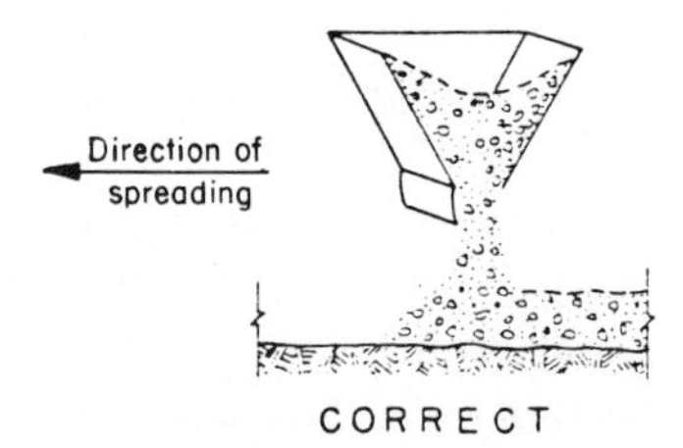

CORRECT

Turn bucket so that separated rock falls on concrete, where it may be readily worked into mass.

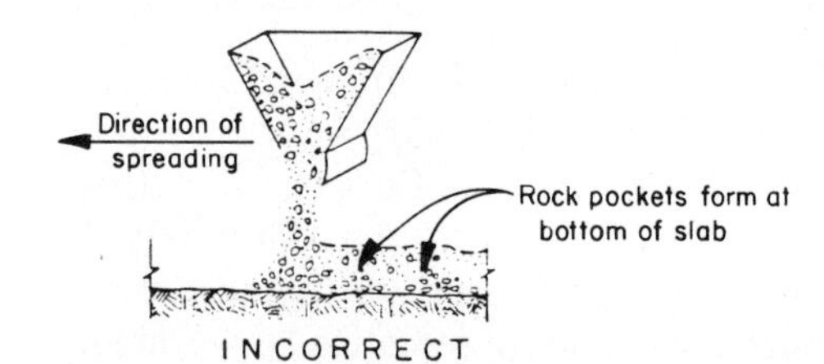

INCORRECT

Dumping so that free rock rolls out on forms or subgrade.

DISCHARGING CONCRETE

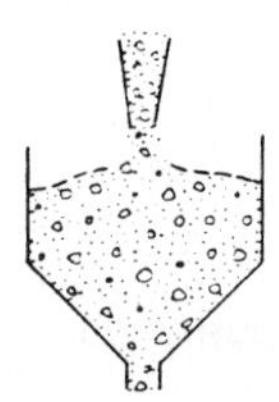

CORRECT

Dropping concrete directly over gate opening.

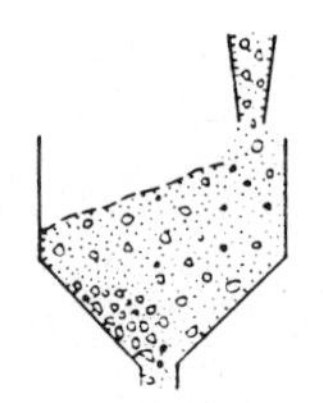

INCORRECT

Dropping concrete on sloping sides of hopper.

FILLING CONCRETE HOPPERS OR BUCKETS

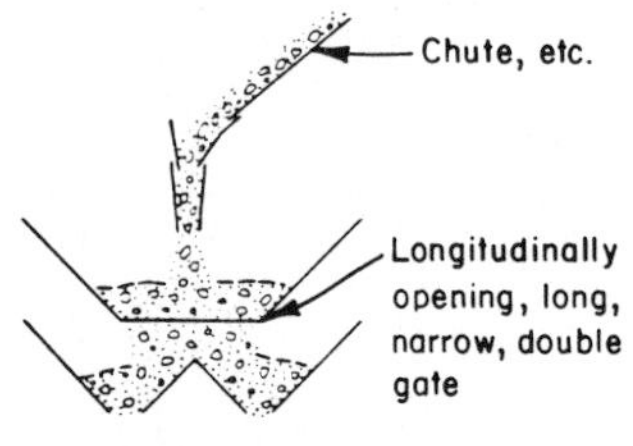

CORRECT

The above arrangement shows a feasible method if a divided hopper must be used. (Single discharge hoppers should be used whenever possible.)

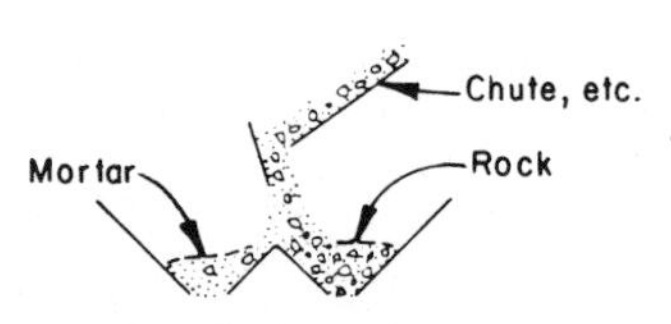

INCORRECT

Filling divided hopper, as above, invariably results in separation and lack of uniformity in concrete delivered from either gate.

DIVIDED CONCRETE HOPPERS

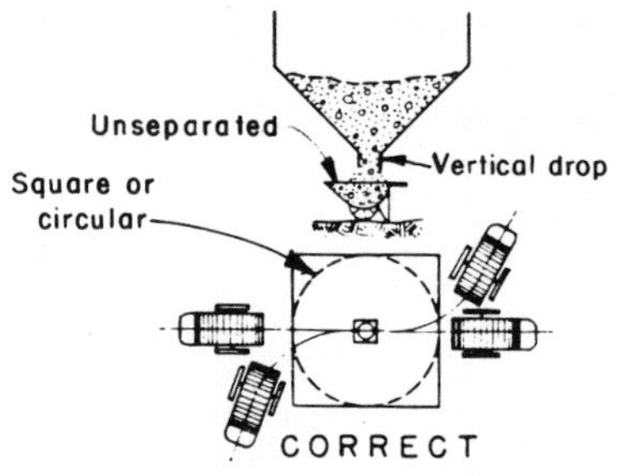

CORRECT

Discharge from center opening permitting vertical drop into center of buggy. Alternate approach from opposite sides permits as rapid loading as may be obtained with objectionable divided hoppers having two discharge gates.

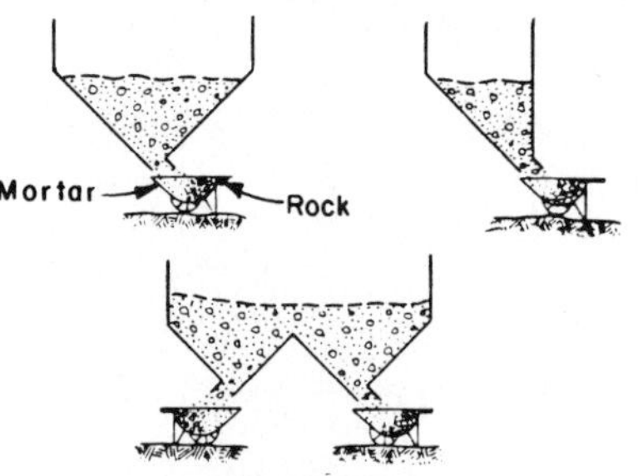

INCORRECT

Sloping hopper gates that are, in effect, chutes without end control that cause objectionable separation in filling the buggies.

DISCHARGE OF HOPPERS FOR LOADING CONCRETE BUGGIES

Figure F-12.—Methods of handling concrete with buckets, hoppers, and buggies. PX-D-25316.

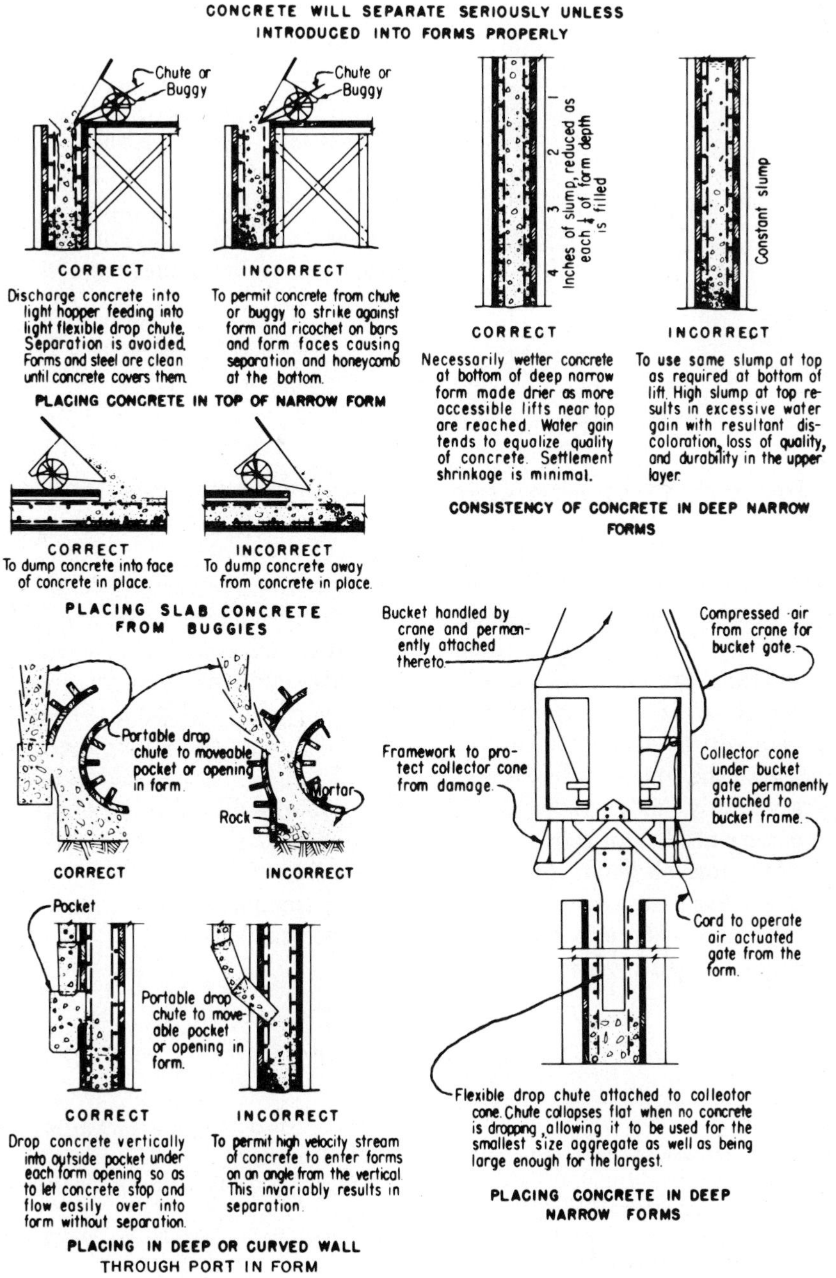

CONCRETE WILL SEPARATE SERIOUSLY UNLESS INTRODUCED INTO FORMS PROPERLY

Chute or Buggy

Chute or Buggy

CORRECT

Discharge concrete into light hopper feeding into light flexible drop chute. Separation is avoided. Forms and steel are clean until concrete covers them.

INCORRECT

To permit concrete from chute or buggy to strike against form and ricochet on bars and form faces causing separation and honeycomb at the bottom.

PLACING CONCRETE IN TOP OF NARROW FORM

CORRECT

To dump concrete into face of concrete in place.

INCORRECT

To dump concrete away from concrete in place.

PLACING SLAB CONCRETE FROM BUGGIES

1 2 3 4

Inches of slump, reduced as each ¼ of form depth is filled

Constant slump

CORRECT

Necessarily wetter concrete at bottom of deep narrow form made drier as more accessible lifts near top are reached. Water gain tends to equalize quality of concrete. Settlement shrinkage is minimal.

INCORRECT

To use same slump at top as required at bottom of lift. High slump at top results in excessive water gain with resultant discoloration, loss of quality, and durability in the upper layer.

CONSISTENCY OF CONCRETE IN DEEP NARROW FORMS

Portable drop chute to moveable pocket or opening in form.

Mortar

Rock

CORRECT

INCORRECT

Pocket

Portable drop chute to moveable pocket or opening in form.

CORRECT

Drop concrete vertically into outside pocket under each form opening so as to let concrete stop and flow easily over into form without separation.

INCORRECT

To permit high velocity stream of concrete to enter forms on an angle from the vertical. This invariably results in separation.

PLACING IN DEEP OR CURVED WALL THROUGH PORT IN FORM

Bucket handled by crane and permanently attached thereto.

Compressed air from crane for bucket gate.

Framework to protect collector cone from damage.

Collector cone under bucket gate permanently attached to bucket frame.

Cord to operate air actuated gate from the form.

Flexible drop chute attached to colleotor cone. Chute collapses flat when no concrete is dropping, allowing it to be used for the smallest size aggregate as well as being large enough for the largest.

PLACING CONCRETE IN DEEP NARROW FORMS

Figure F-13.—Placing concrete in forms. 288-D-2657.

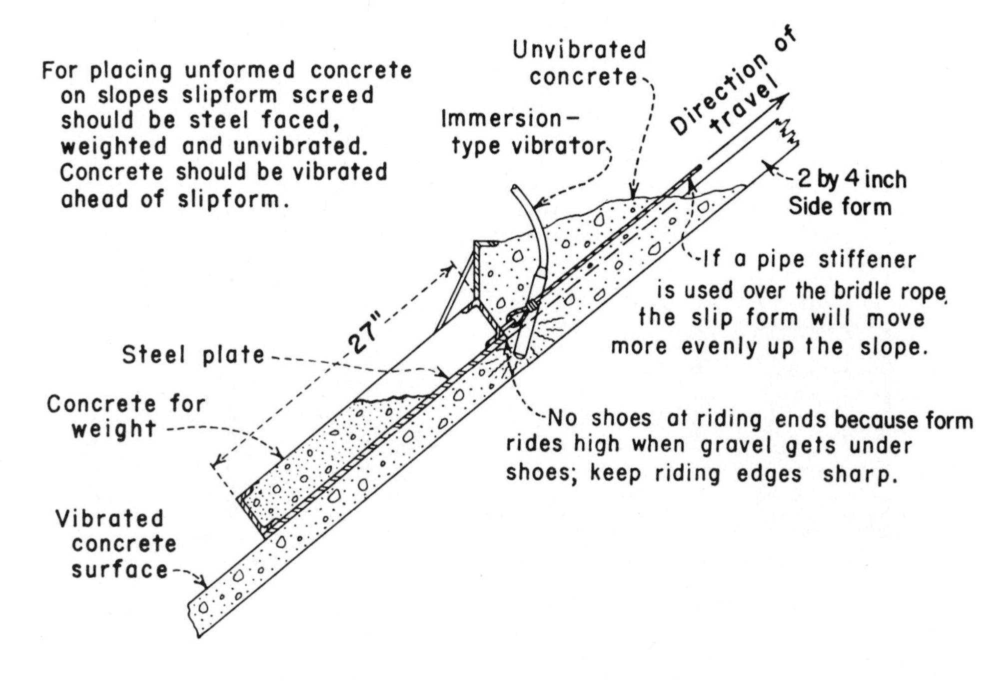

Figure F-14.—Placing unformed concrete on slopes. PX-D-33031, PX-D-25252.

14 days or approved curing compound for 28 days. In warm, dry, windy weather, the corners, edges, and surfaces of concrete dry very quickly. If these portions are prevented from drying so as to fully develop their hardness, it is certain that interior portions of the concrete will be adequately cured. Wet burlap in contact with the concrete is excellent for curing purposes. It not only shades the concrete, but also holds the moisture needed for good curing. Wood forms left in place furnish good protection from the sun, but do not keep the concrete sufficiently moist for good curing. There is no better curing than that provided by well-moistened backfill. Ponding of floors, pavement, and other slabs also provides excellent curing and reduces crazing, cracking, and wear.

Where curing water is not economically available or on vertical or sloping surfaces, it is often necessary to cure concrete by applying a sealing compound to the exposed surfaces immediately after form removal. The sealing compound is designed to restrict evaporation of the mixing water. When it is properly applied and maintained for 28 days, the sealing compound will retain enough moisture for adequate curing.

D. BIBLIOGRAPHY

F.29. *Bibliography.*

[1] *Concrete Manual*, vol. 2, "Test Designations," Bureau of Reclamation, Denver, CO, 1987.

[2] *Concrete Manual* [1], Tests Designations USBR 4128 and 4127.

[3] *Concrete Manual* [1], Tests Designation USBR 4136.

[4] *Concrete Manual* [1], Test Designations USBR 4138 and 4231.

[5] "Lean Mass Concrete as Affected by Water-Reducing, Set-Retarding Agents," American Society for Testing Materials Special Technical Publication No. 266, pp. 38-94, 1960.

[6] *Concrete Manual* [1], Test Designation USBR 4143.

Sample Specifications

G.1. ***Introduction.***—Designs are based on assumptions regarding the quality of work which will be obtained during construction. It is through the means of specifications that the assumed quality is described, and it is important that conformance to the specifications be obtained for all work.

This appendix includes specifications for the various items of work and structure components whose designs are treated in this text. For the construction of a particular dam, these specifications would have to be supplemented by descriptions of items for payment, description and classification of concrete items, and by specifications for other work such as painting, installation of equipment and metalwork, etc. Not all of the specifications included herein are applicable for any one dam as they cover alternative methods and a wide variety of construction details, not all of which would be performed at any one site.

These specifications are abstracted, with slight modifications, from guide specifications normally used by the Bureau of Reclamation. The designation "Contracting Officer," as used in these specifications, applies to the owner of the dam or his authorized representative, as appropriate.

A. ENVIRONMENTAL QUALITY PROTECTION

G.2. ***Landscape Preservation.***[1]—(a) *General.*—The contractor shall exercise care to preserve the natural landscape and shall conduct the construction operations so as to prevent any unnecessary destruction, scarring, or defacing of the natural surroundings in the vicinity of the work. Except where clearing is required for permanent works, approved construction roads, or excavation operations, all trees, native shrubbery, and vegetation shall be preserved and shall be protected from damage by the contractor's construction operations and equipment. The edges of clearings and cuts through trees, shrubbery, and vegetation shall be irregularly shaped to soften the undesirable visual impact of straight lines. Movement of crews and equipment within the right-of-way and over routes provided for access to the work shall be performed in a manner to prevent damage to grazing land, crops, or property.

No special reseeding or replanting will be required under these specifications; however, on completion of the work, all work areas shall be scarified and left in a condition which will facilitate natural revegetation, provide for proper drainage, and prevent erosion.[2] All unnecessary destruction, scarring, damage, or defacing of the landscape resulting from the contractor's operations shall be repaired, replanted, reseeded, or otherwise corrected as directed by the Contracting Officer and at the contractor's expense.

(b) *Construction Roads.*—The location, alinement, and grade of construction roads shall be subject to approval of the Contracting Officer. When no longer required by the contractor, construction roads shall be restored to the original contour and made impassable to vehicular traffic. The surfaces of such construction roads shall be scarified as needed to provide a condition which will facilitate

[1]This section contains basic provisions for all contracts exceeding $10,000. It is to be modified as applicable and supplemented to minimize construction scars and to control unnecessary clearing and defacement of the landscape. Accordingly, provisions may be added to limit, locate, provide for reseeding or replanting, or specify other requirements for such items as temporary construction roads, trenching and backfilling for pipelines in cultivated and residential areas, and operations in borrow areas.

[2]Delete if specifications do not have requirements for landscaping, seeding, or planting.

natural revegetation, provide for proper drainage, and prevent erosion.

(c) *Construction Facilities.*—The contractor's shop, office, and yard area shall be located and arranged in a manner to preserve trees and vegetation to the maximum practicable extent. On abandonment, all storage and construction buildings, including concrete footings and slabs, and all construction materials and debris shall be removed from the site. The area shall be regraded, as required, so that all surfaces drain naturally, blend with the natural terrain, and are left in a condition that will facilitate natural revegetation, provide for proper drainage, and prevent erosion.

(d) *Borrow Areas (and Quarry Sites)*[3].—Borrow pits (and quarry sites)[3] shall be so excavated that water will not collect and stand therein. Before being abandoned, the sides of borrow pits (and quarry sites)[3] shall be brought to stable slopes with slope intersections shaped to carry the natural contour of adjacent undisturbed terrain into the pit or borrow area giving a natural appearance. All rubbish, construction equipment, and structures shall be removed from the site. Waste piles shall be shaped to provide a natural appearance.

(e) *Blasting Precautions.*—In addition to the requirements of the Bureau of Reclamation's *Construction Safety Standards* [1]†, the contractor shall adopt precautions when using explosives which will prevent scattering of rocks, stumps, or other debris outside the work area, and prevent damage to surrounding trees, shrubbery, and vegetation.

(f) *Costs.*—The cost of all work required by this section shall be included in the prices bid in the schedule for other items of work.

G.3. *Preservation of Vegetation.*[4]—

(a) *Preservation.*—Vegetation including trees, shrubs, grass, and other plants that is not specifically required to be cleared or removed for construction purposes shall be preserved and shall be protected from any damage that may be caused by the contractor's construction operations and equipment. Special care shall be exercised where vegetation is exposed to injuries by construction equipment, blasting, excavating, dumping, chemical damage, or other operations; and the contractor shall adequately protect such vegetation by use of protective barriers or other methods approved by the Contracting Officer. The removal of vegetation will be permitted only after prior approval by the Contracting Officer.

The layout of the contractor's construction facilities such as shops, warehouses, storage areas, and parking areas; location of access and haul routes; and operations in borrow and spoil areas shall be planned and conducted in such manner that all vegetation not approved for removal by the Contracting Officer shall be preserved and adequately protected from either direct or indirect damage by the contractor's operations.

Except in emergency cases or when otherwise approved by the Contracting Officer, trees shall not be used for anchorages. Where such use is approved, the trunk shall be wrapped with a sufficient thickness of approved protective material before any rope, cable, or wire is placed.

Where tree climbing is necessary, the use of climbing spurs will not be permitted. If climbing is necessary, safety ropes shall be used.

(b) *Repair or Treatment of Damage.*—The contractor shall be responsible for injuries to vegetation caused by the contractor's operations. The term "injury" shall include, without limitation, bruising, scarring, tearing, and breaking of roots, trunk, or branches. All injured vegetation shall be repaired or treated without delay, at the contractor's expense. If damage occurs, the Contracting Officer will determine the method of repair or treatment to be used for injured vegetation as recommended by an experienced horticulturist or a licensed tree surgeon provided by and at the expense of the contractor. All repairs or treatment of injured vegetation shall be performed under the direction of an experienced horticulturist or a licensed tree surgeon provided by and at the expense of the contractor.

(c) *Replacement.*—Vegetation that, in the opinion of the Contracting Officer, is beyond saving shall be removed and replaced early in the next planting season. The replacements shall be the same species, or other approved species, and of the maximum size that is practicable to plant and sustain growth in the particular environment. Replacement trees and shrubs shall be guyed, as required, watered, and maintained for a period of 1 year. Any replacement tree or shrub that dies shall be removed and replaced, as directed by the Contracting Officer, with such replacements being maintained

[3]Delete when quarry sites are not required.

[4]Include this section in appropriate construction contracts. The paragraph may be modified to fit local conditions and requirements.

†Numbers in brackets refer to entries in the Bibliography, section G.118.

for a period of 1 year from the date of replacement. Replacement vegetation, other than trees or shrubs, shall be maintained until it is established, as directed by the Contracting Officer.

(d) *Cost.*—The cost of all work required by this section shall be included in the prices bid in the schedule for other items of work.

G.4. *Prevention of Water Pollution.*[5]—

(a) *General.*—The contractor's construction activities shall be performed by methods that will prevent entrance, or accidental spillage, of solid matter, contaminants, debris, and other pollutants and wastes into streams, flowing or dry watercourses, lakes, and underground water sources. Such pollutants and wastes include, but are not restricted to, refuse, garbage, cement, concrete, sanitary waste, industrial waste, radioactive substances, oil and other petroleum products, aggregate processing tailings, mineral salts, and thermal pollution.

Unwatering work for structure foundations or earthwork operations adjacent to, or encroaching on, streams or watercourses shall be conducted in a manner to prevent muddy water and eroded materials from entering the streams or watercourses by construction of intercepting ditches, bypass channels, barriers, settling ponds, or by other approved means. Excavated materials or other construction materials shall not be stockpiled or deposited near or on streambanks, lake shorelines, or other watercourse perimeters where they can be washed away by high water or storm runoff, or can in any way encroach upon the watercourse itself.

Turbidity increases in a stream or other bodies of water that are caused by construction activities shall be limited to the increases above the natural turbidities permitted under the water quality standards prescribed for that stream or body of water. When necessary to perform required construction work in a stream channel, the prescribed turbidity limits may be exceeded, as approved by the Contracting Officer, for the shortest practicable period required to complete such work. This required construction work may include such work as diversion of stream, construction or removal of cofferdams, specified earthwork in or adjacent to a stream channel, pile driving, and construction of turbidity control structures. Mechanized equipment shall not be operated in flowing water except as necessary to construct crossings or to perform the required construction.[6]

Waste waters from aggregate processing, concrete batching, or other construction operations shall not enter streams, watercourses, or other surface waters without the use of such turbidity control methods as settling ponds, gravel-filter entrapment dikes, approved flocculating processes that are not harmful to fish, recirculation systems for washing of aggregates, or other approved methods. Any such waste waters discharged into surface waters shall contain the least concentration of settleable material possible. For the purpose of these specifications, settleable material is defined as "that material which will settle from the water by gravity during a 1-hour quiescent detention period."

(b) *Compliance with Laws and Regulations.*—The contractor shall comply with applicable Federal and State laws, orders, regulations, and water-quality standards concerning the control and abatement of water pollution.

Prior to discharging waste water or other pollutants, the contractor shall have a permit to discharge pollutants as required under section 402 of the NPDES (National Pollutant Discharge Elimination System), established under Public Law 92–500, as amended by Public Law 95–217. Prior to discharging dredged or fill materials into navigable waters, the contractor shall have a permit issued by the Corps of Engineers to discharge such materials as provided in section 404 of Public Law 92–500, as amended by Public Law 95–217.[7]

The Bureau of Reclamation has made application for permits to discharge pollutants as required under section 402 of the NPDES, established under Public Law 92–500, as amended by Public Law 95–217. The Bureau has also made application for permits to discharge dredged or fill material into

[5]Include this section in the Environmental Quality Protection section of construction specifications in excess of $10,000 where the work is located near streams or other bodies of water. It may also be used for contracts under $10,000 when appropriate. Modify or delete any inapplicable provisions and add any requirement necessary to cover local polution controls. Applicable State water quality standards for the class of water involved may be quoted as a help and convenience to contractors. For example, see Specifications No. DC-7024 for Cunningham Tunnel, Fryingpan-Arkansas Project.

[6]Delete this section if construction activities are not required to be performed in a stream or other bodies of water.

[7]Check with the Environmental Specialist to determine if these permits are required for a particular job and, if required, whether the Bureau of Reclamation or the contractor will obtain the permits. If the Bureau has obtained the permits prior to the issuance of the specifications, delete this section and include the appropriate information concerning the permits.

navigable waters as required under section 404 of Public Law 92-500, as amended by Public Law 95-217. This is an exception to the section in these specifications for "Permits and Responsibilities" and "Administration of Permits and Responsibilities," which require the contractor to obtain all necessary licenses and permits. When received, the conditions of the permits will be made known to the contractor by the Contracting Officer and the permits will then be transferred to the contractor.

Prior to discharging waste water or other pollutants, or dredged or fill material into navigable waters, the contractor shall have the required permits and abide by nationwide standards for water pollution control.[8]

Where the location of a construction site is such that oil from an accidental spillage could reasonably be expected to enter into or upon the navigable waters of the United States or adjoining shorelines, and the aggregate storage of oil at the site is over 1,320 gallons, or a single container has a capacity in excess of 660 gallons, the contractor shall prepare a SPCC Plan (Spill Prevention Control and Counter Measure Plan) reviewed and certified by a registered professional engineer in accordance with 40 CFR, part 112, as required by Public Law 92-500, as amended by Public Laws 95-217 and 95-576.

The contractor shall submit to the Contracting Officer a certified statement that states the SPCC Plan was reviewed and certified by a registered professional engineer.

The contractor shall also comply with the sanitation and potable water requirements of the Bureau of Reclamation's *Construction Safety Standards* [1].

(c) *Cost.*—The cost of complying with this section shall be included in the prices bid in the schedule for the various items of work.

G.5. *Abatement of Air Pollution.*[9]—The contractor shall comply with applicable Federal, State, and local laws and regulations concerning the prevention and control of air pollution.

In conduct of construction activities and operation of equipment, the contractor shall utilize such practicable methods and devices as are reasonably available to control, prevent, and otherwise minimize atmospheric emissions or discharges of air contaminants.

The emission of dust into the atmosphere will not be permitted during the manufacture, handing, and storage of concrete aggregates, and the contractor shall use such methods and equipment as are necessary for the collection and disposal, or prevention, of dust during these operations. The contractor's methods of storing and handling cement and pozzolans shall also include means of eliminating atmospheric discharges of dust.

Equipment and vehicles that show excessive emissions of exhaust gases due to poor engine adjustments, or other inefficient operating conditions, shall not be operated until corrective repairs or adjustments are made.

Burning of materials resulting from clearing of trees and brush, combustible construction materials, and rubbish will be permitted only when atmospheric conditions for burning are considered favorable and when authorized by appropriate State or local air pollution or fire authorities. In lieu of burning, such combustible materials may be disposed of by other methods as provided in sections G.12 and G.13. Where open burning is permitted, the burn piles shall be properly constructed to minimize smoke, and in no case shall unapproved materials, such as tires, plastics, rubber products, asphalt products, or other materials that create heavy black smoke or nuisance ordors, be burned.[10]

Burning of cleared timber, brush, and rubbish will not be permitted. Cleared timber and brush shall be removed from the site, chipped or shredded, or buried as provided in section G.13. Rubbish, trash, and combustible materials shall be disposed of as provided in section G.12.[10]

Storage and handling of flammable and combustible materials, provisions for fire prevention, and control of dust resulting from drilling operations shall be in accordance with the applicable provisions of the Bureau of Reclamations *Construction Safety Standards* [1].

Dust nuisance resulting from construction activities shall be prevented in accordance with section G.6.

The cost of complying with this section shall be

[8]Include this section when permits have been applied for by the Bureau of Reclamation.

[9]Include this section in appropriate construction specifications for work amounting to $10,000 or more, and in contracts under $10,000 when considered desirable. Insert provisions covering any applicable air quality standards in force for the geographical area involved, including any standards which have been established pursuant to subsection 4(b) of Executive Order 11507.

[10]Use applicable provisions for this section as required by local conditions.

included in the prices bid in the schedule for other items of work.

G.6. *Dust Abatement.*[11]—During the performance of the work required by these specifications or any operations appurtenant thereto, whether on right-of-way provided by the Government or elsewhere, the contractor shall furnish all the labor, equipment, materials, and means required, and shall carry out proper and efficient measures wherever and as often as necessary to reduce the dust nuisance, and to prevent dust which has originated from his operations from damaging crops, orchards, cultivated fields, and dwellings, or causing a nuisance to persons. The contractor will be held liable for any damage resulting from dust originating from his operations under these specifications on Government right-of-way or elsewhere.

The cost of sprinkling or of other methods of reducing formation of dust shall be included in the prices bid in the schedule for other items of work: *Provided,* that payment for applying water used for such purposes, and applied within the right-of-way lines, will be made in accordance with the section in these specifications for "Water for Watering Earth Materials and for Dust Abatement".[12]

G.7. *Noise Abatement.*[13]—(a) *General.*—The contractor shall comply with applicable Federal, State, and local laws, orders, and regulations concerning the prevention, control, and abatement of excessive noise.

Nighttime blasting, the use of jackhammers, pile driving, or other operations producing a high-intensity impact noise may be performed only upon approval of the Contracting Officer.

(b) *Cost.*—The cost of complying with this section shall be included in the prices bid in the schedule for other items of work.

G.8. *Light Abatement.*[14]—The contractor shall exercise special care to direct all stationary floodlights to shine downward at an angle less than horizontal. These floodlights shall also be shielded so as not to be a nuisance to surrounding areas. No lighting shall include a residence in its direct beam.

The contractor shall be responsible for correcting lighting problems when they occur as approved by the Contracting Officer.

The cost of complying with this section shall be included in the prices bid in the schedule for other items of work.

G.9. *Preservation of Historical and Archeological Data.*[15]—(a) Federal legislation provides for the protection, preservation, and collection of scientific, prehistorical, historical, and archeological data (including relics and specimens) which might otherwise be lost due to alteration of the terrain as a result of any Federal construction project.

(b) The contractor agrees that should he or any of his employees, in the performance of this contract, discover evidence of possible scientific, prehistorical, historical, or archeological data, he will notify the Contracting Officer immediately, giving the location and nature of the findings. Written confirmation shall be forwarded within 2 days. The contractor shall exercise care so as not to damage artifacts or fossils uncovered during excavation operations, and shall provide such cooperation and assistance as may be necessary to preserve the findings for removal or other disposition by the Government.

(c) Where appropriate, by reason of a discovery, the Contracting Officer may order delays in the time of performance, or changes in the work, or both. If such delays, or changes, or both, are ordered, the time of performance and contract price shall be adjusted in accordance with the applicable clauses of this contract.

(d) The contractor agrees to insert this section in all subcontracts which involve the performance of work on the terrain of the site.

(e) Except as otherwise provided above, the cost of complying with this section shall be included in the prices bid in the schedule for other items of work.

G.10. *Vegetation Control.*[16]—The contractor

[11]Include this section in contracts where necessary for controlling dust from contractor's operations. Additional provisions should be included where appropriate.

[12]This payment provision may be included when measurement of water for this purpose can be combined with measurement of water for other purposes.

[13]Include this section only in specifications for work in areas where excessive noise may be a nuisance to surrounding area. Additional requirements may be added for work in areas where strict noise control provisions are desirable and noise studies or measurements have been made by the Bureau.

[14]Include this section in specifications for work in areas where contractor lighting may be a nuisance to surrounding areas.

[15]Include this section in specifications for work where there will be alteration to the terrain unless the exclusion of the section is granted by the Bureau archaeologist. Specific project requirements and references to drawings showing archaeological sites should be added to this section when applicable.

[16]Include this section in specifications for work adjacent to crop lands when the field offices determine that it is necessary.

shall be responsible for the removal of all existing mature vegetation, and for the control of all new vegetation within the right-of-way or easement lines, whichever is wider, where such removal is required to protect crops of adjacent landowners.

Removal or control shall be by disking, blading, or spraying. The types of sprays and methods of spraying shall be in accordance with section G.11. All methods of removal and control shall be subject to the approval of the Contracting Officer.

The contractor will be held strictly responsible for all damages to persons or property that occur as a result of the contractor's fault or negligence under the section in these specifications for "Permits and Responsibilities."

Payment for the work of removing existing mature vegetation and for control of new vegetation will be made at the lump-sum price bid in the schedule for removing and controlling vegetation. The cost of complying with this section shall be included in the prices bid in the schedule for other items of work.[17]

G.11. *Pesticides.*[18]—Pesticides include herbicides, insecticides, fungicides, rodenticides, piscicides, surface disinfectants, animal repellents, and insect repellents. Soil-applied herbicide for gravel surfacing shall be in accordance with the section in these specifications for "Soil Applied Herbicide".[19] Should the contractor find it necessary to use other pesticides in work areas of this contract, he shall submit his plan for such use to the Contracting Officer for written approval.[19] Such plan shall be subject to submittal to and review by the Regional Pest Control Specialist before the plan is approved.

Pesticides shall only be those registered with the Environmental Protection Agency in compliance with the Federal Environmental Pesticide Control Act of 1972 or by appropriate State agencies.

The contractor shall read and comply with all labeling requirements when using pesticides.

Requirements contained in the Bureau's *Construction Safety Standards* [1] are applicable to pesticide storage, mixing, and application. In the event there is a conflict between the requirements contained in these standards and other Federal or State codes or standards, the more stringent requirements will prevail.

The cost of complying with this section shall be included in the prices bid in the schedule for other items of work.

G.12. *Cleanup and Disposal of Waste Materials.*[20]— (a) *Cleanup.*—The contractor shall at all times keep the construction area, including storage areas used by him, free from accumulations of waste materials or rubbish.

Prior to completion of the work, the contractor shall remove from the vicinity of the work all plant facilities, buildings, rubbish, unused materials, concrete forms, and other like material belonging to him or used under his direction during construction. All work areas shall be graded and left in a neat manner conforming to the natural appearance of the landscape as provided in section G.2.

In the event of the contractor's failure to perform the above work, the work may be performed by the Government, at the expense of the contractor, and his surety or sureties shall be liable therefore.

(b) *Disposal of Waste Materials:*

(1) *General.*—Waste materials including, but not restricted to, refuse, garbage, sanitary wastes, industrial wastes, and oil and other petroleum products, shall be disposed of by the contractor. *[Except as otherwise provided in section G.13 and the section in these specifications for "Forest Service Requirements," disposal of combustible materials shall be by burying, where burial of such materials is approved by the Contracting Officer; by burning, where burning of approved materials is permitted in accordance with Forest Service regulations and State and local laws; or by removal from the construction area. Except as otherwise provided in section G.27, disposal of noncombustible materials shall be by burying, where burial of such materials is approved by the Contracting Officer, or by removal from the construction area.] Waste materials removed from the construction area shall be dumped at an approved dump.

*[(2) *Disposal of Material by Burying.*—Only materials approved by the Contracting Officer may be buried. Burial shall be in pits at locations shown on the drawings or as otherwise approved by the Contracting Officer. The pits shall be covered by at

[17]Use applicable provision.

[18]Include this section in construction specifications for work exceeding $10,000.

[19]Include when "Soil-Applied Herbicide" section is included in specifications.

[20]Include this section in all construction specifications. Modify or delete any inapplicable provisions and add any necessary requirements not covered.

*Delete or revise as applicable.

least 2 feet of earth material prior to abandonment.]

*[(3) *Disposal of Material by Burning.*—The contractor shall secure the necessary burning permits from the District Forest Ranger and State and local authorities. All burning shall be in accordance with Forest Service Regulations and State and local laws.]

*[All materials to be burned shall be piled in designated burning areas in such a manner as will cause the least fire hazards. Burning shall be thorough and complete and all charred pieces remaining after burning, except for scattered small pieces, shall be removed from the construction area and disposed of as otherwise provided in this section.]

*[The contractor shall, at all times, take special precautions to prevent fire from spreading beyond the piles being burned and shall be liable for any damage caused by his burning operations. The contractor shall have available, at all times, suitable equipment and supplies for use in preventing and suppressing fires (as prescribed by the Forest Service) and shall be subject to all laws and regulations locally applicable for presuppression, suppression, and prevention of fires.]

(4) *Disposal of Material by Removal.*—Material to be disposed of by removal from the construction area shall be removed from the area prior to the completion of the work under these specifications. All materials removed shall become the property of the contractor. Materials to be disposed of by dumping shall be hauled to an approved dump. It shall be the responsibility of the contractor to make any necessary arrangements with private parties and with country officials pertinent to locations and regulations of such dumping. Any fees or charges required to be paid for dumping of materials shall be paid by the contractor.

(c) *Cost.*—The cost of complying with this section shall be included in the prices bid in the schedule for other items of work.

B. EXCAVATION

G.13. *Clearing at Damsite.*—(a) *General.*—The areas to be occupied by the permanent construction required under these specifications and the surfaces of all borrow pits *(and stockpile and wastepile sites) shall be cleared of all vegetation, such as trees, stumps, exposed roots, brush, grass, and weeds; rubbish; and all other objectionable matter as determined by the Contracting Officer.

*[The reservoir area below elevation ______, as shown on drawing ______, shall be cleared of all trees, stumps, and brush 5 feet or more in height, regardless of diameter, and 2 inches or more in diameter, regardless of height. (Trees and stumps in the reservoir area shall either be uprooted or cut off so that the maximum allowable stump height will be 6 inches, as measured on the uphill side of the stump.)[21] Brush in the reservoir area shall be cut off approximately flush with the ground level.]

*[All down timber, branches, and other floatable and combustible material 5 feet or more in length, regardless of diameter, and 2 inches or more in diameter, regardless of length, shall be cleared.]

Trees designated by the Contracting Officer and all other trees outside the clearing limits shall be protected from injury in accordance with section G.3. Clearing will consist principally of removal of ______.

The bidders and the contractor shall, by their own investigation, determine the extent of clearing required in accordance with this section.

Cleared materials shall be disposed of as provided in (b). In accordance with the Government's policy for maximum utilization of timber, every reasonable effort shall be made by the contractor to channel timber resulting from clearing operations into beneficial use. [22]

(b) *Disposal of Materials.*—Subject to approval of the Contracting Officer, materials from clearing operations shall be disposed of by burying; *[burning, reducing to chips and spreading; stockpiling; or removing from the worksite. Burning of materials required to be cleared will not be permitted.]

Disposal of materials by burying shall be performed in accordance with the provisions of section G.12. Materials shall be buried at locations approved by the Contracting Officer. Approved loca-

[21]Insert other items to be cleared such as buildings, fences, and bridges.
*Delete or revise as applicable.

[22]If there is substantial monetary value to be obtained from timber and other materials to be cleared, notify code D-1330. Revisions to this section will be necessary to comply with Federal Procurement Regulations.

tions will be natural or excavated depressions in the reservoir area which are not subject to erosion from streamflow or wave action.

*[Disposal of materials by burning and by removal from the jobsite shall be performed in accordance with provisions of section G.12.]

*[Cut timber, down timber, dead timber, branches, and brush ______ inches and less in diameter, to be disposed of by chipping, shall be reduced to chips of ½-inch maximum thickness. The chips shall be distributed uniformly on the ground surface in approved areas and mixed with the underlying earth so that they will not float or support combustion.]

Cut timber, down timber, dead timber, branches, and other floatable and combustible material over ______ inches in diameter, to be disposed of by stockpiling, shall be trimmed and cut into approximately 4-foot lengths. Such cut materials shall be hauled to stockpiles *[above elevation ______, and at locations as approved by the Contracting Officer.] Cut material shall be neatly stacked in piles.

(c) *Payment.*—Payment for clearing the areas to be occupied by the permanent construction *[and the surfaces of borrow pits (stockpile and wastepile sites), and the reservoir area below elevation ______, will be made at the lump-sum price bid in the schedule for clearing, which lump-sum price shall include the cost of disposing of cleared materials.] Estimates for progress payments for clearing will be made on the basis of percentages of work completed.

For the purpose of progress payments, estimates will be prepared on the following basis:

______________________________.

(d) *Cost.*—*[No separate payment will be made for clearing, and the cost of clearing shall be included in the prices bid in the schedule for the various items of excavation.]

G.14. *Classification of Excavation.*[23]—Except as otherwise provided in these specifications, material excavated will be measured and classified as excavation, to the lines shown on the drawings or as provided in these specifications, and will be classified for payment as follows:

(a) *Rock Excavations.*—For purposes of classifications of excavation, rock is defined as "a sound and solid mass, layer, or ledge of mineral matter inplace; and of such hardness and texture that it cannot be effectively loosened or broken down by ripping in a single pass with a late model tractor-mounted hydraulic ripper equipped with one digging point of standard manufacturer's design adequately sized for use with and propelled by a crawler-type tractor rated between 385- and 410-net flywheel horsepower, operating in low gear." In areas where the use of the ripper described is impracticable, rock is defined as "a sound material of such hardness and texture that it cannot be loosened or broken down by a 6-pound drifting pick." The drifting pick shall be class D, Federal Specification GGG-H-506D, with a handle not less than 34 inches in length.

All boulders or detached pieces of solid rock more than 1 cubic yard in volume will be classified as rock excavation.

(b) *Common Excavation.*—Common excavation includes all earth materials which do not meet the requirements of rock excavation as previously defined in (a). All boulders or detached pieces of solid rock less than 1 cubic yard in volume will be classified as common excavation.

No additional allowance above the prices bid in the schedule for excavation will be made on account of any of the material being wet or frozen.

The Government's representative and the contractor or his representative shall be present during classification of material excavated. On written request of the contractor, made within 10 days after the receipt of any monthly estimate, a statement of the quantities and classifications of excavation between successive stations, or in otherwise designated locations included in said estimate, will be furnished to the contractor within 10 days after the receipt of such request. This statement will be considered as satisfactory to the contractor unless specific objections thereto, with reasons therefor, are filed with the Contracting Officer, in writing, within 10 days after receipt of said statement by the contractor or his representative on the work. Failure to file such written objections with reasons therefor within said 10 days shall be considered a waiver of all claims based on alleged erroneous estimates of quantities or incorrect classification of materials for the work covered by such statement.

G.15. *Classification of Excavation (Alternate).*[24]—Materials excavated will not be classified

[23]When excavations are not classified for payment, use section G.15.
*Delete or revise as applicable.

[24]When excavated materials are classified for payment, use section G.14.

for payment. Except as otherwise provided in these specifications, material excavated will be measured in excavation, to the lines shown on the drawings or as provided in these specifications, and all materials so required to be excavated will be paid for at the applicable prices bid in the schedule for excavation. No additional allowance above the price bid in the schedule will be made on account of any of the material being wet or frozen. Bidders and the contractor shall assume all responsibility for deductions and conclusions as to the nature of the materials to be excavated and the difficulties of making and maintaining the required excavations. The Government does not represent that the excavation can be performed or maintained at the pay lines described in these specifications or shown on the drawings.

Where the terms "rock", "rock excavation", "common", and "common excavation" are used in these specifications, the following definitions shall apply:

(a) *Rock Excavation.*—Rock is defined as "a sound and solid mass, layer, or ledge of mineral matter inplace, and of such hardness and texture that it cannot be effectively loosened or broken down by ripping in a single pass with a late model tractor-mounted hydraulic ripper equipped with one digging point of standard manufacturer's design adequately sized for use with and propelled by a crawler-type tractor rated between 385- and 410-net flywheel horsepower, operating in low gear."

In areas where the use of the ripper described is impracticable, rock is defined as "a sound material of such hardness and texture that it cannot be loosened or broken down by a 6-pound drifting pick." The drifting pick shall be class D, Federal Specification GGG-H-506D, with a handle not less than 34 inches in length.

(b) *Common Excavation.*—Common excavation includes all earth materials which do not meet the requirements of rock excavation as defined in (a).

G.16. *Definitions of Materials.*—Materials excavated will not be classified for payments.[25] For purposes of these specifications, other than for payment, materials of earthwork and embankment construction are defined in detail as follows:

(a) *Rock.*—Rock is defined as "a sound and solid mass, layer, or ledge of mineral matter inplace, and of such hardness and texture that (1) in areas where the use of a ripper-equipped crawler-type tractor is practicable, rock cannot be effectively loosened or broken down by ripping in a single pass with a late model tractor-mounted hydraulic ripper equipped with one digging point of standard manufacturer's design adequately sized for use with and propelled by a crawler-type tractor rated between 385 and 410-net flywheel horsepower, operating in low gear, or (2) in areas where the use of a ripper-equipped crawler-type tractor is impracticable, rock cannot be loosened or broken down by a 6-pound drifting pick. The drifting pick shall be class D, Federal Specification GGG-H-506D, with a handle not less than 34 inches in length.

(b) *Common Material.*—All earth materials which do not meet the requirements of rock as defined in (a).

(c) *Formation.*—Any sedimentary, igneous, or metamorphic material represented as a unit in geology, generally called rock but not necessarily meeting the classification requirements for rock as defined in (a).

(d) *Cobbles.*—Rounded pieces of rock which are not greater than 12 inches, but are larger than 3 inches in maximum dimension.

(e) *Boulders.*—Detached pieces of rock, generally rounded but may be subrounded to angular, which are larger than 12 inches in maximum dimension.

(f) *Rock Fragments.*—Pieces of rock which generally are not rounded.

(g) *Soil Components.*—NOTE.—Soils in nature usually consist of a number of soil components. They are identified by the predominance of one of the components and other criteria given in the Unified Soil Classification System, see chapter 5.

(1) *Clay.*—Plastic soil which passes a United States Standard No. 200 sieve.
(2) *Silt.*—Nonplastic soil which passes a No. 200 sieve.
(3) *Sand.*—Mineral grains which pass a No. 4 sieve and are retained on a No. 200 sieve.
(4) *Gravel.*—Pieces of rock which are not greater than 3 inches in maximum dimension, and are retained on a No. 4 sieve.

(h) *Geologic Definitions of Other Materials:*

Chalk.—A material of variable hardness consisting of a consolidated aggregation of very fine particles, mainly calcium carbonate, which is usually buff in color but may range from white to dark gray.

[25]Delete when materials are classified in accordance with section G.14; when materials are not classified, G.15, is required.

Shale.—A consolidated, partially laminated, fine-grained material having a tendency to split among lamination or bedding planes. It may range from a clay-like material which, when cut or scraped with a knife, produces a slick surface with shiny appearance, to a partially cemented material which, although it can be scratched with a knife, can be cut only with difficulty and produces a dull, fine-grained surface.

Tuff.—A material composed of the finer kinds of volcanic detritus, usually more or less stratified, and in various states of consolidation or induration.

G.17. *Opencut Excavation, General.*—

(a) *General.*—Opencut excavation required for the dam and appurtenant works shall be performed in accordance with this section and sections G.19 through G.22. Opencut excavation in borrow areas shall be in accordance with section G.24. Excavation shall be made to the lines, grades, and dimensions shown on the drawings or established by the Contracting Officer.

Bidders and the contractor shall assume all responsibility for deductions and conclusions as to the nature of the materials to be excavated and the difficulties of making and maintaining the reuired excavations. The Government does not represent that the excavation can be performed to or maintained at the pay lines described in these specifications.

The Government reserves the right, during the progress of the work, to vary the slopes, grades, or the dimensions of the excavations from those specified herein.

All necessary precautions, including control of blasting, shall be taken to preserve the material below and beyond the established lines of all excavation in the soundest possible condition. Any damage to the work due to the contractor's operations, including shattering of the material beyond the required excavation lines, shall be repaired at the expense of and by the contractor. Slopes shattered or loosened by blasting shall be taken down at the expense of and by the contractor.

Excavation for embankment and structure foundations shall be performed in the dry. No excavation shall be made in frozen materials without written approval. No additional allowance above the unit prices per cubic yard bid in the schedule for excavation will be made on account of any of the materials being wet or frozen.

Excavations shall be made to the full dimensions required and shall be finished to the prescribed lines and grades except that individual sharp points of undisturbed ledge rock will be permitted to extend within the prescribed lines not more than 6 inches where the excavation surfaces are not to be covered with concrete.

All *(shale) foundations shall be protected from freezing and air slaking in accordance with the provision of section G.29.

(b) *Structure Foundations.*—The bottom and side slopes of excavation upon or against which concrete is to be placed shall be excavated to the required dimensions as shown on the drawings or established by the Contracting Officer. No material will be permitted to extend within the neatlines of the structure.

If, at any point in rock or formation materials, the natural foundation material is disturbed or loosened, it shall be removed and replaced with concrete.

The bottom and side slopes of excavation in common material upon or against which concrete is to be placed shall be prepared by moistening and tamping or rolling with suitable tools and equipment to form a firm foundation for the concrete structure. If, at any point in common material, the natural foundation material is disturbed or loosened, for any purpose or reason, it shall be consolidated by tamping or rolling or, where directed, it shall be removed and replaced with selected earthfill material moistened and thoroughly compacted in 6-inch layers by tamping or rolling. The cost of all work required in the preparation of structure foundations shall be included in the applicable unit price bid in the schedule for excavation.

Where the material is unsuited to form a firm foundation upon which to place concrete, additional excavation and refill will be ordered in writing by the Contracting Officer, and payment therefor will be made as follows:

(1) Payment for additional excavation when ordered in writing to remove unsuitable foundation materials will be made at the applicable unit price per cubic yard bid in the schedule for excavation for the structure for which the excavation is made.

(2) Payment for concrete placed for refilling additional excavation in rock or formation materials will be made at the applicable unit

*Delete or revise as applicable.

price per cubic yard bid in the schedule for concrete in the structure involved.

(3) Payment for excavation and transportation of selected earthfill materials for use in refilling additional excavation in common material will be made at the unit price bid in the schedule for excavation of the material used for such refill.

(4) In additional excavations where compaction with the roller specified for use on the dam embankment is practicable and desirable, the foundations shall be prepared, and the refill materials shall be selected, placed, moistened, and compacted as provided in section G.29. The selected earthfill materials shall be placed and compacted to an excess depth of 18 inches above the established elevation of the structure foundation, and such excess material shall be excavated to the established elevation of the structure foundation. Payment for placing and compacting refill materials with the roller, as previously described, will be made at the unit price per cubic yard bid in the schedule for earthfill in dam embankment, zone 1, and payment for excavation of the excess roller-compacted earthfill to established grade of the structure will be made at the unit price per cubic yard bid in the schedule for excavation for the structure for which the excavation is made.

(5) In excavations where compaction with the roller specified for use on the dam embankment is impracticable or undesirable, the refilling and compacting of refill material shall be performed in accordance with section G.30, and payment for placing and compacting the refill material will be made only of material required to refill additional excavation as ordered by the Contracting Officer and will be made at the unit price per cubic yard bid in the schedule for specially compacted earthfill, zone 1.

Excess excavation performed for the convenience of the contractor or overexcavation performed by the contractor for any purpose or reason without written orders of the Contracting Officer shall be refilled with material furnished and placed as specified above, except that all such work shall be at the expense of and by the contractor, subject to payment for cement as provided above.

(c) *Excavated Materials.*—So far as practicable, as determined by the Contracting Officer, all suitable materials from excavations for specified permanent construction shall be used in the permanent construction required under these specifications.

Materials shall be selected as follows:[26]

The contractor's blasting and other operations in excavations shall be such that the excavations will yield as much suitable material for such construction as practicable, and shall be subject to the approval of the Contracting Officer. Where practicable, as determined by the Contracting Officer, suitable materials shall be excavated separately from the materials to be wasted and the suitable materials shall be segregated by loads during the excavation operations.The materials shall be placed in the designated final locations directly from the excavation or shall be placed in temporary stockpiles and later placed in the designated locations as directed by the Contracting Officer. In excavating materials which are suitable for use in the dam embankment, the Contracting Officer will designate the depths of cut which will result in the best gradation of materials, and the cuts shall be made to such designated depths.

Excavated materials which, after drainage or drying, are suitable for the impervious rolled earthfill portion of the dam embankment but which, when excavated, are too wet for immediate compaction in the embankment, shall be placed temporarily in stockpiles until the water content is reduced sufficiently to permit them to be placed in the embankment or may be placed on the embankment subject to the provisions of subsection G.29(g), relative to materials in which the water content is greater than that required for proper compaction.

Should cobbles having maximum dimensions of more than 5 inches and boulders be found in otherwise approved earthfill materials, they shall be removed by the contractor either at the site of the excavation or after being transported to the earthfill but before the materials are rolled and compacted. Such rock materials shall be placed in other portions of the dam embankment or wasted, as directed.

If, after excavation, sand, gravel, and cobble fill material has a water content greater than that required for placement and compaction in embankment, the material shall not be placed on the

[26]Insert applicable provisions.

embankment, but shall be placed temporarily in stockpiles and allowed to drain or dry until the water content is reduced sufficiently to permit it to be placed in the embankment.

Excavated materials which are unsuitable for *(or are in excess of) dam embankment or other earthwork requirements, as determined by the Contracting Officer, shall be wasted as provided in section G.27.

The contractor shall be entitled to no additional allowance above the unit prices bid in the schedule on account of the requirements for segregating materials by loads; excavating to designated depths; and draining or drying otherwise suitable materials.

(d) *Measurement and Payment.*—Excavated material including excavation for dam foundation will be measured for payment in excavation to the lines shown on the drawings or described elsewhere in these specifications, and will include only material that is actually removed within the prescribed pay lines.

Where concrete is to be placed directly upon or against the excavations, such excavations shall be sufficient at all points to provide for the minimum dimensions of concrete. Where dimensions of a concrete structure are shown on the drawings or if the elevation of the foundation is indicated, such dimensions shall be considered as the minimum dimensions and such elevation shall be considered as the elevation determining the minimum dimensions of the structure. Where a dimension or an elevation is not indicated on the drawings, minimum dimensions will be established by the Contracting Officer.

Where concrete is to be placed directly upon or against the excavations and the character of the material cut into is such that the material can be trimmed efficiently to accurate dimensions by ordinary excavation finishing methods to the required lines of the concrete structure, as determined by the Contracting Officer, measurement for payment will be made only of the excavation within the neatlines of the concrete structure.

Where concrete is to be placed directly upon or against the excavations and the character of the material cut into is such that the material cannot be trimmed efficiently to accurate dimensions by ordinary excavation finishing methods, as determined by the Contracting Officer, measurement for payment thereof will be made to the prescribed average dimension lines. The prescribed average dimension lines shall be considered as 3 inches outside the neatlines of the concrete for the purposes of measurement, for payment, of excavation. *[Where concrete protective coating is placed for foundation of the ________________________
structure(s) as specified in section G.23, the minimum excavation lines shown on the drawings or established by the Contracting Officer shall be increased by 2 inches, and measurement, for payment, of excavation for the structure will be made to the prescribed average dimension as specified]. No measurement for payment will be made for additional excavation required for application of concrete protective coatings for structure excavation at locations other than those specified in section G.23.

Measurement, for payment, of excavations upon or against which concrete is not required to be placed and excavation for trenches for pipe drains, including excavation for bedding and *(concrete pads), will be limited to the neatlines shown on the drawings or, where not shown on the drawings, to the most practicable lines, grades, and dimensions as established by the Contracting Officer.

Except as otherwise provided in section G.94 for diversion and care of stream during construction and removal of water from foundations, the unit prices bid in the schedule for excavation in opencut shall include the cost of all labor, equipment, and materials for cofferdams and other temporary construction and of all pumping, bailing, draining, and all other work necessary to maintain the excavations in good order during construction and of removing such temporary construction where required.

The unit prices bid in the schedule for excavation in opencut shall also include the cost of:

(1) Transportation of materials from the excavation to points of final use, to disposal areas, to temporary stockpiles, and from temporary stockpiles to points of final use.
(2) Rehandling excavated materials which have been deposited temporarily in stockpiles.
(3) Removal of oversize materials from otherwise suitable materials and disposal of the oversize materials.
(4) Disposal of excavated waste materials.

All excavated materials actually placed in completed earthwork and embankment construction will again be included for payment under appropriate items of the schedule covering such construc-

*Delete or revise as applicable.

tion. No payment will be made for excavation performed in previously placed embankment, refill, or backfill; *[except as provided in (b)].

G.18. *Drilling Line Holes for Rock Excavation.*—Rock excavation, where directed by the Contracting Officer, shall be formed by line drilling and broaching. The diameter of holes for line drilling shall be subject to approval. The spacing of the holes shall be as directed by the Contracting Officer, and shall be sufficiently close to ensure that the rock will break along the desired lines. Light blasting will be permitted in the holes along the sides of the excavation: *Provided*, that whenever, in the opinion of the Contracting Officer, further blasing might injure the rock outside the limits of the excavation, the use of explosives shall be discontinued and the excavation shall be completed by wedging, barring, or other suitable methods.

Measurement for payment for drilling line holes for rock excavation will include only the length of holes actually drilled into the rock along the sides of the excavation as directed by the Contracting Officer and will include only holes drilled at spacings of **(15 inches) or less from center to center of the holes.

Payment for drilling line holes for rock excavation will be made at the unit price per linear foot bid therefor in the schedule, which unit price shall include the costs of light blasting, broaching, wedging, barring, or other methods used in conjunction with line drilling to complete the excavation.

G.19. *Excavation for Grout Cap.*—

(a) *General.*—Excavation for the grout cap shall be performed, by the use of handtools and approved mechanical equipment, in such a manner as to prevent shattering of the sides and bottom of the excavation. At the option of the contractor and with the approval of the Contracting Officer, line drilling and light blasting in blasting holes may be employed: *Provided*, that each successive light blast will fracture and break the material into an open exposed face, or other approved methods may be employed. If line drilling and light blasting are employed, the diameter, spacing, and depth of the line drilling holes and the blasting holes shall be subject to the approval of the Contracting Officer, and the spacing of the holes and the amount, type, and distribution of explosive shall be such as to ensure that the material will break along the desired lines. The blasting shall be limited to approved methods which provide for successive fracturing of the worked face as the work is advanced by use of power tools and handwork. Blasting in line drill holes shall be limited to that blasting required to produce smooth and sound rock or material surfaces even if it is limited to no more than one line drill hole on each side of the grout cap trench per blast. Whenever, in the opinion of the Contracting Officer, further blasting might injure the surfaces outside the limits of the excavations, the use of explosives shall be discontinued. All blasting operations or activities under this section shall be performed in accordance with section G.115 and all Federal, State, and local laws and ordinances.

When an excavation for grout cap crosses a fault or seam, the excavation shall be carried to depths shown on the drawings, or as may be directed, and shall be keyed into the formation on the sides of the fault or seam as directed: *Provided*, that if excavation is required to a greater depth than 8 feet, measured normal to the surface of excavation for dam, such excavation will be ordered in writing in accordance with the section in these specifications for "Changes." The contractor shall furnish all materials to support the sides of the excavation where necessary, and all supports shall be removed before or during the placing of concrete.

(b) *Measurement and Payment.*—Measurement, for payment, of excavation for grout cap will be made to the prescribed average dimension in width, and to the designated depth measured normal to the finished surfaces of excavation for dam embankment foundation.

Payment for excavation for grout cap will be made at the unit price per cubic yard bid in the schedule for excavation for grout cap, which unit price shall include the entire cost of all work described in this section and the cost of furnishing, installing, and removing supports.

G.20. *Excavation for Dam Embankment Foundation.*—(a) *General.*—Excavation for the dam embankment foundation shall consist of all the excavation work listed below, performed to the lines and grades shown on the drawings or established by the Contracting Officer:

(1) Stripping for foundation of dam embankment.

(2) Excavation below stripping for foundation of dam embankment, including cutoff

*Delete or revise as applicable.

**Revise as appropriate.

trench(es) (and ____________________, but not including excavation for grout cap).*

*[(3) Excavation for dam embankment toe drains.

(4) Excavation for open drain ditches.

(5) Excavation for terminal well foundations.

(6) ____________________.]

Insofar as practicable, as determined by the Contracting Officer, suitable material excavated under the provisions of this section shall be *(used in the required construction work or transported to stockpiles for later use in the required construction work, as directed by the Contracting Officer). Excavated materials which are unsuitable for use in the required construction work or are in excess of construction needs, as determined by the Contracting Officer, shall be wasted in accordance with the provisions of section G.27. Excavated materials that may otherwise be suitable for use in the required construction work, but for which it is not practicable, as determined by the Contracting Officer, that they may be used or stockpiled, shall also be wasted in accordance with the provisions of section G.27.

The alinements and excavation lines shown on the drawings are subject to such changes as may be found necessary by the Contracting Officer to adapt the dam foundation excavation *(and other features listed above) to the conditions disclosed by the excavation.

Accurate trimming of the slopes of the excavation will not be required, but the excavation shall conform as closely as practicable to the established lines and grades. Loose rock shall be removed from foundation contacts. Rock cliffs, ledges, overhangs, and sharp irregularities shall be reduced as the Contracting Officer directs, including line drilling and smooth blasting techniques, so as to provide satisfactory foundation contours.

*[Overhanging faces, steep faces, and vertical faces designated by the Contracting Officer shall be excavated by rock shaping methods which do not involve blasting.]

Where, as determined by the Contracting Officer, it is not practicable to excavate local overhanging rock faces or rock faces steeper than ½:1 without detrimental blasting, the rock faces shall be solidly faced with dental concrete to provide abutment contact slopes not steeper than ½:1. Dental concrete shall be in accordance with section G.62.

(b) *Stripping for Foundation of Dam Embankment.*—As provided in section G.21, areas where dam embankment material is to be placed shall first be stripped in accordance with the drawings, these specifications, and as directed by the Contracting Officer.

(c) *Excavation Below Stripping for Cutoff Trench(es).*—The cutoff trench(es) shall be excavated in the dam embankment foundation approximately to the lines and grades shown on the drawings. The cutoff trench(es) shall be excavated *(to sound rock or) to firm ____________________. All loose, soft, or disintegrated material shall be removed from pockets and depressions to the extent directed.

*[Shale formations and other formations designated by the Contracting Officer, which are exposed during the excavation for dam embankment foundation, shall be protected from freezing and surface drying in accordance with the requirements of subsection G.29(c).]

*[(d) *Excavation Below Stripping Outside Cutoff Trench(es).*— Other areas of the dam embankment foundation where shown on the drawings or where directed by the Contracting Officer shall be excavated to sound rock, to firm ____________________, or to an otherwise suitable foundation as determined by the Contracting Officer.]

*[(e) *Measurement and Payment.*—Measurement, for payment, of excavation for dam embankment foundation will be made in accordance with the provisions of section G.17, but as limited by the following dividing surfaces]:

Dividing surfaces between excavation for dam embankment foundation and the following items shall be defined as follows:

*[(1) *Excavation for Structures.*—Within the limits of the dam embankment foundation, the dividing surfaces will be established for measurement for payment purposes by extending the surfaces defining the extent of the excavation for structures work to the original ground surface.]

*[(2) *Excavation for Roadway.*—The dividing surface will be a vertical plane normal to the centerline of the dam crest at dam station ____________________].

*[(3) ____________________].

*Delete or revise as applicable.

Payment for excavation for dam embankment foundation will be made at the applicable unit price per cubic yard bid therefor in the schedule, which unit price shall include all costs as provided in section G.17: *Provided,* that where separate bid items are included in the bidding schedule for excavating and handling materials before and after the materials are stockpiled, the costs of these separate operations shall be included in the applicable unit price.[27]

G.21. *Stripping.*—(a) *General.*—The contractor shall strip all areas of the permanent construction and borrow pits, to the depths directed by the Contracting Officer, to remove all unsuitable materials. The unsuitable materials to be removed by stripping shall include all debris and vegetable matter, including stumps and roots, and all other materials which, in the opinion of the Contracting Officer, are unsuitable for use in the permanent construction.

All stripped materials from borrow areas and permanent construction shall be disposed of in exhausted borrow pits or wasted in approved borrow pits. The borrow pits shall be graded with side slopes not to exceed ______ in a reasonably smooth condition, and the material placed as approved by the Contracting Officer.

(b) *Measurement and Payment.*—Measurement, for payment, for stripping of borrow pits will be made of the areas stripped to the final lines as approved by the Contracting Officer.

Except as otherwise provided for excavation of stripping the borrow areas, no direct payment will be made for stripping, and the cost thereof shall be included in the prices bid in the schedule for the items of excavation for which the stripping is required.

Payment of excavation of stripping the borrow areas will be made at the unit price per cubic yard bid therfore in the schedule, which price shall include the costs of removal of the materials, transportation, stockpiling or disposal, final grading in borrow areas or disposal areas, and all other costs required to complete the work.

G.22. *Excavation, in Opencut, for Structures.*—The item of the schedule for excavation, in opencut, for structures includes all opencut excavation, including stripping, as shown on the drawings, for the concrete structures as follows:

(Usually, this section is used for listing the descriptions and locations of the excavations involved under this excavation pay item, together with the dividing limits for measurement for payment if these excavations are contiguous with other excavations for which separate payment is made. This section is also used for specifications for construction of a concrete dam.)

Measurement, for payment, of excavation, in opencut, for structures will be made as provided in section G.17.

Payment for excavation, in opencut, for structures will be made at the unit price per cubic yard bid therefor in the schedule, which price shall include all costs as provided in section G.17.

G.23. *Protective Coating for Structure Foundations.*—(a) *General.*—Where designated by the Contracting Officer, a protective coating shall be applied to finished excavated foundation surfaces upon or against which concrete will be placed. The protective coating shall be applied only to foundation surfaces which are designated to receive protective coating where, in the judgment of the Contracting Officer, it is deemed necessary to prevent surface drying.

The protective coating shall be concrete protective coating, except an approved sprayed protective coating may be used on foundation surfaces of all structure cutoff excavations and on slopes steeper than 1:1.

Excavation shall not be performed within the final ______ inches of finished surfaces in areas which will require protective coatings until all equipment and facilities required for immediate application of protective coatings are available and in working condition. Areas requiring protection shall be subdivided into units within which the final ______ inches of excavation and the application of protective coating can be completed within one working shift. The work within these units shall be performed by continuous operation, and the application of protective coatings shall follow without delay. The protective coating shall be applied to these unit areas so that finished excavated surfaces will be exposed for the shortest possible period of time, which time shall not exceed ______ hours. Exposed finished excavated surfaces shall be kept

[27]Use when there is a need to include separate pay items in the bidding schedule to provide payment for stage work as it is accomplished, e.g., work before and during stockpiling and work after stockpiling within the same contract. Revise wording as required to agree with bid items used in the schedule.

moist at all times to prevent evaporation of the natural moisture in the material and shall be protected from freezing.

Surfaces to be coated shall be cleaned of all loose material, dirt, dust, mud, standing water, and other foreign matter. Coatings of protective material shall not be applied when air temperature is below 35° F, nor during other adverse weather as determined by the Contracting Officer. Temporary protective coatings, as approved by the Contracting Officer, will be permitted, if necessary, until the permanent protective coatings are applied. Protective coatings damaged by frost, heat, traffic, or other causes shall be removed and replaced or repaired at the expense of and by the contractor as directed, including the cost of removal of any frost or other damaged foundation material below such protective coatings and replacement with compacted earth material or concrete as applicable. Protective coatings shall be covered with structural concrete as soon as practicable, and in no event shall the protective coatings be left exposed for a period exceeding ______ days.

(b) *Sprayed Protective Coating.*—Sprayed protective coating shall be one of the following products or an approved equal:

(1) Polybind, manufactured by Celtite, Inc., Mining Products Division, Huntington, West Virginia.
(2) Genaqua 743, manufactured by The Delta Company, Charleston, West Virginia.
(3) Aerospray 70 Binder, manufactured by American Cyanamid Company, Wayne, New Jersey.

The sprayed protective coating shall be applied to finished excavated surfaces in accordance with the manufacturer's recommendations and by methods approved by the Contracting Officer. The coating shall be applied to a thickness and in such a manner that a uniform coating free from pinholes will be produced which will protect the finished excavated surface from the air.

(c) *Concrete Protective Coating.*—Concrete protective coating shall be applied so that the contact surface is covered to a minimum depth of 2 inches. Where concrete protective coating is applied, the minimum excavation lines shown on the drawings or established by the Contracting Officer shall be increased by 2 inches and the protective coating shall be applied within such increased excavation lines to provide for full dimensions of structural concrete in overlying structures.

The concrete shall conform to the applicable provisions specified in sections G.73 to G.91, inclusive. The method of placing the concrete shall be subject to approval. Concrete for protective coating shall not contain aggregate larger than ¾-inch maximum size. Either water or wax-base curing may be used on concrete protective coating.

The exposed surfaces of concrete protective coating shall not be considered as a construction joint, but shall be cleaned, as approved by the Contracting Officer, immediately prior to placement of the overlying structural concrete on the concrete coating.

(d) *Measurement and Payment.*—Measurement, for payment, of protective coating will be made of the number of square yards of the finished excavated foundation area actually coated at the direction of the Contracting Officer. Payment for protective coating for structure foundations will be made at the unit price per square yard bid therefor in the schedule, which unit price shall include the cost of all work and equipment, and of furnishing the materials required for application of protective coating, except excavation for concrete protective coating and except cement used in concrete protective coating. Concrete placed for protective coating will not be included for payment in other items of the schedule for concrete in the structure involved. Payment for cement used in concrete protective coating will be made at the unit price per ton bid in the schedule for furnishing and handling cement *(for concrete).

Payment for the additional excavation required for application of concrete protective coating will be made at the unit price per cubic yard bid in the schedule for excavation, in opencut, for structures.

Protective coating applied in areas other than as directed by the Contracting Officer shall be at the expense of the contractor.

G.24. *Borrow Areas.*—(a) *General.*—All materials required for the following construction which are not available from excavations required for permanent construction under these specifications, shall be obtained from borrow areas ______, ______, ______, and ______. The locations of the borrow areas are shown on drawing No. ______.

(1) Construction of dam embankment, zones ______, ______, and ______.
*(2) Pervious backfill.
*(3) Bedding for riprap.

*Delete or revise as applicable.

*(4) Selected surfacing.

*(5) ________________.

Explorations in the borrow areas indicate that the materials are variable in nature and texture and contain variable amounts of moisture *[and plus 5-inch material. Approximate percentages of plus 5-inch material encountered in the explorations within borrow area ______ are shown on the logs. The absence of percentages of oversize on any log of explorations within the area does not, however, imply that oversize materials will not be encountered in the vicinity of such explorations.]

Ground-water level encountered in the explorations, as shown on the logs, is for the indicated dates. The absence of a ground-water level or moisture content on any log of explorations within the areas does not, however, imply that ground water or variable moisture content will not be encountered in the vicinity of such explorations.

Bidders are cautioned that wide variation from the nature, texture, moisture content, and the percentage of oversize material as indicated by the explorations, is to be anticipated. Bidders and the contractor must assume all responsibility for deductions and conclusions concerning the nature, moisture content, and texture of materials, the percentages of oversize materials, the total yield of suitable materials, the difficulties of making excavations, of breaking down or removing the oversize materials, of obtaining a satisfactory moisture content, and of obtaining a uniform mixture of materials. *[Some exploratory test pits in the borrow areas will be open for inspection and bidders should inspect the borrow areas and examine the test pits, and bidders are urged to sample and test materials from borrow areas prior to submitting bids.]

The type of equipment used and the contractor's operations in the excavation of materials in borrow pits shall be such as will produce the required uniformity of mixture of each of the types of materials at the borrow pits.

The location and extent of all borrow pits within borrow areas shall be as directed, and the Government reserves the right to change the limits or location of borrow pits within the limits of the borrow areas in order to obtain the most suitable material, to minimize stripping, or for other reasons.

To avoid the formation of pools in borrow pits during the excavation operations, and in borrow pits above elevation __________ after the excavation operations are completed, drainaged ditches from borrow pits to the nearest outlets shall be excavated by the contractor where, in the opinion of the Contracting Officer, such drainage ditches are necessary.

Should any borrow pit be opened near the dam embankment and below the elevation of normal water surface in the reservoir, berms not less than ______ feet wide shall be left between the toe of the dam embankment and the edge of the borrow pit, with a slope of 4:1 to the bottom of the borrow pit. Excavated surfaces of borrow pits adjacent to the reservoir above the normal water surface shall be graded to slopes not steeper than ______. In other areas, the contractor will not be required to excavate surfaces of borrow pits to any specified lines and grades, but such surfaces shall be left in a reasonably smooth and even condition and may require trimming, as directed by the Contracting Officer to provide a neat appearance (and to facilitate measurement for payment.)[28] Borrow pits shall be operated and left in a condition so as not to impair the usefulness nor mar the appearance of any part of the work or any other property of the Government, and shall be left in a condition as required in section G.2. The surfaces of wasted material shall be left in a reasonably smooth and even condition.

*(b) *Roads, Buildings, and Utility Lines in Borrow Areas.*—The road traverses borrow area ______ as shown on drawing No. ______. The road shall be relocated as provided in the section in these specifications for "Roadway Construction, General". *(This road will be relocated by others.) Prior to relocation of the road, the contractor shall not excavate material within 50 feet of the centerline of the road. The contractor shall conduct his operations in such a manner as to permit continued use of the road and to provide safety to the public as provided in the section in these specifications for "Maintaining Public Traffic" until such time as the road has been relocated. *(The contractor shall permit access as necessary to others for the purpose of relocation of this road.)

The buildings located in borrow area ______, as shown on drawing ______, will be disposed of by others. Prior to disposal of the buildings, they shall be protected from damage from the contractor's op-

*Delete or revise as applicable.

[28]Delete or modify when not measured in excavation.

erations. The contractor shall permit access as necessary to others for the purpose of disposal of these buildings.

Power transmission lines, pipelines, and telephone lines traversing the borrow areas, as shown on the drawings, will be relocated by others. Prior to relocation of the utility lines the contractor shall not excavate material within 50 feet of the centerline of any pipe, power transmission, or telephone lines. The contractor shall conduct his operations in a manner to prevent any interference with or damage to the utility lines and to permit access as necessary to others for the purpose of relocation of these utility lines.

(c) *Moisture and Drainage.*—The moisture content of the earthfill material prior to and during compaction shall be in accordance with subsection G.29(e). As far as practicable, the material shall be conditioned in the borrow pits before excavation. If required, moisture shall be introduced into the borrow pits for the earthfill material by irrigation, at least ______ days in advance of excavation operations, *(or at the option of the contractor, moisture may be added at the separation plant.) When moisture is introduced into the borrow pits for earthfill material prior to excavation, care shall be exercised to moisten the material uniformly to produce the required moisture content during compaction, avoiding both excessive runoff and accumulation of water in depressions. The contractor is cautioned to control carefully the application of water and check on the depth and amount of water penetration during application so as to avoid overirrigation:

(Include here information regarding watering tests if any were made)

If at any location in the borrow pits for earthfill material, before or during excavation operations, there is excessive moisture, as determined by the Contracting Officer, steps shall be taken to reduce the moisture by selective excavation to secure the drier materials; by excavating and placing in temporary stockpiles material containing excessive moisture; by excavating drainage ditches; by allowing adequate additional time for curing or drying; or by any other approved means.

The moisture content of sand, gavel, and cobble fill material prior to and during compaction shall be in accordance with section G.34. Borrow pits for sand, gravel, and cobble fill material will not require preconditioning by irrigation but may require preconditioning by draining and lowering the water table below the elevation of borrow excavation. Preconditioning by draining may be accomplished by any approved method, including lowering the water table in the borrow area prior to excavating or stockpiling. If, after excavation, sand, gravel, and cobble fill material has a moisture content greater than that required for placement and compaction in embankment, the material shall not be placed on the embankment, but shall be placed temporarily in stockpiles and allowed to drain or dry until the moisture content is reduced significantly to permit it to be placed in the embankment.

In any event, the contractor will be required to excavate sufficient suitable material in portions of borrow areas ____________ to complete the work under these specifications, regardless of whether overly wet conditions encountered are due to ground water, precipitation, difficulty of draining, or for any other reason. To minimize operations with overly wet material, the contracator will be permitted to utilize portions of the borrow areas which contain dry material and which have been designated as suitable borrow pits to the greatest extent practicable consistent with obtaining suitable material.

The contractor shall be entitled to no additional allowance above the unit prices bid in the schedule on account of the requirement for excavating drainage ditches; for allowing additional time for curing or drying; for stockpiling and rehandling excavated materials which have been deposited temporarily in stockpiles; delays or increased costs due to stockpiling; poor trafficability on the borrow area, the haul roads, or the embankment; reduced efficiency of the equipment the contractor elects to use; or on account of any other operations or difficulties caused by overly wet materials. No additional allowance above the unit prices bid in the schedule will be made because of variation in the proportion between wet and dry materials which are required to be excavated in order to obtain adequate suitable material.

(d) *Stripping and Waste.*—Borrow pit sites shall be cleared as provided in section G.13. Borrow pits will be designated by the Contracting Officer as the work progresses, and stripping operations shall be limited only to designated borrow pits. The contractor shall carefully strip the sites of designated borrow pits of boulders, topsoil, sod, loam, and

---
*Delete or revise as applicable.

other matter which is unsuited for the purposes for which the borrow pit is to be excavated. The contractor shall maintain the stripped surfaces free of vegetation until excavation operations in the borrow pit are completed and the contractor shall be entitled to no additional allowance above the unit prices bid in the schedule because of this requirement. Materials from stripping which are suitable for topsoil shall be selected during stripping operations, temporarily stockpiled adjacent to borrow pits if necessary, and spread over exhausted portions of the borrow pits as directed by the Contracting Officer. Materials from stripping which are not suited for topsoil shall be disposed of in exhausted borrow pits, or in approved areas adjacent to borrow pits, or as provided in section G.27.

If materials unsuitable, or not required, for permanent construction purposes are found in any borrow pit, such materials shall be left in place or excavated and wasted, as directed. Where excavation of such materials is directed, payment for such excavation and disposal of unsuitable or excess materials will be made at (1) unit price per cubic yard bid in the schedule for excavation, stripping borrow pits, or (2) applicable unit price per cubic yard bid in the schedule for excavation in borrow areas and transportation to dam embankment.[29]

(e) *Excavation and Transportation.*—The Contracting Officer will designate the depths of cut in all parts of the borrow pits, and the cuts shall be made to such designated depths. The earthfill materials delivered on the dam embankment shall be equivalent to a mixture of materials obtained from an approximately uniform cutting from the full height of the designated face of the borrow pit excavation. Shallow cuts will be permitted in the borrow areas if unstratified materials with uniform moisture content are encountered.

The contractor shall transport the materials to the dam embankment location designated by the Contracting Officer.

The contractor shall be entitled to no additional allowance above the unit prices bid in the schedule on account of the designation by the Contracting Officer of the various portions of the borrow areas from which materials are to be obtained, on account of the depths of cut which are required to be made, or on account of the zone or location on embankment where materials are hauled.

(f) *Separation Plant.*—Materials from borrow areas ______ shall be separated before placement in dam embankment, zone ______. The contractor shall construct separation plant facilities which will separate cobbles, boulders, and rock fragments having maximum dimensions greater than ______ inches from all other material. Material ______ inches or less in maximum dimension shall be placed in dam embankment zone ______ ; and cobbles, boulders, and rock fragments having maximum dimensions greater than ______ inches shall be placed in ____________: *Provided*, that cobbles, boulders, and rock fragments larger than ______ inches in maximum dimension shall be placed in the outer slopes of ____________or shall be embedded in that zone, so as not to interfere with the compaction operations.

(g) *Measurement and Payment.*—Measurement, for payment, of excavation, stripping borrow pits will be made in excavation and will include only the stripping in locations and to the depths as directed by the Contracting Officer. Payment for excavation, stripping borrow pits will be made at (1) unit price per cubic yard bid therefore in the schedule, which unit price shall include the costs of selecting, stockpiling, and spreading the topsoil over exhausted portions of the borrow pits, or otherwise disposing of materials from stripping, or (2) applicable unit price per cubic yard bid in the schedule for excavation in borrow areas and transportation to dam embankment, which unit price shall include the costs of selecting, stockpiling, and spreading topsoil over exhausted portions of the borrow pits, or otherwise disposing of materials from stripping.[29]

Measurement, for payment, of excavation in borrow areas will be made (in excavation only)[28] and to the excavation lines prescribed by the Contracting Officer. Payment for excavation in borrow areas and transportation to dam embankment *(and for excavation in borrow areas, separation, and transportation to dam embankment) will be made at the applicable unit price per cubic yard bid therefor in the schedule, which unit price shall include all costs of irrigation and unwatering of borrow pits, of conditioning the material properly, and all work *(other than stripping) required by this section. All mate-

[29]Use (1) when haul distance is in excess of 2 miles and/or separation plant is required; use (2) when haul distance is less than 2 miles and/or separation plant is not required.

[28]Delete or modify when not measured in excavation.

*Delete or revise as applicable.

rials from borrow pits placed in dam embankment, zones ____________, in ____________, and in backfill will again be included for payment under the applicable items of the schedule for placing such earthwork.

If the contractor elects to obtain concrete aggregates, gravel for drain, ____________, or other materials for which the cost of furnishing is included in other items of work, no payment will be made for stripping or excavation of such materials obtained from borrow areas. The contractor shall keep his operations for the production of these materials separate and distinct from his other borrow area operations.

G.25. *Rock Deposits* (*Rock Furnished by Contractor*)[30].—Rock fragments of the quality and gradations specified herein shall be furnished by the contractor for use in bedding for riprap and riprap to be placed and stockpiled and for other permanent construction required under these specifications.

(a) *Quality.*—The rock fragments shall meet the following requirements as to quality:

(1) Individual rock fragments shall be dense, sound, and resistant to abrasion and shall be free of cracks, seams, and other defects that would tend to increase unduly their destruction by water and frost actions.

(2) Samples prepared in accordance with applicable designations of the Bureau of Reclamation's *Concrete Manual*[2], shall meet the following requirements when tested by the procedures described in the respective test designations:

Test Designation	Requirements
USBR 4127 - Specific Gravity and Absorption of Coarse Aggregate	Greater than (2.60)*
USBR 4088 - Soundness of Aggregates Using Sodium Sulfate or Magnesium Sulfate	Less than (10 percent)* loss of mass after five cycles.
USBR 4535 - Resistance to Degradation of Large-Size, Coarse Aggregate by Abrasion and Impact in Los Angeles Machine	Less than (40 percent)* loss of mass after 500 revolutions.

*Modify value for each job depending on nature of material available and design considerations.

Samples of ______ and ______[31] from the following locations have been tested and found suitable: (list locations.)

Bidders and the contractor are cautioned that the above mentioned deposits may be variable in quality, and the sizes and quantities of rock fragments that may be obtained from any source are unknown. The contractor will be responsible for furnishing suitable rock fragments, for making necessary arrangements with property owners for rights-of-way, and for payment of required royalities.

(b) *Sampling and Testing.*—The contractor shall furnish to the Contracting Officer, at the damsite, without cost, such samples of rock fragments for testing as may be required by the Contracting Officer from proposed quarry sites and from rock fragments delivered to the damsite. The Contracting Officer reserves the right to make inspections of quarry sites and quarries. The approval of some rock fragments from a particular quarry site shall not be construed as constituting the approval of all rock fragments taken from that quarry, and the contractor will be held responsible for the specified quality and gradation of rock fragments delivered to the damsite. All rock fragments not meeting the requirements of these specifications, as determined by tests and/or inspection at the quarries and damsite, will be rejected.

G.26. *Rock Source* (*Source Furnished by Contracting Officer*)[32].—All rock materials required for construction of (1) ______ and (2) ______ shall be secured from the rock shown on drawing ______. All operations within the rock source shall be subject to approval. The Contracting Officer reserves the right to designate the locations of excavations within the limits of the rock source in order to obtain suitable rock materials for construction purposes. The portions of the rock source to be excavated shall be cleared as provided in section G.13, and shall be stripped of all overburden and loose, soft, disintegrated rock as directed.

The contractor shall produce, by excavation in rock source and selection or processing, sufficient suitable rock fragments reasonably well graded, as determined by the Contracting Officer, up to ______ inches in maximum dimensions for construc-

[30]Use this section when rock is to be furnished by contractor, and not to be used exclusively for riprap; modify section G.43 accordingly.

[31]Designate rock types; e.g., granite, limestone, etc.

[32]Use this section when rock is to be obtained from a source furnished by the Contracting Officer; it is not to be used exclusively for riprap. Modify section G.43 accordingly.

tion of *(rock fines fill in dam embankment, pervious backfill, and bedding for riprap). The contractor shall also produce by excavation in rock source and selection or processing sufficient suitable rock fragments reasonably well graded, as determined by the Contracting Officer, up to ______ cubic yards in volume for construction of *(rockfill in dam embankment and riprap). The type of equipment used and the contractor's operations in the rock source shall be such as will produce the required gradations of rock fragments at the rock source.

All suitable rock fragments shall be transported to points of final use, and all excavated materials unsuitable or in excess of requirements for construction purposes shall be disposed of in excavations in rock source or as directed.

The cost of all work described in this section, including clearing and stripping rock source, shall be included in the schedule for items of constructions in which rock fragments are used.

G.27. *Disposal of Excavated Materials.*—

(a) *General.*—So far as practicable, as determined by the Contracting Officer, all suitable materials from excavation required under these specifications shall be *(stockpiled for future use or) used in the permanent construction as provided in section G.17.

The disposal of all excavated materials that are to be wasted shall be subject to the approval of the Contracting Officer. The contractor will not be required to haul materials to be wasted more than ______ feet, along the most practicable routes, to the designated disposal areas. *(The Contracting Officer will designate disposal areas below El. ______ in the reservoir area.) [Areas designated for disposal of waste material from excavation are shown on drawings ______ and ______ .][33]

Waste piles shall be located where they will not have a detrimental effect on the natural flow of the stream, cross drainage, operation of reservoir, or interfere with the flow of water to or from the spillway or outlet works; the appearance of the completed project, or the accessibility of the completed structures. In no case will waste material be permitted to be disposed of by dumping over the edge from the top of any natural slope.

Special care shall be taken in hauling and disposal of excessively wet materials to prevent turbid water from entering the stream. Such materials shall be disposed of behind dikes of drier waste materials or by other methods approved by the Contracting Officer.

Where directed by the Contracting Officer, waste piles shall be leveled and trimmed to reasonably regular lines.

*[(b) *Corrugated Metal Pipe.*—The contractor shall furnish and install 18-inch corrugated metal pipe culverts at and in the vicinity of waste disposal sites, as directed by the Contracting Officer, so as to provide adequate surface drainage in the area and so as to pass cross drainage from surrounding areas.]

*[The corrugated metal pipe shall be of standard commercial quality and shall be adequate in gage to sustain the anticipated loadings. The ends of the culverts shall be protected as necessary to prevent plugging. The corrugated metal pipe and all appurtenances shall be subject to the approval of the Contracting Officer.]

*[(c) *Cost.*—Except as otherwise provided, the cost of transporting excavated materials from excavation sites to disposal areas or to points of final use, including stockpiling and rehandling, if required, and of disposing of all excavated materials that are to be wasted, as provided in this section, shall be included in the applicable unit prices per cubic yard bid in the schedule for excavation.

*[Measurement, for payment, of 18-inch corrugated metal pipe will be made of the actual length of pipe, installed as directed and approved by the Contracting Officer, and measured in feet along the centerline of the pipe. No allowance will be made for laps at joints.]

*[Payment for furnishing and installing 18-inch corrugated metal pipe will be made at the unit price per linear foot bid therfor in the schedule, which price shall include the cost of all labor, materials, tools, equipment, and expenses required to furnish and install the corrugated metal pipe and all appurtenances, as specified, complete and in place.]

[33]Add drawing numbers when disposal areas are shown on the drawings.
*Delete or revise as applicable.

C. EMBANKMENT

G.28. *Embankment Construction, General.*—

(a) *General.*—For the purpose of these specifications, the term "dam embankment" includes all portions of the dam embankment as follows:

(1) The earthfill, zone 1, portions designated on the drawings by the figure 1 encircled, including specially compacted earthfill, zone 1.

(2) The *(processed) sand and gravel filter zones, zone 2, portions designated on the drawings by the figure 2 encircled, including specially compacted sand and gravel fill, zone 2. Zone 2 material would mostly be used for inclined and horizontal filter layers.

(3) The *(processed) sand and gravel drainage zones, zone 3, portions designated on the drawings by the figure 3 encircled, including specially compacted sand and gravel fill, zone 3. Zone 3 material would mostly be used for inclined and horizontal drainage layers.

(4) The sand, gravel, and cobble fill, zone 4, portions designated on the drawings by the figure 4 encircled, including specially compacted sand, gravel, and cobble fill.

(5) The cobble and boulder fill in dam embankment, zone 5, portions designated on the drawings by the figure 5 encircled.

[34][(6) The sand and sandstone fragments, zone ______ portions designated on the drawings by the figure ______ encircled.

(7) The miscellaneous fill in dam embankment, zone ______ portions designated on the drawings by the figure ______ encircled.

(8) The riprap on the upstream slope of the dam embankment.

(9) The bedding for riprap on upstream slope of the dam embankment.

(10) The soil-cement slope protection on the upstream slope of the dam embankment.

(11) The seeded topsoil cover on the downstream slope of the dam embankment.

(12) The selected surfacing on the crest of the dam embankment.]

Other items of embankment, which are not necessarily a part of the dam embankment, include bedding for riprap, riprap, pervious backfill, seeded topsoil cover, and selected surfacing.

The completed dam embankment shall be to the lines and grades shown on the drawings: *Provided,* that the dividing lines between the downstream *[zones 1 and 2, and ______ and ______ , or ______ and ______ shall vary as directed to accommodate the volume of zones(s) ______ available].

Placing shall be performed in a manner to prevent damage to structures, and all embankment adjacent to either side of a structure shall be kept at approximately the same level as the placing of the embankment progresses.

The contractor's operations shall be such, and he shall handle and place the embankment materials in such a manner, as to prevent segregation of the materials.

(b) *Foundation Preparation.*—No materials shall be placed in any portion of the dam embankment until the foundation for each section has been unwatered, stripped, and suitably prepared, and has been approved by the Contracting Officer. Stripping shall be in accordance with section G.21.

All cavities, depressions, and irregularities, either existing or resulting from removal of rock fragments found within the area to be covered by embankment, and which extend below or beyond the established lines of excavation for dam embankment foundation, shall be filled with embankment materials and compacted as specified for the overlying embankment and/or treated by slush grouting and dental concrete as provided in sections G.61 and G.62.

All joints, shear zones, cracks, openings, and irregularities shall be adequately cleaned out and treated with slush grouting or dental concrete as provided in sections G.29, G.32, and G.33 or in areas where directed by the Contracting Officer.

Materials, other than concrete, shall not be placed at any point on the dam embankment foundation until all curtain grouting of the dam foundation within 100 feet, measured along the slope, of that point has been completed.

(c) *Placing Embankment Materials.*—The suitability of each part of the foundation for placing embankment materials thereon and of all materials for use in embankment construction will be deter-

[34]Delete or revise as necessary to fit design materials and requirements.
*Delete or revise as applicable.

mined by the Contracting Officer. No embankment materials shall be placed in the embankment when either the materials or the foundation or embankment on which it would be placed is frozen.

No brush, roots, sod, or other perishable or unsuitable materials shall be placed in the embankment.

Each load of the material placed in the embankment, whether from excavation for other parts of the work or from borrow pits, shall be placed in the location designated by the Contracting Officer, and the contractor shall be entitled to no additional allowance above the unit prices bid in the schedule on account of this requirement.

In any separate portion of dam embankment being constructed, each layer of each zone shall be constructed continuously and approximately horizontal for the width and length of such portion at the elevation of the layer: *Provided,* that if the embankment is temporarily left low adjacent to the spillway *(or outlet works) to facilitate construction of the structure, embankment placed within the temporary low area will be required to be placed approximately horizontal. Slope requirements given in subsection G.28(c)(2) apply.

The contractor shall maintain the embankment in an approved manner, including maintaining surfaces free of weeds or other vegetation, until final completion and acceptance of all the work under the contract.

The contractor will be permitted to construct separate portions of the dam embankment below original ground surface, subject to the approval of the Contracting Officer. Above original ground surface, construction of the dam embankment shall be subject to the following conditions:

(1) Longitudinal bonding surfaces (surfaces parallel to the centerline crest of embankment) will not be permitted in zone 1. In other portions of dam embankment, longitudinal surfaces between previously constructed embankment and embankment to be constructed shall be subject to approval and shall be not be steeper than 1.5:1.

(2) A temporary gap through the dam embankment, for diversion purposes as described in section G.94, will be permitted: *Provided,* that the slopes of transverse bonding surfaces (surfaces normal to the centerline crest of embankment) between previously completed portions of embankment and embankment to be placed shall be not steeper than 4:1. No other transverse bonding surfaces in zone 1 above original ground surface will be permitted. In zones other than zone 1, transverse bonding surfaces between previously constructed embankment and embankment to be placed shall be subject to the approval of the Contracting Officer and shall not be steeper than 2:1.

During construction of earthfill, zone 1, embankment in the openings at the temporary gap, the contractor shall construct a keyway trench in each 4:1 transverse bonding surface in the previously placed earthfill, zone 1. The keyway trenches shall be excavated in the bonding surfaces to a minimum vertical depth of 5 feet, shall have 4:1 side slopes, and shall have a minimum bottom width of 20 feet. The centerline of the trenches shall be located approximately midway between the upstream and downstream slopes of the zone 1 material. The trenches shall be refilled with earthfill, zone 1, material subject to the provisions of section G.29.

(3) At any cross section above original ground surface, the elevation of the zone 1 portion of the dam embankment shall not exceed the elevation of the immediately adjacent zone _______ portion by more than 1 foot. The allowable difference between all zones should be stated.

During periods of winter shutdown, where exposed above water in the temporary gap for diversion, and at all equipment crossings, the contractor shall protect all zone _______ and _______ embankment material from erosion, excessive saturation, and general contamination. Protection shall include the installation of commercially available protective covering material such as polyethylene sheeting or PVC sheeting, or equal, as approved by the Contracting Officer. For periods of winter shutdown and in the temporary gap for diversion, the sheeting shall be covered by a minimum of 12 inches of zone 1 embankment material. At equipment crossings, the sheeting material shall be covered with a sufficient depth of zone 1 embankment material to prevent damage to the sheeting by the type of equipment using the crossings, or a minimum of 12 inches, whichever provides greater protection.

*Delete or revise as applicable.

The plastic sheeting material shall be factory fabricated into suitably sized sections so that the amount of field seaming is minimized. The placement, joining, and repair of the plastic sheeting shall be in accordance with the recommendations of the manufacturer of the material.

Prior to resuming the placement of zone _____ and _____ material at equipment crossings or after winter shutdown or diversion, the contractor shall remove the plastic sheeting material, the zone 1 embankment material, and any additional items used to hold the sheeting in place or prevent contamination of the underlying materials. If the zone _____ and _____ materials are contaminated or otherwise harmed, the contractor shall restore the zones to their original satisfactory state at his expense. The zone 1 material used in conjunction with the plastic sheeting material may be reused for performing the zone 1 embankment work at the contractor's option if the material is suitable for such use.

At all times, the dam embankment shall be such that surface drainage is away from the zone _____ chimney drain.

(d) *Measurement and Payment.*—Measurement, for payment, of the various items of embankment construction will be made of the materials in place in the completed embankment to the lines, grades, slopes, and thicknesses shown on the drawings, or described in these specifications, or established by the Contracting Officer, and will include embankment for the approach road to the dam crest, and will include crest camber. The cross sections obtained by surveys made after completion of excavation for dam embankment foundation will be used in computing the quantity of dam embankment placed. No allowance will be made in measurement for payment for settlement, shrinkage, and consolidation of the foundation or of the material in the embankment. In measuring embankment for payment, the volume of structures, of specially compacted earthfill, and other work for which items for payment are provided in the schedule will be deducted.

Measurement, for payment, of embankment in the _____________ area which is required to be excavated to minimum lines, in accordance with section G.29, will be made both when originally placed and again when the embankment is replaced. Replacing embankment beyond the minimum lines will be at the contractor's expense.

The dividing surface for measurement for payment between dam embankment items and embankment *[(for service road) (roadway)] placed in accordance with the section in these specifications for "Construction of Road Embankment" shall be a *[vertical plane normal to centerline crest of dam at dam station _____________, the last contact point where the approaching (service road) (roadway) meets the berm of the dam embankment at any point except the crest of the dam].

Payment under all items of embankment construction shall include the costs of preparing the embankment foundations; of placing; of supplementary wetting on the fill, if necessary, and any additional work required on the embankment to accomplish uniform water application; of compacting where compaction is required; of preparing bonding surfaces; and all other operations required to secure adequate bond between embankment in place and embankment to be placed.

[34][Payment for the embankment items will be in addition to payment made for excavation and transportation of the materials, except for furnishing and placing (riprap and bedding for riprap) and (soil-cement slope protection). Payment for (furnishing and placing riprap and furnishing and placing bedding for riprap) (furnishing and placing soil-cement slope protection) shall include all costs in accordance with sections G.42, G.43, and G.117.]

It may be feasible to transport some of the materials which are excavated for other parts of the work and which are suitable for embankment construction directly to the embankments at the time of making the excavations, but the contractor shall be entitled to no additional compensation above the unit prices bid in the schedule by reason of it being necessary, or required by the Contracting Officer, that such excavated materials be deposited temporarily in stockpiles and rehandled prior to being placed in the embankment.

No measurement or payment will be made for excavating keyway trenches in embankment or for refilling the trenches; and the cost of preparing bonding surfaces, including excavating keyway trenches and refilling such trenches in transverse bonding slopes and all other operations required to secure adequate bond between embankment in place and embankment to be placed, shall be in-

[34]Delete or revise as necessary to fit design materials and requirements.
*Delete or revise as applicable.

cluded in unit prices bid for items of constructing embankments.

G.29. *Earthfill in Dam Embankment, Zone 1.*—

(a) *General.*—The earthfill, zone(s) 1 *(and ________) portion(s) of the dam embankment and earthfill placed for the foundations of the ____________ structure shall be constructed in accordance with this section and section G.28.

(b) *Materials.*—Zone 1 of the earthfill portion(s) of the dam embankment shall consist of *(a mixture of) [35][____________ (______), ____________ (________), ______________ (________), and ____________ (_______)], available from borrow pits in borrow areas ___________, *(and _______), *(and from excavations required for the dam and appurtenant works). *(Zone ___________ of the earthfill portion(s) of the dam embankment shall consist of *(a mixture of)[35] [________ (______), _________ (_______), __________ (_______), and _________ (_______)], available from borrow pits in borrow area(s) ______, ______, and ______, *(and from excavations required for the dam and appurtenant works).

The materials selected for zone 1 shall contain a minimum of [36](_______) percent by dry weight of soil particles passing a United States Standard No. 200 sieve and shall have a plasticity index of [36](_______) percent or greater for the portion of the material passing a United States Standard No. 40 sieve. The Contracting Officer will determine the percent soil particles passing the No. 200 sieve and the plasticity index from samples of earthfill materials obtained from uncompacted earthfill materials placed on the dam embankment.

The materials selected for zone ______ shall contain a minimum of [36](_______) percent soil particles passing a United States Standard No. 200 sieve, *[and shall have a plasticity index of [36](_______)percent or greater for the portion of the material passing a United States Standard No. 40 sieve.] The percentage of soil particles passing the No. 200 sieve *(and the plasticity index) will be determined from samples of earthfill materials obtained from uncompacted earthfill material placed in the dam embankment.

The contractor's operations in the excavation of the materials for the earthfill shall be in accordance with sections G.17 and G.24.

Cobbles retained on a screen with 5-inch square openings and boulders shall not be placed in the earthfill. Should cobbles of such size and boulders be found in otherwise approved earthfill materials, they shall be removed by the contractor either at the site of the excavation *(at the separation plant), or after being transported to the earthfill portion(s) of the dam embankment but before the earthfill materials are compacted. Such cobbles and boulders shall be placed in the _______ or _______ portions of the dam embankment or wasted as directed by the Contracting Officer.

(c) *Preparation of Foundations:*

(1) *General.*—No material shall be placed in any section of the earthfill portion(s) of the dam embankment until the foundation for that section has been unwatered, cleaned, and suitably treated and has been accepted by the Government. All portions of excavations made for test pits or other subsurface investigations and all other existing cavities, fissures, and irregularities found within the area to be covered by earthfill, zone 1, *(and _______) which extend below or beyond the established lines of excavation for dam embankment foundation, shall be filled with compacted earthfill or concrete materials as provided below.

(2) *Earth Foundation Surfaces.*—The surfaces of earth foundations upon which earthfill will be placed shall be prepared so that the materials in the top 12 inches of the foundation will be as compact and will provide as satisfactory a bonding surface with the first layer of the earthfill as specified for the subsequent layers of earthfill.

Where directed, the sides of test pits, cavities, or depressions in foundation surfaces shall be shaped so that the side slopes are no steeper than one horizontal to one vertical, and the sides shall be scarified and moistened as necessary to achieve bond between the foundation and the earthfill and the test pit, cavity, or depression filled with earthfill material. The earthfill placed in the prepared test pit, cavity, or depression shall be zone 1 *(or _______) conforming to the overlying embankment material and shall be placed in layers, moistened, and compacted in accordance with the applicable provisions of the following subsections (d), (e), (f), and (g): *Provided*, that where it is impractical to compact the earthfill materials with the specified roller, the earthfill shall be specially compacted in

[35]Insert typical names of soils according to identification by United Soil Classification System. Include Unified Soil Classification System standard symbol in parentheses following typical name.

[36]Limits to be inserted for each job depending on nature of material.

*Delete or revise as applicable.

accordance with the provisions of section G.30.

After all test pits, cavities, and depressions are shaped and filled as directed, and immediately prior to placement of the first layer of earthfill, the surface of the earth foundation beneath the section of the embankment in which the earthfill is to be placed shall be prepared by leveling, loosening thoroughly to a minimum depth of 12 inches by scarifying or disking, and wetting or drying. Cobbles having a maximum dimension greater than 5 inches, boulders, and roots greater than ¼ inch in diameter shall be removed from the loosened foundation material by handwork, raking, or other effective means. The water content of the loosened foundation material shall be increased or decreased as directed by the Contracting Officer to achieve maximum density for the compactive effort to be applied. The loosened foundation surface shall be compacted as specified for the earthfill to be placed in the portion of the embankment overlying the foundation.

(3) *Formation Surfaces.*—Immediately prior to placing the first layer of earthfill, all formation surfaces upon or against which the earthfill portions of the dam embankment are to be placed shall be cleaned of all loose and objectionable materials in an approved manner by handwork, barring, picking, brooming, air jetting, or other effective means. Such surfaces shall be properly moistened and sufficiently cleaned so that the earthfill will adhere firmly to the surfaces, but standing water shall be removed from depressions prior to placement of earthfill. All open joints, cracks, and fissures in the formation surface shall be cleaned of all loose soil material and loose formation material to a depth equal to at least three times their width, or to a depth where the opening is 0.5 inch wide or less, whichever depth is greater, but not to exceed 5 feet, and backfilled as directed by the Contracting Officer with either concrete mortar (slush grout) in accordance with section G.61, or dental concrete in accordance with section G.62. Where open joints, cracks, or fissures are too deep or extensive for effective treatment with concrete mortar or dental concrete, as determined by the Contracting Officer, grout nipples shall be placed in the openings and the openings grouted in accordance with applicable provisions of section G.60. Depressions and other irregularities in the formation surface where, as determined by the Contracting Officer, it is not practical to compact earthfill materials with tamping rollers or mechanical tampers, shall be backfilled with dental concrete as directed and to the extent necessary to permit satisfactory placement and compaction of earthfill materials. Formation overhangs and protrusions which will prohibit the specified placement and compaction of earthfill materials shall be removed as provided in section G.20.

The formation surface remaining after removal of overhangs and protrusions shall be cleaned, and all loose and objectionable material removed prior to placement of the earthfill. Where, as determined by the Contracting Officer, it is not practical to excavate formation overhangs and protrusions, dental concrete shall be used to fill the voids beneath overhangs or to reslope protrusions to a slope not steeper than one horizontal to two vertical. Dental concrete shall be in accordance with section G.62.

Vertical formation surfaces shall be not more than 3 feet in height, and benches of sufficient width shall be provided as necessary so that the average slope of any formation surface is not steeper than one horizontal to two vertical. Resloping of formation surfaces shall be accomplished by the method that results in the least damage to the formation left in place.

All shale *[and [37](____________) formation] surfaces upon which earthfill will be placed shall be protected from air slaking and freezing by leaving [36](______) feet of temporary cover of unexcavated material: *Provided*, that the temporary cover may include portions of the shale [37](and ______ formation) which overlie the anticipated final excavation grade.] The final excavation to remove such temporary cover shall be a continuous operation during nonfreezing weather and shall be followed immediately by placement of earthfill or by the application of protective coatings as provided in section G.23 and placement of concrete. Exposed, finished, excavated *(shale) surfaces shall be kept moist at all times to prevent evaporation of the natural moisture in the material, and such surfaces shall also be protected from freezing temperatures. Exposure of the excavated formation surface upon which earthfill will be placed shall be limited to [36](______) hour(s), which time shall commence at the completion of *(each portion of) the excavation, and which will include the time required for final

[36]Limits to be inserted for each job depending on nature of material.
[37]Include other formations as applicable.
*Delete or revise as applicable.

cleanup and surface treatment. The contractor shall mobilize sufficient equipment, materials, and manpower prior to the start of final excavation in order to limit the exposure time so specified. If the contractor so elects, he may complete the excavation to final grade without leaving a temporary cover of unexcavated material: *Provided*, that time of exposure of the final excavated surface is limited as above: *Provided Further*, that a depth of [36](________) feet of earthfill is placed over the surface to protect it from air slaking and freezing. The earthfill placed for protection of the formation surface shall be earthfill placed and compacted in accordance with these specifications or may be a temporary cover of loose earthfill, in which case the loose earthfill shall be completely removed and the formation surface cleaned and treated prior to placement of compacted earthfill: *Provided*, that the time of exposure between removal of the loose earthfill and placement of compacted earthfill is limited as above.

(d) *Placing.*—The distribution and gradation of the earthfill materials shall be such that the earthfill will be free from lenses, pockets, streaks, voids, or layers of material differing substantially in texture, gradation, or water content from surrounding material. The combined excavation *(separation), and placing operations shall be such that the earthfill materials, when placed on the embankment, will be blended sufficiently in the opinion of the Contracting Officer to secure the highest practicable degree of uniformity and strength. Placing of earthfill materials includes dumping, spreading, and mixing the earthfill materials and any other operations on the surface of the earthfill portion of the embankment necessary to blend earthfill materials to form as homogeneous a layer as practicable prior to compaction. Successive loads of material shall be dumped and spread on the earthfill so as to produce the best practicable distribution of the material, subject to the approval of the Contracting Officer; and for this purpose, the Contracting Officer may designate the locations in the earthfill where the individual loads shall be deposited. The earthfill materials shall be dumped and spread in a direction parallel to the centerline crest of the embankment. When windrows of material are formed as a result of the dumping operations, such windrows shall be parallel to the centerline crest of the embankment.

The material placed in the earthfill shall be spread in level, continuous, horizontal layers such that the layers shall not exceed 6 inches in thickness after being compacted, except that the initial layer of earthfill placed on formation surfaces shall be dumped and spread in a continuous, horizontal layer such that the uncompacted thickness is about 1.25 times the tooth length of the tamping roller to be used for compacting the layer. If the formation surface can be damaged by tamping rollers or is irregular, and compaction of the initial layer is not practicable with tamping rollers as determined by the Contracting Officer, the thickness of the initial layer and compaction thereof shall be in accordance with the provisions of subsection (g) of this section. If, in the opinion of the Contracting Officer, the surface of the prepared foundation or the surface of any previously compacted layer of earthfill is too dry or too smooth to bond properly with the layer of earthfill material to be placed thereon, it shall be moistened and disked or scarified in an approved manner to a sufficient depth to provide a satisfactory bonding surface before the earthfill material is placed. If, in the opinion of the Contracting Officer, the surface of any previously compacted layer of the earthfill in place is too wet for proper compaction of the layer of earthfill material to be placed thereon, it shall be removed, allowed to dry, or be worked with a disk to reduce the water content to the required amount, and then it shall be recompacted before the next succeeding layer of earthfill material is placed.

After a layer of earthfill has been dumped and spread, it shall be disked to break up and blend the earthfill materials. Smooth, hard surfaces and deep ruts in the surface of earthfill resulting from the passage of construction equipment during placing operations shall be removed by disking or scarifying. Disking to obtain a uniform distribution of water content throughout the uncompacted layer, as provided in subsection (e)(2) of this section, may be substituted for disking required to break up and blend the earthfill materials. Disking shall be performed with a heavy disk plow to the full depth of the uncompacted layer. Disks required to break up and blend fill material shall be of the heavy-duty, tandem-axle type with serrated disks having a diameter of 36 inches. The depth of serrations shall be maintained to provide efficient breaking and blending; however, in no case shall serrations be

[36]Limits to be inserted for each job depending on nature of material.
*Delete or revise as applicable.

allowed to wear more than 75 percent of their depth (when new) before being replaced or restored. The equipment shall be so constructed that the operators will be able to make adjustments for the depth of penetration and disking from the towing vehicle without dismounting. Tractors towing the disks shall have sufficient power and traction to scarify to the directed depths. If one pass of the disk does not accomplish the breaking up and blending of the earthfill, additional passes of the disk may be required, but no more than three passes of the disk will be required for the purpose of breaking up and blending the earthfill in any one layer.

Prior to placement of earthfill on or against the surfaces of previously placed and compacted portions of the dam embankment, all previously placed and compacted materials which have become soft or loose due to exposure to weather, which contain erosion channels or cracks, or which are excessively dry, shall be reworked by removing and replacing, or by recompacting as directed by the Contracting Officer. The replaced materials shall be compacted as required by these specifications for the type of material being compacted. Damaged or loosened surfaces shall be recompacted as originally specified for the material being recompacted. No separate payment will be made for removing, replacing, and compacting; or for recompacting loosened material in the previously completed portion of the dam embankment, and the costs thereof shall be included in the applicable price bid in the schedule for the previously completed portion of the dam embankment.

The earthfill on each side of the *(the spillway conduit) and the outlet-works conduit *(and ______________ structure) shall be kept at approximately the same elevation as the placing of the earthfill progresses. The elevation of the earthfill at the dam abutments shall be kept at approximately the same elevation as the layer of earthfill being placed. [38][The *(upstream) (downstream) outer slope of the earthfill portion of the dam embankment above El. _______ shall be compacted thoroughly, shall be reasonably true to line and grade, and all projections of more than 6 inches outside of the neatlines of the earthfill shall be removed at the expense of and by the contractor before the overlying material is placed.]

(e) *Water Content and Density Control:*

(1) *General.*—Each layer of the earthfill material on the embankment shall be compacted by 12 passes of a tamping roller as provided in subsection (g), which shall be the minimum compaction effort to be performed by the contractor. During compaction, the water content of the earthfill materials shall be such that the water content and dry density of the compacted earthfill will be maintained within the control limits specified. The results of testing specially compacted earthfill will not be combined with the results of testing earthfill compacted by tamping rollers.

To determine that the water content and dry density requirements of the compacted earthfill are being met, field and laboratory tests will be make by the Government at frequent intervals on samples of compacted material taken at embankment locations determined by the Contracting Officer. Field and laboratory tests will be made by the Contracting Officer in accordance with test designations USBR 5500, 5505, 7205, and 7240 of the Bureau of Reclamation's *Earth Manual* [3]. The results of all completed earthwork tests will be available to the contractor at the Government laboratory or other designated location.

Materials not meeting the specified water content and dry density requirements, as determined by the tests, shall be reworked until approved results are obtained. If freezing of previously compacted and accepted earthfill has resulted in a decrease in compacted density of the earthfill as determined by the Contracting Officer, the contractor shall rework the earthfill as directed until approved densities are obtained. Reworking may include removal, rehandling, reconditioning, rerolling, or combinations of these procedures. The contractor shall be entitled to no additional allowance above the prices bid in the schedule by reason of any work required to achieve the water content and dry density specified in this section.

(2) *Water Content Control.*—The optimum water content is defined as "the water content of a soil at which it can be compacted to its laboratory maximum dry density by a given compactive effort." The laboratory maximum dry density in pounds per cubic foot is the maximum dry density obtained from a curve of water content versus dry density for a given compactive effort. The procedure and compactive effort used to determine the optimum

[38]To be included when close control of zone line is desirable for placement of filter or drainage materials.

*Delete or revise as applicable.

water content and the laboratory maximum dry density will be as contained in test designations USBR 5500, 5505, and 7240 of the Bureau's *Earth Manual* [3].

As far as practicable, the material shall be brought to the proper water content for compaction in the borrow pit or at the site of required excavation before excavation, as provided in section G.24, and the contractor shall make allowances for water loss during excavation, transportation, and placing operations. *[At the option of the contractor, additional water, if required, may be added at the separation plant.] Supplementary water, if required, shall be added to the material by sprinkling on the earthfill, and each layer of earthfill shall be conditioned by disking or other approved methods so that the water is distributed uniformly throughout the layer.

The water contained in the earthfill material during compaction shall be distributed uniformly throughout the layer of material being compacted. The allowable ranges of water content are based on design considerations. The water content control shall be such that the water content of the portion of the compacted earthfill passing a No. 4 United States Standard sieve, as determined by test performed by the Contracting Officer, shall be within the following limits:

a. Material represented by the samples tested having a water content more than [36](______) percent dry of the optimum water content, or more than [36](_____) percent wet of the optimum water content will be rejected and shall be removed or reworked until the water content is between these limits.

*[b. Within the above limits, and based on a continuous record of tests made by the Government on previously compacted and accepted earthfill, the uniformity of placement water content shall be such that:

1. No more than 16 percent of the samples of accepted embankment material shall be drier than [36](_______) percent dry of the optimum water content, and no more than 16 percent shall be wetter than [36](_______) percent wet of the optimum water content.
2. The average water content of all accepted embankment material and of material represented by any 20 consecutive tests shall be between [36](_______) percent dry of the optimum water content and [36](_______) wet of the optimum water content: *Provided*, that the average water content of accepted embankment materials within[36](_______) feet of vertical structural surfaces and steep or irregular formation surfaces shall be between the optimum water and [36](_______) percent wet of optimum water content.]

*[The Government will inform the contractor when the water content is near or exceeds the limits of uniformity specified above, and the contractor shall immediately make adjustments in procedures as necessary to maintain the water content within the specified limits of uniformity.]

(3) *Density Control.*—Density control of compacted earthfill shall be such that the dry density of the portion of the compacted material passing a United States Standard No. 4 sieve, as determined by tests performed by the Contracting Officer, shall conform to the following limits:

a. Material represented by samples having a dry density less than [36](_______) percent of its laboratory maximum dry density will be rejected. Such rejected material shall be rerolled until its dry density is equal to or greater than [36](_______) percent of its laboratory maximum dry density.

*[b. For all earthfill having a dry density greater than the above limit and based on a continuous record of tests made by the Government on previously compacted and accepted earthfill, the uniformity of dry density shall be such that:

1. No more than 16 percent of the material represented by the samples tested shall be at dry densities less than [36](_______) percent of its laboratory maximum dry density.
2. The average dry density of all accepted embankment material and of material represented by any 20 consecutive tests shall be not less than [36](_______) percent of the average laboratory maximum dry density.]

*[The Government will inform the contractor when the amount of accepted earthfill material having a dry density less than [36](_______) percent of its laboratory maximum dry density is near or exceeds 16 percent of the material compacted and accepted or when the average dry density is near or less than [36](_______) percent of its laboratory maximum dry density. The contractor shall immedi-

[36]Limits to be inserted for each job depending on nature of material.
*Delete or revise as applicable.

ately make adjustments in procedures as necessary to maintain the dry density within the specified limits of uniformity.]

(f) *Rollers.*—Tamping rollers used for compacting the earthfill shall be nonvibratory rollers and may be either towed or self-propelled. The operation of the rollers and the loading used in the roller drums shall be as required to obtain the specified compaction. If more than one roller is used on any one layer of fill, all rollers so used shall be of the same type and essentially of the same dimensions. The design and operation of the tamping rollers shall be subject to the approval of the Contracting Officer, who shall have the right at any time during the prosecution of the work to direct modifications or repairs to the tamping feet, minor alterations in the roller, and variations in the weight, including removal or addition of ballast, as may be found necessary to secure optimum compaction of the earthfill materials. During the compaction operations, the spaces between the tamping feet shall be maintained clear of materials which would impair the effectiveness of the tamping rollers. The rollers shall meet the requirements for towed rollers in subsection (1), or for self-propelled rollers in subsection (2):

(1) *Towed Tamping Rollers.*—Towed tamping rollers shall be drawn by crawler-type or rubber-tired tractors at a speed not to exceed 5 miles per hour. The use of rubber-tired tractors shall be discontinued if the tires leave compacted surfaces which prevent uniform penetration by the feet of the tamping roller. Rollers operated in tandem sets shall be towed in a manner such that the prints of the tamping feet produced by the tandem units are staggered and do not overlap. Tractors used for pulling rollers shall have sufficient power to pull the rollers satisfactorily when drums are loaded with ballast to the maximum extent. The rollers shall meet the following requirements:

a. *Roller drums.*—Tamping rollers shall consist of two or more roller drums mounted side by side in a suitable frame. Each drum of a roller shall have an outside diameter of not less than 5 feet and shall be not less than 5 feet nor more than 6 feet in length. The drums shall be capable of being ballasted. Ballast may be sand or fluid or a mixture of sand and fluid. Provisions for ballast other than sand or fluid shall be as approved by the Contracting Officer. The space between two adjacent drums, when on a level surface, shall be not less than 12 inches nor more than 15 inches. Each drum shall be free to pivot about an axis parallel to the direction of travel. Each drum ballasted with fluid shall be equipped with at least one safety head or with approved equal types. The safety head shall be equal to union-type safety heads as manufactured by Fike Metal Products Corp., 704 South 10th Street, Blue Springs, MO 64015, with rupture disks suitable for between 50- and 75-pounds per square inch rupturing pressure.

The pressure-relief valve shall be a manually operated valve and shall be opened periodically. Personnel responsible for opening pressure-relief valves shall be instructed in the safety procedures for opening such valves and shall be instructed to ascertain that valve openings are free from plugging to assure that any pressure developed in roller drums is released at each inspection.

b. *Tamping feet.*—Each drum shall have tamping feet uniformly spaced over the surface of the drum with at least one tamping foot provided for each 100 square inches of drum surface. The distance measured on the surface of the drum, between the centers of any two adjacent tamping feet, shall be not less than 9 inches. The length of each tamping foot, measured from the outside surface of the drum, shall not be more than 11 inches and shall be maintained at not less than 9 inches. The cross-sectional area of each tamping foot shall be not more than 10 square inches at a plane normal to the axis of the shank 6 inches from the drum surface, and shall be maintained at not less than 7 square inches at a plane normal to the axis of the shank 8 inches from the drum surface. The area of the end bearing surface of each tamping foot shall not be greater than 10 inches. Cupped recesses within the face of each tamping foot will be permitted but shall not exceed 0.5 inch in depth.

c. *Roller weight.*—The weight of a roller when fully ballasted shall not be less than 4,000 pounds per foot of drum length.

(2) *Self-Propelled Rollers.*—Self-propelled rollers shall not be operated at speeds greater than 5 miles per hour. The use of self-propelled tamping rollers in which steering is accomplished through the use of rubber-tired wheels shall be discontinued if the tires leave compacted surfaces which prevent uniform penetration by the feet of the roller.

If use of the self-propelled tamping rollers results in laminations, unbonded surfaces, or inadequate compaction of the earthfill, the Contracting Officer may direct that such rollers be removed from the work and that other self-propelled tamping rollers or appropriate towed tamping rollers be used. The substitution of tamping feet having an end bearing area of up to 14 square inches may be used if the Contracting Officer determines that such substitution will not result in compacted earthfill or lesser density or degree of uniformity than that produced by towed tamping rollers meeting the requirements of subsection (f)(1). When a self-propelled roller is provided with a dozer blade, the blade shall be either removed or rendered inoperable during compaction operations.

Self-propelled tamping rollers may consist of two- or three-drum, side-by-side units which are either in the drive position or are drawn by separate power equipment, may be two-drum units arranged in tandem, or may be four-drum units arranged in tandem and laterally separated by cap and differential. Where the drums are arranged in tandem, the drums must be positioned so that the prints of the tamping feet produced by the tandem drums are staggered and do not overlap. The static weight of self-propelled tamping rollers must be distributed equally to all compaction drums.

In addition to the previous requirements, self-propelled tamping rollers must meet the following requirements:

a. *Roller drums.*—For rollers on which tamper wheels of open-ring construction are used instead of drums, the cylindrical surface which circumscribes the ring surfaces upon which the tamping feet are mounted shall be considered the drum surface for determination of drum area, diameter, and length. Each drum of a roller shall have an outside diameter of not less than 4 feet and shall not be less than 4 nor more than 6 feet in length. Two- or three-drum, side-by-side units that are either in drive position or drawn by separate power equipment shall have a clearance between adjacent drums of not less than 12 nor more than 15 inches. The distance between side-by-side drums on four-drum rollers separated by cab and differential shall be approximately equal, as determined by the Contracting Officer, to the width of one drum. Ballasting of drums will not be required: *Provided*, that the weight of the roller during compaction operations will not be less than the weight specified in subsection (f)(2)c. All drums ballasted with fluid shall be equipped with at least one pressure-relief valve and with at least one safety head or with approved equal types. The safety head shall be equal to union-type safety heads as manufactured by Fike Metal Products Corp., 704 South 10th Street, Blue Springs, MO 64015, with rupture disks suitable for between 50- and 75-pounds per square inch rupturing pressure.

The pressure-relief valve shall be a manually operated valve and shall be opened periodically. Personnel responsible for opening pressure-relief valves shall be instructed in the safety procedures for opening such valves and shall be instructed to ascertain that valve openings are free from plugging to assure that any pressure developed in roller drums is released at each inspection.

b. *Tamping feet.*—The requirements for tamping feet for self-propelled tamping rollers shall be the same as for towed tamping rollers, except for the end bearing area as previously mentioned.

c. *Roller weight.*—The weight of a roller, when being used for compaction of the earthfill, shall not be less than 4,000 pounds per foot of drum length.

(g) *Compaction.*—When each layer or a portion of a layer of earthfill has been blended, leveled, and conditioned to have the water contained therein distributed uniformly throughout the layer, as provided in subsection (e), it shall be compacted by passing the drum of a tamping roller over it 12 times, except that the initial layer of earthfill placed on formation surfaces shall be spread to an uncompacted thickness in accordance with subsection (d), and compacted by passing the drum of a tamping roller over the entire layer 18 times. On rough or irregular formation surfaces or formation surfaces which could be damaged by tamping rollers, as determined by the Contracting Officer, the initial layer of earthfill shall be compacted to a thickness of [36](________) inches by [36](________) passes of a rubber-tired roller *[having a minimum wheel load of 25,000 pounds and tire pressure of 80 to 100 pounds per square inch, and meeting the other requirements for rubber-tired rollers in this section.] When compacted, the dry density of the earthfill shall be uniform throughout the depth of the layer. Passes of the tamping roller or rubber-tired roller shall be carried out so that the compactive effort is uniformly distributed in a systematic manner over the entire layer. When two- or four-drum, self-propelled rollers are used which have drums laterally sepa-

[36]Limits to be inserted for each job depending on nature of material.
*Delete or revise as applicable.

rated by the operator's cab and differential, the uncompacted central portion of the roller path shall not be compacted until the outer portions of the path have been fully compacted.

Where steep abutments, construction activities, or other factors make it impractical or inefficient to complete the required number of drum passes while maintaining the same direction of roller travel, additional passes as needed to bring the total number of drum passes to 12 shall be performed by routing the tamping rollers parallel to the obstructions as approved by the Contracting Officer. Portions of the earthfill which are not accessible to tamping rollers shall be specially compacted with power tampers or other approved methods, and payment made in accordance with the provisions of section G.30.

If, in the opinion of the Contracting Officer, the compacted earthfill material has a water content greater than allowed by subsection (e), the earthfill material shall be worked with a disk or other suitable equipment to reduce the water content to the amount specified, shall be allowed to dry until such time as its water content is within the limits specified in subsection (e), or the material shall be removed from the embankment. If, in the opinion of the Contracting Officer, the compacted earthfill material has a water content less than allowed by subsection (e), water shall be added to the uncompacted earthfill, and the earthfill shall be worked with a disk or other suitable equipment to distribute the water uniformly throughout the uncompacted layer. Compacted earth material which has a water content or dry density which does not meet the limits specified in subsection (e) shall be reworked and rerolled, as directed by the Contracting Officer, to obtain the water content and dry density specified for compacted earthfill.

At locations and at such times as determined by the Contracting Officer, the contractor shall excavate test pits in previously compacted earthfill for the purpose of obtaiing samples of previously compacted earthfill or for determining whether the earthfill contains unbonded layers of earthfill or unblended earthfill materials. Such test pits shall be in accordance with section G.31.

(h) *Measurement and Payment.*—Measurement, for payment, of earthfill in dam embankment will be made of all earthfill compacted in place by tamping rollers, as specified in subsection (f), and of all earthfill compacted by rubber-tired rollers as provided in subsection (g), and as provided in section G.28.

Payment for earthfill in dam embankment, zone(s) 1 *(and ______) will be made at the unit price(s) per cubic yard bid therefor in the schedule, which price shall include all costs of work required under this section and as provided in section G.28, except that payment for [39][specially compacted earthfill, zone(s) 1 *(and ______)] *(pressure grouting foundations, slush grouting, dental concrete, excavation of foundation overhangs and protrusions), and furnishing and handling cement will be made as provided in the applicable sections.

[39][Where portions of the earthfill in dam embankment, zone 1, require special compacting, payment therefor will be made as provided in section G.30.]

*[Payment for pressure grouting foundations, slush grouting, and dental concrete, including furnishing and handling cement, will be made as provided in the applicable sections.]

*[Payment for excavation of formation overhangs and protrusions will be made as provided in section G.20.]

As provided in subsection (d), no separate or additional payment will be made on account of the requirement for reworking previously compacted and accepted earthfill which is loosened by freezing and by other exposure to weather, or which is found to contain unbonded surfaces or inadequate blending of earthfill materials. As provided in subsection (e), no additional payment will be made for any work required including, such as, rewatering and/or reworking the embankment earthfill material to achieve the specified water content or dry density.

G.30. ***Specially Compacted Earthfill, Zone 1.***—(a) *General.*—The specially compacted earthfill, zone 1, shall be constructed in accordance with this section and section G.28. Where compaction of earthfill, zone 1, material by means of the tamping roller specified for compacting earthfill on the dam embankment is impracticable or undesirable, as determined by the Contracting Officer, the earthfill shall be specially compacted as specified herein.

Specially compacted earthfill will be required at the following locations:

(1) Portions of the earthfill in dam embankment

[39]Include only when there is a bid item in the bidding schedule for specially compacted earthfill zone 1 or zones 1 and ______.

*Delete or revise as applicable.

adjacent to structures and structure foundations shown on the drawings as specially compacted earthfill, zone 1.

(2) Portions of the earthfill in dam embankment, zone 1, where designated by the Contracting Officer, at steep and irregular abutments.

(3) Earthfill in dam embankment, zone 1, placed and compacted in depressions and irregularities in foundation surfaces where designated by the Contracting Officer.

(4) Earthfill, zone 1, material placed to refill additional excavation, ordered in writing by the Contracting Officer, in common excavation for structure foundations.

(5) Earthfill material at locations outside the limits of the dam embankment as shown on the drawings or where designated by the Contracting Officer.

(b) *Materials.*—Material used in specially compacted earthfill, zone 1, shall conform to materials required for earthfill in dam embankment, zone 1: *Provided*, that gravel having maximum dimensions of more than 1 inch and cobbles shall not be placed in specially compacted earthfill. The material shall be obtained from excavation required for permanent construction, and excavation in borrow areas in accordance with section G.24.

(c) *Placing.*—All specially compacted earthfill, zone 1, material shall be placed in accordance with the applicable provisions of subsection G.29(d): *Provided,* that earthfill material to be specially compacted may require placement in layers thinner than those specified for roller compaction of earthfill material to obtain the desired compaction with the equipment used.

Where the foundation or compacted surface of any layer is too smooth to bond properly with the succeeding layer, it shall be scarified or otherwise roughened to provide a satisfactory bonding surface before the next layer of earthfill material is placed.

(d) *Compacting.*—When each layer or material has been conditioned to have the required water content, it shall be compacted by special rollers, mechanical tampers, or by other approved methods. All equipment and methods used shall be subject to approval by the Contracting Officer. Adjacent to steep abutments or other restrictive areas as approved by the Contracting Officer, compaction by rubber-tired equipment of a layer of earthfill not to exceed 2 feet in horizontal width may be substituted for compaction by mechanical tampers: *Provided*, that smooth surfaces left by the use of rubber-tired equipment shall be treated as prescribed in subsection (c) prior to placement of the subsequent layer of earthfill. The moisture content and density control shall be equivalent to that obtained in the earthfill placed in the dam embankment in accordance with subsection (d) and (g) in section G.29.

(3) *Measurement and Payment.*—Measurement, for payment, of specially compacted earthfill, zone 1, will be made of the material specially compacted, as provided in this section and in section G.28. Under subsection (a)(2) in this section, measurement, for payment, of specially compacted earthfill at steep and irregular dam abutments will be limited to a width of 2 feet measured horizontally from the average contacts where practicable, or as otherwise determined by the Contracting Officer. Under subsection (a)(3), measurement, for payment of, specially compacted earthfill, zone 1, in depressions and irregularities in foundation surfaces will be made in the most practicable manner as determined by the Contracting Officer.

Payment for specially compacted earthfill, zone 1, will be made at the unit price per cubic yard bid therefor in the schedule, which unit price shall include the cost of roughening or scarifying to provide satisfactory bonding surfaces and of placing, moistening, and specially compacting the earthfill, zone 1, material.

The cost of excavation and transportation of material used in specially compacted earthfill, zone 1, shall be included in the applicable unit price bid in the schedule for excavation of the material.

G.31. ***Test Pits in Compacted Earthfill.***—

(a) *General.*—The contractor shall excavate test pits in compacted earthfill during the progress of the work. Location and times of excavating test pits shall be as necessary to examine or obtain samples of specific portions of the work as determined by the Contracting Officer.

The surface dimensions and depth of each test pit will be determined by the Contracting Officer, but in general no test pit will involve the excavation and backfill of more than 10 cubic yards of earthfill.

The sides of the test pits shall be excavated to as near vertical as practicable, but in accordance with applicable safety requirements to allow inspection of the compacted earthfill by the Government. The contractor shall adjust his operations so that test pits will remain open for ___ hours to facilitate inspection and collection of embankment samples. The test pits shall be backfilled with earthfill conforming to the adjacent embankment materials, which shall be placed in layers, moistened, and compacted in accordance with the applicable provisions of section G.30.

(b) *Measurement and Payment.*—Measurement, for payment, of excavating test pits in compacted earthfill will be made of the number of test pits actually excavated, at the direction of the Contracting Officer, in accordance with this section.

Payment for excavating test pits in compacted earthfill will be made at the unit price per test pit bid therfor in the schedule, which unit price shall include the cost of excavating, backfilling, compacting, and all other work as required under this section.

G.32. *Earthfill in Dam Embankment, Zone 2.*—

(a) *General.*—The earthfill, zone 2, portion of the dam embankment shall be constructed in accordance with this section and section G.28, and to the lines and grades shown on the drawings. Zone 2 earthfill includes the following:

(1) The chimney drain, as shown on the drawings. The chimney drain shall extend from dam station ______ to station ______.

(2) The top and bottom portions of the horizontal drainage blanket, as shown on the drawings. The horizontal drainage blanket extends from dam station ______ to station ______.

(3) The outer portions of the foundation drain, as shown on the drawings. The foundation drain extends from dam station ______ to station ______.

(b) *Materials.*—The zone 2 material shall consist of clean sands obtained from commercial sources or other approved sources. The material shall consist of sound, strong rock, minimally affected by chemical alteration and physical breakdown, and shall meet the quality (durability) requirements for concrete sand listed in section G.78. The zone 2 material shall have the gradation shown in table G-1 when tested inplace in the embankment after compaction.

Table G-1.—Gradation for zone 2 material.

Sieve No.[1]	Total percent, by weight, passing sieve[1]
4	100
8	90–100
16	55–100
30	20–80
50	10–45
100	0–15
200	0

[1]Requires redesign for each job.

Commercial sources of sand and gravel are known to exist in the general area (within 30 miles). It is anticipated that some processing, including washing, will be required in order to meet the specified gradation. In addition to the commercial sources, the Government has performed some explorations in various areas to determine other sources of sand and gravel. Some of the data for commercial sources and other explored sources are included in the section of these specifications for "Records of Construction and Foundation Materials Test Data." The contractor and all prospective bidders are encouraged to visit all sites, conduct additional investigations, and thoroughly investigate all sources before deriving any conclusions. The contractor shall be solely responsible for any conclusions regarding the nature, gradation, and extent of zone 2 material in any source. The Government's data on potential sources is limited, and as such, the Government will not be responsible for any conclusions reached by the contractor and prospective bidders based on this limited information.

The source of zone 2 material shall be subject to the approval of the Contracting Officer. All zone 2 material shall come from the same source, unless impracticable as determined by the Contracting Officer.

(c) *Preparation of Foundations.*—The preparation of foundations, whether inplace foundations or previously placed embankment, shall be in accordance with the requirements outlined in sections G.28 and G.29.

(d) *Placement.*—The zone 2 material shall be placed in continuous, approximately horizontal layers not more than 12 inches in loose thickness.

Successive loads of material shall be dumped so as to secure the best practical distribution of the material and minimize segregation. The material shall be dumped and leveled in an approved manner prior to compaction.

The water content of the zone 2 material before and during compaction shall be uniform throughout each layer of the material. The water content shall be sufficient to attain the required density of the material inplace when compacted. In general, the material shall be thoroughly wetted to obtain the required compaction, but shall not contain water to the extent which will interfere with the trafficability of the contractor's hauling, placing, or compacting equipment.

Water may be applied by sprinkling on the material inplace or by other methods approved by the Contracting Officer.

(e) *Compaction.*—When each layer of material has been placed, the layer shall be compacted by one to six passes of a vibratory roller. One pass of the roller is defined as "the required number of successive roller trips which, by means of sufficient overlay, will insure complete coverage of the entire surface of the layer by the roller." Second and subsequent passes of the roller shall not be made until each pass, as defined above, is completed.

The exact number of passes with the vibratory roller, as approved by the Contracting Officer, shall be that number required to compact the zone 2 earthfill within the following density limits:

Materials represented by samples having a "percent compaction" less than 95 percent shall be rejected. Such rejected material shall be reworked and recompacted so as to satisfy this requirement. Percent compaction shall be defined as "the ratio of the dry density of the inplace material to the maximum laboratory dry density, expressed as a percentage." The maximum laboratory dry density shall be the maximum vibrated dry density determined by either the wet or dry method described in test designation USBR 7250 of the Bureau's *Earth Manual* [3].

The Contracting Officer will inform the contractor when the density of the compacted zone 2 is close to or outside the limits specified above, and the contractor shall immediately make adjustments in procedures as necessary to maintain the density of the compacted embankment within the specified limits.

Vibratory rollers shall be equipped with a smooth steel compaction drum and shall be operated at a frequency of vibration during compaction operations between 1,100 and 1,500 vibrations per minute. Vibratory rollers may be either towed or self-propelled and shall have an unsprung drum weight that is a minimum of 60 percent of the roller's static weight. Vibratory rollers shall have a minimum static weight of 8,000 pounds, a minimum dynamic force of 16,000 pounds when operating at 1,400 vibrations per minute, and an applied force not less than 5,000 nor greater than 9,000 pounds per foot of compaction drum length. The level of amplitude and vibration frequency during compaction will be maintained uniformly throughout the embankment zone within which it is operating. Vibratory rollers shall be operated at speeds not to exceed 1.5 miles per hour. The contractor shall furnish sufficient data, drawings, and computations for verification of the above specifications; and the character and efficiency of this equipment shall be subject to the approval of the Contracting Officer.

The towed roller shall have at lest 90 percent of its weight transmitted to the ground through the compaction drum when the roller is standing in a level position and hitched to the towing vehicle.

The contractor shall furnish to the Contracting Officer adequate data pertaining to the rollers to verify that all the above requirements will be met, and the rollers shall be subject to the approval of the Contracting Officer.

Each pass of the roller shall be offset so that the total compactive effort will be distributed evenly over the entire area. Special attention shall be given by the contractor to ensure that no additional passes are permitted over the area. The roller shall not be allowed to remain stationary on the zone with the vibratory mechanism engaged.

Care shall be taken so that all zone 2 earthfill materials do not become contaminated. Contaminated zone 2 earthfill shall be removed and replaced with suitable material at the contractor's expense. During periods of winter shutdown and at all equipment crossings, zone 2 embankment should be protected as described in section G.28. The contractor shall be solely responsible for protecting the zone 2 earthfill, and ensuring that no contamination occurs. Costs of all protective measures shall be included in the unit price bid in the schedule.

Prior to placing additional zone 2 material at equipment crossings and after winter shutdown, or other substantial delays, the contractor shall remove any protective coverings and shall remove and replace any materials which may have become contaminated as determined by the Contracting Officer. All costs of removing contaminated materials and replacement shall be at the expense of the contractor.

(f) *Optional Method of Construction for Zone 2.*—The contractor may elect to construct the vertical portion of the chimney drain above El. ______, according to the requirements listed in this subsection.

The contractor will be permitted to place horizontal and continuous layers of zone 1 embankment across the full width of the embankment up to a height of 5.0 feet above the zone 2 chimney drain. Upon reaching the maximum height of 5.0 feet, or less, the contractor must stop zone 1 placement and then excavate a ______-foot-wide trench parallel with dam centerline according to the lines and grades specified for the chimney drain. This trench must penetrate through the zone 1 and expose the full width of the underlying chimney drain. The surface of the exposed chimney drain must be thoroughly cleaned off so that it consists solely of clean, uncontaminated zone 2 material, subject to the approval of the Contracting Officer. After approval of the exposed chimney drain, the contractor shall place zone 2 earthfill according to the requirements of subsection (d), and as approved by the Contracting Officer. After placement, the zone 2 material shall be compacted according to the requirements of subsection (e) and as approved by the Contracting Officer. Care must be taken during all construction operations to avoid contaminating the zone 2 material with zone 1 materials. Alternate methods of placement and compaction in this zone will be considered by the Contracting Officer, and may be approved on a trial basis. After the chimney drain has been brought up to the height of the zone 1, the zone 1 placement may resume. The remainder of the chimney drain may be constructed in this manner: *Provided*, that the height of zone 1 placed over chimney drain shall not exceed 5.0 feet.

Should the contractor elect to follow this optional method of chimney drain construction, the entire procedure shall be subject to the approval of the Contracting Officer. All costs of excavation, overbuild, waste, or any other costs shall be included in the unit price bid in the schedule for earthfill, zone 2. Payment for both zone 1 and zone 2 earthfill will only be made to the lines and grades shown on the drawings, and as specified in section G.28.

(g) *Measurement and Payment.*—Measurement, for payment, of earthfill in dam embankment zone 2, will be made as provided in section G.28. Payment for earthfill in dam embankment, zone 2, will be made at the unit price per cubic yard bid in the schedule for earthfill in dam embankment, zone 2, which price shall include all costs of obtaining and transporting material to the site; of processing; of any temporary stockpiling and rehandling; of all special equipment and procedures required to construct zone 2; of placing and compacting; of installing and removal of protection at crossings and during shutdowns; and all other work described in this section and as provided in section G.28.

G.33. *Earthfill in Dam Embankment, Drainage Material, Zone 3.*—(a) *General.*—The earthfill, drainage material, portion of the dam embankment shall be constructed in accordance with this section and section G.28, and to the lines and grades shown on the drawings. Drainage material earthfill includes the following:

(1) The inner portion of the horizontal drainage blanket as shown on drawings ______ and ______. The horizontal drainage blanket extends from dam station ______ to ______.

(2) The inner portion of the foundation drain as shown on drawings ______ and ______. The foundation drain extends from dam station ______ to ______.

(b) *Materials.*—The drainage material shall consist of processed, clean sands and gravels obtained from commercial sources or other approved sources. The material shall consist of sound, strong rock, minimally affected by chemical alteration and physical breakdown, and shall meet the quality (durability) requirements for concrete sand listed in section G.78. The drainage material shall have the following gradation when tested inplace in the embankment after compaction:

Sieve size[1]	Total percent, by weight, passing sieve[1]
1½ inches	100
¾ inch	75–100
⅜ inch	50–100
No. 4	25–60
No. 8	0–30
No. 16	0

[1]Must be redesigned for each job.

Commercial sources of sand and gravel are known to exist in the general area. It is anticipated that processing, including washing, will be required to meet the specified gradation. In addition to the commercial sources, the Government has performed some explorations in various areas to determine other sources of sand and gravel. Some of the data for commercial sources and other explored sources are included in the section of these specifications for "Records of Construction and Foundation Materials Test Data."

The contractor and all prospective bidders are encouraged to visit all sites, conduct additional investigations, and thoroughly investigate all sources before deriving any conclusions. The contractor shall be solely responsible for any conclusions regarding the nature, gradation, and extent of drainage material in any source. The Government's data on potential sources is limited, and as such, the Government will not be responsible for any conclusions reached by the contractor and prospective bidders based on this limited information.

The source of drainage material shall be subject to the approval of the Contracting Officer. All drainage material shall come from the same source, unless impracticable as determined by the Contracting Officer.

(c) *Preparation of Foundations.*—The preparation of foundations, whether inplace or previously placed embankment, shall be in accordance with the requirements outlined in sections G.28 and G.29.

(d) *Placement.*—The drainage material shall be placed in continuous, approximately horizontal layers not more than 12 inches in loose thickness.

Successive loads of material shall be dumped so as to secure the best practical distribution of the material and minimize segregation, as determined by the Contracting Officer. The material shall be dumped and leveled in an approved manner prior to compaction.

The water content of the drainage material before and during compaction shall be uniform throughout each layer of the material. The water content shall be sufficient to attain the required density of the material inplace when compacted. In general, the material shall be thoroughly wetted to obtain the requried compaction, but shall not contain water to the extent which will interfere with the trafficability of the contractor's hauling, placing, or compacting equipment.

Water may be applied by sprinkling on the material inplace or by other methods approved by the Contracting Officer.

(e) *Compaction.*—When each layer of material has been placed, the layer shall be compacted by 1 to 6 passes of a vibratory roller. One pass of the roller is defined as "the required number of successive roller trips which, by means of sufficient overlay, will ensure complete coverage of the entire surface of the layer by the roller." Second and subsequent passes of the roller shall not be made until each pass, as defined above, is completed.

The exact number of passes with the vibratory roller, as approved by the Contracting Officer, shall be that number required to compact the drainage material earthfill within the following density limits:

> Materials represented by samples having a "percent compaction" less than 95 percent shall be rejected. Such rejected material shall be reworked and recompacted so as to satisfy this requirement. Percent compaction shall be defined as "the ratio of the dry density of the inplace material to the maximum laboratory dry density, expressed as a percentage." The maximum laboratory dry density shall be the maximum vibrated dry density determined by either the wet or dry method described in test designation USBR 7250 of the Bureau's *Earth Manual* [3].

The Contracting Officer will inform the contractor when the density of the compacted drainage material is close to or outside the limits specified above, and the contractor shall immediately make adjustments in procedures as necessary to maintain the density of the compacted embankment within the specified limits.

Vibratory rollers used shall be in accordance with subsection G.32(e). The contractor shall furnish to the Contracting Officer adequate data pertaining to the rollers to verify that all the above requirements will be met, and the rollers shall be subject to the approval of the Contracting Officer.

Each pass of the roller shall be offset so that the total compactive effort will be distributed evenly over the entire area. Special attention shall be given by the contractor to ensure that no additional passes are permitted over the area. The roller shall not be allowed to remain stationary on the zone with the vibratory mechanism engaged.

Care should be taken so that all drainage material earthfill does not become contaminated. Contaminated drainage material earthfill shall be removed and replaced with suitable material at the contractor's expense. During periods of winter shutdown and at all equipment crossings, drainage material earthfill should be protected as described under section G.28. The contractor shall be solely responsible for protecting the drainage material earthfill and ensuring that no contamination occurs. Costs of all protective measures shall be included in the unit price bid in the schedule.

Prior to placing additional drainage material at equipment crossings and after winter shutdown, or other substantial delays, the contractor shall remove any protective coverings and shall remove and replace any materials which may have become contaminated as determined by the Contracting Officer. All costs of removing contaminated materials and replacement shall be at the expense of the contractor.

(f) *Measurement and Payment.*—Measurement, for payment, of earthfill in dam embankment, zone 3, drainage material, will be made as provided in section G.28. Payment for earthfill in dam embankment and drainage material, zone 3, will be made at the unit price per cubic yard bid therefore in the schedule, which price shall include all costs of obtaining and transporting material to the site; of processing; of any temporary stockpiling and rehandling; of placing and compacting; of installing and removal of protection at crossings and during shutdowns; and all other work described in this section and as provided in section G.28.

G.34. *Sand, Gravel, and Cobble Fill in Dam Embankment, Zone* ______.—(a) *General.*—The sand, gravel, and cobble fill in dam embankment shall be constructed in accordance with this section and section G.28.

(b) *Materials.*—The materials shall consist of a reasonably well-graded pervious mixture of sand, gravel, and cobbles selected from borrow pits in borrow area ______, in accordance with section G.24. Cobbles and boulders larger than ______ inches in maximum dimensions may be embedded in the fill or may be removed from the fill material and placed in the (*insert location*).

(c) *Preparation of Foundations.*—The foundation for zone ______ shall be prepared by leveling, moistening, and compacting so that the surface materials will be as compact as specified for subsequent layers of zone ______.

(d) *Moisture Control.*—The moisture content of the sand, gravel, and cobble-fill material, prior to and during compaction, shall be distributed uniformly throughout each layer of the material. The moisture content shall be sufficient to attain the maximum relative density of the material inplace, when compacted by the specified compaction procedure as provided in subsection (e). In general, the material shall be thoroughly wetted to obtain the maximum practicable compaction but shall not contain moisture to the extent which will interfere with trafficability of the contractor's hauling, placing, or compacting equipment.

Moisture, as required, may be applied by sprinkling on the fill, or by other approved methods.

(e) *Placing and Compacting.*—The contractor's operations shall be such and he shall handle and place the material in such a manner as to prevent segregation.

The sand, gravel, and cobble material shall be placed in the dam embankment in continuous, approximately horizontal layers not more than 12 inches in compacted thickness. When each layer of material has been conditioned to have the required moisture, as provided in subsection (d), it shall be compacted by four passes of the treads of a crawler-type tractor weighing approximately 40,000 pounds, a vibratory roller as specified in subsection G.36(e), or as provided below. One pass of the treads or roller is defined as "the required number of successive tractor or roller trips which, by means of sufficient overlap, will ensure complete coverage of the entire surface of the layer by the tractor treads or roller drum." Second and subsequent passes of the treads or roller shall not be made until each pass, as defined above, is completed. The government will perform density testing to assure adequate density within the fill.

If the contractor elects to use methods of compaction other than the one specified above, the weight of the compactor, the number of passes, inflation pressures of tires (if rubber-tired compactors are used), and thickness of lift not to exceed 12 inches compacted, shall be such as to result in sand, gravel, and cobble fill in dam embankment compacted within the following limits:

(1) Material represented by samples having a relative density less than [40](______) percent will be rejected. Such rejected material shall be recompacted until a relative density equal to or greater than [40](______) percent is obtained.

(2) Within the above limits, and based on a continuous record of tests made by the Contracting Officer on previously placed and accepted embankment, the uniformity of relative density shall be such that:

*[a. No more than [40](______) percent of the

[40]Limits to be inserted for each job depending on nature of available material.

*Delete or revise as applicable.

material represented by the samples tested shall be at relative densities less than [40](_______) percent.]

The Contracting Officer will inform the contractor when the relative density is close to or outside the limits specified above and the contractor shall immediately make adjustments in procedures as necessary to maintain the relative density within the specified limits.

The relative density of the compacted sand, gravel, and cobble fill material will be determined by the Contracting Officer for the full depth of each compacted layer in accordance with test designation USBR 7250 of the Bureau's *Earth Manual* [3].

(f) *Measurement and Payment.*—Measurement, for payment, of sand, gravel, and cobble fill in dam embankment will be made as provided in section G.28.

Payment for sand, gravel, and cobble fill in dam embankment will be made at the unit price per cubic yard bid therefor in the schedule, which unit price shall include all costs of work required under this section and as provided in section G.28.

G.35. *Miscellaneous Fill in Dam Embankment Zone* _______ [41].—(a) *General.*—The miscellaneous fill, zone _______ portion of the dam embankment shall be in accordance with this section and section G.28.

(b) *Materials.*—The miscellaneous fill, zone _______ portion of the dam embankment shall consist of miscellaneous mixtures of clay, silt, sand, gravel, cobbles, and rock fragments to _______ inches in maximum dimensions. The materials shall be obtained from excavations for permanent construction required under these specifications *(and from borrow areas).

Boulders and rock fragments larger than _______ inches in maximum dimensions shall be removed from otherwise approved miscellaneous fill material, either at the site of excavation or after the material has been placed on the embankment, but before the zone _______ material is compacted. Such oversize boulders and rock fragments shall be placed in _______ (insert location).

(c) *Preparation of Foundations.*—The foundation for zone _______ shall be prepared by leveling, moistening, and compacting so that the surface materials will be as compact as specified for subsequent layers of zone _______.

(d) *Moisture Control.*—Prior to and during compaction, the material in each layer of zone ______ fill material shall have the most practicable moisture content required for compaction purposes as determined by the Contracting Officer. Additional moisture as required may be applied by sprinkling on the dam embankment.

(e) *Placing and Compacting.*—The material shall be placed in the miscellaneous fill in continuous and approximately horizontal layers, not more than _______ inches in thickness after being compacted as herein specified. The combined excavation and placing operations shall be such that the materials, when compacted in the miscellaneous fill, will be sufficiently blended to secure the best practicable degree of compaction and stability.

When each layer of the material has been conditioned to have the proper moisture content, it shall be compacted by six passes of a 50-ton pneumatic-tired roller over each 15-foot horizontal width of the layer , as herein provided. Each pass of the roller shall be offset from the path of the previous pass so that the total compactive effort shall be distributed evenly over the entire horizontal layer of zone _______ embankment.

The pneumatic-tired roller used for compaction shall have a maximum total capacity of 50 tons and shall have a minimum of four wheels equipped with pneumatic tires. The tires shall be of such size and ply as can be maintained at tire pressures between 80 and 100 lb/in^2 for a 25,000-pound wheel load during roller operations. The roller wheels shall be located abreast, and be so designed that each wheel will carry approximately equal loads in traversing uneven ground. The spacing of the wheels shall be such that the distance between the nearest edges of adjacent tires will not be greater than 50 percent of the tire width of a single tire at the operating pressure for a 25,000-pound wheel load. The roller shall have a rigid steel frame provided with a body suitable for balanced loading such that the load per wheel may be maintained at 25,000 pounds.

Tractors used for pulling pneumatic-tired rollers shall have sufficient power to pull the fully-loaded roller satisfactorily under normal conditions of compaction.

(f) *Measurement and Payment.*—Measurement, for payment, of miscellaneous fill in dam embank-

[40]Limits to be inserted for each job depending on nature of available material.

[41]This section may be modified to delete all compaction requirements and to require routing of equipment, in accordance with design requirements.

*Delete or revise as applicable.

ment, zone ______, will be made as provided in section G.28.

Payment for miscellaneous fill in dam embankment, zone ______, will be made at the unit price per cubic yard bid therefore in the schedule, which unit price shall include all costs as provided in section G.28.

G.36. *Rockfill in Dam Embankment, Zone* ______.—(a) *General.*—The rockfill in dam embankment, zone ______, shall be constructed in accordance with this section, section G.28, and to the lines and grades shown on the drawings.

(b) *Materials.*—The rockfill material shall be obtained from excavation for the spillway and from other required excavation. The rockfill shall consist of rock fragments reasonably well graded between 8 and 36 inches (varies for different purposes and material sizes) in maximum dimension of the individual fragments: *Provided,* that the rockfill may contain material less than 8-inch size in quantities not to exceed the amount required to fill the voids in the larger rock. Individual rock fragments larger than 36 inches may be embedded in the rockfill within 6 feet of the downstream slope.

The rockfill immediately adjacent to zone ___ shall be the finer rock materials. Nests of rock materials containing voids will not be permited at the zone ______ contact. Should such voids occur, the contractor shall eliminate the voids by raking out the larger materials or by other approved methods.

(c) *Preparation of Foundation.*—The foundation for the rockfill shall be prepared in accordance with section G.28.

(d) *Placement.*—The rockfill material shall be placed in continuous, approximately horizontal layers having a compacted thickness not greater than 3 feet (revise to meet material sizes and density requirements). In those portions where the rockfill width is less than 10 feet, the uncompacted thickness of the layer may be required to be less than 3 feet.

Successive loads of material shall be dumped so as to secure the best practical distribution of the material and minimize segregation as determined by the Contracting Officer. The material shall be dumped and leveled in an approved manner prior to compaction.

Rockfill shall not be placed against new concrete until the concrete has been in place for at least 28 days.

(e) *Compaction.*—When each layer of material has been placed, the layer shall be compacted by four passes of a vibratory roller. One pass of the roller is defined as "the required number of successive roller trips which, by means of sufficient overlay, will ensure complete coverage of the entire surface of the layer by the roller." Second and subsequent passes of the roller shall not be made until each pass, as defined above, is completed.

The vibratory roller shall be a towed or self-propelled roller as approved by the Contracting Officer and shall have a smooth steel drum with a width not less than 6 feet, a minimum static weight of 20,000 pounds, a minimum dynamic force of 35,000 pounds when operating at 1,400 vibrations per minute, and an applied force not less than 9,000 pounds per foot of compaction drum length.

Any towed roller shall have at least 90 percent of its weight transmitted to the ground through the compaction drum when the roller is standing in a level position and hitched to the towing vehicle.

Rollers shall be operated at speeds not to exceed 1.5 miles per hour and shall at all times during compaction be operated between 1,100 and 1,500 vibrations per minute.

The contractor shall furnish to the Contracting Officer adequate data pertaining to the rollers to verify that all the above requirements shall be met, and the rollers shall be subject to the approval of the Contracting Officer.

The Contracting Officer may direct a reduction in the number of passes required for compaction. Each pass of the roller shall be offset so that the total compactive effort shall be distributed evenly over the entire area. Special attention shall be given by the contractor to ensure that no additional passes are permitted over the area. The roller will not be allowed to remain stationary on the zone with the vibratory mechanism operating.

The roller shall not be operated within 10 feet of the retaining walls with the vibratory mechanism operating. The 10-foot strips immediately adjacent to the retaining walls shall be compacted by placing rockfill materials with 12-inch maximum dimensions in layers not greater than 18 inches thick, and compacting with four pases made with the vibratory mechanism not operating.

(f) *Measurement and Payment.*—Measurement, for payment, of rockfill will be made as provided in section G.28. Payment for placing rockfill in dam embankment, zone ______ will be made at the unit price per cubic yard bid therefor in the schedule, which price shall include all costs of loading, hauling, placing and compacting, including costs of placing in thinner layers adjacent to the retaining wall as described in subsection (e), and as provided in section G.28.

G.37. *Impervious Backfill.*—Impervious backfill shall be placed at ______________ (insert location), ________ and elsewhere as shown on the drawings or as directed. The materials to be used for impervious backfill shall be obtained from excavation for the dam and appurtenant works, or from borrow pits, as directed. The material used for impervious backfill, the amount thereof, and the manner of placing shall be subject to approval.

Measurement, for payment, of impervious backfill will be made of the material inplace about the structure to the prescribed lines, grades, and dimensions. Payment for impervious backfill will be made at the unit price per cubic yard bid therefor in the schedule, which unit price shall include the cost of all work connected therewith, except the excavation, transportation, and compaction of the impervious backfill materials. Where compaction of impervious backfill is required, the compacting shall be performed as provided in section G.38. Payment for compacting impervious backfill will be made at the unit price per cubic yard bid therefor in the schedule, which payment will be in addition to the payment for impervious backfill.

G.38. *Compacting Impervious Backfill*[42].—

(a) *General.*—Where compacting of impervious backfill is required, the materials shall be deposited in uniform layers and compacted as specified in this section. The distribution of materials shall be such that the compacted material will be homogeneous and free from lenses, pockets, streaks, or other imperfections.

The material shall be deposited in horizontal layers not more than 6 inches thick after being compacted. The excavating and placing operations shall be such that the material when compacted will be blended sufficiently to secure the best practicable degree of compaction, impermeability, and stability. Prior to and during compaction operations, the material shall have the optimum moisture content required for the purpose of compaction, as determined by the Contracting Officer, and the moisture content shall be uniform throughout each layer.

Insofar as practicable, as determined by the Contracting Officer, moistening of the material shall be performed at the site of excavation, but such moistening shall be supplemented by sprinkling at the site of compaction if necessary. If the water content is less than optimum for compaction, the compaction operations shall not proceed, except with the specific approval of the Contracting Officer and, if the water content is greater than optimum for compaction, the compaction operations shall be delayed until such time as the material has dried to the optimum water content, and no adjustment in price will be made on account of any operation of the contractor in drying the material or on account of delays occasioned thereby.

When the material has been conditioned as previously specified, it shall be compacted by tamping rollers having staggered and uniformly spaced knobs and of sufficient weight for proper compaction, by hand or power tampers, or by other means or equipment approved by the Contracting Officer. When tamping rollers are used, the tamping knobs and cleaner bars shall be properly maintained and the spaces between the tamping feet shall be kept clear of material which impairs the effectiveness of the tamping roller.

The dry density of the soil fraction in the compacted material shall not be less than 95 percent of the laboratory standard maximum soil density(dry) as determined by the Proctor compaction test for the materials being compacted.

The compaction tests will be made by the Contracting Officer. The standard laboratory maximum soil density is the dry weight per cubic foot of the soil compacted at optimum moisture content by laboratory procedure.The compaction test will be made using a 1/20-cubic-foot compaction mold.

Measurement, for payment, of compacting impervious backfill will be made of the material inplace about the structure to the prescribed lines, grades, and dimensions. Payment for compacting impervious backfill will be made at the unit price per cubic yard bid therefor in the schedule.

G.39. *Pervious Backfill.*—(a) *General.*—Pervious backfill shall be [43](furnished and) placed to the lines and dimensions as shown on the drawings and as directed at the following locations:

(1) ______________

(2) ______________

[42]This section may be used in combination with section G.37, or this type of work may be included in sections G.29 or G.30, as appropriate.

[43]Use applicable provision.

(3) Elsewhere as shown on the drawings or where directed by the Contracting Officer.

(b) *Materials.*—The materials to be used for pervious backfill shall be selected pervious mixtures of sand, gravel, and cobbles, reasonably well graded to ______ inch size except that occasional fragments larger than ______ inches may be used if well distributed in the backfill. The pervious backfill shall not contain more than 5 percent, by weight, of material passing a United States Standard No. 200 sieve. The materials shall [43](be furnished from any approved source) [43](be selected from excavation for permanent construction required under these specifications, or from borrow pits in borrow areas ______, ______, and ______, as directed) [43](and shall be washed or otherwise processed to remove excess fines).

(c) *Placing.*—The material shall be handled and placed in such a manner as to prevent segregation. The method of placing pervious backfill shall be subject to approval. [43][The pervious backfill on either side of each structure shall be kept approximately at the same level as the placing of the backfill progresses.] Pervious backfill shall be placed and roughly leveled off in layers [43][not more than ______ inches thick. Compaction of pervious backfill is not required.] [43][Water shall be added as necessary so that the moisture content shall be uniformly distributed throughout each layer and shall be sufficient to attain the required relative density of the material inplace. The pervious backfill shall be compacted by tampers or roller, treads of crawler-type tractors, surface vibrators, or internal vibrators so that the relative density of the compacted material shall be not less than ______ percent as determined by the Government in accordance with test designation USBR 7250 of the Bureau's *Earth Manual* [3]. The thickness of the horizontal layers after compaction shall not be more than 6 inches if compaction is performed by tampers or rollers; not more than 12 inches if compaction is performed by treads of crawler-type tractors, surface vibrators, or similar equipment; and not more than the penetrating depth of the vibrator if compaction is performed by internal vibrators.]

(d) *Measurement and Payment.*—Measurement, for payment, of pervious backfill will be made of the material inplace about the structures to the prescribed lines, grades, and dimensions. Payment for pervious backfill will be made at the unit price per cubic yard bid therefor in the schedule, which unit price shall include only the cost [43][(of furnishing, and) (of washing or otherwise processing to remove fines), and of placing (moistening, and compacting) the pervious backfill material.] [43][Payment for excavation and transportation of the material will be made at the unit price per cubic yard bid in the schedule for excavation (in borrow area ______) (of the material used.)]

G.40. *Rock Backfill.*—(a) *General.*—Rock backfill shall be [43](furnished and) placed to the lines and dimensions as shown on the drawings and as directed at the following locations:

(1) ____________

(2) ____________

(3) Elsewhere as shown on the drawings or where directed by the Contracting Officer.

(b) *Materials.*—The material used for rock backfill shall be selected angular rock fragments, reasonably well graded, from 3 to ______ inches in minimum and maximum dimensions; and shall be [43][obtained from the same rock source, and be of the same quality, as required for riprap in section G.43; (selected from rock materials from required excavations); or (obtained from borrow area ______)]. The rock backfill shall contain not more than 5 percent, by weight, of material passing a United States Standard No. 200 sieve. Materials less than 3 inches in maximum size may be used in an amount only sufficient to fill the voids in the coarser material.

(c) *Placing.*—The rock fragments shall be placed and spread in layers not more than (varies according to density requirements and gradation) 24 inches thick. Placing shall be performed in a manner to prevent damage to the structures. The method of placing shall be subject to approval. The rock backfill on each side of the structures shall be kept approximately at the same level as the placing of the backfill progresses.

(d) *Measurement and Payment.*—Measurement, for payment, of rock backfill will be made of the rock backfill inplace to the lines, grades, and dimensions shown on the drawings or as established by the Contracting Officer. Payment for rock backfill will be made at the unit price per cubic yard bid therefor in the schedule, which unit price shall include [43][(the cost of furnishing, and) (the cost of all operations required to produce and complete the rock backfill as specified in this section), or (only

[43]Use applicable provision.

the cost of placing the rock backfill material). Payment for excavation, selection, and transportation of material will be made at the unit price per cubic yard bid in the schedule for excavation of the material used.]

G.41. *Filters.*—Graded sand and gravel filters shall be constructed under the *(apron, weir, spillway floor lining) as shown on the drawings or as directed. All materials for the filters shall be furnished by the contractor.

Trenches for the filters shall be excavated to lines, shapes, and dimensions shown on the drawings. Overexcavation in a manner to disturb the compacted foundations will not be permitted, and any material outside of the required lines which is disturbed shall be removed, and shall be replaced at the expense of the contractor in the manner described in section G.17. The sand and gravel shall be placed and tamped into place in such a manner that mixing of sand with gravel in the filter or with foundation or backfill materials will not occur. The graded sand and gravel shall be placed and tamped to the dimensions shown. *[After the graded sand and gravel in the filter have been shaped and compacted to the required depths, surfaces of the filter over which concrete is to be placed shall be covered with a layer of mortar 1 inch thick to provide a covering that will prevent the filter material from being displaced during the placing of the concrete. The mortar coating shall be applied carefully to the required thickness. The consistency of the mortar and methods of application shall be such as to avoid unnecessary filling of the voids in the filter material.]

Materials for filters shall be as follows:

(1) Gravel under the ______________ shall be clean, well-graded gravel from 3/16 to 1½ inches in size.

(2) Sand shall conform to the requirements specified for concrete in section G.78.

Measurement, for payment, of graded sand and gravel in filters will be of the volume of sand and gravel in the completed filter. Payment for graded sand and gravel for filters will be made at the unit price per cubic yard bid therefor in the schedule, which price shall include the cost of furnishing, delivery, handling, placing, and compacting the graded sand and gravel *(and furnishing sand for and mixing and placing the mortar covering). Excavation for filters will be paid for in accordance with section G.17.

G.42. *Bedding for Riprap.*—(a) *General.*—Bedding for riprap shall be in accordance with this section and section G.28. Bedding for riprap shall be placed to the prescribed lines, grades, and thicknesses and at locations shown on the drawings and elsewhere as directed. Bedding for riprap will not be required between riprap and pervious backfill.

(b) *Materials.*—The bedding for riprap materials shall be selected from borrow pits in borrow area ______.

The materials shall be pervious mixtures of sand, gravel, and cobbles reasonably well graded from 3/16 to 6 inches in maximum dimensions, but may contain materials less than 3/16 inch in quantities not to exceed the amount required to fill the voids between the materials larger than 3/16 inch: *Provided*, that the material shall contain not more than 5 percent, by weight, of material passing a United States Standard No. 200 sieve.

Should cobbles and boulders having dimensions of more than 6 inches be found in otherwise approved materials, they shall be removed by the contractor either at the site of excavation or after being placed. Such oversize cobbles and boulders shall be placed in zone ______ or wasted, as directed by the Contracting Officer.

(c) *Placing.*—The bedding need not be compacted in place, but shall be placed in such a manner as will result in uniform layers of bedding for riprap of the specified thickness.

(d) *Measurement and Payment.*—Measurement, for payment, of bedding for riprap will be made of the bedding in place to the established lines and grades and on the basis of the specified thickness, and as provided in section G.28.

Payment for bedding for riprap will be made at the unit price per cubic yard bid therefor in the schedule, which unit price shall include all costs as provided in section G.28.

G.43. *Riprap.*—(a) *General.*—Riprap shall be in accordance with this section and section G.28. Riprap shall be furnished and placed to the prescribed outlines and thicknesses for the protection of slopes, channels, and structures at the locations shown on the drawings and elsewhere as directed by the Contracting Officer.

The contractor shall neatly place in stockpile approximately ______ tons of riprap material at the locations shown on drawing ______. The material

*Delete or revise as applicable.

in this stockpile shall meet the gradation requirements for riprap of nominal thickness of 36 inches.

The contractor shall also neatly place in stockpile approximately ______ tons of riprap material at the locations shown on drawing ______. The riprap in this stockpile shall meet the gradation requirements for riprap of nominal thickness of ______ inches.

*[Prior to any contractor operations in the riprap source, the contractor shall submit, to the Construction Engineer for approval, his plans for developing the source and transporting the materials to the damsite. The plans shall be in sufficient detail to indicate full compliance with this section and section G.2.]

The contractor shall furnish to the Contracting Officer at the site of the work, without cost to the Government, such samples of rock materials for testing as may be required by the Contracting Officer from proposed quarry sites and from rock materials delivered to the damsite.

All rock materials not meeting the requirements of these specifications, as determined by tests and/or inspections at the quarries or at the damsite, will be rejected. All rejected materials shall be disposed of in an approved manner at the expense of and by the contractor.

(b) *Riprap Source.*—Rock for riprap may be obtained from any approved source.

Samples of rock from the riprap sources, located as shown on the drawings, have been tested, and the samples were found to be of suitable quality, and these sources have been approved. Tests have not been made to determine the relative difficulty of obtaining rock fragments of the specified sizes. Bidders and the contractor are cautioned that rock from the above-mentioned sources may be variable in quality and sizes; that only selected locations and strata within the source will produce acceptable rock; and that the quantity of acceptable rock fragments which may be obtained from the sources is unknown.

*[No charge will be made to the contractor for rock materials taken from the riprap source located as shown on the drawings, and used in the work covered by these specifications, or stockpiled in accordance with subsection (a).]

The contractor shall make all arrangements with property owners for right-of-way, and shall pay all costs including any royalties for furnishing materials of approved quality and gradation from any other approved sources.

The Government reserves the right to make inspections of quarry sites and quarries. The approval by the Contracting Officer of some rock fragments from a particular quarry site shall not be construed as constituting the approval of all rock fragments taken from that quarry, and the contractor will be held responsible for the specified quality and gradation of rock fragments delivered to the damsite.

(c) *Quarry Operations.*—The contractor shall clear, strip, develop, and operate the quarries; excavate and transport the rock materials; dispose of waste materials; construct and maintain haul routes; and perform all other operations required to produce acceptable riprap materials. Quarry operations shall also be in conformance with section G.2.

The location and extent of all quarries within the riprap source and all quarry operations shall be subject to approval. The Government reserves the right to change the limits or location of quarries within the riprap source in order to obtain suitable materials.

The contractor shall perform all stripping operations and dispose of waste materials as approved by the Contracting Officer.

Blasting in the quarry shall be so controlled that so far as joint patterns in the quarry will permit, the rock fragments shall meet gradation requirements specified herein. Unsatisfactory blasting procedures will not be permitted.

The contractor shall develop and work the riprap source in a manner to produce sufficient hard, dense, durable rock fragments reasonably well graded to complete the riprap, as specified herein.

The materials for riprap shall be selected to contain the coarsest and the most hard, dense, and durable fragments from the riprap source.

Methods of sorting and loading material in the quarry shall be such as to produce riprap of the highest practicable quality and shall be subject to the approval of the Contracting Officer.

Waste materials shall be disposed of in the exhausted areas of the riprap source or in approved areas adjacent to quarries.

If the contractor elects to use the source located as shown on the drawings, quarry locations shall also meet the following specific requirements.

(1) Removal of riprap material shall commence

*Delete or revise as applicable.

at the scarred area near ______________ with excavation and rimming as necessary for the back slope to blend into existing back slope near______________, and shall proceed down station with back slopes approximately the same as the existing roadway excavation.

(2) A portion of the overburden and unsuitable rock which overlays the riprap source, and some riprap, has been removed by others. The contractor shall remove the remaining overburden and unsuitable rock as necessary. Overburden and small rock shall be stockpiled, if necessary, and used to smooth the final excavated area adjacent. Excess overburden and unsuitable rock shall be removed and wasted in the riprap source disposal area, as shown on drawing ________.

(3) The area behind the top of the cut should not be marred or disturbed.

(4) The floor of the quarry area shall be left at approximately the same elevation as the adjacent area, shall be smoothed as provided in (2), and shall be left so that it will drain.

(5) Adjacent road surfacing and structures shall be protected, and all damage resulting from the contractor's operations shall be repaired by and at the expense of the contractor, and to the satisfaction of the Contracting Officer.

(d) *Quality.*—The rock fragments for riprap shall meet the following requirements as to the quality:

(1) Individual rock fragments shall be dense, sound, and resistant to abrasion; and shall be free from cracks, seams, and other defects that would tend to increase unduly their destruction by water and frost actions.

(2) Samples prepared in accordance with the applicable test designations of the Bureau of Reclamation's *Concrete Manual* [2], shall meet the following requirements when tested by the procedure described in the respective designations shown in table G-2.

(e) *Gradation.*—Riprap shall be reasonably well graded within the limits shown in table G–3.

(f) *Placing.*—The riprap need not be compacted, but shall be placed to grade in a manner to ensure that the larger rock fragments are uniformly distributed and the smaller rock fragments serve to fill the spaces between the larger rock fragments in such a manner as will result in well-keyed, densely placed, uniform layers of riprap of the specified thickness. Hand placing will be required only to the extent necessary to secure the results specified above.

Table G-2.—Requirements of specified test designations.

Test Designation	Requirements
USBR 4127—Specific Gravity and Absorption of Coarse Aggregate	Greater than (2.60)*
USBR 4088—Soundness of Aggregates Using Sodium Sulfate or Magnesium Sulfate	Less than (10 percent)* loss of mass after five cycles.
USBR 4535—Resistance to Degradation of Large-Size, Coarse Aggregate by Abrasion and Impact in Los Angeles Machine	Less than (40 percent)* loss of mass after 500 revolutions.

*Modify value for each job depending on nature of material available and design considerations.

Table G-3.—Riprap gradation requirements—size of rock fragments.*

Nominal thickness of riprap (inches)	Maximum size (lb)	Percent by weight[1]				
		30 to 40%		60 to 70%		0 to 10% less than[2]
		From (lb)	To (lb)	From (lb)	To (lb)	(lb)
18*	500*	250	500*	15	250*	15*
24*	1,250*	626	1,250*	50	625*	50*
36*	4,500*	2,250	4,500*	100	2,250*	100*

*Modify the values shown in this table for each job depending on nature of material available and design considerations.
[1]Sand and rock dust shall be less than 5 percent, by weight, of total riprap material.
[2]The percentage of this size material shall not exceed an amount which will fill the voids in larger rock.

(g) *Measurement and Payment.*—Rock materials for riprap shall be weighed on platform scales furnished at the expense of and by the contractor. The scales shall be approved by the Contracting Officer and shall be tested and sealed, at the expense of the contractor, as often as the Contracting Officer may deem necessary to ensure their accuracy. A weighmaster certified by the State of ______________ and compensated by the contractor shall weigh all materials required to be weighed as herein provided. The scales shall be located in the vicinity of the work at the damsite. Certified copies of the weigh tickets shall be furnished to the Contracting Office.

*[When the water content of the riprap exceeds 4 percent, by weight, of the ovendry weight of the material, as determined by the Contracting Officer, the weight of the material to be paid for shall be determined by deducting the weight of the water in

*Delete or revise as applicable.

excess of 4 percent.]

Measurement, for payment, for furnishing and placing riprap will be made on the number of tons of riprap placed to the lines, grades, and thicknesses shown on the drawings or as established by the Contracting Officer, and will include riprap materials placed in stockpiles in accordance with subsection (a).

Payment for furnishing and placing riprap will be made at the unit price per ton bid therefor in the schedule, which unit price shall include the cost of all operations required to furnish, produce, and place the riprap as specified in this section; the cost of furnishing, testing, and sealing the scales; and all costs as provided in section G.28.

D. TUNNEL AND SHAFT CONSTRUCTION[44]

G.44. ***Tunnel Construction, General.***—Tunnel construction, as used in these specifications, includes the excavation by tunneling methods and other related work for the outlet works between station ______ and ______ including the gate chamber.

Placement of concrete lining for the tunnel and gate chamber shall be in accordance with section G.54.

The locations of the tunnel portals may be moved, at the direction of the Contracting Officer, to accommodate the conditions encountered during excavation operations. If the tunnel portals are moved, all stations and elevations of portal structures and limits of tunnel construction will be changed accordingly.

Tunnel construction shall be in accordance with the applicable sections in these specifications, and payment for the various items of required work will be made at the applicable unit prices bid therefor in the schedule, except that for shotcrete protection of excavated surfaces in tunnel, for furnishing and installing rock bolt tunnel supports, for furnishing and installing steel bearing plates for rock bolt tunnel supports, for furnishing and installing chain link fabric tunnel support, and for furnishing and installing intermediate expansion bolts for chain link fabric, payment will be made at fixed prices stated in the bidding schedule and in accordance with sections G.47, G.50, and G.51.

The tunnels shall be supported where conditions encountered are such as to require support. Approved types of support are shown on the drawings.

Where conditions in the tunnels are suitable for the exclusive use of rock bolt tunnel supports, with or without chain link fabric support, the Contracting Officer will approve the use thereof. Rock bolt tunnel supports and chain link fabric support shall be furnished and installed in accordance with the provisions of sections G.50 and G.51, respectively, and payment therefor will be made at fixed unit prices as prescribed therein.

Rock bolts, bearing plates, and chain link fabric used in conjunction with tunnel support systems, or used in the outlet works gate chamber between station ______ and ______, as described later in this section, will not be included in the measurement for payment for rock bolt tunnel supports, nor for chain link fabric support. Measurement, for payment, for furnishing and installing tunnel support systems will not include reaches of tunnel supported exclusively by rock bolt tunnel supports, with or without chain link fabric support.

Where ground conditions in the tunnels are such that the use of a tunnel support system is required, other than only rock bolt and chain link fabric tunnel supports, the contractor may, at his option, use one of the following systems:

(1) A shotcrete tunnel support system as described in section G.52.
(2) A structural-steel tunnel support system as described in section G.48.
(3) An approved combination of these support systems, with or without rock bolt and chain link fabric tunnel supports.

All supports shall be installed outside of the "A" lines.

Regardless of which tunnel support system is used, payment will be made for furnishing and installing tunnel support systems on the linear foot basis for the actual length of the tunnel supported as approved by the Contracting Officer: *Provided,*

[44] Applicable to tunnels, shafts, gate chambers, and other underground construction for spillways, outlet works, and diversion works. The wording of the text should be revised depending on the actual construction involved.

that payment for furnishing and installing a tunnel support system for the outlet works gate chamber between station ______ and ______ will be made at the lump sum price bid therefor in the schedule.

Where shotcrete is used for tunnel support, measurement, for payment, by the linear foot of furnishing and installing the tunnel support system will be made for the actual length of tunnel supported with shotcrete.

Where structural steel is used for tunnel support, measurement, for payment, of furnishing and installing tunnel support system in each reach of supported tunnel will be the distance between end supports plus 3 feet. Reaches of the tunnels with approved structural steel supports placed at 6-foot centers or less will be considered for payment purposes as supported reaches of the tunnels.

Payment for furnishing and installing tunnel support system will be made:

(1) At the applicable unit price per linear foot bid in the schedule for furnishing and installing tunnel support system for outlet works tunnel between station ______ and ______, and for furnishing and installing tunnel support system for outlet works tunnel between station ______ and ______.

(2) At the lump sum price bid in the schedule for furnishing and installing tunnel support system for outlet works gate chamber between station ______ and ______, which lump sum price will be paid whether or not supports are required.

The prices bid in the schedule shall include the costs of furnishing all materials, including cement, and placing shotcrete for tunnel support; of furnishing and placing all structural steel; or furnishing and placing any approved combinations of the support systems. No separate payment will be made for rock bolt supports, bearing plates, or chain link fabric supports installed in reaches of the tunnel for which payment for furnishing and installing support systems is made either by the linear foot or at the lump sum.

No separate payment will be made for shotcrete protection of excavated surfaces in tunnel in areas supported by shotcrete, unless such protection is specifically directed by the Contracting Officer in accordance with section G.47.

The required dimensions of the tunnel sections vary as indicated on the drawings. No additional payment for support systems will be made due to varying quantities of supports required for these sections.

Nothing contained in these specifications shall prevent the contractor, at his own expense, from erecting such amounts of temporary supports as he may consider necessary, or from using more rock bolt supports, heavier structural steel supports, or greater thicknesses of shotcrete for support than approved by the Contracting Officer. Nothing in these specifications shall be construed to relieve the contractor from the sole responsibility for the safety of the tunnels or from liability for injuries to or deaths of persons or damage to property.

G.45. ***Draining, Lighting, and Ventilating Tunnel During Construction.***—The contractor shall drain the tunnel of water by gravity flow or by pumping as necessary to obtain satisfactory working conditions. Substantial flows of water may be encountered. If substantial flows of water are encountered, the contractor may seal off water entering the tunnel in order to decrease the amount of water to be pumped or drained: *Provided*, that the cost of drilling any grout holes and grouting such holes shall be at the contractor's expense.

The contractor shall adequately light and ventilate the tunnel during all construction operations.

The contractor shall provide all labor and materials for cofferdams and other temporary construction, as necessary, to obtain satisfactory working conditions.

The cost of all work described in this section shall be included in the prices bid in the schedule for other items of work.

G.46. ***Tunnel Excavation.***—(a) *General.*—The tunnel and gate chamber shall be excavated to the lines, grades, and dimensions shown on the drawings or established by the Contracting Officer. No variations in alinement or grade of the tunnel will be permitted except for the tolerances permitted in section G.85.

The general dimensions, arrangements, and details of typical sections are shown on the drawings. The Government does not represent that excavation can be performed within the established "B" lines in all cases for tunnel excavation; however, payment for excavation will be made to the "B" lines in all cases, and overbreak of excavation outside the "B" lines shall be at the contractor's expense regardless of the cause of such overbreak or overexcavation.

The tunnel shall be constructed in such a manner as to permit a thorough inspection of the rock formations penetrated. As each ± 100-foot section of the tunnel is excavated, when directed by the Contracting Officer but not more often than weekly, the excavated surfaces for that section shall be washed clean of dust and loose rock so that the nature and condition of the rock can be observed by the Contracting Officer: *Provided*, that washing will not be required for surfaces required to be protected by shotcrete. Washing shall be accomplished with the minimum amount of water that can be used to clean the excavated surfaces adequately for the inspection.

All final excavated surfaces of the tunnel which are subject to deterioration by air slaking shall, within 1 hour after exposure, be protected by a protective coating of shotcrete as provided in section G.47.

Where supports are required to support the roof and sides of tunnel excavation, they shall be furnished and installed in accordance with sections G.44, G.48, G.50, G.51, and G.52.

Excavated materials shall be disposed of as provided in section G.27.

(b) *Definitions of "A" and "B" Lines.*—The "A" lines shown on the typical sections of the drawings are lines within which no unexcavated material of any kind, no timbering, metal, shotcrete, or other supports shall be permitted to remain. The "B" lines shown on the typical sections are the outside limits to which measurement, for payment, of excavation will be made. Measurement, for payment, will in all cases be made to the "B" lines regardless of whether the limits of the actual excavation fall inside or outside of the "B" lines.

(c) *Locations of "A" and "B" Lines.*—The locations of the "A" and "B" lines for the normal tunnel section are shown on the drawings. The "B" lines in reaches supported only by rock bolts are the same as the "B" lines for unsupported reaches.

(d) *Miscellaneous Requirements.*—The contractor shall use every precaution in his operations to avoid loosening material beyond the "B" lines. All drilling and blasting shall be carefully performed. Any damage to or displacement of tunnel supports and any damage to any other part of the work caused by blasting or any other operations of the contractor shall be repaired at the expense of and by the contractor in an approved manner, except as provided in subsection G.50(c) for rock bolts installed closer than 5 feet from the headings.

The excavation in the crown of unsupported, and rock bolt or shotcrete supported, tunnel sections shall be sufficient to accommodate the concrete discharge pipe between the forms or reinforcement and the excavated or shotcrete surfaces. The excavation in the crown of steel rib supported tunnel sections shall be sufficient to permit the placing of peaked structural steel supports to provide for the concrete discharge pipe as shown on the drawings. No payment will be made for excavation in the crown that is outside the "B" line and is performed to provide for the concrete discharge pipe and for the placing of peaked structural steel supports.

Immediately following excavation in unsupported sections, or in supported sections as directed, all loosened material either inside or outside of the "B" lines that, in the opinion of the Contracting Officer is liable to fall, shall be removed.

Loose material on the bottom surface of the tunnel shall be removed in accordance with section G.53. All material projecting inside the "A" lines shall be removed by the contractor in accordance with section G.53.

(e) *Measurement and Payment.*—Measurement, for payment, of excavation in tunnel will include excavation of the gate chamber, be limited to the specified sectional dimensions shown on the drawings, and will be made along the located centerline of the tunnel only for such reaches as are excavated by tunneling methods.

Payment for excavation in tunnel will be made at the unit price per cubic yard bid therefor in the schedule, which unit price shall include the entire cost of excavating, transporting, and disposing of excavated materials; washing the excavated surfaces clean of dust and loose rock; and maintaining the excavation in satisfactory condition until the concrete lining is placed. No additional allowance above the unit price bid in the schedule will be made on account of the class, nature, or condition of any of the material encountered.

G.47. *Shotcrete for Protective Coating.*—

(a) *General.*—Shotcrete conforming to the requirements specified in this section shall be applied to finished excavated tunnel and gate chamber surfaces as directed.

The shotcrete shall consist of a mixture of cement, sand, and water applied under pneumatic pressure. The shotcrete may be applied by either the dry-mix or wet process.

Shotcrete for protective coating shall be applied only to portions of the excavated surfaces which are subject to deterioration by air slaking, if encountered, and which are designated to be coated with shotcrete, as determined by the Contracting Officer. The final excavated surfaces shall be protected within 1 hour after exposure. The exposed finished excavated surfaces shall be kept moist at all times to prevent evaporation of the natural moisture in the material and shall be protected from freezing.

Loose material shall be removed from the excavated surfaces by methods approved by the Contracting Officer, the removal to be accomplished in such a manner as to not disturb the surfaces to receive the shotcrete. Any surface material which, in the opinion of the Contracting Officer, is loosened or damaged shall be removed to a sufficient depth to provide a base which is sufficiently substantial to receive the shotcrete. Temporary protective coverings, at the contractor's expense and as approved by the Contracting Officer, will be permitted if necessary, until immediately before the shotcrete is to be applied. Any covering damaged prior to time of shotcrete application shall be removed and replaced or repaired by and at the expense of the contractor. The applied shotcrete shall be not less than ½ inch in thickness.

The shotcrete shall be cured by maintaining a relative humidity of 80 percent or higher at the shotcrete surface for a minimum period of 7 days. If the natural relative humidity level in the tunnel drops below 80 percent, the contractor will be required to maintain the specified level by provision of a water mist spray or other approved means.

(b) *Materials.*—The cement, sand, and water shall be in accordance with sections G.75, G.77, and G.78.

(c) *Composition.*—The shotcrete shall be mixed in the proportions of 1 part cement to 4 parts (by weight) of surface dry sand. The shotcrete shall be proportioned on the basis of integral bags of cement unless the quantity of cement is determined by direct weighing, and the amount of sand shall be determined by direct weighing. One bag of cement will be considered as having a net weight of 94 pounds. The sand and cement shall be thoroughly mixed before being fed into the delivery equipment. If the dry mix process is used, the percentage of surface (free) moisture in the sand, as batched, shall be within the range of 3 to 6 percent (by weight) and shall be controlled within such range as may be necessary for the maintenance of uniform feed and to avoid choking in the delivery equipment, hose, or nozzle. The placing machine and its operation shall be subject at all times to the approval of the Contracting Officer. The amount of water used shall be that required to produce shotcrete of suitable consistency, quality, and uniformity which will compact against and adhere to the surface to which the shotcrete is applied, with a minimum amount of rebound.

(d) *Application.*—All shotcrete shall be applied in the presence of a duly authorized inspector. Nozzlemen shall demonstrate, to the satisfaction of the Contracting Officer, the ability to apply quality shotcrete prior to applying shotcrete to the work.

Care shall be taken to prevent formation of sand pockets in the shotcrete and, should sand pockets be formed, they shall be removed and replaced with suitable shotcrete at the contractor's expense. Use of rebound will not be permitted, and rebound accumulations shall be removed and disposed of as approved by the Contracting Officer.

(e) *Measurement and Payment.*—Measurement, for payment, of shotcrete for protective coating will be made of the number of square yards of finished surface of the tunnel and gate chamber as are coated, as directed, on the net area measured at the "B" line as shown on the drawings. Payment for shotcrete for protective coating will be made at the fixed unit price per square yard stated therefor in the schedule. The unit price will include the cost of furnishing all materials and applying the shotcrete coating. No separate payment will be made for the cement used in shotcrete.

G.48. *Structural-Steel Tunnel Support System.*—(a) *General.*—Where structural-steel supports are used to support the roof and sides of the tunnel and gate chamber, they shall be installed as shown on the drawings, as prescribed in this section, and as approved by the Contracting Officer.

The types and designs of the structural-steel supports shall be the responsibility of the contractor, subject to the approval of the Contracting Officer. Acceptable types of steel rib supports are shown on the drawings. These types may be modified by the contractor, subject to the approval of the Contracting Officer. The size, weight, miscellaneous details, and spacing of the supports shall also be subject to the approval of the Contracting Officer. The clear distance between flanges of the installed supports shall not be less than 12 inches.

The structural-steel supports, steel lagging, struts, and other approved structural steel members shall be furnished complete with bolts, nuts, washers, plates, tie rods, and other accessories required for installing the supports.

(b) *Installation.*—The steel supports shall be installed to the proper lines and grades, and shall be maintained by the contractor in the proper condition and alinement until the concrete lining is placed about them.

Structural-steel supports shall be installed as close to the heading being excavated as can reasonably be maintained without damage to the supports.

Improper installation of supports shall be corrected by the contractor within 48 hours after the improperly installed supports are called to his attention. In supported sections, the contractor shall securely brace the supports with spreaders and the minimum practicable amount of blocking and wedges as provided in section G.49.

The contractor may, to facilitate his operations, place structural steel supports a greater distance from the inside finished surface of the concrete lining than shown on the drawings or prescribed by the Contracting Officer: *Provided*, that any increase in the quantity of steel supports and any excavation and concrete lining outside the "B" lines shown on the drawings or described in section G.46 required thereby shall be at the contractor's expense.

Where it is necessary to place structural-steel struts across the invert, the struts shall be placed as approved by the Contracting Officer.

(c) *Measurement and Payment.*—Measurement, for payment, of furnishing and erecting structural-steel tunnel supports will be made of the actual number of pounds of structural-steel supports erected. Measurement in each reach of supported tunnel will be the distance between end supports plus 3 feet. Reaches of the tunnel with approved structural-steel supports placed at 6-foot centers or less will be considered for pay purposes as supported reaches of the tunnel.

Payment for furnishing and erecting structural-steel tunnel supports will be made at the unit price per pound bid therefor in the schedule, which unit price shall include the costs of furnishing and erecting all materials. No separate payment will be made for rock bolt supports, bearing plates, or chain link fabric supports installed in reaches of the tunnel for which structural-steel supports are used.

G.49. *Foot Blocks, Lagging, Blocking, and Spreaders.*—(a) *General.*—The dimensions and quantities of the foot blocks, lagging, spreaders, wedges, and blocking are not shown on the drawings, but shall (in all cases) be as necessary to serve their functions and for safety. The materials used for foot blocks, blocking, wedges, and spreaders may, at the contractor's option, be timber, steel, or concrete. All timber shall be well-seasoned, sound timber of rectangular cross section. All lagging shall be steel or approved precast concrete.

Timber blocking, timber wedges, and timber spreaders shall be removed before placing concrete lining in accordance with section G.53.

(b) *Placement of Lagging and Blocking.*—Except as authorized in specific instances, lagging and blocking shall be placed in the form of open cribbing and shall be arranged to permit the ready flow of concrete through and around the lagging and blocking so that the concrete lining will be in contact with at least one-half of the excavated surface area bounded by the centerlines of adjacent steel supports and any two longitudinal lines 5 feet apart.

(c) *Costs.*—No separate payment will be made for furnishing, placing, and removing blocking, wedges, and spreaders; and the costs thereof shall be included in the prices bid in the schedule for other items of work. No separate payment will be made for furnishing and placing foot blocks and lagging, and the cost thereof shall be included in the prices bid in the schedule for other items of work.

G.50. *Rock Bolt Tunnel Supports.*—

(a) *General.*—Where rock bolt supports are used to support the roof and sides of the tunnel and gate chamber, they shall be of either the expansion anchor type with both ends threaded, expansion anchor type with fixed heads at one end and threaded at the other end, or slot-and-wedge type. The rock bolts shall be installed as shown on the drawings, as prescribed in this section, and as approved by the Contracting Officer.

The rock bolts shall be furnished complete with all accessories, including bearing plates, anchor devices, bevel washers, machine washers, nuts, corrosion preventive compound, lubricant, and other materials required for installation of the rock bolts.The minimum length of bolts shall be 6 feet.

The actual rock bolt and accessories selected by the contractor shall be subject to approval by the

Contracting Officer, which approval will be given after the installed rock bolt has proved itself capable of performing its function in the particular rock encountered. If, during the progress of the work, rock conditions change to such an extent that the installation of any one type of rock bolt anchor or accessory proves unsatisfactory, the contractor shall change to that which will give the desired result.

Two copies of the manufacturer's installation instructions shall be submitted to the Project Construction Engineer for his use at the site.

(b) *Materials*:

(1) *Bolts*:

a. Expansion-anchor type.—The bolts shall be not less than ¾-inch nominal diameter and shall be either bolts with both ends threaded or bolts with fixed heads at one end and threaded at the other end. The threaded ends of the bolts shall have rolled threads at least 8 inches in length.The bolts shall be made of steel conforming to ASTM Designation: A 306, Grade 80.

b. Slot-and-wedge type.—The bolts shall be not less than 1-inch nominal diameter, with the slot at one end and rolled threads at least 8 inches in length at the other end; and shall be made of steel conforming to ASTM Designation: A 306, Grade 60. The slot shall be about ⅛-inch wide and 6 inches long.

(2) *Anchors*:

a. The shells and plugs for the expansion-type anchor shall be malleable iron castings conforming to ASTM Designation: A 47, Grade 32510; or forged steel with a maximum sulphur content of 0.23 percent.

b. The steel wedges for the slot-and-wedge type anchor shall be about 5½ inches long, and shall be tapered from 1/16 by ¾ inch to about ¾ by ¾ inch; and shall be made from steel conforming to ASTM Designation: A 306, or shall be made with cast malleable iron conforming to ASTM Designation: A 47, Grade 32510.

(3) *Bearing Plates.*—The bearing plates shall be ⅜-inch flat steel plates providing not less than a 36-square-inch area for each bolt or, if approved, a length of structural steel channel or other structural shape may be used.

(4) *Washers and Nuts.*—The bevel washers shall be steel or malleable iron. Machine washers shall be hardened steel. All nuts shall be heavy-duty hexagonal nuts.

(5) *Corrosion-Preventive Compound.*—The threads of the bolts and nuts shall be coated at the factory with a coat of corrosion-preventive compound. The compound shall conform to Military Specification, MIL–C–16173D, Grade 1.

(6) *Lubricant.*—Lubricant for threads shall be of molybdenum disulfide base, such as Molykote "G", as manufactured by the Alpha-Molykote Corporation, 65 Harvard Avenue, Stamford, Connecticut, or equal.

(c) *Installation.*—Rock bolt installations shall follow the advancement of the heading. The bolts or bolting pattern shall be advanced to about 5 feet from the face following each blasting operation. Such installation shall be completed within 6 hours following blasting.

The holes for the rock bolts, except where otherwise directed by the Contracting Officer, shall be drilled normal to the rock face. The diameter of the holes and installation of the rock bolts shall be in accordance with the manufacturer's instructions unless otherwise directed. The length of the rock bolt at each location shall be as approved by the Contracting Officer, and the depth of hole shall be suitable for the length of bolt to be installed.

The equipment and methods used to drill the holes, to effectively seat and tighten the rock bolt anchorage in the hole, and to tighten the bolt to the required tension shall be subject to the approval of the Contracting Officer.

Rock bolts shall be installed with flat steel bearing plates or, if approved, with a length of structural steel channel or other structural shape to which one or more bolts are connected. Bevel washers, where needed, shall be placed between the bearing plate and the nut to ensure uniform bearing on the bearing plate. A machine washer shall be placed between the nut or bolthead and the bevel washer, and shall be coated on both sides with lubricant.

Each hole shall be cleaned of all drill cuttings, sludge, and debris before the bolt is inserted. All threads of the rock bolts shall be free from rust, burrs, and other foreign matter. Immediately prior to the installation of the rock bolts, any excess corrosion preventive compound shall be wiped off the threads and the threads shall then be given a liberal coating of the lubricant. Where slot-and-wedge type rock bolts are used, the wedges shall also be coated with the lubricant just prior to insertion into the bolt slot.

Each rock bolt shall be tightened with a controlled torque impact wrench so that the bolt is stressed to not less than 60 nor more than 80 percent of the yield point stress based on the net area of the bolt, except that reduced stresses may be permitted in certain rock types as determined by the Contracting Officer. The torque required to produce the required stress in the bolts will be determined by the Contracting Officer using tests performed at the site. Conformance with the required torque shall be periodically tested with an approved torque wrench.

At periodic intervals, as determined by the Contracting Officer, the contractor shall check and where necessary retighten all rock bolts to the required torque until placement of the concrete lining or completion of the work under these specifications.

If a bolt 5 feet or more from the heading has been damaged or made ineffective by blasting operations, the damage shall be repaired and, if necessary, additional bolts shall be installed to replace the damaged or ineffective bolts, all at the expense of the contractor. If installation of rock bolts closer than 5 feet from the heading is approved by the Contracting Officer, and such bolts are damaged during the blasting operation, payment will be made for repair of the damaged bolts and for any additional bolts required to be installed to replace the damaged or ineffective bolts at the fixed price per linear foot stated in the schedule for furnishing and installing rock bolt tunnel supports.

(d) *Measurement and Payment.*—Measurement, for payment, of furnishing and installing rock bolt tunnel supports will be made of the length of the rock bolts approved for installation in the tunnel and gate chamber, but will not include rock bolts used in combination with tunnel support systems as provided in section G.44. Payment for furnishing and installing rock bolt tunnel supports will be made at the fixed unit price per linear foot stated therefor in the schedule. The unit price will include the cost of drilling the holes; of furnishing and installing rock bolts complete with all accessories except bearing plates; of checking and retightening bolts where necessary; and of performing all other work required to complete the rock bolt installation as provided in this section.

Measurement, for payment, of furnishing and installing steel bearing plates for rock bolt tunnel supports will be made of the weights of the flat steel bearing plates and other structural steel shapes approved for installation in conjunction with rock bolt tunnel supports, but will not include bearing plates used in combination with tunnel support systems as provided in section G.44.

Payment for furnishing and installing steel bearing plates for rock bolt tunnel supports will be made at the fixed unit price per pound stated therefor in the schedule.

G.51. *Chain Link Fabric Tunnel Supports.*— (a) *General.*—Chain link fabric shall be furnished and installed against the excavated rock surfaces as part of the support system for the roofs or sides of the tunnel and gate chamber where and as approved by the Contracting Officer.

(b) *Materials*:

(1) *Chain Link Fabric.*—Federal Specification RR-F-00191E, Part 1, Class 1, Coating A, 2-inch mesh, No. 9 gage (0.148-inch diameter of coated wire).

(2) *Intermediate Expansion Bolts and Nuts.*—Expansion bolts for fastening the fabric at intermediate points between rock bolts shall be 18 inches long, shall be ¾-inch expansion anchor type steel bolts, and shall otherwise be in accordance with subsection G.50(b). Nuts shall be heavy-duty hexagonal nuts.

(3) *Bearing Plates.*—Bearing plates for fastening chain link fabric to intermediate expansion bolts shall be flat steel bearing plates not less than 4 by 4 by ¼ inches in size.

(c) *Installation.*—Where rock conditions require chain link fabric, the fabric shall be placed at the time rock bolts are installed. The fabric shall be placed between the rock surface and the bearing plates.

Where conditions warrant and where approved by the Contracting Officer, the fabric may be placed following the completed rock bolt installation. The chain link fabric placed over installed rock bolts may be held to the rock surface using intermediate expansion bolts or by other methods approved by the Contracting Officer.

The contractor shall lap sections of fabric a minimum of 6 inches where practicable: *Provided*, that at connections where it is impracticable to maintain 6-inch laps, as determined by the Contracting Officer, the contractor will be permitted to extend laps in lieu of cutting along regular lines.

The final layout of the fabric and extent of lapping shall be subject to approval of the Contracting Officer.

Where approved, intermediate expansion bolts

shall be installed at intermediate points for fastening the chain link fabric to the rock. The intermediate expansion bolts shall be installed in such manner that the chain link fabric is held securely between the rock surface and the bearing plate.

(d) *Measurement and Payment.*—Measurement, for payment, of furnishing and installing the chain link fabric tunnel support will be made of the actual number of square yards of chain link fabric installed as support for the roof and sides of the tunnel and gate chamber, including overlaps at joints.

Payment for furnishing and installing the chain link fabric tunnel support will be made at the fixed unit price per square yard stated therefor in the schedule. The unit price will include the cost of furnishing and installing the chain link fabric complete with all accessories, except that payment for intermediate expansion bolts and bearing plates will be made at the fixed price per bolt stated therefor in the schedule. The fixed price will include the cost of drilling the holes, and of furnishing and installing the bearing plates, nuts, and all accessories.

G.52. *Shotcrete Tunnel Support System.*— (a) *General.*—Where shotcrete is used for the support system for the roof and sides of the tunnel and gate chamber, the shotcrete shall be furnished and placed as shown on the drawings, as prescribed in this section, and as approved by the Contracting Officer.

Shotcrete is defined as "concrete conveyed through a hose and pneumatically projected at high velocity onto a surface with the force of the jet impacting on the surface compacting the material."

Shotcrete for tunnel support to be applied under these specifications shall be a mixture of cement, sand, coarse aggregate, water, and an accelerator-hardening admixture. The coarse aggregate shall be 3/8-inch maximum size.

The shotcrete shall be applied by the shotcreting process known as the dry-mix process, which consists of thoroughly mixing the solid materials, feeding these materials into a special mechanical feeder or gun, moving the materials by compressed air to a special nozzle where water is added and intimately mixed with the other ingredients, and the mixture jetted from the nozzle at high velocity onto the surface to receive the shotcrete.

Where shotcrete is used to support the roof and sides of the tunnel, the shotcrete shall be applied to all surfaces of the tunnel, except in the lower 70° of the arc of the tunnel invert.

The thickness of the shotcrete shall be such as to adequately support the tunnel, but in no case shall it be less than 2 inches.

To minimize movement of the surrounding material, the shotcrete for tunnel support shall be applied as soon as practicable and as close to the heading as practicable.

An initial layer of shotcrete support shall be applied over at least the upper 180° of the arch of the tunnel sections. The initial shotcrete layer shall be applied after each heading advance and during or immediately following the mucking operation. The initial shotcrete layer shall be applied to within 12 inches of the excavated face or heading of the tunnel. In no case shall the initial application of shotcrete be delayed more than 4 hours after the blast required to advance the heading.

Placement of the shotcrete tunnel support system to the required dimensions and thicknesses shall be completed within 48 hours following exposure by excavation.

The contractor shall maintain safety in all areas where shotcrete is being applied, including dust protection, satisfactory to the Contracting Officer. Sodium and/or potassium hydroxide, and possibly other chemicals contained in accelerating-hardening admixtures are moderately toxic and, if used in shotcrete, may cause skin and respiratory irritation unless adequate safety measures are taken. To assure adequate protection against toxic materials, nozzlemen and helpers shall, when applying shotcrete containing an accelerating-hardening admixture, wear sandblasting hoods supplied with filtered air free of objectionable or toxic material, in addition to gloves and protective clothing.

Any royalties or other charges required to be paid for equipment and materials selected and used by the contractor for use in and applying shotcrete shall be paid by the contractor.

(b) *Materials*:

(1) *Cement.*—The cement shall be type _____ (low alkali) in accordance with section G.75.

(2) *Sand and Coarse Aggregate.*—The sand and 3/8-inch maximum size aggregate shall be in accordance with sections G.78 and G.79, except that the quantity of material passing a No. 100 sieve may be increased to 14 percent: *Provided*, that a greater quantity of material passing the No. 100 sieve than the specified 14 percent will be permitted if needed to provide added workability and adhering qualities of the shotcrete: *Provided Further*, that the in-

creased quantity does not detrimentally affect the quality and strength of the inplace shotcrete. If fine material is to be added to the sand, it shall be suitably blended with the sand. The contractor may screen the 3/8-inch coarse aggregate to eliminate the plus 3/8-inch material.

(3) *Admixtures.*—The shotcrete shall contain an accelerating-hardening admixture which shall be furnished and added to the mix in powder form. Use of calcium chloride in the shotcrete will not be permitted, and the accelerating-hardening agent shall not contain calcium chloride. The brand and quantity of accelerating-hardening agent used shall be the responsibility of the contractor, shall be such as to conform to the foregoing requirements, and shall produce shotcrete meeting the specified strength and bonding requirements of these specifications.

The admixture shall be stored and maintained in a dry condition until it is introduced into the shotcrete mixture. The dosage of admixture used shall be accurately measured and uniformly dispersed throughout the shotcrete mixture.

(4) *Water.*—Water used in shotcrete shall be in accordance with section G.77.

(c) *Composition.*—The shotcrete shall have a minimum cement content of 7 bags per cubic yard of shotcrete as discharged from the nozzle. The shotcrete shall meet the compressive strength requirements, as determined by tests from test panels, as provided in subsection (d).

The percentage of surface (free) moisture in the sand, as batched, shall be within 3 to 6 percent, by weight; and shall be controlled within this range as may be necessary for the maintenance of uniform feed and to avoid choking in the delivery equipment, hose, or nozzle.

The sand, coarse aggregate, cement, and admixture shall be uniformly added and mixed thoroughly before being fed into the delivery equipment. Machine mixing of the dry ingredients, except the accelerating-hardening admixtures, will be required.

The shotcrete shall be proportioned on the basis of integral bags of cement unless the quantity of cement is determined by direct weighing; the amounts of sand and coarse aggregate shall be determined by direct weighing. The admixture shall be added to the shotcrete mix by a gravimetric/volumetric device, calibrated for the varying percentages required and accurate to within 0.5 percent, and shall be fed to the dry-mix shotcrete as it enters the placing machine. The weighing equipment shall be in first-class operating condition and shall conform to the requirements of Federal Specification AAA-S-121D(1) for such equipment, except that accuracy to within 0.4 percent of the scale capacity will be satisfactory.

(d) *Strength Criteria for Shotcrete and Preconstruction Testing of Shotcrete.*—The contractor shall fabricate test panels for each mixture to be used. At least three test panels shall be fabricated for each mix. The panels shall be prepared under the supervision of the Contracting Officer and shall be submitted in sufficient time to obtain and test cores at the specified ages.

Application of shotcrete to test panels may be accomplished at locations other than the construction site: *Provided*, that (1) equipment used for application is that to be used in tunnel construction, (2) materials used in the shotcrete are the same as those to be used in the work, and (3) application is supervised by a Government inspector.

Fabrication of test panels shall consist of applying not less than 4 inches of shotcrete in one application to a plywood panel not less than 30 inches square. The shotcrete shall be applied to the panels in the same manner and under the same pressures that will be used in the actual work.

After fabrication, the panels shall be wrapped and sealed with polyethylene sheeting, or by any other method that will prevent loss of moisture.

The Government will obtain NX-size cores from the panels, and will test the cores for compressive strength at 8 hours and 28 days age. The test cores will have a length-to-diameter ratio of 2, or be corrected thereto.

The test cores shall attain compressive strengths of not less than 500 lb/in^2 in 8 hours and 3,750 lb/in^2 at 28 days age.

No shotcrete mixture shall be applied to the work under these specifications until the compressive strength of the mixture, as determined from the test cores, meets the specified strength requirements: *Provided*, that the contractor will be permitted to proceed with the shotcreting work if it is determined satisfactory by the Contracting Officer that, by increasing the cement content of the shotcrete over the quantity used for the test panels, the specified strength criteria will be met. However, the contractor should allow adequate lead time for preparation of shotcrete test cores. Failure of a mix to meet specified strength requirements could delay accomplishment of other work.

(e) *Equipment.*—The equipment used by the contractor for mixing and applying shotcrete shall be subject to approval, and shall be capable of handling and applying shotcrete containing the specified maximum size aggregate and accelerating-hardening admixture. The equipment, including mixers, hoses, nozzles, air and water pressure gages, and gaskets, shall be maintained in clean and proper operating condition satisfactory to the Contracting Officer.

A properly operating air compressor of ample capacity shall be used that will maintain a supply of clean, dry air adequate for maintaining sufficient nozzle velocity for the application.

The discharge nozzle shall be equipped with a manually operated water injection system of sufficient pressure to provide an even distribution of water through the aggregate-sand-cement mixture. The water valve shall be capable of ready adjustment to vary the quantity of water, and shall be convenient to the nozzleman.

(f) *Preparation of Surfaces to Receive Shotcrete.*—Surfaces to receive shotcrete shall be prepared as required under section G.46, and, if necessary to provide a suitable bonding surface for the shotcrete, the surfaces shall be cleaned by air or water jets.

The surfaces to receive shotcrete shall, where practicable, be rid of free water when the shotcrete is applied. Suitable weep holes, relief pipe, or other methods of controlling water inflows shall be provided. Where impracticable to control free water, the contractor may apply shotcrete to such surfaces provided the shotcrete adheres readily to the surfaces and prevents the inflow of water through the shotcrete. The contractor may provide and use plastic tubes to collect and drain inflows, where and as approved by the Contracting Officer. The plastic tubes may be left in place and embedded in the shotcrete, but shall not extend into the concrete lining inside of the "A" line.

(g) *Placing.*—Shotcrete shall be placed only in the presence of a duly authorized Government inspector.

Nozzlemen shall demonstrate, to the satisfaction of the Contracting Officer, the ability to apply shotcrete of the required quality prior to their placing of shotcrete in the work.

Shotcrete shall not be applied when freezing conditions prevail at the immediate application site unless adequate provisions are made to protect the surfaces to receive the shotcrete, and the applied shotcrete, from freezing for at least 3 days.

The water pressure at the discharge nozzle shall be sufficiently greater than the operating air pressure to assure that water is intimately mixed with the other materials.

The shotcrete shall be applied by pneumatic pressure from a discharge nozzle held about 2 to 5 feet from the surface, and in a stream as nearly normal as possible to the surface being covered.

The shotcrete shall be applied in layers having a thickness that will assure the shotcrete completely adheres to the surface or preceding layer and no sagging occurs. Any shotcrete which shows evidence of sloughing or separation shall be removed and replaced by and at the expense of the contractor and to the satisfaction of the Contracting Officer.

Care shall be taken to prevent the formation of sand pockets and, should sand pockets be formed, they shall be removed immediately and replaced with suitable shotcrete at the expense of the contractor.

Use of rebound will not be permitted, and rebound accumulations shall be removed and disposed of as approved by the Contracting Officer.

The shotcrete shall be cured as provided in section G.91.

(h) *Costs.*—The costs of furnishing and applying shotcrete for the tunnel support system shall be as provided in section G.44.

G.53. *Preparation for Placing Concrete Lining.*—(a) *General.*—The contractor shall prepare the tunnel and gate chamber excavations for placing concrete lining in accordance with section G.86 and the requirements of this section.

Where appreciable quantities of water flow from the surrounding tunnel excavation, the water shall be excluded from the space to be filled with concrete by grouting; by calking; by diverting with pipes, pans, or other means; or by pumping from sumps until the concrete has hardened and gained sufficient strength to be unaffected by the action of the water through percolation, hydrostatic pressure, or erosion.

All material projecting inside the "A" lines shall be removed by the contractor before concrete is placed in the lining. The removal of such projections within the "A" lines may be performed at any time during the progress of the work: *Provided*, that immediately before the concrete lining is placed, the contractor shall remove all material extending within the "A" lines.

All loose material shall be removed to clean undisturbed surfaces before the concrete is placed.

Timber blocking and timber wedges shall be removed as completely as practicable before concrete lining is placed. Where steel or concrete is used for lagging, blocking, or wedges, such lagging, blocking, and wedges may be left in place and lining concrete placed about them as approved by the Contracting Officer.

All timber spreaders used to brace the structural steel supports shall be removed before the concrete lining is placed.

(b) *Cost.*—No separate payment will be made for preparing the tunnel and gate chamber excavations for placing concrete lining, and for excluding water from spaces to be filled with concrete, and the costs thereof shall be included in the prices bid in the schedule for other items of work.

G.54. Concrete in Outlet Works Tunnel Lining and Gate Chamber.—(a) *General.*—The item of the schedule for concrete in outlet works tunnel lining includes all concrete in the lining between station ______ and station ______, as shown on the drawings.

The item of the schedule for concrete in outlet works gate chamber includes all concrete in the gate chamber between station ______ and station ______, as shown on drawing ______, except second-stage concrete.

If placement of concrete lining is to be started prior to completion of all excavation for tunnels, the distance separating these operations shall be subject to approval.

Pipes shall be furnished and installed in the concrete for backfill grouting and for vents as shown on the drawings and in accordance with section G.55.

Concrete in tunnel linings and in the gate chamber shall conform to the requirements of sections G.73 through G.93.

The tunnel excavations shall be prepared for placement of concrete in accordance with section G.53.

All loose material in the inverts shall be removed before concrete is placed in accordance with section G.53.

The tunnel shall be lined with concrete having minimum thicknesses equal to the radial distance at any point in the perimeter of the tunnel between the finished inside surfaces of the concrete lining and the "A" lines, as shown on the typical tunnel sections of the drawings.

All spaces outside of the minimum required thickness of concrete lining shall be filled completely and solidly with concrete, and special care shall be taken to force concrete into all irregularities in the contact surfaces and to completely fill the tunnel and gate chamber arch.

After placing of concrete lining has been completed, the contractor shall fill with backfill grout, all spaces between the rock surfaces and the concrete lining of the tunnel and gate chamber. Where shotcrete is used for tunnel support, the spaces between the shotcrete and the concrete tunnel lining shall be filled with backfill grout. Where metal lagging, liner plates, or other continuous supports are used, both the spaces between such supports and excavated surfaces, and spaces between such supports and concrete lining shall be filled with backfill grout. The backfill grouting shall be performed in accordance with section G.55.

The finished interior surfaces of the tunnel and gate chamber shall conform accurately to the shape, alinement, grades, and sections shown on the drawings.

The distance between transverse joints in the tunnel linings shall not exceed 50 feet. Waterstops shall be placed in all transverse joints. No waterstops will be required in longitudinal construction joints.

Plane panel forming will be permitted for the horizontal curve of the tunnel lining in accordance with section G.83.

(b) *Measurement and Payment.*—Measurement, for payment, of concrete in outlet works tunnel linings and for concrete in outlet works gate chamber will be made to the "B" lines shown on the drawings. No deductions will be made for rock projections inside the "B" lines or for timber, concrete, shotcrete, and metal supports, struts, lagging, and blocking remaining within the prescribed "B" lines. No measurement for payment will be made for concrete required to be placed outside of the "B" lines due to overbreakage or excess excavation to facilitate the contractor's operations, or for additional excavation to accommodate the concrete discharge pipe.

Payment for concrete in outlet works tunnel linings and for concrete in outlet works gate chamber will be made at the applicable unit price per cubic yard bid therefor in the schedule, which price shall include the entire cost of furnishing all materials, except waterstop, cement, and reinforcing bars; and of placing all concrete, pipe, fittings, and backfill grout as described in section G.55. Payment for cement used in the concrete will be made at the unit price per ton bid in the schedule for furnishing and handling cement for concrete. Payment for furnishing and placing reinforcing bars will be made at the unit price per pound bid therefor in the schedule.

Except as provided below for cement, no payment will be made for furnishing and placing materials required for filling spaces outside of the "B" lines. Payment will be made for cement placed outside the "B" lines: *Provided*, that no payment will be made for cement used in filling spaces outside the "B" lines caused by careless excavation or excavation intentionally performed by the contractor to facilitate his operations, as determined by the Contracting Officer.

Payment for furnishing and placing waterstops in the transverse joints in the linings will be made at the unit price per linear foot bid in the schedule for furnishing and placing waterstops.

No direct payment will be made for excluding water from the spaces to be filled with concrete, and the cost thereof shall be included in the unit prices bid in the schedule for other items of work.

G.55. *Backfill Grouting.*—(a) *General.*—The contractor shall backfill with grout, spaces between the rock surfaces and concrete lining resulting from any cause at the locations described in section G.54. In sections of tunnel and gate chamber which are supported by structural steel ribs with liner plates, continuous metal lagging, or liner plates only, all spaces between the excavated surface and concrete lining shall be filled completely with backfill grout.

The grout shall be injected through pipes and fittings installed in the concrete lining for this purpose. The placing of the grout shall be done at low pressures, not more than 30 lb/in^2 above any hydrostatic pressure. Approximately three backfill grout or vent holes will be required along each 20 linear feet of tunnel, and the holes shall be located and staggered as shown on the drawings or as directed.

(b) *Pipes for Backfill Grouting.*—Metal grout and vent pipes to be embedded in the concrete lining for backfill grouting shall be furnished and placed to extend through the concrete at such points as may be designated by the Contracting Officer. The pipes shall be set so that grout can flow freely between the rock surfaces and concrete lining. The pipes shall end not less than 1 inch back from the finished inside surface of the concrete, and recesses shall be provided to the surface of the lining. The recesses shall be filled with concrete or mortar after grouting operations have been completed, in accordance with section G.89.

The size of the grout and vent pipe shall be a minimum diameter of 1½ inches. Pipes shall be held firmly in position and protected from damage while concrete lining is being placed. Caps or other devices shall be attached to the end of the pipe to prevent entry of concrete or other foreign materials prior to grouting, and to facilitate location of the grout pipe after forms are removed. After embedment in concrete and prior to grouting, a hole with a minimum diameter of 1½ inches shall be extended through each grout and vent pipe to the rock surface. Care shall be taken to avoid clogging or obstructing the pipes before grout hookups are made, and any pipe that becomes clogged or obstructed shall be thoroughly cleaned by and at the expense of the contractor.

Pipe shall be Weight A, Class 1, in accordance with Federal Specification WW-P-406D, and shall be cut and fabricated as required. Pipe fittings shall be malleable iron or steel, Type 1, in accordance with Federal Specification WW-P-521F.

(c) *Composition.*—The grout shall be composed of cement and water; or cement, sand, bentonite, and water. The proportions of cement, sand, and water will be determined by the Contracting Officer. The contractor shall use 2 percent bentonite, by weight of the cement, in grout containing sand. The bentonite shall be a suitable, commercially processed powdered bentonite.

Sand shall be clean and of such fineness that 100 percent will pass a No. 8 standard sieve, not more than 5 percent shall be retained on a No. 16 sieve, not less than 10 nor more than 30 percent will pass a No. 100 standard sieve, and not more than 5 percent shall pass the No. 200 sieve.

Cement for backfill grout shall be in accordance with section G.75. Water for backfill grout shall be in accordance with section G.77.

(d) *Grouting Operations.*—The equipment for mixing and placing backfill grout shall be in accordance with the applicable provisions of section G.60. No backfill grouting operations shall be performed until all concrete within a distance of 50 feet has been in place for at least 7 days. Grout holes adjacent to a grout hookup shall be fitted with valves and left open during grouting operations to facilitate the escape of air and water from pockets in the space surrounding the concrete lining. Where grout is found to flow from adjacent grout connections, the valves shall be closed and used as bleeders.

(e) *Cost.*—No separate payment will be made for backfill grouting, metal grout and air vent pipes, or other materials, except cement, used in backfill grouting. Backfill grout placed within the "B" lines will be included in the quantities of concrete lining paid for in accordance with section G.54. Payment for cement used in backfill grouting, including cement used outside of the "B" lines, will be made at the unit price per bag bid in the schedule for furnishing and handling cement for grouting.

E. PRESSURE GROUTING

G.56. *Requirements for Pressure Grouting, General.*—The general plan for pressure grouting requires that the contractor perform drilling and pressure grouting operations as follows:

(1) Drilling and grouting the foundation of the dam from the grout cap or caps and other locations as directed using high-pressure curtain grout holes.
(2) Grouting of all faults, joints, shear zones, springs, and other foundation defects that may require grouting as determined by the Contracting Officer.
(3) Grouting of the joints between the first- and second-stage concrete of the outlet works gate chamber.
(4) Grouting of the ______ diameter bypass pipe.
(5) Drilling and grouting at other locations as shown on the drawings or as directed by the Contracting Officer.

The drilling and pressure grouting of the foundation and [45](______________) shall be in accordance with the provisions of sections G.59 and G.60. The amount of drilling and pressure grouting required under these specifications is uncertain and, except as otherwise provided in the section in these specifications for "Variation in Estimated Quantities," the contractor shall be entitled to no extra compensation above the unit price bid in the schedule because of any excess or deficiency between the final quantities and the quantities stated in the schedule. The contractor shall be entitled to no additional compensation above the unit price bid in the schedule by reason of the location of the required drilling and grouting. It is expected that the required depth of holes will not exceed ______ feet. If any grout holes are required to be drilled to a depth greater than ______ feet, payment therefor will be made as provided in the section in these specifications for "Changes."

*[Pilot grouting at the ______ site was accomplished in ______(year) under Specifications ______ at locations and with results shown on the drawings. Available data on the pilot grouting is contained in a report entitled [46](______________). The data contained in this report are made available for information purposes only, and it shall be expressly understood that the Government will not be responsible for any interpretations, deductions, or conclusions drawn therefrom by the contractor. Copies of this report may be obtained by request to the Bureau of Reclamation, Attention: Code D-1310, PO Box 25007, Denver, CO 80225.]

*[It is anticipated that grouting the foundation of the dam will require more than average time and grout quantities, and that considerable experimentation will be required to develop satisfactory procedures for drilling and grouting. The contractor shall schedule his operations to allow for these contingencies and provide ample time for drilling and grouting. The contractor shall be entitled to no additional allowance above the price bid in the schedule by reason of interference or delay to other phases of the work caused by drilling and grouting operations, including any necessary experimentation which is required to develop satisfactory procedures.]

Drilling and grouting shall be accomplished

[45]Add other areas in which drilling and grouting will be done, if any.

[46]Include complete description of report, including specifications and contract numbers.

*Delete or revise as applicable.

through a standard pipe placed into the concrete or formation to the minimum distances shown on the drawings. Blanket grouting of rock abutments of the dam foundation, where directed, and the upstream and downstream rows of curtain grout holes shall be done through nipples set in holes drilled in the rock abutments. The pipe and installation of the pipe shall be in accordance with the provisions of section G.58.

The approximate location, spacing, direction, and depth of the grout holes are shown on the drawings. However, the actual location, spacing direction, and depth of each grout hole will depend upon the nature of the rock as disclosed by the foundation excavation and drilling, results of water tests, and/or the results of the actual grouting; and shall be as directed by the Contracting Officer. The order in which the holes are drilled and the manner in which each hole is drilled and grouted, the proportions of cement and water used in grout, type and quantity of admixtures used (if any), time of grouting, pressures used in grouting, and all other details of the grouting operations shall be as directed by the Contracting Officer. Each grout hole shall be as directed by the Contracting Officer, and shall be water tested and grouted in sections or stages located between depths in the hole best suited to treat the geologic defects of the foundation, as determined by the Contracting Officer.

*[Prior to drilling and grouting the dam foundation within 100 feet of the centerline of the outlet works, the tunnel and gate chamber shall be lined for a minimum of 100 feet upstream and downstream from the centerline of the gate chamber, and grouting around the gate chamber and 20 feet upstream and downstream from the centerline of the gate chamber shall be completed.]

*[During foundation grouting operations, the contractor shall be required to periodically record elevations of reference points along the grout cap. The Contracting Officer will determine the required recording intervals during the period of foundation grouting operations. A copy of the recorded elevations, reference point locations, and date of measurement shall be submitted to the Contracting Officer at the time of recording. Grouting operations which lift or otherwise distort the foundation will not be allowed.]

*Delete or revise as applicable.

[47][In the dam embankment foundation above elevation ______ and below elevation ______ between stations ______ and ______ where multiple-row curtians are required, they shall consist of primary rows that are then closed with secondary rows. The number of rows typically will be three. The rows shall be drilled and grouted in the order of the downstream row, first; the upstream row, second; and the middle or closure row last. Drilling and grouting operations in the second and third row on the abutments shall not be initiated until all grouting operations within ______ feet in the preceding row are complete. Between stations ______ and ______, drilling and grouting operations in preceding rows shall be at least ______ feet apart.]

[47][Where multiple rows of grout holes are used, the final spacing of the upstream and downstream row shall be ______ feet in abutment sections above elevation ______, and ______ feet between stations ______ and ______. Along the total length of the grout cap row, intermediate holes shall be drilled and grouted with such final spacing as grouting results show to be necessary to close out the curtain.]

Where practical, each grout hole shall be drilled to its full depth and grouted in stages from the bottom of the hole. Whenever required, due to 50 percent or more water drill loss or due to hole caving and rock jointing, the drilling and grouting shall be performed in successive stages from the collar of the hole downward, such operations consisting in each case of: drilling hole to a limited depth; washing out hole; seating a packer just above the section to be grouted; water testing and grouting that section; cleaning out grout hole by washing or other suitable means before grout in the hole has set sufficiently to require redrilling; allowing grout surrounding grout hole to attain its initial set, drilling hole to an additional depth; and thus successively drilling and grouting the hole at various depths within the stages until the required depth of hole is completely drilled and grouted, all as determined by the Contracting Officer. Redrilling required because of the contractor's failure to clean out a hole before the grout has set shall be performed at the contractor's expense. When grout has been allowed to set in a hole by direction of the Contracting Of-

[47]Delete or revise as required. Where the need for grouting is assumed to be minimal and the grouting is primarily exploratory, provisions for expansion of the grouting to a multiple row curtain where the take in the first grout is greater than anticipated should be made.

ficer, the required redrilling will be paid for at the rate of 50 percent of the unit price per linear foot bid in the schedule for drilling grout holes in stage between depths of 0 and 30 feet, regardless of depth. No additional allowance above the unit prices bid in the schedule for drilling grout holes in stage and hookups to grout holes and connections will be made on account of the requirement for cleaning out holes before further drilling or on account of moving of equipment that may be necessary due to the requirement for such successive stage drilling and grouting.

After holes in an area have been drilled and grouted, it may be found necessary to drill and grout additional holes. In this event, holes shall be drilled through concrete grout cap, if necessary, and into the underlying formation in such locations and to such depths as may be directed. No allowance above the unit prices bid in the schedule will be made for the drilling and grouting of such holes nor for the expense of moving equipment to other locations and returning to a previously drilled area.

All foundation grouting, including the formation around tunnels, shall be completed prior to constructing drains and prior to placing concrete structures, except placing concrete in cutoffs and tunnels wtihin ______ feet of the drains or concrete structures.

Dam embankment foundation grouting shall be performed prior to placing adjoining zone 1 embankment within ______ feet in elevation measured from the collar of the hole being grouted.

Drilling and pressure grouting the formation surrounding tunnels, gate chambers, adit, and shafts shall be done after placing of concrete linings a minimum of ______ feet ahead of the pressure grouting operations. Furthermore, placement of backfill grout shall be completed for all concrete lined sections within a distance of ______ feet ahead of foundation pressure grouting operations.

The joints between first- and second-stage concrete in the river outlet works intake structure and gate chamber shall be grouted after the second-stage concrete has set and cooled to the satisfaction of the Contracting Officer.

G.57. *Drilling Foundation Grout Holes.*—(a) *General.*—Grout holes shall be drilled into the foundations as described in section G.56. The requirements as to location, depth, spacing, and direction of the holes are approximate and subject to revision during the drilling, testing, and grouting. It is expected that the required depth of holes will not exceed ______ feet.

The holes shall be drilled with rotary-type drills, and the use of "rod dope," grease, or other lubricants on the drill rods or in the grout holes will not be permitted, except that an approved neutral liquid soap may be added to the drill water. Drilling with percussion-type drills will not be permitted, except for those portions of the grout holes which are drilled for setting the grout pipe. Drilling equipment and techniques shall be such as to minimize causing a hole to cave or become oversize. Drill water shall be clean, clear water. The minimum diameter of each grout hole shall be not less than that produced by the commercial standard ______-size drill bit.

Unless otherwise directed, the first grout holes within each pattern shall be spaced widely and they shall be drilled, cleaned, and grouted before intermediate holes within the pattern are drilled, cleaned, and grouted. Using this procedure, the drilling, cleaning, and grouting of all holes shall be completed with such final spacing of holes as the grouting results show to be necessary. After holes in a region have been drilled, cleaned, and grouted, and as the construction work progresses, the condition of the surrounding foundations or the development of leaks may require that additional holes be drilled, cleaned, and grouted. No allowance above the unit prices bid in the schedule will be made for drilling such holes or for the expense of moving equipment to other operations and returning to a previously drilled area.

Where practical, each grout hole shall be drilled to its full depth, cleaned, and grouted in stages up from the bottom of the hole. Where necessary because of substantial drill water loss, rock jointing, and/or type of material encountered during the drilling, the grout hole shall be drilled, cleaned, and grouted in successive operations by stages down from the collar of the hole. The method of grouting, stage up or stage down, shall be as directed by the Contracting Officer. Where stage-down grouting is directed, redrilling required because of the contractor's failure to clean out a hole before the grout has set shall be performed at the contractor's expense: *Provided*, that where the grout has been allowed to set by direction of the Contracting Officer, the required redrilling, regardless of depth, will be paid for at the rate of 50 percent of the unit price per linear foot bid in the schedule for drilling grout holes in stage between depths of 0 and 30 feet.

When drilling of each hole or stage of a hole has been completed, clean water shall be circulated through the hole until it is flushed free of drill cuttings. The hole shall then be temporarily capped or otherwise suitably protected to prevent the hole from becoming clogged or obstructed due to caving, or the contractor's failure to protect the hole before it is grouted, and shall be opened by and at the expense of the contractor.

A minimum of ______ NX-size grout curtain check holes up to ______ feet in depth will be required following completion of the grout curtain to check the adequacy of grouting. The location, angle, and depth of these holes shall be as directed by the Contracting Officer and as shown on the drawings. These holes shall be drilled, cleaned, water tested, and grouted in accordance with the requirements for foundation grout holes.

(b) *Measurement and Payment.*—Measurement, for payment, for drilling grout holes, including check holes, into the foundation will be made on the actual depth, up to depth directed, of grout holes drilled into the foundation or concrete, excluding any concrete or grout in embedded pipe, at the direction of the Contracting Officer. Stage depths of drilling grout holes will be measured from the collar of the hole at the exposed surface of the formation or concrete.

Except as otherwise provided for drilling ring and crown grout holes, redrilling after stage down grouting, and for furnishing and placing metal pipe and fittings for foundation grouting, payment for drilling grout holes will be made at the applicable unit price per linear foot bid in the schedule for drilling grout holes into foundation in stages between the depths specified in the schedule, which unit prices shall include the cost of furnishing all labor, materials, tools, and equipment required for drilling the holes, maintaining the holes free from obstructions until grouted, and all incidental work connected therewith.

No allowance above the unit prices bid in the schedule for drilling grout holes in stages will be made because of the requirements for interrupting the drilling of holes to permit grouting, for cleaning out holes before further drilling, or for any amount of moving of equipment that may be necessary due to such successive stage grouting.

G.58. *Pipe for Foundation Grouting.*—

(a) *General.*—Standard black steel pipe for grout connections shall be embedded in concrete or set in holes drilled into the concrete or foundation at the locations shown on the drawings and where directed by the Contracting Officer. Pipes for grouting shall also be set over springs, cracks, or crevices in the foundation, faults, or other foundation defects, where directed. Grout pipes shall be left in place until the Contracting Officer has accepted the grouting as complete. All grout pipes beneath earthfill portions of the embankment shall be cut off flush with the foundation or concrete prior to placement of earthfill.

(b) *Materials*:

(1) *Pipe.*—Standard weight, schedule 40, black steel pipe conforming to the requirements of ASTM A120.

(2) *Pipe Fittings.*—Malleable iron or steel fittings conforming to the requirements of ASTM A197 or A234, respectively.

(c) *Installing Pipe.*—The size and length of the grout pipe and the depth of the holes for setting pipe for foundation grouting shall be as shown on the drawings, or directed. The pipe shall be cut, threaded as necessary, fabricated as required, and placed by the contractor. The grout pipes set in holes drilled into the concrete or formation shall be grouted in place. All material required for grouting the pipes in place shall be furnished by the contractor. All pipe and fittings shall be cleaned thoroughly of all dirt, grease, grout, and mortar immediately before being placed. The pipe and fittings shall be carefully assembled and placed, shall be held firmly in position, and protected from damage until after the grout has set. Care shall be taken to avoid clogging or obstructing the pipes before being grouted, and any pipe that becomes clogged or obstructed from any cause shall be cleaned out or replaced by and at the expense of the contractor.

All pipe and fittings, oakum, lead wool, grout, temporary supports, and other materials required for the work described in this section shall be furnished by the contractor.

(d) *Measurement and Payment.*—Measurement, for payment, will be made only for the weight of pipe and fittings actually installed and left in place as directed by the Contracting Office. Payment for furnishing and placing metal pipe and fittings for foundation grouting will be made at the unit price per pound bid therefor in the schedule, which unit price shall include the cost of providing temporary supports, furnishing and placing all calking materials, furnishing and placing all grout materials required to install the pipe, cutting pipes flush with foundation or concrete, and protecting the pipe from damage and clogging. No additional allowance above the unit price bid in the schedule will be made on account of the varying size, length, or number of pipes required.

G.59. *Hookups to Grout Holes.*—

(a) *General.*—Each drilled hole for grouting shall be hooked onto for pressure grouting. Connections to springs, cracks, or crevices in the formation, or other foundation defects, and connections to existing exploratory holes, where required by Contracting Officer, will be considered as hookups to grout holes.

(b) *Measurement and Payment.*—Measurement, for payment, of hookups to grout holes will be made on the number of each *[stage (packer setting)] hooked onto for the purpose of injecting water and/or grout into a grout hole, will be limited to one hookup per stage, will include only those hookups actually made at the direction of the Contracting Officer, and, where packers are required, will be limited to stages where the packers are seated until the stage is completed.

Payment for hookups to grout holes will be made at the *(fixed) unit price per hookup bid *(stated) therefor in the schedule.

The requirement for stage-down hookups will be determined by the Contracting Officer, and the contractor will be entitled to no additional allowance above the unit price *(set) (bid) in the schedule for hookups to grout holes by reason of any amount or none of the work for this item being required.

G.60. *Pressure Grouting *(Foundations and Outlet Works).*—(a) *General.*—Each drilled hole and grout connection for pressure grouting *(foundations and outlet works) as described in section G.56 shall have grout composed of cement and water forced into it under pressure. All pressure grouting shall be performed in the presence of an authorized representative of the Contracting Officer.

*[In areas where cavities or fissures are encountered or where the quantity of grout injected becomes excessive, sand bulking materials or calcium chloride may be required in the grout mixture. If sand bulking materials are used, an admixture of bentonite may be required as an ingredient of the grout. Where bentonite is used as an admixture, it shall not exceed 2 percent, by weight, of the cement.]

*[Calcium chloride, where required, shall be furnished by the contractor, and payment will be made for the quantities actually used, as directed by the Contracting Officer, and will be made at the invoice cost, free on board damsite, plus 20 percent.]

*[The requirements for sand and calcium chloride will be determined by the Contracting Officer for conditions encountered during the grouting operation, and the contractor shall be entitled to no compensation above the unit price per cubic foot bid in the schedule for furnishing and handling sand bulking materials by reason of any amounts or no sand being required.]

The proportions of cement and water or cement, sand, and water used in mixing the grout; time of grouting; pressure used for grouting; and all other details of the grouting operations shall be as determined by the Contracting Officer. It is anticipated that the water-cement ratio of the grout mixture may vary from 5:1 to 0.8:1 by volume.

Adequate lighting of the grouting areas shall be furnished and maintained by the contractor during any night operations, and the lighting shall be subject to the approval of the Contracting Officer. Communication facilities, as specified in subsection (b), between the grout plant and the holes being grouted shall be furnished by the contractor when required by the Contracting Officer.

*[No grouting of foundation holes shall be permitted within 100 feet of embankment materials, as measured along the slope of the foundation.]

*[Foundation grouting shall be completed to 100 feet on either side of the centerline of the river outlet works (and spillway) prior to construction of the river outlet works 100 feet on either side of the grout curtain.]

*[Grouting holes from within all tunnels, shafts, and gate chambers shall be initiated only after a minimum of 10 days following the placement of the tunnel, shaft, and gate chamber concrete, and after all backfill grouting has been completed.]

(b) *Materials.*—The contractor shall furnish all materials for grout. The materials shall be in accordance with the following:

(1) *Cement.*—The cement shall meet the requirements of ASTM C 150 for *(Type I, Type II,or Type V) cement, *(low alkali), and will be sampled and tested by the Government. Mill certificates for all cement for grouting delivered to the worksite

*Delete or revise as applicable.

shall be furnished by the contractor.

(2) *Water.*—Water shall meet the requirements of water for concrete as specified in section G.77.

(3) *Sand.*—Sand for bulking material shall be clean and well graded and, when tested using standard sieves, shall conform to the following limits:

Sieve No.	Individual percent, by weight, retained on sieve
8	0
16	0 to 5
30	15 to 40
50	50 to 80
100	70 to 90
200	95 to 100

(4) *Bentonite.*—Bentonite shall be a suitable, commercially processed, powdered bentonite such as Volclay, by the American Colloid Co., 5100 Suffield Court, Skokie, Illinois 60076; Big Horn Brand, produced by the Wyo-Ben Products Co., P.O. Box 1979, Billings, Montana 59103; Wyo-Gel, produced by the Federal Bentonite Co., 1019 Jericho Road, Aurora, Illinois 60538; or equal.

(5) *Calcium Chloride.*—Calcium chloride shall be a suitable commercial product, approved by the Contracting Officer.

(6) *Communication Facilities.*—The communication facilities shall be a contractor-furnished page/party telephone system between the grout plant and/or mixing plant and the holes being grouted. The system shall consist of Gai-Tronics Model 490: nine phones in weatherproof Lexan cases interconnected with No. 14 AWG twisted pair interconnect cable, as manufactured by Gai-Tronics Corp., P.O. Box 31, Reading, Pennsylvania 19603, or equal.

(7) *Pressure Gages.*—All pressure gages for use in grouting shall be glycerin filled, plain case, with pressure indicated in pounds per square inch, as manufactured by Marsh Instrument Co., a Unit of General Signal, P.O. Box 1011, Skokie, Illinois 60076, or equal. The rating of each pressure gage shall not be more than three times the pressure rating at which the grout is anticipated to be pumped.

(c) *Plant and Equipment.*—All plant and equipment required to mix and pump the grout into the various stages of the grout holes shall be furnished by the contractor. The apparatus for mixing and placing grout, including circulating line and fittings, shall be of a type and size approved by the Contracting Officer and shall be capable of effectively mixing and stirring the grout and forcing it into the grout holes or grout connections in a continuous, uninterrupted flow at any specified pressure up to a maximum of 200 lb/in^2. Water supply to the mixer shall be adequate at all times to provide the required pumping rate.

If bulk cement is used, the grout plant shall be equipped with such measuring equipment as is necessary to measure the amount of cement placed in grout. Such equipment shall be subject to the approval of the Contracting Officer.

The mixer shall have a minimum volume of 17 cubic feet, and shall be of the high-speed colloidal type equipped with a high-speed, diffuser-type centrifugal mixing pump operating at 1,500 to 2,000 r/min during mixing, that delivers 300 gallons per minute at 60 lb/in^2; and provided with an accurate meter, reading to tenths of a cubic foot, for controlling the amount of mixing water used in the grout. In addition to the grout mixer, a holdover mechanical agitator tank similar in volume to the mixer shall be provided. Suitable provisions shall be made for passing the grout through a standard No. 16 sieve as it is discharged from the mixer. Pump rating curves and complete mixer details, including photographs of the proposed mixing equipment, shall be submitted to the Contracting Officer for approval 10 days prior to use. The Contracting Officer shall have the right to require the contractor to make changes in the equipment which the Contracting Officer determines necessary to make the equipment perform satisfactorily during grouting operations without additional cost to the Government. All grout shall be pumped with a helical-screw, rotor-type pump that produces uniform flow without pulsation. The pump shall have a minimum capacity of 35 gal/min at a pressure of 200 lb/in^2. A standby grout pump shall be included as part of the grout plant.

The grouting equipment shall be maintained in a manner satisfactory to the Contracting Officer and shall be capable of continuous and efficient performance during any grouting operation. The arrangement of the grouting equipment shall be such as to provide a supply and return line from the grout pump to the grout hole.

A manifold consisting of a system of valves and a pressure gage, as shown on drawing ______, shall be located in the line at the collar of the hole to permit continuous circulation and accurate control monitoring of grouting pressure, bleeding, and regulation of flow into the grout hole. The minimum size of the supply line and manifold including valves and fittings shall be from 1 to 1½ inches inside diameter. A pressure gage shall also be placed in the discharge grout pump line at the grout pump. Pressure gages shall be equipped with gage savers when pumping grout, and the gages, with the attached gage savers, shall be checked frequently to assure their accuracy. Broken glass faces of gages shall be replaced immediately. An accurately calibrated, high-precision master gage shall be provided by the contractor for periodic checking of the accuracy of all gages used in the grouting operations. No more than six manifolds shall be operated at any one time.

*[The elevation of the grout pump above the collar of the hole being grouted shall not be exceeded by more than 20 feet, where practicable, to prevent pressure head in the line from exceeding the allowable grouting pressure at the collar of the hole.] The pump shall not be placed more than 200 feet away from hole being grouted.

The grout supply pipes and packers shall be furnished by the contractor. The contractor shall have available at all times, a sufficient number and variety of packers to accomplish the grouting. The packers shall consist of pneumatic tubes or expandable rings of rubber, leather, or other suitable material attached to the end of the grout supply pipe. The packers shall be designed so that they can be expanded to seal the drill holes at the specified elevations and, when expanded, shall be capable of withstanding, without leakage, water pressure equal to the maximum grout pressures to be used for the entire period of time that the packer is in use. The supply pipe to the packer and pipe through the packer shall have a minimum inside diameter of ¾ inch, except where sanded mixes are used. For sanded mixes, the minimum inside diameter of the packer pipe and pipe through the packer shall be 1 inch. The amount of packer grouting that will be required will depend upon the conditions disclosed by the drilling of the grout holes.

(d) *Water Testing and Washing Grout Holes.*—Prior to grouting, each stage shall be tested with clean water under continuous pressure: *Provided*, that each test may be subdivided into subintervals in which each interval shall be tested at different but continuous pressures. Different pressures will be required for different stages of holes to a maximum of 200 lb/in².

Sufficient water shall be made available to develop the desired pressure, and pressure gages and watermeters shall be provided to measure the amount of water pumped and the pressure during the test. Pumps, piping, gages, and meters shall be of a type and capacity approved by the Contracting Officer.

The majority of the water tests will be for periods of 5, 10, and 15 minutes per stage; however, periods of up to 20 minutes may be used to test the rate of take or to the wash stage that intersect rock crevices, seams, or faults containing clay or other washable materials.

If more extensive washing of grout holes is required, such as washing alternately with water and air under pressure to eject materials from adjacent holes, the contractor will be paid for such washing with water and air under provisions of the section in these specifications for "Changes."

(e) *Grouting Procedures.*—Where practical, each grout hole shall be drilled to its full depth and grouted in stages from the bottom of the hole. Where necessary because of substantial drill water loss, rock joining and/or type of material encountered during the drilling, the grout hole shall be drilled, cleaned, and grouted in successive operations by stages down from the collar of the hole. *[Where caving of a grout hole is persistent and the hole does not remain open for grouting, grouting through flush-coupled grout pipe or drill rods extending to the bottom of the drilled stage with a stuffing box at the collar of the hole, may be required. As grouting through the pipe progreses, the pipe shall be withdrawn slowly to prevent loss of the pipe.] The method of grouting, stage up or stage down, shall be as directed by the Contracting Officer. [48][The contractor is cautioned that the (*insert geological description*) has soft zones that may require special packers and great care to prevent washing fines from sides of drill hole.

Where stage-up grouting of a hole is directed by the Contracting Officer, the grouting shall be performed by attaching a packer to the end of the grout supply pipe; lowering grout supply pipe into hole to

*Delete or revise as applicable.

[48]To be used when geology identifies material of this nature; otherwise, delete.

top of bottom stage that is required to be grouted at a given pressure; grouting at required pressure, allowing packer to remain in place until there is no back pressure; withdrawing grout supply pipe and packer to top of next higher stage that is required to be grouted; and thus successively grouting the hole in stages at the specified grouting pressures until entire hole is completely grouted.

Wherever stage-down grouting is necessary, as determined by the Contracting Officer, the drilling, cleaning, and grouting shall be performed in successive operations consisting in each case of drilling the hole to a limited depth, water testing and grouting that section, cleaning out grout hole by washing or other suitable means before grout in hole has set sufficiently to require redrilling, allowing grout surrounding grout hole to attain its initial set, drilling hole to an additional depth, grouting by seating a packer near bottom of previously grouted stage; and thus successively drilling, cleaning, and grouting the hole in stages at various depths until required depth of hole is completely drilled, cleaned and grouted.

*[Whether grout holes are grouted by stage-up or stage-down methods, each hole shall be grouted in stages to best treat the geology and defects of the foundation, as determined by the Contracting Officer: *Provided*, that the maximum stage between 0 and _______ feet and _______ feet of grout hole depth shall be _______ feet, and between _______ and _______ feet of grout hole depth shall be _______ feet.] Once grouting of any stage has started, grouting of that stage shall continue until grouting of that stage is completed, unless otherwise approved by the Contracting Officer.

Pressures as high as practicable but which, as determined by the Contracting Officer, are safe against formation or concrete displacement shall be used in the grouting. Different grouting pressures will be required for grouting different sections of most of the grout holes. In general, the maximum pressures as measured at the collar of the hole shall not exceed 1 lb/in^2 per foot of depth, measured normal from the ground surface to the packer: *Provided*, that the top stage shall be grouted at a maximum of 10 lb/in^2 greater than any initial back pressure.

*[The pressure at the collar shall gradually be added so that the maximum pressure may not exceed 15 lb/in^2 within the first 5 minutes and shall be raised gradually to the maximum pressure within the following 20 minutes only if no leaks or rock movement have occurred.]

If, during the grouting of any hole, grout is found to flow from adjacent grout holes or grout connections in sufficient quantity to interfere seriously with the grouting operation or to cause appreciable loss of grout, such connections shall be capped temporarily. Where such capping is not essential, as determined by the Contracting Officer, ungrouted holes shall be left open to facilitate the escape of air and water as the grout is forced into other holes. Before grout has set, the grout pump shall be connected to adjacent capped holes and to other holes from which grout flow was observed, and grouting of all holes shall be completed at the pressures specified for grouting. When grouting is being done with packers, the pressure of the grout returning from any adjacent hole shall be measured by seating a packer in the adjacent hole immediately above where the grout is entering, and such pressures shall be kept below the allowable pressures for that stage of that hole. If, during the grouting of any hole, grout is found to flow from points in the foundation or any parts of the concrete structure, such flows or leaks shall be plugged or calked by the contractor as directed.

The grouting of any stage of any grout hole or grout connection may be discontinued, at the discretion of the Contracting Officer, after that stage or connection takes grout at the rate of less than 1 cubic foot of the grout mixture in 20 minutes if pressures of 50 lb/in^2 or less are being used, in 15 minutes if pressures between 50 and 100 lb/in^2 are being used, in 10 minutes if pressures between 100 and 200 lb/in^2 are being used, and in 5 minutes if pressures in excess of 200 lb/in^2 are being used. The grouting of any stage shall be discontinued, at the discretion of the Contracting Officer, when less than two bags of cement per hour are being injected when pumping continuously.

So far as practicable, full grouting pressures shall be maintained constantly during grout injections. As a safeguard against formation or concrete displacement, or while grout leaks are being calked, the Contracting Officer may require the reduction of the pumping pressure, or the discontinuance of pumping.

Where grout hole or grout connections take a large amount of grout, the Contracting Officer may

*Delete or revise as applicable.

require that pumping be done intermittently, waiting up to 16 hours between pumping periods to allow grout in the holes to set.

After grouting of holes or connections is completed, pressures shall be maintained using stopcocks or other suitable valve devices until grout has set sufficiently so that it will be retained in the holes or connections being grouted.

Grout not injected into the foundation within 2 hours after mixing shall be wasted, and no payment therefor will be made if, as determined by the Contracting Officer, such wasting was due to the contractor's negligence or equipment breakdown.

After completing the pressure grouting in an area, all grout holes shall be backfilled with a 1:1 grout mixture, by volume, by the tremie method. Backfill grout shall be placed by tremie pipe from the bottom of the hole to the top. No payment for hookups will be made for grout holes required to be backfilled by tremie.

(f) *Measurement and Payment.*—Measurement, for payment, for pressure grouting will be made on the basis of the number of bags of cement, and cubic feet of bulking materials (if required) measured separately, actually forced into the holes or grout connections at the direction of the Contracting Officer, or required to fill permanent pipes. In measuring bulking materials for payment, measurement will be made of the dry volume of the materials, measured in cubic feet, that is actually used in grouting at the direction of the Contracting Officer. One bag of cement will be considered as 94 pounds.

[49][Payment for pressure grouting foundations will be made at the unit price per bag bid therefor in the schedule.]

[49][The quantity of pressure grouting and rate of take in bags per pump hour are uncertain and cannot be accurately estimated. Accordingly, the quantity of pressure grouting stated in the schedule is solely for the purpose of comparison of bids, and the actual quantity may vary widely therefrom. Payment for pressure grouting foundations will be made at the unit price per bag bid therefor in the schedule regardless of the quantity actually injected with the following exceptions:

(1) An adjustment in the schedule price will be made for any stage of a grout hole that accepts grout continuously at the rate of five bags per pump hour or less for a period longer than 3 hours. Payment for bags injected after the 3-hour period will be made at two times the unit price per bag bid in the schedule for pressure grouting foundations provided the rate does not exceed five bags per hour until the stage is complete.

(2) If final average rate in bags per pump hour exceeds 18, the number of bags required to average 18 will be paid for at the unit price bid in the schedule for pressure grouting foundations and the number of bags in excess of the number required to average 18 will be paid for at the rate of 50 percent of the unit price bid in the schedule.]

[49][Progress payments will be based on the quantity actually placed and at the unit price per bag bid in the schedule for pressure grouting foundations including any adjustment under subsection (1). After foundation grouting is completed, the average rate of take in bags per pump hour will be determined by dividing the total number of bags for pressure grouting foundations by the total number of pump hours. The total number of pump hours will consist only of actual grout injection time in hours for all grout pumps. Any adjustment under subsection (2) will then be made.]

[49][Except as provided in this section, the contractor shall be entitled to no extra compensation above the unit price bid in the schedule by reason of increased or decreased quantity or of rate of take in bags per pump hour for pressure grouting.]

[49][The quantity of pressure grouting which will be required is uncertain and the actual quantity may vary widely from that given in the schedule. Accordingly, the quantity stated in the schedule for pressure grouting foundations is solely for the purpose of comparison of bids, and the contractor shall be entitled to no additional compensation by reason of increased or decreased final quantity of pressure grouting. The rate of grout take in bags per hour is also uncertain and may vary widely during grouting. Accordingly, the unit price per bag stated in the schedule will be used by the Government for the purpose of comparison of bids and in determining the actual (adjusted) unit price to be paid to the contractor for pressure grouting foundations.]

Payment for pressure grouting foundations will be made based on the actual rate of grout take in bags per hour during pressure grouting operations in accordance with the following scale:

[49]Select applicable method of payment.

Actual average grout injected in bags per hour	Adjusted unit price per bag
Up to 3.9	3.33 times schedule bid price
4.0 to 7.9	1.67 times schedule bid price
8.0 to 11.9	Schedule bid price
12.0 to 15.9	0.71 times schedule bid price
16.0 to 19.9	0.56 times schedule bid price
20.0 to 29.9	0.40 times schedule bid price
Over 30	0.33 times schedule bid price

[49][The adjusted unit price per bag that will be paid to the contractor for pressure grouting will be determined by the Contracting Officer for each hole grouted on the basis of the numer of hours of actual pumping time during grout injection for all stages of a hole measured to the nearest quarter of an hour and of the number of bags of cement and cubic feet of sand actually forced into all stages of the hole or grout connection. The above actual pumping time will not include periods of reseating packers which fail to seal, malfunctioning of grouting equipment, and slowdowns because of lack or shortage of grout materials such as water and cement. Any grout pumped during these periods will be paid for at 0.33 times the schedule bid price.]

Except as otherwise provided, the above payment for pressure grouting foundations shall include the entire cost of furnishing all labor, materials, tools, and equipment required for washing, grouting, and for calking surface leaks.

Measurement, for payment, for furnishing and handling cement for pressure grouting will be made on the number of bags of cement actually injected into the holes or grout connections, or required to fill permanent pipes at the direction of the Contracting Officer, and will include a reasonable amount for line waste, as determined by the Contracting Officer. One bag of cement will be considered as 94 pounds. Payment for furnishing and handling cement for pressure grouting will be made at the unit price per bag bid therefor in the schedule.

Measurement, for payment, for furnishing and handling sand bulking materials for pressure grouting will be made on the number of cubic feet, dry measurement, actually injected into the holes or grout connections. In measuring sand bulking materials for payment, the volume of 1 cubic foot of dry sand will be considered as ______ pounds. Payment for furnishing and handling sand bulking materials for pressure grouting will be made at the unit price per cubic foot bid therefor in the schedule.

The quantity of sand bulking material required, as shown in the schedule, may not represent the actual quantity used, and payment will be made only for the amounts actually used for the pressure and slush grouting at the direction of the Contracting Officer. Measurement, for payment, for furnishing and handling bentonite will be made of the number of cubic feet, dry measure, actually injected into the holes or grout connections. For measurement purposes, one cubic foot of bentonite will be equivalent to 50 pounds. Payment for furnishing and handling bentonite will be made at the unit price per cubic foot bid therefor in the schedule, which price shall include furnishing, transporting, handling, mixing, and all other related costs.

Payment for calcium chloride will be made for the quantities actually used in grout, as directed by the Contracting Officer, and will be made at the invoice cost plus 20 percent.

No payment will be made for grout or for cement used in grout lost due to improper anchorage of grout pipes or connections, rejected on account of improper mixing, or lost by leakage due to the failure of the contractor to calk surface leaks when directed by the Contracting Officer.

Measurement, for payment, for water tests in grout holes performed in accordance with the provisions of this section will be made of each water test made at the direction of the Contracting Officer. Payment for water tests in grout holes performed at the direction of the Contracting Officer will be made at the unit price per test bid in the schedule for water tests in grout holes.

G.61. *Slush Grouting Foundations.*—

(a) *General.*—The contractor shall supplement foundation pressure grouting by applying slush grouting to cracks, crevices, or broken or fractured portions of the foundation surface under the dam embankment zone(s) 1*(and 1A) and other areas as directed, including such portions of the foundation surface beneath the concrete grout *[(cap) (pad)]. Use of slush grouting shall be only at the direction of the Contracting Officer.

(b) *Materials.*—The slush grout shall be composed of neat cement grout or cement, sand, and water. The ratios of the materials may vary as directed by the Contracting Officer, but the ratio of

[49]Select applicable method of payment.

*Delete or revise as applicable.

sand to cement will not exceed 2 parts sand to 1 part cement. Adequate water shall be mixed thoroughly into the cement or cement and sand mixes to produce a workable mixture for proper placement as approved by the Contracting Officer. The grout mixture shall be prepared by mechanical mixer and shall be used within 30 minutes after mixing. Cement, water, and sand shall be as provided in sections G.75, G.77, and G.78, respectively.

(c) *Placement.*—Slush grout shall be used to fill foundation surface cracks, crevices, and fractures at locations as directed by the Contracting Officer. Slush grout shall not be used to cover exposed areas of the formation.

All joints, cracks, crevices, and fractures to be treated shall be thoroughly cleaned of all loose materials as provided in G.29(c)(3) and shall be wetted immediately prior to placement of the slush grout material. Placement of slush grouting shall be by brooming into all cracks, crevices, and fractures with a stiff-bristled broom or other approved method, but grout layers shall not be left on the foundation beyond the edge of the crack, crevice, or fracture.

Finished surfaces of slush grouting shall be left in a roughened, broomed finish to provide a satisfactory bonding surface to the embankment materials. Finished surfaces shall be cured in accordance with section G.91.

[49][(d) *Measurement and Payment.*—Measurement, for payment, of slush grouting will be made on the basis of the number of bags of cement actually placed at the direction of the Contracting Officer. Measurement, for payment, for cement used in slush grouting will be made of the number of bags of cement that are actually used in the slush grouting. One bag of cement will be considered as 94 pounds.]

[49][(d) *Measurement and Payment.*—Measurement, for payment, of slush grouting will be made of the total number of square yards covered by the slush grouting.]

[49][(d) *Measurement and Payment.*—Measurement, for payment, for slush grouting will be made of the actual volume, measured in cubic yards, of slush grouting that is placed as specified. The volume of slush grout placed will be determined by batch count.]

[49]Select applicable method of payment.

Payment for furnishing and placing slush grouting will be made at the unit price per cubic yard or square yard bid therefor in the schedule, which price shall include all costs of materials, except cement, and the equipment and labor for cleaning, wetting, mixing, placing, and all other work required to perform the slush grouting work as specified.

Payment for cement used in the slush grouting will be made at the unit price per bag bid in the schedule for furnishing and handling cement for slush grouting.

G.62. *Dental Concrete.*—(a) *General.*—The contractor shall place dental concrete in exposed areas of broken, fractured, or sheared portions of the dam foundation surface under the dam embankment *[zone (1, 1A, and 2)]; the spillway structures; and at other locations as directed by the Contracting Officer. Dental concrete shall be used in areas too large to be satisfactorily treated by slush grouting and volumes too small to be satisfactorily filled with contiguous compacted embankment as determined by the Contracting Officer.

(b) *Materials.*—Dental concrete shall be lean concrete conforming to the applicable provisions of sections G.73 through G.89.

(c) *Placing Dental Concrete.*—Where, as determined by the Contracting Officer, it is not practicable to excavate local overhanging rock faces or rock faces steeper than 0.5 horizontal to 1 vertical without detrimental blasting or excessive material excavation, the rock faces shall be solidly faced with dental concrete to provide abutment contact slopes not steeper than 0.5 horizontal to 1 vertical. Formwork shall be used at locations specified by the Contracting Officer.

*[All dental concrete shall be placed following the completion of curtain grouting, unless specifically approved by the Contracting Officer.]

*[Where soft zones or areas exist in the surface of formations, they shall be excavated to the extent directed and backfilled with dental concrete. Soft zones are defined as those zones in the ________ formation which can be hand-excavated with a shovel. Placement of the dental concrete may require the use of form work. Form work shall be used at locations specified by the Contracting Officer.]

*[Dental concrete shall also be used to fill buried river channels and potholes found upon excavation

*Delete or revise as applicable.

of the dam embankment foundation and cofferdam trench to the extent directed by the Contracting Officer.]

Designated voids shall be properly excavated and cleaned of all loose materials as approved by the Contracting Officer. Open joints, shear zones, and fractured areas shall be cleaned as provided in G.29(c)(3). Dental concrete shall be placed as required to form a tight, unfractured foundation surface against which the dam embankment or concrete structure may be placed.

Finished surfaces of dental concrete shall be left in a roughened, broomed finish to provide a satisfactory bonding surface for the embankment materials.

(d) *Measurement and Payment.*—Measurement, for payment, of dental concrete will be made of the actual volume of concrete placed as determined by batch count.

Payment for dental concrete will be made at the unit price per cubic yard bid therefor in the schedule, which unit price shall include the cost of form work, if required, and the cost of all labor and materials required in the concrete construction, except that payment for furnishing and handling cement will be made at the unit price per ton bid therefor in the schedule.

Costs of the excavation, including the cleaning of the excavation of all loose materials, shall be included in the *(applicable) item in the schedule for excavation for dam embankment foundation *(and excavation for structures).

The quantity of dental concrete is uncertain, and the contractor shall be entitled to no additional allowance above the price bid in the schedule by reason of increased or decreased quantities required.

F. CONCRETE SPECIFICATIONS

G.63. *Introduction.*—(a) *General.*—Two different concrete specifications are included herein, one for small quantities of concrete where the structures are relatively simple, and one for more complex work requiring larger quantities of concrete where the structures are such that more detailed coverage of the work and the manner in which the work is to be done is desirable. The specification sections, included herein for work requiring detailed control, do not include all the requirements that would be needed for a mass concrete dam. Normally, additional investigations and specification requirements pertaining to the design of concrete mixes and concrete construction procedures are required for a mass concrete dam.

When a mass concrete dam is to be constructed, it may be desirable to require, prior to installation, review and advance approval of the contractor's plants, equipment, and construction procedures. This would particularly apply to the plants and equipment for processing, handling, transporting, storing, and proportioning concrete ingredients; and for mixing, transporting, and placing concrete. In cases where such is considered desirable, the contractor should be required to submit drawings to and for approval by the Contracting Officer, showing proposed plant arrangement, and furnish a description of the equipment he proposes to use in sufficient detail that an adequate review can be accomplished. The drawings and descriptions should be submitted in sufficient time before plant erection to permit a reasonable time for review, and for any alterations to the plant if inadequacies are noted. Where specific types of equipment or specific procedures are provided in the specifications, the contractor should be permitted to use alternative procedures or types of equipment if such are demonstrated to the satisfaction of the Contracting Officer that equivalent results would be obtained. Approval by the Contracting Officer of the contractor's plants and equipment or their operation, or of any construction procedure, should not be cause to waive or modify the requirements for quality of materials of the finished work.

The specifications are written on the basis that the concrete mixes to be used in the work will be designed and controlled by the purchaser (refered to in the specifications as the Government and/or Contracting Officer) within the maximum water-cement ratio and slump limitations specified, the limitations for quality and grading of aggregates, and the limitations for the other materials as specified, except that for the small job specifications, cement content of the concrete may be specified in lieu of a maximum water-cement ratio requirement. The percentages of sand and each size coarse ag-

*Delete or revise as applicable.

gregate to be used in the mixes are also determined by the purchaser. The quality limitations shown in the specifications for sand and coarse aggregate are considered standard limits. These limits may be reduced when only substandard materials are available within reasonable hauling distance and provided it has been determined by tests of concrete made with such aggregate that durable and good strength concrete can be produced. Under these specifications as written, the quantity of cement used in small jobs can be included in the cost of the concrete or paid for separately; for the large job specifications, the quantity of cement used in the work must be paid for separately. In applying these specifications, the purchaser may have his own engineering personnel or arrange with a separate engineering organization to accomplish testing of proposed aggregates, the design of mixes, and the handling of the control thereof throughout the life of the construction contract. However, if the purchaser desires to have the mix design and control the responsibility of the contractor, the specifications should be revised to provide for such. In this case, the specifications should include specific design compressive strength requirements (such as 4,000 lb/in^2) for the concrete. The mixes should be designed to take into consideration the need for increased average compressive strengths at 28-days' age of standard 6- by 12-inch test cylinders to satisfy the 28-days' age design compressive strength requirements. Criteria generally accepted in Bureau of Reclamation work require that the compressive strength of 90 percent of the test cylinders representing structural concrete be greater than the design compressive strength, see the Bureau's *Concrete Manual*[2].

(b) *Ready-Mixed Concrete.*—The specifications included herein permit the manufacture of concrete from a central plant at the jobsite, by use of concrete from ready-mix plants and by use of truck mixers. The more complete specifications contain specific provisions for a central batching and mixing plant for concrete manufactured at the jobsite or for supplying specification concrete from a ready-mix plant using truck mixers.

(c) *Reference Specifications.*—The materials and procedures that are specified by reference to Federal Specifications, ASTM Standard Specifications, other standard specifications, or codes should be in compliance with the latest editions or revisions thereof in effect on the date bids are received or award of contract is made, whichever is appropriate. Specifications for specific work should contain stipulations providing for such conditions.

1. Concrete Specifications for Small Jobs

G.64. ***Source.***—The following sections have been prepared from guide specifications normally used by the Bureau of Reclamation for less than 100 cubic yards of concrete.

G.65. ***Materials.***—The contractor shall furnish all materials for use in concrete, including cementitious materials, water, sand, coarse aggregate, and specified admixtures; and shall furnish all reinforcing bars [50](and fabric) and materials for curing concrete. Pozzolan, as specified, is an acceptable partial replacement for cement and, if used, shall replace 20 percent, by weight, of cement. Thirty days prior to placement of concrete, the contractor shall submit to the Government the name and manufacturer of each cementitious material, admixture, curing compound, and aggregate source. The Government reserves the right to require submission of manufacturer's test data and certification of compliance with specifications, and to require submission of samples of all concrete materials for testing prior to or during use in concrete.

(a) *Cement.*—Portland cement shall meet the requirements of ASTM designation: C150 for [51](type ——) portland cement [52](except that the maximum percent of tricalcium aluminate allowable in type 1 cement shall be 15 percent), and shall meet the low-alkali and false-set limitations specified therein. The low-alkali limitation for cement may be waived on request if the sand and coarse aggregate do not contain objectionable quantities, as determined by the Contracting Officer, of potentially alkali-reactive particles defined by mortar bar tests and complete petrographic analyses of the proposed aggregate. If the contractor requests waiver of the low-alkali limitation, he will be required to submit petrographic analyses satisfactory to the Contracting Officer unless such analyses have been performed by the Bureau of Reclamation. The cement shall be free from lumps and contamination by water and other foreign matter when used in concrete.

[50]Delete if fabric is not involved.
[51]Determine type of cement to be used.
[52]Include only when type I cement is specified.

(b) *Pozzolan.*—Pozzolan shall meet the requirements of ASTM C618 for class N, F, or C with the following additional requirements:

(1) The maximum percent of sulfur trioxide shall be 4.0 percent for classes F and C.

(2) The maximum percent loss on ignition shall be 8.0 percent for class N and 2.5 percent for classes F and C.

(3) The pozzolanic activity index with lime shall be determined using 2-inch cubes, and the minimum strength at 7 days shall be 900 lb/in^2.

(4) Unless the contractor selects aggregates which are not potentially alkali reactive, pozzolan shall be tested for reduction of mortar expansion at 14 days as specified for class N pozzolan under the optional physical requirements in ASTM C618; however, the cement used in the test shall be low alkali. For the pozzolan to be acceptable, it shall result in an expansion reduction of zero percent or greater when compared to the control test.

(5) Pozzolan shall not decrease the sulfate resistance of concrete. "Lassenite SR" pozzolan, as marketed by Lassenite Industries, Inc., 1475 Terminal Way, Reno NV 89502, and "Sun" pozzolan, as produced by Oregon Portland Cement Co., 111 Southeast Madison, Portland OR 97214, are class N pozzolans that have been found not to detract from sulfate resistance. Class F and C pozzolans will not detract from sulfate resistance if they have an "R" factor less than 2.5. The "R" factor is defined as "(C-5)/F, where C is the calcium oxide content of the pozzolan in percent and F is the ferric oxide content in percent."

(c) *Water.*—Water shall be free from objectionable quantities of silt, organic matter, salts, and other impurities.

(d) *Sand and Coarse Aggregate.*—Sand and coarse aggregate shall consist of clean, hard, dense, durable, uncoated rock fragments that are free from injurious amounts of dirt, organic matter, and other deleterious substances. Sand and coarse aggregate shall meet all requirements of ASTM C33. Coarse aggregate shall conform to ASTM C33 gradings for either size No. 467 (1½ inch to No. 4 United States Standard sieve), or size No. 57 (1 inch to No. 4).

(e) *Air-Entraining Admixture.*—The air-entraining admixture shall conform to ASTM C260: *Provided,* that an air-entraining admixture used with a type F or G chemical admixture shall be a neutralized vinsol resin formulation.

(f) *Chemical Admixture.*—The contractor may use chemical admixtures which conform to ASTM C494, type A, D, F, or G. Chemical admixtures that will introduce more than 0.1 percent chloride, by weight, of cementitious materials shall not be used in concrete for prestressed concrete, bridge decks, or concrete in which aluminum, galvanized metalwork, or other dissimilar steel is to be embedded.

[53][In all other concrete, accelerator may be furnished and used during cold weather as hereinafter provided and shall conform to ASTM C494 for type C or E. In addition, if used as an accelerator, calcium chloride shall meet requirements of ASTM D98 and shall be no coarser than grade A, class 1, or shall be liquid. The portion of mixing water containing other admixtures shall not come in contact with the calcium chloride before entering the mixer.]

(g) *Reinforcing Bars* [50]*(and Fabric).*—Reinforcing bars shall conform to ASTM A615 or A617, grade [54](40 or 60), including supplementary requirements. [50][Fabric shall be electrically welded-wire fabric conforming to ASTM A185 or A497.]

(h) *Curing Compound.*—Wax-base (type I) and water-emulsified, resin-base (type II) curing compound shall conform to the requirements of the Bureau's "Specifications for Concrete Curing Compound," dated October 1, 1980. The curing compound shall be of uniform consistency and quality within each container and from shipment to shipment.

(i) *Polyethylene Film.*—Polyethylene film for curing concrete shall be white in color, shall be 4 mils thick, and shall conform to the requirements of ASTM C171.

G.66. *Composition.*—Unless otherwise directed, the contractor shall design the concrete mix in accordance with these specifications. Mix designs shall provide for the minimum cementitious materials contents as shown in table G-4. Each mix design shall be submitted to the Contracting Officer

[50]Delete if fabric is not involved.

[53]Delete if type V cement is being specified; if concrete is primarily for substation and transmission line foundations, or if use of set-accelerating admixtures will otherwise be prohibited.

[54]Delete or revise as required for grade as appropriate.

Table G-4.—Minimum cementitious materials content.

Nominal MSA in concrete, inches	Min. cementitious materials content without WRA, lb/yd^3	Min. cementitious materials content with WRA, lb/yd^3
1½	565	535
1	620	585

MSA = maximum size aggregate
WRA = water-reducing admixture

Table G-5.—Additional cementitious materials requirements.

Hours of contact between cementitious materials and wet aggregate[1]	Additional cementitious materials required, percent
0 to 2	0
2 to 3	5
3 to 4	10
4 to 5	15
5 to 6	20
Over 6	Batch will be rejected.

[1]The Government reserves the right to require the addition of cementitious materials for shorter periods of contact during periods of hot weather, and the contractor shall be entitled to no additional compensation by reason of the shortened period of contact.

for review prior to use of the concrete mix.

The Contracting Officer will test concrete for compliance with specifications, and reserves the right to design and adjust the concrete mix proportions.

An air-entraining admixture shall be used in such an amount as will effect the entrainment of from 4 to 6 percent air, by volume, of the concrete as discharged at placement.

The slump of the concrete shall not exceed 3 inches, plus or minus 1 inch when placed, nor 5 inches when first mixed.

*[Type C or E chemical admixtures, including calcium chloride, shall not be used in the concrete.]

G.67. ***Batching, Mixing, and Transporting.***—Concrete shall be manufactured and delivered in accordance with ASTM C 94, "Standard Specifications for Ready Mixed Concrete".

When bulk cementitious materials and aggregates are dry batched and hauled to where mixing is accomplished, each batch shall be protected during transit to prevent loss and to limit prehydration of the cementitious materials. Separate compartments with suitable covers shall be provided to protect the cementitious materials, or they shall be completely enfolded in and covered by the aggregates to prevent wind loss. If cementitious materials are enfolded in moist aggregates or otherwise exposed to moisture and delays occur between batching and mixing, the contractor shall, at his own expense, add extra cementitious materials to each batch in accordance with the schedule in table G-5.

G.68. ***Concrete Placement, Curing, and Protection.***—Steel reinforcing bars [50](and fabric) shall be placed as shown on the drawings. Before reinforcement is placed, the reinforcement shall be cleaned of heavy flaky rust, loose mill scale, dirt, grease, or other foreign substances. Reinforcement shall be accurately placed and secured in position so that it will not be displaced during placement of concrete.

Forms shall be used to shape the concrete to the required lines. Exposed unformed surfaces shall be brought to uniform surfaces and given a reasonably smooth, wood-float, or steel-trowel finish as directed. The temperature of the concrete when it is being placed shall be not more than 90° F and not less than 50° F.

The concrete shall be cured with water, curing compound, or polyethylene sheets. If water cured, the concrete shall be kept continuously moist by sprinkling or spraying for at least 14 days after being placed, or by other methods approved by the Contracting Officer. Curing compound, when used, shall be applied in accordance with the procedures contained in the Bureau of Reclamation's *Concrete Manual* [2]. Concrete cured by covering with polyethylene sheeting shall be kept continuously moist for at least 14 days after placement.

The contractor shall protect all concrete against injury until final acceptance by the Government. The concrete shall be maintained at a temperature not lower than 50° F for at least 72 hours after it is placed and, if water cured, shall be protected against freezing temperatures for the duration of the curing period. After the water curing is completed, the concrete shall be maintained at a temperature of not less than 50° F for 72 hours. Where artificial heat is employed, special care shall be taken to vent the heater and to keep the concrete from drying.

G.69. ***Repair of Concrete.***—All concrete that is damaged or defective from any cause; concrete that is honeycombed, fractured, or otherwise defective; and concrete which, because of excessive surface depressions, must be excavated and built up

[50]Delete if fabric is not involved.
*Delete or revise as applicable.

to bring surfaces to prescribed lines shall be removed and replaced; and imperfections and irregularities on concrete surfaces shall be corrected. The repair of damaged or defective concrete and the correction of surface imperfections and irregularities shall be made with *(concrete, dry pack, cement mortar, epoxy-bonded concrete, or epoxy-bonded epoxy mortar), where and as applicable for the type of repair involved, in accordance with Bureau of Reclamation's "Standard Specifications for Repair of Concrete," dated January 4, 1982: *Except*, that epoxy-bonded epoxy-mortar shall not be used for outdoor repairs having a surface area greater than 1 square foot. The cost of furnishing all materials and performing all work required for the repair of concrete and the correction of surface imperfections and irregularities shall be at the expense of the contractor.

G.70. *Payment.*—*[Payment for all concrete required under these specifications, including the cost of furnishing and placing reinforcing bars [50](and fabric), will be made at the lump-sum price bid in the schedule for *(concrete________)].

The lump-sum price bid in the schedule for *(concrete ________) shall include the cost of supplying the cementitious materials quantities specified in section G.66. If the Government requires the contractor to use cement in excess of these amounts, such additional cement will be paid for in accordance with the section in these specifications for "Changes."

G.71. *Cost.*—*[The cost of all labor and materials required for concrete under these specifications, including the cost of furnishing and placing reinforcing bars [50](and fabric), shall be included in the lump-sum price bid in the schedule for (concrete ________)].

*[The lump-sum price bid in the schedule for (concrete ________) shall include the cost of supplying the cement quantities specified in section G.66. If the Government requires the contractor to use cementitious materials in excess of these amounts, such additional cementitious materials will be paid for in accordance with the section in these specifications for "Changes".]

[50]Delete if fabric is not involved.
*Delete or revise as applicable.

2. Concrete Specifications for Large Jobs

G.72. *Source.*—The following sections have been prepared from guide specifications normally used by the Bureau of Reclamation for work involving concrete quantities of 1,000 cubic yards or more.

G.73. *Composition.*—(a) *General.*—Concrete shall be composed of [55](cement) [56](cementitious materials); sand; coarse aggregate; water; and admixtures as specified, all well mixed and brought to the proper consistency.

(b) *Nominal Maximum Size of Aggregate.*—The coarse aggregate to be used in concrete shall be as large as practicable, consistent with required strength, spacing of reinforcement and embedded items, and placement thickness. The size of coarse aggregate to be used will be determined by the Contracting Officer, and may vary incrementally according to the conditions encountered in each concrete placement. [57][If the aggregate source chosen by the contractor has a shortage of the 3-inch nominal maximum size aggregate, the Government will consider a request to use smaller nominal maximum size aggregate in portions of the work. If such a change is granted, it shall be at no additional cost to the Government, and the contractor will not be reimbursed for additional [55](cement) [56](cementitious materials) required as a result of using a smaller size aggregate.]

Generally, *(3-inch nominal maximum size aggregate shall be used in concrete walls greater than 15 inches in thickness and in concrete slabs greater than 9 inches in thickness; 1½-inch nominal maximum size aggregate shall be used in other concrete placements).

*(Nominal maximum size aggregate for concrete canal lining shall be 1½ inches for lining thickness 3 inches and greater and ¾ inch for thickness less than 3 inches.) Smaller coarse aggregate than indicated above shall be used where the Contracting Officer determines that proper placement of concrete is impractical *(with the above-listed aggregate sizes).

(c) *Mix Proportions.*—The mix will be designed and adjusted by the Government. The proportions of ingredients will be established in accordance with

[55]Delete when concrete standard, Conc. 3 Cementitious Materials, is used.
[56]Delete when concrete standard, Conc. 2 Cement, is used.
[57]Revise as necessary. Delete reference to 3-inch aggregate if not applicable.

the Bureau's *Concrete Manual* [2]. The proportions will be adjusted during the progress of the work whenever need for such adjustment is indicated by results of testing of the aggregates and the concrete. Adjustments shall be made as directed to obtain concrete having suitable workability, impermeability, density, strength, and durability without the use of excessive [55](cement) [56](cementitious materials). Suitable strength for structural concrete is that which will assure that [58](90) percent of all test cylinders exceed the design strength. Suitable strength for tunnel lining, canal lining, and all other concrete is that which will assure that 80 percent of all test cylinders exceed the design strength. Unless shown otherwise on the drawings, the design strength at 28 days shall be [58](______ pounds per square inch for structural concrete, ______ pounds per square inch for canal and tunnel lining, and ______ pounds per square inch for lean backfill concrete).

The net water-[55](cement) [56](cementitious materials) ratio, exclusive of water absorbed by the aggregates, shall be sufficiently low to provide adequate durability in concrete. Test designation USBR 4211 of the Bureau's *Concrete Manual* [2] should be used as a guide for determining the maximum water-[55](cement) [56](cementitious materials) ratio to ensure durability of concrete.

Where portland cement plus a pozzolan is used, the pozzolan shall constitute 20 percent, by weight, of the total cementitious materials.

(d) *Consistency.*—The slump of the concrete at the placement [59][shall not exceed *(2 inches ±1 inch for concrete in the tops of walls, bridge piers and abutments, parapets, and curbs; in slabs that are horizontal or nearly horizontal; and in all tunnel inverts placed as slabs with unformed top surface. The slump shall also not exceed 4 inches ±1 inch for concrete in sidewalls and arch of tunnel lining and in tunnel inverts placed monolithically with the sidewalls and arch; and shall not exceed 3 inches ±1 inch for concrete in canal lining and for all other concrete)]. If the specified slump is exceeded at the placement, the concrete is unacceptable. The Government reserves the right to require a lesser slump whenever concrete of such lesser slump can be consolidated readily into place by means of the vibration specified in section G.87. The use of buckets, chutes, hoppers, pumps, transit mix trucks, or other equipment that will not readily handle and place concrete of the specified slump will not be permitted.

When a type F or G chemical admixture is used to fluidize the concrete for an unusual placing condition, the slump shall be appropriate for the placing conditions.

Uniformity in concrete consistency from batch to batch will be required. To maintain concrete at the proper consistency, the amount of water and aggregates batched for concrete shall be adjusted to compensate for variations in the moisture content or grading of the aggregates as they enter the mixer. Addition of water in excess of the design water content to compensate for stiffening of the concrete after mixing, known as retempering, will not be permitted.

G.74. *Concrete Quality Control Measures and Concrete Quality Assurance Program.*—

(a) *Concrete Quality Control Measures.*—As stated in the section of these specifications for "Inspection of Construction", the contractor shall be responsible for providing quality control measures to assure compliance of the concrete with the contract requirements.

(b) *Concrete Quality Assurance Program.*—Independently of the contractor's concrete quality control measures, the Government will conduct a concrete quality assurance program incorporating the tests and the contractor-furnished [60](test facilities and) sampling equipment. As part of the assurance program, the Government will conduct tests to the extent and frequency necessary to ascertain that the concrete constituents, as well as the fresh and hardened concrete, meet the specified levels of quality.

(1) *Tests.*—The Government will obtain samples and conduct tests in accordance with test methods listed in sections G.78 and G.79 and the test methods and specifications as follows:

a. *Sampling hydraulic cement.*–ASTM C183.
b. *Sampling pozzolan.*–ASTM C311.
c. *Sampling aggregates.*–ASTM D75.
d. *Reducing field samples of aggregate to testing size.*–ASTM C702.

[55]Delete when concrete standard, Conc. 3 Cementitious Materials, is used.
[56]Delete when concrete standard, Conc. 2 Cement, is used.
[58]Revise as necessary. Consult with designers.
[59]If the work involves primarily substation and transmission line footings, delete the remainder of this sentence and insert "shall not exceed 3 inches".
*Delete or revise as applicable.

[60]Delete if no test facilities are required.

e. *Absorption of fine aggregate.*-ASTM C128.
f. *Absorption of coarse aggregate.*-ASTM C127.
g. *Total moisture content of aggregate.*-ASTM C566.
h. *Sampling fresh concrete.*-ASTM C172.
i. *Concrete uniformity.*-ASTM C94, annex A1.
j. *Density (unit weight) and yield.*-ASTM C138, except that a 0.25-cubic foot container may be used for nominal aggregate sizes up to 1½ inches [61](and a 0.5-cubic foot container may be used for nominal aggregate sizes up to 3 inches).
k. *Air content.*-ASTM C231.
l. *Slump.*-ASTM C143.
m. *Temperature measurement of fresh concrete.*-ASTM C1064. The temperature will be determined by placing a thermometer in concrete at placement.
n. *Making and curing concrete test specimens in the field.*-ASTM C31, except that the frequency of internal vibrators shall be 10,000 vibrations per minute or greater while in use.
o. *Capping cylindrical concrete specimens.*-ASTM C617.
p. *Compressive strength of cylindrical concrete specimens.*-ASTM C39 for cast cylinders, and ASTM C42 for cores.

(2) [60]*(Test Facilities and) Sampling Equipment.*-The contractor shall provide sampling equipment [60](and testing facilities), for use by the Government as follows:

a. [60][An enclosed building of not less than 200 square feet adjacent to the batch plant, free from plant vibration and excessive plant noises, and furnished with all necessary utilities including lights, compressed air, water, room temperature control, and electrical power.]

b. [62][Mechanical sampling devices for safely obtaining and handling representative test samples of aggregates and other concrete materials during batching and, at central mix plants, mechanical sampling devices for safely obtaining representative concrete samples from a point in the discharge stream as the concrete is discharged from the mixers.]

c. Ample and protected working space near the placement site, and a means for safely procuring and handling representative concrete samples.

d. [60][*Removal of test facilities.*—After tests are completed, the contractor-furnished test facilities shall remain the property of the contractor and shall be removed from the worksite.]

(3) *Contractor-Furnished Drawings and Data.*—The contractor shall submit drawings and data to the *[(Project) Construction Engineer], for approval, showing locations and descriptions of contractor-furnished [60](test facilities and) sampling equipment for Government sampling and testing of concrete and concrete materials not less than 30 days prior to start of installation of the contractor's plants and equipment for processing, handling, transporting, storing, and proportioning concrete ingredients; and for mixing, transporting, and placing concrete. The drawings and data shall provide a description in sufficient detail for an adequate review of the facilities and equipment the contractor proposes to provide the Government for use in the Government's concrete quality assurance program.

One copy of the drawings and data shall be sent to the *[(Project) Construction Engineer], Bureau of Reclamation, ______________, and one copy of the letter transmitting the drawings and data to the *[(Project) Construction Engineer] shall be sent to the Contracting Officer.

(c) *Cost.*—The cost of furnishing drawings and data, sampling equipment, [60](and testing facilities) shall be included in the applicable prices bid in the schedule for concrete.

G.75. *Cementitious Materials.*—(a) *General.*—For purposes of these specifications, cementitious materials shall be interpreted to mean any of the following: portland cement, portland cement plus a pozzolan, or blended hydraulic cement. Also, any of the cementitious materials are suitable for use in all cast-in-plate concrete and concrete products, [63][except portland cement is required for grouting mortar for equipment and metalwork as specified in the section in these specifications for "Grouting Mortar for Equipment and Metalwork."]

Cementitious materials shall be free from lumps and other deleterious matter and shall be otherwise undamaged when used. Before a concrete placement

[60]Delete if no test facilities are required.

[61]Delete if concrete containing aggregate larger than 1½ inches is not specified.

[62]Revise subsection designation letter if required.

[63]Include when applicable and list all other items or concrete products in which portland cement is required. Specifiers should complete attachment to this standard regarding consideration of the use of fly ash and materials containing fly ash.

*Delete or revise as applicable.

is started, sufficient cementitious materials shall be in storage at the batch plant to complete the placement.

Transportation from the place of manufacture to the batch plant shall be by means which will protect the cementitious materials completely from exposure to moisture. Immediately upon receipt at the jobsite, bulk cementitious materials shall be stored in dry, weathertight, properly ventilated bins until the cementitious materials are batched. The bins shall be emptied and cleaned by the contractor when so directed by the Government; however, the intervals between required cleanings will normally be not less than 6 months. Each shipment of bagged cement shall be stored so that it may readily be distinguished from other shipments; and shall be stored in a dry, enclosed area protected from moisture. To prevent undue aging of bagged cement after delivery, the contractor shall use bags of cement in the chronological order in which they were delivered to the jobsite. All storage facilities shall be subject to approval by the Contracting Officer, and shall be constructed to permit easy access for inspection.

(b) *Cementitious Materials Options.*—[64][Cementitious materials shall be furnished by the contractor in accordance with one of the following options:

(1) Type II portland cement only.
(2) Type II portland cement plus a class N, F, or C pozzolan.
(3) Type IP (MS) blended hydraulic cement only.]

(c) *Materials*:

(1) *Portland Cement.*—Portland cement shall meet the requirements of ASTM C 150 for type II cement, and shall meet the optional false-set limitation specified therein. Portland cement shall also conform to the low-alkali limitation, unless the contractor selects aggregates which are not potentially alkali reactive.

(2) *Pozzolan.*—Pozzolan used under the options specified in subsections (b)(2) and (b)(3) shall meet the requirements of ASTM C 618 for class N, F, or C, with the following additional requirements:

a. The maximum percent of sulfur trioxide shall be 4.0 percent for classes F and C.

b. The maximum percent loss on ignition shall be 8.0 percent for class N and 2.5 percent for classes F and C.

c. The pozzolanic activity index with lime shall be determined using 2-inch cubes, and the minimum strength at 7 days shall be 900 lb/in^2.

d. Unless the contractor selects aggregates that are not potentially alkali reactive, pozzolan used under the option specified in subsection (b)(2) shall be tested for reduction of mortar expansion at 14 days as specified for class N pozzolan under the optional physical requirements in table 2A of ASTM C 618; however, the cement used in the test shall be low alkali. For the pozzolan to be acceptable, it shall result in an expansion reduction of zero percent or greater when compared to the control test.

e. Furthermore, pozzolan used under the options specified in subsections (b)(2) and (b)(3) shall not decrease the sulfate resistance of concrete. The following class N pozzolans have been found not to detract from sulfate resistance; therefore, either of them may be used under the options specified in subsections (b)(2) and (b)(3).

1. "Lassenite SR" pozzolan, as marketed by Lassenite Industries, Inc., 1475 Terminal Way, Reno NV 89502, from plant located near Herlong, California.
2. "Sun" pozzolan, as produced by Oregon Portland Cement Co., 111 SE. Madison, Portland OR 97214, from plant located near Lime, Oregon.

Bureau of Reclamation research on class F and C pozzolans has correlated sulfate resistance to a resistance factor, "R." This "R" is defined as "(C-5)/F", where "C" is the calcium oxide content of the pozzolan in percent and "F" is the ferric oxide content in percent. The higher the "R" factor, the lower the sulfate resistance expected for concrete containing the pozzolan. When a class F or C pozzolan is used with type II cement or type IP(MS) blended cement, the "R" factor shall be less than 2.5. Calcium and ferric oxide contents shall be determined in accordance with ASTM C 114.

(3) *Blended Cement.*—Blended cement shall meet the requirements of ASTM C 595 for type IP(MS) portland pozzolan cement, and shall also meet the following constraints:

a. The optional false-set limitation specified in ASTM C 150.

b. The physical requirement of ASTM C595 for

[64]Use these options if there will be moderate sulfate attack.

mortar expansion of type P cement at 14 days, unless the contractor selects aggregates which are not potentially alkali reactive.

c. The pozzolan constituent shall be between 15 and 25 percent, by weight, of the portland pozzolan cement.

d. The amount of pozzolan in the finished cement shall not vary by more than ±3 percent, by weight, of the finished cement from that stated by the contractor in the information submitted to the Contracting Officer as required.

e. Pozzolan used in blended cement shall meet the applicable requirements in subsection (c)(2).

The low-alkali limitation for portland cement and the mortar expansion limit for pozzolan and blended cement may be waived if the contractor selects concrete aggregate sources that have previously been tested by the Bureau of Reclamation and which, as evidenced by petrographic examination or mortar bar tests or both, do not contain potentially deleterious amounts of particles which may react with alkalies in cementitious materials. If available, information regarding the potential alkali reactivity of aggregate from a particular source may be obtained from the *[(Project) Construction Engineer, ______________]. If the potential alkali reactivity of an aggregate source is unknown, the low-alkali limitation and mortar expansion limit shall be met.

At least 30 days before first shipment of any cementitious materials, *(including cementitious materials for use in shotcrete, soil-cement, grout, and precast concrete items such as pipe, beams, and tees,) the contractor shall inform the Contracting Officer, in writing, of the following:

- Names and addresses of cement and pozzolan shipping points.
- Names and addresses of cement and pozzolan suppliers from which contractor will purchase cementitious materials.
- Names and addresses of contractors to whom cement and pozzolan will be shipped, if other than the prime contractor.
- Quantities of cement and pozzolan ordered.
- Whether cement will be ordered in bulk or in bags.
- Purchase order number, contract number, or other designation that will identify cement and pozzolan to be used by the contractor.
- Source and composition of the constituents in blended cement.
- Weight percent of the pozzolan constituent in blended cement.

The contractor shall not change the cementitious materials option selected, or sources of cement and pozzolan for providing cementitious materials under the option, without the written approval of the Contracting Officer.

(d) *Acceptance.*—Cement and pozzolan will be accepted in accordance with Department of Army regulation No. ER1110-1-2002, "Cement and Pozzolan Acceptance Testing."

(1) *Prequalified Producer.*-If cement or pozzolan is supplied from a producer prequalified, as described in appendixes A and B of the above-noted regulation, for the specific material to be supplied, the cement or pozzolan may be shipped directly from the product bin. Prequalification shall include required types and classes and optional limitations such as low-alkali, false-set, or "R" value when specified. A complete test report shall be submitted to the Bureau construction office for each lot of cement or pozzolan from which shipments are supplied.

All cement and pozzolan shipments shall be accompanied by shipping documents containing the following:

- Certification that material meets all applicable requirements of these specifications.
- Type or class of material shipped, including optional limitations such as "MS", "false-set", or "low-alkali", or "R" value.
- Manufacturing location and dates.
- Lot (bin) number.
- Date of shipment.
- Quantity of material shipped.

(2) *Testing for Non-Prequalified Producer.*—If the producer is not prequalified for the specific material to be supplied, the cement or pozzolan shall be sampled and stored in sealed silos, and will be tested by the Government for compliance before it is shipped from the sealed silos.

(3) *Testing for Other Categories.*—When a producer is removed from the list of prequalified producers for the material being supplied, or when the Contracting Officer determines that sealed-silo testing and acceptance are otherwise necessary, acceptance will be by successful tests on cement or pozzolan reserved for Government use in sealed silos.

*Delete or revise as applicable.

(4) *Basis for Acceptance, Removal, and Reinstatement.*—Acceptance, removal, and reinstatement of a producer as prequalified source for a specific material are based primarily on project sample tests and statistical evaluation of past test results. These criteria are listed in Department of Army Regulation No. ER 1110-1-2002.

When so directed by the Contracting Officer, the producer shall test cement for compliance with the false-set limitation at the latest time, prior to shipment, that the cement is still in possession of the cement company. Testing frequency shall be as directed by the Contracting Officer and may be as high as one test per truck (about 25 tons) of cement shipped. Cement failing to meet false-set requirements at any time prior to shipment shall not be shipped for Government use.

The cement producer shall evaluate cement strength uniformity in accordance with ASTM C917. The results shall be reported in tabular and graphical form for all test ages. One copy of each shall be sent to the *(Project) Construction Engineer, and one copy of each shall be sent to the Bureau of Reclamation, Attn D-1510, P O Box 25007, Denver CO 80225.

Cement or pozzolan not meeting specifications requirements may be rejected by the Government at any time prior to its use in concrete, and the contractor shall not be entitled to adjustments in price or completion time by reason of any delays caused by rejection of unacceptable cement or pozzolan, nor for additional expense of handling and replacing rejected cement or pozzolan. Furthermore, concrete made with cement or pozzolan which is subsequently tested and does not meet specifications requirements may be rejected by the Government and shall, if rejected, be removed and replaced by the contractor at his expense.

The contractor may be charged the cost of testing of all cement or pozzolan which has been ordered in excess of the amount used for the work under these specifications. The charges to be made for the Government expense invested in quality assurance of excess cement of pozzolan will be at the rate of $2.00 per ton and may be deducted from payments due to the contractor.

(e) *Measurement and Payment.*—Measurement, for payment, for furnishing and handling cementitious materials will be made on the basis of batch weights and batch counts at the batch plant. When determined appropriate by the Contracting Officer, cementitious materials, either bulk or in bags, used for miscellaneous concrete will be measured for payment in the most practicable manner.

Payment for furnishing and handling cementitious materials will be made at the applicable unit price per ton bid in the schedule, for furnishing and handling the various items of cementitious materials, which unit price shall include the cost of purchasing, transporting, handling, and storing cementitious materials. One ton will be considered as 2,000 pounds.

*[Payment, except as otherwise provided, will be made for cementitious materials used in concrete placed within the pay lines for such concrete. Payment will be made also for cementitious materials used in concrete placed outside the pay lines for such concrete when directed by the Contracting Officer, except that no payment will be made when the requirement for such concrete is determined by the Contracting Officer to be the result of careless excavation or excavation intentionally performed by the contractor to facilitate his operations: *Provided*, that payment for cementitious materials used in concrete placed outside the neatlines for concrete in lining will be limited to the percentage specified in subsection G.54(b).]

[65][Payment for furnishing and handling cementitious materials for foundation grouting, backfill grouting, grouting concrete cooling systems, and contraction joint grouting will be made at the respective unit prices per ton bid therefor in the schedule.]

No payment will be made for cementitious materials used in wasted concrete, mortar, or grout; cementitious materials used in replacement of damaged or defective concrete; cementitious materials used in extra concrete required as a result of overexcavation unless the overexcavation is directed by the Contracting Officer; and cementitious materials used in concrete placed by the contractor in excavations intentionally performed to facilitate the contractor's operations.

The cost of cementitious materials used in items of concrete specified in section G.93 shall be included in the applicable prices bid in the schedule

*Delete or revise as applicable.

[65]Include when separate payment will be made for any of the grouting items listed. Delete those items not applicable to the work involved.

for the items for which such cementitious materials are required.

G.76. *Admixtures.*—(a) *General.*—The contractor shall furnish *(air-entraining and chemical admixtures) for use in concrete. Admixtures shall be of uniform consistency, quality, and strength of solution. Admixtures shall be batched separately in liquid form in dispensers capable of measuring at one time the full quantity of each admixture required for each batch. Measurement shall be either by weighting or by volumetric-admixture dispensers constructed and located such that the full batch quantity of each admixture can be observed in a visual gage by the plant operator. Each admixture [66](except calcium chloride) shall be discharged separately into the mixing water as the water is being discharged into the mixture. [66][Calcium chloride solution shall be added directly from the visual dispenser to the mixer concurrently with the addition of mix water.]

The contractor shall notify the *[(Project) Construction Engineer], in writing, of the manufacturers and specific brand names of all admixtures to be used. The contractor will be advised within 10 days after receipt of notification if admixtures are to be tested and examined by the Government. Written notification of products to be used shall be furnished far enough in advance of planned use so that samples, if required, can be made available to the Government for a testing period of 45 days after receipt of the samples.

If the Government elects to test an admixture, the contractor shall submit a manufacturer's certification containing the following information:

- Name of admixture.
- ASTM designation under which admixture is formulated.
- Admixture type.

In addition, the contractor shall submit the manufacturer's product description, instructions, recommended dosage, chloride content, and precautions to be considered when using the admixture. If available, independent laboratory test date, confirming that the requirements of the applicable ASTM standard have been met, shall be submitted to the Government; such test results may, as determined by the Government, preclude the need for Government testing of the admixture. If the Government electes to test an admixture, one sample containing approximately 1 liter of the admixture shall also be submitted to the Government. The certification, data, and sample shall be fully identified and submitted, shipping costs prepaid, by the contractor in accordance with this section.

The contractor will not be entitled to any reimbursement for delays incurred due to Government testing of admixtures or for delays caused by rejection of the proposed admixtures. Final approval of an admixture will not be given until it has performed satisfactorily at the jobsite.

(b) *Chemical Admixtures.*—Chemical admixtures which will introduce more than 0.1 percent chloride, by weight, of *(cement) (cementitious materials), shall not be used in concrete for bridge decks or in concrete in which aluminum, galvanized metalwork, or prestressing steel is to be embedded.

(1) *Accelerator.*—[67][The contractor may use an accelerating admixture in concrete when the mean daily temperature in the vicinity of the placement has been less than 41° F for 2 of the 4 days prior to placement. Accelerating admixture shall not be used in less severe weather except upon written approval by the Contracting Officer. Request for such approval shall state the reason for using accelerator, amount and brand of accelerator to be used, and location of concrete in which contractor proposes use of the accelerator.]

[67][The accelerator shall conform to ASTM C 494 for type C or E chemical admixtures. The amount of accelerator used [66](except for calcium chloride) shall be that amount necessary to effect the requirements of ASTM C 494. The Contracting Officer reserves the right to adjust quantities of accelerator used, depending on climatic and other job conditions, and the contractor shall be entitled to no additional compensation for such adjustment.]

[67][[66](Calcium chloride used as an accelerator shall meet requirements of ASTM D 98, and shall be no coarser than grade A, class 1, or shall be liquid. The calcium chloride shall be batched in liquid form, in solution with water, to include 1 percent calcium chloride, by weight, of *(cement) (cementitious materials), in the concrete mix. The contractor may request approval by the Contracting

[66]Delete if type V cement is specified or if calcium chloride will otherwise be prohibited.

*Delete or revise as applicable.

[67]If type V cement is specified or if accelerator is not to be used due to mild climate or any other reason, delete this paragraph.

Officer for use of a larger amount of calcium chloride, not to exceed 2 percent, by weight, of *(cement) (cementitious materials), during especially severe weather.)]

[68][Accelerating admixtures shall not be used in the concrete.]

(2) *Water-Reducing and/or Set-Controlling Admixtures.*—The contractor [69](shall) (may) use a water-reducing and/or set-controlling admixture, referred to herein as WRA, in all concrete. The admixture shall conform to ASTM C 494 for type A, D, F, or G chemical admixture [70](except that type E chemical admixture meeting ASTM requirements will also be an acceptable WRA only during cold weather).

[71][If use of the WRA chosen by the contractor is accompanied by abnormal setting of the fresh concrete, or if the WRA does not perform in accordance with these specifications, the contractor shall furnish and use other brands of WRA until an acceptable admixture is found.]

Normally, the amount of WRA used shall be that amount necessary to effect the requirements of ASTM C 494; however, the Contracting Officer reserves the right to adjust the quantities of WRA or eliminate its use, and the contractor shall be entitled to no additional allowances for such adjustments.

(c) *Air-Entraining Admixture.*—An air-entraining admixture shall be used in all concrete. The admixture shall conform to ASTM C 260: *Provided,* that air-entraining admixture used with type F or G chemical admixture shall be a neutralized vinsol resin formulation.

The amount of air-entraining admixture used shall be that amount necessary to effect a total air content in the concrete at the placement as shown in table G-6.

Table G-6.—Total air content.

Nominal maximum size coarse aggregate, inches	Total air, percent by volume of concrete
3/4	6 ± 1
1½	4.5 ± 1
3*	3.5 ± 1

*Delete if 3-inch MSA is not specified.

(d) *Cost.*—The cost of furnishing admixtures and all other costs incidental to their use shall be included in the applicable price bid in the schedule for the concrete in which the admixtures are used.

G.77. Water.—The water used in making and curing concrete, mortar, and grout shall be free from objectionable quantities of silt, organic matter, salts, and other impurities. The Contracting Officer will determine whether such quantities of impurities are objectionable. Such determination will usually be made by comparison of compressive strengths, water requirements, times of set, and other properties of concrete made with distilled or very clean water and concrete made with the water proposed for use. In no case shall mix water contain more than 3,000 milligrams per liter of soluble sulfate.

If any water to be used in concrete, mortar, or grout is suspected by the Contracting Officer of exceeding the soluble sulfate limitation, samples of the water will be obtained and tested by the Government. The water will be tested for soluble sulfate content in accordance with the Bureau of Reclamation "Method of Test for Determining the Quantity of Soluble Sulfate in Solid (Soil or Rock) and Water Samples", dated May 1, 1973.

G.78. Sand.[72]—(a) *General.*—The term "sand" is used to designate aggregate in which the maximum size particle will pass a 3/16-inch (No. 4) test sieve. Sand shall be predominantly natural sand that may be supplemented with crushed sand to make up deficiencies in the natural sand gradings. [73][Crushed sand, if used, shall be produced by a suitable ball or rod mill, or disk or cone crusher, so that the particles are predominately cubical in shape and free from flat and elongated particles. Crusher fines produced by a jaw crusher used other than as a primary crusher shall not be used in production of sand. Crushed sand shall be blended uniformly with the natural sand by routing through the same classifier.]

[68]Delete if accelerating admixtures are permitted.

[69]When less than 2,000 cubic yards of cast-in-place concrete is to be included in the work, or where large quantities of concrete are in small scattered features such as transmission line footings and lateral structures, use "may"; otherwise, use "shall."

[70]Delete if accelerator is not to be used.

[71]Delete if use of WRA is optional.

*Delete or revise as applicable.

[72]For concrete work in the Kansas-Nebraska area, special changes and additions to this paragraph will be necessary. When preparing specifications for concrete work in this area, contact code D-1511, Engineering and Research Center, for specific requirements.

[73]Delete when specifications include a section on "Production of Sand and Coarse Aggregate."

All sand shall be furnished by the contractor from any approved source as provided in subsection(d). [73][Any royalties or other charges required to be paid for materials taken from deposits not owned by the Government and controlled by the Bureau of Reclamation shall be paid by the contractor.]

Sand, as delivered to the batching plant, shall have a uniform and stable moisture content of less than 6 percent free moisture. Variations of moisture in sand as batched shall not exceed 0.5 percent in 30 minutes.

(b) *Quality.*—The sand as batched shall consist of clean, hard, dense, durable, uncoated rock fragments. Sand may be rejected if it fails to meet any of the following quality requirements:

(1) *Organic Impurities in Sand* (ASTM C40).—Color no darker than the specified standard.

(2) *Sodium Sulfate Test for Soundness* (ASTM C88).—[74][Shall have 8 percent maximum weighted average loss, by weight.]

(3) *Specific Gravity* (ASTM C128).—[74][Saturated, surface-dry basis, 2.60 minimum.]

(4) *Deleterious Substances.*—As shown in table G-7.

(c) *Grading.*—The sand, as batched, shall be well-graded, and when tested using standard sieves (ASTM C136), shall conform to the limits in table G-8.

The grading of the sand shall be controlled so that the fineness moduli (ASTM C136) of at least 9 out of any 10 consecutive test samples of finished sand will not vary more than 0.20 from the average fineness modulus of the 10 test samples.

[73](d) *Test and Approval.*—[75][The Bureau of Reclamation tests performed on samples of sand obtained from sources in the following locations indicate that these sources contained, when sampled, materials meeting the quality requirements of these specifications for sand:
(1) ________, (2) ________, (3) ________, etc.
All locations are listed relative to the ________ Meridian.]

Sand from sources [76](__________) will not require the use of low-alkali [73](cement) (or pozzolan meeting the alkali requirements) in accordance with section G.75.

If sand is to be obtained from a deposit not previously tested and approved by the Government, the contractor shall assist the Government in collecting representative samples for preconstruction testing and approval. The samples shall consist of about 200 pounds of sand, and shall be submitted to the Bureau of Reclamation, code D-1511, Building 56, Entrance S-6, Denver Federal Center, Denver CO 80225, at least 60 days before the sand is required for use.

The approval of deposits by the Contracting Officer shall not be construed as constituting the approval of all or any specific materials taken from the deposits, and the contractor will be held responsible for the specified quality of all such materials used in the work.

In addition to preconstruction testing and approval of the deposit, the Government may test the

Table G-7.—Allowable percentages of deleterious substances in sand.

	Maximum percent by weight, as batched
Material passing No. 200 sieve (ASTM C 117)	3
Lightweight material (ASTM C 123, using a solution of zinc chloride)	2
Friable particles (ASTM C 142)	1
Other deleterious substance such as mica, coated grains, soft-flaky particles, and loam	2
Sum of all the above deleterious substances	5

Table G-8.—Sand grading requirements.

Sieve No.	Individual percent, by weight, retained on sieve
4	0 to 5
8	5 to 15*
16	10 to 25*
30	10 to 30
50	15 to 35
100	12 to 20
Pan	3 to 7

*If individual percent retained on No. 16 sieve is 20 percent or less, maximum limit for individual percent retained on No. 8 sieve may be increased to 20 percent.

[73]Delete when specifications include a section on "Production of Sand and Coarse Aggregate."

[74]Revise as advised by Contracting Officer.

[75]Delete when tested and approved sources are not to be listed.

[76]Show location numbers; if all sources require use of low-alkali cement, so state.

sand during the aggregate processing, but final acceptance of sand will be based on samples taken at the batch plant. The contractor shall provide such facilities as may be necessary for procuring representative samples at the aggregate processing plant and at the batch plant.

G.79. Coarse Aggregate.[77]—(a) *General.*—For the purposes of these specifications, the term "coarse aggregate" designates clean, well-graded aggregate of particle sizes within the range of [78](3/16 to 1½ inches), or any size or range of sizes within such limits. Coarse aggregate for concrete shall consist of natural gravel, crushed rock, or a mixture of natural gravel and crushed rock. Jaw crushers shall not be used except as a primary crusher. If crushed coarse aggregate is used with natural coarse aggregate, the crushed aggregate shall be blended uniformly with the natural aggregate by routing both together through the classifying screens. Coarse aggregate shall have no more than 30 percent particles with a maximum to minumum dimension of 3 to 1.

Coarse aggregate for concrete shall be furnished by the contractor from any approved source as provided in subsection (d). Any royalties or other charges required to be paid for materials taken from deposits not owned by the Government and controlled by the Bureau of Reclamation shall be paid by the contractor.

Coarse aggregate, as delivered to the batch plant, shall have a uniform and stable moisture content.

(b) *Quality.*—The coarse aggregate, as batched, shall consist of clean, hard, dense, durable, uncoated rock fragments. Coarse aggregate may be rejected if it fails to meet any of the following quality requirements:

(1) *Los Angeles Abrasion Loss* (ASTM C 131, using grading A).—[74][Shall have a 10 percent maximum loss of weight at 100 revolutions, or 40 percent maximum loss of weight at 500 revolutions.]

(2) *Sodium Sulfate Test for Soundness* (ASTM C 88).—[74][Shall have 10 percent maximum weighted average loss, by weight, after 5 cycles.

(3) *Specific Gravity* (ASTM C 127).—[74][Saturated, surface-dry basis, 2.60 minimum.]

(4) *Deleterious Substances.*—These substances, in any size of coarse aggregate, are as shown in table G-9.

(c) *Finish Screening.*—The coarse aggregate shall be separated into nominal sizes during production of the aggregate. Just prior to batching, the coarse aggregate shall be rewashed by pressure spray and finish-screened on multideck vibrating screens capable of simultaneously removing undersized and oversized aggregate from each of the nominal aggregate sizes. If variations in the water content of the aggregates entering the batcher occur during intermittent batching, a watering screen shall be required after the finish screens to remove excess free moisture. Finish screens may be mounted over the batching plant or on the ground adjacent to the batching plant. Finish screens shall be so mounted that the vibration of the screens will not be transmitted to the batching bins or scales and will not affect the accuracy of the weighing equipment in any other manner.

The method and rate of feed for finish screening shall be such that the screens will not be overloaded and that the screening will result in a finished product which meets the grading requirements of these specifications. Coarse aggregate shall be fed to the finish screens in a combination or alternation of nominal sizes which will not cause noticeable accumulation of poorly graded coarse aggregate in any batching bin. The finish-screened aggregates shall pass directly to the individual batching bins in such a manner as to minimize breakage. Minus 3/16-inch material passing through the finish screens shall be wasted unless routed back through a sand classifier in a manner which causes uniform blending with the natural sand being processed. Water from finish screening shall be drained in such a manner as to prevent aggregate wash water from entering the batching bins and weighing hoppers. Washing and finish screening equipment shall be subject to approval by the Contracting Officer.

[79][When provided adequate substantiation by the contractor that coarse aggregate, as batched, will consistently meet specified grading requirements without final washing or finish screening, the Contracting Officer may waive final washing requirements or finish screening requirements, or both. If

[74]Revise as advised by Contracting Officer.

[77]For concrete work in the Kansas-Nebraska area, special changes and additions to this paragraph will be necessary. When preparing specifications for concrete work in this area, contact code D-1511, Engineering and Research Center, for specific requirements.

[78]When nominal MSA is to be other than 1½ inches, substitute size to be used.

[79]Delete when more than 10,000 cubic yards of concrete are required.

Table G-9.—Allowable percentages of deleterious substances in coarse aggregate.

	Maximum percent, by weight, as batched
Lightweight material (ASTM C123, using a solution of zinc chloride)	2
Friable particles (ASTM C142)	0.5
Other deleterious substances	0.5
Maximum allowable sum of all the above deleterious substances	2

Table G-10.—Coarse aggregate grading requirements.

Nominal MSA	¾ inch	1½ inches	3 inches[1]
Nominal size range, inches	3/16 to ¾	¾ to 1½	1½ to 3
Maximum percent retained on (indicated) oversize test sieve	0% (⅞ inch)	0% (1¾ inches)	0% (3½ inches)
Percent retained on (indicated) test sieve	50 to 75% (⅜ inch)	25 to 50% (1¼ inches)	25 to 50% (2½ inches)
Maximum percent passing on (indicated) undersize test sieve	2% (No. 5)	2% (⅝ inch)	2% (1¼ inches)
Maximum percent passing No. 200 sieve	0.5%	0.2%	0.1%

[1]Delete if 3-inch MSA is not used.

such requirements are waived and grading requirements are not consistently met, the contractor shall implement, within 14 days after notification by Contracting Officer, final washing and finish screening as herein specified.]

(d) *Grading.*—Separation of the coarse aggregate into the specified sizes, after finish-screening, shall be such that when the coarse aggregate is tested in accordance with ASTM C 117 and C 136, it shall meet the grading requirements shown in table G-10.

[73,75][(e) *Test and Approval.*—Bureau of Reclamation tests performed on samples of coarse aggregate obtained from sources at the following locations indicate that these sources contained, when sampled, materials meeting the quality requirements of these specifications for coarse aggregate:

(1) ____________, (2) ____________, (3) ____________, etc.

All locations are listed relative to the ____________ Meridian.]

[73, 75][Aggregate from sources [76](____________) will not require the use of low-alkali *(cement) (or pozzolan meeting the alkali requirements) in accordance with section G.75.

If coarse aggregate is to be obtained from a deposit not previously tested and approved by the Government, the contractor shall assist the Government in collecting representative samples for preconstruction testing and approval. The samples shall consist of about 200 pounds of the 3/16- to ¾-inch coarse aggregate and 100 pounds of [80](the ¾- to 1½-inch coarse aggregate), and shall be submitted to the Bureau of Reclamation, Attn. D-1511, Building 56, Entrance S-6, Denver Federal Center, Denver CO 80225, at least 60 days before the coarse aggregate is required for use.

The approval of deposits by the Contracting Officer shall not be construed as constituting the approval of all or any specific materials taken from the deposits, and the contractor will be held responsible for the specified quality of all such materials used in the work.

In addition to preconstruction testing and approval of the deposit, the Government may test the coarse aggregate during the aggregate processing, but final acceptance of aggregate will be based on samples taken at the batch plant. The contractor shall provide such facilities as may be necessary for procuring representative samples at the aggregate processing plant and at the batch plant.]

G.80. *Batching.*—(a) *General.*—The contractor shall notify the Contracting Officer before batching concrete. Unless inspection is waived in each case, batching shall be performed only in the presence of a duly authorized Government inspector.

The contractor shall provide equipment and shall maintain and operate the equipment as required to accurately determine and control the prescribed amounts of the various materials entering the concrete mixers. The amount of bulk cement, *(pozzolan), sand, and each size of coarse aggregate entering each batch of concrete shall be determined

[73]Delete when specifications include a section on "Production of Sand and Coarse Aggregate."

[75]Delete when tested and approved sources are not to be listed.

*Delete or revise as applicable.

[80]When MSA is to be larger than 1½ inches, change this part of statement to read "each of the other sizes of coarse aggregate".

by individual weighing. Sand and coarse aggregate may be weighed with separate scales and hoppers or cumulatively with one scale and hopper. *[If the batch plant is equipped with automatic interlocking sequential batching controls, the cement and pozzolan may be weighed cumulatively with one scale and hopper so long as weighing is automatically controlled within the specified tolerances and cement is weighed first. If the batch plant is not so equipped, cement and pozzolan shall be weighed separately with individual scales and hoppers. Cement shall be weighed separately with an individual scale and hopper.] Water and admixtures shall be measured by weight or by volume in accordance with this section and section G.76. Where bagged cement is used, it need not be weighed if the concrete is proportioned on the basis of integral bags of cement. [81][Aggregate will be rejected if it contains particles frozen together. During freezing weather, the contractor shall protect aggregate stockpiles containing free water by covering and heating them, or shall screen out frozen material prior to use, or shall do both to prevent or remove frozen particles.]

When bulk *(cement, cementitious materials) and aggregates are dry batched and hauled to where mixing is accomplished, each batch shall be protected during transit to prevent loss and to limit prehydration of the *(cement, cementitious materials). Separate compartments with suitable covers shall be provided to protect the *(cement, cementitious materials), which shall be completely enfolded in and covered by the aggregates to prevent wind loss. If *(cement is, cementitious materials are) enfolded in moist aggregates or otherwise exposed to moisture and delays occur between batching and mixing, the contractor shall, at his own expense, add extra *(cement, cementitious materials) to each batch in accordance with the schedule in table G-11.

(b) *Equipment*:

(1) All weighing and measuring equipment shall be accurate to 0.40 percent over the working range. In addition, the construction and accuracy of equipment shall conform to the applicable requirements of the National Bureau of Standards Handbook 44, "Specifications, Tolerances, and other Technical Requirements for Commercial Weighing and Measuring Devices." [82][The contractor shall schedule and perform monthly static tests to assure that the operating performance of each scale and measuring device is within the 0.40 percent accuracy, and shall provide standard test weights and any other equipment necessary to conduct these tests. The tests shall be made in the presence of a Government inspector and shall be subject to his approval. In addition to monthly tests, the contractor shall perform additional tests when requested by the Government.] The contractor shall make such adjustments, repairs, or replacements as may be necessary to meet the specified requirements for accuracy of measurement.

(2) Each weighing unit shall be springless and shall visibly register the actual weights during the weighing operation and not just indicate when a prescribed weight has been obtained. The clear interval for dial scale graduations shall be not less than 0.03 inch. Each scale graduation shall indicate increments no greater than 2.5 pounds for water and *(cement, cementitious materials), and no more than 10 pounds for aggregate for each cubic yard normally batched. Each batch weight indicator and volumetric dispenser shall be in full view of the operator. Batching controls shall be interlocked so that a new batch cannot be started until the weighing hoppers have been completely emp-

Table G-11.—Additional cement or cementitious materials requirements.

Hours of contact between cement or cementitious materials and wet aggregate[1]	Additional cement or cementitious materials required, percent
0 to 2	0
2 to 3	5
3 to 4	10
4 to 5	15
5 to 6	20
Over 6	Batch will be rejected

[1]The Government reserves the right to require the addition of cement or cementitious materials for shorter periods of contact during periods of hot weather, and the contractor shall be entitled to no additional compensation by reason of the shortened period of contact.

[81]Delete in areas not likely to have extended periods of freezing.
*Delete or revise as applicable.

[82]Delete when less than 5,000 cubic yards are required.

tied of the last batch and the scales register zero weight.

(3) The equipment shall be capable of controlling the delivery of material so that the combined inaccuracies in feeding and measuring during normal operation will not exceed (by individual weight) ±1 percent for water; ±1.5 percent for *(cement, cementitious materials); ±2 percent each for sand, ¾-inch nominal maximum size aggregate, and 1½-inch nominal maximum size aggregate; and ±3 percent for admixtures [83](and 3-inch nominal maximum size aggregate). The weighing hoppers shall be constructed so as to permit removal of materials batched in excess of the prescribed mix design and the above tolerances.

(4) Measuring devices for air-entraining and chemical admixtures shall have sufficient capacity to measure, at one time, the full quantity of the properly diluted solution required for each batch, and shall be maintained in a clean and freely operating condition. If admixtures are measured by a method other than direct weighing, equipment shall be designed for confirmation of the accuracy of each batch quantity using visual-mechanical gauges readily visible from the batch plant operator's station. Admixture batching equipment shall be constructed so that the required batch quantity can only be added once to each batch, and so that each admixture is discharged separately into the batched mixing water as it is being discharged into the mixer.

(5) Equipment for conveying batched materials from weighing hoppers into the mixer shall be constructed, maintained, and operated so as to prevent spillage of the batched materials and overlap of batches.

(6) Equipment for handling *(cement, cementitious materials) in the batching plant shall be constructed and operated so as to prevent noticeable dust during the measuring and discharging of each batch of material.

(7) Aggregate batch bins shall be so constructed as to be self-cleaning during drawdown.

[84][(8) Coarse aggregate shall be deposited in the batch bins directly over the discharge gates. [83](Aggregate larger than ¾-inch nominal size shall be deposited in the batch bins through effective rock ladders unless the contractor can prove to the Contracting Officer's satisfaction that the aggregate will not be subject to breakage and degradation beyond the limits allowable in the specifications as provided in tables G-9 and G-10 in section G.79.)]

(9) Convenient facilities shall be provided for readily and safely obtaining representative samples of *(cement, cememtitious materials), admixtures, sand, and each size of coarse aggregate from the discharge stream between batch bins and weighing hoppers or between batch hopper and mixer.

(10) The water-batching device shall be constructed so that the water will be discharged quickly and freely into the mixer without objectionable dribble from the end of the discharge pipe, and shall be such that leakage will not occur when the valves are closed. In addition, equipment shall be capable of adjusting batch water by as little as 3 pounds per cubic yard and there shall be a means for accurately introducing small increments of water into each mixer after batching for occasional final tempering of the concrete.

(11) The equipment shall be capable of adjustment to compensate for the varying moisture content of the sand and coarse aggregates and to adjust the mix proportions as needed.

(12) The contractor shall inform a Government batch plant inspector prior to and after changes and adjustments in batching equipment and control instrumentation.

G.81. *Mixing.*—(a) *General.*—The concrete ingredients shall be thoroughly mixed in mixers designed to assure uniform distribution of all the component materials throughout the concrete at the end of the mixing period.

The concrete, as discharged from the mixer, shall be uniform in composition and consistency from batch-to-batch. Mixers will be examined regularly by the Government for changes in condition due to accumulation of hardened concrete or mortar or to wear of blades. The adequacy of the mixing will be

[83]Delete if MSA is 1½ inches or less.

*Delete or revise as applicable.

[84]Delete designated requirements in subsections (8) through (12) when less than 5,000 cubic yards of concrete is required.

determined by the Government in accordance with the concrete uniformity requirements of ASTM C 94, annex A1. Samples of concrete for such tests will be taken from any size batch which is commonly mixed during concrete production. For testing purposes, the contractor shall mix, in the mixers to be tested, the size of batch directed by the Government inspector at the batch plant, and shall assist in collection of required samples from that batch.

Any mixer that, at any time, produces unsatisfactory results shall not be used until repaired. If repair attempts are unsuccessful, a defective mixer shall be replaced.

Batch size shall be at least 10 percent of, but not in excess of, the rated capacity of the mixer.

(b) *Central Mixers.*—Water shall be admitted prior to and during charging of the mixer with all other concrete ingredients. After all materials are in the mixer, each batch shall be mixed for not less than 90 seconds. The Government will increase the minimum mixing time required as need is indicated by results of the concrete uniformity tests. Excessive overmixing which requires additions of water to maintain the required concrete consistency will not be permitted. The mixing equipment shall conform to the following additional requirements:

(1) Plant configuration shall be such that the mixing action of each mixer shall be observed from a safe location which can be easily reached from the control station. Provisions shall also be made so that the operator can observe the concrete in the receiving hopper of buckets as it is being dumped from the mixers.
(2) Each mixer shall be controlled with a timing device which will indicate the mixing period and assure completion of the required mixing period.
(3) The batch plant shall be equipped with an interlocking mechanism which will prevent concrete batches from entering mixers which are not empty.

(c) *Truck Mixers.*—Truck mixers shall be equipped with a water-meter, accurate to within 1 percent of the total mix water, located between the water supply and mixer. The water meter shall have a digital indicator. Truck mixers shall also be equipped with a reliable revolution counter for indicating the total number of revolutions of the drum for each batch. The revolution counter shall be visible from the operator control area and shall be reset to zero for each batch. Truck mixers shall have a metal plate attached in a prominent place indicating the manufacturer's recommended drum capacities, in terms of volume, and the maximum and minimum speeds of rotation for both mixing and agitating.

Initial mixing shall be continued for not less than 70 nor more than 100 revolutions of the drum after all the ingredients, except about 5 percent of the water which may be withheld for tempering, are in the drum. The mixing speed shall be not less than 12 nor more than 22 revolutions per minute. No water shall be added after the initial introduction of mixing water for the batch except when, on arrival at the placement, the slump of the concrete is less than specified. Then, such additional tempering water to bring the slump within required limits shall be added: *Provided*, that in no case shall the design water content be exceeded and additional water shall not be added at any later time. After addition of the withheld tempering water, mixing shall be continued at the specified mixing speed for a minimum of 30 revolutions. After a prolonged period of agitation, 10 to 15 revolutions of the drum at mixing speed will be required just prior to discharging. Discharge of the concrete shall be completed before the drum has revolved 300 revolutions.

Each batch of concrete, when delivered at the jobsite from commercial ready-mix plants, shall be accompanied by a written certificate of batch weights and time of batching.

G.82. *Temperature of Concrete.*—Concrete shall be placed at a temperature between 50° F and [85](_______° F). The temperature will be determined by placing a thermometer in the concrete immediately after sampling at the placement site. Then, the temperature of the concrete at the batch plant shall be adjusted to assure that the specified concrete temperature is attained at the placement.

Concrete ingredients shall be heated as necessary, but shall not be heated to a temperature higher than necessary to keep the temperature of the concrete from falling below the specified minimum temperature. Methods of heating concrete ingredients shall be subject to approval.

[85]Usually, a maximum of 80° F should be specified for work involving concrete linings placed during warm, dry weather, and a maximum of 90° F should be specified for structural concrete. Temperature rise considerations in mass concrete usually require maximum temperatures of 70° F or less to be specified for dams.

The contractor shall employ effective means, such as precooling of aggregates and mixing water and placing at night, as necessary to maintain the temperature of the concrete below the specified maximum. The contractor shall be entitled to no additional compensation due to the foregoing requirements.

G.83. *Forms.*—(a) *General.*—Forms shall be used, wherever necessary, to confine the concrete and shape it to the required lines. The contractor shall set and maintain concrete forms so as to ensure completed work is within all applicable tolerance limits. If a type of form does not consistently perform in an acceptable manner, the type of form shall be changed and the method of erection shall be modified by the contractor, subject to approval by the Contracting Officer.

Plumb and string lines shall be installed before, and maintained during, concrete placement. Such lines shall be used by contractor's personnel and by Government inspectors and shall be in sufficient number and properly installed as determined by the Contracting Officer. During concrete placement, the contractor shall continually monitor plumb and string line form positions and immediately correct deficiencies.

Forms shall have sufficient strength to withstand the pressure resulting from placement and vibration of the concrete, and shall be maintained rigidly in position. The design of formwork and placing rate of concrete containing type F or G chemical admixtures shall be adjusted to compensate for the greater hydraulic pressures exerted on the forms by concrete of high fluidity. [86][Where form vibrators are to be used, forms shall be sufficiently rigid to effectively transmit energy from the form vibrators to the concrete, while not damaging or altering positions of forms.] Forms shall be sufficiently tight to prevent loss of mortar from the concrete. Chamfer strips shall be placed in the corners of forms and at the tops of wall placements to produce beveled edges on permanently exposed concrete surfaces. Interior angles of intersecting concrete surfaces and edges of construction joints shall not be beveled except where indicated on the drawings.

[87][Inside forms for circular siphons, in which the siphon barrels are placed monolithically without longitudinal or horizontal construction joints, shall be constructed to cover only the arch and sides, leaving the bottom 65 ±5° of the inside circumference to be placed without forming.]

[88][Inside forms for nearly horizontal circular tunnels having an inside diameter of 12 feet or more shall be constructed to cover only the arch and sides. The bottom 65 ±5° of the inside circumference shall be placed without forming: *Provided*, that the contractor may increase the angle of the inside circumference to be placed without forming on written approval of the Contracting Officer. Request for approval shall be accompanied by complete plans and description of the placing methods proposed to be used.]

[89][Forms for tunnel lining shall be provided with openings along each sidewall and in each arch. Each opening shall be not less than 2 by 2 feet. The openings shall be located in the crown and along each sidewall as follows:

(1) Openings in the crown shall be spaced 8 to 10 feet on centers and shall be located alternately on each side of the tunnel centerline.

(2) Openings in sidewalls of forms for tunnels having an inside diameter less than 12 feet shall be located at midheight of the tunnel and shall be spaced 8 to 10 feet on centers along each sidewall.

(3) Openings in sidewalls of forms for tunnels having an inside diameter of 12 feet or more shall be located along two longitudinal lines in each sidewall, at locations which are satisfactory to the Contracting Officer. The openings along the two selected longitudinal lines in each sidewall shall be staggered and shall be spaced 8 to 10 feet on centers along each longitudinal line.

Chord forming of horizontal curves with straight forms is allowable provided:

(1) The length of chord is less than 1.5 times the square root of the radius of the curve.

(2) The chord shall depart from alignment equal and opposite distances at the ends and the center maintaining the minimum specified concrete thickness between the inside surface of all steel support members and the finished surface of the tunnel lining.]

[86]Delete if form vibrators are not required, as prescribed in section G.87.

[87]Delete if circular siphons are not involved in the work.

[88]Delete if circular tunnels having an inside diameter of 12 feet or more are not involved.

[89]Delete if tunnel linings are not involved. If tunnel linings are involved, delete subsections (2) or (3), whichever is not applicable.

[90][Forms for concrete surfaces for which finish F3 is specified shall not be constructed continuously from lift to lift, but shall be removed after concrete in a lift has hardened and reset from the next lift. The reset forms shall overlap the hardened concrete in the lift previously placed by not more than 1 inch and shall be tightened snugly against the hardened concrete so that, when concrete placement is resumed, the forms will not spread and allow offsets or loss of mortar at construction joints. Additional bolts or form ties shall be used as necessary to hold the reset forms tight against the hardened concrete.]

(b) *Form Sheathing and Lining.*—Wood sheathing or lining shall be softwood or plywood of such kind and quality, or shall be so treated or coated that there will be no chemical deterioration or discoloration of the formed concrete surfaces. The type and condition of form sheathing and lining, and the fabrication of forms for finishes [91](F2, F3, and F4) shall be such that the resulting concrete surfaces will have uniform texture and will meet all applicable finish and tolerance requirements. The ability of form sheathing and lining to withstand distortion caused by placement and vibration of concrete shall be such that formed surfaces will conform with specified tolerances. [90][All voids of joints in the plywood form lining or sheating for finish F3 shall be filled and finished smooth. Where finish F3 is specified, the sheathing or lining shall be placed so that the joint marks on the concrete surfaces will be minimal and will be in alignment both horizontally and vertically.] Where used for form sheathing, softwood lumber shall meet applicable requirements of the latest edition of the "Grading Rules for Western Lumber," as published by the Western Wood Products Association for dressed or worked lumber of the grade hereinafter specified. All common boards shall be surfaced on both edges (S2E) in accordance with the standard grading rules. Plywood used for form sheathing or lining shall be concrete form, class 1, grade B-B, exterior, mill oiled and edge sealed, in accordance with the latest edition of "Product Standard PSI," U.S. Department of Commerce. Materials used for form sheathing or lining shall conform with the requirements of table G-12, or may be other materials producing equivalent results.

[90]Delete if finish F3 is not required.
[91]Delete finishes not required.

Table G-12.—Form sheathing or lining material requirements.

Required finish of formed surface	Wood sheathing or lining	Steel sheathing or lining[1]
F1	Any grade common board, or plywood	Steel sheathing and steel lining permitted.
F2	No. 2 common or better, shiplap, or plywood.	Steel sheathing permitted. Steel lining permitted if approved.
F3	Plywood.	Steel sheathing and steel lining not permitted.
F4	For plane surfaces, plywood shall be used. For warped surfaces, plywood or lumber which is free from knots and other imperfections and which can be cut and bent accurately to the required curvatures without splintering or splitting shall be used. Where required curvature is especially severe, forms may be lined with continuously supported, flexible material such as masonite or thin plywood. Need for such liners and construction and materials are subject to approval by the Contracting Officer.	Steel sheathing permitted. Steel lining not permitted.

[1]Steel "sheathing" denotes steel sheets not supported by a wood backing. "Lining" denotes thin sheets supported by a wood backing.

*[(c) *Uniformity of Forming Material.*—Forms for exposed concrete surfaces to receive finishes F2 and F3 shall be constructed so as to produce a uniform and consistent texture and pattern on the face of the concrete. Metal patches on forms for these surfaces will not be permitted. The form sheathing or lining shall be placed so that all horizontal form marks are continuous across the entire surface. If forms are constructed of plywood form lining or of panels of board lumber, the vertical form marks shall be continuous for the entire height of the surface. If forms for concrete surfaces to receive F2 finishes are constructed of board lumber that is not paneled, the boards shall be cut square, and the

*Delete or revise as applicable.

vertical joints in the boards shall be staggered and shall be made only at studs. The contractor shall use one type of form material for all exposed F2 surfaces and one type of form material for all F3 surfaces. If the contractor elects to use board lumber for forms for F2 surfaces, the lumber shall either be all 6-inch or all 8-inch lumber.]

(d) *Form Ties and Form Anchors.*—Embedded ties for holding forms shall remain embedded and, except where F1 finish is permitted, shall terminate not less than 2 diameters or twice the minimum dimension of the tie, whichever is greater, from the formed surfaces of the concrete.

Ties shall be constructed so that removal of the ends or end fasteners can be accomplished without causing appreciable spalling at the faces of the concrete. Form anchors shall be provided in sufficient number, subject to approval by the Contracting Officer, to ensure that concrete surfaces, after stripping forms, are within applicable tolerances. Form anchors embedded in concrete which are loosened prior to placement of adjoining concrete shall be replaced by other supports firmly embedded in the hardened concrete.

(e) *Cleaning and Oiling Forms.*—At the time the concrete is placed in the forms, the surfaces of the forms shall be free from encrustations of mortar, grout, or other foreign material. Before concrete is placed, the surfaces of the forms, *(except surfaces of rough lumber for surfaces to be plastered), shall be coated with a form oil that will effectively prevent sticking and will not soften or stain the concrete surfaces, or cause the surfaces to become chalky or dust producing.

(f) *Removal of Forms.*—To facilitate satisfactory progress with the specified curing and enable earliest practicable repair of surface imperfections, forms shall be removed within 24 hours after the concrete has hardened sufficiently to prevent damage by careful form removal, and specified repair and curing shall be commenced immediately thereafter. It is the contractor's responsibility to design and build adequate forms, and to leave them in place until the forms can be safely removed. The contractor shall be liable for damage and injury caused by removing forms before the concrete has gained sufficient strength. *[Forms on upper sloping faces of concrete, such as forms on the watersides of warped transitions, shall be removed as soon as the concrete has attained sufficient stiffness to prevent sagging. Any needed repairs or treatment required on such sloping surfaces shall be performed at once and be followed immediately by the specified curing.]

*[To avoid excessive stresses in concrete that might result from swelling of forms, wood forms for wall openings shall be loosened as soon as the loosening can be accomplished without damage to the concrete. Forms for the openings shall be constructed so as to facilitate such loosening. Forms for conduits, siphons, and tunnel lining shall not be removed until the concrete strength is such that form removal will not result in perceptible cracking, spalling, or breaking of edges or surfaces, or other damage to the concrete. Forms shall not be removed from siphon barrels *(and conduits) until the concrete has attained a minimum of 25 percent of the specified 28-day compressive concrete strength as determined by the Government from concrete strength as determined by the Government from concrete cylinders field cured adjacent to the structure to duplicate the curing conditions. Forms shall be removed with care so as to avoid injury to the concrete and any concrete so damaged shall be repaired in accordance with section G.89.]

(g) *Cost.*—The cost of furnishing all materials and performing all work for constructing forms, including any necessary treatment or coating of forms, shall be included in the applicable prices bid in the schedule for the items of concrete for which the forms are used.

G.84. *Reinforcing Bars *(and Fabric).*—

(a) *General.*—Reinforcing bars *(and fabric) shall be cut, bent, and placed in the concrete where shown on the drawings or where directed. The contractor shall furnish all reinforcing bars *(and fabric) required for completion of the work.

(b) *Materials:*

(1) *Reinforcing Bars.*—Reinforcing bars shall be deformed bars conforming to *[ANSI/ASTM A 615, grade (40)(60), including supplementary requirements, or ANSI/ASTM A 617, grade (40)(60).]

*[(2) *Fabric.*—Fabric shall be electrically welded wire fabric, and shall conform to ANSI/ASTM A 185 for smooth steel wire or ANSI/ASTM A 497 for deformed steel wire, except that for wire with a specified yield strength exceeding 60,000 pounds per square inch, the yield strength shall be the stress corresponding to a strain of 0.35 percent.]

(c) *Placing Reinforcing Bars *(and Fabric).*—

*Delete or revise as applicable

The reinforcement shall conform to the requirements shown on the drawings unless otherwise shown on the reinforcement design drawings. [92][Reinforcing bars will be required to be placed in lengths up to *(40)(50)(60) feet.] Splices shall be located where shown on the drawings: *Provided*, that the location of splices may be altered subject to the written approval of the Contracting Officer.

Subject to the written approval of the Contracting Officer, the contractor may, for his convenience, splice bars at additional locations other than those shown on the drawings. To meet design and space limitations on splicing, some bent bars may exceed usual shipping clearances. Cutting and bending of such bars from stock lengths may be required at the site.

Unless otherwise prescribed, placement dimensions shall be to the centerlines of the bars. Reinforcement will be inspected for compliance with requirements as to size, shape, length, splicing, position, and amount after it has been placed.

Before reinforcement is embedded in concrete, the surfaces of the bars *(and fabric) and the surfaces of any supports shall be cleaned of heavy flaky rust, loose mill scale, dirt, grease, or other foreign substances which, in the opinion of the Contracting Officer, are objectionable. Heavy flaky rust that can be removed by firm rubbing with burlap, or equivalent treatment, is considered objectionable.

Reinforcement shall be accurately placed to meet the following tolerances:

*[(1) The amount of concrete covering reinforcement in bridge shall not deviate from that specified by more than 1/4 inch if the cover specified is more than 2 1/2 inches, nor by more than 1/8 inch if the cover specified is 2 1/2 inches or less.

(2) The amount of concrete cover protecting reinforcement *(all other concrete) shall not deviate from that specified by more than 1/2 inch if the specified cover is more than 2 1/2 inches, nor by more than 1/4 inch if the cover specified is 2 1/2 inches or less.

(3) The spacing of reinforcing bars shall not deviate from the required spacing by more than 1 inch.]

Reinforcement shall be secured in position so that it will not be displaced during the placing of the concrete, and special care shall be exercised to prevent any disturbance of the reinforcement in concrete that has already been placed. Bars shall not be field bent to the extent of permanent set, nor straightened, except as approved by the Contracting Officer or as shown on the drawings. Bars bent without approval shall be replaced in conformance with the drawings. Welding or tack welding of reinforcing bars will not be permitted except at locations shown on the drawigns or where approved by the Contracting Officer. Chairs, hangers, spacers, and other supports for reinforcement shall be of concrete, metal, or of other approved material. Where portions of such supports will be exposed on concrete surfaces designated to received F2 *(or F3 finish), the exposed portion of the supports shall be galvanized or of other corrosion-resistant material, except that concrete supports will not be permited. Unless otherwise shown on the drawings, reinforcement in structures shall be so placed that there will be a clear distance of at least 1 inch between the reinforcement and any anchor bolts, form ties, or other embedded metalwork.

[93][(d) *Reinforcement Detail Drawings Prepared by Contractor.*—Reinforcement detail drawings, for any structure, that the contractor may require to facilitate fabrication and placement of the reinforcement shall be prepared by the contractor. Such reinforcement detail drawings shall include bar-placing drawings, bar-bending diagrams, and bar lists.

The contractor's reinforcement detail drawings shall be prepared from reinforcement design drawings included with these specifications, [94](or from supplemental reinforcement design drawings to be furnished by the Government. The position, size, and shape of reinforcing bars are not shown in all cases on the drawings included with these specifications. Supplemental reinforcement design drawings in sufficient detail to permit the contractor to prepare his reinforcement detail drawings will be furnished to the contractor by the Government after final designs have been completed and after equipment data are received from equipment manufacturers. As the supplemental reinforcement design drawings may not be available in time to enable the contractor to purchase prefabricated reinforc-

[92]Dependent on type of cement used.

*Delete or revise as applicable.

[93]Include only when type I cement is specified.

[94]Delete if type V cement is specified, if concrete is primarily for substation and transmission line foundations, or if use of set-accelerating admixtures will otherwise be prohibited.

ing bars, it may be necessary for the contractor to purchase bars in stock lengths, and to cut and bend the bars in the field.)]

[95][(d) *Reinforcement Detail Drawings Prepared by Contractor.*—The contractor shall prepare and submit to the Government, for approval, reinforcement detail drawings for all structures, including bar-placing drawings, bar-bending diagrams, and bar lists.

The contractor's reinforcement detail drawings shall be prepared from reinforcement design drawings included with these specifications [96](and from supplemental reinforcement design drawings to be furnished by the Government). The position, size, and shape of reinforcing bars are not shown in all cases on the drawings included with these specifications. Supplemental reinforcement design drawings in sufficient detail to permit the contractor to prepare his reinforcement detail drawings will be furnished to the contractor by the Government after final designs have been completed and after equipment data are received from equipment manufacturers. As the supplemental reinforcement design drawings may not be available in time to enable the contractor to purchase prefabricated reinforcing bars, it may be necessary for the contractor to purchase bars in stock lengths, and to cut and bend the bars in the field. *[However, the Government-furnished supplemental reinforcement design drawings will be available in accordance with the section in these specifications for "Concrete Placement Schedule."]

The contractor shall submit to the *(______________), for approval, *(three prints)(one print and one reproducible that will permit clear, legible copies to be made) of each of his reinforcement detail drawings at least (____) calendar days before scheduled concrete placement. The Government will require 25 calendar days for review of reinforcement detail drawings, and this review time will apply to each separate submittal or resubmittal as provided in the section of these specifications for "Submittal Requirements." No reinforcement shall be placed in any structure until reinforcement detail drawings describing the reinforcement are approved by the *(______________).

The contractor's reinforcement detail drawings shall be prepared following the recommendations established by the American Concrete Institute's "Manual of Engineering and Placing Drawings for Reinforced Concrete Structures" (ACI 315 R-80) unless otherwise shown on the reinforcement design drawings. The contractor's drawings shall show necessary details for checking the bars during placement and for use in establishing payment quantities.

The contractor's reinforcement detail drawings shall be clear, legible, and accurate. If any reinforcement detail drawing or group of drawings is not of a quality acceptable to the Government, the entire set or group of drawings will be returned to the contractor, without approval, to be corrected and resubmitted. Acceptable reinforcement detail drawings will be reviewed by the Contracting Officer for adequacy of general design and controlling dimensions. Errors, omissions, or corrections will be marked on the prints, or otherwise relayed to the contractor, and one print of each drawing will be returned to the contractor for correction. The contractor shall make all necessary corrections shown on the returned prints. The corrected drawings need not be resubmitted unless the corrections are extensive enough, as determined by the Contracting Officer, to warrant resubmittal. Such Government review and approval shall not relieve the contractor of his responsibility for the correctness of details or for conformance with the requirements of these specifications.

[95][(d) *Reinforcement Detail Drawings Prepared by Contractor.*—The contractor shall prepare and submit reinforcement detail drawings, including bar-placing drawings, bar-bending diagrams, and bar lists, in accordance with the following provisions.

The contractor's reinforcement detail drawings shall be prepared from reinforcement design drawings included with these specifications. At least 60 days before scheduled concrete placement, the contractor shall submit to the *(______________), for approval, *(three prints)(one print and one reproducible that will permit clear, legible copies to be made) of each of his reinforcement detail drawings for the following structures:

(1) _______, (2) _______, and (3) _______.

The Government will require 25 calendar days for review of reinforcement detail drawings, and this review time will apply to each separate submittal

[95]Delete or revise as required for grade.

[96]Use this sentence only if type V cement is specified or if use of set-accelerating admixtures is otherwise prohibited. If an accelerator is to be used, delete this sentence.

*Delete or revise as applicable.

or resubmittal as provided in the section of these specifications for "Submittals Requirements." No reinforcement shall be placed in any structure until reinforcement detail drawings describing the reinforcement are approved by the *(____________).

At least 30 days before scheduled concrete placement, the contractor shall submit to the *(Project) Construction Engineer, for informational purposes, one reproducible of each of his reinforcement detail drawings for all structures not listed above.

The contractor's reinforcement detail drawings shall be prepared following the recommendations established by the American Concrete Institute's "Manual of Engineering and Placing Drawings for Reinforced Concrete Structures" (ACI 315 R-80), unless otherwise shown on the reinforcement design drawings. The contractor's drawings shall show necessary details for checking the bars during placement and for use in establishing payment quantities.

The contractor's reinforcement detail drawings shall be clean, legible, and accurate and checked by the contractor before submittal. If any reinforcement detail drawing or group of drawings requiring approval is not of a quality acceptable to the Government, the entire set or group of drawings will be returned to the contractor, without approval, to be corrected and resubmitted. Acceptable reinforcement detail drawings will be reviewed by the *(Project) Construction Engineer for adequacy of general design and controlling dimensions. Errors, omissions, or corrections will be marked on the prints, or otherwise relayed to the contractor, and one print of each drawing will be returned to the contractor for correction. The contractor shall make all necessary corrections shown on the returned prints. The corrected drawings need not be resubmitted unless the corrections are extensive enough, as determined by the Contracting Officer, to warrant resubmittal. Such Government review and approval shall not relieve the contractor of his responsibility for the correctness of details or for conformance with the requirements of these specifications.]

(e) *Measurement and Payment.*—*[Expect as otherwise provided below, measurement, for payment, of reinforcing bars *(and fabric) will be based on the weight of the bars *(and fabric) placed in the concrete in accordance with the drawings or as directed.]

Measurement, for payment, will include reinforcing bars placed as shown on the drawings and reinforcing bars in splices located as shown on the drawings, and in relocated splices that are approved by the Contracting Officer. No measurement for payment will be made of reinforcing bars in additional splices allowed for the convenience of the contractor.

No measurement for payment will be made for reinforcement used in precast concrete products, reinforcement used in ____________, and reinforcement used in terms of concrete specified in section G.93.

Except as otherwise provided below, the quantities of reinforcing bars for each type of *(switchyard) (substation) concrete foundation for which payment will be made are shown on drawing ______, and regardless of the amount of reinforcing bars placed, payment will be made only on the basis of the quantities of reinforcing bars shown on the drawing.

The quantities of reinforcing bars for which payment will be made for each of the concrete foundations listed below will be added to the drawing ______ after the Government has completed the design of these concrete foudations in accordance with the section in these specifications for "Concrete in Structure":

(1) ______, and (2) ______.

The bidding schedule item "Furnishing and Placing Reinforcing Bars," includes estimated quantities of reinforcing bars for the above-listed foundations.

*[Except as otherwise provided below, payment for furnishing and placing reinforcing bars *(and fabric) will be made at the applicable unit price per pound bid therefore in the schedule for the various size of reinforcing bars *(and fabric)], which unit price shall include the cost of preparing reinforcement detail drawings, including bar-placing drawings and bar-bending diagrams; of submitting the drawings to the Government; of preparing all necessary bar lists and cutting lists; of furnishing and attaching wire ties or other approved supports; and of cutting, bending, cleaning, and securing and maintaining in position reinforcing bars *(and fabric) as shown on the drawings.

The cost of reinforcement used in precast concrete products, reinforcement used in ______, and reinforcement used in items of concrete specified in section G.93 shall be included in the ap-

*Delete or revise as applicable.

plicable price bid in the schedule for the items for which such reinforcement is required.

G.85. *Tolerances for Concrete Constructions.*—(a) *General.*—Tolerances are defined as allowable variations from specified lines, grades, and dimensions, and as the allowable magnitude of the surface irregularities. Allowable variation from specified lines, grades, and dimensions are listed in table G-13, and allowable magnitudes for concrete surface irregularities are listed in table G-14.

The intent of this section is to establish tolerances that are consistent with modern construction practice, yet are governed by the effect that permissible variations may have upon a structure. The Government reserves the right to diminish the tolerances set forth herein if such tolerances impair the structural action, operational function, or architectural appearance of a structure or portion thereof.

Concrete shall be within all stated tolerances even though more than one tolerance may be specified for a particular concrete structure: *Provided,* that the specified variation for one element of a structure shall not apply when it will permit another element of the structure to exceed its allowable variation. Where tolerances are not specified or shown on the drawings for a particular structure, tolerances shall be those specified for similar work. As an exception to the notice in these specifications for "Order of Precedence", specific tolerances shown on the drawings in connection with any dimension shall govern. The contractor shall be responsible for finishing the concrete and for setting and maintaining concrete forms within the limits necessary to ensure that the completed work will be within the tolerances specified. Concrete work that exceeds the tolerance limits specified shall be remedied in accordance with subsections (d) and (e).

(b) *Variations from Specified Lines, Grades, and Dimensions.*—Hardened concrete structures shall be checked by the contractor and will be subject to such inspection and measurement as needed to determine that the structures are within the tolerances specified in table G-13.

Variation is defined as "the distance between the actual position of the structure or any element of the structure and the specified position in plan for the structure or the particular element". Plus or minus variations, shown as (±), indicate a permitted actual position up or down or in or out from the specified position in plan. Variations not designated as plus or minus indicate the maximum deviation permitted between designated successive points on the completed element of construction. Specified position in plan is defined as "the lines, grades, and dimensions described in these specifications or shown on the drawings or as otherwise prescribed by the Contracting Officer".

(c) *Concrete Surface Irregularities*:

(1) *General.*—Bulges, depressions, and offsets are defined as "concrete surface irregularities". Concrete surface irregularities are classified as "abrupt" or "gradual", and are measured relative to the actual concrete surface. See table G-14.

(2) *Abrupt Surface Irregularities.*—Abrupt surface irregularities are defined herein as "offsets such as those caused by misplaced or loose forms, loose knots in form lumber, or other similar forming faults." Abrupt surface irregularities are measured using a short straight edge, at least 6 inches long, held firmly against the concrete surface over the irregularity, and the magnitude of the offset is determined by direct measurement.

(3) *Gradual Surface Irregularities.*—Gradual surface irregularities are defined herein as "bulges and depressions resulting in gradual changes on the concrete surface". Gradual surface irregularities are measured using a template conforming to the design profile of the concrete surface being examined. Templates for measuring gradual surface irregularities shall be provided by the contractor. Templates shall be at least 8 feet in length. The magnitude of gradual surface irregularities is defined herein as "a measure of the rate of change in slope of the concrete surface". Gradual surface irregularities are measured using a template held firmly against the concrete surface, and the magnitude is computed.

The magnitude of gradual surface irregularities on concrete surfaces shall be checked by the contractor to ensure that the surfaces are within specified tolerances. The Government will also make such checks of hardened concrete surfaces as determined necessary to ensure compliance with these specifications. Templates for these surfaces shall be furnished by the contractor and shall be available for use by the Government at all times.

(d) *Repair of Hardened Concrete Not Within Specified Tolerances.*—Hardened concrete which is not within specified tolerances shall be repaired to bring it within those tolerances. Such repair shall be in accordance with section G.89, and shall be

Table G-13.—Variations from specified lines, grades, and dimensions.

TOLERANCES FOR DAM STRUCTURES	
1. Footings for columns, piers, walls, buttresses, and similar members.	
(a) Variation in length and width of dimensions from those specified	−½ inch, + 2 inches
(b) Horizontal misplacement or eccentricity:	
(1) 2 percent of footing width in direction of misplacement, but not more than	2 inches
(c) Reduction in thickness from that specified	5 percent of specified thickess
2. Variation of controlling dimensions for each structure from specified position in plan with reference to dam axis:	
Overall dimensions	Exposed, ± 1 inch Buried, ± 2½ inches
3. Variation from centerline specified in plan for [1](spillway, outlet works, ________):	
(a) For overall length, except for buried construction	±1 inch
(b) For any span less than 20 feet, except for buried construction	½ inch
(c) For buried construction	Twice the above values
4. Variation from specified grade for [1](spillway, outlet works, ____________________):	
(a) For ogee crest of uncontrolled hydraulic structures	±½ inch
(b) For all other surfaces	±1 inch
(c) For any span less than 10 feet	½ inch
5. Variation from plumb, specified batter, or specified curved profile for lines and surfaces of columns, walls, piers, buttresses, arch sections, vertical joint grooves, and arrises:	
(a) Exposed construction, except elevator shafts:	
(1) When overall height of line or surface is:	
10 feet or less	±½ inch
More than 10 feet	±¾ inch
(2) For any two successive intermediate points on the line or surface separated by:	
10 feet	½ inch
20 feet or more	¾ inch
(b) Elevator shafts:	
(1) When overall height of line or surface is:	
10 feet or less	±½ inch
More than 10 feet	±1 inch
(2) For any two successive points on the line or surface separated by:	
10 feet	½ inch
20 feet or more	¾ inch
(c) Buried construction	Twice the values shown in 4(a)
6. Variation in cross-sectional dimensions from those specified for columns, beams, buttresses, piers, and similar members	−¼ inch, + ½ inch
7. Variation in thickness of slabs, walls, arch sections, and similar members from that specified	−¼ inch, +½ inch
8. Variation from plumb or level for invert and sidewalls of each wheel-mounted gate slot, for sidewalls of each penstock stoplog guide, and for similar watertight joints:	
(a) When overall length of line is:	
10 feet or less	±⅛ inch

Table G-13.—Variations from specified lines, grades, and dimensions.—Continued.

More than 10 feet	±¾ inch
(b) For any two successive intermediate points on the line or surface separated by:	
10 feet	⅛ inch
20 feet or more	¾ inch
9. Variation from that specified in distance between vertical sidewalls of each wheel-mounted gate slot and between sidewalls of penstock stoplog guides	−½ inch, + ½ inch
10. Variation in location from specified position in plan of sleeves, floor openings, and wall openings	±½ inch
11. Variation in sizes from those specified for sleeves, floor openings, and wall openings	±¼ inch
TOLERANCES FOR TUNNEL LINING AND MONOLITHIC CONDUITS	
1. Tunnels and conduits with flow velocity less than 20 feet per second:	
(a) Departure from excavated alignment	±2 inches
(b) Departure from specified grade	±1 inch
2. Tunnels and conduits with flow velocity greater than 20 feet per second:	
(a) Departure from excavated alignment	±1 inch
(b) Departure from specified grade	±½ inch
3. Variation in thickness, at any point from that specified:	
(a) Tunnel lining	−0
(b) Conduits	−2.5 percent or ¼ inch, whichever is greater
(c) Conduits	+5 percent or ½ inch, whichever is greater
4. Variation from specified inside dimensions	0.5 percent

[1]Insert applicable structure.

accomplished in a manner approved by the Contracting Officer. Concrete repair to bring concrete within tolerances shall be done only after consultation with a Government inspector regarding the method of repair. The Government shall be notified as to the time when repair will be performed.

Concrete which will be exposed to public view shall be repaired in a manner which will result in a concrete surface with a uniform appearance. [97][Concrete surfaces which may be subject to high-velocity flow, see parts 1 and 3 of table G-14, shall, without exception, be repaired as necessary to bring surfaces within specified tolerances.] Grinding of concrete surfaces exposed to view [97](and surfaces subject to high-velocity flow) shall be limited in depth such that no aggregate particles are exposed more than 1/16 inch in cross-section at the finished surface. Where grinding has caused or will cause exposure of aggregate particles greater than 1/16 inch in cross-section at the finished surface, concrete shall be repaired by excavating and replacing the concrete.

(e) *Prevention of Repeated Failure to Meet Tolerances.*—When concrete placements result in hardened concrete that does not meet specified tolerances, the contractor shall, upon request, submit to the Government an outline of all preventative actions, such as modifications to forms, modified procedure for setting screeds, an different finishing techniques, to be implemented by the contractor to avoid repeated failures. The Government reserves the right to delay concrete placements until the contractor implements such preventative actions which are approved by the Contracting Officer.

[97]Delete when no concrete will be subjected to high-velocity flow.

Table G-14.—Tolerances for concrete surface irregularities.[1]

1. Abrupt irregularities on surfaces subject to high-velocity hydraulic flow:

   [2][(a) F4 surfaces of the ______ for a distance up from the floor varying linearly from ______ at station ______ to ______ at station ______, including formed floor surfaces:]

   Nonparallel to flow .... 1/8 inch
   Parallel to flow .... 1/4 inch

   [3][(b) F4 surfaces of the ______ for adistance up from the floor varying linearly from ______ at station ______ to ______ at station ______, including formed floor surfaces] .... 1/32 inch

   [4][(c) Unformed surfaces of the ______ from station ______ to ______] .... 1/32 inch

2. Abrupt irregularities on surfaces not subject to high-velocity flow:

   (a) F1 surfaces, depressions only .... 1 inch
   (b) F2 surfaces .... 1/4 inch
   (c) F3 surfaces .... 1/8 inch
   (d) U1 surfaces .... 1/4 inch
   (e) U2 surfaces .... 1/32 inch
   (f) U3 surfaces .... None
   (g) U4 surfaces .... 1/16 inch

3. Gradual irregularities on surfaces subject to high-velocity hydraulic flow:

   [2][(a) F4 surfaces and unformed surfaces of the ______ for a distance up from the floor varying linearly from ______ at station ______ to ______ at station ______, including floor surfaces. Measured with templates perpendicular and parallel to the flow] .... 1/16 inch per inch

   [3][(b) F4 surfaces and unformed surfaces of the ______ for a distance up from the floor varying linearly from ______ at station ______ to ______ at station ______, including floor surfaces:]

   (1) Measured with templates perpendicular and parallel to flow .... 1/16 inch per inch
   (2) Measured with template perpendicular to flow .... 1/16 inch per inch
   (3) Measured with template parallel to flow .... 1/32 inch per inch

4. Gradual irregularities on surfaces not subject to high-velocity flow:

   (a) F2 surfaces .... 1/8 inch per inch
   (b) F3 surfaces .... 1/16 inch per inch
   (c) U2 surfaces .... 1/8 inch per inch
   (d) U3 surfaces .... 1/16 inch per inch

[1]Tolerance values should be modified as required for the work. If flow velocities exceed 120 ft/s, additional tolerances must be specified.
[2]Include this provision for hydraulic surfaces, such as spillways, that are subject to velocities from 40 to 90 ft/s.
[3]Include as in footnote 2 for velocities from 90 to 120 ft/s.
[4]Include as in footnote 2 for velocities from 40 to 120 ft/s.

G.86. *Preparations for Placing.*—

(a) *General.*—No concrete shall be placed until all formwork, installation of items to be embedded, and preparation of surfaces involved in the placement have been approved.

The contractor shall supply concrete placement checkout cards satisfactory to the Government, and shall provide a watertight container for such cards at a convenient location near each individual concrete placement site. The cards shall list all the various work items; for example, "Cleanup" and "Embedded items," required prior to placement of concrete. After each work item for an individual placement has been completed, that item on the card shall be signed by the contractor or his representative signifying completion of the required work. Authorized Government personnel will inspect the work during and after completion of each phase of the preparations and, if the work is satisfactory, will sign the checkout card. Approval of preparations for placement will not be complete until the contractor or his representative and authorized Government personnel have approved, by signature, all applicable items for that placement. The use of placement checkout cards may be waived by the Government where their use is impracticable.

All surfaces of forms and embedded materials shall be free from curing compound, dried mortar from previous placements, and other foreign substances before the adjacent or surrounding concrete placement is begun.

Prior to beginning concrete placement, the contractor shall make ready a sufficient number of properly operating vibrators and operators, and shall have readily available additional vibrators to replace defective ones during the progress of the placement. The Government inspector at the placement may require that the contractor delay the start of the concrete placement until the number of working vibrators available is acceptable.

(b) [98][*Tunnel Surfaces.*—The surfaces of tunnels against which concrete is to be placed shall be prepared in accordance with section G.53.]

(c) *Foundation Surfaces.*—All [98](other) surfaces upon or against which concrete is to be placed shall be free from frost and ice, water, mud, and debris.

(1) Rock surfaces shall be free from oil, objectionable coatings, and loose, semidetached and unsound fragments. Immediately prior to placement of concrete, surfaces of rock shall be washed with an air-water jet and shall be brought to a uniform surface-dry condition.

(2) Earth foundations shall be damp when concrete is placed against them. Surfaces shall be thoroughly moist but not muddy to a depth of 6 inches, or to impermeable material, whichever is less.

(d) *Construction Joints.*—A construction joint is defined as "a planned joint where two placements of concrete meet, across which development and maintenance of bond are required, and through which any reinforcement that may be present is not interrupted". All construction joints [99](except ______________) shall be roughened, and all laitance removed in preparation for adjoining concrete. [100][In addition, all construction joints of the ____ shall be roughened to a full amplitude of ¼ inch.] Methods of roughening surfaces and removing laitance may include mechanical abrasion or cutting, sandblasting, acid etching, or high-pressure water jetting of hardened (not green) concrete. Water jetting will normally be at pressures of at least 6,000 pounds per square inch. All methods are subject to the approval of the Contracting Officer. Construction joints [99](including ______________) shall be thoroughly cleaned of loose or defective concrete, coatings, sand, curing compound, and other foreign material on the surface.

After this initial cleanup and at the last opportunity prior to placing concrete, concrete surfaces shall be thoroughly washed with water or air water jets, and shall be uniformly surface dried.

*[(e) *Type B Control Joints and Contraction Joints.*—Type B control and contraction joints serve to provide for volumetric shrinkage of monolithic concrete and for movement between monolithic units at established joints, thus preventing formation of objectionable shrinkage cracks elsewhere in the concrete. Prior to application of wax-base curing compound to type B control and contraction joints, the surfaces of all joints shall be cleaned thoroughly of accretions of concrete or other foreign material by scraping, chipping, or other means approved by the Contracting Officer. Curing compound shall not be removed, but shall remain on these joints and be kept intact until adjoining concrete is placed. Waterstops, reinforcing bars, and other embedded items shall be free of curing compound when adjoining concrete is placed.]

G.87. *Placing.*—(a) *General.*—The contractor shall notify the Contracting Officer before batching begins for placement of concrete. Unless inspection is waived for that specific placement, placing shall be performed only in the presence of an authorized Government inspector. Placement shall not begin until all preparations are complete and the concrete placement check-out card has been signed by the contractor or his representative and the authorized representative of the Contracting Officer, substantiating completion of all preparations for that placement.

All surfaces upon or against which concrete is to be placed shall be prepared in accordance with section G.86. Retempering of concrete will not be permitted. Concrete which has become so stiff that proper placing cannot be assured shall be wasted.

Concrete shall not be placed in standing water except with written permission from the Contracting Officer, and the method of placing shall be sub-

[98]Delete if there are no tunnel surfaces.

[99]In the space provided, list applicable structures or parts of structures for which construction joint preparation will not include roughening the surface and removing laitance. Generally, this is not required in free-flow tunnels.

[100]List applicable structures or parts of structures for which joint preparation includes roughening the surface to a minimum of ¼ inch. This will only be required when shear friction design method assumes the coefficient of friction (μ) to be 1.0λ.

*Delete or revise as applicable.

ject to approval. Concrete shall not be placed in running water, and shall not be subjected to running water until after the concrete has hardened.

Concrete shall be deposited as nearly as practical in its final position and shall not be allowed to flow in such a manner that the lateral movement will cause segregation of the coarse aggregate from the concrete mass. Methods and equipment employed in depositing concrete in forms shall minimize clusters of coarse aggregate. Clusters that occur shall be scattered before the concrete is vibrated.

Forms shall be constantly monitored and their position adjusted as necessary during concrete placement in accordance with section G.83.

All concrete, *(except concrete in tunnel lining and concrete placed on unformed slopes), shall be placed in approximately horizontal layers. The depths of layers shall not exceed 20 inches. The Government reserves the right to require lesser depths of layers where concrete cannot otherwise be placed and consolidated in accordance with the requirements of these specifications. Exposed construction joints shall be made straight and level or plumb except as shown otherwise on the drawings.

Except as shown otherwise on the drawings, construction joints intersecting sloping exposed concrete surfaces shall be inclined near the exposed surface to prevent feather edges. The angle between such an inclined surface and the form shall be not less than 50° nor more than 130°, and that surface angle shall extend into the concrete member for at least 3 inches.

To facilitate consolidation and bond at construction joints, structural concrete placements [101][containing 1½-inch or less nominal MSA (maximum size aggregate)] shall either be started with an oversanded mix or else the concrete immediately above the joint shall be vibrated with twice as much time and effort as normally needed for concrete of that consistency. The oversanded mix shall be placed 2 to 6 inches deep on the joint and shall contain ¾-inch nominal MSA; a maximum net water-*(cement) (cementitious materials) ratio of 0.47, by weight; 2 percent additional sand, by volume of total aggregate, based on standard ¾-inch mix; 6 percent air, by total volume of concrete; and having a maximum slump of 4 inches. [101][Structural concrete placements containing 3-inch nominal MSA shall be started with the above-specified oversanded mix placed 2 to 6 inches deep on the joint.]

*[If concrete is placed monolithically around openings having vertical dimensions greater than 2 feet; or if concrete in decks, floor slabs, beam girders, or other similar parts of structures is placed monolithically with supporting concrete, the following requirements shall be strictly observed:

(1) Concrete shall be placed up to the top of the formed openings at which point further placement will be delayed to accommodate settlement of fresh concrete. If bevels are specified beneath nearly horizontal structural members such as decks, floor slabs, beams, and girders, such bevels being between the nearly horizontal members and the vertical supporting concrete below, concrete shall be placed to the bottom of the bevels before delay of placement.

(2) The last 2 feet or more of concrete placed below horizontal members or bevels shall be placed with a 2-inch or less slump and shall be thoroughly consolidated.

(3) Placing of concrete shall be delayed from 1 to 3 hours, but in no case shall placement be delayed so long that the concrete placed before the delay is not readily penetrated by vibrators.

When consolidating concrete which is placed over formed openings after the delay period has elapsed and placement resumes, it is especially important that adequate consolidation be achieved in the concrete at the interface of the fresh concrete and the underlying plastic concrete. The vibrator shall repeatedly penetrate and thoroughly reconsolidate the upper portion of the underlying concrete which was placed before the delay.]

*[The equipment used in placing concrete tunnel lining, and the methods of operation, shall not cause concrete to be discharged into the forms at high velocity. The end of the discharge line shall be kept well buried in the fresh concrete during placement of the arch and sidewalls to assure complete filling. The depth of this burial shall be from 5 to 10 feet, depending upon the thickness of the arch. The end of the discharge line shall be marked so as to readily indicate the depth of burial at all times. Pneumatic equipment, if used to place the tunnel invert, shall be equipped to prevent separation and segregation of the concrete during discharge.]

[101]Delete when concrete containing aggregate larger than 1½-inch nominal MSA is not specified.

*Delete or revise as applicable.

[102][Where placements are terminated with sloping joints, the contractor shall thoroughly consolidate the concrete at such joints to a reasonably uniform and stable slope. If thorough consolidation at the sloping joints is not obtained, the Government reserves the right to require the use of bulkhead construction joints. The concrete at the surface of such sloping joints shall be clean and surface dry before being covered with fresh concrete. The cleaning of such sloping joints shall consist of the removal of all loose and foreign material.]

In placing concrete on unformed slopes so steep as to make internal vibration of the concrete impractical without forming, the concrete shall be placed ahead of a nonvibrating, slip-form screed extending about 2½ feet back from its leading edge. Concrete ahead of the slip-form screed shall be consolidated by internal vibrators so as to ensure complete filling under the slip form.

A cold joint is an unplanned joint resulting when a concrete surface hardens before the next batch is placed against it. Cold joints are undesirable and should be avoided. However, in the event of equipment breakdown or other unavoidable prolonged interruption of continuous placing when it appears that unconsolidated concrete may harden to the extent that later vibration will not fully consolidate it, the contractor shall immediately consolidate such concrete to a stable and uniform slope. If delay of placement is then short enough to permit penetration of the underlying concrete, placement shall resume with particular care being taken to thoroughly penetrate and revibrate the concrete surface placed before the delay. If concrete cannot be penetrated with a vibrator, the cold joint shall then be treated as a construction joint if the design requirements are such that a construction joint is practical. If a construction joint will impair the structural integrity, as determined by the Contracting Officer, the concrete shall be repaired as determined by the Contracting Officer. Repairs in some instances will include removal of all or a portion of the previously placed concrete, and the contractor will not be entitled to any payment for such work.

Care shall be taken to prevent cold joints when placing concrete in any part of the work. The concrete placing rate shall ensure concrete is placed while the previously-placed, adjacent concrete is plastic so that the concrete can be made monolithic by normal use of the vibrators.

Concrete shall not be placed in rain sufficiently heavy or prolonged to wash mortar from concrete. A cold joint may necessarily result from prolonged heavy rainfall.

The contractor shall be entitled to no additional payment, over the unit prices bid in the schedule for concrete, by reason of any limitations in the placing of concrete required under the provisions of this section.

(b) *Transportation.*—Normally, concrete shall be deposited in its final position in the placement within 90 minutes after the introduciton of the mix water and *(cement) (cementitious materials) into the mixer. This limitation may be waived if the concrete is of such slump and workability and contains the specified entrained air content after the 1½-hour time limit that it can be satisfactorily placed without the addition of water. Furthermore, a time limit less than 90 minutes may be invoked during hot weather or under conditions contributing to quick stiffening of the concrete. The methods and equipment used for transporting concrete from the batch plant and the elapsed time during transportation shall not cause measurable segregation of coarse aggregate or slump loss exceeding 2 inches.

Concrete shall be deposited as near as practical to its final position using buckets, chutes, conveyors, or concrete pumps. The use of aluminum pipe or aluminum chutes for delivery of concrete will not be permitted. Concrete buckets shall be capable of promptly discharging concrete of the specified mix design, and the dumping mechanism shall be capable of discharging, at one location, repeated small portions of concrete from a full bucket. Buckets and conveyors shall be designed for attaching drop chutes or tremmies, which shall be used to deposit concrete whenever the concrete must be dropped more than 10 feet from the bucket to the placing surface.

Concrete pumps shall be equipped with slicklines having a minimum diameter of 5 inches. Pumps and slicklines shall be capable of transporting concrete containing a maximum amount of coarse aggregate and a minimum amount of sand, cement, and water. The minimum proportion of ¾- to 1½-inch aggregate shall be 5.5 cubic feet (solid volume) per cubic

[102]Include for free-flow tunnels only.

*Delete or revise as applicable.

yard of concrete and, dependent upon shape and texture of aggregate used, this proportion will be increased as practical.

Buckets, chutes, hoppers, pumps, transit mix trucks, and other equipment shall readily handle and place concrete of the specified slump. The contractor shall, when directed, replace inadequate transporting equipment with acceptable equipment.

(c) *Consolidation.*—Concrete shall be consolidated by vibration. The vibration shall be sufficient to remove all undesirable air voids from the concrete, including the air voids trapped against forms and construction joints. Close attention and additional effort may be required to adequately consolidate concrete adjacent to construction joints and sloping surfaces. Such close attention and additional effort required to consolidate concrete adjacent to construction joints and sloping surfaces shall be at no additional cost to the Government. After consolidation, the concrete shall be free of rock pockets and honeycomb areas, and shall be closed snugly against all surfaces of forms, construction joints, and embedments.

Except as hereinafter provided, consolidation of all concrete shall be by immersion-type vibrators. Immersion-type vibrators shall be operated in a nearly vertical position and the vibrating head shall penetrate and revibrate the concrete in the upper portion of the underlying layer. Care shall be exercised to avoid contact of the vibrating head with embedded items and with formed surfaces which will later be exposed to view. Concrete shall not be placed upon other plastic concrete until the previously-placed concrete has been thoroughly consolidated.

*[Consolidation of concrete in the sidewalls and arch of tunnel lining shall be by rigidly attached form vibrators supplemented where practicable by immersion-type vibrators.]

Immersion-type vibrators shall be operated at speeds of at least 7,000 vibrations per minute when immersed in concrete. *[Form vibrators shall operate at speeds of at least 8,000 vibrations per minute when consolidating concrete.] The contractor shall immediately replace improperly operating vibrators with acceptable vibrators.

G.88. *Finishes and Finishing.*—(a) *General.*—The classes of finish and the requirements for finishing of concrete surfaces shall be as specified in this section, sections G.83 and G.85, or as otherwise indicated on the drawings. The contractor shall notify the Contracting Officer before finishing concrete. Unless inspection is waived in each specific case, finishing of concrete shall be performed only when a Government inspector is present. Concrete surfaces will be tested by the Government in accordance with section G.85 where necessary to determine whether the concrete surface is within the specified tolerances. Finished concrete which is not within the specified tolerances shall be repaired in accordance with section G.89.

(b) *Formed Surfaces.*—The classes of finish for formed concrete surfaces are designated by the symbols *(F1, F2, F3, and F4). Unless otherwise specified or indicated on the drawings, the classes of finish shall apply as follows:

(1) *F1.*—Finish F1 applies to formed surfaces upon or against which fill material or concrete is to be placed. Form tie rod ends on surfaces which will be in contact with fill material shall be protected from moisture if they are below the maximum water table elevation. Protection shall consist of recessing the tie rod ends and filling the recesses with dry pack or other approved material or by a waterproofing system approved by the Contracting Officer. Form tie rod ends on surfaces which will be in contact with concrete or form tie rod ends in contact with fill material above the maximum water table elevation may be cut off flush with the formed surfaces or may be recessed without filling.

(2) *F2.*—Finish F2 applies to all formed surfaces not permanently concealed by fill material or concrete, or not required to receive finish *(F3 or F4).

(3) *F3.*—Finish F3 applies to formed surfaces, the appearance of which is considered by the Government to be of special importance, such as surfaces of structures prominently exposed to public view.

(4) *F4.*—Finish F4 applies to formed surfaces for which accurate alignment and evenness of surface are of paramount importance from the standpoint of eliminating destructive effects of water.

(c) *Unformed Surfaces.*—The classes of finish for unformed concrete surfaces are designated by the symbols *(U1, U2, and U3). Interior surfaces shall be sloped for drainage where shown on the

*Delete or revise as applicable.

drawings, or as directed. Surfaces that will be exposed to the weather and which would normally be level shall be sloped for drainage. Unless the use of other slopes or level surfaces is indicated on the drawings or directed, narrow surfaces, such as *(tops of walls and curbs), shall be sloped about 3/8 inch per foot of width; and broader surfaces, such as *(walks, roadways, platforms, and decks), shall be sloped about 1/4 inch per foot. Unless otherwise specified or indicated on the drawings, these classes of finish shall apply as follows:

(1) *U1.*—Finish U1 (screeded finish) applies to unformed surfaces that will be covered by fill material or by concrete, *(surfaces of operating platforms on canal structures, and surfaces of subfloors that will be covered by concrete floor topping). Finish U1 is also used as the first stage of finishes U2 and U3. Finish operations shall consist of sufficient leveling and screeding to produce even, uniform surfaces.

(2) *U2.*—Finish U2 (floated finish) applies to unformed surfaces not permanently concealed by fill material or concrete, or not required to receive finish *(U1 or U3). Finish U2 is also used as the second stage of finish U3. Floating may be performed by use of hand- or power-driven equipment. Floating shall be started as soon as the screeded surfaces have stiffened sufficiently, but before bleed water forms, and shall be the minimum necessary to produce a surface that is free from screed marks and is uniform in texture. If finish U3 is to be applied, floating shall be continued until a small amount of mortar without excess water is brought to the surface, so as to permit effective troweling. Joints and edges shall be tooled where shown on the drawings or as directed.

(3) *U3.*—Finish U3 (troweled finish) applies to spillway, floor slabs, and to inverts of tunnel spillways. After bleed water has disappeared, and when floated surface has hardened sufficiently to prevent an excess of fine material from being drawn to the surface, steel troweling shall be started. Steel troweling shall be performed with firm pressure so as to flatten the sandy texture of the floated surface and produce a dense uniform surface, free from blemishes and trowel marks.

G.89. Repair of Concrete.—(a) *General.*—Concrete shall be repaired in accordance with this section, section G.85, and Bureau of Reclamation "Standard Specifications for Repair of Concrete", dated January 4, 1982: *Except*, that epoxy-bonded, epoxy mortar shall not be used for outside repairs having a surface area greater than 1 square foot.

Minor formed surface repairs, such as sack rubbing or surface grinding, shall be completed within 2 hours after form removal. Dry-pack, concrete replacement less than 10 inches thick, and portland cement mortar repairs shall be completed within 7 days of the original concrete placement, or shall utilize approved epoxy-resin bonding systems. Repairs involving epoxy-resin bonding systems shall be performed after 7 days and before 60 days from the original placement. Concrete replacement over 10 inches thick and all other repairs shall be completed within 60 days after the original placement.

(b) *Types of Repairs.*—[103][Repair of concrete in ____________[104](and to such other areas as directed by the Contracting Officer), shall be made with concrete replacement, epoxy-bonded concrete, dry-pack, portland-cement mortar, epoxy-bonded epoxy mortar, or injected epoxy resin where and as applicable for the type of repair involved, as provided in the "Standard Specifications for Repair of Concrete".

Recesses resulting from removal of tie rod ends shall be filled with dry pack or other approved material unless the recesses are later to be covered by concrete; or are later to be covered by fill material and are above the maximum water table elevation.

[105][Repair of concrete [106](on surfaces required to receive finish F3) [106](in the following areas of the

---

*Delete or revise as applicable.

[103]Insert description of existing structure or portions thereof for which use of concrete, epoxy-bonded concrete, and epoxy-bonded epoxy mortar repairs will be required. Delete this subsection when use of epoxy-bonded concrete and epoxy-bonded epoxy mortar repairs are not mandatory for any part of the work.

[104]Include this phrase only when the extent and location of any portion of the repairs to be made cannot be determined until after award of contract. Normally, this phrase will only apply to repair of existing concrete, such as previously constructed stilling basins, where the repair areas are under water and the full extent of repairs required are to be determined after award of contract.

[105]Include this paragraph when repair of specific surfaces of concrete will be limited to concrete, dry-pack, or epoxy-bonded concrete, such as for surfaces which, for architectural purposes, the use of portland-cement mortar or epoxy mortar repairs are not desired. List the surfaces to which this provision will apply.

[106]Delete or revise as required. The two parts of this sentence that are in parentheses are alternates, and only one will be used. If the part referring to finish F3 is used, insert a period after "Standard Specifications" and delete balance of sentence.

work) shall be made with concrete replacement, dry-pack, or epoxy-bonded concrete, where and as applicable for the type of repair involved, as provided in the "Standard Specifications for Repair of Concrete":

(1) ______, (2) ______, and (3) ______.]

[107][All other repairs shall be made with concrete replacement, dry-pack, or portland cement mortar; or with epoxy-bonded concrete, epoxy-bonded epoxy mortar, or injected epoxy resin; where and as applicable for the type of repair involved, as provided in the "Standard Specifications for Repair of Concrete".]

When concrete surfaces are repaired with epoxy-bonded epoxy mortar, the surfaces of the finished epoxy mortar shall, in areas visible to the public, be lightly ground or otherwise prepared to eliminate gloss and produce a surface color and texture that closely matches the surrounding concrete surfaces.

[108][(c) *Samples.*—The contractor shall submit samples of epoxy-bonding agent and graded sand for use in mix design of epoxy mortar in accordance with the "Standard Specifications for Repair of Concrete".]

[109][(d) *Cost.*—The cost of furnishing all materials and performing all work required in the repair of concrete shall be borne by the contractor.]

G.90. *Protection.*—The contractor shall protect all concrete against damage until final acceptance by the Government. Concrete shall not be loaded, forms and shoring shall not be removed, and backfill shall not be placed against concrete until the concrete has gained sufficient strength to safely support its weight and all imposed loads.

Fresh concrete shall be protected against erosion, rain, hail, sleet or snow, contamination from foreign materials, and damage from foot traffic until the concrete has hardened. [110][Hardened concrete surfaces that received U2 or U3 finishes shall be protected against damage from foot traffic and other construction activity by covering with protective mats or plywood or by other effective means.] Methods of protection shall be subject to approval by the Government.

[111][Whenever freezing temperatures are imminent, the contractor shall enclose exposed concrete with warmth-retaining sheets or other insulating means, and maintain the concrete at a temperature of not less than 50° F for 72 hours after placement. In addition, concrete being water-cured shall be protected from freezing for the duration of the curing cycle. Then, after discontinuance of the water curing, this concrete shall be maintained at a temperature of not less than 50° F for 72 hours.

Where artifical heat is employed, special care shall be taken to prevent the concrete from drying. Use of unvented combustion heaters will not be permitted during the first 24 hours of curing unless sunformed concrete surfaces are sealed from the resulting carbon-dioxide-rich environment.]

Discontinuance of protection against cold temperatures shall be such that the drop in temperature of any portion of the concrete will be gradual and will not exceed 5° F per hour and 40° F in 24 hours [112](for thin sections and 5° F per hour and 20° F in 24 hours for massive sections greater than 36 inches).

When precipitation [111](or freezing weather) appears imminent, the contractor shall immediately make ready at the placement site all materials which may be required for protection of concrete. The government may delay placement of concrete until adequate provisions for protection against weather are made.

Concrete curing membranes shall be kept intact, and other curing materials and processes shall be maintained as necessary to assure continuous curing for the minimum specified curing time. Protection of curing membranes and other curing methods shall be as described in section G.91.

G.91. *Curing.*—[113](a) *General.*—The contractor shall furnish all materials and perform all work required for curing concrete.

[114][Concrete shall be cured either by water curing or by the use of white wax-base or white water-

[107]When the paragraphs noted by footnotes 103 and 105 are deleted, delete the word "other". This paragraph will apply for all repairs except when specific features or surfaces are to be limited to specific methods of repair listed in footnotes 103 and 105.

[108]Include this subsection when submission of samples is considered necessary. Normally, samples will be specifically required only when high-velocity flow surfaces are involved in the work, such as those surfaces in spillways and outlet works.

[109]Delete this subsection and substitute "Measurement" and "Payment" statements when specifications are being prepared for repair work for which payment will be made.

[110]Delete when U2 or U3 finishes are not required.

[111]Delete or revise as required, especially in areas not subject to freezing.

[112]Delete if no massive sections exist.

[113]This subsection, G.91(a), should be modified to suit conditions at each job.

[114]In general, the first requirements will be used for work involving concrete dams, concrete structures appurtenant to earth dams, canal and lateral linings and structures, tunnel linings and structures, and similar types of concrete work where appearance may not be a requirement.

emulsified resin-base curing compound, except as otherwise provided].

[115][Concrete in tunnel lining need not be sealed for curing if the relative humidity at the placement site continuously exceeds 85 percent. Otherwise, tunnel lining shall be cured by water curing or application of curing compound. The Government will provide equipment and monitor the relative humidity.]

[116][Surfaces of concrete that will remain prominently exposed shall be cured by the use of a clear, resin-base curing compound, either CRC-101 or water-emulsified resin-base curing compound. These surfaces include the following: (list surfaces here)].

*[Concrete surfaces that will receive a finish of cement-base coating shall be cured by the use of either white wax-base, curing compound, or white water-emulsified, resin-base, curing compound. These surfaces include the following: (list surfaces here)].

[117][Surfaces of construction joints shall be water-cured or cured by covering with polyethylene film or cured by the use of white wax-base or white water-emulsified resin-base curing compound. Immediately prior to placement of concrete on or against these surfaces, concrete shall be prepared in accordance with section G.86.

[118][Contraction joint surfaces and type "B" control joint surfaces shall be cured by the use of wax-base curing compound. All extraneous concrete accretions and other foreign materials shall be removed from the surfaces of contraction joints and type "B" control joints to provide a smooth, clean surface prior to application of the curing compound.]

All concrete surfaces shall be treated as specified to prevent loss of moisture from the concrete until the required curing period has elapsed or until immediately prior to placement of other concrete or backfill against those surfaces. Only sufficient time to prepare construction joint surfaces and to bring them to a surface-dry condition shall be allowed between discontinuance of curing and placement of adjacent concrete.

As soon as unformed concrete surfaces have been finished, as specified, and have attained a dull appearance free from bleed water and moist sheen, they shall be treated as specified herein.

Forms shall be removed within 24 hours after the concrete has hardened sufficiently to prevent structural collapse or other damage by careful form removal. Where required, repair of all minor surface imperfections shall be made immediately after form removal. Minor surface repair shall be completed within 2 hours after form removal and shall be immediately followed by the initiation of curing by the applicable method specified herein. Concrete surfaces shall be kept continuously moist after form removal until initiation of curing.

(b) *Materials.*—Materials used for curing shall meet the following requirements:

(1) *Water.*—Water used for curing shall meet the applicable requirements of section G.77 for water used in mixing and curing concrete.

(2) *Curing Compound.*—Wax-base (type I) and water-emulsified, resin-base (type II) curing compounds shall conform to the requirements of "Specifications for Concrete Curing Compound" dated October 1, 1980. The CRC-101 curing compound shall conform to the requirements of "Specifications for Clear Resin-Base Curing Compound, CRC-101", dated January 1, 1981. Curing compounds shall be of uniform consistency and quality within each container and from shipment to shipment.

(3) *Polyethylene Film.*—Polyethylene film for curing concrete shall be [119](clear or) white and shall conform to the requirements of ASTM C 171.

[120][(c) *Sampling, Testing, and Certification.*—The Government will test or require approved manufacturer's certification of all curing compound prior to use.

The contractor shall furnish copies of all purchase orders for curing compound to the Contracting Officer's representative at the jobsite. Copies of

[115]Delete if no tunnel lining.

[116]Include this requirement when specific surfaces are to be cured by application of clear curing compound. Clear curing compound is used for curing concrete exposed to view in powerplants, large pumping plants, concrete tanks, retaining walls, and other structures where appearance is a requirement.

[117]Revise if construction joints will not be cured by application of curing compound.

[118]Include if contraction joint and type "B" control joints are involved in the work. Modify if such joints are to be cured by other means.

*Delete or revise as applicable.

[119]Delete reference to clear polyethylene if the reflectance of white sheeting is required to prevent the temperature of the concrete from becoming excessive due to the sun's radiation, such as with thin, horizontal slabs in a warm climate.

[120]Revise as required to include those requirements applicable to the specified types of curing compound.

the purchase orders shall be furnished far enough in advance of planned use so samples of curing compound, if required as stated below, will be available to the Government to allow a testing period of at least 45 days. The contractor will be informed in writing whether materials covered by each purchase order will be accepted solely on manufacturer's certification of compliance or if testing by the Government will also required. Within 16 days after receipt of the certifications, the Government will notify the contractor whether the certifications conform to specification requirements.

Manufacturer's certification, if required, shall be furnished to the Contracting Officer's representative at the jobsite. The manufacturer shall certify that the material is within 1 percent (by weight of each individual constituent) of the same composition as material which previously has been found to comply with the specifications when completely tested, and shall specify identification data including Bureau of Reclamation solicitation/specifications number, batch number, materials identification, and quantity. In addition, compliance certification from the manufacturer of the CRC–101 curing compound shall include the composition of the materials furnished.

Samples of curing compound, if required, shall be 1 quart in size and, included with each sample, shall be a certification that the sample is from the actual batch from which shipments are to be furnished. Samples and accompanying certifications shall be fully identified as previously described and shall be submitted, shipping costs prepaid, by the contractor.

The contractor shall be responsible for the accuracy of all certifications submitted and data contained therein whether submitted by him, a manufacturer, or a subcontractor. The costs and delays that result from rejection of materials or inadequate certifications shall be the responsibility of the contractor.

[121][(d) *Water Curing.*—Concrete cured with water shall be kept wet for at least 14 days from the time the concrete has attained sufficient set to prevent detrimental effects to the concrete surfaces. The concrete surfaces to be cured shall be kept wet by covering them with water-saturated material; by using a system of perforated pipes, mechanical sprinklers, or porous hose; or by other methods which will keep all surfaces continuously (not periodically) wet. All curing methods are subject to approval by the Contracting Officer.]

[122][Water curing of concrete shall be discontinued after 6 days during periods when the mean daily temperature in the vicinity of the worksite, as determined by the Contracting Officer, is less than 40° F.]

[123][(e) *Curing with Wax-Base or Water-Emulsified Resin-Base Compound.*—Curing by wax-base or water-emulsified resin-base or CRC-101 curing compound shall be by application to designated concrete surfaces to provide a water-retaining film. The curing compound shall be reapplied as necessary to maintain a continuous, water-retaining film on the surface for 28 days. The curing compound shall be mixed thoroughly and spray-applied to the concrete surface in one coat to provide a continuous, uniform film over the concrete. The coverage rate shall not exceed 150 square feet per gallon for wax-base or water-emulsified resin-base compound, and 200 square feet per gallon for CRC-101 compound. On rough surfaces, the coverage rate shall be decreased as necessary to obtain the required continuous film. Special care shall be taken to ensure ample coverage with the compound at edges, corners, and rough surfaces; and to keep curing compound off waterstops and reinforcing bars. Equipment for applying curing compound and the method of application shall be in accordance with the provisions of chapter 6 of the Bureau's *Concrete Manual* [4].]

[124][In applying CRC-101 curing compound, care shall be taken to produce a uniform, continuous film, and to avoid sagging, puddling, and excessive thickness. To prevent sagging on surfaces which are not horizontal, application shall consist of two or more passes over each point on the surface, using a cross-spraying technique, and with a time interval between passes not exceeding 30 minutes. The application shall be performed by personnel qualified, as determined by the Contracting Officer, in using the specified spray techniques. The compound shall be applied in a manner conforming with safe control

[121]Include this subsection when water curing is required or permitted for any part of the concrete work.

[122]Delete in areas of mild climate.

[123]Include this subsection when curing by application of wax-base or water-emulsified resin-base curing compound is required or permitted for any part of the concrete work.

[124]Include when curing by application of clear resin-base curing compound is required or permitted for any part of the work.

proceedings outlined in the Bureau of Reclamation's "Occupational Health and Safety" data sheet on CRC-101 curing compound.

To assure bond of curing compound, the contractor shall, where and as directed by the Contracting Officer, remove excessive form oil from concrete surfaces by washing with a solution of trisodium phosphate, followed by a thorough rinsing of the surfaces with clear water. The trisodium phosphate wash will be required when it is determined by the Contracting Officer that the amount of form oil on the concrete will impair the bond of the curing compound or when surfaces are exposed to public view.

Where curing compound is to be applied, formed concrete surfaces shall be kept continuously moist by repeated light spraying with water until immediately prior to application of curing compound. Curing compound shall be applied as soon as the surface film of moisture has disappeared, but while the concrete still has a damp appearance.

After application of the curing compound has been completed and the coating is dry to touch, all remaining required concrete repairs shall be performed without delay in accordance with section G.89. Completed repairs shall be moistened and coated with curing compound in accordance with the foregoing requirements.]

[125][(f) *Polyethylene Film Curing.*—Curing by this method shall be by completely covering the designated concrete surfaces with polyethylene film to provide an airtight, water-retaining film over the entire concrete surfaces for at least 14 days. As soon as the concrete has hardened sufficiently to prevent damage, all surfaces shall be throughly moistened by spraying them lightly with water and then covering them completely with polyethylene film. Edges of the polyethylene strips shall be lapped to effect a seal to adjacent strips and, at the extreme edge of the curing area, held tightly against the concrete surface. The polyethylene film shall be adequately secured to withstand wind and to prevent circulation of air inside the curing film.]

[126][(1) *Protection of Curing Membranes.*—Curing compound membranes shall be maintained to provide a moistureproof membrane for curing concrete for the minimum period specified. Curing compound that is damaged, or that peels from concrete surfaces within 28 days after application, shall be repaired without delay by moistening the concrete and applying additional compound in a manner satisfactory to the Contracting Officer.

Polyethylene film curing shall be sustained for at least 14 days. The polyethylene film shall be protected as necessary to keep it intact, and the concrete surface shall be kept moist for the full curing period.]

Where foot traffic or other construction activity is necessary on concrete being cured by curing compound or polyethylene film, the curing membrane shall be protected by covering with sand or earth not less than 1 inch thick, with plywood, or by other effective means approved by the Contracting Officer. Protective covering shall not be placed on curing compound until the compound is dry. The contractor shall remove protective coverings before final acceptance of the work.

(g) *Cost.*—The cost of furnishing all materials and performing all work for curing concrete shall be included in the price bid in the schedule for the concrete on which the particular curing methods are required.

G.92. *Measurement of Concrete.*—Measurement, for payment, of concrete required to be placed directly upon or against surfaces of excavation *[except concrete in canal lining] *[and concrete in tunnel lining] will be made to the lines for which payment for excavation is made. *[Measurement, for payment, of concrete in canal lining will be made to the neatlines shown on the drawings. Measurement, for payment, of concrete in tunnel lining will be made in accordance with section G.54]. Measurement, for payment, of all other concrete will be made to the neatlines of the structures, unless otherwise specifically shown on the drawings or prescribed in these specifications.

[127][In the event cavities resulting from overexcavation, as determined by the Contracting Officer, are required to be filled with concrete, the materials furnished by the Government and used for such refilling will be charged to the contractor at their cost to the Government at the point of delivery to the contractor.]

In measuring concrete for payment, the volume of all openings, recesses, ducts, embedded pipes,

[125]Include this subsection when curing by polyethylene film is required or permitted for any part of the concrete work.

[126]Revise as required to include those requirements applicable to the types of curing specified.

[127]Delete if no concrete materials are to be furnished by the Government.

*Delete or revise as applicable.

woodwork, and metalwork, each of which is larger than 100 square inches in cross section, will be deducted.

G.93. ***Payment for Concrete.***—Payment for *(all) concrete *(in various parts of the work) will be made at the *[unit price(s) per cubic yard bid therefore in the schedule for ______________ applicable unit price(s) per cubic yard therfore in the schedule], which unit price(s) shall include the cost of furnishing all materials and performing all work required for the concrete construction, except that payment for furnishing and handling *(cement) (cementitious materials) and payment for furnishing and placing reinforcing bars *(and fabric) will be made at the respective unit price(s) bid therefore in the schedule.

G. MISCELLANEOUS

G.94. ***Diversion and Care of Stream During Construction.***[128]—(a) *General.*—The contractor shall furnish all materials for and shall construct and maintain all cofferdams, channels, flumes, drains, sumps, and/or other temporary diversion and protective works necessary for diversion and care of the stream during construction.

After having served their purpose, all cofferdams or other temporary diversion and protective works downstream from the dam shall be removed from the stream channel, or leveled to give a sightly apperance, so as not to interfere in any way with the operation or usefulness of the reservoir, and in a manner approved by the Contracting Officer. All cofferdams or other temporary diversion and protective works constructed upstream from the dam and not a part of the permanent dam embankment shall be removed or leveled and graded to the extent required to prevent obstruction in any degree whatever of the flow of water to the spillway or outlet works.

The contractor shall be responsible for and shall repair at his expense any damage to the foundations, structures, or any other part of the work caused by floods, water, or failure of any part of the diversion or protective works.

(b) *Plan.*—Prior to beginning any work on the diversion and care of the stream, the contractor shall submit to the Bureau of Reclamation, Attention: D-1300, P.O. Box 25007, Denver, Colorado 80225, for review and approval, a stream diversion plan showing the proposed method for the diversion and care of the stream during construction. For payment purposes, the plan shall contain not more than the number of major divisions of work specified in subsection (e). The plan may be placed in operation upon approval, but nothing in this section shall relieve the contractor from full responsibility for the adequacy of the diversion and protective works.

The hydrographs of ______________ and discharge curves for the spillway and outlet works *(and for diversion) are shown on the drawings solely for the information of the contractor in timing his construction operations to prepare for such flood storage and/or to bypass such flow as may be necessary. The Government assumes no responsibility for any deductions, interpretations, or conclusions which may be made from the curves.

(c) *Diversion and Care of Stream.*—Except as otherwise provided, the contractor shall not interrupt nor interfere with the natural flow of ______________ through the damsite for any purpose without the written approval of the Contracting Officer.

The contractor shall at all times pass the full flow of the stream through the damsite, except that the contractor will be permitted to reduce such flow in the amount of water used for construction purposes as provided in the section of these specifications for "Water for Construction Purposes"; and during the period of closure of the outlet works, the contractor will be permitted to store inflow. [129](______________).

For the purpose of stream diversion, the contractor will be permitted to use any method, as approved by the Contracting Officer, which may include a gap in the dam embankment, temporary pipes or flumes, and/or use of the outlet works.

[128]Specifications presented herein are for the case where the plan for diversion and care of water is designed by the contractor and approved by the Contracting Officer. There are cases where it is prudent for the designer to provide the scheme for diversion and care of water and, if so, provisions for that specific design would be included in the appropriate provision of the specifications.

*Delete or revise as applicable.

[129]Add pertinent information on downstream requirements for water.

*[Prior to initiation of construction of the dam embankment in the diversion gap above the elevation of the diversion channel, the flow of the stream shall be diverted through the outlet works. Embankment construction shall be in accordance with section G.28.]

The contractor shall provide such temporary timbering and other protection as may be necessary to assure smooth, unobstructed flow through the outlet works, and shall provide approved protection of recesses and other surfaces for receiving second-stage concrete and for waterstops.

Rock fragments or other solid materials shall be cleaned from the outlet works prior to diversion and shall be prevented from being washed through the outlet works tunnel. Approved protective works may be required at the entrance to the outlet works to keep the outlet works free of debris. The contractor shall repair at his own expense any damage resulting from the use of the structures for diversion purposes:

[130](______________________________).

(d) *Cleanup and Reservoir Regulation.*—After having served their purpose, all materials placed for temporary diversion and protection shall remain the property of the contractor and shall be removed from the site.

After completion of the spillway structure and of all second-stage concrete in the outlet works structure, *(and prior to the time full downstream releases will commence), the stilling basins shall be unwatered and all sediment, rocks, and debris shall be removed from the hydraulic flow surfaces; and all drainage outlets shall be inspected and cleaned as necessary.

After *(placement of all second-stage concrete and) installation and testing of gates and other metalwork and equipment in the outlet works structure, the Government will operate the gates and regulate the flow in the river, and reserves the right to commence storage in the reservoir.

(e) *Payment.*—Payment for diversion and care of the stream during construction will be made at the lump-sum price bid therefor in the schedule. Except as otherwise provided in section G.17, the lump-sum price bid in the schedule for diversion and care of the stream during construction shall include the cost of furnishing all labor, equipment, and materials for constructing and maintaining cofferdams, dikes, channels, flumes, temporary timberings, and other temporary diversion and protective works; removing or leveling such works, where required; disposing of materials; diverting the stream; making required closures; cleaning the outlet works prior to and after diversion; and all other work required by this section.

The contractor's plan for diversion and care of the stream shall be in such form as to allocate the total lump-sum price to not more than [131](___ major divisions) of the work to be performed under the item of the schedule for diversion and care of the stream during construction. Each major division of work shall be outlined and identified by title, and the plan shall show the proportionate part of the total lump-sum price allocated to each such major division of work. The above allocation of the lump-sum price shall be subject to the approval of the Contracting Officer and, when approved, shall become a part of the contract. In preparing monthly estimates for progress payments, consideration will be given to the percentage of each major division of work performed during the month for which such estimate was prepared.

G.95. *Removal of Water from Foundations.*[132]—(a) *General.*—The contractor shall furnish, install, maintain, and operate all necessary pumping and other equipment for removal of water from the various parts of the work, and for maintaining the foundations and other parts of the work free from water as required for constructing each part of the work.

(b) *Plan.*—Prior to beginning any work on removal of water from foundations, the contractor shall submit to the Bureau of Reclamation, Attention: D-1300, P.O. Box 25007, Denver, Colorado 80225, for review and approval, a plan showing his proposed method for removal of water from foundations. For payment purposes, the plan shall be in not more than ___ major divisions as provided in subsection (d). The plan may be placed in operation

[130]Add special statements covering what contractor will and will not be permitted to do; work to be accomplished before permanent construction may be used for diversion purposes; and work to be accomplished before final closure can be made.

*Delete or revise as applicable.

[131]Number of divisions to be determined for each contract, but will not exceed 12.

[132]Specifications presented herein are for the case where the plan removal of water from the foundation is designed by the contractor and approved by the Contracting Officer. There are cases where it is prudent for the designer to provide a foundation dewatering system and, if so, provisions for that specific design would be included in the appropriate provisions of the specifications.

upon approval, but nothing in this section shall relieve the contractor from full responsibility for the adequacy of the water removal installation.

(c) *Removal of Water from Foundations.*—The contractor's method of removal of water from foundations shall be subject to the approval of the Contracting Officer. The use of a sufficient number of properly screened wells or other equivalent methods will be approved for dewatering. Where excavation of the cutoff trench in the embankment foundations and excavation for the outlet works and spillway structures extends below the water table in common material, the portions below the water table shall be dewatered in advance of excavation. The dewatering shall be accomplished in a manner that will prevent loss of fines from the foundation, will maintain stability of excavated slopes and bottom of the excavation, and will result in construction operations generally being performed in the dry.

*[Protective coating for structure foundations shall be in accordance with section G.23].

The contractor will also be required to control seepage along or from the bottom of the dam embankment cutoff trench, which may require supplementing the approved dewatering systems by pipe drains leading to sumps from which the water shall be pumped. Such pipe drains shall be uniform diameter for each run, shall be provided with grout connections and returns at 25-foot intervals, and shall be embedded in clean reasonably well-graded gravel or like material. No drain shall extend more than 15 feet in the upstream-downstream direction, nor more than 25 feet in a direction parallel to the dam centerline: *Provided*, that trench drains of the upstream and downstream edges of the cutoff trench may be continuous. Drains in the upstream-downstream direction shall be uniformly staggered at stations not closer together than 25 feet on center.

During the placing and compacting of the embankment material in the dam embankment cutoff trench and in the foundation excavation outside the cutoff trench, the water level at every point in the cutoff trench shall be maintained below the bottom of the embankment until the compacted embankment in the cutoff trench at that point has reached a depth of 10 feet, after which the water level shall be maintained at least 5 feet below the top of the compacted embankment. When the embankment has been constructed to an elevation which will permit the dewatering systems to maintain the water level at or below the designated elevations, as determined by the Contracting Officer, the pipe drains and sumps, including surrounding gravel, shall be filled with grout composed of water and cement or clay.

(d) *Payment.*—Payment for removal of water from foundations will be made at the lump-sum price bid therefor in the schedule. Except as otherwise provided in section G.17, the lump-sum price bid in the schedule for removal of water from foundations shall include the cost of furnishing all labor, equipment, and materials for maintaining the work free from water as required for grouting drains and sumps, and all other work required by this section.

The contractor's plan for removal of water from foundations shall be in such form as to allocate the total lump-sum price to not more than ___ major divisions of the work to be performed under the item of the schedule for removal of water from foundations. Each major division of work shall be outlined and identified by title, and the plan shall show the proportionate part of the total lump-sum price allocated to each such major division of work. The above allocation of the lump-sum price shall be subject to the approval of the Contracting Officer and, when approved, shall become part of the contract. In preparing monthly estimates for progress payments, consideration will be given to each major division of work performed during the month for which such estimate was prepared.

G.96. *Concrete or Cement-Bound Curtain.*—The contractor shall construct a mixed-in-place cement-bound curtain, or a concrete or cement-bound curtain constructed by other methods that will be equivalent to a mixed-in-place cement-bound curtain. At least 30 days before beginning any work on the curtain, the contractor shall submit, for approval, plans and specifications for the work. The contractor shall furnish all materials and equipment required to construct the curtain. The curtain shall have a minimum effective thickness of 12 inches and shall be constructed to the depths and elevations shown on the drawings, or established by the Contracting Officer, and as close as practicable to the established lines. The cement used in the curtain shall be portland cement conforming to the requirements of section G.75. Particular efforts should be directed toward maintaining a continuous, unbroken cutoff by bonding around the end of

*Delete or revise as applicable.

the previously placed "pile" whenever shutdown periods occur and construction is again resumed. The curtain, when completed, shall provide a reasonably impervious barrier to the passage of subsurface flows. Any royalties due because of the mixed-in-place cement-bound curtain or other type concrete or cement-bound curtain being placed by patented methods, or use of patented materials, shall be paid by the contractor.

Measurement, for payment, of the curtain will be made of the area of curtain placed, based on the depth and length of the curtain along the centerline of the curtain as shown on the drawings or established by the Contracting Officer. Payment for constructing the curtain will be made at the unit price per square yard bid therefor in the schedule, which unit price shall include the cost of all labor, materials, and equipment required to complete the cutoff curtain, regardless of the type of curtain constructed: *Provided*, that payment for furnishing and handling cement will be made at the unit price per barrel bid therefor in the schedule.

G.97. *Steel Sheet Piling.*—(a) *General.*—Steel sheet piling shall be driven in locations as shown on the drawings. The piling shall be driven to the depths shown on the drawings or prescribed by the Contracting Officer, with the top of each pile at the prescribed elevation. Where required, the tops of piling shall be cut off to the required elevation. The piling shall be driven as close as practicable to the established lines and in a manner to ensure interlocking throughout the entire length of each pile. The method of driving shall be subject to approval. All materials shall be furnished by the contractor.

A cast steel driving head shall be used for driving the steel sheet piling. Piles ruptured in the interlock or otherwise injured in driving shall be pulled and new piles driven. Should boulders be encountered, the contractor shall make every effort to drive the piling to the required depth, either by moving or shattering the boulder or by approved deviations in the line of the piling. If at any time the forward edge of the steel piling wall is found to be out of plumb, the piling already assembled and partly driven shall be driven to the required depth, and taper piles shall then be used to bring the forward edge plumb before additional piling is assembled or driven. The maximum permissible taper in a single pile shall be ¼ inch per foot of length. Where welding of piles is required for field connections, the welding shall be by approved methods. Cutoff pieces 3 feet and longer may be welded or spliced in an approved manner to provide longer piles or additional piles. The steel sheet piling, taper piles, and special intersections shall be manufactured from steel conforming to ASTM A 328. Manufacturer's certification of compliance with the specifications shall be furnished by the contractor.

The piling shall have a continuous interlock rolled integral with the pile throughout its entire length. The interlock shall permit an angular movement between adjoining piles of not less than 10° in either direction from the centerline. Piling shall be equal to ________. The weight per square foot of piling shall be not less than ________ pounds.

(b) *Measurement and Payment.*—Measurement, for payment, of steel sheet piling will be made of the piling remaining in place and to the area projected normal to the established line of piling. Payment for furnishing and driving steel sheet piling will be made at the unit price per square foot bid therefor in the schedule, which price shall include the costs of welding of field connections, taper piles and special intersections, cutting of tops, and pulling and replacing unsatisfactory piling.

[133][In addition to the payment for piling remaining in place, an allowance will be made for actual length of cutoffs, but not to exceed 3 feet for each pile. Payment for cutoff will be made at a unit price of 60 percent of the unit price per square foot bid in the schedule for furnishing and driving steel sheet piling.]

G.98. *Saturation of Dam Foundation by Flooding to Promote Consolidation.*—Saturation of the dam foundation by flooding will be required in the embankment area as outlined on the drawings. The saturation of the dam foundation will be accomplished by progressively flooding separate sections of the foundation. The flooding shall be such that complete saturation of the foundation will be accomplished and a continuous water cover to a minimum depth of 12 inches shall be maintained. Before flooding is started, the excavation for the dam foundation shall be completed as provided in section G.20. At such time as is approved by the Contracting Officer, the contractor shall begin saturation of the foundation by flooding with water. The flooding operations shall be continued until the desired penetration and saturation has been at-

[133]Include this provision when there are indications that piling will meet refusal before reaching depths shown on drawings.

tained: *Provided*, that the contractor will not be required to provide plant capacity sufficient to supply water in excess of ____ gallons per day: *Provided Further*, that the contractor will not be required to maintain continuous flooding of any individual section to a minimum depth of 12 inches for longer than 60 days. In the event of plant failure, the maximum time limit of 60 days for any section will be extended by the same number of days as pumping is interrupted by plant failure, if the desired penetration and saturation has not been attained prior to that time. Additional pumping, if required in any section beyond the 60-day period, except where extension of the 60-day period is due to failure of plant, will be ordered in writing by the Contracting Officer and payment thereof will be made as extra work.

The quantity stated in the schedule for water for saturation of dam foundation is an estimate only of the amount to be required, and the contractor shall be entitled to no additional compensation above the unit prices bid in the schedule by reason of any amount or none being required. The contractor shall be responsible for, and shall repair at his own expense, any damage to the dam foundation or any part of the work caused by excessive pumping or failure of pipelines or temporary dikes. No payment will be made for water lost due to failure of any part of the contractor's water-supply system or dikes. The saturation of the dam foundation shall be scheduled so that as short a time as practicable will elapse between the time the saturation is completed and the earth embankment is placed. Measurement, for payment, of water for saturation of dam foundation will be made by metering the water near the point or points of discharge into the dam foundation. Meters furnished and installed by the contractor shall be tested for accuracy prior to use. Payment for water for saturation of dam foundation will be made at the unit prices per million gallons bid therefor in the schedule, which unit prices shall include the cost of all water and the cost of all labor, materials, and operations required for continuously flooding the dam foundation as described in this section, including the cost of constructing, maintaining, and removing the necessary temporary dikes: *Provided*, that the cost of all plants shall be included in the unit price bid in the schedule for water for saturation of dam foundation less than ____ gallons.

G.99. *Topsoil for Seeding.*—The item of the schedule for topsoil for seeding consists of loading, hauling, placing, spreading, and rolling selected topsoil material. The topsoil shall be placed on the downstream slope of the dam embankment at locations shown on the drawings or designated by the Contracting Officer. All operations involved in the placing, spreading, and rolling of the topsoil shall be subject to the approval of the Contracting Officer. Selected topsoil shall be obtained from approved stockpiles of materials from excavation for dam embankment foundation, from stripping from borrow areas, or from other approved sources. The material shall contain the most fertile loam available from approved sources and shall be free from excessive quantities of grass, roots, weeds, sticks, stones, or other objectionable materials. Areas to receive topsoil shall be brought to within 1 foot of the prescribed final cross section at all points, and finished smooth and uniform before the topsoil is applied. Topsoil shall be evenly placed and spread over the graded area, and compacted in two layers, each by one pass of a roller weighing not less than 50 pounds per linear inch of drum length. Topsoil shall not be placed when the subgrade is frozen or in a condition otherwise detrimental to proper grading and seeding as determined by the Contracting Officer.

Measurement, for payment, for topsoil will be by volume, compacted in place within the lines shown on the drawings or as established by the Contracting Officer. Payment for topsoil for seeding will be made at the unit price per cubic yard bid therefor in the schedule, which unit price shall include the cost of loading, hauling, placing, spreading, and rolling the topsoil, and shall also include the cost of excavating additional suitable topsoil material if sufficient quantity of such material is not obtained from approved stockpiles.

G.100. *Water for Seeded Areas.*—It is expected that it will be necessary to irrigate the seeded areas in preparing the seedbed and to promote germination and growth of the plants. The frequency of application and quantities of irrigation water used will be determined by the Contracting Officer. The contractor shall provide a temporary sprinkler irrigation system of pipelines or mobile water tanks to provide for uniform application of water over the entire seeded areas and complete control of the amount of water at all times to eliminate erosion. The contractor shall repair at his own expense any damage to the slopes or any part of the work caused by excessive or irregular application of irrigation water. The quantity stated in the schedule for water for seeded areas is an estimate only of the amount to be required, and the contractor shall be entitled to no additional compensation above the unit price bid in the schedule by reason of any amount or none being required.

Measurement, for payment, of water for seeded areas will be made by metering the delivery pipeline, using meters furnished and installed by the contractor, or by tank gallonage delivered through the sprinkler heads and applied to the seeded areas. Payment for water for seeded areas will be made at the unit price per thousand gallons bid therefor in the schedule, which unit price shall include the cost of all labor, materials, plant, and operations required for sprinkler irrigation of the seeded areas as described in this section, including the cost of removing the pipelines, if used.

G.101. *Seeding.*—(a) *General.*—Seeding shall consist of ground preparation, furnishing and planting approved seed, furnishing and placing mulch, and furnishing and spreading approved commercial fertilizer. Except for placing, spreading, and rolling topsoil, all seeding operations shall be performed in accordance with provisions of this section. The areas to be seeded are: (list specific areas).

All excavation surfaces composed of rock and excavated slopes with a slope of 1:1 or steeper, shall be excluded from the seeded areas.

The limits to which the described surfaces are to be seeded shall be as prescribed by the Contracting Officer.

If directed, areas within the right-of-way lines shall be seeded where construction operations have removed the existing grass cover, where such areas have otherwise been denuded of grass cover, or where due to other reasons grass seeding is determined to be necessary.

The contractor shall maintain the seeded areas until final acceptance thereof, and any damage caused to the seeded areas by the contractor's operations shall be repaired by and at the expense of the contractor.

(b) *Seedbed Preparation*:

(1) *Where Topsoil for Seeding is Required.*—The contractor shall place, spread, and roll topsoil over the areas to be seeded in accordance with section G.100. The surfaces of the topsoil shall be maintained smooth and even until they are seeded. If these surfaces are disturbed and loosened by the contractor's operations, he shall smooth and reroll them before starting the seeding operations, and the costs thereof shall be at the contractor's expense.

(2) *Where Topsoil for Seeding is not Required.*—The contractor shall prepare the areas to be seeded to provide a firm, well-packed condition suitable for establishing grass stands just prior to sowing the seed.

Where required, the contractor shall scarify the ground to prepare a proper seedbed. No separate payment will be made for either compacting or scarifying areas to be seeded, and all cost of seedbed preparation shall be included in the unit price per acre bid in the schedule for seeding.

(c) *Seeds.*—Seed and seeding mixtures shall be free of all prohibited noxious weed seeds and shall not contain more than 0.5 percent, by weight, of restricted noxious weed seeds. Prohibited and restricted noxious weeds shall be those as classified by the State seed department.

All seed containers must be sealed and labeled to comply with existing (insert State) seed laws and regulations or in accordance with U.S. Department of Agriculture rules and regulations under the Federal Seed Act, if shipped in interstate commerce. All different grass species specified shall be separately packaged and labeled, and shall be uniformly and thoroughly mixed after they are received on the job.

The contractor shall furnish and sow a uniform seed mixture composed of the seeds listed as follows:

Seed required for 1 acre[1]

Kind of seed	Pounds of pure live seed per acre
Creeping red fescue	11
Chewing fescue	8
Newport blue grass	5
Perennial rye grass	3
Dutch white clover	3

[1]Sample table, revise as appropriate.

(d) *Sowing Periods.*—Seeding shall be done at such times of the year when climatic conditions of temperature and moisture are most adaptable for growth. Unless otherwise approved, seeding shall not be performed between ______ and ______ of each year.

(e) *Mulching.*—The contractor shall furnish and uniformly place, after seeding, a minimum of 2 tons per acre of hay or straw mulch on all seeded areas or, as an alternate, the contractor may hydromulch in accordance with subsection (h). Mulch material shall be reasonably free of mold or other evidence of decomposition and weed seed. The major portion of the mulch material in place shall exceed 12 inches in length. The mulch material shall be firmly anchored with a "IMCO" treader or equivalent. The treader shall be operated at a depth of 3 to 4 inches and crosswise to all slopes. Mulch will be anchored at 6- to 12-inch intervals across the slope. The cost of mulching shall be included in the unit price bid in the schedule for seeding.

(f) *Sowing Seed*:

(1) *Method.*—The mixture specified herein shall be sown by drilling with either an approved disc or shoe-type grass drill, an approved hydroseeder, or by mechanical or hand braodcasting.

(2) *Drill Seeding.*—If the drill seed method is used, the drill shall be regulated to uniformly distribute the seed at the rate specified herein on the areas to be seeded. Where possible to safely operate equipment, as determined by the Contracting Officer, drilling shall be done crosswise to the general slope. The drill shall be regulated so that the seed is properly placed in the soil and covered with soil to a depth of ___ to ____ inches. In the event the drill is equipped with an approved fertilizer attachment which will uniformly distribute fertilizer, up to ____ pounds of the nitrogen and ____ pounds of the phosphorous may be applied simultaneously with the drilling of the seed. The balance of the fertilizer shall be broadcast or drilled in prior to or after seeding of grass.

(3) *Hydroseeding.*—Seeding with an approved hydroseeder will be acceptable, provided wind velocities permit uniform distribution of the seed and fertilizer slurry on the areas to be seeded. In hydroseeding operations, the mixture of seed and fertilizer specified herein shall be properly mixed with water to form a slurry. The slurry mixture shall be prepared immediately prior to application, and shall be promptly applied on the areas to be seeded and fertilized. Slurry mixtures prepared more than 1 hour prior to application are not acceptable.

The hydroseeder shall be designed so as to ensure seed and fertilizer being uniformly applied at the rates per acre specified herein. The hydroseeder shall be equipped with a paddle-type agitator and recirculation pump that will continually stir and mix the slurry to prevent settling of solids in corners and bottom of tank, and maintain a uniform mixture of seed, fertilizer, and water at all times during the entire seeding operation.

Immediately after the slurry mixture is applied to the soil surface, the seed shall be properly covered with soil to the depths prescribed using a rotary hoe, Dunham packer, spike tooth harrow, or other acceptable implements as approved by the Contracting Officer. Covering seed by dragging a log chain or similar device will not be permitted. Seed applied around structures shall be properly covered with soil using a hand rake or float.

(4) *Broadcast Seeding.*—Broadcast seeding by either a mechanical broadcaster or by hand is acceptable only on areas inaccessible to the basic method employed, which may be either drill seeding or hydroseeding.

a. Mechanical broadcasting.—A mechanical broadcaster of either the centrifugal type or pull type similar to fertilizer spreaders is acceptable. Any equipment of this type used for broadcast seeding shall be designed and regulated to ensure that the proper seeding rate per acre specified herein is uniformly applied on areas to be seeded. When this method is used, seed and fertilizer may not be applied in the same mixture simultaneously, but each shall be broadcast separately.

b. Hand broadcasting.—Hand broadcasting may be performed only on small, inaccessible areas as approved by the Contracting Officer. Seed application may be performed by using an approved hand broadcaster or by broadcasting the seed by hand from a sack or other suitable container. Whichever means is used, the seed shall be uniformly applied at the rates specified herein. When using this method, both the seed and fertilizer shall be broadcast separately.

Immediately after broadcasting the seed by either mechanical or hand methods, the seed shall be properly covered with soil to the depths prescribed using a spike tooth harrow, rotary hoe, Dunham packer, or other acceptable implements. Covering broadcast seed by dragging a log chain or similar device will not be permitted. Seed broadcast around structures shall be covered with soil by a hand rake or float.

[*(g) *Fertilizer.*—The contractor shall furnish and apply commercial fertilizer at the minimum rate per acre of ____ pounds of actual nitrogen and _____ pounds of actual phosphorus. The fertilizer

*Delete or revise as applicable.

shall be packaged and labeled showing the guaranteed analysis and net weight per bag when received on the job.

Fertilizer may be applied prior to seeding by suitable mechanical spreaders, blowers, or hydraulic equipment. Fertilizer may also be applied when seeding as specified in subsections (f) (2) and (3)].

(h) *Hydromulching.*—As an alternate to other methods of seeding, fertilizing, and mulching herein specified, application by an approved hydromulcher will be acceptable. Wood cellulose fiber mulch or other approved material to be used in hydromulching shall contain no germination or growth-inhibiting factors. The mulching material shall be dyed an appropriate color to allow visual metering of its application, and shall have the property of becoming evenly dispersed and suspended when agitated in water. When sprayed uniformly on the surface of the soil, the fibers shall form a blotter-like ground cover which readily absorbs water and allows infiltration to the underlying soil. Weight specifications from the suppliers, and for all applications, shall refer only to air dry weight of the fiber, a standard equivalent to 10 percent moisture. The mulch material shall be supplied in packages marked by the manufacturer to show the air dry weight content. Suppliers shall be prepared to certify that laboratory and field testing of their product has been accomplished and that it meets all the foregoing requirements.

The application by hydromulcher shall be done in the following manner: mulching material shall be added to water slurry in hydraulic seeder after proportionate quantities of grass seed and fertilizer materials. All slurry ingredients shall be mixed to form a homogeneous slurry. Slurry mixtures prepared more than 1 hour prior to application are not acceptable. Using the color of the mulch as a metering agent, the operator of the hydraulic seeder shall spray-apply the slurry mixture uniformly to the prepared seedbed to correspond with per acre requirements of all materials. Wood cellulose fiber mulch shall be applied at a minimum rate of 1,000 pounds per acre. Other approved mulching material shall be applied at an equivalent effective rate per acre. The Contracting Officer will verify, by inspections of tank loading and spray application, that materials applied correspond with the per acre requirements.

(i) *Measurement and Payment.*—Measurement, for payment, of seeding will be made along the surface of the areas actually seeded as directed. Payment for seeding will be made at the unit price per acre bid therefor in the schedule, which price shall include the cost of all labor, materials, and equipment required for preparation of seedbed (except for placing, spreading, and rolling topsoil); cost of furnishing and spreading fertilizer; cost of furnishing, sowing, and covering the seed; and the cost of furnishing and placing the mulch.

G.102. ***Joints and Edges in Concrete.*—**

(a) *Construction Joints.*—Construction joints are joints which are purposely placed in concrete to facilitate construction; to reduce initial shrinkage stresses and cracks; to allow time for installation of embedded metalwork; or to allow for subsequent placing of other concrete. Bond is required at construction joints regardless of whether or not reinforcement is continuous across the joint.

The location of all construction joints in concrete work shall be subject to approval of the Contracting Officer, and the joints shall be constructed in accordance with sections G.86 and G.87.

(b) *Contraction Joints.*—Contraction joints are joints placed in concrete to provide for volumetric shrinkage of a monolithic unit or movement between monolithic units. The joints shall be so constructed that there will be no bond between the concrete surfaces forming the joint. Except as otherwise provided for dowels, reinforcement is never continuous across a contraction joint.

Contraction joints of the types shown on the drawings shall be constructed at the locations shown. The joints shall be made by forming the concrete on one side of the joint and allowing it to set before concrete is placed on the other side of the joint. *(Except for contraction joints to be grouted, the) *(The) surface of the concrete first placed at the contraction joint shall be coated with curing compound before the concrete on the other side of the joint is placed. The curing compound shall conform to the Bureau's "Specifications for Concrete Curing Compound", dated October 1, 1980.

*[Where elastomeric sealer is specified for construction joints in concrete, it shall conform to the Bureau of Reclamation's "Specifications for Elastomeric Canal Joint Sealer", dated August 1, 1983.]

*[Contraction joints to be grouted do not require curing compound, and shall be constructed in ac-

*Delete or revise as applicable.

cordance with the details shown on the drawings and section G.86: *Provided*, that where coated with curing compound at the option of the contractor, contraction joints to be grouted shall be lightly sandblasted without exposing appreciable areas of aggregate, in order to remove the curing compound before placing adjacent concrete.]

(c) *Control Joints.*—Control joints are joints placed in concrete to provide for control of initial shrinkage stresses and cracks of monolithic units. Control joints shall be constructed as provided in subsection (b) for contraction joints: *Provided*, that reinforcing bars are always continuous across control joints.

(d) *Expansion Joints*:

(1) *General.*—Expansion joints shall be constructed between the ______________ as shown on the drawings. Preformed bituminous joint filler shall be placed in all expansion joints. The contractor shall furnish and place the preformed bituminous joint filler. The joint filler shall cover the entire surface of the concrete at each joint, and shall be laid against the concrete and held rigidly in place while the concrete is placed on the other side of each joint. All joints in the joint filler shall be tight-fitting butt joints.

(2) *Materials.*—Preformed bituminous joint filler, Federal Specification HH–F–341F, type 1.

(e) *Edges.*—The contractor shall tool or chamfer edges of concrete where shown on the drawings and elsewhere as required.

(f) *Cost.*—*[Except for furnishing and placing waterstops, furnishing and installing metal seals, and furnishing and placing sponge rubber filler ______________, (the) (The) cost of furnishing all materials and performing all work for constructing construction joints, contraction joints, control joints, and expansion joints; and for tooling or chamfering concrete edges shall be included in the applicable prices bid in the schedule for the concrete for which the joints and edges are required or for the items which include the concrete for which the joints and edges are required.]

G.103. *Rubber Waterstops.*—(a) *General.*—The rubber waterstops shall be installed in *[construction, contraction, control, and expansion joints of the ______________ where shown on the drawings or where directed: *Provided*, that PVC waterstops conforming to section G.104 may be furnished and installed in lieu of rubber waterstops, except rubber waterstops shall be installed in all monolithic concrete siphon barrel joints.]

*[Type "A", "B", "G", and "H" rubber waterstops shall be in accordance with the details shown on drawing ________, and type "D", "E", and "F" rubber waterstops shall be in accordance with the details shown on drawing ________].

The contractor shall furnish the waterstops and all material and equipment for splicing waterstops, for fastening waterstops to forms and to supporting reinforcing bars, and for completing installation of the waterstops. The contractor shall also furnish all materials for splices and all field splicing molds, and the electrical energy for heating the molds. The contractor shall provide suitable support and protection for the waterstops during the progress of the work and shall repair or replace, at his expense, any damaged waterstops which, in the opinion of the Contracting Officer, have been damaged to such an extent as to affect the serviceability of the waterstops. All waterstops shall be protected from oil, grease, and curing compound.

*[Waterstop that is not embedded in concrete at station ________, as shown on drawing ________, shall be protected from damage by a covering approved by the Contracting Officer.]

(b) *Material*:

(1) *Rubber Waterstop.*—The rubber waterstops shall be fabricated from a high-grade, tread-type compound. The basic polymer shall be a natural or synthetic rubber. The material shall be compounded and cured to have the listed physical characteristics shown in table G-15.

(2) *Gum Rubber and Rubber Cement.*—Gum rubber and rubber cement shall be suitable for making field connections in rubber waterstops as described in subsection (g).

*[(3) *Connection Plates.*—Connection plates shall be made from No. 16 United States Standard gauge stainless steel plates. The stainless steel plates shall be class 321, 347, or 348, condition A; and shall have any suitable finish, all in accordance with Federal Specification QQ–S–766C.

(4) *Bolts, Nuts, and Washers.*—Bolts, nuts, and washers shall be made of corrosion-resisting steel containing 18 percent chromium and 8 percent nickel, or 17 percent chromium and 9 percent nickel.

(c) *Fabrication.*—The rubber waterstops shall be molded or extruded and cured in such a manner

*Delete or revise as applicable.

Table G-15.—Rubber waterstop physical characteristics.

Type of Test	Method of test ANSI/ASTM	Required	
		Natural rubber	Synthetic rubber
Tensile strength, pounds per square inch, minimum	D 412	3,500	*3,000
Tensile strength at 300 percent elongation, pounds per square inch, minimum	D 412	1,450	1,150
Elongation at break, percent, minimum	D 412	500	*450
Shore durometer (type A)	D 2240	60 to 70	60 to 70
Change in weight, water immersion, percent maximum (2 days at 70 °C)	D 471	5	5
Compression set (constant deflection), percent of original deflection, maximum	D 395, Method B	30	30
Accelerated aging (96 hours at 70 °C), percent of tensile strength before aging, minimum	D 573	80	80
Percent of elongation before aging, minimum	D 573	80	80
Ozone cracking resistance (7 days at 0.5 p/m at 30 °C) 20 percent elongation	D 1149	No cracks	No cracks

*Polychloroprene shall have a minimum tensile strength of 2,000 pounds per square inch, and a minimum elongation of 350 percent.

that any cross section will be dense, homogeneous, and free from porosity and other imperfections. The following minor surface defects will be acceptable:

(1) Lumps and depressions not exceeding ¼ inch in longest lateral dimensions and 1/16 inch deep, with no limit to the frequency of occurrence.

(2) Lumps and depressions between ¼ and ½ inch in longest lateral dimension and 3/32 inch deep, as long as the frequency of occurrence does not exceed six in a 50-foot length and there is at least 2 inches between any two such defects.

(3) Marks resulting from the tubing operation or handling during manufacturing, with no limit to width or frequency of occurrence as long as the thickness of material below the mark is not less than the minimum thickness.

(4) Coarse or grainy surface texture.

(5) Suck-back along flash lines of molded goods if not more than 1/16 inch wide, 1/16 inch deep, and not more than 2 feet long.

The tolerances, shown on the drawing, shall govern all cross-sectional dimensions. Any defects which are not within the above limitations shall either be repaired as approved by the Contracting Officer or shall be removed from the finished product by cutting out a length of waterstop containing such defects and splicing the waterstop at that point. All factory splices shall be molded splices. Molded splices shall be made by vulcanizing the splices in a steel mold for a time sufficient to produce maximum strength in the splice. All molded splices shall withstand being bent 180° around a 2-inch-diameter pin without any separation at the splice.

*[Rubber waterstops for joints in the barrel or box portions of siphons, culverts, or other pressure conduits shall be furnished in continuous circular hoops. The hoops shall be fabricated from a straight-strip waterstop with the ends spliced together with molded splices to form a closed ring of the specified circumferential length. A tolerance of ± 2 inches will be permitted in the circumferential length of each hoop.]

*[(d) *Special Waterstop Intersections.*—Special waterstop intersections, types 1 through ______, as shown on drawing ______, shall be fabricated by molding or by lap splicing. The lap splices shall be made by removing the side bulbs and center bulb from the intersecting pieces over the entire overlapping area flush with the webs to provide flat contact surfaces. The open half of the center bulb shall be plugged to form a watertight lap. The contact surfaces of the two overlapping pieces shall then be buffed smooth and coated with rubber cement. A piece of uncured gum rubber shall be applied to one of the contact surfaces, and the two pieces of waterstop shall then be placed together in the position shown on the drawings and be vulcanized by the best approved methods. During the vulcanizing period, the contact surfaces shall be held

*Delete or revise as applicable.

firmly together by placing metal plates on both sides of the waterstop and applying clamps to the metal plates. Suitable gum rubber and rubber cement shall be applied to the butt ends of waterstop at these joints to assure obtaining a continuous watertight seal around the intersection. The lap splice shall withstand being bent 180° around a 6-inch-diameter pin without any separation at the splices.]

(e) *Tests*:

(1) *General.*—Rubber waterstops shall be subject to laboratory tests before shipment. Material for tests shall be furnished by the manufacturer and all tests shall be made at the place of the manufacturer of the rubber waterstops.

Except as otherwise provided in subsection (2), general sampling procedures shall be in accordance with section 6 of Federal Test Method Standard No. 601/Gen.

(2) *Sampling for Tests.*—Samples for laboratory tests to determine physical properties of the compound shall be taken at random to obtain the number of test units listed in table G-16 from each separate purchase order.

At the option of the manufacturer, laboratory tests to determine physical properties of the rubber waterstops required to be furnished under these specifications shall be performed on test specimens cut from (a) test units taken from the finished rubber product, or (b) substitute samples furnished in accordance with section 6, Federal Test Method Standard No. 601/Gen.

(3) *Methods of Tests.*—Tests shall be made in accordance with the methods specified in subsection (b)(1).

(4) *Data Furnished by Manufacturer.*—One certified copy of all laboratory test reports representing each shipment of waterstop shall be mailed to the *(Project) Construction Engineer, Bureau of Reclamation, ______________. One copy of the transmittal letter shall be mailed to the Contracting Officer, ______________.

(f) *Shipping and Storing.*—Rubber waterstops may be shipped in rolls to facilitate handling, but if any roll of waterstop is not to be installed in a structure within 6 months after receipt of the material, the roll shall be loosened. All waterstops shall be stored in as cool a place as practicable, preferably at 70° F or less. Waterstops shall not be stored in the open or where they will be exposed to the direct rays of the sun.

Table G-16.—Number of test units.

Size of purchase order	No. of test units
500 lin ft or less	1
501 to 1,000 lin ft	2
1,001 to 5,000 lin ft	4
5,001 to 10,000 lin ft	8
Over 10,000 lin ft	15

(g) *Installation.*—The waterstops shall be installed with approximately one-half of the width of the material embedded in the concrete on each side of the joint. Care shall be exercised in placing and vibrating the concrete about the waterstops to ensure complete filling of the concrete forms under and about the waterstops and to obtain a continuous bond between the concrete and the waterstops at all points around the periphery of the waterstops. In the event the waterstop is installed in the concrete on one side of a joint more than 1 month prior to the scheduled date of placing the concrete on the other side of the joint, the exposed waterstop shall be covered or shaded to protect it from the direct rays of the sun during the exposure.

*[(1) *Field Splices in Type "A", "B", "G", and "H" Rubber Waterstops.*—All field splices in type "A", "B", "G", and "H" rubber waterstops shall be molded splices. All molded splices shall be made by vulcanizing the splices in a steel mold as follows: adjoining ends at splices shall be beveled at an angle of 45° or flatter using a saw and miter box so that ends to be spliced together will be pressed together when mold is closed. The beveled ends and sides for at least ¼ inch back from the ends shall be buffed thoroughly to provide clean, rough surfaces. All buffed surfaces shall be given two thin coats of rubber cement, and each coat shall be permitted to dry thoroughly. A piece of gum rubber cut to the same dimensions as the beveled face shall then be applied to the end of one strip after removing the cloth backing from the gum rubber. The adjoining strip shall then be placed accurately in position, and all edges shall be stitched thoroughly together with a suitable handstitcher. The mold shall be heated to 290 °F before splice is placed in mold. The prepared splice shall be placed in the mold with splice in center of mold, and mold shall be closed tightly to prevent slipping during vulcanizing process. The

*Delete or revise as applicable.

splice shall remain in the mold 25 minutes after the mold is closed completely, during which time the mold shall be maintained at 290° F.

Each finished splice shall withstand a bend test by bending the waterstop 180° around a 2-inch-diameter pin without showing any separation at the splice.]

*[(2) *Field Splices in Type "D", "E", and "F" Rubber Waterstops.*—All field splices and intersections in type "D", "E", and "F" rubber waterstops, including connections to metal seals, shall be made as shown on drawing ______].

(h) *Measurement and Payment.*—Measurement, for payment, for furnishing and installing the various types of rubber waterstops will be made of the number of linear feet of waterstops in place, measured along the centerline of the waterstop, *(with no allowance for lap at splices and intersections.)

Payment for furnishing and installing the various types of rubber waterstops will be made at the applicable unit price per linear foot bid in the schedule for furnishing and installing the various types *(and sizes of rubber or PVC) waterstops, which unit prices shall include the cost of furnishing all materials, performing tests, making field splices and intersections, installing waterstops, *(of making connections), (of making connections to metal seals), and of furnishing and installing coverings for protecting waterstops from damage.

G.104. *PVC Waterstops.*—(a) *General.*—The PVC waterstops shall be installed in *(construction, contraction, control, and expansion joints of the ______________) where shown on the drawings or where directed. [134][If PVC waterstops are furnished and installed in lieu of rubber waterstops, they shall conform to the details shown on drawing ______. If PVC waterstops are furnished, a 9-inch PVC waterstop shall be furnished in lieu of a type "A" rubber waterstop, and a 6-inch PVC waterstop shall be furnished in lieu of a type "H" rubber waterstop.]

The contractor shall furnish the waterstops and all materials and equipment for splicing waterstops, for fastening waterstops to forms and to supporting reinforcing bars, and for completing installation of the waterstops. The contractor shall provide suitable support and protection for the waterstops during the progress of the work and shall repair or replace, at his expense, any damaged waterstops which, in the opinion of the Contracting Officer, have been damaged to such an extent as to affect the serviceability of the waterstops. All waterstops shall be protected from oil, grease, and curing compound.

[135][(b) *Drawings and Data Furnished by Contractor.*—At least 60 days prior to installing any waterstop, the contractor shall submit drawings and data to the Government for approval.]

[135][(1) *Drawings.*—The contractor shall submit four sets of drawings, except for the 6- and 9-inch-type waterstops shown on drawing ______, showing details of the waterstops, including dimensions, shapes, and details of intersections and splices between waterstops of the same sizes and of different sizes. The details of intersections and splices shall show all expected connections required for the work under these specifications.

One set of drawings will be returned to the contractor either approved, not approved, or conditionally approved, and also marked to indicate changes, if required. All drawings that are not approved or that require changes shall be revised and resubmitted for approval, and shall show all changes with revision dates. Drawings conditionally approved shall be resubmitted for approval, if directed.

Any fabrication or procurement of materials performed prior to approval of the drawings will be at the contractor's risk. The Government will have the right to require the contractor to make any changes in his drawings which may be necessary to make the finished installation conform to the requirements and intent of these specifications without additional cost to the Government. Approval by the Government of the contractor's drawings shall not be held to relieve the contractor of any part of the contractor's obligations to meet all requirements of these specifications or the responsibility for the correctness of the contractor's drawings.]

[135][(2) *Data.*—The contractor shall submit detailed laboratory test reports on the physical properties, listed in subsection (c), of the compound which will be used in the waterstops to be furnished, together with a copy of the purchase order for the waterstops, and a manufacturer's certificate stating

[134]Use or revise as required only if PVC waterstop may be used in lieu of rubber waterstop.

*Delete or revise as applicable.

[135]Delete or revise as required. Designers will determine if drawings are to be required for approval. Data should normally be required unless quantities of waterstops are small.

that the waterstops, as furnished, will meet all requirements of these specifications. If the contractor purchases the waterstops under more than one purchase order, the data and samples required by this subsection shall be submitted for each separate purchase.

(3) *Addresses for Submittals.*—The approval drawings and data shall be forwarded to the Bureau of Reclamation, P.O. Box 25007, Denver CO 80225. A copy of each letter transmitting the approval (drawings and data) shall be forwarded by the contractor to the *(Project) Construction Engineer, Bureau of Reclamation, ______________].

(c) *Material.*—The PVC waterstops shall be fabricated from a compound, the basic resin of which shall be domestic virgin PVC. No reclaimed PVC or manufacturer's scrap shall be used. The compound shall contain any additional resins, plasticizers, stabilizers, or other materials needed to ensure that, when the material is compounded, the finished product will have the physical characteristics listed in table G-17.

(d) *Fabrication.*—All waterstops shall be molded or extruded in such a manner that any cross section will be dense, homogeneous, and free from porosity and other imperfections. The 6- and 9-inch-type waterstops shall be fabricated in accordance with detail dimensions and tolerances shown on drawing ________.

[136][The ________-inch waterstop shall have a center bulb of ________-inch inside diameter and ____ -inch outside diameter; shall be ________ inches in width; shall have not less than ________ longitudinal ribs on each side of the bulb, with the ribs evenly distributed between the rib adjacent to the bulb and the edge of the waterstop, and with ________-inch-minimum to ________-inch-maximum rib height; and shall have a web thickness of ________ inch adjacent to the center bulb and a web thickness of ________ inch near the edge.]

(e) *Inspection and Tests*:

(1) *General.*—All waterstops shall be sampled at the jobsite, tested, and approved by the Government before installation. The contractor shall have the waterstop available at the jobsite in sufficient time to allow 30 days for testing after samples obtained by the Government have been received at the Bureau of Reclamation laboratories in Denver, Colorado.

(2) *Samples for Tests.*—A representative sample not less than 12 inches long shall be cut from each 500 feet of each size and type of finished waterstop: *Provided*, that a minimum of four samples shall be taken for each size and type from each separate purchase order. Each sample shall be marked so that it may be identified with the specific length of waterstop from which it is taken.

(3) *Methods of Tests.*—Test specimens will be prepared from the samples in accordance with the U.S. Army Corps of Engineers Specification CRD–C–572–74, single copies of which may be obtained free of charge from the Director, U.S. Army Engineer Waterways Experiment Station, P.O. Box 631, Vicksburg, MS 39180. Tests will be made in accordance with the methods specified in subsection (c).

(f) *Installation.*—Waterstops shall not be installed until [135](drawings, data, and) field-sampled materials have been approved. The location and embedment of waterstops shall be as shown on the drawings, with about one-half of the width of the waterstop embedded in the concrete on each side of the joint. To eliminate faulty installation that may result in joint leakage, particular care shall be taken that the waterstops are correctly positioned and secured during installation. All waterstops shall be installed so as to form a continuous watertight diaphragm in the joint unless otherwise shown. Adequate provision shall be made to completely protect the waterstops during the progress of the work.

Concrete surrounding the waterstops shall be given additional vibration, over and above that used for adjacent concrete placement, to assure complete embedment of the waterstops in the concrete. Larger pieces of aggregate near the waterstops shall be removed by hand during embedment to assure complete contact between the waterstop and surrounding concrete.

Prior to starting installation of the waterstops, the contractor shall furnish to the *(Project) Construction Engineer, Bureau of Reclamation, ______________, a copy of the manufacturer's recommendations for installing and making splices in the waterstops. Splices of waterstops shall be fab-

[136]Use or revise this paragraph if sizes other than 6 or 9 inches are required.

*Delete or revise as applicable.

[135]Delete or revise as required. Designers will determine if drawings are to be required for approval. Data should normally be required unless quantities of waterstops are small.

Table G-17.—PVC waterstop physical characteristics.

Type of Test	Method of test	Required
Tensile strength, pounds per square inch, minimum	ASTM D 683, speed D, specimen type IV	2,000
Ultimate elongation, percent minimum	ASTM D 638, speed D, specimen type IV	300
Stiffness in flexure, pounds per square inch, minimum	ASTM D 747	600
Low temperature brittleness at minus 35 °F	ASTM D 746	No cracking or chipping
Volatile loss, change in weight, percent allowed	ASTM D 1203, method A, 0.08-inch-thick specimen	0.50
Tensile strength after accelerated test, percent of tensile strength before extraction test	U.S. Army Corps of Engineers Specification CRD-C-572-74	80
Ultimate elongation after accelerated extraction test, percent of ultimate elongation before extraction test, minimum	U.S. Army Corps of Engineers Specification CRD-C-672-74	80
Change in weight after effects of alkalies test, percent allowed	U.S. Army Corps of Engineers Specification CRD-C-572-74	+0.25,−0.10
Change in Shore durometer hardness after effect of alkalies test, percent allowed	U.S. Army Corps of Engineers Specification CRD-C-572-74	±5

ricated only by personnel who have demonstrated to the satisfaction of the Contracting Officer that they are sufficiently skilled to fabricate the required splices. Splices in the continuity or at the intersections of runs of plastic waterstops shall be performed by heat sealing the adjacent surfaces in accordance with the manufacturer's recommendations. A thermostatically controlled electric heat source shall be used to make all splices. The correct temperature at which splices should be made will differ with the materials compounded, but should be sufficient to melt but not char the plastic material. All splices shall be neat with the ends of the joined waterstops in true alignment. A miter-box guide and portable saw shall be provided and used to cut the ends to be joined to ensure good alignment and contact between joined surfaces. The spliced areas, when cooled and bent by hand to as sharp an angle as possible, shall show no sign of separation.

Where splices are required between waterstops of different sizes, the splices shall be made as recommended by the manufacturer of the waterstops, [135][and drawings showing the details of the splices shall be submitted to the Government, for approval, as required in subsection (b)(1)].

(g) *Measurement and Payment.*—Measurement, for payment, for furnishing and installing the various sizes of PVC waterstops will be made of the number of linear feet of waterstops in place measured along the centerline of the waterstop with no allowance for lap at splices and intersections.

Payment for furnishing and installing the various sizes of PVC waterstops will be made at the applicable unit price per linear foot bid [134](therefor) in the schedule [134](for furnishing and installing the various types and sizes of rubber or PVC waterstops), which unit price shall include the cost of furnishing all materials, preparing and submitting [135](drawings and) data, furnishing required samples of finished waterstops, making field splices and in-

[134]Use or revise as required only if PVC waterstop may be used in lieu of rubber waterstop.

[135]Delete or revise as required. Designers will determine if drawings are to be required for approval. Data should normally be required unless quantities of waterstops are small.

tersections, and installing the waterstops; and of furnishing and installing coverings for protecting waterstops from damage.

G.105. ***Sponge Rubber Filler for Concrete Joints.***—(a) *General.*—Elastic filler material consisting of sponge rubber shall be furnished and placed in the joints in concrete where shown on the drawings. *[Elastomeric sealer, packing, and sealing compound shall also be furnished and placed in the joints where shown.]

(b) *Materials:*

(1) *Sponge Rubber.*—The sponge rubber shall conform to Federal Specification HH-F-341F, type 2, class A, sponge rubber: *Provided,* that the load required to compress the test specimen to 50 percent of its thickness before test shall be not less than 50 nor greater than 150 pounds per square inch. Sponge rubber shall be stored in as cool a place as practicable, preferably at 70 °F or less, and in no case shall the rubber be stored in the open, exposed to the direct rays of the sun.

(2) *Copper Nails.*—Copper nails shall conform to Federal Specification FF-N-105B for common copper wire nails.

[137][(3) *Adhesive.*—Adhesive for fastening the sponge rubber in place shall be a nonbituminous adhesive as recommended by the manufacturer of the filler material.]

*[(4) *Elastomeric Sealer.*—Elastomeric sealer shall conform to the Bureau of Reclamation's "Standard Specifications for Elastomeric Canal Joint Sealer," dated August 1, 1983.]

*[(5) *Packing.*—Graphited asbestos packing shall be sheets conforming to Federal Specification HH-P-46E.]

*[(6) *Sealing Compound.*—Sealing compound shall conform to Interim Federal Specification TT-S-00227E, type 1, gray color.]

(c) *Installation.*—The sponge rubber filler shall be cut to the size and shape of the joint surface. The filler shall be secured to the concrete in an approved manner, with copper nails embedded in the first-placed concrete in such a manner that the nails will protrude from the joint surface to be covered at about 12-inch centers, [137](or by adhesive applied between the filler and the first-placed concrete.)

Joints between adjoining portions of the filler material shall be sufficiently tight to prevent concrete from seeping through such joints. *[Where elastomeric sealer material is required, the joint filler shall be set back from the edge of the joint to provide the proper recess for installing elastomeric sealer.] Elsewhere, unless otherwise shown on the drawings or directed, the edges of the sponge rubber filler shall be placed flush with the finished surface of the concrete or to the bottom edge of chamfers.

*[The concrete to which the elastomeric sealer is to adhere shall be clean and free from foreign substances including curing compound and standing water.]

*[Graphited asbestos packing sheets shall be cut to the required sizes and cemented in place with linoleum cement.]

[138][(d)*Measurement and Payment.*—Measurement, for payment, of sponge rubber joint filler will be made of the area of material in place. Payment for furnishing and placing sponge rubber joint filler will be made at the *(applicable) unit price per square foot bid therefor in the schedule, *(which unit price shall include the cost of furnishing and placing elastomeric sealer, graphited asbestos packing, and sealing compound.)]

[138][(d)*Cost.*—The entire cost of furnishing and placing sponge rubber filler *(and elastomeric sealer, graphited asbestos packing, and sealing compound) in joints shall be included in the unit price per cubic yard bid in the schedule for concrete in which the material is placed.]

G.106. ***Metal Seals.***—(a) *General.*—Metal seals of corrosion-resisting metal shall be placed in joints in the structures where shown on the drawings.

(b) *Materials.*—The contractor shall furnish all materials for metal seals, including metal strip, materials for [139](welding) (brazing), and washers and nails for fastening the seals to the forms. Materials for metal seals shall conform to the following:

[139][(1) *Copper.*—Copper strip conforming to Federal Specification QQ-C-576b, 0.032-inch thick, soft annealed.]

[139][(1) *Corrosion-Resisting Steel.*—Federal Specification QQ-S-766c, class 321, 347, or 348, condition A (annealed), hot- or cold-rolled finish, No. 20 gauge, United States standard (0.0375 inch thick).]

---

[137]Delete if adhesive will not be acceptable.

*Delete or revise as applicable.

[138]Use applicable payment provision.

[139]Use applicable term or delete as required.

(2) [139](Welding) (Brazing) material for joining the individual lengths of metal seals shall be of a type and composition approved by the Contracting Officer.

(c) *Installation.*—Metal seal connections shall be as shown on the drawings. The seals shall be joined carefully together by [139](welding) (brazing) so as to form continuous watertight diaphragms in the joints. Before any seal is embedded in the concrete, the seal shall be tested with soapy water to assure that all welds are tight. Additional vibration, over and above that used for [139](mass) concrete placement, shall be employed near the seal to assure complete embedment in the concrete. Large pieces of aggregate near the seal shall be removed by hand during embedment to assure complete contact between the seal and the surrounding concrete. [139][The bottom end of the vertical seals shall be embedded a minimum of 12 inches into sound rock as shown on the drawings.] The contractor shall replace or repair any metal seals punctured or damaged. Provision shall be made to support and protect the seals during the progress of the work.

(d) *Measurement and Payment.*—Measurement, for payment, of metal seals will be made of the linear feet of seals in place, and no allowance will be made for lap at joints. Payment for furnishing and installing metal seals will be made at the unit price per linear foot bid therefor in the schedule, which unit price shall include the cost of forming, [139](welding) (brazing), and maintaining the metal seals free from damage during the progress of the work.

G.107. *Metal Waterstops.*—(a) *General.*—Metal waterstops shall consist of plates of 3/16 by 8-inch wrought iron, bent and welded to the size and shape of the structure at the joint and coated with plastic compound. The metal plates, welding rods, and plastic compound shall be furnished by the contractor.

(b) *Placing.*—The waterstops shall be located in the concrete of the structures as shown on the drawings. The contractor shall cut, shape, and weld the plates and place them in the construction joints as herein provided. The exposed half of the metal waterstops shall be coated completely to a thickness of about 1/16 inch with plastic compound applied cold. Adequate provisions shall be made to support and protect the metal waterstops during the progress of the work. The contractor shall replace or repair any waterstops that are damaged before final acceptance of the work.

(c) *Materials:*

(1) *Wrought-Iron Plates.*—The wrought-iron plates shall conform to ASTM A 42.

(2) *Plastic Compound.*—The plastic compound shall consist of asphalt dispersed in water by means of a mineral emulsifying agent. The compound shall be heavy-bodied, of smooth plastic consistency, and free from lumps and sediment. When applied at room temperature in one coat to a smooth metal surface at a thickness of 1/16 inch and the specimen is then immediately placed in a vertical position, the compound shall be tightly adherent and shall not run or sag while the coating is drying and after it has dried. The asphalt compound shall comprise at least 50 percent, by weight, of the compound, shall have a softening point (ASTM D 36) of 100 to 130° F, a penetration at 77° F (ASTM D 5) of 60 to 120, and a ductility at 77° F (ASTM D 113) of not less than 100 centimeters. The ash content shall be not more than 18 percent, as determined by ASTM D 128.

(3) *Welding Rods.*—Welding rods shall be of a type and composition approved by the Contracting Officer.

(d) *Payment.*—Payment for furnishing and placing metal waterstops will be made at the unit price per linear foot bid therefor in the schedule, which unit price shall include the cost of cutting, welding, placing, and coating the metal waterstops.

G.108. *Anchor Bars.*—(a) *General.*—Where shown on the drawings or directed, the contractor shall drill holes in the [140](rock) (formation material) (concrete) for anchor bars, and grout the bars in place. The anchor bars shall be reinforcing bars and shall be used for anchoring the concrete [141](______________) in place. The contractor shall furnish the anchor bars and all materials for the grout.

The dimensions of the anchor bars and the locations and depths of the anchor-bar holes shall be as shown on the drawings or as directed. *[The diameter of each anchor-bar hole shall not be less than 1.5 times the diameter of the anchor bar specified for that hole.]

[139]Use applicable term or delete as required.

[140]Select or add the type of material into which holes will be drilled.

[141]List structures requiring anchor bars.

*Delete or revise as applicable.

The depth of holes shown on the drawings for receiving the bars are the minimum depths to be drilled. [142][In overbreak areas, longer bars will be required to provide a constant embedded length and maintain the top of the anchor bar hook in the position shown on the drawings.] [142][In overbreak areas, no adjustment in bar lengths will be required. The contractor shall maintain the top of the anchor bar hook in the position shown on the drawings.]

Where excavation is required in areas where anchor bars will be placed, the holes for the anchor bars shall not be drilled until the excavation has been completed.

(b) *Materials.*—Anchor bars shall be in accordance with section G.84. Bars shall be cut and bent to the shapes and dimensions shown on the drawings prior to being grouted in place.

Grout shall consist of cement, water, and sand mixed in the proportions and to the consistency prescribed by the Contracting Officer. Cement, water, and sand shall be in accordance with sections G.75, G.77, and G.78, respectively.

(c) *Placing.*—Anchor bars shall be cleaned thoroughly before being placed. The holes shall be cleaned thoroughly and shall be completely and compactly filled with grout. The anchor bars shall be moistened with water and forced into place before the grout takes its initial set and, where practicable, shall be vibrated or rapped until the entire surface of the embedded portions of the bars is in intimate contact with the grout. Special care shall be taken to ensure against any movement of bars which have been placed until the grout has set.

(d) *Measurement and Payment.*—Measurement, for payment, of drilling holes for anchor bars and grouting bars in place will be based upon the length of holes required to be drilled to receive the bars. Payment for drilling holes for anchor bars and grouting bars in place will be made at the unit price per linear foot bid therefor in the schedule, which unit price shall include the cost of furnishing materials for grout, *(except cement), of drilling the holes, and of grouting the bars in place.

Payment for furnishing and placing the anchor bars will be made at the *(applicable) unit price per pound bid in the schedule for furnishing and placing reinforcing bars. *[Payment for furnishing and handling cement will be made at the unit price per ton bid therefor in the schedule for furnishing and handling cement for concrete in structures.]

[142]Select applicable wording.

*Delete or revise as applicable.

G.109. *Drainage, General.*—All drains shall be constructed at the locations shown on the drawings or as directed by the Contracting Officer. Care shall be taken to avoid clogging or damaging the drains during the progress of the work, and should any drain become clogged, damaged, or obstructed from any cause before final acceptance of the work, the drain shall be cleaned out in a manner approved by the Contracting Officer or replaced by and at the expense of the contractor. No pipe which has been damaged shall be used in the work if, in the opinion of the Contracting Officer, the pipe is unfit for use.

G.110. *Dam Embankment Toe Drains.*—(a) *General.*—The contractor shall furnish all material for and shall construct dam embankment toe drains as shown on the drawings. Beneath the dam embankment, the drains shall consist of ______-inch-diameter perforated pipe embedded in graded gravel or crushed rock, and in well-graded sand bedding materials. The drain outfalls, extending beyond the dam embankment, shall consist of ______-inch-diameter nonperforated pipe embedded in backfill materials.

The pipe shall be laid to lines and grades as directed by the Contracting Officer. No portion of the dam embankment toe drain system shall be placed with adverse slopes. End plugs or stoppers shall be placed on the upper ends of the drains. A suitable temporary end plug or end cover shall be placed on pipe ends during shutdown periods.

The discharge ends of outfall drains shall be covered with stainless steel or noncorrosive screens of about ½-inch mesh or other suitable device for preventing animals from entering the pipe.

The pipe shall be hauled and handled in such a manner as to avoid damage to the pipe and coating. The contractor shall not use rope, cable, or chain slings for handling the pipe, but may use canvas slings not less than 12 inches in width.

(b) *Materials*:

(1) *Pipe, Fittings, and Couplings.*—The pipe, fittings, and couplings shall be *(at the contractor's option) (corrugated metal) (clay sewer) (asbestos cement) meeting the following specifications:

a. Corrugated metal pipe.—The corrugated metal pipe, fittings, and coupling bands shall be in accordance with Federal Specification WW-P-405B, class I or II, series A, shape 1, coating G for asbestos-impregnated, bituminous-coated, corrugated metal pipe. The nominal gauge thickness of the zinc-coated metal shall be No. 14 gauge for 12-inch-diameter pipe, No. 12 gauge for 18-inch-diameter pipe, and ________.

b. Clay sewer pipe.—The clay sewer pipe, fittings, and couplings shall be in accordance with ANSI/ASTM C 700, standard strength, bell and spigot, perforated, and nonperforated.

c. Asbestos-cement pipe.—The asbestos-cement pipe, fittings, and couplings shall be in accordance with ANSI/ASTM C 508, type II, for sizes 4- through 12-inch diameter.

d. End plugs or stoppers.—End plugs or stoppers shall be suitable for use with [143](________) pipe.

(2) *Bedding Materials.*—The bedding materials shall be furnished by the contractor, and may be obtained from approved sources of aggregate for concrete, or may be produced by screening the desired sizes from selected material from approved deposits. The bedding materials adjacent to the drainpipes shall consist of graded gravel or crushed rock, clean and well graded from 3/16 to 1½ inches in size, as approved by the Contracting Officer, and may contain up to 10 percent, by weight, of the total particles smaller than 3/16-inch size. Well-graded sand shall meet the requirements of section G.78.

(c) *Constructing Drain:*

(1) *General.*—Excavation for the drain trenches shall be in accordance with section G.20. Where additional excavation for pipe trenches is directed in accordance with section G.17, such additional excavated volume shall be refilled and compacted in accordance with section G.29.

(2) *Perforated Drains.*—A minimum ____-inch-thick layer of well-graded sand bedding material shall be tamped in place on the bottom surface of the trench. The graded gravel or crushed rock shall then be placed over the sand bedding and shall be shaped and tamped to provide equal bearing under the lower half of the pipe.

The pipe shall be laid and joined together so that the perforations are symmetrical about the vertical centerline and below the horizontal centerline.

End plugs or stoppers shall be cemented in place on the upper ends of the drains. The pipe shall be covered with the minimum thickness of bedding materials as shown on the drawings. The bedding materials shall be carefully placed and tamped about the pipe so as not to disturb the pipe and to hold it securely in position while the overlying material is being placed.

The pipe trench shall be kept free of water which might impair pipe-joining operations. The methods of lowering the pipe into the trenches and placing pipe in position shall be such as to prevent getting dirt inside of the pipe and coupling, and to prevent damage to the pipe. Before and during assembly of a joint, all parts shall be free of mud, ice, oil, or grease.

The joining of pipe sections shall be made with materials, fittings, and couplings consistent with the type of pipe used. The pipe sections shall be fitted together spigot to bell, and the joints shall be drawn together so that the bells and spigots are fully engaged.

(3) *Nonperforated Drain Outfalls.*—When the surface on which the drain is to be placed has reached an elevation about one-fourth the diameter of the pipe above the prescribed elevation of the invert of the pipe, the material shall be excavated carefully to the established shape, lines, and grades, and prepared to provide a firm and uniform bearing for the pipe.

As each unit of pipe is laid, sufficient backfill material shall be tamped about the pipe to hold it rigidly in place until the joints are completed. The joining of pipe sections shall be such as to produce a watertight line for the conveyance of water.

After the joints are completed, the backfill shall be placed and compacted to the finished ground surface as directed by the Contracting Officer. The backfill shall be placed carefully on each side of the pipe simultaneously in such a manner as to prevent disturbing or damaging the pipe and joints.

(d) *Measurement and Payment.*—Measurement, for payment, for furnishing ____-inch-diameter perforated pipe and constructing dam embankment toe drains, and for furnishing ____-inch-diameter nonperforated pipe and constructing drain outfalls, will be made along the centerline of the pipe from end to end of the pipe in place, and no allowance will be made for laps at joints.

Payment for furnishing ____-inch-diameter perforated pipe and constructing dam embankment toe drains will be made at the unit price per linear foot bid therefor in the schedule, which unit price shall include the cost of furnishing all materials for and preparing and placing the bedding material around

[143]Insert type of pipe specified.

the pipe, furnishing all materials for and making joints in the pipe, and furnishing and installing end plugs or stoppers.

Payment for furnishing ____-inch-diameter nonperforated pipe and constructing toe drain outfalls will be made at the unit price per linear foot bid therefor in the schedule, which unit price shall include the cost of preparing the pipe foundation, furnishing all materials for making joints in pipe, and furnishing and installing the screens or other suitable devices at the ends of the pipe.

Measurement, for payment, of excavation for drain trenches will be made to the minimum lines shown on drawing ________, but will not include excavation in previously placed embankment. Payment for excavation for drain trenches will be made at the appropriate unit price per cubic yard bid in the schedule for excavation for dam embankment foundation. Payment for refilling and compacting refill where additional excavation is directed for pipe trenches will be made at the unit price per cubic yard bid in the schedule for ____________.

Payment for placing and compacting backfill for the nonperforated drain outfall trenches will be made at the unit price per cubic yard bid in the schedule for ______________.

G.111. *Structure Underdrains.*—(a) *General.*—The contractor shall furnish all materials for and construct ________-inch diameter *(and ________-inch-diameter) structure underdrains under the [144](______________________________) structures to the dimensions and lines as shown on the drawings.

The pipe for structure underdrains shall be perforated, except that pipe required to be embedded in structural concrete shall be nonperforated pipe and shall be constructed with caulked joints.

Drains under the ______________ structures shall be perforated pipe placed in ________ inches of crushed rock or gravel and ________ inches of sand as shown on the drawings.

(b) *Materials:*

(1) *Perforated Pipe, Fittings, and Couplings.*—The perforated pipe, fittings, and couplings shall be either:

a. Perforated concrete sewer pipe.—Class 1, in accordance with ASTM *(C 14, C 14M), perforated in accordance with the provisions for perforated clay pipe as set forth in ASTM C 700.

b. Perforated clay pipe.—Standard strength, bell and spigot, conforming to ASTM C 700.

c. Perforated asbestos-cement underdrains.—Type II, in accordance with ASTM C 508, with couplings of flexible materials as recommended by the pipe manufacturer.

d. Perforated PVC underdrain pipe.—SDR35, in accordance with ASTM D 3034, and the perforations in accordance with the provisions for perforated clay pipe as set forth in ASTM C 700. Couplings shall be as recommended by the pipe manufacturer.

(2) *Nonperforated Pipe, Fittings, and Couplings.*—The nonperforated pipe, fittings, and couplings shall be either:

a. Concrete sewer pipe.—Class 1, bell and spigot, in accordance with ASTM *(C 14, C 14M).

b. Asbestos-cement nonpressure sewer pipe.—Type II, class 1500, in accordance with ASTM C 644 (sizes 4, 5, and 6 inches) and C 428 (8 inches and larger).

c. Clay pipe.—Standard strength, bell and spigot, conforming to ASTM C 700.

d. PVC underdrain pipe.—SDR35, in accordance with ASTM D 3034. Couplings shall be as recommended by the pipe manufacturer.

(3) *Bedding Materials.*—The bedding material around the perforated pipe drains shall consist of crushed rock or gravel, clean and well graded from [145](3/16 to 1½ inches) in size, as approved by the Contracting Officer, and may contain up to 10 percent, by weight, of the total particles smaller than [145](3/16-inch) size.

The bedding material shall be furnished by the contractor, and may be obtained from approved sources of aggregate for concrete, or may be produced by screening the desired sizes from selected material from approved deposits.

Sand shall be furnished by the contractor, and shall meet the requirements of section G.78.

(4) *Burlap.*—Burlap shall be 40 inches in width, 10 ounces per linear yard, in accordance with Federal Specification CCC–C–467C.

(5) *Lean Concrete Pads.*—Concrete for lean concrete pads shall be in accordance with sections G.73 through G.89.

(6) *Rigid Plastic Foam.*—Rigid plastic foam shall be 24 inches wide and 2 inches thick, equal to Styrofoam SM brand plastic foam insulation, as man-

[144]Include the names of structures.

*Delete or revise as applicable.

[145]Revise sizes of gravel as required.

ufactured by Dow Chemical Company, 2020 Dow Center, Midland, Michigan, 48640.

(c) *Constructing Drains*:

(1) *General.*—Excavation for the drains shall be in accordance with section G.22.

(2) *Perforated Pipe.*—The bell end of bell-and-spigot pipe shall be laid upgrade with the spigot end placed concentrically in the bell. Joints of asbestos-cement pipe shall be constructed as recommended by the pipe manufacturer.

The pipe shall be laid so that perforations are symmetrical about the vertical centerline and above the horizontal centerline.

Stoppers *(strainers) at the upstream ends of drains shall be cemented in place.

When required, the lean concrete pad shall be placed and the pipe shall be worked into the fresh concrete to ensure continuous support under the total length of the pipe. Special care shall be taken to avoid plugging the perforations.

The crushed rock or gravel bedding material shall be carefully placed and tamped about the pipe so as not to disturb the pipe, after the pipe has been laid, and to hold the pipe securely in position while the overlying material is being placed. The bedding material shall be covered with a layer of burlap before the overlying concrete is placed. Burlap shall extend to at least 6 inches outside of the excavation lines of the drains, and rigid plastic foam shall extend 3 feet each side of the centerline of the drain or 6 inches outside of the excavation lines of the drain, whichever is greater.

(3) *Nonperforated Pipe.*—For bell-and-spigot pipe, the ends of the pipe shall fit closely with the bell end upgrade, the spigot end shall be placed concentrically in the bell, and the joints shall be packed with oakum and caulked: *Provided*, that at the contractor's option, the joints of concrete sewer pipe may be constructed using a rubber gasket in accordance with ASTM C 443. Asbestos-cement pipe units shall be securely joined as recommended by the pipe manufacturer.

The pipe to be embedded in concrete shall be installed in the locations shown on the drawings, and held securely in place during placement of the surrounding concrete.

Where pipe is to be laid in a sand blanket, the sand shall be carefully placed and tamped about the pipe so as not to disturb the pipe after the pipe has been laid and to hold the pipe securely in position while the overlying material is being placed.

(d) *Measurement and Payment.*—Measurement, for payment, for furnishing *(____-inch-diameter) (various sizes of)sewer pipe and constructing structure underdrains, will be made along the centerlines of the perforated and nonperforated pipe from end to end in place, and no allowance will be made for lap at joints.

Payment for furnishing *(____-inch-diameter) (various sizes of) sewer pipe and constructing perforated or nonperforated pipe underdrains for structures will be made at the applicable unit price per linear foot bid therefor in the schedule, which unit price shall include the costs of furnishing all materials for the underdrains, except *(cement) (cementitious materials) for lean concrete pads, of placing the pipe and making joints, of placing crushed rock or gravel, sand blanket, burlap covering, lean concrete pads, and all other work necessary to complete the drains for structures.

Payment for *(cement) (cementitious materials) used in lean concrete pads will be made at the unit price per ton bid in the schedule for furnishing and handling *(cement) (cementitious materials).

Measurement, for payment, of excavation for underdrains will be made only to the neatlines shown on the drawings or as directed, and payment for such excavation will be made at the unit price per cubic yard bid in the schedule for excavation for structures.

G.112. *Drilling Drainage Holes.*—

(a) *General.*—Drainage holes shall be drilled through the concrete lining, steel reinforcement or tunnel supports, if encountered, and into the surrounding formation in the locations and to the depths shown on drawing ______.

The contractor will be permitted to furnish and install approved pipe inserts to form holes in the concrete lining. Pipe inserts shall be smooth cut and flush with the concrete surface.

Drainage holes shall be drilled from the inside of the tunnel with approved rotary drills, and shall be not less than 2 inches in diameter. Drainage holes shall not be drilled until all grouting of the formation within 150 feet has been completed.

Prior to placement of PVC slotted pipe and sand pack, each hole shall be thoroughly cleaned of any foreign and slough material. No additional compensation will be made for any additional cleanup or the use of temporary pipe casing during con-

*Delete or revise as applicable.

struction and placement of slotted pipe and sand pack.

The PVC slotted pipe, with approved stopper cemented in place and metal pipe assembly, shall be centered in each hole and properly braced in a vertical position during the placement of the sand pack material.

(b) *Materials*:

(1) *Sand Pack.*—Selected sand shall be used for the sand pack and obtained from an approved source. Sand must be clean and graded to pass a United States Standard No. 16 sieve and be retained on a No. 30 sieve, as approved by the Contracting Officer.

(2) *PVC (Polyvinyl-Chloride) Slotted Pipe.*—The PVC slotted pipe shall meet the following requirements as approved by the Contracting Officer:

ASTM Designation.......................... D 1785
Diameter.......................... 2 inches nominal
Strength.......................... Schedule No. 40
Slots.......... Three transverse slots per row, 0.020 inch wide, 1-inch minimum slot length, and 140 slots per foot of pipe.

(3) *Metal Pipe and Fittings.*—All metal pipe and fittings shall be in accordance with the section in these specifications for "Metal Pipe, Fittings, and Valves".

(c) *Measurement and Payment.*—Measurement, for payment, for drilling and constructing drainage holes will be made of the number of drainage holes drilled to the depths shown on the drawings.

Payment for drilling and constructing drainage holes will be made at the unit price per hole bid therefor in the schedule, which price shall include the cost of furnishing all materials, except _____ and ____________; placement of metal/plastic pipe assemblies and sand pack; cleanup; and all other work necessary to complete the work.

Payment for ____________________________ will be made at the unit price per pound bid in the schedule for ____________.

Payment for ____________ will be made at the lump sum bid in the schedule for ____________.

G.113. *Cast Iron Pipe Drains.*—A ____-inch cast iron soil pipe drain shall be installed under and through the spillway floor to drain the spillway ______ upstream from spillway station ______ as shown on the drawings. The cast iron soil pipe, fittings, and joint material shall be furnished and installed by the contractor as shown on the drawings or as directed by the Contracting Officer.

Materials shall conform to the following specifications:

(1) Cast iron soil pipe and fittings, hub-and-spigot pattern, Class XH, Federal Specification WW–P–401.
(2) Jute caulking, Type II (tarred), Federal Specification HH–P–117.
(3) Caulking lead, Type I, Federal Specification QQ–C–40.

The spigot ends of cast iron soil pipe and fittings shall be placed concentrically in the hubs, and all joints shall be packed with tarred jute or similar material thoroughly caulked with suitable caulking tools so as to leave 2 inches in the bell for lead. Joints shall be poured full of molten lead in one operation. The lead shall be retained in the joints by suitable joint runners, and after the lead has cooled sufficiently, it shall be caulked tightly. Pipe to be embedded in concrete shall be held firmly in position while the concrete is being placed.

Measurement, for payment, for furnishing and installing ____-inch-diameter cast iron soil pipe spillway drain will be made from end to end of the pipe in place, and no allowance will be made for lap at joints. Payment for furnishing and installing ____-inch-diameter cast iron soil pipe spillway drain will be made at the unit price per linear foot bid therefor in the schedule.

G.114. *Dry-Rock Paving for Open Drains.*—Dry-rock paving shall be placed on a bedding of sand and gravel or crushed rock as lining for open drains, as shown on the drawings. The quality of the bedding material and rock used for dry-rock paving shall be equivalent to materials for bedding for riprap and riprap. The overall thickness of the finished bedding and paving at any point shall be not less than 15 inches. The dimensions of the paving stones normal to the face of the paving, for not less than two-thirds of the surface area of the paving, shall be not less than 12 inches, and the dimensions normal to the face of the paving of any stone forming the surface of the paving shall be not less than 8 inches. The paving stones shall have an average volume of not less than 1/6 cubic foot, and not more than 25 percent of the pieces shall be less than 1/9 cubic foot in volume. Stones of the same dimensions normal to the face of the paving shall be distributed uniformly throughout the paving. Rock materials may be selected from materials for bedding for riprap and riprap furnished by the contractor. The stones shall have roughly squared and reasonably flat upper faces; shall be hand-placed, with close joints, to the established lines and grades; and the spaces between the stones shall be filled with spalls and gravel or crushed rock.

Measurement, for payment, of bedding and dry-rock paving will be made on the basis of the 15-inch thickness and on the basis of the area of finished surface of rock paving in place to the lines shown on the drawings or established by the Contracting Officer. Payment for dry-rock paving for open drains will be made at the unit price per square yard bid therefor in the schedule, which unit price shall include the cost of procuring, handling, hauling, and placing bedding and paving materials. Payment for excavation for open drains, to the lines and grades established by the Contracting Officer, will be made at the applicable unit price per cubic yard bid in the schedule for excavation for the structure involved.

G.115. *Blasting for Rock.*[146]—(a) *General.*—The contractor shall perform blasting where needed, in accordance with the requirements of this section and the Bureau's *Construction Safety Standards* [1]. Where there is a conflict between the requirements of this section and the requirements of the safety standards, the more stringent requirements shall govern.

The contractor shall erect proper warning signs, of adequate number and size, stating that blasting operations are taking place in the area, and such signs shall be clearly visible to all traffic entering the area. The contractor shall establish a reliable audible blast-warning system, and use watchmen to ensure that all personnel in the area are properly warned and kept at a safe distance from the impending blast.

All blasting shall be carefully performed, and any damage to the work, environment, and adjacent property shall be repaired by and at the expense of the contractor. All necessary precautions shall be taken to preserve the material below and beyond the established lines of all excavation in the soundest possible condition. Material beyond the required lines which is shattered or loosened by the contractor's operations shall be removed by and at the expense of the contractor. Where necessary, as determined by the *(Project) Construction Engineer, blasting mats shall be used to protect adjacent property and installations.

[147][(b) *Blasting Plans.*—Prior to starting any blasting for rock excavations, the contractor shall submit to the *(Project) Construction Engineer, for approval, a two-part conceptual blasting plan not later than [148](40) calendar days after the date of receipt of notice to proceed and at least *(20 calendar days) prior to initiating any blasting.

Part 1 of the conceptual plan shall include a complete summary of proposed transportation, handling, storage, and use of explosives. Part 2 shall include the proposed general concept for the blasting, including controlled blasting techniques and controls of noise, dust, fly rock, airblast, and vibrations. Test blasts planned by the contractor shall be included in part 2.

In addition to the conceptual plan, individual shot plans shall be submitted on a day-to-day basis, to the *(Project) Construction Engineer for approval so that the plans are received by at least 24 hours before the scheduled time for the shooting provided for in the plan. The *(Project) Construction Engineer or his authorized representative will observe the loading of shotholes for test blasting and any excavation blasting to ensure that loading is in accordance with the approved plans. Individual shot plans shall include drilling patterns; number, location, inclination, diameter, and depth of drilled holes; amount, type, and distribution of explosive per hole; pounds of explosives per square foot for presplitting; powder factor; time delays; weight of explosives in each delay; sequence of firing; time of blast; and total pounds of explosives in place, at any one time, within the area to be excavated under this contract; and any other data which the Contracting Officer may deem pertinent to his determination of the contractor's intent and purpose to produce smooth and sound rock surfaces at the surfaces of excavation, and to protect adjacent structures. No blasting will be permitted until the contractor's blasting plans for rock excavation have been approved by the *(Project) Construction Engineer and other conditions required by the Bureau's *Construction Safety Standards* [1] have been met.

[146]Use this section when blasting will be needed in open excavation. Additional damage control limitations may be needed. Consult with designers and blasting experts.

[147]Use where submittal of a blasting plan by the contractor is required.

[148]Insert number of calendar days in which contractor shall submit his blasting plans if other than 40 days.

*Delete or revise as applicable.

In addition to blasting plans, all blasting operations, and all personnel supervising blasting operations, shall be subject to the approval of the *(Project) Construction Engineer. Approval of the blasting plans, of all blasting operations, and of blasting agents by the *(Project) Construction Engineer, and compliance by the contractor with provisions for protection of life and property, shall not relieve the contractor of his responsibility or liability for the safety of persons and property.

The blasting plans shall be transmitted to the *(Project) Construction Engineer, Bureau of Reclamation, ____________. A copy of each letter transmitting the blasting plans to the *(Project) Construction Engineer shall be sent to the Contracting Officer.]

[149][(c) *Blasting Techniques.*—Where blasting is required in performing required excavations for the [150](____________), the contractor shall use "line drilling", "presplitting", or other controlled blasting techniques as approved by the *(Project) Construction Engineer in all locations where *(vertical, sloping) surfaces are to be left exposed or where concrete or backfill *(about the pumping plant structure) is to be placed against vertical or sloping excavated surfaces; and for all trench excavations under the [151](____________).

The "line drilling" technique involves the use of a single row of closely spaced, unloaded, small diameter holes along the neat excavation line to provide a plane of weakness to which the primary blast can break. The spacing and loading of the blastholes adjacent to the line drill holes shall be reduced from the spacing and loading of the main blastholes so as to break the rock between the line drill holes and produce smooth rock surfaces with a minimum amount of overbreak or underbreak.

The "presplitting" blasting technique involves the use of a single row of holes drilled along the neat excavation lines of a face and firing these holes before any adjoining main excavation area is blasted. The presplitting may be accomplished during the primary blast by delaying the primary holes so that the presplit holes will fire ahead of them. These presplit holes shall be spaced, loaded, and fired simultaneously so as to produce a tensional split or crack between the holes to which subsequent blasts can break, thus resulting in smooth rock surfaces with a minimum amount of overbreak or underbreak.

[152](As the rock excavations approach the required elevations of the structure foundations, the contractor shall either stop the bottom of the blastholes 5 feet above final grade and drill and blast the final 5 feet of rock to be excavated as separate operations, or drill the blastholes to other required depths and stem, but not load with explosive, the bottom 5 feet of blastholes and blast the final 5 feet of rock to be excavated as a separate operation.)

If, at any point in excavation the contractor's drilling and blasting operations do not result in the specified surfaces of excavation, the contractor shall immediately adjust his procedures such that the surfaces of the finished excavations meet the specified requirements.]

[153][*Cost.*—The cost of blasting, [147](including the cost of preparing and submitting blasting plans), shall be included in the applicable prices bid in the schedule for the items of work for which the blasting is required.]

[154][*Cost.*—The cost of blasting, [147](including the cost of preparing and submitting blasting plans), shall be included in the applicable prices bid in the schedule for rock excavation and for other items of work for which the blasting is required.]

G.116. *Information as to Subsurface Investigations.*—All available samples and cores recovered in subsurface investigations may be inspected by bidders at the office of the Contracting Officer.

*[Arrangement for inspection of available samples and cores can be made through the office of the Contracting Officer.]

The Contracting Officer does not represent that the available cores and samples show the conditions that will be encountered in performing the work, and represents only that any such cores or samples show conditions encountered at the particular point for which such cores or samples were obtained. Bidders must assume all responsibility for deductions and conclusions which may be made as to the nature

[149]Use these techniques where smooth and sound rock surfaces at the surfaces of the excavation are required.
[150]Insert name of structures for which these techniques are required.
[151]Insert names of structures under which trench excavation in rock is required.
*Delete or revise as applicable.

[147]Use where submittal of a blasting plan by the contractor is required.
[152]Check depth of excavation to see if this paragraph is applicable.
[153]Use if material is unclassified.
[154]Use if material is classified.

of the materials to be excavated, the difficulties of making and maintaining the required excavation, and of doing other work affected by the geology at the site of the work.

*[Solely for the convenience of bidders, logs (as abstracted by the Contracting Officer) of the core drilling and subsurface explorations are included in the drawings. The complete logs of all holes, including any available percolation tests and core recovery data, are available for examination by bidders at (insert name and address).

*[Bidders must make their own determinations as to whether the abstracted data properly and adequately reflect the information shown on the complete drill logs, as well as whether the complete logs and the abstracted logs properly and adequately reflect the information shown by the available cores and samples.] Bidders may obtain their own samples and perform tests on the soils and rock materials to determine the unit weights, evaluate shrinkage and swell factors, and other properties which the bidder believes to be significant in arriving at a proper bid.

*[Bidders are cautioned that the Contracting Officer disclaims responsibility for any opinions, conclusions, interpretations, or deductions that may be expressed or implied in any of the information presented or made available to bidders; it being expressly understood that the making of deductions, interpretations, and conclusions from all of the accessible factual information is the bidder's sole responsibility.]

G.117. *Soil-Cement Slope Protection.*—

(a) *General.*—Soil cement slope protection on the ______________ shall consist of a combination of soil, portland cement, and water; uniformly mixed, placed, compacted, finished, and cured in accordance with these specifications. The soil-cement slope protection shall be constructed to the lines, grades, and dimensions shown on the drawings or established by the Contracting Officer.

(b) *Materials*:

(1) *Cement.*—Cement for the soil-cement shall be furnished by the contractor and shall be in accordance with the applicable provisions of section G.75.

(2) *Water.*—The water used in soil-cement shall be free from objectionable quantities of organic matter, alkali, salts, and other impurities; and in accordance with the provisions of section G.77.

(3) *Soil.*—The soil for soil-cement shall be a selected non-plastic material of the following gradation:

Sieve Size	*Total percent, by weight, passing sieve*[1]
No. 200	7 to 20
No. 100	20 to 40
No. 50	35 to 65
No. 30	50 to 75
No. 16	65 to 85
No. 8	75 to 95
No. 4	85 to 100
⅜ inch	90 to 100
¾ inch	93 to 100
1 inch	100

[1]Site-specific gradation, modify as required for each job.

Soil material introduced into the mixing unit shall contain no clay balls larger than 1 inch in size. It may be necessary to screen the soil on a 1-inch sieve prior to introducing the soil into the mixer to remove such clay balls.

The soil material shall be obtained from borrow area ________ or ________, as shown on the drawings. The contractor's excavation operations in the borrow area and selection of material shall be such as will result in the required gradation of materials when incorporated in the soil-cement slope protection. The contractor shall conduct his operations to fully utilize in embankment construction all the suitable clayey material which is removed for access to the soil-cement material.

The ground-water level elevation indicated in the exploratory holes within the borrow areas are shown on the logs. However, the absence of a ground-water level on any log of exploratory holes within the area does not imply that the ground-water level will not be encountered in the vicinity of such exploratory holes.

(c) *Plant and Equipment*:

(1) *Mixing Plant.*—Mixing of the soil, cement, and water to be used in the soil-cement mixture shall be accomplished in a stationary mixing plant. The mixer shall be an approved twin-pugmill type or a continuous-mixing type designed for either weight or volume proportioning. The plant shall have a rated capacity of at least 200** cubic yards

*Delete or revise as applicable.

**Revise as appropriate.

per hour and shall be designed, coordinated, and operated so as to produce a uniform mixture within the limits required by these specifications. Facilities for efficiently storing, handling, and proportioning unmixed materials shall be provided at the plant. A water supply sufficient for the rated capacity of the plant shall be provided. Prior to the start of any soil-cement placement, the contractor's proportioning and mixing equipment shall be checked with respect to meeting specifications requirements. Proportioning checks shall be made at various plant operating speeds to cover the range of planned operating speeds. Actual batch weight checking will be required. Proportioning checks shall also be performed periodically during construction.

Satisfactory means shall be provided to obtain the proper amount of cement, soil, and water. All measuring devices shall be sensitive to a 2 percent variation above or below the actual weight in pounds required. Proportioning may be on the volume basis: *Provided*, that the sensitivity specified for the weight basis is maintained.

The plant shall be equipped with a positive, adjustable governor for controlling the mixing time of each batch. The mixing time shall be considered as the interval between the time the cement contacts the soil and water and time the mixture leaves the mixing unit.

Batching plants designed for weight proportioning shall include means for accurately weighing soil and cement in a weight box or hopper suspended on scales, ample in size to hold a full batch without hand raking or running over. The weight box or hopper shall be supported on fulcrums and knife edges so constructed that they will not be easily thrown out of alinement or adjustment. Scales may be either of the beam type with over-and-under indicator, or springless-dial type, and shall be of a standard make and design, sensitive to one-half of one percent of the maximum load that may be required. If the beam-type scale is used, there shall be included a separate beam for soil and cement, each beam being connected so as to actuate the over-and-under indicator, and a tare beam for balancing the hopper.

A scale check shall be conducted at least once each month or as often as the Contracting Officer deems necessary to ensure accuracy, at the expense of the contractor.

Plants designed for continuous mixing shall include a means for accurately proportioning soil and cement, and shall be equipped to ensure positive interlocking control of the flow of soil and cement from bins.

(2) *Transportation Equipment.*—Trucks for transporting the soil-cement mixture shall have tight, clean, smooth beds and protective covers.

(3) *Spreader.*—The equipment for spreading the soil-cement mixture shall be suitable for the purpose and shall be capable of discharging the mixture in layers to produce reasonably smooth uniform surfaces. The equipment shall be controllable so as to produce layers which, when compacted, will each be approximately of the specified thickness and will meet all the requirements of these specifications.

(4) *Compaction Equipment*:

a. Tamping rollers.—Tamping rollers used for compaction of soil-cement shall conform to the following requirements:

1. Roller drums.—Each drum of a roller shall have an outside diameter of not less than 4 feet, and shall be not less than 4 feet in length. The space between two adjacent drums, when on a level surface, shall be not less than 12 nor more than 15 inches. Each drum shall be free to pivot about an axis parallel to the direction of travel. Each drum of ballasted rollers shall be equipped with at least one pressure-relief valve and with at least one 2-inch safety head, as shown on drawing ________, or with approved equivalent types.

The safety head shall be of the Union type with rupture disks suitable for 60 pounds per square inch rupturing pressure. The pressure-relief valve shown is a manually operated valve and shall be opened periodically. Personnel responsible for opening pressure-relief valves shall be instructed to ascertain that valve openings are free from plugging to assure that any pressure developed in roller drums is released at each inspection.

2. Tamping feet.—At least one tamping foot shall be provided for each 100 square inches of drum surface. The spaces measured on the surface of the drum, between the centers of any two adjacent tamping feet, shall be not less than 9 inches. The length of each tamping foot from the outside surface of the drum shall be maintained at not less than 8 inches. The cross-sectional end area of each tamping foot shall be maintained at not less than 5 nor more than 7 square inches.

3. Roller weight.—The weight of a roller when fully loaded shall be not less than 2,000 pounds per foot of length of drum.

The loading used in the roller drums and operation of the rollers shall be as required to obtain the desired compaction. If more than one roller is used on any one layer of fill, all rollers so used shall be of the same dimensions.

Tractors used for pulling rollers shall have sufficient power to pull the rollers satisfactorily when drums are fully loaded with sand and water. Self-propelled tamping rollers which meet all the foregoing requirements will be permitted. During the operation of rolling, the tamping feet shall be maintained free of materials that would impair the effectiveness of the tamping rollers.

b. Pneumatic-tire rollers.—Pneumatic-tired rollers may be either of the towed or self-propelled type. Roller wheels shall be located abreast in not more than two rows and be so designed that each wheel will carry approximately equal loads during compaction. The tires shall be of such size and ply as can be maintained at tire pressures between 80 and 100 pounds per square inch for a 10,000-pound wheel load.

The roller shall have a rigid steel frame provided with a body suitable for ballast loading such that the load per wheel may be varied from 4,000 to 10,000 pounds. The character and efficiency of this equipment shall be subject to the approval of the Contracting Officer. Tractors used for pulling towed rollers and power systems used for self-propelled rollers shall be sufficient to pull fully loaded towed rollers or to propel fully loaded self-propelled rollers satisfactorily under the normal conditions of compaction.

(5) *Watering Equipment.*—Watering equipment consisting of pumps, water tanks, sprinklers, or other approved equipment, shall be furnished by the contractor. Adequate equipment, subject to the approval of the Contracting Officer, shall be available at all times to provide water as required for curing and protection of permanently exposed slopes and for moistening compacted surfaces that are to receive an overlying layer of soil-cement, all as provided in this section. Water trucks or sprinklers for adding water to inplace layers of soil-cement shall be equipped with fog-type sprayers.

(6) *Inspection of Plant and Equipment.*—The Contracting Officer shall have access at all times to all parts of the plant for checking the adequacy of the equipment in use, for inspecting the operation of the plant, and for verification of weights or proportions and character of material.

The contractor may at any time be requested to weigh selected truck loads of soil-cement to assure proper mixing plant calibration.

(7) *Safety Requirements.*—Adequate and safe stairways to the mixer platform and guarded ladders to other plant units shall be placed where required for accessibility to all plant operations. All gears, pulleys, chains, sprockets, and other dangerous moving parts shall be thoroughly guarded and protected. Ample and unobstructed space shall be provided on the mixing platform. A clean and unobstructed passage shall be maintained at all times in and around the truck loading space. This space shall be kept free of droppings from the mixing platform.

A positive lockout procedure shall be developed for all maintenance and cleaning operations. This procedure should be included in the contractor's safety program, and approved by the Contracting Officer prior to equipment setup.

(d) *Preparation of Foundation.*—The surface of the dam embankment upon which soil-cement slope protection is to be placed shall be firm and compact, and shall be true to the lines and grades shown on the drawings. If loose material is placed on the slope to bring the slope to line and grade, such material shall be compacted by special rollers, mechanical tampers, or other approved methods, to a degree equivalent to that obtained in the dam embankment in accordance with section G.29. The embankment surface shall be moistened and kept moist until overlying soil-cement is placed.

Surfaces in the channels and side slopes upon which soil-cement slope protection is to be placed shall be similarly compacted: *Provided*, that the degree of compaction shall be equivalent to not less than 85 percent of average Proctor maximum dry density or not less than 65 percent of relative density for the top 8 inches.

(e) *Proportioning and Mixing*:

(1) *General.*—The soil, cement, and water shall be accurately measured and conveyed into the mixer in the proportionate amounts necessary to meet the specified requirements. All ingredients shall be mixed for at least 30 seconds or longer as may be necessary to ensure a thorough, uniform, and in-

timate mix of the soil, cement, and water; and until the resulting mixture is homogeneous and uniform in appearance.

(2) *Cement Content.*—The approximate amount of cement shall be 12** percent by dry weight of soil. The exact amount of cement required will be determined by the Contracting Officer.

(3) *Water Content.*—Water shall be added and mixing shall be continued until a thorough, uniform, and intimate mixture of soil-cement and water is obtained as determined by the Contracting Officer. When mixing is completed, the percentage of moisture in the mixture on a basis of ovendry weight shall be such that at time of compaction it will be within 1 percentage point dry to 1 percentage point wet of the Bureau of Reclamation laboratory standard optimum condition as defined in section G.29.

(f) *Transporting Soil-Cement Mixture.*—The soil-cement mixture shall be transported from the mixing plant to the work site in trucks having tight, clean, and smooth beds. Haul time shall not exceed 30 minutes, and shall be considered to mean the time elapsed from the time the material leaves the mixer until the same material is spread on the fill to the specified thickness. The contractor shall protect the soil-cement mixture if transported during unfavorable weather. Any loads excessively wet by rain will be subject to rejection. Equipment shall not be operated on a finished compacted layer of the soil-cement, except where specifically permitted, and any damage resulting to the soil-cement from such operation shall be repaired at the expense of and by the contractor.

(g) *Placing Soil-Cement.*—The soil-cement mixture shall be placed and distributed in such a manner as to produce a reasonably smooth uniform surface in layers of such uncompacted thickness that, when compacted, each layer will be about 6 inches in thickness. In general, soil-cement shall be placed in horizontal layers: *Provided*, that the contractor will be permitted to place the material in sloping layers to accommodate compacting equipment if such sloping layers are not steeper than 8:1. Each successive layer in a section shall be placed and compacted as soon as practicable after the preceeding layer is completed.

The soil-cement mixture placed on channel side slopes shall be similarly placed: *Provided*, that the contractor shall place and compact material normal to the centerline of the structure: *Provided Further*, that in order to attain proper compaction and bonding between layers, the layer thickness may be reduced, as directed by the Contracting Officer.

Compacted surfaces of soil-cement that are to receive an overlaying or adjacent layer of soil-cement shall be kept moist continuously until placement of the overlaying or adjacent layer of soil-cement: *Provided*, that the contractor will not be required to keep such surfaces moistened for longer than 7 days. The surface of the compacted soil-cement shall be scarified to a depth of about ⅛ inch with a power-driven steel broom within 1 to 3 hours, depending on set after compacation. The contractor shall clean off bonding surfaces thoroughly by power brooming prior to placing the next layer of soil-cement. Equipment operating on soil-cement layers shall be routed so as not to disrupt or damage the layers, and no equipment shall be operated over the finished edges of the soil-cement on the dam slope unless proper protection is provided. Transverse joints at stoppages of work shall be trimmed to form straight joints and with as steep a taper as possible. When lanes of soil-cement are placed in adjacent layers, the longitudinal joints shall be trimmed within 3 hours of placement to form straight vertical joints prior to the placement of the adjacent lane. Soil-cement materials removed in brooming, smoothing, or trimming the layers after the time limits specified for transporting and compacting the layers shall be wasted.

Soil-cement shall not be mixed or placed when the air temperature is below 45° F: *Provided*, that if the temperature is 40° F or above, soil-cement slope protection may be placed if the temperature is rising. Soil-cement shall not be placed if, in the judgment of the Contracting Officer, weather conditions are unsuitable.

(h) *Compaction.*—The soil-cement mixture shall be compacted by six passes of a tamping roller followed by four passes of the fully loaded pneumatic-tired roller: *Provided*, that compaction of channel-side slopes shall be made with a fully loaded pneumatic-tired roller with an adequate number of passes to attain an equivalent density, as approved by the Contracting Officer.

One pass of either type roller is defined as "the required number of successive roller trips, which by means of sufficient overlay, will ensure complete coverage of the entire surface by the roller". Second

**Revise as appropriate.

and subsequent passes of the roller shall not be made until each previous pass, as defined above, has been completed. The specified moisture content shall be maintained uniformly throughout the layer of material being compacted. The compaction operations shall proceed in such a manner that the length of time between completion of spreading operations of the soil-cement mixture and completion of compaction by both tamping and pneumatic-tired rollers shall not exceed 1 hour for each layer. If necessary, water shall be added and incorporated during the compaction operation to maintain the uncompacted mixture at its optimum moisture content. If, in the opinion of the Contracting Officer, the surface of a layer of soil-cement has been rutted or compacted unduly by hauling equipment to reduce the effectiveness of compaction by the tamping roller, the contractor will be required to scarify such surfaces, as directed, prior to compacting with the tamping roller.

When any of the compaction operations are interrupted prior to completion of compaction by both types of rollers so that the mixture which has not been completely compacted is left unworked for more than 30 minutes for any reason, or when the soil-cement mixture, before completion of compaction, is wetted by rain so that the average moisture content exceeds the tolerance given in subsection (e)(3) at the time of final compaction, the entire layer affected, as determined by the Contracting Officer, shall be removed and replaced in accordance with these specifications at the expense of the contractor and no payment will be made for cement used in the removed material.

(i) *Protecting and Curing Surfaces of Soil-Cement.*—All surfaces of soil-cement that will remain exposed permanently shall be water cured by fog spraying or, at the option of the Contracting Officer, may be cured by providing a moist earth covering. Soil-cement surfaces cured with water shall be kept wet for a minimum of 7 days immediately following placement of the soil-cement: *Provided*, that during the prescribed period of water curing when temperatures are such that soil-cement surfaces may freeze, water curing shall be discontinued and such surfaces shall be protected against freezing by application of a moist earth covering.

If a protective covering of moist earth is used for curing or protecting soil-cement other than at locations to be used for haul ramps, covering shall have a minimum thickness of 6 inches. Portions of the soil-cement facing that are to be used for haul ramps shall be protected by a layer of earth of sufficient thickness, as determined by the Contracting Officer (at least 2 feet are required), to preclude any damage to the soil-cement facing by the hauling equipment. All surfaces to be cured and/or protected by moist earth covering shall be kept wet until the earth cover is applied, after which the earth covering shall be kept moist until the soil-cement surface has been subjected to a total curing time of 7 days following placement of the soil-cement.

The earth material used for curing or for protective covering, including that used for haul ramps, may be obtained from any approved source; but no measurement for payment will be made for excavation, transportation, or placement of the materials. The contractor will be required to remove the earth material after the curing period.

(j) *Measurement and Payment.*—Measurement, for payment, for furnishing and placing soil-cement slope protection, will be made of the soil-cement in place after compaction to the lines, grades, and dimensions shown on the drawings, or established by the Contracting Officer, and on the basis of the prescribed thickness. No measurement, for payment, of soil-cement slope protection will be made of soil-cement which, after compaction, lies outside of the line of the embankment slope as shown on the drawings. Trimming and removal of excess soil-cement will not be required.

Payment for furnishing and placing soil-cement slope protection will be made at the unit price per cubic yard bid therefor in the schedule, which unit price shall include the cost of all labor, materials, and equipment required for the completion of the soil-cement construction including excavation, transportation, and processing of earth materials; mixing, placing and spreading soil-cement; compaction by both tamping and pneumatic-tired rollers; and water curing or furnishing and placing moist earth cover for curing or for protection: *Provided*, that payment for furnishing and handling cement used in soil-cement slope protection will be made at the unit price per ton bid in the schedule for furnishing and handling cement for soil-cement as provided in section G.75.

No measurement or payment will be made for excavation of soil-cement materials. The entire cost of excavation, transportation, processing, and all other operations required in the borrow area to complete the soil-cement slope protection shall be included in the unit price bid in the schedule for furnishing and placing soil-cement slope protection.

H. BIBLIOGRAPHY

G.118. *Bibliography.*

[1] *Construction Safety Standards*, revised 1987, Bureau of Reclamation, Denver, CO.

[2] *Concrete Manual*, vol. 2, "Test Designations," Bureau of Reclamation, Denver, CO, 1987.

[3] *Earth Manual*, vol. 2, "Test Designations," Bureau of Reclamation, Denver, CO, 1987.

[4] *Concrete Manual*, 8th ed., Bureau of Reclamation, Denver, CO, 1975.

Typical Checklist of Dams and Structures for On-Site Inspections

OPERATIONS

Attendance at Dam ______________________

- Dam tender's training ______________________
- Residence ______________________

Written Instructions? Yes No

- Adequate Yes No

Communications

- Type ______________________
  - Normal ______________________
  - Standby ______________________
- Adequate ______________________

Auxiliary Power

- Test during examination ______________________
- Condition ______________________
- Adequate ______________________

Access Roads ______________________

- Adequate under adverse conditions ______________________

Oil Containment ______________________

SPCC Plan ______________________

Landslides ______________________

Restricted ______________________

Signs ______________________

EARTH DAM

Upstream Face

Riprap ______________________

Erosion—Beaching ______________________

Vegetative growth ______________________

Settlement ______________________

Debris ______________________

Downstream Face

Rock ______________________

Erosion—Sinkholes ______________________

Vegetative growth ______________________

Crest

Roadway ______________________

Guardrails ______________________

Curb ______________________

Parapet wall ______________________

Settlement ______________________

Lighting ______________________

Abutments ______________________

Seepage and Drainage

Location ______________________

Toe drain ______________________

Measurement ______________________

EARTH DAM—Continued

Method __________
Amount __________
Change in flow __________
Records __________

Performance Instruments

Surface settlement points __________
Piezometer well __________
Readings __________
Other __________

CONCRETE DAM

Upstream Face __________
Downstream Face __________

Crest

Roadway __________
Walks __________
Parapet wall __________
Lighting, etc. __________

Galleries

Concrete __________
Metalwork __________
Electrical __________
Ventilation __________
Drains and drainage __________

Elevator Shaft

Metalwork __________
Equipment __________
Safety inspection __________

CONCRETE DAM—Continued

Abutments ______

Foundation at Downstream Toe of Dam ______

Seepage Around Dam

- Location ______
- Amount ______
- Measurement methods ______

Performance Instruments and Devices

- Uplift measurements ______
- Drain flow ______

SPILLWAY

Approach Channel

- Channel ______
- Log boom ______

Control Structures

- Crest ______
- Walls ______
- Apron ______

Chute

- Walls ______
- Floor ______
- Drains ______

Stilling Basin

- Walls ______
- Floor ______

Outlet Channel

- Riprap ______
- Erosion ______

SPILLWAY—Continued

- Vegetation ____
- Structural
  - Hoist deck ____
  - Bridge ____
- Gates
  - Mechanical features
    - Hoists ____
    - Cables ____
    - Gates ____
    - Protective coatings ____

OUTLET WORKS

- Inlet Structure ____
  - Trashracks ____
  - Concrete ____
  - Gate Chamber ____
    - Gates
      - Operation at time of examination ____
      - Exercising frequency ____
      - Mechanical ____
      - Electrical ____
      - Protective coatings ____
      - Posted operating instructions ____
  - Ventilation ____
  - Seepage ____
  - Concrete ____
  - Access tunnel ____

OUTLET WORKS—Continued

Concrete ______

Metalwork ______

Outlet Conduit ______

Metalwork ______

Protective coatings ______

Concrete ______

Cavitation ______

Control Facilities ______

Control house ______

Structural condition ______

Roof ______

Walls ______

Housekeeping ______

Metalwork ______

Protective coatings ______

Gates

Operation at time of examination ______

Exercising frequency ______

Mechanical ______

Electrical ______

Protective coatings ______

Posted operating instructions ______

Chute ______

Floor ______

Walls ______

Drains ______

Stilling Basin ______

Outlet Channel ______

Vegetation ______

Gravel bars, etc. ______

Appendix I

Conversion Factors

INTERNATIONAL SYSTEM (SI METRIC)/U.S. CUSTOMARY CONVERSION FACTORS

LENGTH

To convert from	To	Multiply by	To convert from	To	Multiply by
angstrom units	nanometers (nm)	0.1	feet	millimeters	304.8
	micrometers (μm)	1×10^{-4}		meters	0.3048
	millimeters (mm)	1×10^{-7}		inches	12
	meters (m)	1×10^{-10}		yards (yd)	0.333 333
	mils	$3.937\ 01 \times 10^{-6}$	yards	meters	0.9144
	inches (in)	$3.937\ 01 \times 10^{-9}$		inches	36
micrometers	millimeters	1×10^{-3}		feet	3
	meters	1×10^{-6}	meters	millimeters	1×10^{3}
	angstrom units (A)	1×10^{4}		kilometers (km)	1×10^{-3}
	mils	0.039 370		inches	39.3701
	inches	$3.937\ 01 \times 10^{-5}$		yards	1.093 61
millimeters	micrometers	1×10^{3}		miles (mi)	$6.213\ 71 \times 10^{-4}$
	centimeters (cm)	0.1	kilometers	meters	1×10^{3}
	meters	1×10^{-3}		feet	$3.280\ 84 \times 10^{3}$
	mils	39.3701		miles	0.621 371
	inches	0.039 370	miles	meters	$1.609\ 34 \times 10^{3}$
	feet (ft)	$3.280\ 84 \times 10^{-3}$		kilometers	1.609 34
centimeters	millimeters	10		feet	5.28×10^{3}
	meters	0.01		yards	1.76×10^{3}
	mils	393.701	nautical miles	kilometers	1.853 24
	inches	0.393 701	(nmi)	miles	1.151 55
	feet	0.032 808			
inches	millimeters	25.4			
	meters	0.0254			
	mils	1×10^{3}			
	feet	0.083 333			

AREA

To convert from	To	Multiply by	To convert from	To	Multiply by
square milli-	square centimeters (cm^2)	0.01	square meters	hectares	1×10^{-4}
meters	square inches (in^2)	1.55×10^{-3}		square feet	10.7639
square centi-	square millimeters (mm^2)	100		acres	$2.471\ 05 \times 10^{-4}$
meters	square meters (m^2)	1×10^{-4}		square yards (yd^2)	1.195 99
	square inches	0.155	acres	square meters	$4.046\ 86 \times 10^{3}$
	square feet (ft^2)	$1.076\ 39 \times 10^{-3}$		hectares	0.404 686
square inches	square millimeters	645.16		square feet	4.356×10^{4}
	square centimeters	6.4516	hectares	square meters	1×10^{4}
	square meters	6.4516×10^{-4}		acres	2.471 05
	square feet	$6.944\ 44 \times 10^{-3}$	square kilo-	square meters	1×10^{6}
square feet	square meters	0.092 903	meters	hectares	100
	hectares (ha)	$0.092\ 903 \times 10^{-6}$		square feet	$1.076\ 39 \times 10^{7}$
	square inches	144		acres	247.105
	acres	$2.295\ 68 \times 10^{-5}$		square miles (mi^2)	0.386 102
square yards	square meters	0.836 127	square miles	square meters	$2.589\ 99 \times 10^{6}$
	hectares	$8.361\ 27 \times 10^{-5}$		hectares	258.998
	square feet	9		square kilometers (km^2)	2.589 99
	acres	$2.066\ 12 \times 10^{-4}$		square feet	$2.787\ 84 \times 10^{7}$
				acres	640

VOLUME—CAPACITY

To convert from	To	Multiply by
cubic millimeters	cubic centimeters (cm^3)	1×10^{-3}
	liters (l)	1×10^{-6}
	cubic inches (in^3)	$6.102\ 37 \times 10^{-5}$
cubic centimeters	liters	1×10^{-3}
	milliliters (ml)	1
	cubic inches	0.061 023
	fluid ounces (fl. oz)	0.033 814
milliliters	liters	1×10^{-3}
	cubic centimeters	1
cubic inches	milliliters	16.3871
	cubic feet (ft^3)	$5.787\ 04 \times 10^{-4}$
liters	cubic meters	1×10^{-3}
	cubic feet	0.035 315
	gallons	0.264 172
	fluid ounces	33.8140
gallons	liters	3.785 41
	cubic meters	$3.785\ 41 \times 10^{-3}$
	fluid ounces	128
	cubic feet	0.133 681
cubic feet	liters	28.3169
	cubic meters (m^3)	0.028 317
	cubic dekameters (dam^3)	$2.831\ 69 \times 10^{-5}$
	cubic inches	1.728×10^{3}
	cubic yards (yd^3)	0.037 037
	gallons (gal)	7.480 52
	acre-feet (acre-ft)	$2.295\ 68 \times 10^{-5}$
cubic miles	cubic dekameters	$4.168\ 18 \times 10^{6}$
	cubic kilometers (km^3)	4.168 18
	acre-feet	3.3792×10^{6}
cubic yards	cubic meters	0.764 555
	cubic feet	27
cubic meters	liters	1×10^{3}
	cubic dekameters	1×10^{-3}
	gallons	264.172
	cubic feet	35.3147
	cubic yards	1.307 95
	acre-feet	$8.107\ 13 \times 10^{-4}$
acre-feet	cubic meters	$1.233\ 48 \times 10^{3}$
	cubic dekameters	1.233 48
	cubic kilometers	$1.233\ 48 \times 10^{-6}$
	cubic feet	4.356×10^{4}
	gallons	$3.258\ 51 \times 10^{5}$
cubic dekameters	cubic meters	1×10^{3}
	cubic feet	$3.531\ 47 \times 10^{4}$
	acre-feet	0.810 713
	gallons	$2.641\ 72 \times 10^{5}$
cubic kilometers	cubic dekameters	1×10^{6}
	acre-feet	$8.107\ 13 \times 10^{5}$
	cubic miles (mi^3)	0.239 913

ACCELERATION

To convert from	To	Multiply by
feet per second squared	meters per second squared (m/s^2)	0.3048
	G's	0.031 081
meters per second squared	feet per second squared (ft/s^2)	3.280 84
	G's	0.101 972
G's (standard gravitational acceleration)	meters per second squared	9.806 65
	feet per second squared	32.1741

VELOCITY

To convert from	To	Multiply by
feet per second	meters per second (m/s)	0.3048
	kilometers per hour (km/h)	1.097 28
	miles per hour (mi/h)	0.681 82
meters per second	kilometers per hour	3.6
	feet per second (ft/s)	3.280 84
	miles per hour	2.236 94
kilometers per hour	meters per second	0.277 778
	feet per second	0.911 345
	miles per hour	0.621 371
miles per hour	kilometers per hour	1.609 34
	meters per second	0.447 04
	feet per second	1.466 67
feet per year (ft/yr)	millimeters per second (mm/s)	$9.665\ 14 \times 10^{-6}$

FORCE

To convert from	To	Multiply by
pounds	newtons (N)	4.448 22
kilograms (force)	newtons	9.806 65
	pounds (lb)	2.204 62
newtons	pounds	0.224 809
dynes	newtons	1×10^{-5}

MASS

To convert from	To	Multiply by
grams	kilograms (kg)	1×10^{-3}
	ounces (avdp)	0.035 274
ounces (avdp)	grams (g)	28.3495
	kilograms	0.028 350
	pounds (avdp)	0.0625
pounds (avdp)	kilograms	0.453 592
	ounces (avdp)	16
kilograms	kilograms (force)-second squared per meter ($kgf \cdot s^2/m$)	0.101 972
	pounds (avdp)	2.204 62
	slugs	0.068 522
slugs	kilograms	14.5939
short tons	kilograms	907.185
	metric tons (t)	0.907 185
	pounds (avdp)	2×10^{3}
metric tons (tonne or megagram)	kilograms	1×10^{3}
	pounds (avdp)	$2.204\ 62 \times 10^{3}$
	short tons	1.102 31
long tons	kilograms	$1.016\ 05 \times 10^{3}$
	metric tons	1.016 05
	pounds (avdp)	2.24×10^{3}
	short tons	1.12

TEMPERATURE

To convert from	To	Multiply by
degrees Celsius	kelvins (K)	$t_K = t_{\circ C} + 273.15$
degrees Fahrenheit	degrees Celsius	$t_{\circ C} = (t_{\circ F} - 32)/1.8$
degrees Fahrenheit	kelvins	$t_K = (t_{\circ F} + 459.67)/1.8$
degrees Rankine	kelvins	$t_K = t_{\circ R}/1.8$

VOLUME PER UNIT TIME FLOW

To convert from	To	Multiply by
cubic feet per second	liters per second (l/s)	28.3169
	cubic meters per second (m^3/s)	0.028 317
	cubic dekameters per day (dam^3/d)	2.446 57
	gallons per minute (gal/min)	448.831
	acre-feet per day (acre-ft/d)	1.983 47
	cubic feet per minute (ft^3/min)	60
gallons per minute	cubic meters per second	$6.309\ 02 \times 10^{-5}$
	liters per second	0.063 090
	liters per minute	3.785 41
	cubic dekameters per day	$5.450\ 98 \times 10^{-3}$
	cubic feet per second (ft^3/s)	$2.228\ 01 \times 10^{-3}$
	acre-feet per day	$4.419\ 19 \times 10^{-3}$
acre-feet per day	cubic meters per second	0.014 276
	cubic dekameters per day	1.233 48
	cubic feet per second	0.504 167
cubic dekameters per day	cubic meters per second	0.011 574
	cubic feet per second	0.408 735
	acre-feet per day	0.810 713
cubic meters per second	acre-feet per day	70.0456
	cubic feet per second	35.3147
	gallons per minute	$1.585\ 03 \times 10^4$
	liters per second	1×10^3
	million gallons per day	22.8245
million gallons per day (mgd)	cubic meters per second	0.043 813

FORCE PER UNIT AREA PRESSURE—STRESS

To convert from	To	Multiply by
pounds per square inch	kilopascals (kPa)	6.894 76
	[1]meters-head	0.703 091
	[2]mm of Hg	51.7007
	[1]feet of water	2.306 73
	pounds per square foot (lb/ft^2)	144
	std. atmospheres	0.068 046
pounds per square foot	kilopascals	0.047 880
	[1]meters-head	$4.882\ 60 \times 10^{-3}$
	[2]mm of Hg	0.359 033
	[1]feet of water	0.016 019
	pounds per square inch	$6.944\ 44 \times 10^{-3}$
	std. atmospheres	4.7254×10^{-4}
short tons per square foot	kilopascals	95.7605
	pounds per square inch (lb/in^2)	13.8889
[1]meters-head	kilopascals	9.806 36
	[2]mm of Hg	73.5334
	[1]feet of water	3.280 84
	pounds per square inch	1.422 29
	pounds per square foot	204.810
[1]feet of water	kilopascals	2.988 98
	[1]meters-head	0.3048
	[2]mm of Hg	22.4130
	[2]inches of Hg	0.882 401
	pounds per square inch	0.433 514
	pounds per square foot	62.4259
kilopascals	newtons per square meter (N/m^2)	1×10^{-3}
	[2]mm of Hg	7.498 55
	[1]meters-head	0.101 975
	[2]inches of Hg	0.295 218
	pounds per square foot	20.8855
	pounds per square inch	0.145 039
	std. atmospheres	$9.869\ 26 \times 10^{-3}$
kilograms (f) per square meter	kilopascals	$9.806\ 65 \times 10^{-3}$
	[2]mm of Hg	0.073 556
	pounds per square inch	$1.422\ 73 \times 10^{-3}$
millibars (mbar)	kilopascals	0.1
bars	kilopascals	100
std. atmospheres	kilopascals	101.325
	[2]mm of Hg	760
	pounds per square inch	14.70
	[1]feet of water	33.90

[1]Column of H_2O (water) measured at 4 °C.
[2]Column of Hg (mercury) measured at 0 °C.

MASS PER UNIT VOLUME DENSITY AND MASS CAPACITY

To convert from	To	Multiply by
pounds per cubic foot	kilograms per cubic meter (kg/m³)	16.0185
	slugs per cubic foot (slug/ft³)	0.031 081
	pounds per gallon (lb/gal)	0.133 681
pounds per gallon	kilograms per cubic meter (kg/m³)	119.826
	slugs per cubic foot	0.232 502
pounds per cubic yard	kilograms per cubic meter	0.593 277
	pounds per cubic foot (lb/ft³)	0.037 037
grams per cubic centimeter	kilograms per cubic meter	1×10^{3}
	pounds per cubic yard	$1.685\ 55 \times 10^{3}$
ounces per gallon (oz/gal)	grams per liter (g/l)	7.489 15
	kilograms per cubic meter	7.489 15
kilograms per cubic meter	grams per cubic centimeter (g/cm³)	1×10^{-3}
	metric tons per cubic meter (t/m³)	1×10^{-3}
	pounds per cubic foot (lb/ft³)	0.062 430
	pounds per gallon	$8.345\ 40 \times 10^{-3}$
	pounds per cubic yard	1.685 56
long tons per cubic yard	kilograms per cubic meter	1.328 94
ounces per cubic inch (oz/in³)	kilograms per cubic meter	$1.729\ 99 \times 10^{3}$
slugs per cubic foot	kilograms per cubic meter	515.379

VISCOSITY

To convert from	To	Multiply by
centipoise	pascal-second (Pa · s)	1×10^{-3}
	poise	0.01
	pounds per foot-hour (lb/ft · h)	2.419 09
	pounds per foot-second (lb/ft · s)	$6.719\ 69 \times 10^{-4}$
	slug per foot-second (slug/ft · s)	$2.088\ 54 \times 10^{-5}$
pascal-second	centipoise	1×10^{3}
	pounds per foot-hour	$2.419\ 09 \times 10^{3}$
	pounds per foot-second	0.671 969
	slug per foot-second	0.020 885
pounds per foot-hour	pascal-second	$4.133\ 79 \times 10^{-4}$
	pounds per foot-second	$2.777\ 78 \times 10^{-4}$
	centipoise	0.413 38
pounds per foot-second	pascal-second	1.488 16
	slug per foot-second	0.031 081
	centipoise	$1.488\ 16 \times 10^{3}$
centistokes	square meters per second (m²/s)	1×10^{-6}
	square feet per second (ft²/s)	$1.076\ 39 \times 10^{-5}$
	stokes	0.01
square feet per second	square meters per second	0.092 903
	centistokes	$9.290\ 30 \times 10^{4}$
stokes	square meters per second	1×10^{-4}
rhe	1 per pascal-second (1/Pa · s)	10

Index

* U.S. GOVERNMENT PRINTING OFFICE:1999 573-693